Helmholtz's Treatise

on

PHYSIOLOGICAL OPTICS

Translated from the Third German Edition

Edited by
James P. C. Southall
Formerly Professor of Physics in Columbia University

complete in three volumes bound as two

Volumes I and II

Dover Publications, Inc.
New York   New York

Published in Canada by General Publishing Company, Ltd., 30 Lesmill Road, Don Mills, Toronto, Ontario.

Published in the United Kingdom by Constable and Company, Ltd., 10 Orange Street, London WC 2.

This Dover edition, first published in 1962, is an unabridged and corrected republication of the English translation of *Handbuch der physiologischen Optik* originally published by The Optical Society of America in 1924. Volumes I and II originally appeared as two separate volumes.

Standard Book Number: 486-60015-7
Library of Congress Catalog Card Number: 62-1421

Manufactured in the United States of America
Dover Publications, Inc.
180 Varick Street
New York, N. Y. 10014

Helmholtz's Treatise

on

PHYSIOLOGICAL OPTICS

Translated from the Third German Edition

Edited by

James P. C. Southall

Formerly Professor of Physics in Columbia University

Volume I

Handbuch

der

Physiologischen Optik

von

H. von Helmholtz.

Dritte Auflage

ergänzt und herausgegeben in Gemeinschaft mit

Prof. Dr. A. Gullstrand und **Prof. Dr. J. von Kries**
Upsala   Freiburg

von

Professor Dr. W. Nagel
Rostock

Erster Band

Mit 146 Abbildungen im Text

Einleitung herausgegeben von Prof. Dr. **W. Nagel**
Die Dioptrik des Auges herausgegeben von Prof. Dr. **A. Gullstrand**

Hamburg und Leipzig

Verlag von Leopold Voss

1909.

PREFACE TO THE ENGLISH TRANSLATION

HELMHOLTZ's "Popular Scientific Lectures" have spread his fame far and wide among educated people everywhere. His great work "On the Sensations of Tone as a Physiological Basis for the Theory of Music" has long been accessible to English readers (3rd ed., 1895). While he was professor at Heidelberg and still a comparatively young man, nearly three-score years ago he composed the preface to the first edition of his monumental work on light and vision, in all their intricate and manifold relations to each other; and already considerably more than a decade has passed since the publication of the posthumous third edition of the *Physiologische Optik* which was brought up to date and greatly enlarged under the collaboration of NAGEL, GULLSTRAND and v. KRIES. Yet in all these years there has been no English translation of this great classical treatise; and unfortunately no similar work in English of any kind. It is interesting to note that both YOUNG and HELMHOLTZ, the two great pioneers in Physiological Optics, started on their careers in the medical profession, and each of them afterwards gained his greatest renown in Physics. Apart from its own intrinsic value, the treatise on Physiological Optics is a model of scientific method and logical procedure that has hardly ever been excelled in these respects.

The meeting of the Optical Society of America in 1921 in Rochester, N. Y., was made notable by the celebration of the hundredth anniversary of the birth of HELMHOLTZ. On that occasion it was proposed to commemorate this event in a more useful and substantial way by bringing out the long-delayed English translation of the Physiological Optics, and accordingly a special committee was appointed to have charge of this business. After due deliberation the committee decided that under the circumstances the third German edition was beyond question the one to be reproduced in English, not simply because it was the last and, so to speak definitive edition, but because, besides containing the original HELMHOLTZ text absolutely unchanged, each of the three principal divisions of the subject, namely, let us say, the physical, the physiological and the psychological portions, had been supplemented and enriched by recent additions, all of the highest value and importance. This plan involved, however, a much bigger undertaking and much greater expense than had perhaps been contemplated at first. But luckily for the success of the project, there was one member of the committee who was determined that no obstacles should stand in the way; and it is literally true that without the continual advice and encouragement of Mr. ADOLPH LOMB, the achievement would never have been accomplished. He was resolved at all costs that this great thesaurus of physiological optics should henceforth be at the disposal of ophthalmologists and scientific investigators in England and America in their own tongue. And certainly the very existence of this book in English should lead to new treatises and new text-books which are sorely needed at present.

The editor has received also valuable assistance from other sources without which he could hardly have accomplished his own task. Herewith appended is a list of those collaborators who have lent their aid in the arduous work of translation:

R. P. ANGIER, Yale University (Volume III, v. KRIES's Appendix, I., Nos. 6, 7 and 8).

M. DRESBACH, Albany Medical College (Volume II, §§22, 23, 24 and 25).

HARRY S. GRADLE, Chicago, Ill. (Volume III, §§27, 28).

DAVENPORT HOOKER, University of Pittsburgh (Volume I, §§1, 2, 3, 4, 5, 6, 7, 12, and GULLSTRAND's Appendix IV).

WILLIAM KUNERTH, Iowa State College (Volume III, §§26, 29).

JAKOB KUNZ, University of Illinois (Volume III, v. KRIES's Note on §31, and §§32 and 33, and v. KRIES's Appendix I., Nos. 1, 2, 3, 4, 5).

HENRY LAURENS, Yale University (Volume II, §§17, 18. 18A, and Appendices of W. NAGEL and v. KRIES)

A. LOMB and H. C. LOMB, New York City (new matter contributed by v. KRIES to Volumes II and III).

G. W. MOFFITT, Frankford Arsenal (Volume III, v. KRIES's Appendix II).

L. T. TROLAND, Harvard University, and E. J. WALL, Wollaston, Massachusetts (Volume II, §§19, 20, 21).

L. D. WELD, Coe College (Volume I §§8, 9, 10, 11, 13, 14, and part of 15, Volume III, §3 except v. KRIES's Note on this section).

W. WENIGER, Oregon State Agricultural College (Volume III, §30).

The single object that has been kept steadily in mind throughout was a faithful rendition of the original, at the same time without being too literal and awkward. And while I believe every word has been carefully scrutinized, I must still hope that the indulgent critic will be disposed to overlook many shortcomings. At the same time I wish it to be clearly understood that the editor, and the editor alone, assumes all responsibility for the version as it stands. He has had to exercise the right of revising the preliminary manuscripts without returning them to the various collaborators for their approval.

In no sense is this work a new edition of the Physiological Optics. Nevertheless, it does contain some new and original material of distinct value, notably as follows: 1. A chapter on Ophthalmoscopy by Professor GULLSTRAND, taken by his permission from his book entitled *Einführung in die Methoden der Dioptrik des Auges des Menschen* (Leipzig, 1911), which is inserted at the end of the first volume; 2. Several special contributions prepared by Professor v. KRIES, which will appear at various places in the second and third volumes; and finally, 3. An article by Dr. CHRISTINE LADD-FRANKLIN on her colour theory and related matters, which will be found at the end of the second volume. Here and there throughout the entire work the editor and his associates have ventured to insert a few explanatory footnotes and occasional, more or less haphazard, references to more recent literature. Anything like a complete bibliography in the ever-widening domain of this vast subject would have to be a separate task in itself and was manifestly out of the question here. This is something that I hope will be systematically undertaken perhaps also by the Optical Society of America; and the sooner, the better, if it is ever to be done at all. The additional footnotes are indicated by the sign ¶ prefixed to them; in each instance the initials of the responsible writer being appended in parentheses at the end.

With a few necessary modifications now and then, the plates and illustrations have been reproduced from the original copper plates purchased directly from the German publishers. The latter, by the way, together with Professor GULLSTRAND and Professor v. KRIES, have coöperated in the most friendly and helpful way to make the English edition in every way worthy of its handsome prototype. This is also true of the American printers, who, as will be seen, have spared no pains to make the book useful and suitable from every point of view.

To my friend and colleague Mr. C. L. TRELEAVEN I am under many obligations for assisting me in reading the proof-sheets. My wife has likewise aided me in this labour. And, last, but not least, let me inscribe here, *magna cum laude*, the name of Miss RUTH TOWNSEND, who has diligently copied the entire manuscript thus far, besides taking time to perform some of HELMHOLTZ's experiments as she went along!

As these lines are being written, the first volume is about ready to be issued from the press, and the manuscript of the second volume is now in the hand of the printers. I trust the entire treatise in three volumes will be completed before the end of another year.

JAMES P. C. SOUTHALL

Department of Physics,
Columbia University,
New York, N.Y.
June 1 1924

The first section of this treatise appeared in 1856, the second in 1860, and the third partly at the beginning and partly toward the close of 1866. The long interval that elapsed before the publication of the final instalment was due in part to outside influences (two changes of residence and occupation involving other scientific undertakings) and partly also to internal causes. Of late years the theory of visual perceptions has been the subject of much investigation and has just begun to develop its rich contents and the absorbing interest which it possesses. It might be a fair question to ask whether it is now indeed quite feasible to carry out the general plan of this book and of the encyclopedia to which it belongs and to bring even to a preliminary conclusion a work which treats of this youthful and at the same time effervescing field of knowledge. However, owing to the peculiar nature of this domain of science, it is hardly to be expected that a final answer can be very soon given to some of the questions that are still debatable. The whole region is closely entangled with physiological problems of the utmost difficulty, and moreover the investigators who can make advances are necessarily limited, because they must have long practice in the observation of subjective phenomena before they are qualified to do more than see what others have seen before them. Unless a person is duly cautious about this kind of experimental work, he may have to pay for it afterwards by some impairment of his eyesight. The result is that just here where psychical processes intervene there appears to be much greater room for individual peculiarities than in other regions of physiology.

Finally, however, an effort had to be made to introduce law and order in this region and to rid it of the curious contradictions which have heretofore impeded progress. I have proceeded on the conviction that law and order even if they are not fundamentally sound are better than contradictions and lawlessness. Accordingly, I have taken as my guide the principle of the empiristic theory as expounded in §§26 and 33 concerning which I am persuaded more and more, the longer I ponder over it, that it is the only safe guide through the labyrinth of the facts known at present. Along this route other pioneers have already preceded me whose labours, perhaps in consequence of a certain predilection for direct mechanical explanations that are characteristic of the materialistic tendency of the day, have on the whole not won such favour as they probably deserved. The reason for this may be due to the fact that my predecessors have always been busy with single chapters in the theory of the visual perceptions, and their opinions, to be of weight, should be placed in the right perspective with respect to the whole subject. I have been at much pains to develop this connection completely.

The inconveniences resulting from not waiting to publish the entire work before the appearance of the two earlier portions I have endeavoured to remedy by collecting the recent literature on the subject in a supplement and calling attention at least briefly to the most important facts that have been ascertained since the publication of the first parts of this book. Fortunately, none of these new observations have necessitated any essential modification of the previous conclusions and opinions.

As far as possible and with the means at my command, I have tried to follow the literary plan of the encyclopedia for which these volumes were intended. The more recent literature will be found to be fairly complete; but the earlier writings I have frequently had to compile from secondary sources and cannot guarantee their accuracy. The execution of a really trustworthy history of physiological optics would be of itself an undertaking that would demand the time and strength of an investigator over a long period of years, and such a work would hardly be worth the labour until the science itself was in a much maturer state than it is at present.

In the preparation of this treatise the chief aim which I have had in view has been to verify all the fairly important facts by the evidence of my own eyes and by my own experience. Those methods of observation which seemed to me the most reliable have been selected always for description, and if they are sometimes different from those of the original investigator, I hope no one will suppose that these variations are introduced without purpose and merely for the sake of novelty.

I trust that competent judges will bear in mind the difficulty and intricacy of the problem to be solved when they are disposed to find fault with the book which is here submitted to them.

H. HELMHOLTZ

Heidelberg, December, 1866

PREFACE TO THE THIRD EDITION

The first edition of HERMAN VON HELMHOLTZ's Treatise on Physiological Optics, which was published in 1866, has long been out of print, and even the second edition published in 1885 is no longer to be found in the bookshops. The demand for the book has not ceased and will not cease for a long time to come, for no new treatise has superseded HELMHOLTZ's work. Containing in its scope such a wealth of material presented in the simplest and clearest fashion, the "Physiological Optics" bears the stamp of a genuinely classical treatise which will always retain its value, even if new investigations lead to some modifications here and there of the points of view which HELMHOLTZ himself entertained.

To preserve a work of this character for the scientific world and for the book-trade is not simply a pious duty of mere historical value but is also a practical service in a very real sense. And so when the publishers announced that a new edition was needed and appealed to me to undertake it, I was glad to coöperate with them, although I was aware of the enormous difficulties which were necessarily involved.

It was obvious from the outset that the mere reproduction either of the first or of the second edition without any changes whatever would not be satisfactory at all. Undoubtedly, for a long time to come a new impression of the original text would be found to be valuable and useful. And yet in view of the wealth and significance of much of the new material of research, it seemed as if it might be a matter of almost universal regret if there were no reference to it whatever, whereas by taking some account of recent progress in this domain of science the value of the entire work might be essentially enhanced. If a new edition along these lines appeared practicable instead of simply a new impression of the original text, evidently this was the best solution. Of course, I had to admit that an adequate revision of the entire work was probably beyond the power of any single individual and certainly beyond my power. But this difficulty was quickly disposed of in the most satisfactory way when Professor GULLSTRAND and Professor VON KRIES consented to join me in the enterprise and to edit the parts on the Dioptrics of the Eye and the Visual Perceptions, respectively; thus leaving me free to devote my labours exclusively (except for certain essentially technical problems) to revising the second part of the book, which is concerned with the subject of the Visual Sensations.

The principal difficulty thereafter was to decide on the nature and plan of the revision. It was immediately apparent that we could not hope to satisfy every desire in this respect. However, this problem also was soon clarified and settled by consultations among the editors themselves and also with the publishers and Madam ELLEN v. SIEMENS, *neé* v. HELMHOLTZ, who represented the author's heirs. All were unanimously of the opinion that a revision in the sense of producing an entirely new work in which the text of the original was freely employed was out of the question. Undoubtedly, such a procedure might have resulted in a uniform, well rounded work which would be useful for reference. But this is exactly what HELMHOLTZ meant when he spoke of an editor who had become so completely merged and, as it were, melted in his work as to have lost all identity of his own. A compilation of this sort may indeed be desirable one of these days, but that is for future times to determine. At present (we were all agreed on that point) the time was not ripe for this. The significance of HELMHOLTZ's own views is still too great to suffer what he wrote and his mode of presenting these ideas to be submerged and more or less obliterated by being restated and re-edited. The facts and problems of physiological optics as they appeared to HELMHOLTZ should be still accessible for general information on this subject.

Under the circumstances there was nothing else to be done but to preserve the text of the original work intact, and at the expense of a certain unity and uniformity in the work as a whole to limit the revision to supplementary chapters. The unavoidable disadvantage of this method will be less evident wherever such additions are substantially in harmony with the author's own views and opinions and appear therefore as a sort of super-structure on the basis of his ideas. However, the circumstances of the case are found to be quite different in the separate parts of the treatise. In the theoretical and for the most part solid territory belonging to the physiology of both the sensations and the perceptions of vision, the editors considered the conditions so far favourable for their plan that even where it was necessary to record a notable advance of scientific investigation since the date of the appearance of the first edition of the Physiological Optics, a natural outcome of this kind should not involve at all an adverse attitude towards the theories of HELMHOLTZ. It is precisely because the editors believe that in such questions as these it is necessary to start from the fundamental conceptions as HELMHOLTZ represented them that they decided to undertake the revision of the work. The plan of arrangements of the separate divisions will be explained further on.

The decision to reproduce the original text with supplements having been reached, the next question was whether to use the text of the first or second edition. Undoubtedly, the natural thing was to select the later version for this purpose. How could an editor choose to disregard any alterations or additions which had been made by the author himself? If, therefore, in spite of so obvious an objection, the editors have preferred the text of the first edition, there must have been special reasons that were responsible for this decision. Foremost of these was the consideration that the whole imperishable significance of HELMHOLTZ's achievements in the domain of the physiology of vision, the elegant physical methods which he adopted and improved, his painstaking observations of the sensations themselves and the allied psychical phenomena, the mathematical analysis and philosophical and critical discussion, all these characteristic features are essentially interwoven with the first edition of the Physiological Optics. It is the classical work that marked the dawn of a new era in the science of the physiology of the senses.

However, there was another reason also for preferring the text of the original edition. Curiously enough the changes and additions which were introduced in the second edition seem to be called in question and discarded at present to a far greater extent than the contents of the first edition.* The explanation of this is hardly to be attributed to the fact that at the time when HELMHOLTZ was at work on the second edition, he was diverted from the task by other absorbing labours and consequently could not give to physiological optics the same undivided strength and interest as formerly, and so had not been able to keep pace with the more recent developments in this domain of science. A sufficient answer to that is that at this very time, under his influence and with his collaboration, A. KÖNIG's important researches were begun and had aroused his keenest interest. Through these investigations he had become acquainted with part of a newly explored region. Subsequent study of these phenomena and better knowledge of them placed the results in a somewhat different light and suggested the probability of a different interpretation. It is easy for us looking backwards to see now how, on account of the unfinished state of these researches, the beginning of the year 1890 happened to be a singularly unfortunate time for a new edition of the Physiological Optics. Thus at the present time it is not only easier but wiser to undertake the revision on the safe basis of the first edition instead of attempting to reconcile the tentative investigations in the second edition. This criticism applies, of course, to only one part of physiological optics; but it is the very part in which the changes in the second edition are most numerous.

* It will be of interest to read the review of the second edition written by Professor J. McKEEN CATTELL and published in *Science*, N.S. Vol. VIII, pp. 794-796. Dec. 2, 1898. (J. P. C. S.)

Accordingly, it was decided to reproduce word for word the text of the first edition, including the supplements which HELMHOLTZ had added himself. With regard to the contributions of the editors, the best plan seemed to be to allow as much latitude as possible to each of them to present the subject in his own way. Occasional brief comments and corrections are to be found in footnotes; whereas the more extensive notes are placed at the conclusions of the various single sections. In each of the three main divisions of the work certain subjects required to be revised with perfect freedom and in more detail. Parts of a new chapter arising in this fashion may be inserted in between the sections of the original text and the other parts appended at the end of the main division. In these supplementary portions certain regions of physiological optics which HELMHOLTZ merely touched on or ignored entirely and which modern investigations have opened up for the first time are examined, whereas in other chapters recent theoretical views are presented.

A revision of the introduction on the anatomy of the eye appeared to be unnecessary. HELMHOLTZ's treatment of this subject is a model of terseness and clearness and enables an ordinary reader to obtain a sufficient grasp of the matter; whereas a complete revision going more in detail would exceed the scope of the work.

Of the three main divisions of the entire book the first one of the "Dioptrics of the Eye" required special consideration owing to the very considerable progress which has been made recently in the study of the actual image-process in optical systems as compared with the ordinary more or less imperfect methods of Dioptrics that have long been in vogue. Consequently, mere minor alterations and additions in the original text were not adequate here for the purpose in hand, and therefore it seemed better to present this whole subject from these new standpoints.

While it was not to be gainsaid that a complete new treatment of this division was advisable for the reasons mentioned above, on the other hand it began to be evident very soon that this plan necessarily involved such a disproportionate augmentation of this part of the book that it had to be abandoned for a compromise. And so the editor of this subject has endeavoured to limit himself mainly to the essential facts in the region where notable advances have taken place and to present these modern ideas in as simple a form as possible for a reader who was not versed in higher mathematical analysis. An outline of the new theory as a whole is given here for the first time, including also the hitherto unknown laws of optical imagery in media of variable index of refraction which could not be omitted because, first of all, they are essential for finding the data of a schematic eye that will agree with the facts as they are now known, and also because these considerations are of importance in connection with the effort to substitute a new theory of accommodation in place of HELMHOLTZ's theory, whereas undoubtedly this attack as well as others of a similar kind are to be regarded as affording new supports to the author's views on this subject.

In the region of the "Sensations of Vision" the main question to be decided first of all was whether HELMHOLTZ's conception of the structure and action of the mechanism of colour-perception could still be considered as an adequate explanation of all the new observations that have been made in the last four decades; and if not, whether these ideas should be discarded perhaps altogether, or, finally, whether it would be really profitable to introduce here additional supplementary hypotheses. The editor's position on this question is that there is no reason whatever to abandon the fundamental ideas of the colour-theory which HELMHOLTZ espoused; although the assumption of the organization of the mechanism of colour-perception in three components is no longer sufficient to give an entirely satisfactory account of all the known facts of colour-vision. However, in the theory of the separate functions of the rods and cones of the retina an opportunity is afforded of making certain phenomena intelligible that are ignored in HELMHOLTZ's original statement of the retinal functions. Since this theory of the twofold function of the retina is fundamentally and essentially bound up with the differences of vision in bright and feeble illumination and with the so-called adaptation of the eye, a special chapter had, first of all, to be devoted to this subject in order to explain how the light-sense and colour-sense are related to the state of adaptation of the eye. The purpose of another chapter is to describe and estimate comparatively recent advances in laboratory methods of measurement of the colour-sensitivity of the eye (spectrophotometry, colorimetry, peripheral and flicker reactions, etc.). And, finally, a third chapter here treats of the abnormalities of the colour-sense as to their bearing on the theory of colour-vision.

With respect to the last of the three main divisions of the treatise, the comprehension and explanation of the "Perceptions of Vision" will probably depend for a long time to come on personal opinions that are hardly open to discussion, because here we are concerned with a whole set of debatable propositions that cannot be submitted to experiment or direct observation but are determined by considerations of a philosophical and psychological nature. The corner-stone in HELMHOLTZ's theory of the visual perceptions, the doctrine of "empiricism," as he called it, has to be described by a word which in our opinion begs the question, and indeed is utterly opposed to it, that is, a conception, which, while it may still be justifiable and is fundamentally so, being supported by the same identical facts, is nevertheless subject to the same doubts and difficulties now as it was forty years ago. And inasmuch as it was HELMHOLTZ's intention in 1894 to republish this part of the book for the second edition without any considerable alterations, it can perhaps be positively affirmed that the facts which had come to life meantime, supposing he was aware of them then, would certainly not have altered at all his main convictions on this subject. Under such circumstances it might therefore seem permissible to limit the revision of this portion of the work merely to certain simple statements of fact without attempting any explanations of the theoretical and fundamental questions which they involved.

And yet a desire of presenting the opposite aspect of the matter in relation to a whole set of items, together with numerous other considerations which will be duly mentioned as they arise, appeared to make such a restriction impractical, so that at last the editor felt obliged to attempt a general and independent review of the fundamental questions that are aroused by the battle-cry of "empiricism" and "nativism" (or intuitionalism). To this third main division of the work another chapter also has been added dealing with binocular optical instruments, which is a subject entirely within the scope of the work and which indeed was discussed at some length in the original edition, but which of late years has received such extensive and important practical developments in the construction of new apparatus that it was deemed advisable to present the whole matter in a more thorough and systematic way.

In outward appearance and mechanical execution the publishers have spared neither pains nor expense. The page is larger in size and the letter-press more agreeable to the eye. The paper likewise is better than it was in the former editions, and since the actual text has been augmented by additions considerably beyond that of the first and even of the second edition, it has been found necessary to issue the work in three volumes, as a single volume would have been entirely too unwieldy. Following the author's example in the second edition, the illustrations have been distributed in these volumes in the places in the text where reference to them occurs instead of assembling them in plates as in case of the first edition.

The bibliography which was prepared by ARTHUR KÖNIG for the second edition has not been included in the present edition. It would certainly have needed to be brought up to date, and in that case it would have required a whole volume by itself. Besides, the expenditure of time and labour would have been out of proportion to its value, since nowadays good journals are available containing periodical lists and abstracts of the literature of the subject, notably, for example, the "Zeitschrift für Psychologie und Physiologie der Sinnesorgane" which was started by A. KÖNIG himself and is specially devoted to the physiology of the senses.

The bibliographies of the first edition (together with those contained in the supplements) have been retained as containing references to early investigations in physiological optics which otherwise might be difficult to trace. The citations in the new parts of the work will be found in footnotes.

For convenience of reference and comparison with the two preceding editions, the corresponding page numbers of the first edition are given at the top of each page, as was done in the second edition. In place of these numbers, the contributions of the various editors, GULLSTRAND, v. KRIES and NAGEL, are indicated at the top of the page by the initial letter of the author's name, G., K. or N. The editors' comments in the footnotes are indicated in the same way.

A portrait of H. v. HELMHOLTZ will appear as a frontispiece of the next volume that is issued.

W. NAGEL

Rostock, September, 1909

The first volume of the third edition of the "Handbuch der physiologischen Optik" appeared in 1909. The next volume to be issued was the third dated 1910; which was followed by the second volume in 1911.

PREFACE TO THE SECOND VOLUME

With the appearance of the second volume the new edition of the Physiological Optics reaches its completion, later and differently from what was anticipated when the work was begun. Professor W. A. NAGEL to whom was entrusted the revision of the second volume suffered an accident late in March, 1910, which developed into a severe illness resulting in his death. When his work was interrupted he had completed the revision of the original text together with the minor additions thereto. Of the new chapters which were to be included in this volume the first one on Adaptation, Twilight Vision and Duplicity Theory had likewise been written and printed and the first proof of it corrected. When it became necessary to entrust the completion of the work to other hands, the publisher begged me to undertake the task; and I have complied with this wish not without many misgivings but influenced finally by the fact that my personal relations with NAGEL made me acquainted with his views in the main, and since my opinions were not materially divergent from his at any point I was perhaps in the best position to continue what he had already begun and to bring it to a conclusion to some extent as he had intended. The task was indeed all the more difficult for me because NAGEL had already planned the remaining chapters in detailed fashion (as indicated by numerous preliminary memoranda) but except for a very summary outline had not prepared any formal manuscript on the subject. Here therefore I was obliged in the main to follow my own judgment. On the other hand with respect to the first of the new chapters, apart from the fact that it had already been put in type as stated above, it was due to the author and his memory not to alter that materially. It may therefore very well be that the disadvantages, to some extent unavoidable in the whole work, a certain lack of unity and perhaps also of completeness, will be more apparent in this volume than in the first and third volumes. Should this be the case, the special difficulties incident to the change of editorship may be alleged by way of explanation and excuse.

The alphabetical index of subjects for all three volumes will be found at the end of this volume; and likewise a few corrections.

v. KRIES

Freiburg, April, 1911

Table of Contents of Volume I

_____

Anatomical Description of the Eye

Physiological Optics

Part I

The Dioptrics of the Eye

Appendices by A. Gullstrand

Anatomical Description of the Eye

§1. General Structure of the Organ of Vision

The eyes of animals may distinguish only light from darkness or may perceive form as well.

1. *Distinguishing only light and darkness.* This is probably the case in the "eyespots" of the lowest forms of animal life (annelids, intestinal worms, starfish, sea-urchins, jelly-fish, infusoria, etc.). The only essential for this purpose is a nerve sensitive to light, the peripheral end of which lies exposed to the exterior under a transparent covering. In most cases, the peripheral end of this nerve is surrounded by pigment of one colour or another and is thus rendered visible. However, it has not been ascertained whether all pigmented "eyespots" in the lower animal forms actually serve for the perception of light. On the other hand, the reactions to light of some lower animals without "eyespots" force us to the conclusion that nerves, sensitive to light but unaccompanied by pigment, may be present in transparent animals, though an investigator has no way of recognizing them.

2. *Distinguishing not only light and darkness, but form as well.* The ability to do this requires an apparatus of separate nerve fibres in order to perceive light coming from separate luminous points. It is no longer necessary for each nerve fibre to receive light rays from all parts of the environment, but only from one small portion of it. Thus to each individual nerve fibre corresponds a certain field of vision, and consequently it is possible to distinguish which elementary fields of vision of the entire area perceived contain luminous bodies and which do not. The smaller the size of each single field of vision and the larger their total number, the more minute will be the portions of surrounding bodies which may be perceived. In the highest development of the organ of vision, the size of these separate elements becomes imperceptibly small in proportion to that of the total field. The requirement for clear vision in such an organ might be expressed by saying, light coming from a single illuminated point in the environment must fall only upon a single point of the nervous substance or retina that is sensitive to light.

The subdivision of the light coming from different parts of the environment is brought about either (1) by means of funnel-shaped, opaque septa (the composite eyes of invertebrates), or (2) by the refraction of light at curved refracting surfaces (the simple eyes of invertebrates and the eyes of vertebrates).

1

There is no sharp line of demarcation between eyes which perceive only light and darkness and those which also perceive form. Even in the lowest forms of animal life, the layers of pigment surrounding the light-sensitive nerves are so arranged that light can fall only on the exposed sides at the ends of the fibres. By moving its body, an animal with such eyespots would be able to ascertain from which direction most light comes, in very much the same way as a human being determines the direction of radiant heat by means of his cutaneous sensation or as a patient with an entirely opaque crystalline lens is able to make out the position of a window in a room. The pigment layers of the eyespots are thus seen to have a very important function. In forms such as the leeches and planaria, in which a transparent, spherical or conical body lies in front of the nervous substance, different parts of the retina may be impressed in different degrees by light coming from different directions. From this type there occurs a gradual differentiation of structure through the simple eyes of crustacea, arachnids and insects (which usually have something on the order of a lens and vitreous humor beyond the cornea) to those of the molluscs and especially of the cephalopods, whose eyes are quite like those of vertebrates. That clearness of vision in such eyes is, in general, directly proportional to their linear dimensions, may be inferred because the miscroscopical elements of animal tissues, especially those of the nervous system, are more or less of the same size in all classes of animals, and also because clearness of vision is essentially dependent upon the number of individual receptive elements present, which must be approximately proportional to the extent of the posterior surface of the vitreous humor of the simple eye.

Compound eyes occur in crustacea, where they often appear as an aggregate of conically elongated simple eyes. They are best developed among insects. Their outer surface is somewhat spherical and often composes more than one-half or even as much as two-thirds of the surface of a sphere. At the centre of the sphere lies a club-shaped swelling of the optic nerve, from which fibres run out radially in all

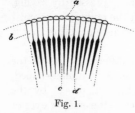

Fig. 1.

directions towards conically shaped and radially arranged vitreous bodies. The bases of these latter are turned towards the cornea, which generally presents on its outer surface a rather flat, six-sided or four-sided facet for each cone, whereas on the inner surface it often has lens-like swellings. The individual transparent cones are separated from one another by the funnel-like pigment layers which surround them. The accompanying illustration (Fig. 1), taken from JOH. MÜLLER,[1] represents a number of such cones from the eye of a nocturnal butterfly. The facets of the cornea are indicated by the letter a, the transparent cones by b, the fibres of the optic nerve by c, and the pigment between them by d.

If each cone were provided with only one nerve fibre, the field of vision would be divided only into as many parts as there were cones. Recently, however, GOTTSCHE[2] has demonstrated that an optical image of objects in front of the eye is thrown on the inner ends of the

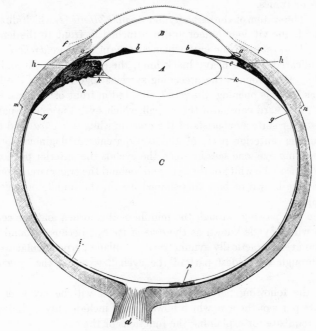

Fig. 2.

cones. Consequently, if a number of perceptive nerve elements were present, there might be still another subdivision of individual impressions in each cone. If there were only one nerve element for each cone, the refraction of the light would still have a functional significance, because light falling parallel to the axis of the cone is concentrated on the end of the nerve fibre, and that from other adjacent points in the field of vision is prevented from reaching it more effectively by this means than by septa.

[1] *Zur vergleichenden Physiologie des Gesichtssinnes.* Leipzig 1826. S. 349. Taf. VII. Fig. 5.

[2] J. MÜLLERS *Archiv. für Anat. u. Physiol.* 1852. S. 483.

Fig. 2 represents a horizontal section of the human eye magnified five times. The eyes of vertebrates are similar to the human eye in all important features. These eyes contain the following transparent elements:

1. The aqueous humor in the anterior chamber of the eye *B*.
2. The crystalline lens *A*.
3. The vitreous humor *C*.

These are enclosed by three concentrically situated systems of membranes or tunics.

1. The system of the *retina* (*i*) and *Zonula Zinnii* (*e*) which directly surrounds the vitreous humor and is attached in front to the lens *A*.

2. The system of the *uvea*, which consists of the *choroid* (*chorioidea*) (*g*) (indicated by the heavy black line), the ciliary body (*h*) and the *iris* (*b*). It surrounds the preceding systems together with the lens, and has but one opening, the *pupil*, situated in front of the lens.

3. The hard capsule of the eyeball, which, over the greater part of its posterior surface, consists of the opaque white *sclerotica*, and over the smaller anterior part, of the transparent cartilaginous *cornea*. In the living eye, one sees between the eyelids the anterior portion of the *sclerotica* (the white of the eye) and, behind the transparent convex cornea, the brown or blue ring-shaped iris, in the middle of which is the pupil.

The line passing through the middle of the cornea and the centre of the whole eye is known as the *axis of the eye*, because around this line the eye is practically symmetrical. A plane perpendicular to the axis through the widest part of the eyeball is called the *equatorial plane*.

In the following paragraphs a description will be given of the separate parts of the eye, which however will include only such details as are requisite for explaining the functions of the eye.[1]

The principal reference works on the comparative anatomy and physiology of the eye are:

J. Müller, *Zur Physiologie des Gesichtssinnes.* Leipzig 1826. S. 315.

R. Wagner, *Lehrbuch der vergleichenden Anatomie.* 1835.

J. Müller, *Handbuch der Physiologie des Menschen.* Coblenz 1840. Bd. II, S. 305.

R. Wagner, *Lehrbuch der speziellen Physiologie.* 1843. S. 383.

v. Siebold und Stannius, *Lehrbuch der vergleichenden Anatomie.* Berlin 1848.

Bergmann und Leuckart, *Anatomisch-physiologische Übersicht des Tierreichs.* Stuttgart 1852.

---

[1] ¶The description of the anatomy of the eye given in the next six sections is not only brief, as the author implies, but also in many respects inaccurate according to our present knowledge, as will be occasionally pointed out in footnotes. (D. H.)

The following give good descriptions of the structure of the human eye:

TH. SÖMMERING, *Abbildungen des menschlichen Auges.* Frankfurt a. M. 1801.—In Latin also.

C. F. TH. KRAUSE, *Handbuch der menschlichen Anatomie.* Hannover 1842. Bd. I, T. II.
S. 511—551.—Contains also earlier literature on the anatomy of the eye. S. 733-745.

E. BRÜCKE, *Anatomische Beschreibung des menschlichen Augapfels.* Berlin 1847.

W. BOWMAN, *Lectures on the parts concerned in the operations on the eye and on the structure of
⌐the retina and the vitreous humour.* London 1849.

A. KÖLLIKER, *Mikroskopische Anatomie oder Gewebelehre des Menschen.* Leipzig 1854.
Bd II, S. 605.—More recent literature also, S. 734-736.

DUJARDIN, Remarques sur certaines dispositions de l'appareil de la vision chez les insectes.
C. R. XLII, 941. Inst. 1856, 194.

§2. Sclerotica and Cornea

The sclerotica of the eye (σκληρòν, *tunica albuginea, sclerotica dura,*
tough membrane) encloses the greater part of the eyeball, controls its
form and protects it from external injury. Its outer form is distinctly
different from that of a sphere; the posterior side being quite flattened,
while along the equator it is a little indented above and below and on
the right and left sides by the pressure of the rectus muscles of the eye.
In between these four places it bulges considerably. In most individuals the greatest diameter of the eyeball passes from a point on the
upper nasal side to one on the lower temporal side. In front the
sclerotica passes over into the very convex cornea; at the back a little
toward the nasal side, it is perforated for the passage of the optic
nerve (*nervus opticus*), (Fig. 2, *d*), and is here continuous with the
fibrous covering of the latter. The sclerotica is thicker both in front
and behind than it is at the equator of the eye, as shown in the figure.
The anterior thickening is caused by the attachment of the tendons
of the motor muscles of the eye to the sclerotica and their fusion with
it. The place of insertion of the internal rectus is at *m*, and that of
the external rectus is at *n*.

The sclerotica is composed of fibrous tissue. It is white, only
slightly translucent, flexible and quite inelastic. It may be classed
with the collagenous substances on the basis of its chemical composition. Microscopically, it consists of a very dense felt-work of connective tissue fibres, which in the main run parallel to the surface,
thereby making it possible to split the tunic in imperfect layers.
Between these, as in other tendons, lies a network of very delicate
elastic fibres which show thickenings containing nuclear remnants at
those places where their cells of origin were once located.

The cornea is set into the anterior margin of the sclerotica and has
the general shape of a very convex watch-glass. Its anterior surface
closely approximates the form of a segment of a prolate spheroid
generated by the revolution of an ellipse around its axis major. The
end of this axis lies at the centre of the cornea. The shape of the

posterior surface is not definitely known. In adults the cornea is somewhat thinner in the middle than at the periphery.

The cornea consists of the following layers from the outside inwards:

1. An *epithelium*,[1] composed of stratified, flat cells of horny consistency (pavement epithelium), indicated in the figure by the broken line *ff*. It is continuous with the conjunctiva of the eyelids. The anterior surface is kept smooth and moist by a continual flow of tear fluid.

2. The fibrous layer of the cornea (*Substantia propria corneae*)[2] is the thickest of them all and is left white in the figure. Its chemical composition places it among the cartilages, as on boiling it gives chondrin. It consists of a felt-work of fibres similar to those of the sclerotica except that the fibres are united in flat bundles lying parallel to the surface of the cornea; and hence the cornea also may be divided in imperfect layers. In the adult the cornea contains no blood vessels. However, between the bundles of fibres, there is a system of branched nucleated cells resembling undeveloped elastic tissue as found in many organs rich in connective tissue. It is possible that these cells may carry on the necessary exchange of fluids for the nutrition of the substance of the cornea. The substance of the cornea appears to be entirely transparent by ordinary illumination. However, if considerable light is concentrated by a convex lens on a point of the cornea, it appears cloudy, as the amount of light reflected by the surfaces of its microscopical components becomes sufficient to be visible under these conditions.

3. The posterior homogeneous membrane (*Membrana Descemeti, Membrana Demoursii*, etc.) is a structureless, transparent, fragile membrane, 0.007 to 0.015 mm in thickness. It rolls up when separated from the cornea. It resembles elastic tissue[3] in its resistance to the action of boiling water, acids and hydroxides. On the surface next the aqueous humor, it bears a layer of large polygonal epithelial cells,[4] indicated by the dotted line on the inner surface of the cornea (Fig. 2).

The plane of union between cornea and sclerotica is not perpendicular to the surface of the eyeball, but passes inwards and backwards,

[1] ¶The corneal epithelium (*conjunctiva*) is composed of about five rows of cells; one row of cylindrical cells, the basal cells; two rows of polyhedral cells in the middle layer; and the external layer of two rows of flattened cells. (D. H.)

[2] ¶The anterior homogeneous membrane or membrane of Bowman is now regarded as the second layer of the cornea, the *substantia propria* being the third. (D. H.)

[3] ¶Sasse (Zur Chemie der Descemet'schen Membran, *Unters. d. physiol. Inst. Univ. Heidelberg*, Bd. 2, 1879) has demonstrated that the tissue of the anterior and posterior homogeneous membranes is not identical with elastic tissue. (D. H.)

[4] ¶This layer is usually considered as a separate layer, the endothelium of the cornea. (D. H.)

the sclerotica overlapping on the outer surface, the cornea on the inner. On the inner surface the margin of the cornea forms a fairly regular circle. On the outer surface, on the contrary, it appears to be a horizontal oval, as the sclerotica overlaps it above and below more than on the sides. At this plane of union, the fibres of the cornea are directly continuous with those of the sclerotica.

Fig. 3.

The membrane of DESCEMET, however, acts quite differently at the border of the cornea. A cross-section of this region is shown in Fig. 3, where the sclerotica is marked S, the cornea C, its external epithelium c, passing over into the conjunctiva D, and the membrane of DESCEMET d. From f a network of elastic fibres arises between the membrane of DESCEMET and the substance of the cornea, while the former appears to end abruptly at this point. By the separation of this layer of elastic fibres from the sclerotica and its fusion with the lamella a, the canal of SCHLEMM is formed further back. This is a ring-shaped canal situated at the boundary between cornea and sclerotica. Laterally it is bounded by the sclerotica, but its medial wall consists of elastic tissue in front and of fibrous tissue behind. To this inner wall the muscular portions of the uvea are attached. The canal of SCHLEMM appears to carry blood.

Although measurements of the dimensions of the eye are of the greatest importance in physiological optics, many difficulties are usually involved in executing them, in the first place because the form of the entire eyeball and of its individual parts varies greatly in different eyes, and, secondly, because after death the eye undergoes many changes. The individual variations are so great that the averages of observations on different eyes should be used only with great caution. For the determination of exact and accurate results, all important measurements must be made on the same eye.

The external form of the eyeball is determined by the pressure of the fluids which it contains. Immediately after death a majority of its blood vessels empty themselves, which naturally produces a diminution in the pressure. The volume of the fluids inside the eye gradually becomes reduced still further by endosmotic paths, so that the eyeball becomes flaccid and the tunics, especially the cornea, become wrinkled. Either measurements on the form of the eyeball must be made on very fresh eyes, or the pressure must be artificially restored, as BRÜCKE[1] did, by passing a canula through the optic nerve and connecting it with a vertical tube containing a column of water about 0.4 m in height. These methods suffice for the measurement of the different diameters of the eyeball, but in order to measure one of the most

[1] E. BRÜCKE, *Anat. Beschreibung des menschl. Augapfels.* Berlin 1847. S. 4.

important optical elements of the eye, the convexity of the cornea, it is not sufficient merely to restore the pressure approximately. The radius of curvature at the vertex of the cornea becomes greater in direct proportion to the pressure, as the writer has found by a method of measurement described below. The reason of this is probably to be found in the fact that a membranous covering which contains fluid must approach more and more the form of a sphere in proportion as the internal pressure of the fluid increases, because for a given superficial area a sphere has the greatest volume. When this happens in the eye, the constriction between the cornea and the sclerotica must be pushed out and as a result the cornea becomes less convex.

Under these circumstances it is evidently an essential requirement to determine all the more important dimensions of the eyeball as far as possible by measurements of the eyes of living persons.

The earlier measurements of the eye were usually made with compasses. C. KRAUSE, who carried out a very extensive system of measurements, measured the external dimensions of the eye with this instrument. Then he cut the eyes in half along a line which had been previously marked out, using a razor to section the cornea, iris and lens, and cutting the sclerotica with scissors. Next he laid the halves in a bowl full of egg-albumen solution with the cut surfaces just below the surface of the fluid. Thus he measured the dimensions of the cross sections partly with compasses, partly with a barred glass micrometer in the ocular of a microscope of low magnification, and partly with a glass ruled in squares which he laid upon the surface of the fluid. He had many opportunities of using very fresh eyes. The external measurements of the sclerotica obtained from these may be considered as thoroughly reliable, but the convexity of the cornea, which depends upon the pressure of the fluids, must have been greatly altered in the sectioned eyes.

KRAUSE's table for the form of eight eyeballs is appended below. No. I is that of a drowned man 30 years old; No. II is the right eye of a man 60 years old who died from having his throat cut; Nos. III and IV are the left and right eyes of a man 40 years old who was hanged; Nos. V and VI and Nos. VII and VIII are the left and right eyes of two men, 20 and 21 years old, respectively, both of whom were executed by the sword. The measurements are given in Paris lines.[1]

| No. | Axis of the eye | | Diameter | | | | | |
| | outer | inner | transverse | perpendicular | | diagonal | | smaller |
				outer	inner	larger outer	inner	
I.	10.9	9.85	10.9	10.8	9.9	11.25	10.3	
II.	11.05	10.0		10.3	9.4	11.1	10.2	11.05
{ III.	10.7	9.8	10.7	10.5	9.6	11	10.2	10.6
{ IV.	10.5	9.5	10.6	10.3	9.5	10.9	10.1	10.7
{ V.	10.8	9.55	10.9	10.55	9.6	11.3	10.35	11
{ VI.	10.8	9.55	11	10.6	9.45	11.3	10.2	11.1
{ VII.	10.65	9.4	10.75	10.3	9.45	10.75	9.6	10.75
{ VIII.	10.65	9.45	10.75	10.3	9.15	10.9	9.75	10.7

BRÜCKE has made measurements on eyes which were distended by a water pressure of 4 decimetres. He maintains that the axis of the eyeball varies between 23 and 26 mm, the greatest horizontal diameter between 22.8 and 26 mm, and the greatest vertical diameter between 21.5 and 25 mm.

[1] 1 Paris line = 2.2558 mm. N.

C. KRAUSE compares the inner convexity of the sclerotica with the surface of an ellipsoid of revolution. The axes which he has calculated and his results concerning the thickness of the cornea and sclerotica at different points are given in the following table.

No.	Thickness of the Sclerotica			Semi-axes of the ellipsoid of the posterior corneal surface		Thickness of the cornea	
	along the optic axis	at the equator	at the corneal border	major	minor	centre	edge
I.	0.55	0.45	0.35	5.12	4.45	0.4	0.5
II.	0.5	0.35		5.05	4.15	0.35	0.5
III.	0.45	0.4	0.35	5.12	4.23	0.4	0.5
IV.	0.5	0.4	0.3	5.07	4.41	0.4	0.45
V.	0.65	0.4	0.3	5.14	4.58	0.5	0.55
VI.	0.65	0.5	0.3	5.05	4.43	0.48	0.55
VII.	0.55	0.5	0.4	5.05	4.41	0.53	0.63
VIII.	0.6	0.5	0.4	4.93	4 19	0.5	0.62

C. KRAUSE's measurements of the form of the cornea have been omitted, because his method does not appear to the writer to be sufficiently trustworthy in such an important matter. It may be observed that he pronounced the anterior surface of the cornea to be spheroidal and the posterior surface to be that of a paraboloid of revolution near its vertex. In the case of several corneae examined by the writer the thickness in the middle half of the cross section was found to be nearly constant and increased rapidly only near the periphery, so that in the middle of the vault the two surfaces appeared to be almost concentric.

KOHLRAUSCH attempted to measure the radius of curvature of the cornea in the living eye by determining the size of the reflex image in it. For purposes of examination, the patient sat on a very masssive stool with a high back. His head was held by a special apparatus so that he could be comfortable and passive at the same time. He fixed his eyes on a little white spot in the centre of the objective of a KEPLER telescope placed two to three feet away. The telescope was directed towards the eye in such a manner that the white spot lay in the same horizontal plane as the vertex of the cornea. Two fine threads were stretched parallel to each other in the focal plane of the ocular. These two parallel lines could be moved nearer together or farther apart by means of a screw. On either side, and in the same horizontal plane, a light was placed whose rays fell upon the eye through a round opening in a small screen and were reflected from the cornea in such a manner that two small images of the luminous points were seen through the telescope. When the threads were exactly aligned on these images, a finely divided rule was placed in front of the eye and the separation of the images in the cornea read off on it. The radius of the cornea may be approximately calculated from the follov/ing data: (1) the amount of separation of the images, (2) the distances of the eye from the openings in the screen and from the centre of the objective, and (3) the distance between the two points last mentioned.

KOHLRAUSCH obtained an average of 3.495 Paris lines (7.87mm) for measurements on twelve eyes, the smallest value being 3.35, the highest 3.62. The probable error of the individual observations was calculated as 0.02 Paris lines.

By a similar, but not accurately described method, SENFF determined not only the radius of curvature, but also the ellipticity of the cornea, his results being given in the following table.

	Radius of curvature at vertex	Square of the eccentricity	Axis major	Axis minor	α
Right eye. Vertical	7.796	0.1753	9.452	8.583	3.6°
Right eye. Horizontal	7.794	0.2531	10.435	9.019	2.9°
Left eye. Vertical	7.746	0.4492	11.243	8.344	1.6°

SENFF calls the angle between the vertex of the ellipse and the end point of the axis of the eye the angle α. In the vertical section the vertex of the ellipse lies below the end point of the axis of the eye, and in the horizontal section it is situated more outwards. Apparently what SENFF means here by the "axis of the eye" is the line which is hereafter defined as the "visual axis" (*Gesichtslinie*) of the eye.

In making these measurements the greatest difficulty is to keep the patient's eye and head steady. In any method in which images are measured and in which it is necessary to read the mark on a scale which corresponds to one edge of the corneal image and then to read that which coincides with the other edge, even the slightest movement of the head from side to side between the two readings will add to or subtract from the size of the image as measured. Accordingly, the author has constructed an instrument whereby it is possible to make these and other measurements of the eye accurately and quite independently of small movements of the head, and which is therefore called an *ophthalmometer*, although it may be advantageously used also for making many other measurements besides, especially measurements of optical images.

If an object is observed through a glass plate with plane parallel faces, which is held obliquely to the line of vision, it will be seen in its natural size, but shifted slightly to one side. This displacement increases as the angle is diminished between the direction of the rays of light and the surface of the plate. The ophthalmometer is essentially a telescope, adapted to vision at short distances, having two glass plates placed close together, in front of its objective. They are so adjusted that over one half of the objective, the observer sees through one plate, and over the other half through the other plate. If the two plates are in a plane perpendicular to the axis of the telescope, only a single image of the object in question will be seen. If, however, both plates are rotated a little in opposite directions, the single image will be divided into two images, whose distance apart will increase with the angle through which the plates are turned. This separation of the twin images may be calculated from the angles which the plates make with the axis of the telescope. If the two images of a line which is to be measured are so adjusted that they just touch at their ends, the length of the object-line is equal to the distance between a pair of corresponding points of the two images and may be calculated from it.

The instrument itself is shown in Fig. 4 in vertical section and in Fig. 5 in horizontal section, one-half actual size. The rectangular box $B_1B_1B_2B_2$ containing the adjustable glass plates is attached to the end of the telescope A next the object-glass. In Fig. 4, the side wall of the box has been removed and all parts in the lower half are drawn as though sectioned in the middle vertical plane. The base of the box is formed by a strong rectangular frame, shown in Fig. 4, running around the box; and to it thin brass plates are fastened to form the walls, as may be seen in Fig. 5. Conical holes are drilled in the middle of the horizontal portion of the frame, in which the axles CC of the two plates rotate. Outside the box each axle has a cylindrical disc d which is graduated in degrees on the curved surface. At a there is a vernier scale reading

to tenths of a degree. Inside the box, each axle carries a toothed wheel *ee*
and a metal frame *g* in which the glass plate *f* is fastened. The frame of each
plate has only three sides, the side turned towards the other glass plate being
missing. The two glass plates constituted originally a single plane parallel

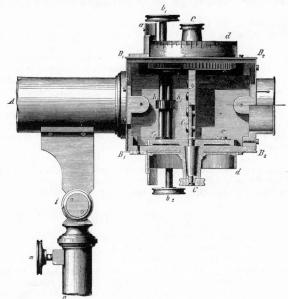

Fig. 4.

plate. A complete metal frame was made for this plate and fastened between
the surfaces of the two toothed wheels. Then the axles were rounded off on a
lathe and finally the frame was cut through in the middle. The glass plate
was cut through in the same manner, and each half fastened in its corresponding half of the frame. Thus an exact adjustment of the positions of the plates
on the two axles was accomplished. The toothed wheels are moved by the
sprockets c_1 and c_2 which are rigidly connected with the axles b_1c_1 and b_2c_2.

Moreover, each of these axles has a
sprocket *h* in the middle. If the
knob at b_1 is turned, the lower
toothed wheel controlling the lower
glass plate will be moved by means
of the sprocket c_1. Furthermore,
the sprocket h_1 engages with the
sprocket h_2 and rotates the second
axle b_2c_2 by an equal amount in the
opposite direction. As a result of
this the sprocket c_2 acts upon the
upper toothed wheel connected with
the upper glass plate and turns it

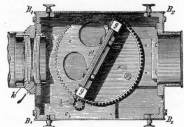

Fig. 5.

through an angle almost as large as that of the lower plate. The rotation of each plate is measured by the graduated discs attached to the axles
on the outside of the box.

It is necessary to employ two plates which are rotated at approximately the same angle because the images of the object viewed through the plates will not only be displaced laterally, but will also be brought a little nearer together. If the amount of this approximation is unequal for the two images of the same object, the telescope cannot be focused exactly on both simultaneously.

The objective of the telescope is composed of two lens-systems k and l. The achromatic doublet k is used by itself when the telescope is to be focused on a distant object. Its double convex crown glass lens, as usual, is turned towards the object. On the other hand, when the object is very close, a single lens-system does not give a good image, because it is designed to concentrate parallel rays at a point. Hence, the writer has inserted a second achromatic doublet l, with its crown glass lens turned towards the other doublet. If now the object is in the first focal plane of this second system, the rays that issue from it will be bundles of parallel rays, which in turn will be concentrated by the first system at its second focal point. Thus sharper images are obtained. In the writer's own instrument the focal lengths of k and l are 6 inches and 16 inches, respectively. The telescope is supported on an upright n in which a cylindrical bar fits so that the instrument can be turned and at the same time raised or lowered. The telescope itself is fastened to this bar by a hinge joint i. Thus the axis of the telescope can be pointed in any direction. And, finally, the box with the glass plates can be turned around the end of the telescope.

Let us proceed now to show how the shifting of the images may be found from the angle of rotation of the glass plates.

In Fig. 6 $A_1A_1A_2A_2$ represents one of the glass plates; and the straight lines a_1c_1, c_1c_2, and c_2a_2 show the path of a ray which traverses it. The normals to the two faces at entrance and emergence are $b_1c_1d_2$ and $b_2c_2d_1$, respectively. The angle of incidence $b_1c_1a_1$, which is equal to the angle $b_2c_2a_2$, is marked a, and the angle of refraction $d_2c_1c_2$, which is equal to $c_1c_2d_1$, is marked β. The thickness of the plate is denoted by h. The luminous point a_1 appears to an eye below the plate to lie in the prolongation of a_2c_2 backwards. If x denotes the length of the perpendicular a_1f drawn from a_1 to the prolongation of the emergent ray, this distance x will be the apparent lateral shifting of the luminous point. Now

$$x = c_1c_2.\sin \angle c_1c_2f$$
$$c_1c_2 = \frac{h}{\cos \beta}$$
$$\angle c_1c_2f = \angle d_1c_2f - \angle d_1c_2c_1$$
$$= a - \beta$$
$$x = h.\frac{\sin(a-\beta)}{\cos\beta}.$$

The angle a is measured by the instrument. The thickness of the glass plate h must be known, as well as its index of refraction n with respect to air. Then

$$\sin a = n.\sin \beta,$$

from which β may be calculated, and then all the factors for computing the value of x are known. If two rotatable glass plates are used, as in the instrument above described, the separation E of two luminous points, whose images have been superposed, will be twice as great as x; that is,

$$E = 2h\frac{\sin (a-\beta)}{\cos \beta}.$$

Lacking other ways of doing it, the magnitudes denoted by n and h can be ascertained by measurements made with the instrument itself, by finding the angle through which the plates have to be turned to superpose each division of an accurate scale on the next following division or on every second or third

division, etc. In this way a series of correlated values is obtained for x and a,
from which h and n may be calculated by
a suitable process of elimination. If
many observations are to be made, it is
well to prepare a table for E for every
degree from 0° to 60°.[1]

The same adjustment of the double
images that is found for a rotation of a
degrees occurs also for a rotation of $-a$
and likewise for $(180° - a)$ or $(a - 180°)$.
In order to eliminate errors in the disc
scale and in the parallelism of the faces
of the glass plates, it is advisable to repeat
each measurement in these four positions
and to take the average of the four results
thus obtained.

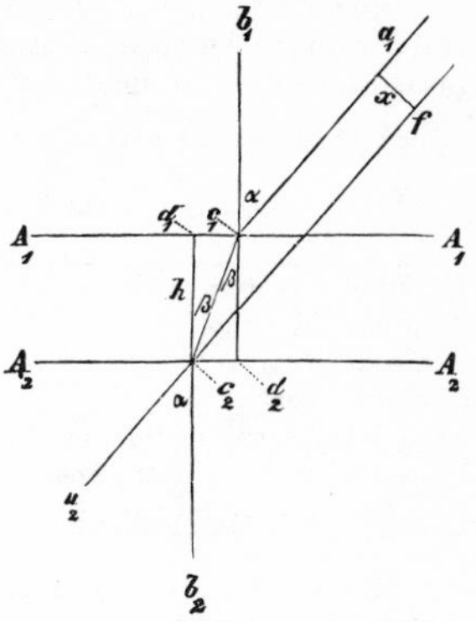

Fig. 6.

One of the most important advantages
of the ophthalmometer is that the linear
magnitude of the apparent distance of its double images is independent of
the distance of the object, so that it is not necessary to know the latter in
order to make the measurements.

If the instrument described is used for the measurement of a corneal
image, small movements of the head of the subject do not introduce a disturbing factor, inasmuch as both images will always move in the same way, and
their relative positions will not be altered. If at the same time the object
which is responsible for the corneal image is far enough away, so that small
movements of the head are negligible in comparison with its distance, the size
of the image also will not be noticeably affected by these movements, and the
head can be kept steady enough by providing an easy support for the chin.

A bright window may be chosen as object for the image in the cornea. If
the parallel boundaries of two images of such a bright surface are adjusted in
contact in the ophthalmometer, the eye of the observer will be quite sensitive
to any overlapping or separation of the two images, which will be noticeable
at once in virtue of a white or black line between the two uniformly illuminated
fields. On the other hand, a scale placed far enough away may
be used as object if one of its divisions is marked by a small lamp and another
preferably by two such lamps placed close together. The measurement in this
case consists in adjusting one of the images of the single lamp midway between
that of the pair of lamps. This method of adjustment is capable of great
accuracy, as has been observed by BESSEL in the measurement of stellar
parallaxes with the heliometer.

The calculation of the radius of curvature of the cornea is very simple
provided the reflex image as measured is relatively small in comparison. In
this case the size of the object is to its distance from the eye in the same ratio
as the size of the image is to half the radius of curvature; so that the latter
may then be calculated from this proportion. The ellipticity of the cornea
may also be determined in this way, by measuring the size of the reflex image
in each position of the eye when, by appropriate variations of the point of
fixation, the eye is made to turn through successive known angles, both laterally and vertically. Thus the various values of the radius of curvature over
the different parts of the cornea are calculated first of all, whence are computed
the elements of the ellipsoid which the cornea approximately resembles in
form.

---

[1] In the first edition h occurs here instead of E, evidently an error in the manuscript
or a typographical error. N.

Appended below are the elements of the horizontal sections of the cornea of three women between 25 and 30 years of age, with whose eyes a series of measurements were made by the author.

Designation of the Eye	O.H.	B. P.	J. H.
Radius of curvature at the vertex............	7.338	7.646	8.154
Square of the eccentricity..................	0.4367	0.2430	0.3037
Semi-axis major..........................	13.027	10.100	11.711
Semi-axis minor..........................	9.777	8.788	9.772
Angle between axis major and visual axis.....	4. 19'	6° 43'	7° 35'
Horizontal diameter of the area.............	11.64	11.64	12.092
Distance of the vertex from the base........	2.560	2.531	2.511

The centre of the anterior surface of the cornea in all three of these eyes corresponds almost exactly with the vertex of the ellipse. The visual axis lies on the nasal side of the forward extremity of the axis major of the corneal ellipsoid.

Measurements of the eyeball will be found in the following:

1723–30. PETIT in *Mem. de l'Acad. des sciences de Paris.* 1723. p. 54.—1725. p. 18.—1726. p. 375.—1728. p. 408.—1730. p. 4.

1738. JURIN, *Essay upon distinct and indistinct vision.* p. 141 in SMITH's *Compleat System of Optics.*

1739. HELSHAM, *Course of Lectures on Natural Philosophy.* London 1739.

1740. WINTRINGHAM, *Experimental Inquiry on some parts of the animal structure.* London, 1740.

1801. TH. YOUNG, *Philos. Transact.* 1801. p. 23.

1818. D. W. SOEMMERING, *De oculorum hominis animaliumque sectione horizontali.* Göttingen 1818. p. 79*.

1819. BREWSTER in *Edinburgh Philos. Journal.* 1819. No. I. p. 47.

1828. G. R. TREVIRANUS, *Beiträge zur Anat. und Physiol. der Sinneswerkzeuge.* Bremen 1828. Heft I. S. 20*.—This work contains a summary of the results of earlier investigators.

1832. C. KRAUSE, Bemerkungen über den Bau und die Dimensionen des menschlichen Auges, in MECKELS *Archiv. für Anatomie und Physiol.* Bd. VI. S. 86* (Description of the methods and measurements in two eyes.) Extract from this in POGGEN-DORFFS *Ann.* XXXI. S. 93*.

1836. C. KRAUSE in POGGENDORFFS *Ann.* XXXIX. S. 529* (Measurements of 8 human eyes).

1839. KOHLRAUSCH über die Messung des Radius der Vorderfläche der Hornhaut am lebenden menschlichen Auge, in OKENS *Isis.* Jahrg. 1840. S. 886*.

1846. SENFF in R. WAGNERS *Handwörterbuch der Physiol.* Bd. III. Abt. 1. Art.: Sehen. S. 271*.

1847. E. BRÜCKE, *Beschreibung des menschl. Augapfels.* S. 4 and 45*.

1854. H. HELMHOLTZ, in GRAEFES *Archiv. für Ophthalmologie.* II. S. 3.

1855. SAPPEY, *Gazette medicale.* No. 26, 27.

1857. ARLT, *Archiv. f. Ophthalmologie.* III, 2. S. 87.

1858. NUNNELEY, *On the organs of vision.* London. p. 129.

1859. J. H. KNAPP, *Die Krümmung der Hornhaut des menschlichen Auges. Habilitationsschrift.* Heidelberg 1859. Also: *Arch. f. Ophthalm.* VI, 2. S. 1-52.

1860. MEYERSTEIN, Beschreibung eines Ophthalmometers nach HELMHOLTZ. POGGENDORFFS *Ann.* CXI. S. 415-425, and HENLE u. PFEUFERS *Zft.* XI. S. 185-192.

1861. v. Jäger, *Über die Einstellung des dioptrischen Apparates im menschlichen Auge.* Wien.

1864. R. Schelske, Über das Verhältnis des intraoculären Druckes zur Hornhautkrümmung. *Arch. f. Ophthalm.* X, 2. S. 1-46.

§3. The Uvea

The *tunica uvea*[1] derives its name from its resemblance to a dark grape from which the stem has been removed. The opening for the stem corresponds to the pupil. The dark colour of this tunic is produced by the layer of pigment cells on its inner surface and in its stroma. The uvea is attached to the sclerotica in two places, namely, in the rear at the entrance of the optic nerve (Fig. 2, *d*) and in front at the inner wall of Schlemm's canal *a*. The portion marked *abba*, which is the iris, lies in front of and within this latter line of attachment, right behind the cornea. The posterior portion, which lies in contact with the inner surface of the sclerotica, is called the *choroid (chorioidea)*.

The choroid, composed chiefly of blood vessels bound together by a characteristic connective tissue, forms a thin, dark membrane in the posterior portion of the eyeball. Kölliker considers this connective tissue to be undeveloped elastic tissue. It consists of branched cells, some of which are pigmented, having very finely divided processes which are felted together. This peculiar stroma binds the arteries and veins of the choroid together beneath the sclerotica.[2] Inside this layer lies the looser layer of capillary vessels (*membrana chorio-capillaris*), which in turn is covered by the pigment cells on the surface towards the retina.[3] These pigment cells form a single layer towards the posterior part of the choroid, but become stratified[4] towards the ciliary body. Their nuclei are to be seen usually as a lighter area between the black pigment granules. In Fig. 7 (copied from Kölliker) a surface view of these cells is shown at *a* and a side view at *b*. The pigment granules, which are small, flattened and rod-like, 0.0016 mm in length, are shown at *c*. These granules may be destroyed by chlorine and potassium hydroxide.

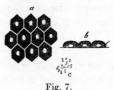

Fig. 7.

In front, the *ciliary muscle (tensor chorioideae, musculus* Brückianus) is attached to the outer surface of the choroid, while the *ciliary proc-*

---

[1] ¶*Tunica uvea* (*uva*, L., a grape), uveal tract, more frequently termed *tunica vasculosa,* includes the *tunica chorioidea* (Choroid from Greek *chorion,* meaning a membrane, formerly spelled chorioid), the ciliary body and the iris. (D. H.)

[2] ¶The tunica choroidea is usually divided into three layers, from without inwards: *lamina suprachorioidea, lamina vasculosa, lamina choriocapillaris.* (D. H.)

[3] ¶The pigment cells, which are the sole derivatives of the outer layer of the optic cup, are, in consequence of this fact, now considered the outermost layer of the retina. (D. H.)

[4] ¶This is an error. The retinal pigment cells are not stratified at any point, though they may appear so in oblique sections. (D. H.)

esses (*processus ciliares*) arise from its inner surface. They are plaited and contain a network of blood vessels. The section in Fig. 2 is represented as passing through a ciliary process *c* on the left side, while on the right side it passes between two such processes, so that there only the ciliary muscle *h* is visible. The fibres of the ciliary muscle originate at the inner wall of Schlemm's canal where the elastic and collagenous tissues unite (at *a* in Figs. 2 and 3); whence they extend backwards along the external surface of the choroid and are inserted in this membrane. The fibres of this muscle are of the so-called visceral type, such as we find in most of the involuntary muscles. They are provided with longitudinally oval nuclei and are not cross-striated. Brücke, who discovered this muscle, maintained that it stretched the choroid (together with the retina and hyaloid membrane closely attached to it at *g*) over the vitreous humor. Donders, on the other hand, supposes that the choroid constitutes its fixed point of origin, and that it stretches the elastic part of the inner wall of Schlemm's canal and consequently pulls the base of the iris backwards. Both of these actions probably occur together (see §12).

The ciliary processes are membranous folds of the choroid, which lie in the meridional planes of the eye. They are from 70 to 72 in number. They arise in the neighbourhood of the anterior border of the retina[1] (Fig. 2, *g*), increasing in height as they pass forwards and attain their greatest height near the external edge of the lens. From this point their height rapidly falls off, and their anterior extremities blend with the posterior surface of the iris. Their projecting sharp boundaries are often free from pigment and stand out as white lines when the ciliary region is viewed from behind through the vitreous humor. The ciliary processes contain a large number of blood vessels bound together by a stroma similar to that found in the choroid.

The *iris*, the most anterior part of the tunica uvea, forms a movable diaphragm for the eye. It arises in common with the ciliary muscle at the inner wall of Schlemm's canal at the posterior edge of the fibrous portion and is bound to the elastic portion of this inner wall (Fig. 3, *b*) by a network of elastic fibres which run freely through the aqueous humor. These elastic fibres form the *ligamentum iridis pectinatum*. Thence the iris extends medially to its pupillary margin, lying on the anterior surface of the lens, and consequently is slightly arched in front. It contains smooth muscle fibres, forming two muscles:

1. The *pupillary sphincter* (*musculus contractor sive sphincter pupillae*), surrounds the pupillary margin in the form of a ring about 1 mm wide. It lies in front of the pigment layer, but behind the chief nerves and vessels passing to the pupillary margin. Its fibres run in

[1] ¶At the *ora serrata*. (D. H.)

concentric circles and so decrease the size of the pupil by their contraction.

2. The *dilatator of the pupil (musculus dilatator pupillae)*. The fibres of this muscle originate in the inner wall of SCHLEMM's canal and perhaps also in the fibres of the *ligamentum pectinatum*. They proceed to the posterior surface of the iris, bound together in a network passing medially to lose themselves in the substance of the sphincter.

The stroma of the iris is connective tissue. It is covered behind by the layer of pigment cells and in front by epithelium. This stroma frequently contains pigment cells, in which case the colour of the iris is brown. In their absence from the stroma, this semi-opaque medium in front of the dark posterior pigment cells causes the iris to appear blue.

The arrangement of the blood vascular system of the tunica uvea is very characteristic. As already indicated, the vessels make up the greatest portion of the mass of this coat. Its arteries (*arteriae ciliares posticae breves*, for the choroid and ciliary processes; *arteriae posticae longae* and *anticae*, for the iris) enter through the sclerotica, and communicate with the veins not only through a fine capillary network, as elsewhere in the body, but also through rather large connecting vessels which arise in the arteries of the choroid in delicate, fan-like arches and reunite to enter the veins (*venae vorticosae*). The *arteriae ciliares posticae breves*, about 20 small twigs, penetrate the sclerotica on its posterior surface, and branch dichotomously as they pass forwards. One portion pours blood through a capillary network which lies on the inner side of the choroid to supply the retina and the other supplies the veins through the wide communicating vessels of the *venae vorticosae*. Some of these veins (*vasa vorticosa*) leave the eyeball at its equator, and others (*venae ciliares posticae*) at the posterior portion of the sclerotica. Most of the branches of these arteries, however, pass forwards into the ciliary processes and form there a vascular network, from which recurrent branches pass into the anterior arches of the vortices. The vascular net of the iris receives some tributaries from that of the ciliary processes, but gets the greater volume of its blood supply through special vessels. Some of these penetrate the sclerotica at the back (*arteriae ciliares posticae longae*) and run forwards between the choroid and the sclerotica as far as the ciliary muscle, while others penetrate in front (*arteriae ciliares anticae*). These vessels form two anåstomosing or interlacing vascular circles, one on the peripheral border of the iris (*circulus arteriosus iridis major*), the other near the pupillary margin (*circulus arteriosus iridis minor*). The iris is thickest over the latter and has a bulge on its anterior surface at this place.

In an uninjured eye the iris is visible through the cornea. Refraction causes it to appear nearer the cornea and therefore more convex than it actually is. On the other hand, if the eye of a cadaver is placed under water (which has approximately the same index of refraction as the aqueous humor), refraction is almost abolished, and then the iris appears but slightly convex in its natural form and position. In order to obtain a correct image of the iris of the living eye, J. CZERMAK[1] invented an instrument called the *orthoscope.* For all practical purposes it is a small box with glass walls which is used in such a manner that the eye to be examined forms its back side. Having been

 applied to the eye, it is then filled with water. The instrument illustrated in Fig. 8 has a bottom *fcb*, and a side wall *gab*, placed next the nose, both made of sheet metal. Their free edges are shaped to fit the face closely. The front *abcd* and the side *cdef* are made of flat glass plates. In order to make the edges against the face water-tight, CZERMAK recommended placing kneaded bread-crumbs on the face and pressing

Fig. 8. the rim of the instrument into them. The eye being shut at first, water from 29 to 33° C is poured into the box and the eye opened. Seen from the side, the cornea appears as a transparent, convex bladder, while the iris is seen to be an almost flat curtain across its base.

In this method there might be some doubt as to whether the form of the iris were not changed a little either by the refraction between the cornea and the water or by that between the cornea and the aqueous humor. A correct knowledge of the form and position of the iris is very important for the theory of the accommodation of the eye. Therefore, other methods of examination will be described here. An easy way of observing the iris relief is as follows: A light is placed a little to one side in front of the eye to be observed, and with the aid of a convex lens of 2-inch focus and relatively large aperture its rays are concentrated on a point of the cornea, so as to form there an image of the source. The cornea appears opaque at the illuminated spot. The focal point on the cornea constitutes a new source of illumination, from which the rays proceed directly to the iris without further refraction. If they fall on it obliquely, shadows of various lengths will be seen on the iris, due to the thickening which contains the *circulus arteriosus minor.* By means of these shadows, the amount of the forward or backward displacement of individual parts of the iris may easily be determined. When this method is used, the iris of a myopic eye is often so flat that there are no deep shadows on it. In normal eyes, on the contrary, prominent shadows are found surrounding the pupil. If the illuminating focal point is about 1 mm from the edge of the cornea, the shadows will frequently extend to the peripheral edge of the iris.

In order to realize the important fact that the iris lies close against the lens in the living eye, the same process may be employed, except that the focal point of the convex lens should be made to fall a little to one side on the anterior surface of the crystalline lens. Strongly illuminated in this way, the substance of the crystalline lens appears milky, and no shadows are cast by the iris. This is even better shown by the reflex from the anterior surface of the lens. In Fig. 9, C_1C_2 represents a convex spherical mirror, with a dark screen *DE* having an opening *FG* placed in front of it. The observer's eye is supposed to be at *A* and a source of light at *B*. If the ray of light *BF* passing the edge of the aperture at *F* is reflected at *H* along the line *HA*, the eye can get no light reflected from the part of the mirror between *H* and C_1 except such light as may come from the dark rear surface of the diaphragm

[1] J. CZERMAK, *Prager Vierteljahrsschrift für prakt. Heilkunde.* Bd. XXXII. S. 154. 1851.

For example, light emanating from the point K of the diaphragm will be reflected into the eye along JA. Therefore, the eye must see a dark area of the surface of the mirror between F and H whenever the edge of the diaphragm is not in intimate contact with the reflecting surface. The validity of this statement may be tested on any convex reflecting surface, as for example a convex metal knob, for which there has been made a suitable black diaphragm with round opening. Only in case the edge of the opening lies close against the surface can the reflex images of surrounding objects in the mirror reach the edge of the diaphragm.

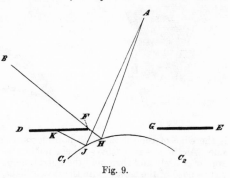

Fig. 9.

If, however, there is a little space between the diaphragm and the reflecting surface, a dark line will be seen between the edge of the opening next the eye and the image in the mirror.

The surfaces of the crystalline lens also reflect some light, but not very much. These reflexes[1] may be seen when the eye is in a dark room where there is only one source of illumination. The light is adjusted in front of the eye a little to one side of the prolongation of the optical axis. The observer looks into the eye from the other side, in such fashion that his visual axis makes about the same angle with the optical axis as the incident rays. Near the prominent bright corneal reflex two other much fainter reflex images may be seen. The larger of the two is an erect, rather indistinct image of the flame reflected in the anterior surface of the lens. The smaller one is a sharp, inverted image reflected in the posterior surface of the lens. These reflex images are known to ophthalmologists as SANSON's images. If either the light or the observer's eye is moved during the examination, the position of the image also changes, and hence the first of these reflex images may be shifted voluntarily along the anterior surface of the lens to any desired spot in the edge of the pupil. In this case the image will always be seen without any black line between it and the pupillary margin on the side next the observer. At least, the writer has always found this to be the case under normal conditions without artificial dilatation of the pupil, and this fact unequivocally demonstrates that the pupillary margin of the iris rests against the lens.

The distance from the pupillary plane to the vertex of the cornea has been measured by C. KRAUSE on sectioned eyes. However, it should be borne in mind that the attachment of the lens to the sclerotica by means of the ciliary processes is not sufficiently strong to prevent considerable change of position in the process of sectioning.

If the living eye is observed from the side so that the pupil is just visible in front of the edge of the sclerotica, convincing evidence will be obtained that the pupillary plane lies behind a plane passed through the external cornea-scleral junction. On the edge of the cornea there will be seen in perspective

---

[1] Discovered by PURKINJE. See his treatise: *De examine physiologico organi visus et syst. cutanei.* Vratisl. 1823. In the diagnosis of diseases as used by SANSON (*Leçons sur les maladies des yeux.* Paris. 1837). Its origin was more exactly ascertained by H. MEYER (HENLES und PFEUFERS *Zeitschrift f. rationelle Medizin.* 1846. Bd. V.).

as shown in Fig. 10, two streaks in front of the pupil. The one nearer the
pupil is bright and is a distorted image of the iris. The other, a dark streak,

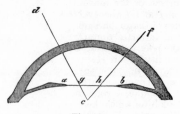

Fig. 10.   Fig. 11.

is the edge of the sclerotica as it projects over the cornea on the opposite
side. As the observer moves his eye farther back still, the pupil and iris disappear entirely and then only the scleral margin can be seen behind the still
visible edge of the cornea. As the rays of light, after penetrating the cornea,
proceed in straight lines through the aqueous humor, it naturally follows that
the iris lies farther back than a line joining a pair of opposite points on the
external margin of the cornea.

If the radius of curvature at the vertex of the cornea is known, the distance
of the pupillary plane from the vertex of the cornea can be calculated quite
accurately by finding the apparent position of the iris as compared with the
apparent position of the image of a luminous point in the corneal mirror. The
reflex image of a distant luminous point lies a little behind the plane of the
pupil, as may easily be verified by looking at the eye from different
sides and noting the position of the image with respect to the border of the
pupil.

In Fig. 11, let *ab* represent the pupil, *c* the apparent position of the reflex
image, and *dc* and *fc* two different directions in which the observer looks at
the point *c*. From *d* the point *c* will be seen to be beyond the point *g* in the
pupillary plane, and therefore apparently nearer *a*. From *f* it will appear
behind the point *h*, and therefore apparently nearer *b*. The simplest way to
ascertain the position of the point *c* would be to measure its apparent distance
in perspective from both edges of the pupil, which might be done with the
ophthalmometer. However, the almost continual variations in the diameter
of the pupil render this difficult.

Accordingly, the writer found it better to proceed a little differently.
Suppose that the elliptical axes of the eye to be examined have been measured

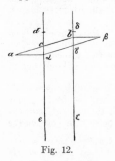

Fig. 12.

and the position of the visual axis determined with
respect to them. A lamp may then be placed in front
of the eye in a given position with respect to the
visual axis; and the position of its reflex image in the
cornea can be calculated according to the theory of
the imagery of a spherical mirror. Consequently,
it will be assumed in what follows that the position
of this reflex image is known. If the lamp, the
point of fixation and the ophthalmometer are all so
adjusted that the two corneal images of the source
as seen in the ophthalmometer can be so arranged
that one is on one edge of the pupil and the other on
the other edge, it may be inferred that, as seen from
the ophthalmometer, the reflex image lies in per-
spective beyond the centre of the pupil. In Fig. 12 *ed* and *eδ* are two straight
lines supposed to be parallel to the axis of the telescope of the ophthalmometer;

and *ab* and *αβ* represent the double images of the horizontal diameter of the pupil. It is assumed that the centre of the pupil, the lamp, the axis of the telescope and the visual axis of the eye that is being measured are all in the same horizontal plane. According to the theory of this instrument as given in §2 above, all lines connecting corresponding points of the double images must be of equal length and perpendicular to the axis of the telescope, and the double images themselves must be geometrically congruent. Hence it follows that *aα* and *bβ*, and also *ab* and *αβ*, are equal and parallel to each other. Now suppose that *d* and *δ* are the corresponding double images of the luminous point, and that such a position of the eye has been found that *d* is covered by *a* and *δ* by *b*, in other words, so that the lines *de* and *δε*, which are parallel to the axis of the telescope, pass through *a* and *b*, respectively. According to the theory of parallel lines,

$$d\delta : b\beta = a\gamma : \gamma\beta$$
$$d\delta : a a = cb : ac.$$

But since the distances between corresponding points of the double images are equal, therefore:

$$d\delta = a a = b\beta.$$

Consequently,

$$a\gamma = \gamma\beta$$

and

$$cb = ac.$$

The points *c* and *γ*, behind which the points *d* and *δ* appear in perspective, are therefore the centres of the pupillary images.

By suitable measurements it is now easy to determine what angle the line *ed*, or the axis of the telescope, makes with the visual axis of the observed eye. Thus the position of the line *ed* in the horizontal section of the eye is given by a point and the angle which it makes with another line of known direction, namely, with the visual axis. The centre of the pupil also lies in the line *ed*.

All that remains to be done now is to make a second observation of the same sort in another direction. Thus we find a second straight line of known direction, along which the centre of the pupil lies. Accordingly, the centre of the pupil must be at the point of intersection of this pair of lines, and its distance from the cornea can be found by geometrical construction or by calculation.

The method of observation is as follows: In Fig. 13 *A* represents the eye to be measured, which gazes through a hole in a screen so as to keep its position fairly fixed. At some distance from it there is a horizontal scale *CD*. Suppose a perpendicular is drawn from the eye to the scale meeting it at *B*. Here a diaphragm is placed

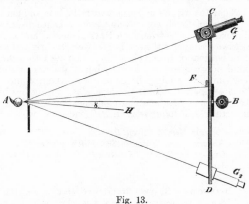

Fig. 13.

with a small hole in it, and a lamp behind the hole. The light from the lamp goes through the hole and reaching the eye is reflected from the cornea. At F there is an adjustable mark which is used as the point of fixation of the eye. The ophthalmometer is placed first at G_1 and then at G_2, equidistant from B in both positions. Marks may be made on the table for the tripod of the ophthalmometer, as the adjustment of the telescope has to be changed during the experiment. The patient is told to look steadily at the fixation mark F, and to follow all its movements. The observer, making his first observation at G_1, adjusts the glass plates of the ophthalmometer until one of the double images of the luminous point in the cornea coincides with the edge of the pupil. If now the other double image does not also coincide with the other edge of the pupil, the marker F is moved along the scale until this occurs, and the scale division noted. This same procedure is repeated from the second position of the ophthalmometer at G_2.

The distance AB must be measured in divisions of the scale CD; and then the angle FAB can be found by the formula:

$$\frac{FB}{AB} = \tan \angle FAB.$$

Knowing the axis major AH of the corneal ellipsoid and the angle FAH, the angle BAH may be calculated. This angle is needed to find the position of the reflex image in the cornea. In the same way the angle G_1AH is found, which establishes the direction along which the observer viewed the eye at A. The centre of the apparent pupil (as it looks through the cornea) will lie therefore in a line parallel to G_1A, which passes through the apparent position of the corneal image.

The method by which the actual position of the centre of the pupil may be calculated from its apparent position will be given in §9 and §10.[1]

The results of the measurements made with the ophthalmometer on the corneae of three eyes are as follows:

		O. H.	B. P.	J. H.
Distance of the pupillary plane from the vertex of the cornea..............................	apparent	3.485	3.042	3.151
	actual	4.024	3.597	3.739
Distance of the centre of the pupil from the corneal axis on nasal side..................	apparent	0.037	0.389	0.355
	actual	0.032	0.333	0.304

That the iris lies in contact with the lens and is convex in front, has been a subject of much controversy among anatomists.[2] The older anatomists assumed this to be true, until PETIT denied it and asserted that the so-called *posterior chamber* of the eye lies between the iris and the lens, as a result of his investigations on frozen eyes. In frozen eyes, thin sheets of ice are sometimes found between iris and lens. Almost all later anatomists accepted PETIT's view, until very lately STELLWAG VON CARION and CRAMER again asserted the close apposition of iris to lens. The author has been able to make direct observations by the method mentioned above which appear to confirm this. Nevertheless, BUDGE (1855) has defended the work of PETIT.

1728.   PETIT in *Mém. de l'Acad. Roy. des sciences.* 1728. p. 206 and p. 289.
1850.   STELLWAG VON CARION in *Zeitschrift d. Wiener Ärtze.* 1850. Heft 3, S. 125.
1852.   CRAMER in *Tijdschrift der Nederl. Maatschappij tot bevord. der Geneeskunst.* 1852. Jan.

[1] HELMHOLTZ in GRAEFES *Archiv. für Ophthalmologie.* Bd. 1. Abt. 2, S. 31.

[2] ¶See the supplement to this section which quite adequately presents the present viewpoint. (D. H.)

1853. CRAMER: *Het Accommodatievermogen der Oogen.* Haarlem. bl. 61*.
1855. J. BUDGE *über die Bewegung der Iris.* Braunschweig. S. 5-10 (also gives earlier literature of the subject.)
      HELMHOLTZ in GRAEFES *Archiv. für Ophthalmologie.* Bd. I. Abt. 2, S. 30.

Supplement (from the first edition, pp. 820 et seq., 1867)

There now appears to exist a general agreement that the central part of the iris lies in apposition to the lens in the normal eye. The only differences of opinion are in regard to the extent of the free space between the peripheral portion of the iris and the anterior borders of the ciliary processes and the folds of the zonule. The difference is on the question as to whether this space is only a cleft, as CRAMER, VAN REEKEN, ROUGET and HENKE maintain, or whether there is an open annular space, corresponding to a posterior chamber, as ARLT supposes. The ciliary processes are empty of blood after death and have collapsed. As it is impossible to know exactly how much they would be enlarged were the vessels filled with blood, the matter is difficult of solution.

In Figs. 2 and 3 above the ciliary processes are perhaps represented as being too close to the iris. The relations of these parts were taken from dried specimens (as Fig. 3) in which the angle of the pigment layer between the ciliary processes and iris appears to have been drawn out and flattened by the drying. In fresh preparations, the ciliary processes are separated from the iris at their anterior ends by a much deeper cleft than is shown in the diagrams.

1855. VAN REEKEN. Onteedkundig onderzoek van den toestel voor accommodati van het Oog. *Onderzoekingen gedaan in het Physiol. Laborat. der Utrechtsche Hoogeschool.* Jaar VII 248-586
—— ROUGET in *Gaz. med. 1855.* No. 50
1860. W. HENKE. Der Mechanismus der Akkommodation für Nähe und Ferne. *Archiv. für Ophthalm.* VI, 2. S. 53-72.
1863. O. BECKER. Lage und Funktion der Ciliarfortsätze in lebenden Menschenauge. *Wien. Mediz. Jahrbücher.* S. 159.

The discovery of H. MÜLLER and ROUGET concerning the ciliary muscle should be mentioned. They have shown that there is a large mass of circularly arranged muscle fibres, running parallel to the equator of the lens, on the medial side of the muscle toward the ciliary processes and between its previously described meridional fibres. The action of these fibres will be further discussed in the supplement to §13.

1856. C. ROUGET. Recherches anatomiques et physiologiques sur les appareils érectiles. Appareil de l'adaptation de l'oeil. *C. R.* XLII, 937-941. *Institut.* 1856. p. 193 to 194. *Cosmos.* VIII, 559-560.
—— H. MÜLLER. Réclamation de priorité. *C. R.* XLII, 1218-1219.
—— C. ROUGET. Résponse à une réclamation de priorité addresée par M. MÜLLER. *C. R.* XLII, 1255-1256. *Instilt.* 1856. p. 245. *Cosmos.* IX, 9.
1857. H. MÜLLER. Über einen ringförmigen Muskel am Ciliarkörper. *Archiv. für Ophthalmol.* III, 1.
—— ARLT. *Zur Anatomie des Auges.* Ibid., III, 2.
1858. H. MÜLLER. Einige Bemerkungen über die Binnenmuskeln des Auges. Ibid. IV, 2. p. 277-285.

The existence and position of the *dilatator pupillae* is still subject to much discussion.[1] The blood vessels of the iris are plentifully supplied with muscle

---

[1] ¶The existence of the *musculus dilatator pupillae* is amply proved by the work of GRYNFELTT (*Le muscle dilatateur de la pupille chez les Mammiferes*, 1899) and others. (D. H.)

fibres. Some anatomists have described various layers of fibres in addition
to those of the vessels, which they considered as forming a *dilatator pupillae*.
Others have denied the existence of such fibres.

J. HENLE. *Handbuch der systematischen Anatomie des Menschen.* II, 635. Braunschweig.
1866.

§4. The Retina

The retina is a superficial expansion of nerve substance spread over
the fundus of the eye between the choroid and the vitreous humor.

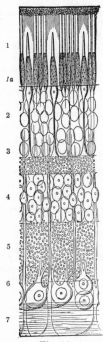

Fig. 14.

It is quite transparent when fresh, but a
cloudy white *post mortem*. It is thickest
(0.22 mm) at the back of the eye. The place
where the optic nerve enters, situated somewhat towards the nasal side (Fig. 2, *d*), is
white, whereas a little towards the temporal
side (at *p*) there is a yellow spot (*macula lutea
retinae*), the seat of clearest vision. Towards
the front the retina gets thinner (0.09 mm at
the anterior edge) and ends in a serrated edge
(*ora serrata retinae*), where the ciliary processes begin, or at any rate its nervous elements are not found beyond here.[1] It is
closely attached at this place to the choroid
and the hyaloid membrane which is a transparent structureless sac enclosing the vitreous
humor. The membranous parts which form
its anatomical continuation from here on
(*pars ciliaris retinae* and *Zonula Zinnii*) have
an entirely different structure and physiological significance.

The retina is composed partly of the usual
microscopical components of the nervous
system (nerve fibres, ganglion cells and nuclei), and partly of certain characteristic
elements, the so-called rods (*bacilli*) and cones (*coni*). Fig. 14
represents a cross section through the layers of the retina at the
equator of the eye. It is taken from MAX SCHULTZE, but with
its dimensions altered by SCHWALBE.[2] The various layers in the

---

[1] ¶The pigment layer of the retina (*pars ciliaris retinae*) is contained over the ciliary
body and the posterior surface of the iris as far as the *rima pupillae*. (D. H.)

[2] In the first edition reference was made to a figure after KÖLLIKER on a special plate.
This was changed in the second edition by HELMHOLTZ himself to M. SCHULTZE's semi-
schematic figure as shown above. N.

order that they occur beginning with the one next the choroid are as follows:[1]

1. The *layer of rods and cones* (Fig. 14, 1). The rods are cylindrical in shape, from 0.063 to 0.081 mm in length and 0.0018 mm in diameter, made of a substance of high index of refraction. They are arrayed close together like the stakes in a palisade. Their outer knobs end abruptly; inwardly, they are continued as fine fibres which pass into the next layer. The cones are found between the rods. They are thicker (from 0.0045 to 0.0065 mm) and shorter than the rods and are composed of similar substance. The external extremity of each cone runs out into an ordinary rod (*cone rod*), while at the inner end it is continued as a pear shaped nucleated cell-body which is separated from the cone by a slight constriction lying in the next succeeding layer ("Zapfenkorn," as KÖLLIKER called it or cone nucleus according to VINTSCHGAU).

The cones, which are distributed between the rods, occur less frequently out towards the periphery of the retina and are far more concentrated towards the yellow spot, where there are no rods at all. In Fig. 15 *A* represents a surface view of this layer at the equator of the eye, *B* the edge of the yellow spot, and *C* the yellow spot itself. The little circles

Fig. 15.

indicate rods and the larger ones cones, in which the cross section of the cone rod is shown. This layer is probably the one where the impression of light is obtained.

The layers of the retina which come next are:

2. The *outer nuclear layer* (Fig. 14, 2). (Separated from the layer of rods and cones by the *membrana limitans externa*, 1 *a*;—an observation inserted in the text by NAGEL.)

3. The *outer reticular* (*molecular*) *layer* (Fig. 14, 3).

4. The *inner nuclear layer* (Fig. 14, 4).

5. The *inner reticular* (*molecular*) *layer* (Fig. 14, 5).

These layers consist of fine fibres proceeding from the rods and cones (*radial fibres*, fibres of MÜLLER[2]): They are imbedded in a fine granular

---

[1] ¶The retinal pigment cells, indistinctly shown at the top of Fig. 14, form the outermost layer. Modern names of the layers have been substituted in the English translation. (D. H.)

[2] ¶The fibres of MÜLLER (radial fibres, sustentacular cells) extend throughout the entire retina from the *membrana limitans externa* to the *membrana limitans interna*, which appear to be formed by the ramifications of the terminal fibres of these cells. Their nuclei lie in the inner nuclear layer. These cells have no nervous function. Consequently, the statement in the next paragraph that the processes of the ganglion cells "in part seem to be united with the fibres of MÜLLER," is evidently a mistake. (D. H.)

substance and are much branched. Between them lie the *molecular bodies*, from 0.004 to 0.009 mm in diameter, attached to the fibres of MÜLLER.

6. The *layer of ganglion cells* (Fig. 14, 6) consists of large nerve or ganglion cells with many processes. One such cell, from the eye of an elephant, is shown in Fig. 16, which is copied from CORTI. Each cell contains a nucleus (Fig. 16, *a*). The processes of these cells in part pass out as fibres of the optic nerve and in part seem to be united with the fibres of MÜLLER. This layer is thickest in the yellow spot where it may be from eight to ten cells deep. It becomes thinner towards the periphery of the retina, where its cells cease to form a continuous layer.

7. The *layer of nerve fibres*. From the place where the optic nerve enters the eye its fibres spread out radially all over the retina, except in the yellow spot, which they go around. This layer is, naturally, thickest (0.2 mm) near the entrance of the optic nerve and becomes thinner towards the outer limit of the retina (0.004 mm at its margin).

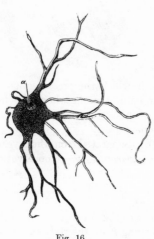

Fig. 16.

These fibres are of extremely fine calibre. They usually become varicose after death. Their thickness varies greatly (from 0.0005 to 0.0045 mm). As to their final terminations, nothing definite is known so far. Some of them are known to unite with the processes of the ganglion cells, and probably this is true of all of them.[1]

The inner ends of the fibres of MÜLLER, which have dense arborizations here, pass through the layer of nerve fibres. Their ultimate ends are attached to a glassy membrane which clothes the retina on its inner surface (*membrana limitans interna*).

The *yellow spot*, the most important part of the entire retina for vision, may be differentiated from the surrounding portions by its yellow colour, which is due to a pigment found in all layers except the layer of rods and cones. The layer of nerve fibres is lacking here, and in the layer of rods and cones the cones

---

[1] ¶Except for a few centrifugal fibres, probably vaso-motor in function, all the fibres of this layer are axones of the ganglion cells. (D. H.)

alone are present. In its centre there is an extremely transparent indented place or hollow, the *fovea centralis*, which is very easily torn and consequently was considered for some time to be a foramen. At the margin of the yellow spot the layer of ganglion cells is thicker than in all the other parts of the retina, but it gets thinner again in the *fovea centralis* and consists of only a few layers of cells at this point. The inner granular layer is probably absent entirely at the centre of the fovea. The inner nuclear layer and the outer granular layer become considerably thicker, whereas the outer nuclear layer gets thinner, towards the yellow spot. According to H. MÜLLER, the inner nuclear layer is also thinner in the fovea. According to REMAK and KÖLLIKER, all layers except the ganglion cells and cones are absent in the *fovea centralis*.[1] REMAK also states that here there is a very yellow glassy substance interposed between the cones and the choroid.

In spite of their importance, the relations of the structures in the yellow spot are in many respects but little understood. The delicate structures of this region dis-integrate very shortly after death. Besides, owing to the fact that the macula has hitherto been found only in the human eye,[2] all the more delicate investigations of this area have been necessarily made on the eyes of executed criminals, and such oppor-tunities are rare.

Fig. 17.

The *fovea centralis* is readily seen with an ophthal-moscope by virtue of its pecu-liar light reflex (see §16). Here is situated the point of the retina for direct vision, where the image of the point of fixation of the field of view is focused.

The *vessels of the retina* (*arteria* and *vena centralis retinae*) enter the eye through the centre of the optic nerve and branch out in all direc-tions from this point. At first, they lie directly under the *membrana limitans interna* in the layer of nerve fibres. Then they penetrate into

[1] ¶There is some question as to the constitution of the tunica retina at the fovea. It would appear from sections that the cones, a few elements of the outer nuclear and the outer reticular layers constitute with the external and internal limiting membranes the entire retina at this point. (D. H.)

[2] ¶The macula and the fovea have been found in all classes of vertebrates by a number of investigators, though it is lacking in most fishes, in many amphibia and reptiles and in a few mammals. (D. H.)

the layer of ganglion cells and even into the external molecular layer, in both of which they form a large-meshed capillary net. The position and form of this vascular arborization is important for certain optical phenomena (see §15), and therefore a drawing is inserted here (Fig. 17), which was made by DONDERS from an injection preparation. The arteries are shown in outline, the veins in solid black. In the yellow spot there are no larger vessels and in the fovea even capillaries are absent. The fovea is surrounded by a wreath of terminal capillary branches.

At the anterior edge (*ora serrata*) the retina passes over into a layer of cells (*pars ciliaris retinae*) which together with the *membrana limitans* (*interna*) covers over the ciliary processes and the posterior surface of the iris. Here it appears to become changed into pigment cells, and is closely attached to the underlying structures.

Inasmuch as the dimensions of the retina and its elements are of much importance in connection with many optical phenomena, attached herewith is a résumé of certain measurements, as made by various observers, the results being all expressed in mm. These data derived from the works of C. KRAUSE, E. H. WEBER, BRÜCKE, KÖLLIKER and VINTSCHGAU are indicated below by the abbreviations *Kr., W., B., Ko.* and *V.*, respectively.

Diameter of the optic nerve at its point of entrance: *Kr.*, 2.7 and 2.14; *W.*, 2.09 and 1.71.

Diameter of the vessels contained in it: *W.*, 0.704 and 0.63.

Distance of the centre of the optic nerve from the centre of the yellow spot: *W.*, 3.8. *Kr.*, 3.28 and 3.6. Distance between the centre of the optic nerve and the inner edge of the yellow spot: *Ko.*, 2.25 to 2.7.

Horizontal diameter of the yellow spot: *Kr.*, 2.25; *W.*, 0.76; *Ko.*, 3.24.

Vertical diameter of the yellow spot: *Ko.*, 0.81.

Diameter of the *fovea centralis: Ko.*, 0.18 to 0.225.

Distance between the *ora serrata* and the edge of the iris on nasal side: *B.*, 6; on temporal side, 7.

Thickness of the retina near the optic nerve: *Ko.*, 0.22.

Thickness of the retina at the back of the eye: *Kr.*, 0.164, *Ko.*, 0.135.

Thickness of the retina at the equator: *Kr.*, 0.084.

Thickness of the retina at its anterior margin: *Ko.*, 0.09.

Thickness of the layers in the yellow spot: *Ko.*, ganglionic layer, 0.101 to 0.117; inner molecular layer, 0.045; inner nuclear layer, 0.058; outer molecular layer, 0.086; outer nuclear layer, 0.058; layer of rods and cones, 0.067.

Diameter of the ganglion cells: *B.*, 0.01 to 0.02; *Ko.*, 0.009 to 0.036, usually between 0.013 and 0.022.

Diameter of the nuclei: *B.*, 0.006 to 0.008; *Ko.*, 0.004 to 0.009. Of the cone-cells: *V.*, 0.0068.

Diameter of the rods: *B.* and *Ko.*, 0.0018; *V.*, 0.0010.

Length of the rods: *B.*, 0.027 to 0.030; *Ko.*, 0.063 to 0.081.

Diameter of the cones: *Ko.*, 0.0045 to 0.0067; *V.*, 0.0034 to 0.0068. In the yellow spot: *Ko.*, 0.0045 to 0.0054.

Length of the cones: *V.*, 0.015 to 0.020.

The newer (1845–1854) works on the structure of the retina are:

1845. F. PACINI in *Nuovi Annali delle scienze nat. di Bologna.* 1845.
1851. H. MÜLLER in SIEBOLD und KÖLLIKERS *Zeitschrift für wiss. Zoologie.* 1851. S. 234.
　　—*Verhandl. der Würzburger med. Ges.* 1852. S. 216. Ibid. III. 336 and IV. 96.

1850. CORTI in J. MÜLLERS *Archiv.* 274.—*Zeitschr. für wissensch. Zoologie. V.*—
      J. HENLE in *Zeitschr. für ration. Medizin.* N. F. II. 304 and 309.
1852. A. KÖLLIKER *Verhandl. der Würzburger med. Ges.* III. S. 316*.
1853. A. KÖLLIKER u. H. MÜLLER *C. R. de l'Acad. d. Sc.* 1853. Sept. 23.—Plate drawing
      of the retina by these same authors in ECKER *Icones physiologicae**.
      R. REMAK in *C. R. de l'Acad. d. Sc.* 1853. Oct. 31. and *Allgem. med. Zentralz.*
      1854. No. 1*. *Prager Vierteljahrsschr.* XLIII. S. 103.
      *M. DI VINTSCHGAU in *Sitzbr. d. Wiener Akad.* XI. 943*.
1854. *A. KÖLLIKER *Mikroskopische Anatomie.* Leipzig 1854. II. 648-703*.
      Some measurements have been copied from:
      C. KRAUSE, *Handbuch der menschlichen Anatomie.* Hannover 1842. I, 2. S. 535*.
      E. BRÜCKE, *Anat. Beschr. d. menschl. Augapfels.* Berlin 1847. S. 23.
      E. H. WEBER in *Sitzber. d. Sächs. Ges. d. Wiss.* 1852. S. 149-152.

Supplement (from the first edition, pp. 822 et seq. 1867)

The more delicate anatomy of the retina has been much studied by anatomists and more complete information is at hand. As a result of his own work and that of other observers, J. HENLE distinguishes the following layers in his latest compilation:

Mosaic layer. . . . . { 1. Layer of rods and cones
{ 2. External limiting membrane
{ 3. Nuclear layer (granular layer)

External fibre layer. . . . . .4. External fibre layer

Nervous layer { Grey substance. . { 5. External granular layer
{ 6. External ganglionic layer
{ 7. Internal granular layer
{ 8. Internal ganglionic layer
{ White substance. .9. Layer of nerve fibres

Boundary membrane. . . . . .10. *Limitans hyaloidea.*

Of these, 1, the layer of rods and cones; 3, the outer nuclear layer; 4 and 5, the outer reticular (molecular) layer; 6, the internal nuclear layer; 7, the inner reticular (molecular) layer; 8, the layer of ganglion cells; and 9, the expansion of the optic nerve are all enumerated in the list given above (p. 25).

The rods of the hindmost layer of the retina are themselves each composed of two rod-like members joined together, the inner of which is thicker (0.0018 to 0.0022 mm in diameter) and consists of a less highly refracting substance than that of the outer (0.0013 to 0.0018 mm in diameter). The basal portion of the *rods* reaches the same height as the thicker bottle shaped basal segment of the *cones*. The external portion of the cones, the *cone rods* mentioned above, lie in a row with the external portions of the rods, but they are shorter and therefore do not extend as far towards the choroid. The diameter of the thicker inner part of the cones gets to be as much as from 0.004 to 0.006 mm. Only in the fovea where there are no rods between the cones the latter are thinner. (Their basal ends measure from 0.002 to 0.0025 mm according to M.SCHULTZE, and in a small region from 0.0015 to 0.002 mm according to H. MÜLLER, and between 0.0031 and 0.0036 mm according to WELCKER). According to M. SCHULTZE, the cones of the yellow spot are further differentiated by being nearly twice as long as those in other parts of the retina.

HENLE states that the *outer nuclear layer* contains many superposed layers of ellipsoidal granules which, in fresh condition, exhibit a characteristic and very delicate cross striation. Each granule, as a rule, shows three bright bands separated by darker ones giving the optical effect of layers of two alternating substances passing through the granule parallel to the surface of the retina. In well fixed preparations these granules may be been in fairly regular rows perpendicular to the surface of the retina. Their reaction to reagents is so essentially different from that of nerve cells that they may be readily distinguished. Their long axis, perpendicular to the surface of the retina, measures from 0.006 to 0.007 mm. The shorter axis is not much more than half as long.

The *cone nuclei* ("Zapfenkörner," above mentioned) extend also into the nuclear layer. Each of them contains a nucleus and is continued towards the inner layers as a smooth shining cylindrical fibre, 0.0015 mm in diameter, which penetrates the thickness of the nuclear layer and enters the external granular layer with or without a cell-like enlargement.

According to M. SCHULTZE, this fibre appears to break up here into a large number of very fine fibres which enter the external granular layer and become lost in it. In the rods likewise originate delicate nerve fibres which are connected with the granules of the external granular layer. They correspond to the cone fibres but are much finer, and have an enlargement as they approach the external granular layer in which they also become lost.

A special fibre layer (known as HENLE's *external fibre layer*) is to be found in general only in and around the yellow spot and around the *ora serrata*, along the outer edge of the retina. The fibres in the yellow spot run radially out from the centre of the fovea in all directions, proceeding principally parallel to the surface of the retina. However, they sometimes pass out of the granular layer in small bundles and join the horizontal layer of fibres, or they may leave this layer to penetrate into the layer of nerve fibres and the outer granular layer. These fibres apparently represent the connections between the cones of the fovea and the nerve cells which are found in large numbers in its vicinity. On account of their great number, however, HENLE doubts whether they all serve this purpose. The role that these fibres apparently play in the production of HAIDINGER's tufts in polarised light is explained in §25.

Nothing of importance has been recently discovered with respect to the other front layers of the retina. A large number of the radially arranged fibres of MÜLLER, especially those which unite to form the *membrana limitans hyaloidea*, are connective tissue fibres. According to MAX SCHULTZE, the nerve fibres proper can be recognized by their varicose appearance, but, beyond their procedure in the foremost layer of the retina which forms the expansion of the optic nerve, nothing very definite is known.

In the fundus of the fovea the two layers of nerve cells have united with each other and with the nuclear layer. Behind these lie the cones. All the other layers are absent.

1856. H. MÜLLER. Anatomische Beiträge zur Ophthalmologie. *Archiv. für Ophthalmologie.* II, 2. S. 1. III, 1. S. 1. IV, 1. S. 269.
Idem, Anatomisch-physiologische Untersuchungen über die Retina bei Menschen und Wirbeltieren. SIEBOLD und KÖLLIKER *Zft. für wissensch. Zoologie.* VIII, 1. *C. R.* XLIII. Oct. 20.

1857. C. BERGMANN. Anatomisches und Physiologisches über die Netzhaut des Auges. *Zft. für rationelle Medizin.* (3) II. 83.

1858. NUNNELEY. On the structure of the retina. *Quarterly Journal of microscop. science.* 1858. July. 217.

1859. RITTER. Über den Bau der Stäbchen und äusseren Endigungen der Radialfasern an der Netzhaut des Frosches. *Archiv. für Ophthalm.* V, 2, S. 101.
M. SCHULTZE. *De retinae structura penitiori.* Bonn.

1859. E. v. WAHL. *De retinae textura in monstro anencephalo. Dissert.* Dorpat.

1860. W. MANZ. Über den Bau der Retina des Frosches. *Zft. für ration. Medizin.* (3) X, 301.
G. BRAUN. Eine Notiz zur Anatomie und Bedeutung der Stäbschenschichte der Netzhaut. *Wiener Sitzungsber.* XLII, 15-18.
W. KRAUSE. Über den Bau der Retinastäbchen beim Menschen. *Göttinger Nachrichten.* 1861. No. 2. *Zft. für ration. Medizin.* (3) XI, 175.

1861. M. SCHULTZE. *Sitzungsber. der niederrheinischen Ges.* 1861. S. 97. *Archiv. für Anatomie und Physiol.* 1861. S. 785. *Archiv. für mikrosk. Anatomie.* II, 175-286. RITTER in *Archiv für Ophthalm.* VIII, 1.

1862. H. MÜLLER. Bemerkungen über die Zapfen am gelben Fleck des Menschen. *Würzburger naturwiss.* Zft. II, 218.
Idem, Über das Auge des Chamäleon. Ibid. III, 10.

1863. SCHIESS. Beitrag zur Anatomie der Retinastäbchen. *Zft. für ration. Medizin.* (3) XVIII, 129.
H. WELCKER. Untersuchung der Retinazapfen bei einem Hingerichteten. Ibid. XX, 173.
W. KRAUSE. Ibid. XX, 7.

1865. BLESSIG. *De Retinae textura. Dissert.* Dorpat.

1866. J. HENLE. *Handbuch der systematischen Anatomie des Menschen.* II, 636-670.

§5. The Crystalline Lens

The crystalline lens is a transparent, colourless double convex body less curved in front than behind. It is enclosed in a structureless glassy membrane (the *capsule of the lens*), which resembles in all respects the membrane of DESCEMET. Like the latter, it also, according to BRÜCKE, has a layer of epithelium on its anterior surface where it is in contact with the aqueous humor; but HENLE and KÖLLIKER deny this. Its posterior half is fused with the hyaloid membrane. The substance of the lens is of a gelatinous consistency in the outer layers, but becomes stiffer in the centre or *core* of the lens. The entire organ is highly elastic in the fresh condition, yielding easily to any external force, but quickly and completely recovering its former shape.

The crystalline humor is a double refracting medium. If examined between two crossed NICOL prisms, the black cross with coloured rings is seen which is a characteristic appearance of the section of a uni-axial crystal perpendicular to the optical axis.

The mass of the lens consists of a peculiar protein, the so-called *globulin* or *crystallin*. Its microscopical elements are fibres of hexagonal

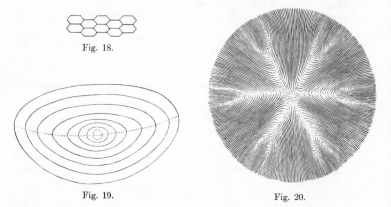

Fig. 18.

Fig. 19.   Fig. 20.

cross section, from 0.0056 to 0.0112 mm broad, and from 0.002 to 0.0038 mm thick. They are smaller and of a firmer consistency in the core of the lens than in the outer layers. Their broader surface lies parallel to the surface of the lens, and thus the lens may easily be split in this direction in concentric layers like an onion. Fig. 18 shows a cross section of the fibres in normal apposition; and Fig. 19 shows the direction of the layers in a cross section of the lens. In each individual layer the fibres extend generally from the axis of the lens to its periphery. The characteristic star-shaped figures, such as that shown in Fig. 20 from the outer layers of the lens, are found only near the axis where the fibres bend back again. In the core layers the star has only three rays, which make angles of 120° with each other. The stars of the posterior and anterior surfaces are turned through 60° with respect to each other. In the outer layers, however, the three principal rays of the stars are much broken up into secondary rays so that much more intricate and irregular figures occur.

Close under the capsule there is a layer of cells instead of fibres which disintegrate after death and form the *liquor Morgagnii*. According to BRÜCKE, similar cells also unite the ends of the fibres in the rays of the star, at any rate in the outer layers. BOWMAN and KÖLLIKER, however, maintain that a structureless substance exists at these places. The latter explains also the cell-like structures on the posterior surface of the lens as swollen and flattened ends of the lens fibres that are attached here to the capsule. Thus in each half of the lens there are three planes passing through the axis, and corresponding to the principal rays of the star (*central planes*, BOWMAN), in which the structure of the lens is different from that found elsewhere. In the superficial layers these planes are further subdivided. Doubtless, certain irregularities in the refraction of light rays are dependent on this latter fact.

We have by no means a clear idea of the distribution of the fibres in the lens. THOMAS[1] has described peculiar figures made by the ends of the fibres on the surfaces of sections of dried lenses, consisting mainly of two systems of concentric circles. These do not admit of any explanation on the basis of present knowledge as to the distribution of the fibres of the lens.

As a result of his measurements, KRAUSE considers the anterior surface of the lens as a portion of a flattened ellipsoid of revolution and the posterior surface as a paraboloid of revolution. He gives the following values of the different constants, in Paris lines, for the eight eyes specified in §2:

No.	Axis of the whole lens	Axis of the front half	Axis of the rear half	Anterior Surface Semi-axis of ellipse major	Anterior Surface Semi-axis of ellipse minor	Distance from the cornea	Posterior Surface param-eter	Posterior Surface distance from the retina	Diam-eter
I.	2	0.85	1.15	2.05	0.95	1.2	4.49	6.65	4.1
II.	1.9	0.78	1.1	2	0.91	1.35	4.99	6.8	4
III.	2.4	0.98	1.42	2	1.14	1.25	4.99	6.1	4.1
IV.	2.2	0.95	1.25	2.05	1.10	1.35	4.51	5.9	4.1
V.	1.85	0.65	1.2	2.03	0.83	1.25	4.83	6.4	4
VI.	2.35	0.8	1.55	1.95	0.98	1.2	4.53	6.0	4.1
VII.	1.8	0.78	1.02	2.03	0.95	1	4.09	6.65	4
VIII.	1.85	0.85	1	2	0.94	1	3.79	6.55	4

[1] THOMAS, *Prager mediz. Vierteljahrsschr.* 1854. Bd. I. Ausserord. Beilage S. 1.

KRAUSE's data on the distances of the two surfaces of the lens from the cornea and retina are included above, although, as formerly observed, the correctness of these results appears very dubious to the writer. Moreover, the latter's measurements of the thickness of the lens in the eyes of living persons do not agree with those made on lenses of cadavers. Inasmuch as the thickness of the lens is changed in near and far vision, the discussion of these investigations will be postponed until we come to the theory of accommodation in §12.

Literature concerning the structure of the lens:

1845.   A. HANNOVER in J. MÜLLERS *Archiv.* 1845. S. 478*.

1846.   HARTING in VAN DE HOEVEN EN DE VRIESE *Tijdschrift* XII. S. 1.

1847.   *E. BRÜCKE, *Beschr. d. menschl. Augapfels.* Berlin. S. 27-30*.

1849.   W. BOWMAN, *Lectures on the parts concerned in the oper. on the eye.* London.

1851.   H. MEYER in J. MÜLLERS *Archiv.* 1851. 202*.

1852.   GROS in *C. R. de l'Acad. d. Sciences.* 1852. April.

1852.   D. BREWSTER. On the development and extinction of regular doubly refracting structures in the crystalline lenses of animals after death. *Phil. Mag.* (4) III, 192-193.

1854.   *A. KÖLLIKER, *Mikroskopische Anatomie.* Leipzig. II. 702-713*.
        THOMAS in *Prager med. Vierteljahrsschrift.* 1854. Bd. 1. S. 1.*

1859.   G. VALENTIN. Neue Untersuchungen über die Polarisationserscheinungen der Kristallinsen des Menschen und der Tiere. *Archiv für Ophthalm.* IV, I, 227-268.

———.   D. BREWSTER, On certain abnormal structures in the crystalline lenses of animals and in the human crystalline. *Rep. of Brit. Assoc.* 1858. 2, p. 7.

1863.   F. J. v. BECKER. Über den Bau der Linse bei dem Menschen und den Wirbeltieren. *Archiv für Ophthalm.* IX (2), 1-42.

§6.   The Aqueous and Vitreous Humors

The aqueous humor (*humor aqueus*) fills the space between the cornea, iris and lens. The space comprised between the posterior surface of the cornea, the anterior surface of the iris and the pupillary plane is called the *anterior chamber of the eye*. On the other hand, the space which was supposed to lie between the pupillary plane, the posterior surface of the iris and the anterior surface of the lens was called the *posterior chamber of the eye*. However, as a matter of fact, this is only a potential space or capillary gap under normal circumstances,[1] as the posterior surface of the iris is close against the anterior surface of the lens. The iris seems to become separated from the lens only after strong artificial dilatation of the pupil with belladonna.

The aqueous humor therefore fills the anterior chamber of the eye.[2] It is clear, colourless and consists of water containing about 2% of solids the chief of which are sodium chloride and extracts. Its index of refraction differs very little from that of water.

The cavity of the eyeball between the lens and the retina is filled with the *vitreous humor* (*corpus vitreum, humor vitreus*) which in turn

---

[1] ¶Except at its base. (D. H.)

[2] ¶The aqueous humor also fills the posterior chamber of the eye. (D. H.)

is contained in the *hyaloid membrane* (*membrana hyaloidea*). The vitreous humor is a gelatinous mass of slight coherence. When it is cut, a thin non-viscous fluid drips from it, which has an alkaline reaction and contains from 1.69 to 1.98% of solids, about half of which is inorganic material (sodium chloride, a little sodium carbonate, traces of lime, sulphuric acid and phosphoric acid). The organic part seems to consist chiefly of mucin containing traces of some protein compound. The index of refraction of the vitreous humor likewise differs little from that of water, but is somewhat higher than that of the aqueous humor.

In the embryo the vitreous humor has a cellular structure, but subsequently only a few remnants of these cells are found, such as membranes, granules, and granular lumps[1] that move about in it but not with perfect freedom. The vitreous humor apparently owes its consistency to a rather small amount of very much swollen organic substance (mucin or fibrous material). Small amounts of fibrous tissue which have differentiated from a watery fluid often give rise to similar soft gelatinous masses from which fluid runs out if the continuity of the coagulum is mechanically disturbed. If the vitreous humor is hardened in reagents that precipitate the mucin, as, for example, in a solution of lead acetate or of chromic acid, the sections of it are found to contain sometimes uniform condensations. However, it is still extremely doubtful whether these can be considered as membranes that pass through the vitreous humor.

HANNOVER infers that the presence of these bands indicates that flat membranes are present in the vitreous humor of the human eye which all intersect in a line proceeding from the place where the optic nerve enters the eye to the posterior surface of the lens; and that these membranes extend from this line to the exterior of the vitreous humor where they are inserted in the hyaloid membrane, so that the structure of the vitreous humor would be like that of an orange.

The deductions as to the structure of the vitreous body which may be drawn from entoptical phenomena will be considered later.

The *hyaloid membrane* is a very delicate, glassy membrane without structure which at the back part of the eye rests against the *membrana limitans interna* of the retina, being attached thereto over the entire surface during life,[2] but after death only at the place of entrance of the optic nerve and at the *ora serrata*. From the *ora serrata* it is continued as a thinner membrane over the posterior surface of the capsule of the

---

[1] ¶These remnants are frequently noticeable as the shadowy "*muscae volitantes*," noted at times by the observer in his own eye. (D. H.)

[2] VINTSCHGAU in *Sitzbr. d. Wiener Akad.* XI. 943 and BUROW in J. MÜLLERS *Archiv.* 1840.

lens with which it is united (Fig. 2, *k*). Another membrane, the so-called *zonula Zinnii* (*ligamentum suspensorium lentis*) is inserted between it and the ciliary portion of the retina. This is regarded by many anatomists as an anterior layer of the hyaloid membrane.

The zonule is folded like a ruff so as to follow the surface of the ciliary processes. The anterior or outer border of its folds is closely attached to the *membrana limitans* in the hollows between the folds of

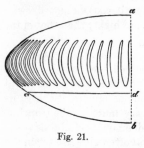

Fig. 21.

the ciliary processes. The posterior or inner border of its folds, corresponding to the summits of the ciliary processes, lies in apposition to the hyaloid membrane. In Fig. 2 the zonule is indicated by the line *e*. On the right it passes between two ciliary processes, while on the left it goes over the summit of one of them. In this manner it reaches the border

of the lens and is attached to its capsule in a wavy line. A quadrant of the lens is shown in Fig. 21, projected on a plane passed through the axis of the lens *ab*. The line of attachment of the hyaloid membrane is indicated by *cd*. Above this is seen the serrated line of attachment of the zonule.

The cleft-like space between the zonule and the hyaloid membrane is called the *canal of* PETIT (*canalis Petiti*). If it is inflated after the zonule has been laid free from the anterior surface, the invaginated folds of the zonule bulge outwards so that the whole has the appearance of an Ionic egg-molding, and hence PETIT, who discovered it, named it "*canal godronne.*" With stronger inflation, the evaginated portions of the membrane tear, leaving only the tougher anterior edges of the folds as bands which bind the lens to the vitreous humor. The anterior edges of the folds are attached also to the ciliary portion of the retina which dips down between the ciliary processes; and this in turn is attached to the pigment layer. Fibres of attachment are also present here. According to BRÜCKE, they arise from the fibres between which the nerve cells of the retina are embedded. The fibres are attached to the *ora serrata* at those places which correspond to the interval between each pair of ciliary processes and pass forward in the bottom of these grooves. BRÜCKE thinks that the zonule itself is a structureless membrane, but HENLE and KÖLLIKER maintain that it is fibrous. The zonule and its fibres are as resistant to chemicals as is elastic tissue.

The zonule secures the position of the lens inasmuch as it attaches the latter to the ciliary body. Under tension the zonule may exert a pull on the equatorial edge of the lens thereby tending to elongate the equatorial diameter, reduce the axial thickness, and flatten the surfaces of the lens.

Literature on the structure of the vitreous humor:

PAPPENHEIM, *Spezielle Gewebelehre des Auges.* 842. S. 181.

E. BRÜCKE in J. MÜLLERS *Archiv.* 1843. S. 345 and 1845. S. 130.

HANNOVER, ibid. 1845. S. 467 and in: *Das Auge.* Leipzig. 1852.

BOWMAN in *Dublin Quarterly Journal of Med. Science.* 1848. Aug.; also in *Lectures on the Parts conc. in the oper. on the eye.* London 1849. p. 94.

*E. BRÜCKE, *Beschr. d. menschl. Augapfels.* Berlin 1847.

VIRCHOW in *Verhandl. d. Würzburger phys. med. Ges.* II. 1851. 317 and in *Archiv für pathol. Anat.* IV. 468 and V. 278.

*KÖLLIKER, *Mikrosk. Anatomie* II. 713.

DONDERS en JANSEN in *Nederlandsch Lancet* 1846. II. 454.

*A. DONCAN, *De corporis vitrei structura.* Dissert. Utrecht 1854. Abridged in *Onderzoekingen ged. in het physiol. Laborat. der Utrechtsche Hoogeschool.* Jaar VI. S. 172.

§7. Surroundings of the Eye

The eyeball lies imbedded in loose adipose tissue in the bony orbit or *socket of the eye (orbita)*. This is very nearly conical in form. The base of the cone is the external opening of the orbit in the face; its apex lies posteriorly and somewhat medially. Fig. 22 shows the positions of

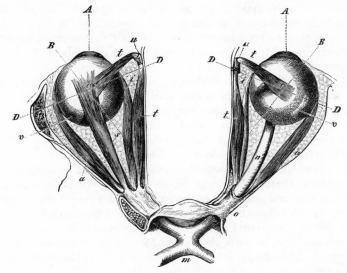

Fig. 22.

the eyes in both orbits. From the posterior side of the right eyeball in the figure, the optic nerve *n* may be seen to arise, entering the cranial cavity through a hole *o* (*foramen opticum*) situated at the apex of the orbit, and uniting and crossing with the nerve from the opposite side in the *chiasma nervorum opticorum* at *m*. The continuations of the optic nerve from the chiasma to the brain are known as the optic tract (*tractus opticus*). The fibres of each *tractus opticus* pass partly into the optic nerve of its own side, partly into that of the opposite side, and a small part through the *tractus opticus* of the opposite side back into the brain. Some observers have also found fibres which pass from one optic nerve through the chiasma into the other.

There are six muscles whose function is to turn the eyeball in its socket, namely:

1. The *internal rectus i*, and

2. The *external rectus a*. Both of these originate in the vicinity of the *foramen opticum* at the apex of the orbit and are inserted on the inner (medial) and outer (lateral) sides of the eyeball, respectively. They turn the eye around its vertical axis.

3. The *superior rectus*, removed from the right side of Fig. 22 in order to show the optic nerve, marked *s* on the left side; and

4. The *inferior rectus*, which lies on the under side of the orbit, just as the superior rectus shown in the figure lies on the upper side. These two muscles also originate in the vicinity of the *foramen opticum* and are inserted in the upper and lower sides of the eyeball. They turn it around a horizontal axis, indicated by the line *DD* in Fig. 22, which passes from the nasal side of the eye, a little to the front, to the temporal side, a little to the back, making an angle of about 70° with the optical axis (*A*) of the eye.

5. The *superior oblique muscle t* arises from the edge of the *foramen opticum* and proceeds to the upper nasal side in the front part of the orbit, where its tendon passes through a small pulley *n* (*trochlea*), which is attached to the upper anterior edge of the orbit. Here it turns at an angle and is inserted in the upper side of the eyeball at *C*. The muscle exerts a pull in the direction of its tendon.

6. The *inferior oblique muscle*, not shown in the figure, arises from the front nasal border of the orbit, passes under the eyeball towards the temporal side, and is inserted in the posterior outer side of the eyeball at *v* in Fig. 22. The axis of rotation (*BB*) of the oblique muscles of the eye is likewise horizontal and passes from the outside in front to the inside behind, making an angle of about 75° with the axis of rotation of the superior and inferior recti and an angle of 35° with the optical axis of the eye.

The optical axis of the eye may be turned in any desired direction by the action of these six muscles combined in different ways. The eyeball is capable of rotation also about the optical axis itself. As an introduction to the subject, it would appear to be justifiable to assume provisionally a common axis of rotation for the two muscles of a pair. Anyhow it simplifies very much the comprehension of the movements which the muscles of the eye have to produce.

The eyeball is protected in front by two *eyelids* (*palpebrae*). Each of them contains a cartilaginous plate which is covered on the outer surface by the external skin and on the inner by a mucous membrane, the *conjunctiva*, which is continued over the eyeball. It is loosely attached to the white of the eye but fuses with the cornea at its border. The surface of the *conjunctiva* and the anterior surface of the cornea are kept continually moist by three different secretions. These are: (1) the secretions of the Meibomian glands which lie on the inner surface of the eyelids under the *conjunctiva*. This fatty secretion perhaps affects mainly the edges of the lids and prevents the overflow of tears, but it may also spread over the cornea in oily drops, especially when the lids are moved strongly. (2) The mucous of the mucous glands of the conjunctiva which are most numerous in the folds between the lids and the eyeball. (3) The tears, secreted by the lachrymal glands. There are two of these glands situated in the upper outer side of each orbit. They pour out their watery secretion, which contains only about 1% of solids, through from seven to ten fine ducts above the outer angle of the eye between the upper lid and the eyeball. From this point the tears spread over the entire surface of the *conjunctiva* and are taken up at the inner angle of the eye by two small openings, the *puncta lacrymalia*. These are the orifices of the two *lachrymal canals* which empty into a wider canal, *ductus nasolacrymalis*, from which they finally reach the nose.

The *conjunctiva* of the eye is extraordinarily sensitive. The slightest contact with a foreign body causes pain and involuntary movement of the eyelids or *winking*. By this means and by the continuous flow of tears across the *conjunctiva*, the anterior surface of the cornea is kept clean and bright at all times, which is a necessary condition for clear vision. The larger particles of dust floating in the air, insects, etc., are kept out by the *eyelashes*.

MORE RECENT BIBLIOGRAPHY ON ANATOMY OF THE EYE[1]

ADDARIO, C., 1902: Ueber die Matrix des Glaskörpers im menschlichen und tierischen Auge, *Anat. Anz.*, Bd. 21, S. 9-12.
    1904–05: La matrice ciliare delle fibrille del vitreo, loro forma e disposizione, nonche lore rapporti colla neuroglia della retina visiva periferica nell'occhio umano adulto, *Arch. di Ottalmol.*, vol. 12, p. 206-262.

[1] ¶This alphabetical list, compiled by Dr. HOOKER, for the English translation, is inserted here for convenience of reference. Although it does not pretend to be a complete list by any means, it will undoubtedly be useful for the purpose in view. (J. P. C. S.)

AGABABOW, A., 1904: Ueber die nerven des Sclera, *Arch. f. mikr. Anat.*, Bd. 63, p. 701-709.

AREY, L. B., 1915: The occurrence and the significance of photo-mechanical changes in the vertebrate retina—an Historical Survey, *Jour. Comp. Neur.*, vol. 25, p. 535-554.

1916: The function of the efferent fibers of the optic nerve of fishes, *Jour. Comp. Neur.* vol. 26, p. 213.

1919: A retinal mechanism of efficient vision, *Jour. Comp. Neur.*, vol. 30, p. 343-353.

BACH, L. and SEEFELDER, R., 1911: Atlas zur Entwicklungsgeschichte des menschlichen Auges, Part I, Leipzig.

BALDWIN, W. M., 1912: Die Entwicklung der Fasern der Zonula Zinnii im Auge der weissen Maus nach der Geburt, *Arch. f. mikr. Anat.*, Bd. 80, S. 274-305.

BARATZ, W., 1902: Das Wachstum des Auges und seine Besonderheiten beim Neugeborenen, *Inaug. Diss.*, St. Petersburg, (Abstr. in *Schwalbe's Jahresberichte, N. S.*, Bd. 9).

BARTELS, M., 1920: Aufgaben der vergleichenden Physiologie der Augenbewegungen, *Arch. f. Ophthal.*, Bd. 101, S. 299-332.

BELL, E. T., 1906: Experimentelle Untersuchungen ueber die Entwicklung des Auges bei Froschen, *Arch. f. mikr. Anat.*, Bd. 68, S. 279-296.

1906: Experimental studies on the development of the eye and the nasal cavities in frog embryos, *Anat. Anz.*, Bd. 29, 185-194.

BELL, E. T., 1907: Some experiments on the development and regeneration of the eye and nasal organ in frog embryos, *Arch. f. Entw.-Mech.*, Bd. 23, p. 457-478.

BERNARD, H. M., 1904: Studies in the retina. 4. The continuity of the nerves through the vertebrate retina, *Quart. Jour. Micr. Sci., N. S.*, vol. 47, p. 303.

BIELSCHOWSKY, M., und POLLACK, B., 1904: Zur Kenntnis der Innervation des Säugetierauges, *Neurol. Centralbl.*, Jg. 23, S. 387.

BODDAERT, G., 1871: Zur Histologie der Cornea, *Centralbl. f. d. med. Wissen.*, 9 Jahrg., S. 337-339.

BODEN AND SPRAWSON, 1892: The pigment cells of the retina, *Quart. Jour. Micr. Sci., N. S.*, vol. 33.

BONNEFON, 1920: Le régime circulatoire dans la choroïde et le corps ciliaire, ses rapports avec l'ophthalmotonus et la sécrétion de l'humeur aqueuse, *Ann. d'ocul.*, T. 157, p. 504-507.

BRUCH, C., 1854: Ueber Bindegewebe, *Zft. f. wiss. Zool.*, Bd. 6, S. 145-207.

BRUECKNER, A., 1907: Ueber Persistenz von Testen der tunica vasculosa lentis, *Arch. f. Augenheilk.*, Bd. 56, Suppl., S. 5-149.

BRYCE, T. H., 1908: Embryology, in QUAIN's *Anatomy*, Eleventh Edition, vol. 1.

CAJAL, S. RAMON Y., 1893: La rétine des vertebrés, *La Cellule*, T. 9, p. 119-257.

1896: Nouvelles contributions a l'étude histologique de la rétine, etc., *Jour. de l'Anat. et de la Physiol.*, T. 32.

CAMERON, J., 1905: The development of the retina in Amphibia: An embryological and cytological study, *Jour. of Anat. and Physiol.*, vol. 39, p. 332.

CARINI, A., 1899: Osservazioni sull'origine del vitreo, *Monitore Zool. Ital.*, T. 10, p. 33-39.

CHIEWITZ, J. H.: 1887: Die Area and Fovea centrales retinae beim menschlichen Fetus, *Internat. Zeitschr. f. Anat. u. Physiol.*, Bd. 4, S. 201-226.

CHILD, C. M., 1921: *The Origin and Development of the Nervous System*, Chicago.

CIRINCIONE, G., 1903: Ueber die Genese des Glaskörpers bei Wirbeltieren, *Anat. Anz.*, Bd. 23, Erg. Heft, S. 51-60, Verh. Anat. Gesell., 17 Vers.

Ueber die Genese des Glaskörpers bei Wirbeltieren, *Centralbl. prakt. Augenheilk.*, Bd. 27, S. 161-169.

1904: Ueber den gengewärtigen Stand der Frage hinsichtlich der Genesis der Glaskörpers, *Arch. f. Augenheilk.*, Bd. 50, S. 201-217.

COLE, W. H., 1922: The transplantation of skin in frog tadpoles, with special reference to the adjustment of grafts over eyes and to the local specificity of integument, *Jour. Exp. Zool.*, vol. 35, p. 353-410.

CORNING, H. K., 1900: Ueber die vergleichende Anatomie der Augenmuskulatur, *Morph. Jahrb.*, Bd. 29, S. 94-140.

COSMETTATOS, G. F., 1910: Récherches sur le développement de la membrane pupillaire chez l'homme, *Arch. d'Ophthal.*, T. 30, p. 480–498.

DEDEKIND, F., 1908: Beiträge zur Entwicklungsgeschichte der Augengefässe des Menschen, *Anat. Hefte*, Bd. 38, S. 1-29.

DEMOURS, 1741: Observations sur la cornée, Histoire d. l'Acad. roy. d. sciences avec les *Mem. d. Math. et d. Physique*, p. 68-71.

DESCEMET, 1758: An sola lens crystallina čataractae sedes, *Dissertatio*, Paris.

1768: Observations sur la choroïde, *Mem. d. math. et de phys. presentés à l'Acad. roy. des Sciences*, T. 5, p. 177-189.

DETWILER, S. R., 1916: The effect of light on the retina of the tortoise and the lizard, *Jour. Exp. Zool.*, vol. 20, p. 165-191.

1920: Studies on the retina; The structure of the retina of Phrynosoma cornutum, *Jour. Comp. Neur.*, vol. 32, p. 347-356.

1921: Studies on the retina; Histogenesis of the visual cells in Amblystoma, *Jour. Comp. Neur.*, vol. 33, p. 493-508.

DEWEY, K. W., 1920: A contribution to the study of the lymphatic system of the eye, *Anat. Rec.*, vol. 19, p. 125-143.

DEYL, J., 1896: Ueber den Eintritt der arteria centralis retinae beim Menschen, *Anat. Anz.*, Bd. 11, S. 687-692.

DOGIEL, A. S., 1890: Die Nerven der Cornea des Menschen, *Anat. Anz.*, Bd. 5, S. 483.

1895: Die Structure des Nervenzellen der Retina, *Arch. f. mikr. Anat.*, Bd. 46, S. 394.

DRAGENDORF, O., 1903: Experimentelle Untersuchungen ueber Regenerationsvorgänge am Auge und an der Linse bei Hühnerembryonen, Univ. Rostock. i. M.

DRYAULT, A., 1904: Appareil de la vision; in POIRER and CHARPY, *Traité d'anatomie humaine*, vol. 5.

DUBOIS, E. et CASTELAIN, F., 1907: Contribution a l'étude de l'innervation motrice de l'Iris, *Arch. d'Ophthal.*, T. 27, p. 310.

DUBREUIL, G., 1907: La glande lacrymale de l'homme et des mammiferes, *Rev. gen. Ophthal.*, Année 26, p. 339.

DUCLOS, J., 1895: *Étude sur les dimensions du cristallen* (thesis), Bordeaux.

VAN DUYSE, 1904: *Elements d'embryologie et teratologie de l'oeil*, Paris.

DWIGHT, T., 1897: The anatomy of the orbit and the appendages of the eye; in *System of Diseases of the Eye*, ed. by NORRIS and OLIVER, vol. 1, pp. 69-108.

EKMAN, G., 1914: Experimentelle Beiträge zum Linsenbildungsproblem bei den Anuren mit besonderer Berücksichtigung von Hyla arborea, *Arch. f. Entw.-Mech.*, Bd. 39, S. 328-351.

1914: Zur Frage nach der frühzeitigen Spezifizierung der verschiedenen Teile der Augenanlage, *Arch. f. Entw.-Mech.*, Bd. 40, S. 122-130.

EYCLESHYMER, A. C., 1893: The development of the optic vesicles in Amphibia, *Jour. Morph.*, vol. 8, p. 189-193.

FALCHI, F., 1888: Sur l'histogenese de la retine et du nerf optique, *Arch. Ital. de biol.*, T. 9, p. 382-399.

1888: Ueber die Histogenese des retina und des nervus opticus, GRAEFES *Arch. f. Ophthal.*, Bd. 34, (2), S. 67-108.

FESSLER, F., 1920: Zur Entwicklungsmechanik des Auges, *Arch. f. Entw.-Mech.*, Bd. 46, S. 169-201.

FISCHEL, A., 1900: Ueber die Regeneration der Linse, *Anat. Hefte*, Bd. 14.

FISCHEL, A., 1921: Ueber normale und abnorme Entwicklung des Auges; I. Ueber Art und Ort der ersten Augenanlage sowie die formale und kausale Genese der Cyclopie; II. Zur Entwicklungsmechanik der Linse, *Arch. f. Entw.-Mech.*, Bd. 49, S. 383-462.

FRITSCH, G., 1900: Vergleichende Untersuchungen menschlicher Augen, *Sitzungsber. d. Königl. Preuss. Akad. d. Wissen. zu Berlin*, Bd. 30, S. 1-18.

1908: Ueber den Bau und die Bedeutung der histologischen Elements in der Netzhaut des Auges besonders am Ort des deutlichsten Sehens bei verschiedenen Menschenrassen, *Anat. Anz.*, Bd. 32, Erg.-heft, S. 141-145, Verhand. d. Anat. Gesell.

FRITZ, W., 1906: Ueber die membrana Descemetii und das ligamentum pectinatum iridis bei den Säugetieren und beim Menschen, *Sitzber. k.k. Akad. Wiss. Wien. Math-natur-wiss.*, Kl., Bd. 115.

FRORIEP, A., 1891: Ueber die Entwicklung des Sehnerven, *Anat. Anz.*, Bd. 6, S. 155.

— 1905: Ueber die Einstülpung der Augenblase, *Arch. f. mikr. Anat.*, Bd. 66, S. 1-11.

— 1905: Die Entwicklung des Auges der Wirbeltiere; in HERTWIG's Handbuch, Bd. II, 2.

FUCHS, H., 1905: Zur Entwicklungsgeschichte des Wirbeltierauges; I. Ueber die Entwicklung der Augengefässe des Kaninchens, *Anat. Hefte*, Bd. 28, S. 1-251; 194-216.

GABRIELIDES, A., 1895: Récherches sur l'embryogenie et de l'anatomie comparée de l'angle de la chambre anterieure chez le poulet et chez l'homme. Muscle dilatateur de la pupille; Thesis, *Arch. d'ophthal.*, T. 15, p. 176-193, Paris.

GRYNFELLT, E., 1898: Sur le développement du muscle dilatateur de la pupille chez le lapin, *Comptes Rend. Acad. Sci.*, T. 127, p. 966-968, Paris.

— 1899: *Le muscle dilatateur de la pupille chez les Mammiferes*, Firmin-Montane, Montpellier.

GUTMANN, G., 1888: Ueber die Lymphbahnen der Cornea, *Arch. f. mikr. Anat.*, Bd. 32, S. 593-602.

HAEMERS, A., 1903: Régeneration du corps vitré, *Arch. d'ophthal.*, T. 23, p. 103-114.

HAMBURGER, C., 1921: Einiges Kritische und Experimentelle zur Ernährung des Auges, *Klin. Monatsbl. f. Augenh.*, Bd. 66, S. 403-409.

HARTINGER, H., 1921: Zur Messung der Kammertiefe und des Irisdurchmessers, *Zft. f. ophthal. Optik*, Bd. 9, S. 135-143.

HEERFORDT, C., 1900: Studien ueber den musculus dilator pupillae, samt Angabe von gemeinshaftlichen Kennzeichen einiger Fälle epithelialer Muskulatur, *Anat. Hefte*, Bd. 14, S. 487-558.

— 1900: Berichtigung zum Aufsatz ueber den musculus dilatator pupillae, etc., *Anat. Hefte*, Bd. 15, S. 721.

HENCKEL, FR., 1898: Beiträge zur Entwicklungsgeschichte des menschlichen Auges, *Anat. Hefte*, Bd. 10, S. 485-510; also as *Med. Dissert. Giessen*.

HERZOG, H., 1902: Ueber die Entwicklung der Binnenmuskulatur des Auges, *Arch. f. mikr. Anat.*, Bd. 60, S. 517-586.

HESSE, R., 1898: Die Sehorgane des Amphioxus, IV Abt. in Untersuchungen ueber die Organe der Lichtempfindung bei niederen Tieren, *Zft. f. wiss. Zool.*, Bd. 63.

— 1904: Ueber den feineren Bau des Stäbchen und Zapfen einiger Wirbeltiere, *Zool. Jahrb.*, Suppl. 7, (*Fetschr. zum. Geburtst.* A. WEISMANN), S. 471.

HIRSCH, K., 1906: Ist die fetale Hornhaut vascularisiert? *Klin. Monatsbl. f. Augenheilk.*, Bd. 44, N. S., Bd. 2, S. 13-30.

HOWARD, A. D., 1908: The visual cells in vertebrates, chiefly in Necturus maculosus, *Jour. Morph.*, vol. 19, p. 561-631.

JACOBI, E., 1905: Ueber die Neuroglia des Sehnerven, *Klin. Monatsbl. f. Augenheilk.*, Bd. 43, S. 129-137.

JEANNULATOS, P., 1896: Étude de la formation de la chambre anterieure. Embryogenie de la membrane pupillaire, part qu'elle prend dans l'évolution d'iris, *Arch. d'ophthal.*, T. 16, p. 529-554.

— 1896: *Récherches embryologiques sur la mode de formation de la chambre anterieure chez les mammiferes et chez l'homme. Embryogenie de la membrane pupillaire, part qu'elle prend dans l'évolution de l'iris*, (thesis), Paris.

JOHNSTON, J. B., 1905: The morphology of the vertebrate head from the viewpoint of the functional divisions of the nervous system, *Jour. Comp. Neur.*, vol. 15, p. 175-275.

KEIBEL, F., 1886: Zur Entwicklung des Glaskörpers, *Arch. f. Anat. u. Physiol.*, Anat. Abt., S. 358-368.

— 1889: Ueber die Entwicklung des Sehnerven, *Deutsche med. Wochenschr.*, Bd. 15, S. 116.

— 1906: Die Entwicklungsgeschichte des Wirbeltierauges, *Klin. Monatsbl. f. Augenheilk.*, Bd. 44, N. S. Bd. 2, S. 112-132.

KEIL, R., 1906: Beiträge zur Entwicklungsgeschichte des Auges vom Schwein, mit besonderer Berücksichtigung des Verhaltens der fetalen Augenspalte, *Anat. Hefte*, Bd. 32.

KESSLER, L., 1897: *Zur Entwicklung des Auges der Wirbeltiere*, Leipzig.

KIRIBUCHI, K., 1898: Ueber das elastische Gewebe im menschlichen Auge, nebst Bemerkungen ueber den Musculus dilatator pupillae, *Arch. f. Augenheilk.*, Bd. 38, S. 177-184.

KNAPE. V., 1909: Ueber die Entwicklung der Hornhaut der Hühnchens, *Anat. Anz.*, Bd.
34, S. 417-424.

KÖLLIKER, A., VON, 1903: Ueber die Entwicklung und Bedeutung des Glaskörpers,
Anat. Anz., Bd. 23, S. 49-51, Erg.-heft, Verh. Anat. Gesellsch. 17 Vers.
1904: Die Entwicklung und Bedeutung der Glaskörpers, *Zeitschr. f. wiss. Zool.*,
Bd. 76, S. 1-25.

KOLMER, W., 1904: Ueber ein Strukturelement der Stäbchen und Zapfen der Froschretina,
Anat. Anz., Bd. 25, S. 102.

KRUECKMANN, E., 1906: Ueber die Entwicklung und Ausbildung der Stützsubstanz im
Sehnerven und in der Netzhaut, *Klin. Monatsbl. f. Augenheilk.*, Bd. 44, N.S., Bd. I, S.
162-191.

LANGE, O., 1901: Zur Anatomie des Auges des Neugeborenen. 1. Zur Anatomie des
Ciliarmuskels der Neugeborenen, *Klin. Monatsbl. f. Augenheilk.*, Bd. 39, S. 1-6.
2. Suprachorioidealraum, zonula Zinnii, ora serrata und sogenannte physiologische
Exkavation der Sehnervenpapille, *Klin. Monatsbl. f. Augenheilk*, Bd. 39, S. 202-213.
1908: *Einblicke in die embryonale Anatomie und Entwicklung des Menschenauges.
Nach eigenen Präparaten dargestellt*, Wiesbaden.

LAURENS, H. and WILLIAMS, J. W., 1917: Photomechanical changes in the retina of
normal and transplanted eyes of Amblystoma larvae, *Jour. Exp. Zool.*, vol. 23, pp.
71-84.

LAURENS, H. and DETWILER, S. R., 1921: Studies on the retina; The structure of the
retina of Alligator mississippiensis and its photomechanical changes, *Jour. Exp. Zool.*,
vol. 32, p. 207-234.

LEBER, TH., 1908: Die Zirkulations und Ernährungsverhältnisse des Auges; in GRAEFE-
SÄMISCHS *Handbuch der gesamten Augenheilkunde*, 2d ed. Bd 2, 2. (Published 1903).

LEBER, TH., and PILZECKER, A., 1906: Neue Untersuchungen ueber den Flüssigkeits-
wechsel des Auges, *Arch. f. Ophthal.*, Bd. 64, S. 1-127.

LeCRON, W. L., 1906-07: Experiments on the origin and differentiation of the lens in the
Amblystoma, *Am. Jour. Anat.*, vol. 6, p. 245.

LENHOSSEK, M., 1903: *Die Entwicklung des Glaskörpers*, Leipzig.

LEWIS, W. H., 1903: Wandering pigmented cells arising from the epithelium of the
optic cup, with observations on the origin of the m. sphincter pupillae in the chick,
Am. Jour. Anat., vol. 2, pp. 405-416.
1904: Experimental studies on the development of the eye in Amphibia; 1. On the
origin of the lens. Rana palustris, *Am. Jour. Anat.*, vol. 3, pp. 505-536.
1905: Experimental studies on the development of the eye in Amphibia; II. On the
cornea, *Jour. Exp. Zool.*, vol. 2, pp. 431-446.
1907: Experimental studies on the development of the eye in Amphibia; III. On the
origin and differentiation of the lens, *Am. Jour. Anat.*, vol. 6, pp. 473-509.
1907-08: Lens formation from strange ectoderm in Rana sylvatica, *Am. Jour. Anat.*,
vol. 7, p. 45.
1907: Experiments on the origin and differentiation of the optic vesicle in Amphibia,
Am. Jour. Anat., vol. 7, p. 259.

LUBOSCH, W., 1909: Besprechung einen neuen Theorie der Licht- und Farbenempfindung
nebst einem Exkurs über die stammesgeschichtliche Entstehung des Wirbeltierauges,
Morphol. Jahrb., Bd. 39, S. 146-153.

MAGITOT, A., 1910: Étude sur le développement de la rétine humaine, *Ann. d'Ocultistique*,
T. 143, p. 241.

MALL, F. P., 1893: Histogenesis of the retina in Amblystoma and Necturus, *Jour. Morph.*,
vol. 8, pp. 415-432.

MENCL, E., 1907: Neue Tatsachen zur Selbstdifferenzierung der Augenlinse, *Arch. f. Entw.-Mech.*, Bd. 25, S. 431-450.

MERKEL, FR., 1873, *Die Muskulatur der menschlichen Iris*, Rostock.

MERKEL, FR., u. KALLIUS, E., 1910: Makroskopische Anatomie des Auges, GRAEFE-SÄMISCH, *Handb. d. ges. Augenheilk*, 2. Auf., Bd. I, 1 Abt., Kap. I.

MÖRNER, C. T., 1893: Untersuchung der Proteinsubstanzen in den lichtbrechenden Medien des Auges; II. Die Hornhaut. III. Die Glasmembranen der lichtbrechenden Medien, *Zft. f. physiol. Chemie*, Bd. 18, S. 213-256.

MUENCH, K., 1906: Ueber die Mechanik der Irisbewegung, *Arch. f. Ophthal.*, Bd. 44, p. 339.

NEAL, H. V., 1909: The morphology of the eye muscle nerves, *Proc. 7th Int. Zool. Congr.*, pp. 204-214.

    1918: The history of the eye muscles, *Jour. Morph.*, vol. 30, pp. 433-453.

NUSSBAUM, M., 1892: Vergleichende Studien über die Orbita des Menschen und der Tiere, *Sitzb. Niederrh. Ges.*

    1893: Vergleichendanatomische Beiträge zur Kenntniss der Augenmuskeln, *Anat. Anz.*, Bd. 8, S. 208.

    1899: Ueber Entwicklung der Augenmuskeln bei den Wirbeltieren, *Sitzb. Niederrh. Ges.*

    1901: Die Pars ciliaris retinae des Vogelauges, *Arch. f. mikr. Anat.*, Bd. 57, S. 346-353.

    1901: Entwicklung der Binnenmuskeln des Auges der Wirbeltiere, *Arch. f. mikr. Anat.*, Bd. 58, S. 199-230.

    1902: Zur Anatomie der Orbita, *Anat. Anz.*, Bd. 21, Erg. heft. S. 137-143, Anat. Vers.

    1912: Entwicklungsgeschichte des menschlichen Auges; in GRAEFE-SÄMISCHS *Handbuch der gesamten Augenheilk*, (2d ed., Part 15, pp. 35-59. Published in Part I of Bd. 2 in 1908) III. Aufl., I. Teil, VIII. Kap.

OGAWA, C., 1921: Experiments on the regeneration of the lens in Diemyctylus, *Jour. Exp. Zool.*, vol. 33, pp. 395-407.

OPIN, 1906: Contribution a l'histologie du chiasma chez l'homme. La commissure de Hannover, *Arch. d'Ophthal.*, T. 26, p. 545.

PARKER, G. H., 1908: The origin of the lateral eyes of vertebrates, *Am. Nat.*, vol. 42.

    1909: The Integumentary nerves of fishes as photoreceptors and their significance for the origin of the vertebrate eyes, *Am. Jour. Physiol.*, vol. 25, pp. 77-80.

VAN PEE, P., 1903: Récherches sur l'origine du corps vitré, *Arch. de Biol.*, T. 19, pp. 317-385.

PIERSOL, G. A., 1897: The Microscopic Anatomy of the Eyeball, NORRIS and OLIVER, *System of Diseases of the Eye*, vol. 1. pp. 217-382.

PIPER, H., 1905: Ueber die Funktionen der Stäbchen und Zapfen und über die physiologische Bedeutung des Sehpurpur, *Med. Klinik.*, Jg. I., Nr. 25, S. 629; Nr. 26, S. 658.

POOLE, F. S., 1905: The relations of the superior oblique muscle of the eye in the mammals, *Jour. of Anat. and Physiol.*, vol. 39, p. 154.

PROKOPENKO, P., 1903: Ueber die Vertheilung der elastischen Fasern im menschlichen Auge, *Arch. f. Ophthal.*, Bd. 55, S. 94-120.

RABL, C., 1898: Ueber den Bau und die Entwicklung der Linse; I. Selachier und Amphibien, *Zft. f. wiss. Zool.*, Bd. 63.

    1899: 2. Reptilien und Vögel, *Zft. f. wiss. Zool.*, Bd. 65.

    1900-03: 3. Säugetiere. Rückblick und Schluss, *Zft. f. wiss. Zool.*, Bd. 67.

    1900: *Ueber den Bau und Entwicklung der Linse*; Leipzig.

    1903: Zur Frage nach der Entwicklung des Glaskörpers, *Anat. Anz.*, Bd. 22, S. 573.

    1918: Ueber die bilaterale oder nasotemporale Symmetrie des Wirbeltierauges, *Arch. f. mikr. Anat.*, Bd. 90, S. 261-444.

RECKLINGHAUSEN, VON, 1861: Eine Methode, mikroskopische Hohle und solide Gebilde voneinander zu unterscheiden, *Arch. f. path. Anat.*, Bd. 19, S. 451.

RETZIUS, G., 1894: Ueber den Bau des Glaskörpers und der zonula Zinnii in dem Auge des Menschen und einiger Tiere, *Biolog. Untersuch.*, N.S., Bd. 6, S. 66-87.

REUTER, K., 1897: Ueber die Entwicklung der Augenmuskulatur beim Schwein, *Anat. Hefte*, Bd. 9, S. 365, (Also as *Inaug. Diss. Göttingen*, pp. 21).

ROCHON-DUVIGNEAUD, 1920: La vision et l'oeil de l'homme à point de vue de l'anatomie et de physiologie comparées, *Bull. et. Mem. Soc. d'anthrop. de Paris*, 7 S, p. 1-29.

SASSE, 1879: Zur Chemie der DESCEMET'schen Membran, *Untersuch. d. physiol. Inst. d. Univ. Heidelberg*, Bd. 2.

SCHAPER, A., 1904: Ueber einige Fälle atypischer Linsenentwickelung unter abnormen Bedingungen, *Anat. Anz.*, Bd. 24, S. 305.

⎯1899: Bemerkung zur Struktur der Kerne der Stäbchen-Sehzellen der Retina, *Anat. Anz.*, Bd. 15, S. 534-538.

SCHMIDT-RIMPLER, H., 1903: Die Farbe der Macula lutea, *Arch. f. Ophthal.*, Bd. 57, p. 24.

SCHÖN, W., 1895: Zonula und ora serrata, *Anat. Anz.*, Bd. 10, S. 360-364.

⎯ 1895: Der Uebergangsraum der Netzhaut oder die sogenannte ora serrata, *Arch. f. Anat. u. Entwickl.*, S. 417-422.

SCHREIBER, L., 1904: Ueber vitale Indigkarminfärbung der Hornhaut, nebst Bemerkungen ueber das Verhalten des Indigkarmins im Blute und im Auge, *Arch. f. Ophthal.*, Bd. 58, S. 343-367.

SCHULTZE, O., 1892: Zur Entwicklungsgeschichte des Gefässsystems in Säugetierauge, KÖLLIKER's *Festschrift*; Leipzig.

⎯ 1902: Ueber die Entwicklung und Bedeutung der ora serrata des menschlichen Auges, *Verh. Phys.-med. Gesel.*, N. S., Bd. 34; Wurzburg.

SEEFELDER u. WOLFRUM, 1906: Zur Entwicklung der vorderen Kammer und des Kammerwinkels beim Menschen, nebst Bemerkungen ueber ihre Entstehung bei Tieren, *Arch. f. Ophthal.*, Bd. 63, S. 430-451.

SEIDEL, E., 1920: Weitere experimentelle Untersuchungen ueber die Quelle und den Verlauf der intraokulären Saftströmung, *Arch. f. Ophthal.*, Bd. 101, S. 189; Bd. 102, S. 366-382; Bd. 102, S. 383-414.

⎯ 1921: Weitere experimentelle Untersuchungen ueber die Quelle und den Verlauf der intraokulären Saftströmung, *Arch. f. Ophthal.*, Bd. 105, S. 162-169.

⎯ 1921: Weitere experimentelle Untersuchungen ueber die Quelle und den Verlauf der intraokulären Saftströmung, *Arch. f. Ophthal.*, Bd. 106, S. 176-186.

SLONAKER, J. R., 1897: A comparative study of the area of acute vision in vertebrates, *Jour. Morph.*, vol. 13, p. 445-502.

⎯ 1902: The eye of the common mole, Scalopo aquaticus machrinus, *Jour. Comp. Neur.*, vol. 12, p. 335-366.

⎯ 1918: A physiological study of the anatomy of the eye and its accessory parts of the English sparrow (Passer domesticus), *Jour. Morph.*, vol. 31, p. 351-459.

⎯ 1921: The development of the eye and its accessory parts of the English sparrow (Passer domesticus), *Jour. Morph.*, vol. 35, p. 263-357.

SPAMPANI, G., 1901: Alcune richerche sull'origine et la nature del vitreo, *Monit. Zool. Ital.*, Anno 12, p. 145-153.

SPEMANN, H., 1901: Ueber Correlationen in der Entwicklung des Auges, *Anat. Anz.*, Bd. 19, Erg.-heft, S. 61-79, Verh. Anat. Gesellsch., 15 Vers.

⎯ 1903: Ueber Linsenbildung bei defekter Augenblase, *Anat. Anz.*, Bd. 23, S. 457.

⎯ 1904: Ueber Linsenbildung nach experimentelle Entfernung der primären Linsenbildungszellen, *Comptes rendus 6ieme. Cong. intern. de Zoologie*.

⎯ 1905: Neue Tatsachenzum Linsenproblem, *Zool. Anz.*, Bd. 28.

⎯ 1907: Ueber Linsenbildung nach experimenteller Entfernung der primären Linsenbildungszellen, *Zool. Anz.*, Bd. 31.

⎯ 1912: Zur Entwicklung des Wirbeltierauges, *Zool. Jahrb.*, Bd. 32.

⎯ 1912: Ueber die Entwicklung umgedrehter Hirnteile bei Amphibienembryonen, *Zool. Jahrb.*, Suppl. 15, Bd. 3, S. 1-48. (*Festschrift für* J. W. SPENGEL).

STOCKARD, C. R., 1907: The artificial production of a single median cyclopean eye in the fish embryo by means of sea water solutions of $MgCl_2$, *Arch. f. Ent.-Mech.*, Bd. 23, S. 249-258.

⎯ 1906-07: The embryonic history of the lens in Bdellostoma stouti in relation to recent experiments, *Am. Jour. Anat.*, vol. 6, p. 511-515.

1910: The independent origin and development of the crystalline lens, *Am. Jour. Anat.*, vol. 10, p. 393-423.

1910: The experimental production of various eye abnormalities and an analysis of the development of the primary parts of the eye, *Arch. f. vergl. Ophthal.*, Bd. 1, S. 473-480.

1913: An experimental study of the position of the optic anlage in Amblystoma punctatum, with a discussion of certain eye defects, *Am. Jour. Anat.*, vol. 15, p. 253-289.

STRAHL, H., Zur Entwicklung des menschlichen Auges, *Anat. Anz.*, Bd. 14, S. 298.

SUTTON, J. E., 1920: The fascia of the human orbit, *Anat. Rec.*, vol. 18, p. 141-157.

SZENT-GYÖRGYI, A., 1917: Untersuchungen ueber den Bau des Glaskörpers des Menschen, *Arch. f. mikr. Anat.*, Bd. 89, S. 324-386.

SZILY, A., 1902: Zur Anatomie und Entwicklungsgeschichte der hinteren Irisschichten, mit besonderer Berücksichtigung des musculus sphincter iridis beim Menschen, *Anat. Anz.*, Bd. 20, S. 161-175.

1902: Beitrag zur Kenntnis der Anatomie und Entwicklungsgeschichte der hinteren Irisschichten, mit besonderer Berücksichtigung des musculus sphincter pupillae des Menschen, *Arch. f. Ophthal.*, Bd. 53, S. 459-498.

1904: Zur Glaskörperfrage, *Anat. Anz.*, Bd. 24, S. 417-428.

1908: Ueber das Entstehen eines fibrillären Stützgewebes im Embryo und dessen Verhältnis zur Glaskörperfrage, *Anat. Hefte*, Bd. 35, Heft 107, S. 651-757.

TARTUFERI, F., 1903: Ueber das elastische Hornhautgewebe und ueber eine besondere Metallimprägnationsmethode, *Arch. f. Ophthal.*, Bd. 56, S. 419-438.

VERMES, L., 1905: Ueber die Neurofibrillen der Retina, *Anat. Anz.*, Bd. 26, p. 601.

VIRCHOW, H., 1901: Fächer, Zapfen, Leiste, Polster, Gefässe im Glaskörperraum von Wirbeltieren, sowie damit in Verbindungstehende Fragen, *Ergeb. Anat. u. Entwickl.*, Bd. 10, S. 720-844.

1910: Mikroscopische Anatomie der aüsseren Augenhaut und des Lidapparates, GRAEFE-SÄMISCH, *Handb. d. ges. Augenheilkunde*, 2 Aufl., Bd. I, II Kap.

VOLL, A., 1892: Ueber die Entwicklung der membrana vasculosa retinae, KÖLLIKER's *Festschrift*.

VOSSIUS, A., 1883: Beiträge zur Anatomie des nervus opticus, *Arch. f. Ophthal.*, Bd. 29, Pt. 4, S. 119-150.

VOSSIUS, A., 1921: Persistierendes Blutführendes Pupillarmembrangefäss. Ein Beitrag zur Frage des Blutdruckes in den intraocularen Gefässen, *Arch. f. Ophthal.*, Bd. 104, S. 320-324.

WACHS, H., 1920: Restitution des Auges nach Extirpation von Retina und Linse bei Tritonen, (Neue Versuche zur WOLFF'schen Linsenregeneration) II, *Arch. f. Entw.-Mech.*, Bd. 46, S. 328-390.

WEISS, L., 1897: Ueber das Wachstum der menschlichen Auges und ueber die Veränderung der Muskelinsertionen am wachsenden Auge, *Anat. Hefte*, Bd. 8, Heft 25, S. 191-248.

WERBER, E. J., 1916: On the blastolytic origin of the 'Independent' lenses of some teratophthalmic embryos and its significance for the normal development of the lens in vertebrates, *Jour. Exp. Zool.*, vol. 21, p. 347-367.

WHITNALL, S. E., 1922: *The anatomy of the human orbit and accessory organs of vision*, London.

WILCKENS, M., 1861: Ueber die Entwicklung der Hornhaut des Wirbeltierauges, *Zft. f. rat. Med.*, s. Reihe, Bd. 11, S. 167-174.

WOLFF, G., 1895: Entwickelungsphysiologische Studien. I. Die Regeneration der Urodelenlinse, *Arch. f. Entw.-Mech.*, Bd. 1, S. 380-390.

WOOD, C. A., 1917: *The fundus oculi of birds*, Chicago.

ZUERN, J., 1902: Vergleichend histologische Untersuchungen ueber die Retina und die Area Centralis retinae der Haussäugetiere, *Arch. f. Anat. u. Entw.-Suppl. Bd.*

Physiological Optics

§8.   Subdivisions of the Subject

Physiological Optics is the science of the visual perceptions by the sense of sight.   The objects around us are made visible through the agency of light proceeding thence and falling on our eyes.   This light, reaching the retina, which is a sensitive portion of the nervous system, stimulates certain sensations therein.   These are conveyed to the brain by the optic nerve, the result being that the mind becomes conscious of the perception of certain objects disposed in space.

Accordingly, the theory of the visual perceptions may be divided into three parts:

1.   *The theory of the path of the light in the eye.*   Since we are here chiefly concerned with the refraction of the rays, and only incidentally with regular or diffuse reflection, this subdivision of the subject may be entitled *the dioptrics of the eye.*

2.   *The theory of the sensations of the nervous mechanism of vision;* in which the sensations are considered by themselves without taking account of the possibility which they afford of recognizing external objects.

3.   *The theory of the interpretation of the visual sensations,* dealing with the impressions which these sensations enable us to form of the objects around us.

Thus the difference between *physiological optics* and *physical optics* is that, whereas the former is concerned with the properties and behaviour of light only as they pertain to visual perceptions, the latter investigates optical phenomena and laws independently of the human eye.   Physical optics is intimately connected with visual phenomena partly because the eye itself is an optical instrument and is employed for purposes of observation and partly also because it affords the most convenient means of recognizing the existence and propagation of light and of distinguishing one kind of light from another.

For the benefit of such readers as are not thoroughly familiar with the principles of physical optics, the following brief summary of the characteristic properties of light which are of most importance in physiological optics, together with definitions of some of the physical terms that are to be employed later, is inserted at this place.

Nearly all physicists nowadays regard light as a form of motion

in an hypothetical medium known as the luminiferous aether.   The
wave theory of light, as it is called, gives a satisfactory
explanation of all the phenomena, and is the basis of
this explanation.[1]

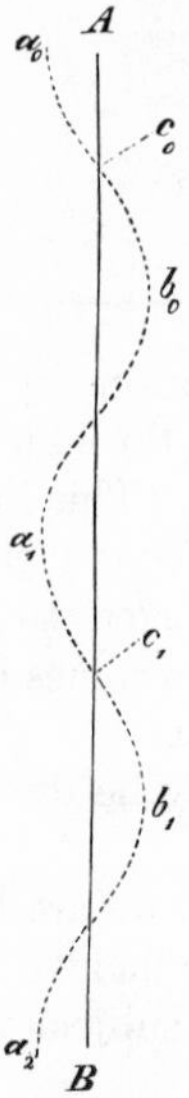

A good idea of the mode of motion of the aether
particles along a ray of light, according to the fundamental assumption of the wave theory, may be obtained
by holding in the hand the upper end of a moist string
or a slender chain AB, Fig. 23, and, as it hangs vertically, giving it a rapid lateral motion to and fro.   The
string will then assume a wave form, as indicated by
the dotted line in the figure, and this wave form will
travel continuously from the upper to the lower end.
As the waves travel down the string, each particle of
the string must remain at the same height above the
floor, but is free to vibrate to right and left or to and
fro in a straight line, or to move in a horizontal circle
or ellipse about its central equilibrium position, in
accordance with the similar movements of the hand.

The vibrations of a row of aether particles, along
which a ray of light is being propagated, would be
exactly like the motions of the single parts of
the string.   Each element of the aether remains always in the vicinity of its original normal position, and merely oscillates in a
straight or curved path about this point.   It is not the aether particles
themselves that are propagated as light, but only the wave form into
which they continue to arrange themselves in their movements and
changing *phases* of displacement and velocity.   The paths of the aether
particles lie in planes which are *transverse* or perpendicular to the
directions of propagation of the waves of light; just as, in the case of
our string, the waves travel vertically towards the floor while each
particle of the vibrating cord continues to describe a horizontal path
at a constant level.   In this respect waves of light are different from the
waves in elastic fluids, such as sound waves in air, for example, in
which the particles perform *longitudinal* vibrations *parallel* to the
direction of propagation.

If the path of the vibrating particles of aether in a train of light
waves is rectilinear, the light is said to be *plane-polarised*;[2] whereas if

Fig. 23.

---

[1] ¶HELMHOLTZ explains here the wave theory in terms of the ideas that were prevalent
in the middle of the last century, long before the modern electromagnetic theory of light, as
developed by MAXWELL and HERTZ, had superseded the earlier notions of the mode of
propagation of light.   (J. P. C. S.)

[2] ¶As to the beginnings of the theory of the polarisation of light, see:

NEWTON's *Optics* (1719), HUYGENS' *Traité de la lumière* (1690), MALUS in *Mémoires de*

the path is circular or elliptical, the rotation taking place in either direction around the orbit, the light is said to be *circularly* or *elliptically polarised*. Two plane-polarised rays whose directions of vibration are perpendicular to each other are said to have *mutually perpendicular polarisation*. Natural light, as it issues from luminous bodies, behaves usually as a uniform mixture of all kinds of differently polarised light; such light is said to be *unpolarised*. It is primarily through the agency of refraction and reflection that we obtain light with an excess of one kind of polarisation, or with one kind only.

If each aether particle concerned in the propagation of light traverses exactly the same path always in the same time and with the same velocity, the light itself is said to be *simple, monochromatic*,[1] or *homogeneous*, and the interval of time required for it to traverse its path once is known as the *period of vibration*. The most striking characteristic whereby light of different vibration periods may be distinguished by the eye is that of colour. Natural light from luminous bodies is usually not simple light of constant period, but consists of trains of waves of almost innumerable frequencies of vibration continually changing in value. Light of this kind is said to be *mixed* or *composite*. The white light of the sun is mixed light. Mixed light may be most readily separated into its monochromatic components by being refracted through a transparent prism, due to the fact that wave-trains of different periods will proceed in different directions after refraction. We may compare the vibrations in a beam of natural light to those which our string would make, if the hand holding it were to execute horizontal movements in various periods and directions, without, however, ever getting very far from its mean position.

Light is propagated with prodigious speed. Its velocity in interstellar space, as determined by astronomical observations, is found to be not less than 310,177.5 Km per second.[2] In all other transparent media the velocity is less than *in vacuo* and depends also on the frequency of vibration.

In crystalline bodies and other media whose molecular structure is different in different directions (*double refracting substances*), the

---

physiques et de chimie de la Societé d'Arcueil, tome II (1809), and FRESNEL'S *Oeuvres complètes*, tomes I, II, published in Paris in 1868. (J. P. C. S.)

[1] ¶A thing may be "simple" from one point of view and at the same time very complex in other ways. The word "monochromatic" (*einfarbig*) is used in physics to describe light of a definite wave-length or frequency, and this usage is so general there that it can perhaps now never be changed. The expression "single frequency light" is awkward, but it is more accurate and less misleading. (J. P. C. S.)

[2] ¶The mean value of the speed of light *in vacuo* is usually given nowadays as 300,000 Km per second. MICHELSON'S measurements in 1879 gave 186,380 miles per second. (J. P. C. S.)

velocity is also not the same for different directions of propagation and of polarisation.

If a ray of monochromatic, plane-polarised light travels along the line AB, Fig. 23, the aether particles which were originally in that line will now take the wave-form $a_0b_0a_1b_1a_2$, which moves forward with uniform velocity. This results in the formation of alternate loops to right and left, which are of equal length. The length of two such loops, c_0c_1, or more generally, the distance at a given instant from any point on one loop to the corresponding point of the next loop which has the same displacement, is called the *wave-length*. While the crest of the wave is travelling from a_0 to a_1, another crest must be formed at a_0, and the aether particle A must have performed a complete vibration; so that the light travels forward through one wave-length during the time of one vibration period. That is, the wave-length is equal to the vibration period multiplied by the velocity of propagation. Hence it follows that, for light of given vibration period traversing different transparent media, the wave-length must always be proportional to the velocity of propagation; and also that the wave-length in dense transparent substances is in general less than in empty space.

Wave-lengths may be measured by means of interference phenomena, and the corresponding vibration periods then calculated. Interference depends upon the fact that two rays of light will reinforce each other if they give rise to aether movements in the same direction, while if these movements are in opposite directions, they tend to neutralize each other. If two parts of one original ray are made to follow different paths and are then re-united, they will reinforce each other, provided the lengths of the paths are equal or differ by exactly one, or two, or more whole wave-lengths. From observations upon such interference effects it has been found that the wave-lengths of light corresponding to the so-called visible spectrum vary from 0.00039 to 0.00069 mm, and hence that the number of vibrations within the limits of visibility is from 451 to 789 million millions per second.[1]

The disturbances imparted to the surrounding aether by a luminous point-source in an isotropic medium proceed from it uniformly with the same speed in all directions. The result is that the wave expands in spherical form, while the amplitudes of the aether vibrations diminish in proportion as the radius of the sphere increases. It is to be noted, however, that the intensity of the light is proportional to the

---

[1] ¶The visible spectrum extends from about 723 $\mu\mu$ at the red end to 397 $\mu\mu$ at the violet end. these being the wave-lengths in vacuo. (1 $\mu\mu$ is one millionth of a millimetre or ten Ångström units.) Taking the velocity of light as 300 million metres per second, the limiting frequencies of the visible spectrum will be found to be comprised between about 415 and 756 million millions of vibrations per second, corresponding roughly to a range of somewhat less than one octave. (J.P.C.S.)

square of the amplitude of vibration, and that it therefore varies *inversely as the square* of the distance from the source. With respect to the propagation of light, any surface on which the particles of aether are all exactly in the same phase of vibration is called a *wave-surface* or wave-front.

The term *ray of light* requires a special explanation. Mathematically it may be defined as a line perpendicular to the wave-front. Thus, so far as spherical waves are concerned, the rays of light may be regarded as radii of all the concentric spherical surfaces, maintaining their same directions as long as the light continues to travel unhindered in the same transparent medium. As a matter of fact, the vibrations of the aether particles lying along a ray of light are not strictly independent of the movements of the particles along adjacent rays. However, interruptions of these neighbouring vibrations, produced, for example, by the interposition of an opaque body, are found to have little effect on the motions of the aether particles of the original ray under ordinary conditions, especially so far as the eye is concerned. In such circumstances, therefore, the vibrations of the aether particles belonging to a ray may be regarded as practically constituting an isolated mechanism, and as taking place independently of the vibrations in the adjacent rays. The theory of the propagation of light is thereby very greatly simplified. So we are accustomed, in ordinary practice, to assume that each ray of light travels in a straight line, unaffected by the rays adjacent to it; and indeed the inaccuracy arising from such assumption is generally altogether negligible. However, this method of explanation of the expansion of spherical light waves along rays or lines of propagation leads us astray when the light passes through an opening whose dimensions are small enough to be comparable with the wave-length. We find then that appreciable quantities of light are propagated laterally beyond the opening. And in general, wherever light travels past the edge of an opaque obstacle, a small part of it is deflected or, as we say, *diffracted*, from the direct path. In such cases, the phenomena can be explained only by taking into account the action of the entire wave. So far as the physics of the eye is concerned, however, we may tacitly assume that the propagation of light in an isotropic medium is rectilinear.

There is a very marked difference between light and sound in this connection, though it is really only one of degree. The dimensions of most natural objects are so large in comparison with a wave-length of light that the latter magnitude is practically negligible. Nearly all the light goes right on past the side of the obstacle in straight lines, and it is only by the use of special apparatus that we can detect the slight diffraction effects at the edges. Sound waves, on the other hand, are several inches or feet in length, and therefore exhibit a great deal of diffraction when passing among obstacles. Common experience shows us that we can see only in straight lines, although we can hear around corners. We cannot, therefore, explain sound propagation in terms of "sound rays," as it would lead us too far from the actual facts. It is on this account that the theory of sound has always been so much more difficult to present than that of light. To this same peculiarity of light the eye owes its ability of judging correctly the precise position of a luminous body from the direction of the rays of light that come from it into the eye, whereas the ear possesses a similar faculty only to a very limited extent. On the other hand, any intervening opaque object prevents the eye from seeing what is behind it, whereas the ear can easily hear sounds proceeding from behind an obstacle. It thus happens that the phenomenon of wave diffraction involves certain distinct advantages and disadvantages in the case of both these senses.

When a ray of light is incident upon the boundary surface separating two different transparent media, as a rule a portion of it is turned back (*reflected*) and continues in the first medium, while another portion passes on into the second medium, but generally not without being bent aside or *refracted* from its original direction. If the surface of separation is perfectly smooth and *polished*, and the media are not double refracting, there will be only one reflected ray (*regular reflection*) and only one refracted ray. But if the surface is rough, the light will be scattered by reflection and refraction in many or all directions, even if the incident rays were all parallel (*diffuse reflection* and *refraction*).

As light proceeds through a material medium, its intensity may continue undiminished; no matter how far it travels, in which case the medium is said to be *transparent*. Empty space itself is probably the only example of an absolutely transparent medium. On the other hand, the intensity of the light may gradually diminish, which indeed can happen in two ways. Thus there may be in the medium itself innumerable minute foreign particles, tiny fractures, slight changes of structure, etc., which produce an internal scattering or refraction of the light (*false internal dispersion*), causing the medium to appear cloudy and self-luminous throughout; or the light may simply vanish without having been scattered (*absorption*). As absorption usually is different for light of different wave-lengths, white light is generally coloured after passing through a medium of this nature, and the medium itself appears coloured. Colourless transparent media are those which transmit all rays of visible light without appreciable absorption. They may, however, absorb certain invisible rays, as the infra-red or the ultra-violet of solar radiation; that is, they may behave towards these rays as coloured media do towards visible light.

The absorption of light is frequently accompanied by chemical actions, probably always by heat, and sometimes by new light. In the last case, each part of the illuminated medium radiates light in all directions which differs, however, in colour and composition from that which was absorbed. The substance becomes self-luminous. This phenomenon is called *phosphorescence* if it persists after the illumination is cut off, and *fluorescence* (or *true internal dispersion*) if it lasts only during illumination. Light derived from a fluorescent substance is in general of longer wave-length than that of the incident light, and its colour and composition are independent of the latter. In one sense, therefore, fluorescence results in an alteration of the wave-length or refrangibility of the light, and it often happens that light which is invisible to the eye or almost so on account of its short wave-length may be detected by allowing it to fall on a fluorescent material such as the acid sulphate of quinine, uranium glass, extract of horse-chestnut bark, amber, etc.

Following is a list of works which deal in a general way with physiological optics:

1600. FABRICIUS AB AQUAPENDENTE, *de visione*. Ven. Fol.
1604. J. KEPLER, *Paralipomena ad Vitellionem*. Frankf. Cap. 5.
1613. FRANCISCI.AGUILONII, *opticorum libri sex*. Antwerpiae.
1619. SCHEINER, *Oculus sive fundamentum opticum, in quo radius visualis eruitur, sive visionis in oculo sedes cernitur et anguli visorii ingenium reperitur*. Oenip.
1738. R. SMITH, *A compleat system of optics* with J. JURIN'S *Essay upon distinct and indistinct vision*. Cambridge 1738.—Translated in German by KÄSTNER. Altenb. 1755.
1740. LE CAT, *Traité des sens*. Rouen.
1746. P. CAMPER, *dissert. de visu*. Lugd. Batav.
1759. PORTERFIELD, *Treatise on the eyes, the manner and phaenomena of vision*. Edinb.
1766. HALLER, *Elementa physiologiae hum.* Lausanne 1757. Bern 1766.
1819. J. PURKINJE, *Beiträge zur Kenntnis des Sehens in subjektiver Hinsicht*. Prag.
1825. J. PURKINJE, *Beobachtungen und Versuche zur Physiologie der Sinne*. Bd. II. *Neue Beiträge zur Kenntnis des Sehens*. Berlin.
      LEHOT, *Nouvelle théorie de la vision*. Paris.
1826. J. MÜLLER, *Zur vergleichenden Physiologie des Gesichtssinnes*. Leipzig.
1828. MUNCKE, Article: Gesicht und Sehen in GEHLERS *physikalischem Wörterbuche*. Leipzig.
1830. A. HUECK, *Das Sehen seinem äusseren Prozesse nach*. Dorpat u. Göttingen.
1831. D. BREWSTER, *A treatise on optics*.
1834. C. M. N. BARTELS, *Beiträge zur Physiologie des Gesichtssinnes*. Berlin.
1836. A. W. VOLCKMANN, *Neue Beiträge zur Physiologie des Gesichtssinnes*.
1837. J. MÜLLER, *Lehrbuch der Physiologie des Menschen*. Coblentz. Bd. II. S. 276-393.
1839. F. W. G. RADICKE, *Handbuch der Optik*. Bd. II. S. 211-281.
1842. BUROW, *Beiträge zur Physiologie und Physik des menschlichen Auges*. Berlin.
1844. MOSER über das Auge in DOVE's *Repertorium der Physik*. Berlin. Bd. V.

1845. TH. RUETE, *Lehrbuch der Ophthalmologie.*
1846. VOLCKMANN, Article: Sehen in R. WAGNERS *Handwörterbuch d. Physiologie.* Braunschweig.
1852. C. LUDWIG, *Lehrbuch der Physiologie des Menschen.* Heidelberg. Bd. I. S. 192 -263.
1847–53. BRÜCKE, *Berichte über physiologische Optik in Fortschritte der Physik.* Bd. I to V.

PART FIRST

The Dioptrics of the Eye

§9. Laws of Optical Imagery for a System of Spherical Refracting Surfaces.[1]

It is mainly through the agency of refraction that the course of the rays of light is altered in the human eye. Here, however, there is not just one refracting surface, but a whole series of them. Accordingly, let us proceed to consider the general laws of refraction of light in isotropic media, especially of successive refractions at each of a series of curved surfaces, since these laws form the theoretical basis of the first division of this work.

When a ray of light is incident on a surface separating two isotropic media, the directions of the corresponding reflected and refracted rays may be found as follows. Let *ab*, Fig. 24, represent the interface between the two media, which we shall call the *refracting surface*. The straight line *fc* indicates the path of an incident ray; *dc* is a line perpendicular to *ab* at *c*, called the *incidence normal*; and the straight lines *ch* and *cg* represent the paths of the reflected and refracted rays, respectively. The plane containing the normal and the incident ray is called the *plane of incidence*, the

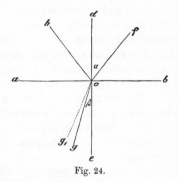

Fig. 24.

angle between these lines being the *angle of incidence* (angle *dcf* or *a* in the figure); the angle between the normal and the reflected ray (angle *hcd* in the figure) being the *angle of reflection*; and that between the normal and the refracted ray (angle *gce* or *β*) being the *angle of refraction*.

When the media are isotropic, (1) the reflected and refracted rays both lie in the plane of incidence; (2) the angle of reflection is equal to the angle of incidence; and (3) the angle of refraction and the angle of incidence are so related that the sines of these angles are in the same ratio as the velocities of propagation of light in the two media.

The ratio of the velocity of light in vacuo to that in a given medium is called the *absolute index of refraction* of that medium. Thus if *c* is the velocity in vacuo and c_1, c_2 the velocities in the first and second media, whose indices of refraction are denoted by n_1, n_2, respectively, then:

[1] See the first of the Appendices to Part I. G.

$$n_1 = \frac{c}{c_1} \quad , \quad n_2 = \frac{c}{c_2}$$

$$\frac{\sin \alpha}{c_1} = \frac{\sin \beta}{c_2}$$

or
$$n_1 \sin \alpha = n_2 \sin \beta.$$

The law of refraction is usually expressed in this last form. By definition the absolute index of vacuum is unity. For air at ordinary pressures it differs so little from unity (its value being 1.00029 at 0° C and 760 mm pressure), that for most purposes the difference is negligible.

The velocities of different kinds of monochromatic light are all the same in vacuo, but in transparent liquids and solids light of different colours is propagated at different speeds. As a rule, the shorter waves (blue and violet) travel more slowly than the longer waves (red and yellow) in the same medium, and hence the index of refraction of the medium is greater for the former than for the latter. Accordingly, the violet rays are said to be *more refrangible* than the red. Owing to this difference of refrangibility, the different coloured components of white light after refraction generally proceed in different directions through a liquid or solid; so that this affords a means of separating them. In Fig. 24, the upper medium is supposed to be less dense than the lower one. The refracted ray *cg* is bent towards the incidence normal *ce*. The deviation is greater for the violet rays than for the red rays. Thus, if the violet light takes the route *cg*, the red component of the beam *fc* will proceed in a direction cg_1, and be separated from the more refrangible colours.

In the eye, we are concerned with the refraction of light at spherical or approximately spherical surfaces. Now in any case of this kind the laws of refraction are greatly simplified when the light falls on the surface nearly normally, so that the angles of incidence are all very small. Moreover, another simplification is introduced in the case of a system of spherical surfaces if they are so adjusted that their centres of curvature all lie on one straight line, called the *optical axis* of the system. A system of spherical surfaces which fulfills this last condition is called a *centered optical system*. A bundle of rays composed of straight lines which all intersect in a single point is said to be *homocentric*.[1] When a homocentric bundle of rays is refracted through a centered system of spherical refracting surfaces, all the angles of incidence being small, the emergent rays will likewise all meet again at a single point, or proceed as if they were diverging from a luminous point, that is, the bundle of emergent rays will be homocentric also. This point at which the rays are again united is called the *optical image*

---

[1] ¶A better term is "monocentric." (J. P. C. S.)

of the original point-source. If now the light were sent back through the system from the point where the image is formed, retracing the same paths the rays would be converged at the original luminous source; and hence these two points, where the source and its image are located, are called *conjugate foci* of the rays.

An optical image is said to be *real*, provided the rays, after their various refractions, actually converge to a focus there. A real image, therefore, must be beyond the refracting surfaces. If the emergent rays apparently diverge from a point nearer the source than the furthermost refracting surface, the image is said to be *virtual*. We say *"apparently,"* because in this case the rays of light themselves do not actually intersect, but only their geometrical prolongations.

Convex glass lenses (burning glasses, convergent lenses) produce real images of distant objects, as shown in Fig. 25, where the lens is represented by *cd* and the luminous point by *a*. The incident rays *ac* and *ad* are refracted through the lens along *cf* and *de*, and actually intersect at *b*, so as to form a real image there. Proceeding on their way, they diverge from *b* as if it were itself an original luminous source.[1]

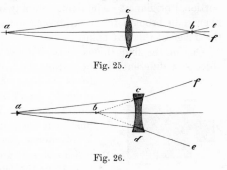

Fig. 25.

Fig. 26.

Concave glass lenses (divergent lenses), on the other hand, give virtual images of real objects, as shown in Fig. 26, which is lettered in the same way as Fig .25. In this case the emergent rays themselves do not actually intersect, but when they are traced back, they intersect "virtually" at *b*; so that to an eye placed between *f* and *e* it would appear as if the source were actually at *b*.

When several luminous points lie in a plane perpendicular to the axis and so near it that their rays all meet each of the surfaces in turn at very small angles of incidence, the images of these points, whether real or virtual, will also lie in a transversal plane perpendicular to the axis, and will have a relative geometrical arrangement similar to the distribution of the luminous points themselves. If these are the luminous points of an object, the optical image of the object will be similar to it.

---

[1] ¶This statement is not strictly accurate, because, whereas the luminous point *a* emits rays in all directions, the rays proceeding beyond *b* are confined to a definite cone of rays. (J. P. C. S.)

The *camera obscura* affords a good illustration of the formation of real images of objects which at the same time is very similar to the way they are produced in the eye. It consists of a box *A* (Fig. 27), blackened on the inside, with a focusing tube mounted in the front side which contains one or more glass lenses *l*. The back of the box is a ground glass plate *g*. If the camera is pointed towards a distant luminous object, and care taken to shade the ground glass, there may be seen upon it an inverted image of the object in its natural colours. If the lens is properly focused, the image will be sharply defined. This means that with a suitable lens situated at the proper distance from the ground glass screen, the rays from any given point of the object will be brought to a focus at some point on the screen. This point will receive all the light which enters the instrument from the corresponding point of the object, and will therefore have the same colour and proportional brilliancy. The light from any other part of the object will likewise be brought to its own proper focus, and will not overlap upon the image of the first point.

One of the first things to be noticed here is that the images of objects at different distances from the instrument are not sharply in

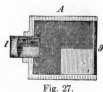

Fig. 27.

focus on the screen at the same time; and in order to get an image of a near object, the lens tube must be pulled out more; and pushed in for a distant object. The reason is, of course, that the images of unequally distant objects are themselves unequally distant from the lens, so that they cannot all be in focus on the screen at once.

Moreover, in case the diameter of the lens is large in proportion to the length of the camera, another thing that will be observed is that the borders of bright parts of the image are fringed with colour, generally blue or orange. Owing to the difference of refrangibility of light of different wave-lengths, the foci for different colours do not lie exactly at the same distance back of the lens, and the coloured images, therefore, do not exactly coincide. This phenomenon is known as *chromatic aberration*. It can be almost completely avoided by the use of a suitable combination of lenses made of different kinds of glass. Optical instruments constructed in this way, so as to be free from chromatic aberration, are said to be *achromatic*.

However, even with monochromatic light it will be found that the images formed in the *camera obscura* and other optical instruments of large aperture are more or less blurred or indistinct. This is because the rays coming from a single point are not refracted by a spherical surface exactly to a focus, but only approximately. In order for the focus to be exact, the angles of incidence must be infinitely small. This second kind of aberration is called *spherical aberration*. An *aplanatic*[1] instrument is one in which the effect is minimized as far as possible by a suitable combination of the refracting surfaces. Perfect aplanatism, generally speaking, is not attainable with spherical refracting surfaces; and for that purpose other curved surfaces which are in fact surfaces of revolution of the second or fourth order have to be used; but hitherto they have been but little employed in actual optical instruments.

Provided certain points on the axis of a centered system of spherical refracting surfaces, known as the *cardinal points* of the system, have been previously located, it is a comparatively simple matter to find the position and size of the image of an object produced by the so-called "paraxial" rays, and also to determine the procedure of any such ray. There are three pairs of these points, namely, the two *focal points*, the two *principal points*, and the two *nodal points*.

The side of the system from which the light comes will be called the *first side*, and the other side to which it goes, the *second side*. The indices of refraction of the first and last media will be denoted by $n\prime$ and $n\prime\prime$, respectively.

The *first focal point* is the point where an incident ray must cross the optical axis in order to emerge from the system in a direction parallel to the axis; and the *second focal point* is the point where an emergent ray, which was originally parallel to the axis, crosses the axis. The *second principal point* is the image of the *first;* that is, the principal points are a pair of conjugate points on the optical axis, so that a ray which before refraction is aimed at the first principal point will issue from the system along a straight line which passes through the second principal point. The *principal planes* of the system are the pair of conjugate planes perpendicular to the axis at the principal points; and the characteristic property of these planes is that an object lying in the first principal plane is reproduced by an image in the second principal plane which has exactly the same dimensions as the object and is oriented the same way. The principal points are the only pair of conjugate points of the system for which this condition is satisfied. The two nodal points are likewise a pair of conjugate points on the axis, characterized in this case by the fact that an incident ray which is directed to the *first nodal point* will emerge from the system in the same direction along a line which passes through the *second nodal point*.

The distance of the first principal point from the first focal point is called the *first focal length* of the optical system. It is reckoned as

---

[1] ¶The term "aplanatic," as commonly used nowadays, implies also the fulfillment of ABBE's so-called "sine condition." (J. P. C. S.)

positive when the first principal point lies beyond the first focal point in the direction of the incident light. Thus, in Fig. 28, suppose that the light goes along the axis from A towards B; and let $f\prime$, $f\prime\prime$ designate the focal points; $h\prime$, $h\prime\prime$ the principal points; and $k\prime$, $k\prime\prime$ the nodal points. In this case the first focal length $f\prime h\prime$ is a positive step along the axis. The *second focal length*, on the contrary, is defined as the distance

Fig. 28.

of the second focal point from the second principal point, that is the step $h\prime\prime f\prime\prime$, which is also a positive step in the adjoining diagram.[1]

The step from the first focal point to the first nodal point is the same as that from the second principal point to the second focal point; and, similarly, the step from the second focal point to the second nodal point is the same as that from the first principal point to the first focal point; that is,

$$\left. \begin{array}{l} f\prime k\prime = h\prime\prime f\prime\prime \\ h\prime f\prime = f\prime\prime k\prime\prime \end{array} \right\} \quad . \quad . \quad . \quad . \quad . \quad . \quad . \quad (\alpha)$$

Hence it follows also that

$$k\prime h\prime = k\prime\prime h\prime\prime = f\prime h\prime - f\prime\prime h\prime\prime \quad . \quad . \quad . \quad . \quad (\beta)$$

Moreover, the interval between the principal points is equal to that between the nodal points, that is,

$$h\prime h\prime\prime = k\prime k\prime\prime \quad . \quad . \quad . \quad . \quad . \quad . \quad (\gamma)$$

Finally, the ratio of the focal lengths is equal to that of the indices of refraction of the first and last media: therefore

$$\frac{f\prime h\prime}{n\prime} = \frac{h\prime\prime f\prime\prime}{n\prime\prime}. \quad . \quad . \quad . \quad . \quad . \quad . \quad (\delta)$$

Accordingly, if the first and last media are the same $(n\prime = n\prime\prime)$, as is the case in most optical instruments, but not in the eye, the two focal lengths are equal and the principal points and nodal points are one and the same pair of conjugate points on the axis.

---

[1] ¶According to the author's definitions, the focal lengths ordinarily, therefore, have the same sign; but nowadays they are both usually defined in the same way, so that generally the two focal lengths are opposite in sign. (J. P. C. S.)

The first focal point, principal point and nodal point are considered as being in the first medium and are concerned with the incident rays; whereas the second focal point, principal point and nodal point are to be regarded as being in the last medium and having to do with the emergent rays.

The focal planes are perpendicular to the optical axis at the focal points. Incident rays which meet in a point in the first focal plane will emerge from the system as a bundle of parallel rays. According to the definition of the nodal points, the direction of this bundle of parallel rays will be parallel to a straight line drawn from the point of intersection of the incident rays in the first focal plane to the first nodal point.

A bundle of parallel rays in the first medium will be brought to a focus at a point in the second focal plane; and the position of this focus will be found by drawing the straight line which is parallel to the incident rays and passes through the second nodal point.

These rules enable us to find the path of a ray in the last medium when we know how it goes in the first, and to determine the position of the image of a given luminous point.

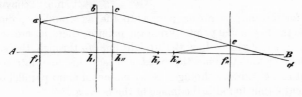

Fig. 29.

Thus, for example, being given the path ab (Fig. 29) of a ray in the first medium, suppose it is required to find its path in the last medium. Let a designate the point where the straight line ab crosses the first focal plane, and let b designate the point where it crosses the first principal plane. The image of the point b lies in the second principal plane, since one principal plane is the image of the other. And since, by the definition of these planes, the image of b must be exactly as far from the axis in the same direction, it must lie at the point c found by drawing a straight line through b parallel to the axis until it meets the second principal plane. Every ray originating at b or passing through this point must, therefore, emerge from the system along a straight line which goes through c.

Thus, the continuation of the ray ab goes through the point c. Now connect the point a with the first nodal point k, by a straight line and draw cd parallel to ak,. Then cd is the continuation of ab in the last medium; because, since a is a point in the first focal plane, all incident rays that go through it will emerge in parallel directions, and since ak, may be considered as one such ray and since the continuation of it must be parallel to ak,, it follows that the continuation of the ray ab in the last medium must also be parallel to ak,.

Or we may also use the property of the second focal plane to make this construction, as follows: Draw the straight line bc parallel to the optical axis meeting the second principal plane at c; and through the second nodal point draw k,,e parallel to ab meeting the second focal plane at e. The straight line ce is the path of the emergent ray.

Or suppose it is required to construct the image of a given luminous point a (Fig. 30). All that is necessary here is to construct the paths

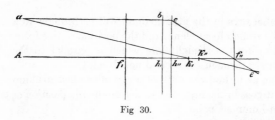

Fig 30.

of two rays coming from a and to determine their ultimate point of intersection. When the given point a is not on the axis, the rays most convenient to use for this purpose are ac, parallel to the axis, and ak,, directed towards the first nodal point. From the point c where ac crosses the second principal plane, draw the straight line cf,, through the second focal point, and determine the point e where this line intersects a straight line k,,e drawn through the second nodal point parallel to ak,. The point e thus found is the image of the point a.

That the rays ac and ak, will, after refraction, follow the paths ce and k,,e, respectively, follows immediately from the foregoing rules and definitions.

If a lies on the axis, one of the rays will follow the axis itself, without deviation. It will then be necessary to construct just one other ray, and the image will be its intersection with the axis.

Having thus briefly outlined the results of the theory for the benefit of those who wish only to know the facts, let us proceed now to the complete mathematical treatment of the subject.

Refraction at a Spherical Surface

In Fig. 31, let a designate the centre of the spherical surface cb, and p the position of a luminous point outside it. A ray proceeding from p towards the centre meets the surface normally and continues along the same straight line aq. Another ray, proceeding along pc,

meets the surface at *c* and is refracted there into the second medium.
The first question is, what
is its new path? By the law
of refraction given above,
it must remain in the plane
of incidence determined by
the incident ray and the
normal at the point of
incidence. The radius of

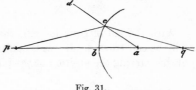

Fig. 31.

a sphere being everywhere perpendicular to its surface, the incidence
normal in this case is simply the prolongation of the radius *ac*, and the
plane of incidence is the plane containing the lines *pc* and *ad*. The line
pq also lies in this plane, since it contains the points *p* and *a* that are
on *pq*. The refracted ray, therefore, must intersect the straight line
pa in some point *q*. Where is this point with reference to the point *b*?
Should the ray happen to be parallel to *pa*, the intersection *q* may
be regarded as at an infinite distance. Its position depends on the
fact that

$$n' \sin (pcd) = n'' \sin(qca) \quad . \quad . \quad . \quad . \quad . \quad (1)$$

where n' and n'' denote the indices of refraction of the first and second
media, respectively.

By the law of sines in trigonometry, we derive the following
relations from the triangles *apc* and *aqc:*

$$\frac{\sin (pca)}{\sin (cpa)} = \frac{ap}{ac}$$

$$\frac{\sin(qca)}{\sin(cqa)} = \frac{aq}{ac}.$$

Dividing the second of these equations by the first, and noting that the
sine of the angle *pca* is equal to the sine of its supplement *pcd*, we
obtain:

$$\frac{\sin(pcd)}{\sin(qca)} \cdot \frac{\sin(cqa)}{\sin(cpa)} = \frac{ap}{aq}.$$

Equation (1) may be written:

$$\frac{\sin(pcd)}{\sin(qca)} = \frac{n''}{n'}$$

and from the triangle *pcq* we have:

$$\frac{\sin(cqa)}{\sin(cpa)} = \frac{cp}{cq}.$$

Combining the last three equations, we find:

$$\frac{n'' \cdot cp}{n' \cdot cq} = \frac{ap}{aq} \quad . \quad . \quad . \quad . \quad . \quad . \quad (2)$$

When the point p is infinitely far away, cp and ap may be considered as being ultimately equal, and hence in this case:

$$n_{'}.cq = n_{''}.aq \quad . \quad . \quad . \quad . \quad . \quad . \quad (2a)$$

With the aid of equation (2), the path of the refracted ray may easily be constructed. If this is performed, not only for one single ray, but, by varying the position of the point c, for a number of other rays

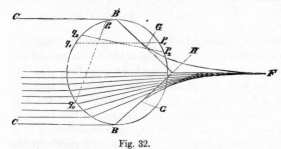

Fig. 32.

also, it will be found that the refracted rays as thus determined do not all intersect each other exactly at one point, and that their successive points of intersection lie along a curved (*caustic*) line, as shown in Fig. 32 for the case when the incident rays are parallel. In this diagram BB represents the spherical refracting surface and CC the incident rays; GFG is the caustic line, which is the enveloping curve of the bundle of refracted rays. The rays that pass closest to the centre meet at the cuspidal point F.

If the discussion is confined to the case of such rays as are incident on the refracting surface nearly normally, it is obvious from Fig. 31 that the ratio $\dfrac{cp}{cq}$ becomes more and more nearly equal to the ratio $\dfrac{bp}{bq}$, when the point c is taken nearer and nearer to b. In this case equation (2) becomes:

$$\frac{n_{'''}.bp}{n_{''}.bq} = \frac{ap}{aq} \quad . \quad . \quad . \quad . \quad . \quad . \quad (2b)$$

Putting the radius $ab = r$, and employing also the following symbols: $bp = f_{'}$, $bq = f_{''}$, $ap = g_{'}$, $aq = g_{''}$, we have therefore

$$\left.\begin{array}{l} f_{'} + r = g_{'} \\ f_{''} \quad\;\; = g_{''} + r. \end{array}\right\} \quad . \quad . \quad . \quad . \quad . \quad . \quad (2c)$$

Equation (2b) becomes:

$$\frac{n_{'}.f_{'}}{n_{'}.f_{''}} = \frac{f_{'} + r}{f_{''} - r}$$

or

$$\frac{n_{''}(g_{'} - r)}{n_{'}(g_{''} + r)} = \frac{g_{'}}{g_{''}}.$$

Thence, by a simple transformation, we may write:

or

$$\left. \begin{array}{l} \dfrac{n'}{f'} + \dfrac{n''}{f''} = \dfrac{n''-n'}{r} \\[2mm] \dfrac{n''}{g'} + \dfrac{n'}{g''} = \dfrac{n''-n'}{r}, \end{array} \right\} \qquad . \quad . \quad . \quad . \quad (3)$$

from which the required distances f'' or g'' may be found.

If F'' and G'' denote the values of f'' and g'' when the luminous source p is infinitely far away, that is, when $f' = g' = \infty$, we find:

$$\left. \begin{array}{l} F'' = \dfrac{n''r}{n''-n'} \\[2mm] G'' = \dfrac{n'r}{n''-n'}. \end{array} \right\} \qquad . \quad . \quad . \quad . \quad . \quad . \quad (3a)$$

Similarly, if f'' and g'' are made infinite, the values of f' and g' are:

$$\left. \begin{array}{l} F' = \dfrac{n'r}{n''-n'} = G'' \\[2mm] G' = \dfrac{n''r}{n''-n'} = F'' \end{array} \right\} \qquad . \quad . \quad . \quad . \quad (3b)$$

Equations (3) may now be written simply as follows:

$$\left. \begin{array}{l} \dfrac{F'}{f'} + \dfrac{F''}{f''} = 1 \\[2mm] \dfrac{G'}{g'} + \dfrac{G''}{g''} = 1. \end{array} \right\} \qquad . \quad . \quad . \quad . \quad (3c)$$

Solving the first of these equations for f', and then for f'', we obtain:

$$\left. \begin{array}{l} f' = \dfrac{F'f''}{f''-F''} \\[2mm] f'' = \dfrac{F''f'}{f'-F'}. \end{array} \right\} \qquad . \quad . \quad . \quad . \quad . \quad . \quad (3d)$$

Whenever either of these values turns out to be negative, it means that the corresponding point, p or q, lies on the opposite side of the refracting surface from that indicated in Fig. 31.

Remarks. 1. If the light, instead of originating at p in the first medium were to come from q in the second medium, qc would be the incident ray and cp the corresponding refracted ray. Thus rays diverging from q and meeting the surface nearly normally, would be brought to a focus at p. This leads at once to the formulae for refraction when the light falls on the concave side of the spherical surface. All that is necessary is to interchange the terms *first medium* and *second medium* and the subscripts in the symbols; whereupon the original equations (3) become

$$\frac{n'}{f'} + \frac{n''}{f''} = \frac{n'-n''}{r}$$
$$\frac{n''}{g'} + \frac{n'}{g''} = \frac{n'-n''}{r}.$$

But these differ from (3) only in the sign of the right-hand term in each case; so that all we have to do is to consider r negative in order that equations (3) may apply also to the case of a concave surface. The same thing is true with respect to equations (3a), (3b), (3c) and (3d), which are all derived from (3).

2. If q is the image of p, then p is also the image of q. This mutual relation is expressed by saying that a pair of such points are *conjugate foci*, without implying which one of them is the source of light. Moreover, as far as the law of refraction is concerned, it is immaterial whether the point from which the light comes belongs to an actual material body, and is self-luminous or not, or is merely a point of intersection of previously refracted rays. Thus, the source may be only a virtual focus of such rays, which has to be constructed by producing the ray paths backwards until these lines intersect at a point on the other side of the surface at which the rays were refracted.

3. Another thing to be noted is that the laws of the *reflection* of rays at a curved mirror may also be deduced from equations (3) by simply putting $n_{\prime\prime} = -n_{\prime}$. Hereafter we shall need these formulae to investigate the reflex images in the refracting surfaces in the eye. Some writers prefer, however, to use special symbols for the mirror formulae. When $-n_{\prime}$ is substituted for $n_{\prime\prime}$ in equations (3), we obtain:

$$\frac{1}{f_{\prime}} - \frac{1}{f_{\prime\prime}} = -\frac{2}{r}.$$

When r is positive, that is, according to the above, when the mirror is convex, then for $f_{\prime} = \infty$, the value of $f_{\prime\prime}$ is equal to $\dfrac{r}{2}$ and is positive, so that the focus of the mirror lies behind it and is therefore virtual. For a concave mirror, r is negative and $f_{\prime\prime}$ is found to be negative also; that is, the focus of a concave mirror is in front of it and is therefore real. Usually, however, it is convenient to reckon the distance of the image from the mirror as positive when the image is real. Therefore, the signs of $f_{\prime\prime}$ and of the radius (r) of the mirror must be taken opposite to those used in case of refraction; so that the fundamental equation has to be written:

$$\frac{1}{f_{\prime}} + \frac{1}{f_{\prime\prime}} = \frac{2}{r}.$$

4. If r is infinite, the refracting surface is plane; in which case, according to (3a), the focal lengths become infinite also, and the first of equations (3) is transformed into

$$\frac{n_{\prime}}{f_{\prime}} + \frac{n_{\prime\prime}}{f_{\prime\prime}} = 0$$

or

$$f_{\prime\prime} = -\frac{n_{\prime\prime}}{n_{\prime}} f_{\prime} \qquad \ldots \qquad (3e)$$

In a plane refracting surface, therefore, the image lies on the same side of the surface as the source, but at a different distance.

Image of an Object in a Spherical Refracting Surface

Hereafter in speaking of an object whose image is formed in a curved refracting surface, it is to be understood that the term refers to a plane object placed perpendicular to the axis of the optical system; and furthermore that it is of very limited size and, for the purposes of the image, emits only such rays as meet the refracting surface nearly normally and therefore at very small inclinations to the optical axis.

When the image of a luminous point is produced by a spherical refracting surface, the straight line joining this point with the centre of the surface may be considered as the axis; but for an object as above defined the axis is the straight line drawn through the centre of the surface perpendicular to the plane of the object.

In Fig. 33, the straight line sp represents the object and the straight line pr drawn through the centre (a) of the spherical refracting surface perpendicular to sp is the optical axis. The image of a point s near the axis is formed at t, whose position is given by two rectangular coördinates,

Fig. 33.

ar and rt, parallel and perpendicular to the axis, respectively.

Considering the luminous point s by itself, its image, as we have seen, must lie somewhere on the straight line sa. Put $sa = y_{\prime}$, and $at = y_{\prime\prime}$; then according to equation (3c):

$$\frac{G_{\prime}}{\gamma_{\prime}} + \frac{G_{\prime\prime}}{\gamma_{\prime\prime}} = 1 \qquad \ldots \qquad (4)$$

Now put $pa = g_{\prime}$, $ar = x$ and angle $sap = a$; then

$$\gamma_{\prime} = \frac{g_{\prime}}{\cos a}$$

$$\gamma_{\prime\prime} = \frac{x}{\cos a}.$$

Substituting these values in (4), we find:

$$\frac{G_{\prime}}{g_{\prime}} + \frac{G_{\prime\prime}}{x} = \frac{1}{\cos a}.$$

Now by the conditions as to the size of the object, the angle a must be very small, and by putting $\cos a = 1$, we shall neglect only a small quantity of the second order of smallness; and then we may write:

$$\frac{G'}{g'} + \frac{G''}{x} = 1.$$

If g'' denotes the distance from a of the image of the axial point p, then

$$\frac{G'}{g'} + \frac{G''}{g''} = 1,$$

and hence

$$x = g'' \qquad \ldots \quad \ldots \quad \ldots \quad (5)$$

That is, the point r at the foot of the perpendicular tr is the image of p.

Accordingly, the images of all points lying in a plane perpendicular to the axis at p are found to be approximately in a plane perpendicular to the axis through the image of p. Thus having first located the point r which is the image of the axial point p, the image of any other point in the object may be found by simply drawing a line from the given point through the centre of the spherical refracting surface, and the point where it crosses the transversal image-plane at r will be the required image. It follows from the principles of elementary geometry that the image and the object are similar.

It is easy to find the ratio of the corresponding linear dimensions of the object and its image. For example, let the height of the object ps be denoted by β', and the corresponding length in the image rt by β''; then

$$-\frac{\beta'}{\beta''} = \frac{g'}{g''} \quad , \qquad \ldots \quad \ldots \quad \ldots \quad (6)$$

where the minus sign has to be inserted in the formula so that it will apply to the cases of both erect and inverted images. Combining this equation with equations (2c), (3a), (3b) and (3c), we find:

$$\frac{\beta''}{\beta'} = \frac{G''}{G' - g'} = \frac{G'' - g''}{G'} \qquad \ldots \quad \ldots \quad (6a)$$

or

$$\frac{\beta''}{\beta'} = \frac{F'}{F' - f'} = \frac{F'' - f''}{F''} \qquad \ldots \quad \ldots \quad (6b)$$

When the refracting surface is plane, the focal lengths become infinite, and for this case equation (6b) becomes

$$\frac{\beta''}{\beta'} = 1 \qquad \ldots \quad \ldots \quad \ldots \quad \ldots \quad (6c)$$

Accordingly, the image in a plane refracting surface is exactly as large as the object.

Generalization of the preceding results. Now let us inquire how the focal points, principal points and nodal points, as above defined, are applicable in the case of a single spherical refracting surface.

The *focal points* are the points where rays intersect in one medium that proceed parallel to the axis in the other medium. The positions of the focal points can be found from equations (3a) and (3b), because the magnitudes denoted by F, F, and G, G, are the distances of the focal points from the vertex and centre of the refracting surface, respectively.

The *focal planes* are the transversal planes perpendicular to the axis at the focal points. Since the conjugate point to either focal point is infinitely far away, the same statement must be true with respect to any point in one of the focal planes, provided it is not too far from the axis. In other words, rays which meet in a point in either focal plane will be parallel to each other in the other medium.

The characteristic property of the *principal points* is that object and image lying in the *principal planes*, which are perpendicular to the axis at these points, have precisely the same dimensions in all respects. For these planes, therefore, $\beta = \beta$. According to equations (6b), this means that here $f = f = 0$, which conditions must both be satisfied, as shown by equations (3d). Consequently, the two principal points of a spherical refracting surface coincide with each other at the vertex, so that object and image are here coincident.

The peculiar property of the *nodal points* is that a ray which is directed towards the first nodal point before refraction will proceed through the second nodal point after refraction in the same direction as before. The two nodal points of a spherical refracting surface also coincide, both being at the centre of the surface; because any ray whose path in the first medium is directed towards the centre of curvature will proceed into the second medium not only in the same direction but along the same straight line.

The constructions given above which were based on the properties of these special points and planes are, therefore, applicable also to the case of a single refracting surface.
The process is
simpler here be-
cause every point
in the first prin-

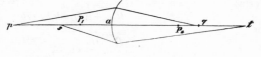

Fig. 34.

cipal plane is its own image, and also because a ray directed to the first nodal point proceeds straight on along the same line.

The two equations (3c), similar in form, enable us to determine the abscissa of the axial image-point, with reference, however, to two different points as origins of measurement. More general equations of the same simple type are obtained by taking as origins in the two media any pair of conjugate points on the axis. For example, suppose the points designated by s, t and p, q in Fig. 34 are two pairs of conjugate points on the axis of a spherical refracting surface, whose focal points are P_1 and P_2; and let us introduce here the following symbols:

$$sa = f_1, \qquad\qquad P_1a = F_1,$$
$$ta = f_2, \qquad\qquad P_2a = F_2,$$
$$pa = \varphi_1,$$
$$qa = \varphi_2,$$
$$ps = h_1, \qquad\qquad qt = -h_2,$$
$$P_1s = -H_1, \qquad\qquad tP_2 = -H_2,$$

then

$$(a) \quad \frac{F_1}{f_1} + \frac{F_2}{f_2} = 1$$

$$(\beta) \quad \frac{F_1}{\varphi_1} + \frac{F_2}{\varphi_2} = 1$$

$$(\gamma) \quad \varphi_1 - f_1 = h_1,$$
$$(\delta) \quad \varphi_2 - f_2 = h_2,$$
$$(\epsilon) \quad F_1 - f_1 = H_1,$$
$$(\zeta) \quad F_2 - f_2 = H_2.$$

Substituting in (β) the values of φ_1 and φ_2 as obtained from (γ) and (δ), we obtain

$$\frac{F_1}{h_1 + f_1} + \frac{F_2}{h_2 + f_2} = 1,$$

or

$$F_1(h_2 + f_2) + F_2(h_1 + f_1) = (h_1 + f_1)(h_2 + f_2).$$

Writing (a) in the form,

$$F_1f_2 + F_2f_1 = f_1f_2,$$

and subtracting this equation from the one above, we get:

$$F_1h_2 + F_2h_1 = h_1h_2 + h_1f_2 + h_2f_1$$

or

$$(F_1 - f_1)h_2 + (F_2 - f_2)h_1 = h_1h_2,$$

which by virtue of equations (ϵ) and (ζ) may be put in the following form:

$$H_1h_2 + H_2h_1 = h_1h_2,$$

or

$$\frac{H_1}{h_1} + \frac{H_2}{h_2} = 1 \quad . \quad . \quad . \quad . \quad . \quad . \quad . \quad (7)$$

Thus if distances along the axis are reckoned from any given pair of conjugate foci a formula of this same simple type is always obtained. Since the centre of curvature of the refracting surface and likewise any point on the surface coincides with its conjugate point, these points are their own images, and equations (3c) prove to be only special examples of the general formula (7).

If the point s coincides with the first focal point, equation (7) is confusing, because now both H_2 and h_2 become infinite. But in this case the corresponding equation can be obtained easily from the first of equations (3d), as follows:

$$f, = \frac{F, f,,}{f,, - F,,}.$$

By subtracting $F,$ from both sides the preceding equation may be written:

$$f, - F, = \frac{F, F,,}{f,, - F,,} \qquad \cdots \qquad (7a)$$

If in this equation we put $f, - F, = l,, f,, - F,, = l,,$, where $l,, l,,$ denote the distances of axial object-point and image-point measured, in opposite directions, from the first focal point and the second focal point, respectively, the connection between a pair of conjugate points is given in its simplest form, as follows:

$$l, l,, = F, F,, \qquad \cdots \qquad (7b)$$

In terms of the same magnitudes, formula (6b) for the magnification-ratio becomes

or
$$\left. \begin{array}{l} \dfrac{\beta,}{\beta,,} = -\dfrac{l,}{F,} \\[2mm] \dfrac{\beta,,}{\beta,} = -\dfrac{l,,}{F,,} \end{array} \right\} \qquad \cdots \qquad (7c)$$

Connection between the linear magnification and the angular magnification. In Fig. 35 let sp and qr represent an object and its image in a spherical refracting surface whose axis is pq. Let a_1, a_2 denote the angles which a ray coming from p makes with the axis before and after refraction, respectively; each of these angles being reckoned as positive or

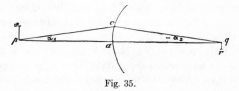

Fig. 35.

negative according as the ray in question leaves the axis above or below it, respectively. Thus $\angle cpa = a_1$, $\angle cqa = -a_2$. Also, as before, let $ps = \beta_1$, $qr = \beta_2$, $ap = f_1$ and $aq = f_2$. Since by hypothesis the slopes of the rays are all small, the arc ac may be considered here as a short straight line perpendicular to the axis at a; and so we may then write:

$$ac = f_1 \tan a_1,$$
$$ac = -f_2 \tan a_2,$$

and therefore

$$f_1 \tan a_1 = -f_2 \tan a_2 \qquad \ldots \qquad \ldots \qquad (A)$$

Moreover, from equations (3d) and (6b):

$$\frac{f_2}{f_1} = \frac{F_2}{f_1 - F_1} = \frac{f_2 - F_2}{F_1},$$

$$\frac{\beta_2}{\beta_1} = \frac{F_1}{F_1 - f_1} = \frac{F_2 - f_2}{F_2}.$$

From (3a) and (3b), $\dfrac{F_2}{F_1} = \dfrac{n_2}{n_1}$; and hence

$$\frac{f_2}{f_1} = -\frac{n_2}{n_1} \cdot \frac{\beta_2}{\beta_1}.$$

Combining this equation with equation (A), we obtain the relation sought, namely:

$$n_1 \beta_1 \tan a_1 = n_2 \beta_2 \tan a_2 \qquad \ldots \qquad \ldots \qquad (7d$$

This important result expresses the relation between the linear magnification and the angular magnification without involving directly the distance of the object or the focal lengths of the refracting surface.[1]

Centered System of Spherical Refracting Surfaces

Let us proceed now to investigate the imagery in the case of a symmetrical optical instrument consisting of a system of spherical refracting surfaces whose centres all lie on a straight line which is therefore the axis of symmetry or *optical axis* of the system.

The light is incident in the *first medium*, whose index of refraction is denoted by n_1, on the *first surface*; the *second medium*, of index n_2, is the medium comprised between the first surface and the *second surface*, etc.; and the *last medium* of all is the medium beyond the last or mth surface, whose index of refraction is denoted therefore by n_{m+1}, since the number of media is always one more than the number of surfaces. As above, the radius of a surface is counted positive or negative according as the surface is convex or concave towards the side of the instrument from which the light comes. Moreover, it should be stated here once for all that when an image is said to lie in a certain medium, this means that it is the focus of the rays in their passage

---

[1] ¶This is a famous law in geometrical optics, sometimes called the "HELMHOLTZ equation" or the "LAGRANGE-HELMHOLTZ equation," because, although HELMHOLTZ discovered it independently and recognized its peculiar importance, he himself attributed it to LAGRANGE who had published a special case of the general law in 1803. But ROBERT SMITH in his *Compleat System of Opticks* (Cambridge 1738) had enunciated this law for a system of infinitely thin lenses long before LAGRANGE, so that nowadays it is sometimes referred to as the "SMITH-HELMHOLTZ equation." (J. P. C. S.)

through this medium, no matter where the image may be situated in space and no matter whether it is real or virtual.

It has been shown that a narrow bundle of rays that all meet a spherical refracting surface nearly normally will be homocentric after refraction, if it were homocentric before refraction. And this remains true no matter how many times the rays are refracted in traversing a centered system of spherical refracting surfaces. If the object is composed of a number of luminous points all lying in a transversal plane perpendicular to the optical axis, the new foci after the first refraction will also lie in a parallel plane in the second medium in similar geometrical arrangement; and the same thing is true after each successive refraction from one medium to the next; so that the image formed in the last medium, that is, the resultant image in the entire system, will lie in a certain transversal plane perpendicular to the optical axis and will be geometrically similar to the object.

Since the image formed in each medium may be regarded as an object with respect to the next spherical refracting surface, the position and size of the final image may be computed without any particular difficulty, although even for a moderate number of refractions, the formulae become very complicated.

Our problem therefore is to derive, if possible, some general laws applicable to any number of refracting surfaces; which is particularly necessary in dealing with the optical system of the human eye, because the crystalline lens has a variable index of refraction and is to be regarded therefore as composed of innumerable surfaces or layers; so that it is no easy matter to trace the path of a ray of light in the eye.

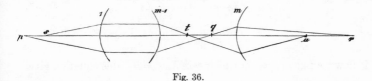

Fig. 36.

1. First of all, let us show that the law found in equation (7) for the case of a single spherical refracting surface is true also of a centered system of such surfaces.

In Fig. 36 the first surface is marked 1, the next to the last $m-1$, and the last m. The point in the first medium designated by s and the point in the last medium designated by u are a pair of conjugate points on the optical axis with respect to the entire system; and the points p and r are another pair of conjugate axial points. Putting $ps = h_1$, and $ur = h_{m+1}$, what we have to prove is that

$$\frac{H_1}{h_1} + \frac{H_2}{h_{m+1}} = 1,$$

where H_1, H_2 denote the distances of the first and second focal points of the system from the points s and u, respectively. In order to show that this is a general law, it will first be proved that if it is true for a system of $(m-1)$ surfaces, it is true also for a system of m surfaces. Then, since we know it is true for one surface, it holds for two; and therefore for three; and so on indefinitely.

The images of the points s and p in the first $(m-1)$ surfaces are formed in the mth medium at the points t and q respectively; put $tq = h_m$. Let L_1, L_2 denote the distances of the two focal points of the system of $(m-1)$ surfaces from the points s, t, respectively; and let M_1, M_2 denote the distances of the two focal points of the mth or last surface from the points t, u, respectively. These distances must be measured from the points s, t and u, and considered as positive when they extend in the same direction as that in which the light traverses the axis. Now by hypothesis:

$$\frac{L_1}{h_1} + \frac{L_2}{h_m} = 1,$$

and for the refraction at the last surface:

$$-\frac{M_1}{h_m} + \frac{M_2}{h_{m+1}} = 1.$$

Dividing the first of these equations by L_2 and the second by M_1, and then adding them, we get:

$$\frac{L_1}{L_2} \cdot \frac{1}{h_1} + \frac{M_2}{M_1} \frac{1}{h_{m+1}} = \frac{1}{L_2} + \frac{1}{M_1}$$

or

$$\frac{M_1 L_1}{M_1 + L_2} \cdot \frac{1}{h_1} + \frac{M_2 L_2}{M_1 + L_2} \cdot \frac{1}{h_{m+1}} = 1.$$

If now we put $h_1 = \infty$ in which case $h_{m+1} = H_2$, this equation gives:

$$H_2 = \frac{M_2 L_2}{M_1 + L_2},$$

and if we put $h_{m+1} = \infty$, so that $h_1 = H_1$, then

$$H_1 = \frac{M_1 L_1}{M_1 + L_2}.$$

Hence, finally

$$\frac{H_1}{h_1} + \frac{H_2}{h_{m+1}} = 1 \qquad \cdots \cdots \cdots \quad (8)$$

as we set out to prove.

For every real value of h_1, positive or negative, according to this equation, there is one corresponding value of h_{m+1}, and only one such value; and, conversely, to each value of h_{m+1} corresponds one value of h_1. Therefore either of the two conjugate foci may be taken anywhere on the optical axis; and whenever the position of one of these points is given, that of the other is uniquely determined.

2.   In every optical system there is one pair of conjugate foci, and only one pair, for which object and image in the corresponding conjugate planes at right angles to the axis are equal in every respect. This pair of conjugate planes is the pair of *principal planes* of the optical system; and the corresponding points on the axis are the *principal points*. The focal lengths of the optical system are to each other in the same ratio as the indices of refraction of the first and last media.

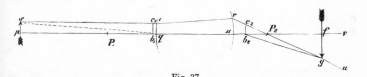

Fig. 37.

The construction of the image of any object is very simple. Suppose that p (Fig. 37) is the point where the optical axis meets the object ps, where s is any other point of the object near p. Think of the object as moving along the axis, so that the point s traces out a straight line st parallel to the axis. If the straight line st is the path of a ray of light, this ray will always go through the point s, no matter what the distance pq is. Now all rays parallel to the axis will emerge from the system so as to cross the axis in the last medium at the second focal point P_2. If the straight line ru which crosses the axis at P_2 is the path of the emergent ray corresponding to the incident ray st, the image of the point s will always remain on this line.   Let the straight line fg perpendicular to the axis be the image of the object ps. As p moves along the axis, its conjugate point f must move also along the axis while the point g conjugate to s will move along the straight line ru. Evidently the size of the image fg will vary directly as the distance P_2f; as we know already from equations (6a) and (6b) is the case with a single refracting surface. Also since, according to equation (8), P_2f can have any value whatsoever, positive or negative, the same is true as to the size of the image, provided the length of the image is reckoned as negative when the image is inverted.   Thus there is only one position of the object ps for which its image will be precisely equal to it in both size and direction; suppose that this position is b_1c_1 and that the image then is b_2c_2. The pair of conjugate points b_1, b_2 are therefore the positions of the so-called *principal points* of the system.

Employing the following symbols,

$$sp = c_2b_2 = \beta_1,$$
$$fg = -\beta_2,$$
$$b_1P_1 = F_1, \qquad\qquad b_1p = f_1,$$
$$b_2P_2 = F_2, \qquad\qquad b_2f = f_2,$$

we have here

$$\frac{c_2b_2}{fg} = \frac{b_2P_2}{P_2f}$$

or

$$-\frac{\beta_1}{\beta_2} = \frac{F_2}{f_2 - F_2},$$

but by equation (8)

$$\frac{F_1}{f_1} + \frac{F_2}{f_2} = 1 \quad . \quad . \quad . \quad . \quad . \quad . \quad . \quad (8a)$$

and hence we get

$$\frac{\beta_1}{\beta_2} = \frac{F_2}{F_2 - f_2} = \frac{F_1 - f_1}{f_1} \quad ; \quad . \quad . \quad . \quad . \quad . \quad (8b)$$

a formula that corresponds to equation (6b) for a single refracting surface. Let l_1, l_2 denote the distances of object and image from the first and second focal points, respectively, that is, put

$$l_1 = f_1 - F_1,$$
$$l_2 = f_2 - F_2.$$

Accordingly, eliminating f_1, f_2 from equations (8a) and (8b), we find the so-called image-equations for a centered system of spherical refracting surfaces, in their simplest forms, as follows:

$$l_1l_2 = F_1F_2 \quad . \quad . \quad . \quad . \quad . \quad . \quad . \quad (8c)$$

$$\left.\begin{array}{l} \dfrac{\beta_1}{\beta_2} = -\dfrac{l_1}{F_1} \\[2mm] \dfrac{\beta_2}{\beta_1} = -\dfrac{l_2}{F_2} \end{array}\right\} \quad . \quad . \quad . \quad . \quad . \quad . \quad (8d)$$

These results should be compared with equations (7b) and (7c) which were obtained for a single surface.

Finally, in order to find the ratio of the focal lengths F_1 and F_2, let us apply equation (7d) to the case of the incident ray whose path is along the straight line joining s and b_1 and which emerges therefore along a straight line which goes through g and crosses the axis at b_2. Let γ' denote the size of an object in the first principal plane, and let γ'', γ''', etc., and γ_{m+1} denote the sizes of the successive images of this object formed after each refraction. By the characteristic property of the principal planes the last image of all must be of the same size as the object, that is, $\gamma_{m+1} = \gamma'$. Moreover, let a', a'', . . . a_{m+1} denote the angles which the ray sb_1 makes with the axis in each medium in succession from the first to the last; so that, for example,

$$\angle sb_1 p = -a',$$
$$\angle gb_2 f = -a_{m+1}.$$

Now according to equation (7d)

$$n'\gamma'\tan a' = n''\gamma''\tan a'',$$
$$n''\gamma''\tan a'' = n'''\gamma'''\tan a''', \text{ etc.,}$$

and, consequently,

$$n'\gamma'\tan a' = n_{m+1}\gamma_{m+1}\tan a_{m+1} \quad . \quad . \quad . \quad . \quad (9)$$

or since $\gamma' = \gamma_{m+1}$,

$$n'\tan a' = n_{m+1}\tan a_{m+1} \quad . \quad . \quad . \quad . \quad (9a)$$

Moreover, according to the notation above,

$$sp = \beta_1 \quad = -f_1\tan a',$$
$$fg = -\beta_2 = -f_2\tan a_{m+1},$$

and consequently

$$\frac{n'\beta_1}{f_1} = -\frac{n_{m+1}\beta_2}{f_2}.$$

Substituting here the value of f_2 as obtained from equation (8a), we get

$$\frac{n'\beta_1}{f_1-F_1} = -\frac{n_{m+1}\beta_2}{F_2}$$

and according to equation (8b),

$$\frac{\beta_1}{f_1-F_1} = -\frac{\beta_2}{F_1}.$$

From these two equations we derive immediately the fundamental relation between the focal lengths of an optical system, namely:

$$\frac{n'}{n_{m+1}} = \frac{F_1}{F_2} \quad . \quad . \quad . \quad . \quad . \quad . \quad (9c)$$

3.   In every optical system there is one, and only one, pair of *nodal points*. If a ray crosses the axis in the first medium at the first nodal point, the corresponding ray in the last medium will cross the axis at the second nodal point along a line which is parallel to the original direction of the ray.   The transversal conjugate planes through these points perpendicular to the axis are called the *nodal planes*.   The second nodal point is the image of the first, since rays that meet at the first point must meet again at the second point.   The distances between the nodal points and focal points of an optical system are inversely proportional to the indices of refraction of the first and last media.

If equation (9) is applied to the nodal points we must put $a_r = a_{m+1}$, and thus we obtain:

$$n_r\gamma_r = n_{m+1}\gamma_{m+1}.$$

Hence, we see that the linear dimensions of object and image lying in the nodal planes are likewise inversely proportional to the indices of refraction of the first and last media.

Since the size of the image is proportional to its distance from the second focal plane, this distance can be found, provided the size of the image is given. If the image lies in the second principal plane, it has the same size as the object and its distance from the second focal point is F_2. On the other hand, if the image is formed in the second nodal plane, its size, as has just been shown, will be

$$\gamma_{m+1} = \frac{n_r}{n_{m+1}}\gamma_r.$$

If G_2 denotes its distance in this case from the second focal point, then

$$\frac{\gamma_r}{\gamma_{m+1}} = \frac{F_2}{G_2},$$

and therefore by equation (9c),

$$G_2 = \frac{n_r}{n_{m+1}}F_2 = F_1 \quad . \quad . \quad . \quad . \quad . \quad . \quad (10a)$$

Accordingly, the distance between the second principal plane and the second nodal plane is

$$a_2 = F_2 - G_2$$
$$= F_2 - F_1.$$

The nodal planes are a pair of conjugate planes; and if a_1 denotes the distance of the first nodal plane from the first principal plane, that is, if

$$a_1 = G_1 - F_1,$$

then by equation (8a), we have:

$$-\frac{F_1}{a_1} + \frac{F_2}{a_2} = 1,$$

hence

$$a_1 = a_2 = F_2 - F_1$$
$$G_1 = F_2 \quad . \quad . \quad . \quad . \quad . \quad . \quad . \quad (10b)$$

and

$$\frac{G_1}{G_2} = \frac{n_{m+1}}{n_1} \quad . \quad . \quad . \quad . \quad . \quad . \quad . \quad (10c)$$

*The Cardinal Points of a Compound Optical System, Composed of Two
Systems with Axes in Same Straight Line*

The two component systems are designated in Fig. 38 by A and
B. The focal points and principal points of system A are designated
by $p_\prime$, $p_{\prime\prime}$ and $a_\prime$, $a_{\prime\prime}$, respectively; and the focal points and principal
points of system B are designated by $\pi_\prime$, $\pi_{\prime\prime}$ and $a_\prime$, $a_{\prime\prime}$, respectively.
Let d denote the distance of the first principal point of system A from
the second principal point of system B; this interval being taken as
positive when, as in Fig. 38, the point $a_\prime$ lies beyond the point $a_{\prime\prime}$.
The focal lengths of the first system are $a_\prime p_\prime = f_\prime$ and $a_{\prime\prime} p_{\prime\prime} = f_{\prime\prime}$, and

Fig. 38.

those of the second system are $a_\prime \pi_\prime = \varphi_\prime$ and $a_{\prime\prime} \pi_{\prime\prime} = \varphi_{\prime\prime}$. Evidently,
the first focal point ($\pi_\prime$) of system B is the image of the *first focal
point* ($t_\prime$) of the compound system as formed by system A. Hence, a
ray which in the first medium crosses the axis at $t_\prime$ will, after traversing
system A, cross the axis at $\pi_\prime$ and emerge finally in the last medium
along a straight line parallel to the axis; because by definition this
must be the case with a ray that crosses the axis originally at the first
focal point of the compound system. Since $a_{\prime\prime} \pi_{\prime\prime} = d - \varphi_\prime$, we have:

$$a_\prime t_\prime = \frac{(d - \varphi_\prime) f_\prime}{d - \varphi_\prime - f_{\prime\prime}} \quad . \quad . \quad . \quad . \quad . \quad (11a)$$

Similarly, the *second focal point* ($t_{\prime\prime}$) of the compound system is the
image of the second focal point ($p_{\prime\prime}$) of system A in system B. Hence

$$a_{\prime\prime} t_{\prime\prime} = \frac{(d - f_{\prime\prime}) \varphi_{\prime\prime}}{d - \varphi_\prime - f_{\prime\prime}} \quad . \quad . \quad . \quad . \quad . \quad (11b)$$

The *principal points* of the compound system are a pair of conjugate points with respect to it. Accordingly, there must be a point on
the axis which is the image of the first principal point in system A, and
at the same time whose image in system B is at the second principal
point of the compound system. Suppose this point is at s in Fig. 38 and
that $r_\prime$, $r_{\prime\prime}$ are the principal points of the compound system. If s
is the image of $r_\prime$ in system A, and if $r_{\prime\prime}$ is the image of s in system B,
then $r_{\prime\prime}$ is the image of $r_\prime$ in the compound system. This is one of the
conditions that these points must satisfy; the other condition being
that object and image in the principal planes must be equal in every
way. Suppose, therefore, that an object of height $\beta_\prime$ is set up at the

point r,, and that the image of this object in system A is formed at s and has the height σ; and that the image of σ in system B is formed at r,, and has the height β,,. Putting $x = a$,,s, and $y = sa$,, we get from equation (8b):

$$\frac{\beta,}{\sigma} = \frac{f,,}{f,, - x}$$

$$\frac{\beta,,}{\sigma} = \frac{\varphi,}{\varphi, - y}.$$

Now if we are to have here $\beta, = \beta,,$, then

$$\frac{f,,}{f,, - x} = \frac{\varphi,}{\varphi, - y}$$

or

$$\frac{x}{f,,} = \frac{y}{\varphi,} \qquad \cdot \quad \cdot \quad \cdot \quad \cdot \quad \cdot \quad \cdot \quad \cdot \quad (11c)$$

or

$$\frac{a,,s}{a,,p,,} = \frac{a,s}{a,\pi,}.$$

Thus, we have the following rule for finding the point s in the medium common to the two component systems A and B, which is conjugate with respect to both systems to the principal points $(r,, r,,)$ of the compound system $(A+B)$: Divide the interval between the second principal point $(a,,)$ of system A and the first principal point $(a,)$ of system B in two parts which are in the same ratio as the second focal length of system A is to the first focal length of system B.

Since $x + y = d$, then according to equation (11c),

$$\frac{x}{f,,} = \frac{d - x}{\varphi,}$$

$$\frac{d - y}{f,,} = \frac{y}{\varphi,}.$$

Hence,

$$x = \frac{df,,}{\varphi, + f,,}$$

$$y = \frac{d\varphi,}{\varphi, + f,,}.$$

By using the above value of x, the distance $a,r, = h,$ of the first principal point of the compound system from the first principal point of system A may be found, as follows:

$$h, = \frac{xf,}{x - f,,}$$

$$h, = \frac{df,}{d - \varphi, - f,,} \qquad \cdot \quad \cdot \quad \cdot \quad \cdot \quad \cdot \quad \cdot \quad (11d)$$

Similarly, the distance $a''r'' = h''$ of the second principal point of the compound system from the second principal point of system B is given by

$$h'' = \frac{\varphi''y}{y - \varphi'}$$
$$h'' = \frac{d\varphi''}{d - \varphi' - f''} \quad \cdot \quad \cdot \quad \cdot \quad \cdot \quad \cdot \quad \text{(11e)}$$

Thence, we obtain the following expressions for the focal lengths (F', F'') of the compound system:

$$\left. \begin{aligned} F' &= a't' - a'r' \\ &= \frac{\varphi'f'}{\varphi' + f'' - d} \\ F'' &= a''t'' - a''r'' \\ &= \frac{\varphi''f''}{\varphi' + f'' - d} \end{aligned} \right\} \quad \cdot \quad \cdot \quad \cdot \quad \cdot \quad \text{(11f)}$$

Having found the positions of the principal points and focal points, we can easily locate the nodal points; because the distance of the first nodal point from the first focal point is equal to the second focal length, and the distance of the second nodal point from the second focal point is equal to the first focal length.

But if it is required to find the positions of the nodal points without having ascertained those of the principal points, a process similar to the above can be employed, by utilizing the fact that the lengths of conjugate lines in the nodal planes are inversely proportional to the indices of refraction of the respective media.

For example, in Fig. 38 suppose that the points designated by a', a'' and α', α'' are the nodal points of systems A and B, respectively; and that the points designated by r', r'' are the nodal points of the compound system; so that now

$$\begin{aligned} a'p' &= f'' & \alpha'\pi' &= \varphi'' \\ a''p'' &= f' & \alpha''\pi'' &= \varphi' \\ a''s &= x & \alpha's &= y. \end{aligned}$$

Then

$$a'r' = \frac{xf''}{x - f'}$$
$$\alpha''r'' = \frac{y\varphi'}{y - \varphi''}.$$

Let β' denote the height of an object in the first medium placed at r', and let σ denote the height of its image in system A, which will be formed at $s;$ and, finally, let β'' denote the height of the image of σ in system B, which will be formed at $r'';$ then according to the property of the nodal points,

$$\frac{\beta'}{\sigma} = \frac{a'r'}{x} = \frac{f''}{x-f'}$$

$$\frac{\beta''}{\sigma} = \frac{a''r''}{y} = \frac{\varphi'}{y-\varphi''}.$$

If n', n'' denote the indices of refraction of the first and last media, and if ν denotes the index of refraction of the intervening medium between the two components of the compound system, we must have for the nodal planes:

$$n'\beta' = n''\beta'',$$

and hence

$$\frac{n'f''}{x-f'} = \frac{n''\varphi'}{y-\varphi''}.$$

But

$$n'f'' = \nu f',$$

therefore

$$n''\varphi' = \nu\varphi'',$$

and

$$\frac{f'}{x-f'} = \frac{\varphi''}{y-\varphi''}$$

$$\frac{x}{f'} = \frac{y}{\varphi''}$$

or

$$\frac{a''s}{a''p''} = \frac{a's}{a'\pi'}.$$

This same equation was obtained above as equation (11c) on the assumption that the points designated by a', a'', a', a'', r' and r'' were the principal points. Accordingly, the positions of the nodal points of the compound system, with respect to those of the component systems, are found by exactly a similar process as was used for finding the principal points.

The simplest case is when the compound system is a combination of two spherical refracting surfaces, and it will be worth while to give the special formulae for this system. If the radii of the first and second surfaces are denoted by r_1 and r_2, respectively, and if d denotes the distance of the vertex of the second surface from that of the first; and, finally, if n_1, n_2, n_3 denote the indices of refraction of the three media in their actual order, then by equations (3a) and (3b):

$$f_1 = \frac{n_1 r_1}{n_2 - n_1} \qquad\qquad \varphi_1 = \frac{n_2 r_2}{n_3 - n_2}$$

$$f_2 = \frac{n_2 r_1}{n_2 - n_1} \qquad\qquad \varphi_2 = \frac{n_3 r_2}{n_3 - n_2}.$$

By way of abbreviation, put

$$n_2(n_3 - n_2)r_1 + n_2(n_2 - n_1)r_2 - (n_3 - n_2)(n_2 - n_1)d = N.$$

Then the focal lengths are

$$F_1 = \frac{n_1 n_2 r_1 r_2}{N} \left.\right\}$$
$$F_2 = \frac{n_2 n_3 r_1 r_2}{N} \left.\right\} \qquad \cdots \qquad \cdots \qquad (12)$$

The distances of the principal points from the two surfaces are

$$h_1 = \frac{n_1 (n_2 - n_3) d r_1}{N} \left.\right\}$$
$$h_2 = \frac{n_3 (n_1 - n_2) d r_2}{N} \left.\right\} \qquad \cdots \qquad \cdots \qquad (12a)$$

and the distance of these points from each other is

$$H = d \cdot \frac{(n_2 - n_1)(n_3 - n_2)(r_1 - r_2 - d)}{N} \qquad \cdots \qquad \cdots \qquad (12b)$$

For $d = 0$, we have $h_1 = h_2 = H = 0$, and

$$F_1 = \frac{n_1 r_1 r_2}{(n_3 - n_2) r_1 + (n_2 - n_1) r_2}$$
$$F_2 = \frac{n_3 r_1 r_2}{(n_3 - n_2) r_1 + (n_2 - n_1) r_2}.$$

If in these equations we put $r_2 = r_1$, we obtain:

$$F_1 = \frac{n_1 r_1}{n_3 - n_1}$$
$$F_2 = \frac{n_3 r_1}{n_3 - n_1}.$$

In this case the focal points and principal points are exactly the same as if there were only a single refracting surface; the result is independent of n_2. Therefore:

In considering any system of refracting spherical surfaces, we may think of each surface as replaced by an infinitely thin layer of arbitrary index of refraction, bounded by concentric spherical surfaces, without in any way altering the optical properties of the system.

This proposition will serve later to simplify many of our discussions.

Lastly, the formulae will be given for lenses with spherical surfaces surrounded by the same medium on both sides $(n_3 = n_1)$:

$$F_1 = F_2 = \frac{n_1 n_2 r_1 r_2}{(n_2 - n_1)[n_2 (r_2 - r_1) + (n_2 - n_1) d]} \qquad \cdots \qquad (13)$$

In this case the nodal points are the same as the principal points, and their distances from the two vertices are:

$$h_1 = \frac{n_1 d r_1}{n_2 (r_2 - r_1) + (n_2 - n_1) d} \left.\right\}$$
$$h_2 = -\frac{n_1 d r_2}{n_2 (r_2 - r_1) + (n_2 - n_1) d} \left.\right\} \qquad \cdots \qquad (13a)$$

these distances being reckoned positive or negative according as the principal points are outside the lens or inside it, respectively. The interval between the principal points is

$$H = d.\frac{(n_2-n_1)(d+r_2-r_1)}{n_2(r_2-r_1)+(n_2-n_1)d} \quad \cdots \quad \cdots \quad (13b)$$

The optical centre of the lens is the point on the axis which is conjugate to the first nodal point with respect to the first surface, and to which therefore the second nodal point is conjugate with respect to the second surface; its distances from the two surfaces are proportional to the radii.

Evidently, so far as the position and size of the image is concerned, two optical systems are equivalent in their effects, provided their focal points and principal points have the same positions; and provided also the first and last media of the two systems are the same; because the ratio of the indices of refraction of these media cannot be changed without altering the ratio of the focal lengths. Thus, one optical system can be substituted for another one if they both have the same focal length and the same interval between the pair of principal points, the first and last media being the same for both systems. In a system composed of two refracting surfaces, the two factors above mentioned involve only the four magnitudes denoted by r_1, r_2, n_2 and d and therefore a system with only two refracting spherical surfaces may always be substituted for a centered system of any number of surfaces; in the sense that the images in the two cases will be exactly the same as to both size and position. As a matter of fact, we may even impose two other conditions on the simple system, as, for example, that the interior medium shall have a certain index of refraction, etc.

We shall now consider the several kinds of lenses;[1] that is, systems composed of two refracting surfaces separated by a distance less than either radius of curvature, surrounded on the outside by a single medium, which has a lower index of refraction than that of the interior medium. We shall often have occasion to speak of systems of this kind, which may be classified by their form, as follows:

1. *Double Convex Lens*, in which both surfaces are convex, that is, r_1 is positive and r_2 negative, and hence, according to formula (13), the focal lengths are positive. As the distances of the principal points from the surfaces are both negative, these points lie inside the lens; but since

---

[1] ¶The author seems to have specially in mind here ordinary glass lenses surrounded by air. It is perfectly possible, however, to think of an air lens surrounded by glass. Nor is it necessary that the thickness of the lens should be limited as stated in the text. Moreover, a perfectly general definition must include astigmatic lenses (cylindrical lenses, toric lenses, etc.) and other aspherical lenses. (J. P. C. S.)

the interval between them is positive, the first principal point is in front of the second. The positions of the focal points (p_1, p_2) and the principal points (h_1, h_2) of a double convex lens are indicated in Fig. 39, where the first and second numerals designate the first and second surfaces. A *plano-convex* lens is a special form of double convex lens in which one of the radii of curvature is infinite, and consequently

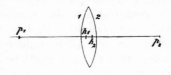

Fig. 39.

one of the principal points lies at the vertex of the curved surface.

2. *Double Concave Lens*, in which both surfaces are concave, that is, r_1 is negative and r_2 positive, and hence the focal lengths are negative. Here also the distances of the principal points from the surfaces are both negative, that is, these points lie inside the lens; and since they are separated by a positive interval, the first principal point lies in front of the second, as shown in Fig. 40,

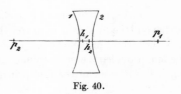

Fig. 40.

which is a diagram of a double concave lens, the same letters being used here to designate the focal points and principal points as in Fig. 39. A *plano-concave* lens is a special form of double concave lens with the radius of one surface infinite, so that, just as in a plano-convex lens, one of the principal points coincides with the vertex of the curved surface.

3. *Meniscus Lens*, in which both radii are positive or both negative, It is sufficient to consider simply the case when both radii are positive, as all we have to do then is to turn the lens around in order to have the case when both radii are negative. The focal lengths are positive, provided

$$n_2(r_2+d-r_1)>n_1d;$$

but they become infinite when these two expressions are equal, and negative when the left-hand member is less than the right-hand member. The expression within the parentheses is the distance of the centre of curvature of the second surface from that of the first. If the second centre lies beyond the first, the lens will be thicker in the middle than at the edge; but in the opposite case, it will be thinner in the middle. Thus, the focal lengths of a meniscus lens are positive or negative according as the lens is, or is not, thicker in the middle than it is at the edge. The first principal point of a meniscus lens lies before the convex surface (that is, on its convex side), when the focal length is positive; and may be very far away if the focal length is very great, and infinitely far when the focal length is infinite. When the focal length is negative, the first principal point is situated beyond the convex surface (that is, on its concave side), and likewise recedes to infinity when the focal length becomes infinite. The second principal point of a meniscus lens lies in front of the concave surface of the

Fig. 41.

lens (that is, on its convex side), when the focal length is positive, and beyond this surface when the focal length is negative, being at infinity when the focal length is infinite. For a positive focal length, the second principal point always lies beyond the first, that is, nearer the lens. If the focal length is negative, the second principal point lies beyond the first, that is, farther from the lens provided the lens is thinner at the middle than towards the edge; but it lies in front of the first principal point when the lens is thicker

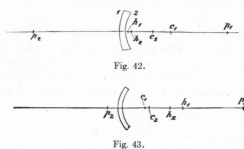

Fig. 42.

Fig. 43.

in the middle and yet has a negative focal length. If the two surfaces of the lens are concentric, the two principal points coincide with each other at the common centre of curvature. A meniscus lens with positive focal length is shown in Fig. 41. Both meniscus lenses in the next two diagrams have negative focal lengths, but the one in Fig. 42 is thinner in the middle than out towards the edge, whereas it is just the other way in Fig. 43. In all three lenses the centres of the first and second surfaces are designated by c_1 and c_2, respectively. The focal points are never inside the lens, and are always on opposite sides of it.[1]

In case the focal lengths of the system are equal, the image-equations (8a) and (8b) become:

$$\frac{1}{f_1} + \frac{1}{f_2} = \frac{1}{F} \quad \cdot \quad \cdot \quad \cdot \quad \cdot \quad \cdot \quad \cdot \quad (14)$$

or

$$f_2 = \frac{F f_1}{f_1 - F} \quad \cdot \quad \cdot \quad \cdot \quad \cdot \quad \cdot \quad \cdot \quad (14a)$$

[1] This remark applies only to the type of lenses last mentioned. G.

and

$$\frac{\beta_2}{\beta_1} = \frac{F}{F - f_1} = \frac{F - f_2}{F} \qquad . \quad . \quad . \quad . \quad . \quad . \quad (14b)$$

In the case of lenses with *positive focal length* (*convergent* or *positive* lenses, as they are called), the image of an infinitely distant object ($f_1 = \infty$) lies beyond the lens in its second focal plane, is real and inverted, and is infinitely small as compared with the object itself. As the object is brought nearer the lens, the image, which is still real and inverted, recedes from the lens and gets bigger, until finally when the object arrives in the first or anterior focal plane ($f_1 = F$), both the distance and size of the image are infinite. This is easily seen from equation (14), which may be written

$$\frac{1}{f_2} = \frac{1}{F} - \frac{1}{f_1},$$

by giving f_1 any values from ∞ to F, in which case the corresponding values of f_2 will be found to increase from F to ∞. The image is inverted, that is, the sign of

$$\beta_2 = -\beta_1 \frac{F}{f_1 - F}$$

continues negative so long as f_1 is greater than F; and as f_1 diminishes from ∞ to F, β_2 assumes all negative values from 0 to $-\infty$.

Similarly, it may be shown that as the object proceeds from the first focal plane to the first principal plane, f_2 assumes all positive values from ∞ to 0; so that the image now is virtual and erect and lies in front of the lens on the same side as the object, proceeding from infinity until it arrives in the second principal plane, where it has the same size as the object.

Finally, for negative values of f_1, the object itself is virtual, and in this case f_2 will always be positive and numerically less than f_1, the image being real and erect and smaller than the virtual object.

Thus a convergent lens converges parallel incident rays to a real focus on the other side of the lens. Convergent incident rays are made still more convergent, and divergent incident rays less divergent or even convergent, according as they proceed from a point on the axis nearer to or farther from the convergent lens than the first focal point.

Lenses with negative focal lengths are called *divergent* or *negative* lenses, because they make parallel incident rays divergent, divergent rays still more divergent, and convergent rays less convergent or even divergent. If the absolute value of the focal length is denoted by P, that is, if $P = -F$, then for a divergent lens

$$\frac{1}{f_2} = -\frac{1}{P} - \frac{1}{f_1}$$

$$\beta_2 = \beta_1 \frac{P}{f_1 + P}.$$

Thus the values of f_2 corresponding to all positive values of f_1 will be found to be negative, so that as f_1 decreases from ∞ to 0, f_2 will vary from $-P$ to 0, and β_2 from 0 to β_1. A divergent lens therefore gives a virtual image of a real object anywhere in front of the first principal plane, the corresponding image being erect, smaller than the object, and nearer the lens and in front of the second principal plane. The values of f_2 corresponding to negative values of f_1 that are numerically less than P are positive, and as f_1 assumes all values between 0 and $-P$, f_2 has all positive values, and β_2 changes from β_1 to ∞. Thus convergent incident rays are made less convergent provided they are directed originally to a point on the axis nearer the lens than the focal point. For negative values of f_1 numerically greater than P, f_2 and β_2 are both negative, and in such cases the image in a divergent lens is virtual and inverted. As f_1 varies from $-P$ to $-\infty$, f_2 varies oppositely from $-\infty$ to $-P$, and β_2 from $-\infty$ to 0. Hence rays originally converging towards a point *beyond* the further focal point are made divergent by a divergent lens.

The distance e between a pair of conjugate points on the axis is equal to $f_1 + a + f_2$, where a denotes the interval between the principal points; e being counted as positive when the image point lies beyond the object-point. Substituting for f_2 its value, we obtain as the expression for this distance

$$e = \frac{f_1^2}{f_1 - F} + a.$$

Differentiating this equation with respect to f_1, we have:

$$\frac{de}{df_1} = \frac{f_1^2 - 2f_1 F}{(f_1 - F)^2}.$$

Hence, $de = 0$, that is, this interval e is a maximum or minimum, provided either $f_1 = 0$ or $f_1 = 2F$. As a matter of fact, whether the focal length of the lens is positive or negative, e is a minimum for $f_1 = 2F$ and a maximum for $f_1 = 0$, as is easily seen from the expression for e.

The following is a partial list of works which contain a treatment of the theory of refraction by a centered system of spherical surfaces:[1]

---

[1] ¶This list is by no means complete. For example, H. CODDINGTON's *A Treatise on the Reflection and Refraction of Light* (London 1829) should certainly be included, as well as Sir W. R. HAMILTON's papers on "Theory of systems of rays" in *Trans. Roy. Irish Acad.*, xv (1828), 69-174; xvi (1830), 3-62, 93-126, and xvii (1837), 1-44. (J. P. C. S.)

1738. COTES in SMITH, *A compleat system of opticks*. Cambridge. Vol. II.
       p. 76.

1757, 1761. EULER in *Histoire de l'Acad. roy. de Berlin pour* 1757. p. 283.—Ibid., *pour*
       1761. p. 201.

1765. EULER, *Précis d'une théorie générale de la dioptrique* in *Hist. de l'acad. roy.
       des sc. de Paris*, 1765. p. 555.

1778, 1803. LAGRANGE in *Nouv. Mém. de l'acad. roy. de Berlin pour* 1778. p. 162.—Ibid.
       1803. p. 1.

1882. PIOLA in *Effemeridi astron. di Milano per* 1822.

1830. MÖBIUS in CRELLES *Journal für Mathematik*. Bd. V. S. 113.

1841. *BESSEL in *Astronom. Nachrichten*. Bd. XVIII. S. 97.
       *GAUSS, *Dioptrische Untersuchungen*. Göttingen.—Reprint from *Abhandl. d.
       Kön. Ges. d. Wiss. zu Göttingen*. T. 1. for years 1838–43.

1844. ENCKE, *De formulis dioptricis*. *Ein Programm*. Berlin.
       MOSER, Ueber das Auge, in DOVE's *Repert. d. Physik*. Bd. V. S. 289.

1851. LISTING, Art. Dioptrik des Auges, in R. WAGNERS *Handwörterbuch d.
       Physiologie*. Bd. IV. S. 451.

§10. Optical System of the Eye[1]

In its optical behaviour the eye is essentially like a *camera obscura*.[2]
In order for a luminous point to be seen distinctly, the light diverging
from it must be refracted by the media of the eye and thereby converged at some point of the retina. On the surface of this membrane a
real optical image is projected of the external objects in view, which is
inverted and very much reduced in size. By carefully removing a
central portion of the sclerotica and choroid coating at the back of a
freshly enucleated eye, thus exposing the retina from behind, and then
pointing the cornea towards a bright object, a small, inverted image,
as above described, can actually be seen on the retina, sharply defined.[3]
A still better plan is that of GERLING,[4] in which a small portion of the
retina is removed with a needle and a little plate of glass or mica
inserted in the opening. It is quite easy to observe the retinal image
in the eye of a white rabbit, the choroid of which is devoid of pigment.
In this case it is not even necessary to remove the hard coating, as the
image can be seen through it, not as distinctly, of course, as when the
retina itself is directly exposed, but clearly enough to recognize and
locate it. It is even possible to see the image sometimes through the
sclerotica of the eye of a live individual, especially if he is blond and
has bright blue eyes which usually contain scant pigment in the
choroid coating. The patient is taken into a dark room and made to
turn his eye towards the temporal side, so as to expose the white eye-

[1] See Appendix II on "Refraction of Rays in the Eye" at end of Part I. G.

[2] ¶This comparison was made by J. B. PORTA (1545–1615), the inventor of the "pinhole
camera" and *camera obscura*. (J. P. C. S.)

[3] ¶This experiment was performed by C. SCHEINER (1573–1650), first, with eyes of
sheep and oxen and, in 1625, with a human eye. KEPLER had already inferred that the
image must be formed on the retina, although PORTA seems to have supposed that it was
focused in or on the crystalline lens. (J. P. C. S.)

[4] POGGENDORFF, *Ann.* XLVI. 243.

ball well around towards its rear surface. When a candle is held a little to one side of the averted eye, its image will be visible on the inner side of the retina, and frequently it sparkles so clearly through the translucent coatings of the eye that its inverted position, the tip of the flame, and the wick at its base, can be recognized.[1]

The best method of investigating the retinal image in the living eye is with an ophthalmoscope, which will be described in §16. With the aid of this instrument, it is possible to look directly in the eye from the front and see clearly not only the retina itself and its blood vessels but the optical images that are projected on it. That this is actually the case is proved by the fact that if the eye under examination is focused on an object that is bright enough, a distinct and sharply defined image of it may be seen by the observer on the surface of the retina.

As has already been mentioned in describing this membrane, there is in the fundus of the eye a small area of the retina of peculiar structure known as the yellow spot. At its centre is a small depression, the *fovea centralis*, where the blood vessels which ramify all over the rest of the retina are entirely lacking. Here there is nothing but nerve tissue; and in fact the retinal membrane itself at this particular place appears to be composed entirely of nerve cells and cones. Physiologically, as the place of direct vision, it is of the highest importance. Whenever we look directly at anything and fix it in the eye, its image falls on the fovea.[2] This fact, which had long been inferred from the special structure of the yellow spot, can be verified directly with the ophthalmoscope. When the entire retina is illuminated, the location of the yellow spot is easily recognized by the absence of blood vessels. In the middle of this veinless area, where the fovea is, there is a peculiar bright place, described first by Coccius,[3] which he explains as a reflex from the foveal cavity. Moreover, Donders[4] has shown that this bright reflex appears always at that part of the retinal image that corresponds to the point of fixation in the field of view, and the writer has verified this observation. From the position of the so-called foveal reflex it is possible to tell exactly the point of fixation of the eye in the field of view, and by directing the patient to look first at one place and then at another, the observer can watch the reflex being focused at the corresponding place in the retinal image. The method of procedure will be described in §16.

[1] Volkmann, Article: Sehen in Wagners *Handwörterbuch d. Physiologie.* S. 286-289.

[2] ¶This is called direct vision or foveal vision. (J. P. C. S.)

[3] *Ueber die Anwendung des Augenspiegels.* Leipzig 1853. S. 64.

[4] *Onderzoekingen gedaan in het Physiolog. Laborat. d. Utrechtsche Hoogeschool.* Jaar VI. S. 133.

Usually the optical image on the retina is not perfectly sharp except in the vicinity of the axis of the eye, and farther off it is not so well defined. Ordinarily, therefore, the point of fixation is the only point in the field of view that is seen distinctly at any one time, everything else being more or less vague. The vagueness of indirect vision is apparently due to diminished sensitivity of the retina outside the foveal region, because even a short distance out when the image is still sharply outlined the impression is not very distinct. The eye is an optical contrivance of remarkably wide field of view, but it is only within a very limited part of this field that the images are clear-cut. The entire field is like a drawing which is carefully executed to delineate the most important central part of the picture, while the surroundings are simply sketched in, more and more lightly out towards the borders.

However, in virtue of the mobility of the eye, it can be quickly focused on the various parts of the field in succession. A human being cannot attend to more than one object at a time, and the one point that he can see distinctly is enough to occupy him fully at that moment. Still, the attention is often distracted by the details, and then, in spite of the vagueness of the broad field of view, the eye is capable of taking in at a rapid glance the main features of the whole surroundings, and of noting immediately the sudden appearances of new objects in the remoter parts of the field.

The field of view of a single eye is determined by the diameter of the pupil and its position with respect to the edge of the cornea. By observing his own eye in a mirror in a dark room, with a light placed to one side, the author found that he could perceive the presence of the light so long as rays from it fall on the opposite edge of the pupil and enter the pupil itself. Therefore any light which passes through the cornea and enters the pupil must fall on some sensitive part of the retina. It is true that the pupil lies somewhat farther back than the outer edge of the cornea, but owing to the refraction by the cornea, rays can enter the pupil through the edge of the cornea even when they were originally perpendicular to the optical axis of the eye. Thus the field of view of the eye is approximately a hemisphere, which is wider than that of any artificial optical instrument. There are, of course, individual variations in different eyes, depending on the diameter and position of the pupil. In near vision the pupil is displaced a little towards the cornea, thereby increasing the field somewhat; as the author can readily see in his own eye by holding a bright light at the outer edge of the field.

Part of the field of view of each eye separately is intercepted above and below and on the inside by cheeks, eyebrows, and nose; on the outside, however, the field is entirely unobstructed. But both eyes together, directed straight ahead into the distance, command an horizontal arc of 180° or more. The extent of the field is greatly increased beyond this by the rotary movements of the eyes, which will be discussed later.

Rays from a distant point entering the eye are first refracted by the cornea so that, without being again intercepted, they would come to a focus about 10 mm beyond the retina. Thus converging, they traverse the anterior chamber of the eye and arrive at the crystalline lens, where they are made still more convergent and may, therefore, be brought to a focus on the retina itself.

The main refraction occurs at the cornea. Next in importance are the refractions at the anterior and posterior surfaces of the crystalline lens. However, there are refractions also in the interior of the lens at the boundaries of its separate layers, since these latter have different densities. All these refracting surfaces may be regarded approximately as surfaces of revolution around a common axis. Although in most human eyes the axis of the various surfaces are apparently not strictly coincident, the variations are so slight as to be negligible in effect so far as the position and size of the image are concerned; so that the eye may be regarded as a *centered* optical system.

The axis of this system, or the *axis of the eye*, as we call it, coincides approximately with the straight line joining the vertex of the cornea with a point on the retina between the yellow spot and the place where the optic nerve enters the eyeball.

The positions of the *focal points*, *principal points* and *nodal points* of the eye are subject to rather considerable individual variations. Measurements of different eyes and of each of their refracting surfaces are often found to differ to a rather surprising extent, when we consider the refinement of construction and adjustment required in such an organ. Moreover, it will be seen later on that even in the same eye, the cardinal points change their positions during the act of accommodation. About all that can be said definitely as to the positions of the cardinal points in the normal eye, adjusted for distant vision, is that the *two principal points are very close together, as are also the two nodal points*. Both principal points lie near together about midway in the anterior chamber of the eye, while the nodal points are very near the posterior surface of the crystalline lens, and the second focal point is on the retina.

Since it is necessary for many purposes to have at least approximate values of the optical constants of the eye, the values of Listing's schematic eye are tabulated herewith. They were obtained by compiling the measurements available at the time as well as possible and expressing the results in simple integers.

The data assumed by LISTING are as follows:

1. Index of refraction of air........................... 1
2. Index of refraction of aqueous humor...............103/77
3. Index of refraction of crystalline lens............... 16/11
4. Index of refraction of vitreous humor...............103/77
5. Radius of curvature of cornea..................... 8 mm
6. Radius of curvature of anterior surface of lens........10 "
7. Radius of curvature of posterior surface of lens....... 6 "
8. Distance between anterior surfaces of cornea and lens.. 4 "
9. Thickness of lens................................. 4 "

From these data he calculated the following:

1. The first focal point is located 12.8326 mm in front of the cornea, and the second focal point 14.6470 mm beyond the posterior surface of the lens.

2. The first principal point is 2.1746 mm, and the second principal point 2.5724 mm, beyond the anterior surface of the cornea, so that their distance apart is 0.3978 mm.

3. The first nodal point is 0.7580 mm, and the second nodal point 0.3602 mm, in front of the posterior surface of the lens.

4. Accordingly, the first focal length of the eye is 15.0072 mm, and the second focal length is 20.0746 mm.

The positions of the principal points h', h'', the nodal points k', k'', and the focal points F', F'', as found by LISTING, are shown in Fig. 44. Among the data employed in these calculations, the only ones about which there might be some question are the index and radii of the lens. However, the focal length of the lens as calculated from these data agrees so well with direct measurements of this magnitude as made by the writer, that the optical effect of the lens in LISTING's schematic eye cannot, at any rate, differ essentially from that of the natural eye. The values that are important for the refraction of the cornea are based on sufficiently reliable measurements. There is no reason to doubt, therefore, that LISTING's model agrees about as well with the actual facts as can be expected with the wide range of variation that exists in individual eyes.

With the cardinal points of the eye as given above, the construction described in §9 can be used to trace the path of a given incident ray after its last refraction, and likewise the position of the image of a luminous point anywhere near the axis of the eye. Since, as just seen, the two nodal points of the eye as well as the two principal points are very close together, each pair may be regarded as a pair of coincident points, without seriously impairing the accuracy of the results. Thus is obtained a still simpler optical model, which LISTING calls the *reduced eye.*[1] The double principal point of this eye is 2.3448 mm beyond the anterior surface of the cornea, and the nodal point (κ in Fig. 44) is 0.4764 mm in front of the posterior surface of the lens, the focal points being unchanged. The optical behaviour of this reduced eye is equivalent to that of a single spherical refracting surface whose centre and vertex are at the nodal point and principal point, respectively, the first medium being air and the second medium the aqueous or vitreous humor. The radius of curvature of such a surface would be 5.1248 mm. Many problems, in which only the size and position of the image are required, are greatly simplified by using this equivalent spherical surface. In Fig. 44 the surface is shown as the dotted arc *ll*, with its centre at κ.

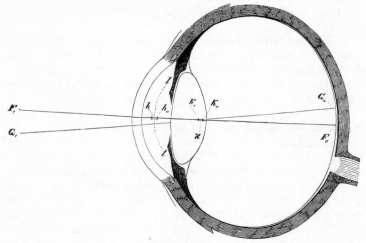

Fig. 44.

If, as often happens, we know in advance that the image is focused on the retina, and all we wish to do is to find the position of the image of a given point, the nodal points are sufficient for the purpose; and if it is permissible to regard the nodal points as coincident, as in the reduced eye, the position of the image may be located by drawing a straight line from the luminous point to the nodal point and prolonging it to meet the retina. A straight line drawn in this way may be called a *line of visual direction*. The nodal point considered as single is therefore the point of intersection of all the lines of visual direction. The two parts of such a line that are in the air in front of the cornea and

---

[1] ¶Listing's reduced eye is very similar to the "simplified eye" imagined by Huygens in the first part of his *Dioptrica* (1652). (J. P. C. S.)

beyond the lens in the vitreous humor·are parts of the actual path of a certain ray, which may be called a *direction ray*. The path of a direction ray coincides with a line of visual direction except along the part of its path that is comprised between the anterior surface of the cornea and the posterior surface of the lens.

If, however, it is desired to make the exact construction, using the two separate nodal points, it is necessary to distinguish between *two lines of direction* which are parallel to each other, one being drawn from the luminous point to the first nodal point and the other through the second nodal point to the image point on the retina. The part of the first line which is outside the eye and the part of the second line in the vitreous humor are portions of the path of a single ray, namely, the so-called *direction ray* above mentioned.

That one of the direction rays which comes from the point of fixation and therefore proceeds to the fovea is called the *visual axis;* or, rather, the visual axis is the line drawn from the point of fixation to the first nodal point of the eye. Formerly, the yellow spot was generally supposed to be located at the terminus of the optical axis of the eye, and the visual axis and optical axis were regarded as identical. However, the writer's investigations have shown that these lines are quite distinct from each other. As a matter of fact, the part of the visual axis lying in front of the eye is on the nasal side and usually somewhat above the optical axis, so that the *fovea centralis* is on the temporal side and usually a little *below* the optical axis. In Fig. 44, which represents a horizontal section of the eye, the visual axis is shown by the lines $G'G''$, and the optical axis by the line $F'F''$, in their relative positions as found by the writer in a normal eye. The upper part of the diagram represents the outer or temporal side of the eye, and the lower part the nasal side.

In studying the refraction of the several media of the eye, it is convenient to consider the eye as a compound optical system composed of two partial systems, the cornea and the crystalline lens. The corneal system is bounded by air on one side and the aqueous humor on the other side. The aqueous humor is also the first medium of the lenticular system, and the vitreous humor is the last medium.

Beginning with the cornea, we find the problem of its optical performance is materially simplified by the fact that this system is merely a thin shell whose two surfaces have nearly the same curvature and whose index of refraction is only slightly greater than that of the aqueous humor. In §9 in connection with equations (12), (12a) and (12b) it was shown that at any interface between two media an infinitely thin layer of arbitrary index of refraction, bounded by surfaces of equal curvature, can be inserted in the system without having any effect

on the procedure of the rays.   Here let us suppose, therefore, that such
a layer of liquid material is interposed in front of the cornea, as in fact
is actually found there in the layer of tears that moisten the outer
surface of the cornea.   Thus the whole corneal system, apart from the
air in front of the eye, may be considered as a lens like a watch-crystal
surrounded by aqueous humor on both sides.   A lens of this description has a very long focus and does not, therefore, appreciably deflect
the light traversing it.   Consequently, we may just as well consider
the aqueous humor as extending clear out to the anterior surface of the
cornea; and indeed this assumption is usually made in discussing the
geometrical optics of the cornea, and is almost necessary for the reason
that, while the measurements of the outer surface of the cornea are
accurate enough, the data with respect to the inner surface are not
sufficiently reliable.

If the focal length is supposed to be infinite, it follows from equation
(13), §9 that

$$n_2(r_2-r_1)+(n_2-n_1)d=0,$$

where n_1 denotes the index of refraction of the aqueous humor, n_2
that of the corneal substance, d the thickness of the cornea, and
r_1, r_2 the radii of the anterior and posterior surfaces, respectively.
But as a matter of fact this equation is not true in case of the cornea.
If it is written

$$(r_2+d)-r_1=\frac{n_1d}{n_2},$$

where (r_2+d) is equal to the distance of the centre of curvature of the
posterior surface from the vertex of the anterior surface, we can see
that it implies that the centre of curvature of the posterior surface lies
beyond that of the anterior surface, in which case the corneal substance
would be thicker in the middle than out towards the edge, which as a
rule is contrary to the fact.   Regarding the cornea as a lens immersed
in aqueous humor, we find that it actually has a very long, negative focal
length, and is a meniscus lens of the type described towards the end
of §9.

Taking $r_1=8$ mm, $r_2=7$ mm, $d=1$ mm and (a c c o r d i n g   t o
W. Krause) $n_2=1.3507$, $n_1=1.3420$, the focal length of the cornea
immersed in aqueous humor is found by equation (13) to be equal to
-8.7 metres; a value which, as compared with the dimensions of the
eye, may be regarded as practically infinite.   This result has been
confirmed by the writer's measurements with the ophthalmometer.
The size of an object as seen through a glass vessel with vertical parallel
walls which was filled with water was measured with this instrument.
When a freshly dissected human cornea was immersed in the water

and the object observed through it, the reduction in the size of the image could not be detected with the ophthalmometer. Whatever change may have occurred in the appearance of the image, it was so slight as to escape notice.

In order to get an idea as to what extent the actual refraction of the eye differs from what it would be if the index of refraction of the cornea were really equal to that of the aqueous humor, the optical constants of the cornea may be calculated by equation (12), §9, by putting $n_1 = 1$, $n_3 = n$, $n_2 = n + \Delta n$, $r_1 = r$, $r_2 = r - \Delta r$, where the magnitudes denoted by Δn, Δr and the thickness of the cornea (d) must all be regarded as very small in comparison with n and r. Substituting these values, at the same time neglecting the higher powers of the small quantities, we find for the focal lengths:

$$F_1 = \frac{1}{n} F_2 = \frac{r}{n-1} \left\{ 1 - \Delta n \cdot \frac{(n-1)d - n\Delta r}{n(n-1)r} \right\} \quad . \quad . \quad . \quad (1)$$

The difference between this and the value $\dfrac{r}{n-1}$, obtained by putting $\Delta n = 0$ is a small magnitude of the second order. Likewise, the distance (x) of the first principal point from the anterior surface of the cornea calculated as above turns out to be

$$x = \frac{d \cdot \Delta n}{n(n-1)} \quad . \quad . \quad . \quad . \quad . \quad . \quad (1a)$$

The interval (a) between the two principal points is indeed of the third order of smallness, namely:

$$a = \frac{d^2 \Delta n}{nr} \quad . \quad . \quad . \quad . \quad . \quad . \quad . \quad (1b)$$

For calculation of images, therefore, it is accurate enough to assume that refraction occurs simply at the anterior surface of the cornea and to put the index of refraction of the cornea equal to that of the aqueous humor.

The second part of the optical system of the eye is composed of the crystalline lens, bounded by the aqueous humor in front and the vitreous humor behind, The indices of refraction of these two humors are so nearly the same that the difference may be ignored. In an optical system surrounded by the same medium on both sides, the principal points coincide with the nodal points. Thus, just as in an ordinary glass lens surrounded by air, these two pairs of points in the optical system of the crystalline lens are identical. But the crystalline lens differs essentially from a glass lens because the density of its substance is not uniform but increases from the outside towards the central part. Being ignorant of the exact law of this increase, we are not in position

to trace in detail the passage of the rays through the lens, or to determine the exact positions of its focal points and principal points; and we
have therefore to be contented with finding their approximate positions. In this connection the following propositions may be stated.

1. *The focal length of the crystalline lens is less than it would be if the
index of refraction of the entire lens were uniform and equal to the index of
the lens-core.*

In order to demonstrate this important fact, imagine the crystalline
lens resolved, according to its natural lamellar structure, into the core,
which is an almost spherical double convex lens of positive focal length,
and the separate layers surrounding it, which near the axis of the eye
correspond to lenses of meniscus type, which get thicker, or at least
not thinner, towards the edge; and for which, therefore, $r_1 \geqq r_2 + d$
(see end of §9), where r_1 denotes the radius of the convex surface, r_2
that of the concave surface, and d the thickness of the lens. In such
cases, according to equation (13), §9, the focal length is negative.
The positions of the principal points h_1, h_2 and of the focal points
p_1, p_2 in a lens of this type are shown in Fig. 42.

Referring to Fig. 45, let a', a'', designate the vertices of the lens,
c', c'' the centres of the two surfaces, and h', h'' the positions of the
principal points. This lens will produce a virtual, erect and reduced

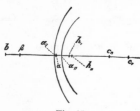

Fig. 45.

image (β) of an object situated at a
point b in front of the first (convex) surface. As shown in §9, this image lies
not only in front of the second principal
point, but invariably also in front of
the second surface of the lens; for if
$bh' > a'h'$, then $\beta h'' > ah''$, where a is
the point on the axis of the lens conjugate to the vertex a'. But the image

of the point a' is due to a single refraction at the second surface of
the lens, and since the focal length of this surface is negative, the
image (a) of a' will be nearer to the surface and in front of it. Therefore, β, which is farther back than a, must necessarily be in front of
the posterior surface of the lens.

Now it may also be shown that for an object (b) in front of the first
vertex (a') of the lens, the image (β) will be nearer the second surface
when the index of refraction is greater. It is easy to see that this is so
when the object is at a' and its image at a. Thus, by equations (3),
§9, putting $aa'' = q$, we have:

$$\frac{n_2}{d} - \frac{n_1}{q} = \frac{n_1 - n_2}{r_2}$$

or

$$q = \frac{n_1 r_2 d}{n_2 r_2 + (n_2 - n_1)d}.$$

Evidently, the value of q decreases as n_2 increases. Now if it can be shown that, when n_2 becomes greater, the image of b approaches nearer to a, this means that under these circumstances this image also approaches the second surface of the lens. Put $bh' = f'$, $a'h' = p$ (which corresponds to the length $-h'$ in equations (13a) of §9); then the distance of the second principal point from the image (β) is

$$\beta h'' = \frac{f'F}{F - f'}$$

where F denotes the focal length of the lens; and the distance of the same principal point from the point a which is the image of a' is

$$ah'' = \frac{pF}{F - p}.$$

Subtracting, we find for the interval between these two images:

$$\beta a = \frac{(f' - p)F^2}{(F - f')(F - p)}$$

$$= \frac{f' - p}{\left[\dfrac{F - p}{F} - \dfrac{f' - p}{F}\right]\dfrac{F - p}{F}}.$$

Putting

$$C = \frac{F - p}{F}$$

and substituting the values of F and $p = -h'$ as given by equations (13) and (13a), §9, we have:

$$C = 1 + \left(1 - \frac{n_1}{n_2}\right)\frac{d}{r_2}.$$

If the absolute value of the focal length is denoted by P, that is, if

$$P = -F = \frac{n_1 r_1 r_2}{\left(1 - \dfrac{n_1}{n_2}\right)[n_2(r_1 - r_2 - d) + n_1 d]},$$

then

$$\beta a = \frac{(f' - p)}{\left[C + \dfrac{f' - p}{P}\right]C}.$$

From the expressions above, it is evident that C increases and P decreases when n_2 is increased, whereas $(f' - p)$, which does not involve n_2, remains unchanged. Either increase of C or decrease of P results in diminishing βa, and, hence, increase of the index of refraction causes reduction of the interval βa.

Thus far we have studied the effect of a single one of the lenses obtained by dividing the crystalline body in its layers. Suppose now that all these meniscus lenses on one side of the core are mounted together in their natural position and surrounded by aqueous humor introduced between each pair of adjacent layers of different densities

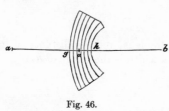

Fig. 46.

in the crystalline lens; and isolate that part of it on one side of the nucleus; thereby obtaining a system like that represented in Fig. 46, where ab is the axis, and g and h are the two opposite vertices of the combination. Let a designate the position of a luminous point on the axis in front of the convex side. From what was proved above with respect to a single lens of this type, evidently the image of a in the first lens will lie in front of the second surface of this lens and therefore also in front of the first surface of the second lens. Similarly, the image of this image in the second lens will lie in front of the second surface of that lens, and so on for each lens in succession; and, consequently, the final image of a in the entire system will lie somewhere in front of the last refracting surface, at a, say.

Evidently, too, as the point a approaches the vertex g, the point a will approach the vertex (h) of the farther surface. For the image of a real object in a simple negative lens is nearer the lens, when the object is nearer; and since the image produced by each lens of the system acts as object for the next lens, therefore when a approaches the first surface, its image moves along the axis in the same direction, and so on for each image in succession.

The conclusion is that if the index of refraction of one of the layers were increased, the image a would thereby fall nearer h. Until the layer which is supposed to be altered is reached, there would be, of course, no change in the path of the rays or in the successive images; but the image in that layer will be nearer h than it would have been, and, consequently, the last image (a) will be nearer. If, therefore, this final image is to stay where it was originally before the index of one layer is increased, the object a must be moved farther back so as to increase the distance ag.

Consider now the whole crystalline lens as composed of two such systems of meniscus lenses B and C (Fig. 47), with its double convex core (A) comprised between them. If the crystalline lens as a whole

forms a real inverted image
at b of a luminous point a in
front of the lens, the system
of layers B must produce an
image at a point α in front of
the anterior surface of the
core. Similarly, the resultant
image at b is the image in
system C of a point β lying on

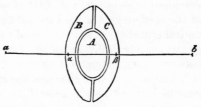

Fig. 47.

the axis beyond the posterior surface of the core at the place where
the rays intersect after having traversed the core and before being
refracted by system C. Like any double convex lens, therefore, the
core itself must produce a real inverted image of α at the place
marked β; which it will do, provided α lies in front of its first focal
point. If a were removed to an infinite distance, b would be at the
second focal point of the optical system of the crystalline lens.

If now the index of refraction of one of the layers of B is supposed
to be increased, α will thereby be brought closer to the anterior surface
of A, and, consequently, the image of α formed by B at β and the image
of β formed by C at b will be displaced forwards in the direction of the
incident light. Similarly, an increase of the index of refraction of one
of the layers of C will produce a displacement of b away from the
crystalline lens, without having any effect on the position of β.

*If, therefore, the index of refraction of a single layer of the crystalline
lens is increased, the second focal point of the lens will thereby be made to
recede farther from its posterior surface.*

Thus even if the index of refraction of each layer of the crystalline
lens were increased until it was equal to that of the core, the focal
point would not be infinitely far away, because ultimately the entire
lens in this case would be formed of the same material as the core and
would be a simple homogeneous double convex lens of finite focus.

The same argument applies, of course, as to the position of the first
focal point; and so it has been shown that the focal points of the crystalline lens are both nearer the lens than they would be if all its layers
were of the same density and index as the core.

2. *The interval between the principal points of the crystalline lens
is less than it would be for a lens of the same external form with constant
index of refraction equal to that of the core.*

The *optical centre* of the crystalline lens is a point on the axis which
is conjugate in turn to each of the principal points.[1] Wherever it is,

---

[1] ¶The optical centre of the crystalline lens is the point where the curved line crosses the
axis which represents the path of the ray inside the lens that was directed originally towards
the first principal point. (J. P. C. S.)

the same method as was used above for finding the focal point may be employed to show that the effect of increasing the index of refraction of the single layers of the lens will be to draw the two images of the optical centre closer to the external surfaces of the lens; and hence the greater, algebraically speaking, will be the value of the distance between them. Suppose now that the layers have the same index of refraction as that of the core; the optical centre of this new homogeneous lens will not, in general, be at the same place with that of the original crystalline lens. Since the interval between the principal points of a convergent or positive lens is the maximum of all intervals between pairs of conjugate points (see end of §9), the interval between the principal points of this new homogeneous lens will be in any case greater than that between the images of the optical centre of the original lens that are formed by the new lens; and hence it is also greater than the distance of the principal points of the unaltered lens from each other.

Moreover, it may be shown that the interval between the principal points of the crystalline lens is positive; that is, that the second principal point lies beyond the first; provided we assume, as is evident from the form of the layers, that the radii of curvature of their surfaces, taken near the axis, exceed the distances of these surfaces from the core. The image in a spherical refracting surface of a point between the vertex and the centre is nearer the surface than the point itself. Therefore the image of the centre of the core formed by the anterior half of the lens falls in front of, and that formed by the posterior half falls beyond, that point. The two corresponding images of the centre of the core are thus separated by a positive distance. And since the interval between the principal points is algebraically greater than that between any other pair of conjugate points, it likewise must be positive.

The principal points of a lens with the same external form as the crystalline lens of the human eye and with an index of refraction the same as that of the core would be about $\frac{1}{4}$ mm apart; so that the separation of the principal points of the crystalline lens itself must be very small indeed.

Measurements of the indices of refraction of the transparent media of the human eye were made many years ago by CHOSSAT[1] and BREWSTER,[2] who seem, however, to have examined only a small number of eyes; and quite recently W. KRAUSE[3] has carried out an extensive series of such measurements. BREWSTER introduced the substance under examination between the curved surface of a convex lens, mounted as the objective of a microscope, and a plane glass plate set perpendicular to the instrumental axis. This

[1] *Bulletin des sc. par la Société philom. de Paris.* A. 1818. June. p. 294.

[2] *Edinburgh Philos. Journal.* 1819. No. 1. p. 47.

[3] *Die Brechungsindices der durchsichtigen Medien des menschl. Auges von* Dr. W. KRAUSE, Hannover 1855.

altered the focal length of the microscope. BREWSTER measured the object-distance of the microscope before and after the insertion of the refracting substance, and also after inserting water of known index of refraction. CA-HOURS and BECQUEREL[1] suggested measuring the size of the microscope image, which is also the method used by W. KRAUSE, whose process is the one here described.

An ordinary KELLNER microscope, the lower part of which is represented by Fig. 48, was arranged for the purpose by substituting a double convex crown glass lens of about 30 mm focus in place of the objective, its fastening *b* being screwed into the tube *a* of the microscope. The lens was set in a black hollow depression in which it was screwed tight by means of the casing *d* in the middle of which there was an opening 2.6 mm in diameter. The lens was pressed air-tight against the rim of this aperture, and below it was mounted a plane crown glass plate *e*, held in place by a conical ring *f*, fitted upon the conical surface of *d* but not so tightly as entirely to exclude the air in between. The specimen of ocular medium to be tested was placed in the ring *f* on the middle of the flat plate, and the ring pressed against the mounting *d* with sufficient force to insure that the glass plate was perpendicular to the instrumental axis. The lens could thus be easily removed and cleaned after each measurement.

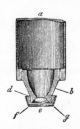

Fig. 48.

The eyepiece was provided with a glass micrometer divided in thirtieths of a Vienna line[2]; another scale divided in tenths of a line was mounted upon the microscope stage. The instrument being adjusted so that both scales were clearly in focus at the same time, the number of divisions of one micrometer that corresponded to one scale division of the other micrometer was determined. Similar measurements were made with air and with distilled water substituted for the transparent humor.

Equations (12) of §9 may be employed for the reduction of the results. It is true that these equations apply to two refracting surfaces only, whereas KRAUSE's apparatus involves four, namely, the two surfaces of the plate and the two surfaces of the lens. But the system may be divided into two parts, the first being the plate and the second being the lens, the focal lengths of the former being infinite. Denoting the first (lower) and second (upper) focal lengths of the plate by $f,$, $f,,$, respectively, corresponding to the notation in equations (11a) to (11f), §9, those of the lens by $\varphi,$, $\varphi,,$, and the distance of the second principal point of the plate from the first principal point of the lens by d; we find, from the last of equations (11f), when $f,,$ is made infinite, that the second (upper) focal length of the whole system is

$$F,, = \varphi,,.$$

The first focal length has the same value, since the first and last media are the same (air). Putting $f,, = \infty$ in equation (11e), we find that the second principal point of the whole system coincides with that of the lens. Accordingly, in this case the second principal point and the second focal point are the same as if the medium contained between the flat plate and the lens extended upwards indefinitely. According to the notation used in equation (12), §9, let us denote the index of refraction of the substance that is being investigated by n_1, that of the glass lens by n_2, and that of the air by $n_3 = 1$. The expression for F_2 as given by that equation will then correspond to the focal length F of our system:

[1] *L'Institut. Scienc. math., phys. et natur.* 1840. p. 399.

[2] ¶Vienna line = 2.195 mm. (J. P. C. S.)

$$F = \frac{n_2 r_1 r_2}{n_2(1-n_2)r_1 + [n_2 r_2 - (1-n_2)d](n_2 - n_1)}.$$

If F_0 denotes the focal length of the objective, when distilled water of index n_0 is inserted between the plate and the lens, and if Φ denotes the focal length when this space contains air, we have two other similar formulae, which, together with the one above, may be put in the following form:

$$\left.\begin{array}{l} FA - n_2 r_1 r_2 = n_1 F B \\ F_0 A - n_2 r_1 r_2 = n_0 F_0 B \\ \Phi A \ - n_2 r_1 r_2 = \Phi B \end{array}\right\} \quad \cdot \quad \cdot \quad \cdot \quad \cdot \quad \cdot \quad (2)$$

in which A and B are abbreviations for the following expressions:

$$A = n_2[(1-n_2)r_1 + n_2 r_2 - (1-n_2)d],$$
$$B = n_2 r_2 - (1-n_2)d.$$

Subtracting the second of equations (2) from the first, and the third from the second, we obtain:

$$(F - F_0)A = (n_1 F - n_0 F_0)B$$
$$(F_0 - \Phi)A = (n_0 F_0 - \Phi)B.$$

Eliminating A and B by division, we have:

$$\frac{F - F_0}{F_0 - \Phi} = \frac{n_1 F - n_0 F_0}{n_0 F_0 - \Phi}.$$

Accordingly,

$$n_1 = 1 + (n_0 - 1)\frac{F_0(F - \Phi)}{F(F_0 - \Phi)} \quad \cdot \quad \cdot \quad \cdot \quad \cdot \quad (2a)$$

Thus knowing the three focal lengths F, F_0 and Φ and the index of refraction (n_0) of distilled water, we are in a position to determine the index of refraction (n_1) of the substance to be measured. The focal lengths, however, may be calculated from measurements of the images under the different conditions. Thus, if b denotes the size of a scale-division of the lower micrometer, and if β denotes the absolute size of its image in the focal plane of the ocular (that is, disregarding the change of sign due to inversion), then by equation (8b), §9:

$$\frac{\beta}{b} = \frac{f_2 - F}{F}$$

or

$$F = \frac{f_2 b}{b + \beta} \quad , \quad \cdot \quad \cdot \quad \cdot \quad \cdot \quad \cdot \quad \cdot \quad (2b)$$

where F denotes the focal length of the optical system of the objective and f_2 denotes the distance of β from the second principal point of this system. Having measured b and β, we would, therefore, still have to know f_2 in order to find F. But on the assumption that f_2 is constant, which is practically the case in KRAUSE's apparatus, this quantity may be eliminated from the expression for n_1, and consequently does not have to be known. If β, β_0 and $\mathfrak{b}$ denote the values corresponding to the three focal lengths F, F_0 and Φ, we have three equations of the form of equation (2b) which combined with equation (2a) enable us to eliminate the focal lengths as well as f_2, and thus to obtain finally;

$$n_1 = 1 + (n_0 - 1)\frac{\mathfrak{b} - \beta}{\mathfrak{b} - \beta_0} \quad \cdot \quad \cdot \quad \cdot \quad \cdot \quad \cdot \quad (2c)$$

By this method, therefore, it is not even necessary to know the size of the object b under the microscope; and all we need to have is some object of constant dimensions.

In these measurements the value of f_2 is constant, provided the positions of the eyepiece micrometer and the second principal point of the objective system are not altered. The latter will not be absolutely stationary, when different liquids are introduced between plate and lens, unless the upper surface of the lens is plane. The distance of the second principal point from the second surface of the lens is denoted by h_2 in equation (12a), §9. Except when r_2 is infinite, this distance depends on the index of refraction (n_1) of the substance that is inserted on the lower side of the lens. But if r_2 is infinite, then

$$h_2 = -\frac{n_3 d}{n_2},$$

in which therefore h_2 is independent of n_1. Accordingly it might be better to use a plano-convex lens for this purpose with its plane side up, instead of a double convex lens. However, the error introduced by employing a double convex lens is extremely small, provided the thickness of the lens is negligible in comparison with the length of the instrument.

In BREWSTER's measurements the index of refraction of distilled water was taken as .1.3358, which according to FRAUNHOFER's data about corresponds to the E line in the green, that is, to rays of medium refrangibility. KRAUSE, taking LISTING's advice, based his work on the rays of greatest intensity, for which, according to FRAUNHOFER, the index of refraction of water is 1.33424. The results obtained by CHOSSAT, BREWSTER and KRAUSE for the human eye are here tabulated. W. KRAUSE measured twenty eyes from ten individuals, and found very considerable variations in them.

Table of indices of refraction of media of human eye

| Observer | | Cornea | Aqueous humor | Vitreous humor | Crystalline lens | | |
					Outer layer	Middle layer	Core
CHOSSAT		1.33	1.338	1.339	1.338	1.395	1.420
BREWSTER			1.3366	1.3394	1.3767	1.3786	1.3839
$n_0 = 1.3358$							
	Max.	1.3569	1.3557	1.3569	1.4743	1.4775	1.4807
W. KRAUSE	Min.	1.3431	1.3349	1.3361	1.3431	1.3523	1.4252
$n_0 = 1.3342$	Mean	1.3507	1.3420	1.3485	1.4053	1 4294	1.4541
HELMHOLTZ			1.3365	1.3382	1.4189		
$n_0 = 1.3354$							

The writer's own measurements, the results of which are also included in the table above, were made in the following way. The fluid specimen to be measured was inserted between a plane glass plate and the concave surface of a small plano-concave lens, and the image produced by this system was measured with the ophthalmometer; whence the focal lengths were calculated. Incidentally, the radius of the curved surface of the lens could be found directly with the ophthalmometer, by the same method as was described in §2 for measuring the radius of curvature of the cornea. Under these circumstances, it was unnecessary to assume a value for the index of refraction of distilled water, because it was measured also and found in this way to be 1.3351, which is intermediate between that assumed by BREWSTER and that assumed by KRAUSE.

KRAUSE made another series of measurements of the indices of refraction of calves' eyes, especially with a view to finding out whether the indices suffered any noticeable change of value in the first twenty-four hours after death. He made measurements on twenty specimens immediately after the animals had been killed, and on twenty others after they had been kept twenty-four hours at a temperature of 19° C. The average results are as follows:

	Immediately after death	24 hours after death
Cornea	1.3467	1.3480
Aqueous humor	1.3421	1.3415
Vitreous humor	1.3529	1.3528
Outer layer of lens	1.3983	1.4013
Middle layer of lens	1.4194	1.4211
Core of lens	1.4520	1.4512

Accordingly, there is not any noticeable change in the indices of refraction of the media of a calf's eye in the first twenty-four hours after death, and it is a reasonable inference that the same is true in case of the human eye.

Since it is not possible to calculate the focal lengths of the several layers of the crystalline lens directly from their forms and indices of refraction, the author has inserted below the results of direct measurements of the optical constants of the crystalline lenses of two human eyes, which he was able to make about twelve hours after death.

When the lens is extracted from the eye and exposed to the air its outer surface soon dries and shrivels up, and if kept in water it swells and loses its transparency. The author therefore adopted the plan of surrounding the lens with vitreous humor. The lens is, moreover, remarkably sensitive to every little tension or pressure, but as long as it is surrounded by its elastic and tight-fitting capsule, these effects are only temporary. During the measurements, therefore, the lens has to be kept in such a position that it will not be

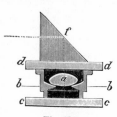

Fig. 49.

subjected to external stresses of any sort. This was accomplished by using the apparatus shown in section in Fig. 49, which is actual size. In the centre there is a hollow brass cell divided on the inside at *bb* by a horizontal partition, concave above, with a circular opening in the middle. The mounting of the objective from an old microscope was convenient for the purpose. Upon the lower rim of this mounting was cemented a plane-parallel glass plate, *cc*, care being taken, however, not to use any appreciable thickness of cement. The lower part of the brass cylinder having been first filled with vitreous humor, the crystalline lens was very carefully transferred from the eye, without being injured or bruised, to the position shown, and laid, flat side downwards, on the opening in the diaphragm *bb*. The upper part of the brass tube was then filled level to the brim with vitreous humor and covered over with a second glass plate *dd*, thus giving the humor a plane upper surface. As it was not convenient to set the ophthalmometer in a vertical position, a right-angle isosceles glass prism *f* was mounted on the glass plate *dd*, which reflected the light from below in a horizontal direction. The whole apparatus was conveniently mounted on the body of a microscope, from which all the lenses and the small diaphragm below had been removed. A brass plate provided with a GRAVESAND slit, the opening of which was to serve as the object to be viewed through the crystalline lens, was mounted first on the stage of the microscope, and afterwards close to the under side of the glass plate cc, between it and the upper end of the microscope tube. The illumination was produced by adjusting the microscope mirror so as to reflect light from below up through the slit in the brass plate. The width of the image of the slit in the crystalline lens was measured with the ophthalmometer.

In making the calculation it is necessary to know the distance between the knife-edges of the slit and the under surface of the plate cc. Let this be denoted by a_1 when the brass plate lies on the microscope stage, and by a_2 when it is close to the under surface of the glass plate. The greater a_1 and the smaller a_2 can be made, the more reliable are the results. We must also know the thickness c of the plate cc, its index of refraction n_c (approximately at least), the distance b between its upper surface and the upper edge of the opening bb, and the index of refraction n_2 of the vitreous humor with respect to air. Let b_1 denote the interval between the edges of the slit as it lies on the microscope stage at a distance a_1 from the plate cc; β_1 the width of the image of this interval as seen through the crystalline lens (which here is negative, on account of the inversion); and b_2, β_2 the corresponding magnitudes for the other position of the slit; and, finally, let f denote the required focal length of the lens in vitreous humor, and x the distance of its first nodal point from the plane of the upper edge of the opening bb. From equations (3e) and (6c), §9, concerning refraction in plane plates, it follows that the rays proceed in the vitreous humor before passing through the lens as if they had come from a source of size b_1 or b_2, located at the distance

$$\left(na_1+\frac{n}{n_c}c+b+x\right) \text{ or } \left(na_2+\frac{n}{n_c}c+b+x\right),$$

respectively. The size of the image β_1 or β_2 will evidently not be altered further by the subsequent refractions at the surfaces of the upper glass plate. Accordingly, we may write

$$\frac{\beta_1-b_1}{\beta_1}=\frac{na_1+\dfrac{n}{n_c}c+b+x}{f}$$

$$\frac{\beta_2-b_2}{\beta_2}=\frac{na_2+\dfrac{n}{n_c}c+b+x}{f};$$

which give by subtraction:

$$\frac{\beta_1-b_1}{\beta_1}-\frac{\beta_2-b_2}{\beta_2}=\frac{n(a_1-a_2)}{f},$$

whence the focal length of the crystalline lens surrounded by vitreous humor is found to be:

$$f=\frac{n\beta_1\beta_2(a_1-a_2)}{b_2\beta_1-b_1\beta_2},$$

and the value of x can be found by substituting this value in either of the two original equations. In making the calculation it is necessary to keep in mind that when a_1 is greater than the focal length, the image will be inverted, and hence β_1 will be negative. A slight correction has to be made in the value of x thus obtained, due to the fact that the curved surface of the lens extends a little below the plane of the opening bb on which it rests, so that x is not exactly equal to the distance of the nodal point from the anterior surface of the lens.

This correction is easily calculated from the diameter of the opening and the radius of curvature of the lower or front lens surface.

By simply turning the lens over, the distance of the second nodal point from the other surface of the lens may be found in the same manner.

The reduced thickness of the glass plate c/n_c may be determined from observations with the ophthalmometer, by inserting it between the slit and a small glass lens, for which the focal length and positions of the nodal points are known, just as it was originally inserted between the slit and the crystalline lens. The value of b also is similarly obtained, and the same equations as were used in calculating x and f may be employed to find b and c/n_c when the two former magnitudes have been ascertained.

The curvatures of the surfaces of the lens in the vicinity of the axis may be found either by reflection, as already explained, or by refraction. For this purpose, the lens is left in the brass cell, and the part of the vitreous humor over its upper surface is removed. The slit is then placed in front of the prism f, a little to one side of the axis of the ophthalmometer, and its reflected image measured; or it is left lying on the microscope stage and the measurement made on the dioptric image thus formed. It has already been explained how the measurement of the reflected image is utilized. In the dioptric method, suppose the symbols b_1, β_1, and f have the same meanings as before, but let β_3 denote the size of the image formed with the upper layer of vitreous humor removed, and let y denote the distance of the second nodal point from the upper surface of the lens (supposed to be surrounded by the vitreous humor). Then, if the radius of curvature at the vertex of the upper surface is denoted by R, it may be found from the equation

$$R.\frac{n(\beta_1-\beta_3)}{(n-1)\beta_3}=f\frac{b_1-\beta_1}{b_1.}-y.$$

The focal length of the crystalline lens with its peculiar structure has been found to be shorter than that of a lens of the same external form made of homogeneous substance of the same density and index of refraction as those of the core of the lens. Consequently, a homogeneous lens exactly like the crystalline lens in shape and size and of the same focal length would have to be made of some material of even greater index of refraction than that of the core itself. The index of refraction of this imaginary lens fulfilling these specifications has been called by SENFF the *total index* of the crystalline lens. It is quite different from the average index of refraction obtained by taking the arithmetical mean of the values for all the layers, exceeding, as it does, the highest of all the values of the index of refraction in the crystalline lens. Herewith is appended a summary of the data derived from measurements of human lenses made by the author, the dimensions being in millimetres. The focal lengths and principal points are given on the supposition that the lens is surrounded by vitreous humor. The radii of curvature were obtained by the reflection method.

1. Focal length.................................45.144 to 47.435
2. Distance of first principal point from anterior surface. 2.258 " 2.810
3. Distance of second principal point from posterior surface............................. 1.546 " 1.499
4. Thickness of lens............................. 4.2 " 4.314
5. Radius of curvature of anterior surface at vertex....10.162 " 8.865
6. Radius of curvature of posterior surface at vertex... 5.860 " 5.889
7. Total index of refraction....................... 1.4519 " 1.4414

However, whether the form and focal length are the same for lenses measured after death as in the unaccommodated living eye is rendered doubtful by certain of the writer's measurements. The smallest values of the thickness of the lens as found by measurements of dead eyes are occasionally more than half a millimetre greater than the writer found for the same distance in the eyes of three live individuals.[1] The method of measuring the distance between the pupil and the front of the cornea was explained in §3. The anterior surface of the lens is close against the edge of the pupil, and so the thickness of the lens can be found as soon as the distance of the posterior surface of the lens from the cornea is obtained.

The cornea and lens are represented in Fig. 50 by AA and B, respectively. Light comes to the eye along some direction such as Cc, and, after refraction first at the cornea and then at the anterior surface of the lens, is partially

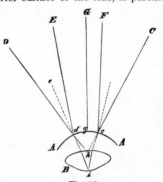

reflected at i at the posterior surface of the lens. The reflected ray emerges by the path idD, so as finally to enter the eye of the observer. If now the source of light C and the observer's eye D are interchanged, the light will again proceed along the same path, only in the reverse direction, $DdicC$, being reflected, as before, at the same point i on the posterior surface of the lens. The patient's eye is directed steadily towards a point of fixation and the straight line Gg represents the visual axis of his eye. These things, having all been previously determined by suitable measurements, we can find the angles between the lines Cc, Dd

Fig. 50.

and Gg. In order to locate the points c and d on the cornea, suppose the observer's eye is at D, and let a small source of light be so adjusted at a place E in front of the eye that the observer at D will see the reflex of this light in the anterior surface of the cornea and at the same time the reflex from C in the posterior surface of the crystalline lens. This coincidence occurs when the ray Ed is reflected to D, that is, when the bisector de of the angle EdD is normal to the cornea. Now if the angle EdD or the angle between Ed and Gg has been found by suitable measurement, it is easy to calculate the angle between ed and Gg; and hence, from the form and curvature of the cornea, as obtained by previous measurements, the length of the arc dg can be found, that is, the position of d with respect to g. The position of the point c is ascertained in the same way. Thus, the positions of the points c, d and the directions of the lines Cc, Dd are known; and the point h where these lines meet is the apparent place of the reflex image in the posterior surface of the crystalline lens, that is, the place where it appears to be as seen through the intervening ocular media.

In making the measurement the sources of light C and E are arranged on a horizontal graduated bar several feet from the eye under examination. The source C should be as large and bright as possible, but E should be small and coloured by a blue glass to facilitate observing its reflection. The observer looks through a small telescope, which is also mounted on the grauated bar to enable him to locate its position. The telescope and lamp C can then be interchanged, as desired.[2]

The mean apparent position of the posterior surface of the lens, as found by observations of this kind with three different eyes, was not far in front of the centre of curvature of the cornea. The displacement produced by the

[1] v. Graefes *Archiv. für Ophthalmologie.* Bd. I. Abt. 2. S. 56.

[2] The details of this method are described in Graefes *Archiv.* I, 2, p. 51.

refraction at the cornea may be calculated. Since a spherical refracting surface has very little effect on the apparent position of an object located near its centre, individual variations in the value of the index of the refraction of the aqueous humor are unimportant so far as the final result is concerned. The same is true with respect to the refraction of the lens for a point on its posterior surface, since this surface too is very near the second principal point of the lens. The results of the author's measurements of the interval between the principal points of the dead crystalline lens were not reliable because in the case of such very small magnitudes all the other errors are cumulative; and so he has borrowed the correction that has to be made for the lenticular refraction from the data of LISTING's schematic eye. The apparent forward displacement of the posterior surface of the lens, due to refraction through the lens, is somewhat less than the interval between the principal points. It has been shown that the distance between the principal points in the natural lens is less than in a homogeneous lens of the same form·and of index of refraction equal to that of the core; consequently, the correction deduced from LISTING's lens must be rather too large, and tends therefore to give slightly too large a value of the calculated thickness.

The mean results for the three eyes examined, as deduced from two series of concordant observations, were as follows:

	O.H.	B.P.	J.H.
Radius of curvature of cornea	7.338	7.646	8.154
Apparent distance of posterior surface of lens from vertex of cornea	6.775	7.003	6.658
Actual distance	7.172	7.232	7.141
Distance of pupillary plane from vertex of cornea	4.024	3.597	3.739

Assuming the anterior surface of the lens to lie in the pupillary plane, these results give for the thickness of the lens in the unaccommodated living eye: 3.148   3.635   3.402

Adding to these the correction necessary because of the convexity of the anterior lens surface, the edge of the pupil itself being assumed to have no appreciable thickness, we obtain the values: 3.414   3.801   3.555

The values of the pupillary diameter and the curvature of the anterior surface of the lens used in calculating this correction were obtained by actual measurements in each of the eyes concerned. These final results also are still less than the smallest values of the thickness heretofore obtained from dead lenses, which vary, according to the elder KRAUSE, from 4.0 to 5.4 mm.

The fact, observed by the younger KRAUSE, that the index of refraction of the lens from a calf's eye remains practically unchanged 24 hours after death, makes it improbable that the thickening of the lens is due to absorption of water; for in that case we should expect a decrease of the index of refraction. It seems likely, therefore, that the observed change is of the same nature as what takes place in the act of accommodation. This will be referred to again in §12.

There still remains to be stated what has been learned to date about the cardinal points of the eye. The conclusions here given are based on LISTING's schematic eye, which certainly departs very little from the actual average, as is verified in some measure by the writer's investigations. At any rate, wherever it is necessary or permissible to use mean values in the computations of physiological optics, the numerical data for the individual eye in question being unknown, it is probable, in view of the very large individual variations that exist, that the data of LISTING's schematic eye will be found just as reliable and satisfactory as the actual mean values, supposing that the latter were known. Accordingly, LISTING's constants will be used in this treatise, with occasional comments, when necessary, explaining how they are sometimes different from what seem to be the actual mean values.

LISTING gives 8 mm as the radius of the cornea; although, according to the measurements of SENFF as well as those of the author, it appears to be somewhat less than this. The average of the values of the index of refraction of the cornea obtained by W. KRAUSE is rather higher than BREWSTER's value $103/77 = 1.3379$ which is adopted by LISTING. On both accounts LISTING's data for the focal lengths of the cornea are somewhat greater than the observed average. According to equations (3a) and (3b), §9, the first focal length of the cornea is

$$F_1 = \frac{r}{n-1},$$

where n denotes the index of refraction of the aqueous humor and r denotes the radius of the cornea; and the second focal length is

$$F_2 = \frac{nr}{n-1}.$$

In LISTING's schematic eye,

$$F_1 = 23 \tfrac{9}{13}, \quad F_2 = 31 \tfrac{9}{13}.$$

If we put $r = 7.8$, which is the result of SENFF's measurements and which agrees also approximately with the mean of the writer's determinations, and if, following W. KRAUSE, we take $n = 1.342$, we get:

$$F_1 = 22.81, \qquad F_2 = 30.61.$$

The index of refraction of the lens in LISTING's schematic eye is $16/11$; the thickness of the lens is 4 mm, and the radii are 10 and 6 mm. Accordingly, for a lens immersed in aqueous humor, we find by equations (13), (13a), and (13b), §9, that the focal length is 43.796 mm, the interval between the principal points 0.2461 mm, the distance of the first principal point from the anterior surface 2.3462 mm, and the distance of the second principal point from the posterior surface 1.4077 mm. These values agree very closely with the results of the writer's earlier direct measurements of two dissected human lenses. He is not aware of any other direct measurements of the focal lengths of eyes of human beings. The reason why it is not practicable to calculate the focal lengths from the form and indices of the component layers of the lens has already been explained. It follows from the theorem proved in the earlier part of this section, that the assumption, made by most earlier opticians, of an equivalent homogeneous crystalline lens having the same figure and the average index of refraction of the actual lens, is essentially incorrect; and that, on the contrary, such an artificial lens would have to have a higher index than that of the densest part of the actual crystalline lens. For example, SENFF[1] found this *total index of refraction* of the crystalline lens of an ox to be 1.539, whereas the actual indices for the outer layer and for the core were 1.374 and 1.453, respectively. The two values of the total index found by the author from his measurements, namely, 1.4519 and 1.4414, are both less than the above and correspond, say, with the average of the values given by W. KRAUSE for the core. (His results were: maximum, 1.4807; minimum, 1.4252; mean, 1.4541.) LISTING had previously chosen the value $16/11 = 1.4545$, which agrees well enough with both KRAUSE's work and the writer's investigations.

If we assume that there is always the same difference between the optical properties of the crystalline lens before and after death as was shown by the writer's experiments, LISTING's schematic eye would probably correspond to an eye that was accommodated for near vision, the focal length of the lens when relaxed being somewhat longer, and its thickness somewhat less.

The value assumed by LISTING for the distance between the anterior surfaces of cornea and lens is 4 mm. This corresponds to the near-sighted eye designated as O. H. in the author's measurements. In near-sighted eyes the

---

[1] VOLKMANN, Art. "Sehen" in R. WAGNERS *Handwörterbuch d. Physiologie.* Bd. III· S. 290.

anterior chamber is usually deeper and the iris flatter. The other two eyes in the author's experiments were normal, and in both of them the depth was less; but in all three the posterior surface of the lens was in front of the centre of curvature of the cornea. This leads the writer to suspect that the lens is somewhat nearer the cornea in normal eyes than LISTING has assumed. The difference is too small, however, to be of much importance.

Being given the focal lengths of the cornea and lens and the positions of the principal points of the latter, the cardinal points of the eye as a whole may be found by means of equations (11a) to (11f), §9, The values calculated by LISTING from his data have already been recorded.

For finding the position of the image on the retina, the nodal points of the eye are the most convenient of all the cardinal points, and, luckily, the locations of these points is known now with considerable certainty.

By the method given in §9 for finding the nodal points, the point on the axis of the eye which is conjugate to each of the nodal points in succession is found to lie between the nodal point of the cornea (which is its centre of curvature) and the first principal point of the lens; its distances from these points being to each other as the lesser focal length of the cornea, is to that of the lens, namely, about 1 to 2. In LISTING's schematic eye, the distance of the first principal point of the lens from the centre of curvature of the cornea, which he found to lie on the posterior surface of the lens, is 1.627 mm. But according to measurements of living eyes as made by the author, the posterior surface of the lens may be as much as 1 mm in front of the centre of curvature of the cornea, which might make the above distance about 2.6 mm. Thus, the point, which is conjugate to each nodal point in succession, would be from 0.54 to 0.87 mm in front of the centre of curvature of the cornea, the range of variation being, therefore, very small. The first nodal point is its image as formed by the cornea. The image of an object just a little in front of the centre of curvature of a spherical refracting surface is only a very short distance in front of the object itself. It we take LISTING's values of the focal lengths of cornea and lens, the first nodal point proves to be 0.758 mm in front of the centre of curvature of the cornea. On the other hand, if the point, which is conjugate to this nodal point with respect to the optical system of the cornea is assumed to be 0.87 mm in front of the centre of curvature of the cornea, the first nodal point will be found to be 1.16 mm in front of the centre. We shall, therefore not go far wrong by assuming that in normal eyes the first nodal point is from 3/4 to 5/4 mm in front of the centre of curvature of the cornea.

VOLKMANN[1] endeavoured to determine experimentally the position of the nodal point in the human eye. The fact was mentioned above that when the light from a candle enters the eye sidewise, the image of the flame, especially in the case of a blond individual, can be seen at the inner corner of the eye. VOLKMANN measured the distance of this image from the cornea, and at the same time the angle between the incident rays and the visual axis. He then constructed a horizontal section of the eye to a suitable scale, marked on it the point where the retinal image was visible through the sclerotica, and drew through this point a line intersecting the optical axis at the same angle as that between the incident rays and the visual axis. The point of intersection was taken as the nodal point. The mean of his measurements with five persons gave the position of the nodal point as 8.93 mm beyond the cornea. Undoubtedly, this value is somewhat too large, as it makes the nodal point lie beyond the centre of curvature of the cornea, whereas it must necessarily lie in front of that point. The error in VOLKMANN's result is explained by the fact that he was as yet unaware of the distinction between the optical axis

[1] R. WAGNERS *Handwörterbuch d. Physiologie.* Art. "Sehen." S. 286.*

and visual axis, and also because the definition of nodal points and principal points are valid only for much smaller angles of incidence than he used in these experiments. BUROW[1] found, moreover, in repeating VOLKMANN's experiments with the eyes of white rabbits, that for very wide angles of incidence the retinal image falls nearer the optical axis than it should if all the direction lines intersected in a point. Both of these influences would have the effect of making the distance from cornea to nodal point, as determined by VOLKMANN's method, somewhat too large.

We shall now explain how the centering of the eye and the positions of the optical axis and the visual axis may be determined. The method utilizes the reflex images formed by the cornea and lens surfaces of a bright source of light placed in front of the eye.

Concerning the appearance of these reflex images and the best methods of observing them, the reader is referred to §12. In Fig. 51, *cd* represents the axis of an accurately centered eye; the eye of the observer is at *a* and the source of light at *b*. Suppose *ab* is perpendicular to *cd*, and *ac = cb*. With this arrangement, everything being symmetrical, it is clear that the light from *b*, falling upon the three reflecting surfaces at their vertices, where they intersect the axis *cd*, will in each case be reflected to *a*. If the observer and the source of light are interchanged, the same thing will occur again, and the three reflected points will appear in the same perspective, on account of the bilateral symmetry of the whole apparatus. Since the anterior surface of the lens is about half-way between the cornea and the posterior surface of the lens, the image in the anterior surface of the lens should, for either position of the light and observer, appear about halfway between the other two images.

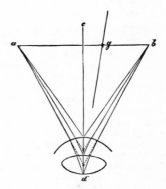

Fig. 51.

The following method may now be employed to ascertain the adjustment of any given eye. Let a horizontal graduated scale be placed along the line *ab*, suitable openings being provided at *a* and *b* for the observer and the source of light. The eye under examination is brought into some convenient position *d*, on the perpendicular bisector *cd*, and its owner is directed to look fixedly at some adjustable object, *g*, which is then moved up or down and to right or left until the observer can see the reflex from the anterior surface of the lens lying between those from the cornea and the posterior surface of the lens. The observer then changes place with the light and notes whether, with the fixation mark unchanged, the three images remain in the same relative positions as before. If the eye under examination were correctly centered, it would be possible to find a position for the object *g* such that this would be the case.

The writer has never examined a human eye that quite fulfilled this condition. If the three reflexes are in the right positions when viewed from one side, they are not so when viewed from the other, and in order to adjust them in the right positions again, the point of fixation (*g*) has to be shifted more or less. For each of the three eyes on which this method was tried, it was found necessary to place the fixation point *g* somewhat above the plane *abd*. The visual axis was invariably found to lie on the nasal side of the line *cd*, its

[1] *Beiträge zur Physiologie d. menschl. Auges.* S. 56-60.

horizontal projection making the following angles with *cd* under the given conditions:

Eye	Light coming from the nasal side	from the temporal side
O. H.	3° 47′	4° 57′
B. P.	5° 6′	8° 12′
J. H.	5° 43′	7° 44′

These results show that *the human eye is not exactly centered.* But the differences between the corresponding angles for different eyes is comparatively small; and we may, therefore, assume the line *cd*, found from the experiments, as the approximate position of the so-called optical axis, and take the arithmetical mean of the above results as the angle between this assumed optical axis and the horizontal projection of the visual axis. This optical axis also coincides well enough with the axis of the cornea as found by the author and passes through the centre of its circumference.

The pioneer in physiological optics who was the first to have a clear conception of the refraction of light in the eye and of the formation and position of the image on the retina was KEPLER. It is true that MAUROLYCUS had previously compared the crystalline lens of the eye with a glass lens, and asserted that it converges the rays towards the axis, but he could not admit that it forms an inverted image on the retina, because we should then have to see everything upside down. PORTA also, who invented the *camera obscura,* compared the eye with that instrument, but he supposed that the image was formed on the crystalline lens. KEPLER, who had already investigated the general theory of optical instruments, was the first to realize the existence of the inverted retinal image and the condition for distinct vision, namely, that the rays from each point of the object shall be brought to a focus at some point of the retina. KEPLER's theory was extended by the work of the celebrated Jesuit philosopher SCHEINER,[1] who made further investigations on the structure of the eye and the refraction in its transparent humors. He verified the fact that optical images are projected on the retina in the case of the eyes of certain beasts, by exposing the back part of the retina so that the image could be seen, and in 1625 in Rome he performed the same experiment on a human eye. He assumed that the refractivities of the aqueous humor and the crystalline lens were the same as those of water and glass, respectively, while the vitreous humor was intermediate between the other two in this respect. Finally HUYGENS[2] constructed an artificial model of the eye, by means of which he demonstrated the principal phenomena of vision, the application of spectacles, etc.

With the exception of a few amateurish and wholly impossible propositions that have been put forth in opposition to it, KEPLER's theory has received practically universal acceptance from the first. For example, N. TH. MÜHLBACH[3] and CAMPBELL[4] denied the existence of the retinal image, and LEHOT[5] advanced the idea that a three-dimensional image of the object is formed within the vitreous humor. PLAGGE[6] worked on the theory that the eye is a mirror

[1] *Oculus.* Inspruck 1619.

[2] *Dioptrica* in *Opera posthuma.* Lugduni 1704. p. 112.

[3] *Inquisitio de visus sensu.* Vindob. 1816.

[4] *Annals of philosophy.* X. 17.—*Deutsches Archiv.* IV. 110.

[5] *Nouvelle Théorie de la Vision.* Paris 1825.

[6] HECKERS *Annalen.* 1830. S. 404.

and that the image used in vision is the reflection in the cornea. J. READE[1] concurred in this opinion and attributed vision to the presence of nerves in the cornea. MAYER[2] opposed PLAGGE's view, but advanced an equally remarkable one of his own, namely, that the retina acts as a concave mirror. Likewise, ANDREW HORN[3] imagined the vitreous humor to be the reflector and the resulting image to act upon the optic nerve.

As to the positions of the cardinal points of the eye, there was some difficulty at first concerning the second focal point. According to calculations based on the measured dimensions and indices of refraction, this point seemed to be beyond the retina. This error was due to using in the calculation the mean index of refraction of the layers of the crystalline lens, which we now know to be incorrect.[4] VALLÉE[5] concluded that it was necessary to assume a gradual increase in the index of refraction of the vitreous humor towards the back of the eye. PAPPENHEIM[6] was willing to admit this explanation, provided even a slight change of the sort can be demonstrated to exist. Until the development of GAUSS's theory, considerable confusion prevailed among physicists and physiologists as to the location of the nodal points of the eye. This was because the theory of optical instruments up to that time had dealt exclusively with systems of refracting surfaces at comparatively negligible distances apart, as, for example, the lenses of the objective of a telescope; whereas in the eye the distances between the refracting surfaces are quite considerable as compared with the focal length of the whole system. Owing to the imperfect development of the theory, there appears to have been some uncertainty as to the proper standpoint from which to attack the problem. Many attempts were made to locate a point on the optical axis of the eye that would correspond to the optical centre of a glass lens; such that a ray directed towards it would not be ultimately deviated by refraction in traversing the ocular media. If it is permissible to consider the two nodal points as coincident, their common position would correspond to the required optical centre. One trouble, especially, was that this point was also confused with the point of intersection of the so-called *lines of sight* drawn from points at different distances in the field of view that appeared to be all in the same line of vision. This point, however, i⸴ essentially different from the nodal point of the eye, and is, in fact, the centre of the entrance-pupil of the eye, as will be shown in the next section. MUNCKE[7] supposed that the two points were identical and located them in the middle of the lens; whereas BARTELS[8] placed them at the centre of the cornea. The place where the straight lines meet that connect the various points of the object with the conjugate points of the retinal image was called by VOLKMANN[9] the *point of intersection of the direction rays*; and, subsequently, after MILE's objections, the *point of intersection of the direction lines*. By means of experiments upon the eyes of white rabbits, he showed that these lines all intersect at a point, and found its location, which necessarily lies between the two nodal points. His result showed that, in the

[1] *Annals of philos.* XV. 260.

[2] MUNCKE, Art. "Gesicht" in GEHLERS *Wörterbuch.* The reference given there is wrong.

[3] *The seat of vision determined.* London 1813.

[4] MOSER in DOVES *Repertorium.* V. 337-349.*—FORBES, *Proc. Edinb. Roy. Soc.* 1849. Dec. p. 251.

[5] *Comptes rendus.* 1845. XIV. 481.

[6] Ibid. XXV. 901.

[7] GEHLERS *physik. Wörterbuch (neu bearb.)* Leipzig 1828. Art. "Gesicht." Bd. IV. 2. S. 1434.*

[8] *Beiträge zur Physiol. d. Gesichtssinns.* Berlin 1834. S. 61.

[9] *Neue Beiträge zur Physiol. d. Gesichtssinns.* Leipzig 1836. Kap. IV.—POGGENDORFFS *Ann.* XXXVII. 342.

rabbit, at least, it was beyond the lens. By a different method he tried to find the same point in the case of the living human eye. Two hair-sights about 6 inches from the eye were viewed through two small peep-holes placed nearer the eye, the latter being so adjusted that both hairs were seen at the same time in the centres of the openings. Each hair and its corresponding peep-hole thus constituted a line of sight. VOLKMANN might therefore have been able to find the point of intersection of the direction lines in this way if it had been possible for the subject to see both hairs through their respective openings at the same time without turning the eye. This is, however, a very difficult thing to do, because the subject can look directly at only one of the hairs at a time, the other being seen indirectly on a less sensitive portion of the retina. The probable result was that the subject looked first at one hair and then at the other, the lines of fixation therefore intersecting at the centre of rotation of the eye; and accordingly this was the point that VOLKMANN took to be the place of intersection of the direction lines.

MILE,[1] KNOCHENHAUER[2] and STAMM[3] took exception to VOLKMANN's conclusions. MILE pointed out that the direction lines and lines of sight are not necessarily identical, and defined the point of intersection of the direction lines as being the centre of the cornea, assuming the effect of refraction by the lens to be negligible. Thence he concluded that the direction lines do not necessarily have to pass through the centre of the blur circle projected on the retina by a luminous point out of focus. KNOCHENHAUER tried to simplify MILE's proof that the coincidence of images in the field is independent of the direction lines, and thereby to avoid the assumption, at that time generally accepted but in fact only approximately true, that the point of intersection of the direction lines is the same for objects at different distances. BUROW[4] also rejected VOLKMANN's conclusions, but used his method to determine the centre of rotation of the eye, and worked out an independent method of finding the point of intersection of the direction lines. This method, however, was not successful, for reasons subsequently given by LISTING.

The first to apply the theoretical work of GAUSS[5] and BESSEL[6] to the optical system of the eye was MOSER,[7] who, from the available data at that time as to the form of the refracting surfaces and the indices of refraction, computed the positions of the nodal points (which, by the way, he called principal points). The values which he found for the distances of these points from the cornea were 3.19 and 3.276 Paris lines (7.18 and 7.37 mm). But since he had assumed BREWSTER's average value of the index of refraction of the crystalline lens (1.3839), which means that the rays from a distant source come to a focus beyond the retina, he concluded that the radius of the cornea should be diminished from 3.39′′′ to 2.88′′′, and on this supposition he deduced the new values 2.835′′′ and 2.890′′′ (6.38 and 6.50 mm) for the distances from cornea to nodal points.

LISTING[8] investigated the properties of the principal points and nodal points of the eye (giving the latter their name), found their approximate positions, and particularly called attention to the fact that if the lens is to be treated as made of some homogeneous material, the index of refraction as-

[1] POGGENDORFFS *Ann.* XLII. 37-71. 235-263.* Reply by VOLKMANN, ibid. XLV. 207 to 226.*

[2] Ibid. XLVI. 248-258.*

[3] Ibid. LVII. 346-382.*

[4] *Beiträge zur Physiologie u. Physik d. menschl. Auges.* Berlin 1841. S. 26-93.

[5] *Dioptrische Untersuchungen.* Göttingen 1841.

[6] *Astronomische Nachrichten.* XVIII. Nr. 415.

[7] DOVE, *Repertorium d. Physik.* V. 337, 373.

[8] *Beitrag zur physiologischen Optik.* Göttingen 1845.

signed to it must exceed the actual index of its densest part. It was then that VOLKMANN[1] made his later attempt, as above mentioned, to find experimentally the positions of the nodal points in living human eyes. Finally, LISTING[2] published a complete mathematical theory of the subject, including a calculation of the numerical data based upon the best measurements available at the time.

1575. FR. MAUROLYCI *Photismi de lumine et umbra ad Perspectivam et radiorum incidentiam facientes.* Venetiis 1575. Messinae 1613.—A later complete edition of his optical writings has the title: FR. MAUROLYCI, *Abbatis Messanensis, theoremata de lumine et umbra, ad Perspectivam et radiorum incidentiam facientia; Diaphanorum partes seu libri tres, in quorum primo de perspicuis corporibus, in secundo de Iride, in tertio de organi visualis structura et conspicillorum formis agitur: Problemata ad Perspectivam et Iridem pertinentia. His accesserunt* CHRISTOPH. CLAVII *e. S. J. notae.* Lugduni 1613.

1583. JO. BAPT. PORTAE *Neap. de refractione Optices parte libri novem.* Neapoli 1583. Liber III-VIII.

1602. *JO. KEPLER *ad Vitellionem paralipomena, quibus astronomiae pars optica traditur.* Francofurti 1604. Cap. V.

1611. KEPLER, *Dioptrice, seu demonstratio eorum, quae visui et visibilibus; propter conspicilla non ita pridem inventa, accidunt.* Augustae Vindelicorum 1611.

1619. C. SCHEINER, *Oculus, sive fundamentum opticum.* Innspruck 1619. London 1652.

1695. HUYGENS ([†]1695), *Opera posthuna. Dioptrica.* Lugduni 1704. p. 112.

1759. W. PORTERFIELD, *A treatise on the eye.* Edinb. 1759. Vol. I. Book 3. Chap. 2*.

1776. J. PRIESTLEYS *Geschichte der Optik;* translated in German by G. S. KLUEGEL. Leipzig 1776 (Early history; calculation of focal lengths, S. 465)*.
       RUMBALL, *Annals of Philos.* II. 376.

1813. ANDREW HORN, *The seat of vision determined.* London 1813.

1816. N. TH. MÜHLBACH, *Inquisitio de visus sensu.* Vindobonae 1816.
       MAGENDIE, *Précis élémentaire de Physiologie.* Paris. Vol. I. p. 59.

1817. CAMPBELL, *Annals of Philos.* X. 17. *Deutsches Archiv.,* IV. 110.
       J. READ, *Annals of Philos.* XV. 260.

1825. C. J. LEHOT, *Nouvelle Théorie de Vision.* 1825.

1828. G. R. TREVIRANUS, *Beiträge zur Anatomie und Physiologie der Sinneswerkzeuge.* Bremen 1828. Kap. I*.
       MUNCKE in GEHLERS *Physikalischem Wörterbuch; neu bearbeitet.* Leipzig 1828. Art. Gesicht. IV. 2. S. 1364*.

1830. PLAGGE, HECKERS *Annalen* 1830. S. 404.

1834. BARTELS, *Beiträge zur Physiolgie des Gesichtssinns.* Berlin 1834. S. 61.

1836. A. W. VOLKMANN, *Untersuchung über den Stand des Netzhautbildchens.* POGGENDORFFS *Ann.* XXXVII. 342*.—*Neue Beiträge zur Physiologie des Gesichtssinns.* Leipzig 1836. Kap. IV.

1837. JOH. MILE, Über die Richtungslinien des Sehens. POGGENDORFFS *Ann.* XLII. 37 and 235*.

1838. VOLKMANN, POGGENDORFFS *Ann.* XLV. 207*. (Reply to above.)

1839. GERLING, Über die Beobachtung von Netzhautbildern. POGGENDORFFS *Ann.* XLVI. 243*.
       KNOCHENHAUER, Über die Richtungsstrahlen oder Richtungslinien beim Sehen. POGGENDORFFS *Ann.* XLVI. 248*.

1841. A. BUROW, *Beiträge zur Physiologie und Physik des menschlichen Auges.* Berlin 1841. S. 16-93*.

1842. VALLÉE, *Comptes rendus.* XIV. 481.
       W. STAMM, Über VOLKMANNS Richtungslinien des Sehens. POGGENSDORFFS *Ann.* LVII. 346*.

---

[1] R. WAGNERS *Handwörterbuch d. Physiologie.* Art. "Sehen." S. 286.*
[2] Ibid., Art. Dioptrik des Auges.

1843. A. W. VOLKMANN, J. MÜLLERS *Archiv. f. Anat. u. Physiol.* 1843. S. 9 (reply to BUROW).

1844. *L. MOSER, Über das Auge, in DOVES *Repertorium d. Physik.* S. 337-349*.

1845. J. B. LISTING, *Beitrag zur physiologischen Optik.* Göttingen 1845 (abstract of *Göttinger Studien*). S. 7-21*.
      L. L. VALLÉE, *Comptes rendus.* XX. 1338.—*Institut.* No. 393. p. 166.

1846. *A. W. VOLKMANN, Art. "Sehen" in R. WAGNERS *Handwörterbuch der Physiologie.* III. 1. S. 281-290*.

1847. F. C. DONDERS, *Holländische Beiträge zu den anat. u. physiol. Wissensch.* I. S. 107-112.

1849. J. D. FORBES, Note respecting the dimensions and refracting power of the eye. *Proceedings Edinb. Roy. Soc.* 1849. p. 251.—SILLIMAN'S *Journal.* (2) XIII. 413.

1851. *J. B. LISTING, Art. "Dioptrik des Auges" in R. WAGNERS *Handwörterbuch d. Physiol.* IV. 451-504*.

1854. H. HELMHOLTZ, GRAEFES *Archiv. für Ophthalmologie.* I. 2. S. 1-74*.

Measurements of the indices of refraction:

1710. HAWKSBEE, *Phil. Transact.* 1710. p. 204.

1785. A. MONRO. II. *On the structure and physiology of fishes.* p. 60.

1801. TH. YOUNG, *Phil. Transact.* 1801. I. 40*.

1818. CHOSSAT, *Bulletin des sc. par la Société philomat. de Paris.* A. 1818. June. p. 294.—*Ann. de ch. et de ph.* VII. p. 217.

1819. D. BREWSTER, *Edinb. Philos. Journ.* 1819. No. 1. p. 47.

1840. CAHOURS et BECQUEREL, *Institut.* 1840. p. 399.

1847. S. PAPPENHEIM, *Comptes rendus.* XXV. 901. — *Arch. d. sc. ph. et natur.* VII. 78. QUESNEL, *Revue scient.* XXXII. 144.

1849. BERTIN, *Comptes rendus.* XXVIII. 447. — *Institut.* 1849. No. 796. p. 105. — *Ann. d. ch. et de ph.* XXVI. 288. — *Arch. d. sc. ph. et nat.* XII. 45. — POGGENDORFFS *Ann.* LXXVI. 611.

1850. ENGEL, *Prager Vierteljahrsschrift für prakt. Heilk.* 1850. I. 152.
      H. MAYER, ibid. 1850. IV. Beilage and 1851. IV. 92.

1852. RYBA, ibid. 1852. II. 95.

1855. W. KRAUSE, *Die Brechungsindizes der durchsichtigen Medien d. menschl. Auges.* Hannover 1855*.

Supplement.—DONDERS gives the following summary of the results of a large number of measurements of the curvature of the cornea at its intersection with the visual axis. The values are given in millimetres.

A. Males

1.	20 under 20 years	7.932
2.	51 under 40 "	7.882
3.	28 over 40 "	7.819
4.	11 over 60 "	7.809

Mean	7.858
Maximum	8.396
Minimum	7.28

B. Women

1.	6 under 20 years	7.720
2.	22 under 40 "	7.799
3.	16 over 40 "	7.799
4.	2 over 60 "	7.607

Mean	7.799
Maximum	8.487
Minimum	7.115

C.   According to Static Refraction

1.   27 Emmetropes.................................7.785
2.   25 Myopes....................................7.874
3.   26 Hypermetropes.............................7.96

1852—61.   L. L. Vallée, Théorie de l'œil. *C. R.* XXXIV, 321–323; 718–720; 720–722;
           789–792; 872–876. XXXV, 679–681. LI, 678–680. LII, 702–703; 1020 to
           1021. *Mém. des savants étrangers.* XII, 204–264. XV, 98–118; 119–140.

1857.   W. Zehender, Über die Brewstersche Methode zur Bestimmung der Bre-
           chungsexponenten flüssiger und festweicher Substanzen. *Archiv für Ophthalmol.*
           III, 2 S. 99.

1858.   N. Lubimoff, Recherches sur la grandeur apparente des objets. *C. R.* XLVII,
           24–27. *Ann. de chimie* (3), LIV. 13–27.

1860.   Breton, Note sur une propriété du cristallin de l'œil humain. *C. R.* L, 498–499.

1864.   Giraud Teulon, Nouvelle étude de la marche des rayons lumineux dans l'œil.
           Ann. d'oculistique, 1864.

—   F. C. Donders, *On the anomalies of accommodation and refraction of the eye.*
           London. p. 38–71.

§11. Blur Circles on the Retina[1]

When light from a luminous point reaches the eye, the part of the
bundle of rays that are admitted through the pupil forms a cone of
rays beyond it, with its circular base in front and with its apex,
representing
the image of
the luminous
point, turned
away from the
incident light.

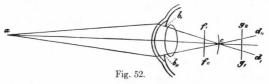

Fig. 52.

Beyond this focus, the rays diverge again. In Fig. 52, the luminous point is supposed to be at *a*, and the pupil is represented by
b,b,,; the rays converge to the point *c*, *cd,* and *cd,,* being the prolongations of the rays *b,c* and *b,,c*, respectively. When the point of
convergence is exactly on the surface of the retina, the luminous
point (*a*) affects just this single point (*c*) of the retina, and thus the
image of *a* is distinct. But when the retina lies a little in front of or
beyond the focus, so as to cut the cone of rays at *f,f,,* or at *g,g,,*, it
will be illuminated, not at one point only, but over a small circular
area corresponding to the cross section of the cone. An area of the
retina thus illuminated by an external luminous point-source is called
a *circle of diffusion* or *blur circle*. The circular form corresponds, of
course, to the roundness of the pupil. If its form or the base of the
cone of incident rays is altered, as may be virtually accomplished by
placing just in front of the cornea an opaque screen having a small
hole of any desired outline whose diameter is less than that of the
pupil, the area of diffusion will assume a correspondingly different
shape. If the spot falls on the central part of the retina, it will be

[1] Consult Appendix III at the end of Part I. G.

geometrically similar to the opening. The small diffusion images formed when the focus is close to the retina present, however, striking exceptions to these rules, and will be discussed later in §14.

The production of blurred images may be easily reproduced experimentally by adjusting a small source of light, or, better still, an illuminated pinhole in a screen, at a suitable distance in front of a convex lens, and catching the light on a white card beyond the lens which can be moved to and fro parallel to its axis. It will be found that a distinct, punctual image is formed only when the card is in a certain definite position; elsewhere it expands into a round spot of light or blur circle. When the luminous object is a bright line, as, for example, a narrow illuminated slit, the circles of diffusion from

Fig. 53.

the various points of this line will overlap, as shown in Fig. 53b, and there will appear on the screen, in place of the sharp line a, a bright figure similar to that of c. When the source of light is a clear-cut, uniformly bright area, the centre of the diffusion image will be uniformly bright, but the outer portions will fade and seem to blend gradually into the brightness of the surroundings.

Diffusion images of this same sort may be projected on the retina of the eye. Naturally, we cannot move the retina arbitrarily to and fro with respect to the lens like the paper card in the above experiment, but we can move the luminous point nearer the eye or farther from it, so that its image moves back and forth in the vitreous humor. As in the case of any optical system of spherical refracting surfaces, the images formed by the eye of objects at different distances lie at different points along the axis. The image of an infinitely distant point lies in the second focal plane, and that of a nearer point lies beyond it. Therefore, if one of these images lies on the retina, it is sharply defined, while the other necessarily produces a blur circle on it. Evidently, therefore, *objects at different distances from the eye cannot be seen distinctly at the same time.* To verify this, one has simply to hold a veil or some other transparent texture about six inches in front of one eye, and about two feet beyond it an open book. He can see at pleasure either the threads of the mesh or the letters of the printed page with perfect distinctness, but he cannot see both distinctly at once. When the threads stand out sharply, the letters are blurred, and *vice versa.* Moreover, if the eye looks steadily in the same direction, first, at the farther object and then at the nearer, it will be noticed that every such change requires a conscious effort.

The experiment may be varied in many ways. Go to a window, for example, and hold a needle vertically about six inches in front of the eye, so that it appears to cross the horizontal window-bar at right angles. If you look at the needle, you will also see the window-bar as an indistinct dark band, or if you look at the window-bar or at the view outside, you will see the needle simply as a blurred vertical band in the field of view. Again, look through a small hole at the more distant objects beyond, and you may see either those objects or the edge of the hole distinctly, but never both at the same time. The first form of the experiment, however, is the most striking and also the best calculated to make it clear that the phenomenon is not due to any change in the direction of vision.

It is to be noticed, in all these cases, that while one may not see clearly two unequally distant objects at once, still they may be seen distinctly one at a time, and that the transition from one to the other is entirely under the control of the observer.

This peculiar process whereby the eye is enabled to see distinctly objects at different distances is called *accommodation* or *adaptation*[1] of the eye to distance.

When the object is far away, a very considerable change of distance will make but slight alteration in the position of its image. Thus, if an eye is accommodated for an infinite distance, the blur circles of object-points even as close as twelve metres say, are so tiny that the distinctness is not seriously impaired. But when the eye is accommodated for near vision, a slight change of distance one way or the other will cause the object to be entirely out of focus. That segment of the visual axis where, for a given state of accommodation, an object can be seen without being indistinct is what J. Czermak has called the "line of accommodation." The length of this segment increases with its remoteness from the eye, and becomes infinite when its distance is very great.

These effects may be easily verified by keeping the eyes fixed on a needle or similar object erected an inch or more in front of a printed page. If the observer moves his eye as near the needle as he can without being unable to see it distinctly, the page appears blurred; but if the observer now moves his eye away from the needle, still fixing it steadily, the printed page becomes clearer and clearer.

The reason we are able to "sight," and to tell whether two points at different distances are exactly in line with the eye, is just because the blur circle of a distant object is very small when the eye is accommodated for another distant object. Strictly speaking, only one of the points sighted can be seen distinctly at one time, while the others

[1] The latter term is no longer used in this sense. G.

appear more or less blurred; and the exact alignment of two points may be obtained by simply getting the sharp image of one point into apparent coincidence with the centre of the blur circle of the other. A line passing through two such apparently coincident points is called a *line of sight*. All lines of sight intersect at one point within the eye, namely, at the centre of the image of the pupil formed by the cornea, known as the *point of intersection of the lines of sight*.[1]

That the change taking place during the process of accommodation is an actual alteration of the optical image itself, and not simply a mode of sensation of the retina, as some physiologists have supposed, may be proved in the most convincing manner by the use of the ophthalmoscope. With this instrument, which will be described in §16, the fundus of the eye can be seen distinctly, including the retina with its blood vessels and the images projected on it. If the patient's eye is fixed on a given object, what we find is that the image of a light at the same distance away will be sharply focused on the retina, and at the same time the veins and other anatomical details of the retina will be clearly visible in the vicinity of this bright image. Now suppose the light is moved much nearer; its image will become indistinct, but the details of the retinal membrane remain as sharply defined as before. Attempts at seeing the changes of the retinal images in dead eyes from which the rear portions of the sclerotica and choroid have been removed or in the living eyes of white rabbits, whose sclerotica is nearly transparent, are both unsatisfactory and likely to fail, because the images thus observed are usually not exact enough to enable the investigator to recognize minute variations in them. Even in a living eye noticeable alterations of the image, due to accommodation, do not occur unless the object itself is comparatively small and precise like a thread or a printed word. Large objects may be still recognized by form even when the accommodation is not correct.

But on the retina of a dead eye all the finer details are effaced, as will be seen by artificially magnifying the image until it looks to the observer as large as it would have seemed to the observed eye, when its retina was still sensitive.

These accommodation phenomena and the varying positions of the ray-focus with respect to the retina are still better demonstrated by an experiment due to SCHEINER. Two pinholes are made in a card at a distance apart less than the diameter of the pupil of the eye. With one eye closed, the observer looks through both holes at a small

---

[1] ¶This point coincides, therefore, with the centre of the entrance-pupil of the eye. (J. P. C. S.)

  Since the act of sighting requires central visual acuity, we are justified in speaking only of one line of sight; which is the one along the ray that after refraction in the eye proceeds to the *fovea centralis*. G.

object sharply delineated against a contrasting background, for example, at a needle held in front of a bright window. The needle should be adjusted at right angles to the line joining the two holes. If the eye is focused on the needle itself, it appears single; but if it is focused on something else, nearer or farther away, the needle appears double. In the former case, one of the openings may be covered with the finger without producing any effect except a darkening of the whole field. But when the needle is seen double, one of the images will disappear when one of the holes is closed. Thus, if the eye is focused on an object beyond the needle, the image that vanishes is the one on the opposite side from the hole that is closed; whereas if the eye is focused on an object nearer than the needle, the image that vanishes will be on the same side as the hole that is closed. If any difficulty is experienced in accommodating the eye without having definite objects to look at, it is a good plan to use two pins, a vertical one about six inches away and a horizontal one about two feet away, and to look at one in order to see the other double, adjusting the card so that the line joining the holes is always placed at right angles to the needle that is to be seen double.

Now suppose three holes are made in the card, all within an area whose diameter is less than that of the pupil; then there will be three images of the needle. If the holes are arranged as in Fig. 54*a*, and if the eye is accommodated for a point nearer than the needle, its three images will appear as shown in *b*, with their knobs in the same relative positions as the holes. But if the accommodation is for a point beyond the needle, the images will be reversed, as in *c*, so that their knobs form an inverted pattern of the holes. It makes no difference whether a needle is used against a bright background, or some bright object against a dark background, or an illuminated hole or slit in an opaque screen; the results are always the same.

Fig. 54.

The explanation of these effects is easily found by making corresponding experiments with a glass lens. In Fig. 55, *b* represents a convex lens in front of which there is an opaque screen with two holes in it at *e* and *f*. Rays diverging from a luminous point *a* are focused by the lens on the other side of it at the point *c*. Consequently, all the rays of the two bundles that go through the openings *e* and *f* will meet at *c*; and hence if a white card be placed perpendicular to the axis of the lens at *c*, there will appear on it merely a single bright spot, which is the image of *a*. But if the card is moved either way so as to come into the position *mm* or *ll*, the two bundles of rays will fall on it separately, and two bright spots will appear.[1] We have only to imagine the glass lens replaced by the optical system of the eye and the white card by the retina. If the two pencils converge on the retina, only one image is seen; if before or beyond it, there are two. The position of the card at *mm* corresponds to the accommodation of the eye for an object farther than *a*, and the position at *ll* for a nearer object. There is one apparent contradiction. In the experiment with the glass lens, when the upper opening *e* is covered, it is the upper spot on *m*, or the lower spot on *l*, that disappears; and this seems at first sight to be exactly the reverse of what occurs in the eye. The discrepancy is easily explained. For it must be remembered that the retinal image is always inverted, and that the image of what appears

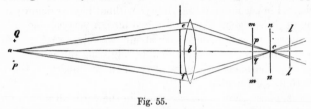

Fig. 55.

to us as the higher of two objects really lies lower on the retina, and *vice versa*. When, therefore, the retina, supposed to be at *m*, intercepts light coming from *a* at two places *p* and *q* on opposite sides of the axis, the impression produced on the observer is that *p*, which is above the axis, is due to an object *P* lying below the axis·in the field of view, and that *q*, which is below the axis, is due to an object *Q* lying above the axis. Consequently, if the opening *e* is closed, the effect on the retina at *p* ceases and causes the observer to suppose that the object at *P* has been extinguished. It is just the reverse when the eye is focused for an object nearer than *a*, in which case the retina corresponds to the card placed at *ll*.

Similar results are obtained with a screen perforated with three openings, as in Fig. 54*a*. There will be three bright spots on the white card if it be placed either at *m* or at *l;* if at *m*, the spots will be arranged in the same manner as the pin-holes, if at *l*, in the reverse order. The same apparent contradiction occurs in comparing this with the eye, and is explained in the same manner.

If a screen with one pin-hole in it is moved laterally up or down in front of the glass lens (Fig. 55), the bright spot at *c* will remain stationary when the card is placed at *nn;* but when the

---

[1] ¶L. D. WELD, Some Precise Methods of Focusing Lenses. *School Science and Math.*, XVIII, p. 547 (1918); in which a modification of this principle is given as a simple method of finding the focus of a lens. (J. P. C. S.)

card is at *mm* in front of *c*, the spot moves on the card up or
down just in the same way as the opening; and when the card is
at *ll* beyond *c*, the spot moves up or down just opposite to the way
the hole moves.   Likewise, if the eye be directed, through a small hole
in a card, towards a needle and accommodated for a more distant
point in the same line, any slight lateral movement of the card will
result in the apparent displacement of the pin in the opposite direction; but if the accommodation be for a point nearer than the needle,
the displacement will be in the same direction.   These phenomena
are easily explained, with reference to Fig. 55, imagining that the
perforated screen has only one opening which is situated first at *e*
and then at *f*.

A screen with a narrow opening in it may be placed in front of the
eye to enable
it to get a dis-
tinct view of
an object for
which the eye
is not accom-
modated. In
such case the
cone of rays
entering the
eye has a very

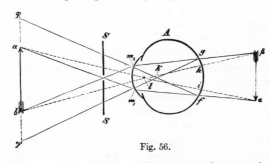

Fig. 56.

small aperture and a correspondingly small cross section anywhere
along its route, so that the blur circles on the retina will be small also.

An object held close in front of the eye gives a blurred image; but
if it is viewed through a small opening, the image gets more distinct,
as above stated, and also appears larger.   The apparent magnification
increases as the opening is moved away from the eye.   These phenomena may be explained by reference to the diagram in Fig. 56; where
a and *b* represent two points of the luminous object, *SS* the perforated
screen, and *A* the eye.   The only rays that reach the eye from *a* and
b are am_1 and bm_2, respectively.   If *aβ* represents the image of *ab*
formed by the optical system of the eye, these rays am_1, bm_2 proceed
after their refraction towards *a* and *β*, and meet the retina at *f* and *g*,
respectively.   Connect each of these latter points by straight lines
with the nodal point of the eye, designated by *k;* these lines correspond
to rays which seem to enter the eye from the points *γ* and *φ* where
they intersect the plane of the object; and the resultant sensation on
the retina is naturally interpreted as corresponding to an object *γφ*,
larger therefore than the real object *ba*.

As the perforated screen S is moved from the eye towards the object, evidently the points m_1, m_2, and likewise the lines m_1a, $m_2\beta$ that determine the positions of the points f and g on the retina will recede from the axis; and accordingly the retinal image fg becomes larger than before.

If the screen is removed, each point of the object will be reproduced by a blur circle on the retina. The centres of the blur circles corresponding to a and b will then be nearer each other on the retina than f and g, where the images of a and b appeared when the screen was in place. The centre of the blur circle is determined by the chief ray of the bundle of rays, that is, by the ray which goes through the centre (l) of the pupil. The straight lines $a\alpha$, $b\beta$, intersecting at l, meet the retina at i and h, which are, therefore, the centres of the blur circles corresponding to the points a and b when the screen is removed. The distance ih is evidently less than fg.

On the other hand, if one looks through a small opening towards a distant object with the eye accommodated for near vision, the object will appear diminished in size in proportion as the opening is farther from the eye.

The range of distances for which the human eye can accommodate varies greatly with the individual. The limits of this range are called the *near point* and *far point of accommodation*. In normal eyes the near point is usually about four or five inches away, while the far point is very much farther, perhaps sometimes even infinitely far away. However, it seems to be very unusual for the far point to be at an infinite distance, even in the case of persons who live in the open and are accustomed to look only at distant objects. People almost always describe a ray-shaped figure as a star, and the fact that it appears so to most persons indicates that that is the way a star looks to them; which shows that their eyes are not accommodated for infinity, as will be explained in §14.[1]

A *near-sighted* or *myopic* eye is one for which the far point is a short distance away, sometimes only a few inches from the eye; the near point being, of course, even closer. A *far-sighted* or *presbyopic* eye, on the other hand, is one for which the near point is quite a little distance away, perhaps several feet from the eye; but the far point does not generally seem to have receded to the same relative extent, but rather to have remained stationary. Thus, the amplitude of

---

[1] ¶The argument here proves nothing. Even if geometrical optics alone were competent to decide the intricate questions that are involved in the appearance of a star, a sufficient answer to the above reasoning would be to remind the reader that the image on the retina is never absolutely punctual in the sense of point-to-point correspondence; and that a luminous point for which the eye was able to accommodate, might easily look like a star. (J. P. C. S.)

accommodation of the eye is greatly reduced, that is, the capacity of varying its refracting power is perhaps almost entirely gone. In certain exceptional cases where either the eye has become malformed by disease, or the crystalline lens has been extracted in the operation for cataract, the eye is so far-sighted that it is only able to focus on the retina a bundle of converging incident rays and requires, therefore, a weak convex lens to see distinctly an object at infinity. Near-sightedness is usually the result of occupation or habits requiring the close and minute examination of small objects. Far-sightedness is more commonly met with in old age, hence the Greek name presbyopia (from πρεσβυς meaning an old man). Moreover, among sailors, shepherds, hunters and other persons whose attention is concentrated chiefly on remote objects, there are cases where the eye is unable to accommodate for near vision and seems to have become incapacitated by lack of practice. This defect is commonly remedied by the use of spectacles. Concave glasses are used to correct near-sightedness by bringing the image of a distant object so near the eye that it is not farther than the far point. On the other hand, a far-sighted individual needs a convex lens which will produce an image of a near object farther away where the eye can be accommodated to see it.

When the eye is immersed under water, the refraction at the cornea becomes almost negligible, and the crystalline lens by itself is unable to focus the image on the retina; and now the eye is, to so speak, extremely far-sighted and requires a powerful convex spectacle glass to discern clearly anything at all.

In order to calculate the size of a blur circle on the retina, it should be remarked in the first place that all rays which outside the eye are aimed at the apparent pupil (which is the image of the pupil as seen through the cornea)[1] pass through the real pupil after having been refracted at the cornea, and that they proceed in the vitreous humor as if they had come from the virtual image[2] of the pupil in the lens. This follows immediately from the theory of optical images. A given point of the actual pupil and the corresponding point of its image in the cornea are conjugate points so far as the refraction at the cornea is concerned. Rays originating at any point of the actual pupil and emerging from the eye appear to be coming from the image of that point; and, conversely, rays proceeding in the air and converging towards a point of the apparent pupil must, after refraction at the cornea, come to a focus at the corresponding point of the actual pupil.

In LISTING's schematic eye the iris is supposed to be half a millimetre in front of the anterior surface of the lens, and accordingly its

---

[1] The *entrance-pupil* as it is now called. G.

[2] The *exit-pupil*. G.

image in the crystalline lens is found to be 0.055 mm beyond the
iris itself and magnified in the ratio of 16 to 15. If, however, the pupil
is supposed to be in contact with the anterior surface of the lens, as
is more natural, the enlargement is found to be only about 1/18
(3/53, to be exact), and the image is 0.113 mm beyond the pupil.
Retaining the other data of LISTING's schematic eye, we must,
therefore, put the distance of the lenticular image of the pupil from
the cornea equal to 18.534 mm. On the other hand, this same pupil
is magnified by the cornea by 1/7 (13/90, to be exact) and appears to
be 0.578 mm in front of its actual position.

The magnitudes of blur circles on the central part of the retina
may be found now as follows. In Fig. 57 let the straight line gf
represent the optical axis, and let the straight line gq perpendicular to gf

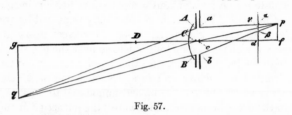

Fig. 57.

represent an object in front of the eye, whose image in the eye is fp.
Since only a small portion of the retina in the vicinity of the axis is
to be considered, it may be represented by a straight line da perpendicular to the axis. Moreover, let the image of the pupil in the lens
and its image in the cornea be represented by ba and BA, perpendicular
to the axis at c and C, respectively. The rays ap and bp, coming from
the edge of the (exit) pupil, intersect the retina at a and β, and $a\beta$,
therefore, is the diameter of the blur circle on the retina corresponding
to the object-point q. By geometry, since ab and ad are parallel,

$$ap : ap = ab : a\beta$$
$$ap : ap = cf : df,$$

and therefore $$a\beta = \frac{ab \cdot df}{cf} \qquad . \qquad . \qquad . \qquad . \qquad . \qquad . \qquad . \qquad . \qquad (1a)$$

If the retinal plane coincides with the second focal plane of the eye,
and if D designates the position of the first focal point, as in equation (8),
§9, let us put $CD = H_1$, $cd = H_2$, $Cg = h_1$ and $cf = h_2$ (instead of h_{m+1});
so that we may write immediately:

$$\frac{H_1}{h_1} + \frac{H_2}{h_2} = 1,$$

or $$\frac{H}{h_1} = \frac{h_2 - H_2}{h_2} = \frac{df}{cf},$$

and hence $$a\beta = ab \cdot \frac{H_1}{h_1}. \qquad \cdots \qquad \cdots \qquad \cdots \qquad (1b)$$

If c designates the centre of the image of the pupil in the lens, that is, if $bc = ca$, the point γ where the straight line cp meets the retina is the centre of the blur circle.   For since

$$ac:bc = a\gamma:\beta\gamma,$$
$$ac = bc,$$

consequently, $$a\gamma = \beta\gamma.$$

Accordingly, the ray that proceeds to the centre of the blur circle is the ray in the vitreous humor that comes from the centre of the so-called exit-pupil of the eye.   In the anterior chamber of the eye this same ray goes through the centre of the real pupil, and its prolongation in the air goes through the centre of the so-called entrance-pupil.[1]

One result of this is, that if the centres of the blur circles on the retina corresponding to two points at unequal distances from the eye coincide, the ray proceeding from the centre of the exit-pupil to this common centre on the retina must belong to both bundles of rays.   The part of this common ray which lies outside the eye must necessarily pass through both luminous points and its prolongation must go through the centre of the entrance-pupil of the eye.   Even if one of the blur circles on the retina contracts to a single point at the centre of the other, the above statements will still be correct.

When two points at different distances are aligned with each other as when we "sight" from one to the other, the image of one falls on the retina at the centre of the blur circle of the other; or, supposing both points are indistinct, the centres of their blur circles coincide. The straight line connecting such a pair of points is what we have already called a *line of sight*.   As just explained, it must coincide with the ray that is aimed at the centre of the entrance-pupil, so that this centre is therefore the point of intersection of all lines of sight.

This subject is closely related to the *visual angle*.   When it is said that objects subtending equal visual angles have the same apparent size, the common vertices of the angles must be at the point of intersection of the lines of sight.   However, it is usual to assume that the vertex of the visual angles is at the point of intersection of the direction lines, that is, at the first nodal point.   On the other hand, if the extremities of the object are viewed in succession one after the other, the vertex of the visual angle in this case should be taken at the centre

---

[1] ¶Although the terms "entrance-pupil" and "exit-pupil" were suggested by ABBE long after the first edition of HEMHOLTZ's *Optik* was published, and, of course, do not occur in the original text, they are employed in the translation. Incidentally, it may be noted here that HUYGENS in his *Dioptrica* constantly makes use of the same ideas as conveyed by these terms. (J. P. C. S.)

of rotation of the eye. Of course, when the object is very far away, these distinctions do not affect the visual angle, but they are not unimportant when the object is near by.

Appended below is a brief table, computed by LISTING for his schematic eye on the assumption that the retina coincides with the second focal plane of the eye and that the pupil is 4 mm in diameter. In this table l_1 denotes the distance of the luminous point in front of the first focal plane, l_2 the distance of the image beyond the retina, and z the diameter of the blur circle. The calculation is based on equation (8c), §9, namely,

$$l_1 l_2 = F_1 F_2$$

and on equation (1a) §11. The product $F_1 F_2$ in LISTING's schematic eye is 301.26, or 300 in round numbers, the distances being expressed in mm.

l_1 in metres	l_2 in mm	z in mm
∞	0	0
65	0.005	0.0011
25	0,012	0.0027
12	0.025	0.0056
6	0.050	0.0112
3	0.100	0.0222
1.5	0.200	0.0443
0.75	0.40	0.0825
0.375	0.80	0.1616
0.188	1.60	0.3122
0.094	3.20	0.5768
0.088	3.42	0.6484

This table shows how little the position of the image varies as long as the object is far away, and how rapidly it recedes beyond the retina when the object is near at hand and comes nearer and nearer.

Various instruments called *optometers* have been devised for measuring the range of accommodation of the eye.

Here may be mentioned first the simple, every-day method of distinguishing near-sight and far-sight by finding how far off the letters on a printed page or details of some other suitable object can be seen most conveniently. Of course, no great accuracy can be attained in this way. Printed letters are never so small as not to be legible over a considerable range of accommodation. For example, the author can read print like that on this page at a distance of at least 13 inches, with his eyes accommodated for his far point 3 feet away. Again, not being able to accommodate nearer than 3.6 inches, he can read the same print when it is only 2.7 inches from his eye. Another thing to be noted here is that the apparent size of an object is bigger when it is brought near the eye, so that, other things being equal, its details can be more clearly made out than when it is farther away. Thus, tiny objects which are hard to see are sometimes examined even nearer than the near point of the eye, because the larger apparent size may more than compensate for the slight indistinctness of the details, and it may be better seen than it could be with exact accommodation under a smaller visual angle. It is evident that in order to use this method for measuring the range of accommodation, we must take different objects for different distances, each of them being just large enough to be recognized distinctly when the eye is accommodated for that particular distance.

PORTERFIELD[1] was the first to propose using SCHEINER's experiment for measuring the range of accommodation distances, and designed an optometer on this principle, which was afterwards improved by THOMAS YOUNG.[2] The latter uses a fine white thread stretched on the black surface of a graduated bar. One end of the thread is close to the eye, which looks along the thread through two small peepholes or slits in an opaque screen, and sees the thread as a pair of straight lines which intersect each other at the point for which the eye is accommodated. This point may be located without difficulty, and its distance from the eye is the distance of accommodation of the eye at that particular instant. The method may be modified by using any other small objects whose distances from the eye can be varied. The objects chosen for the experiment must be small enough to be just distinctly visible through the holes in the screen, as, for example, slender needles against a bright background, or fine holes and slits in dark screens. The eye must be sure to look through both openings at once, otherwise errors are liable to be made. The field of view in these experiments is contracted to the comparatively large blurred images of the two apertures, which partly overlap each other as shown in Fig. 58, *a* and *b*. Double images of a needle, as indicated at *g*, can be seen only in the bright middle region *c* that is common to both openings, but not on either side in any part of the field that corresponds to one aperture alone. In this latter region the image is always

Fig. 58.

single, as at *h*; which is the reason why persons sometimes have difficulty in succeeding with the experiments unless they have practised with the apparatus.

Another similar method for finding the range of accommodation and especially for ascertaining the far point is more accurate, in the writer's opinion, than that of looking through two openings. Daylight or light from a candle flame is admitted through a small opening in a screen. To an eye not accommodated for it a small point of light like this looks like a star with five or six rays (see §14 below), whereas, when the eye is properly accommodated, it appears as a fairly well defined bright spot even if it is not uniformly round. Now move a screen slowly from one side in front of the pupil; and what generally happens in this case is that the pattern of light that is seen begins to fade away on one side, and this occurs on the same side as that from which the screen is interposed, provided the eye is accommodated for a point nearer than the luminous point, but on the opposite side if the eye is focused for a point beyond the source of light. But if the eye is accommodated for the luminous point, the image gets uniformly darker all over, or else it is eclipsed

[1] An Essay concerning the Motions of our Eyes. *Edinb. medical Essays.* Vol. I. p. 423. IV. 185 (1747).

[2] *Phil. Transactions.* 1801 P. I. p. 34.

in some irregular way, as for example, by closing in from both top and bottom when the shutter is introduced from one side.[1]

An easier way than SCHEINER's, especially for an inexperienced observer, which depends on the chromatic aberration of the eye, will be described in §13.

RUETE's optometer is designed to insure against intentional deception on the part of the person examined. It is a box-shaped hood through which passes a tube. The patient looks with one eye through the tube at a book, only a few words of which can be seen, and whose distance he has no means of estimating except by the accommodation of the eye itself. Various sizes of type are used and at various distances; and any attempt at deception is practically certain to involve the subject in self-contradictions.

HASNER's optometer consists of a board mounted horizontally on a tripod, provided at one end with a mask fitting over the upper part of the face, in order to hold the eyes steadily in one position. The board has a graduated scale, to measure the distance from the eyes, and another scale also to register the angle of convergence of the two eyes when they are directed towards any point along its length. The instrument is intended to facilitate measurements of the range of accommodation and various experiments concerning the phenomena of single and double binocular vision.

Artificial eye-models for the demonstration of KEPLER's theory of vision and the use of spectacles have been described by HALLER,[2] HUYGENS,[3] WOLF,[4] ADAMS[5] and KRIES.[6]

KEPLER[7] was not only the first to give a correct interpretation of the refraction of light in the eye, but he was also aware of the necessity of an accommodation of the eye for different distances and supposed that blurred vision was due to the lack of proper accommodation. SCHEINER[8] described the phenomena that occur in imperfect accommodation when the observer looks through two holes in a screen. Explanations of these experiments were given by DE LA HIRE,[9] who, however, denied the possibility of accommodation for different distances; and later by J. DE LA MOTTE[10] and PORTERFIELD,[11] the latter of whom also corrected DE LA HIRE's erroneous conclusions. MILE[12] first noted the singular apparent motions of an object lying outside the range of accommodation of the eye, as seen through a narrow aperture which is itself in motion; and these phenomena were afterwards described more fully by H. MAYER,[13] as connected with the theory of accommodation. A complete discussion of the cause of blur circles on the retina, their overlapping, etc., was given by JURIN.[14]

As to the use of spectacles, there is a place in PLINY's *Naturalis historia*[15] which seems to be a reference to them. He mentions certain concave emeralds

---

[1] ¶The description of these phenomena appears to have been first given by CZERMAK. (J. P. C. S.)

[2] *Elem. Physiolog.* V. 469.

[3] *Dioptrica.* Lugduni 1704. p. 112.

[4] *Nützliche Versuche.* III. 481.

[5] *Essay on vision.* London 1792.

[6] German translation of the preceding essay. Gotha 1794.

[7] *Paralipomena.* p. 200.

[8] *Oculus.* p. 37 and 41. Similar experiments, p. 32 and 49.

[9] *Journal des Sçavans*, 1685; and in *Accidens de la vue.* 1693.

[10] *Versuche und Abhandl. der Gesellschaft in Danzig.* Bd. II. S. 290.

[11] *On the eye.* Vol. I. Book 3. Chap. 3.

[12] POGGENDORFFS *Ann.* XLII. 40.

[13] *Prager Vierteljahrsschrift.* 1851. Bd. IV. S. 92.

[14] *Essay on distinct and indistinct vision.* SMITH's *Optics.* Cambridge 1738.

[15] L. XXXVII. c. 5.

that had a curious property of "converging the vision" (*visum colligere*), and for that reason should never be cut. The emperor NERO, who was near-sighted (PLINY, I. II, c.34), is said to have viewed gladiatorial combats through an emerald of this kind. Subsequently, from the beginning of the 14th century we come across accounts in which spectacles are mentioned as a new discovery. A Florentine nobleman, SALVINUS ARMATUS, who died in 1317, is referred to on his epitaph as the inventor of spectacles.[1] ALEXANDER DE SPINA, a monk of Pisa, who died in 1313, is said to have seen a pair of spectacles worn by somebody who made a secret of the invention; but they were imitated and used by many persons.[2] MAUROLYCUS (1494 to 1575) afterwards tried to explain the theory of such lenses, but the explanation, like his theory of vision, was incorrect. He supposed that the visual rays, each emanating from a separate part of the object, are made more convergent or more divergent by the lens, as in fact is the case only for rays proceeding from a single point of the object; and it was not until KEPLER began to study the question that a correct and complete theory of the use of spectacles was published.[3]

Literature:

1575. FR. MAUROLYCUS, *De lumine et umbra.* Lib. III.

1583. J. B. PORTA, *De refractione.* Lib. VIII.

1604. J. KEPLER, *Paralipomena ad Vitellionem.* p. 200.

1619. SCHEINER, *Oculus.* p. 32–49.

1685. DE LA HIRE, *Journal des Sçavans.* Ann. 1685. — *Accidens de la vue* 1693. §II. (Consequences of SCHEINER's experiment.)

1709. DE LA HIRE, *Mém. de l'Acad. de Paris.* An.1709. p. 95 (Vision in water).

. . . . DE LA MOTTE, *Versuche und Abhandlungen der Gesellschaft in Danzig.* Bd. II. S.290. (Theory of SCHEINER's experiment.)

1738. JURIN, *Essay on distinct and indistinct vision in* SMITH, *System of optics.* Cambridge 1738.

1759. PORTERFIELD, *On the eye.* p. 389–423.* (Theory of SCHEINER's experiment.)

1792. G. ADAMS, *An essay on vision.* London. 2d edition, translated in German by F. KRIES. Gotha 1794. (Particularly about spectacles.)

1800. J. BISCHOFF, *Praktische Abhandlung der Dioptrik.* Stuttgart. 2. Aufl. (About spectacles.)

1801. TH. YOUNG, *Philos. Transact.* P. I. p. 34. (Optometer.)

1810. GILBERT in his *Annalen d. Physik.* XXXIV. 34 and XXXVI. 375. (Vision in water.)

. . . . WOLLASTON, Improved periscopic spectacles. *Phil. Mag.* XVII. NICHOLSON's *Journal,* VII. 143. 241.

. . . . JONES on WOLLASTON's *spectacles.* NICHOLSON's *Journal.* VII. 1902 and VIII. 38.

1821. G. TAUBER, Anweisung für auswärtige Personen, wie dieselben aus dem optisch-okulistischen Institute zu Leipzig Augengläser bekommen können. Leipzig. 3 Aufl.

1824. MUNCKE, Über Sehen unter Wasser. POGGENDORFFS *Ann.* II. 257. GEHLERS *physik. Wörterbuch,* neu bearb. Leipzig 1828. Art. Gesicht. S. 1383–1386.* About spectacles, see also 1403–1410.*

1825. PURKINJE, *Zur Physiologie der Sinne.* II. S. 128.*

1830. HOLKE, *Disquisitio de acie oculi dextri et sinistri in mille ducentis hominibus.* Lipsiae.

1837. J. MILE in POGGENDORFFS *Ann.* XLII. S. 51.*

1840. HENLE in J. MÜLLERS *Lehrbuch der Physiologie.* Bd. II. S. 339–341.*

---

[1] VOLKMANNS *Nachrichten von Italien.* Bd. I. S. 542. The tablet in the Church of Mary Magdalene at Florence has since been removed, but it read:

> *Qui giace Salvino degli Armati*
> *Inventore degli Occhiali.*
> *Dio gli perdoni le peccata.*

[2] SMITH's *Optics. Remarks* p. 12.

[3] *Paralipomena.* p. 200.

1845. Young's *optometer*. *Phil. Mag.* XXVI. 436.
185C. J. Czermak, *Verhandl. d. Würzburger physik. Gesellschaft.* Bd. I. S. 184.
1851. Peytal, Nouvel instrument à l'usage de la vue myope. *Institut.* No. 841. p. 53.
       No. 857. p. 180.
       H. Mayer, *Prager Vierteljahrsschrift für prakt. Heilkunde.* XXXII. S. 92.*
       v. Hasner, ibid. S. 166. (Optometer.)
1852. Th. Ruete, *Der Augenspiegel und das Optometer.* Göttingen. S. 28.*
1854. Jo. Czermak, *Wiener Sitzungsberichte.* Bd. XII. S. 322.*

Supplement

The theory of the individual variations of the refraction of the eye has been very thoroughly worked out by Donders in his valuable treatises on this subject, which has resulted already in the most useful applications in ophthalmic practice, not simply directly for the correction of defective vision by means of glasses, but also indirectly for the relief of a whole series of obscure ailments that are due to imperfect refraction and accommodation.

The great contribution made by Donders consists particularly in the distinction which he has made between the phenomena pertaining to *abnormal degrees of refraction* when the eye is passive and relaxed and those which depend on the amplitude of *accommodation* and hence on refractive conditions brought about by muscular effort.

The idea that the passive eye is accommodated for far vision, which is very decidedly supported by the evidence of the subjective sensation, and which is also at the basis of the argument as presented above, is carried still further by Donders, who has pointed out that, when the sphincter of the pupil and the accommodation have been paralyzed by certain mydriatics, particularly by atropin (the alkaloid of belladonna), the eye is automatically adjusted for its far point, without being able to alter its state of refraction. If there were some muscular mechanism whose contraction could reinforce the accommodation for far vision, we should be forced to admit the very unlikely assumption that this muscle had not been paralyzed by the atropin but was subjected to a sort of permanent spasm.

Moreover, pathological observations indicate that whenever the mechanism of the eye becomes affected by paralysis of the *nervus oculomotorius*, the eye invariably is focused all the time for its normal far point. And there is no case on record to show that when the movements of the eye are paralyzed the far point had come nearer the eye.

Accordingly, the maximum distance of accommodation occurs when the eye is relaxed. The normal position of the far point may be considered as infinitely distant.[1] Donders uses the term *emmetropic*

[1] ¶The author here records a change in his views on this subject, as previously expressed. (J. P. C. S.)

(from ἔμμετρος, *modum tenens*, and ὤψ, *oculus*) to describe an eye of this sort, so as to avoid the vagueness of the word "normal" and the expression "normal vision." An emmetropic eye may be subject to various defects, and is not necessarily "normal" by any means.

If the far point of the eye is at a finite distance in front of it, it is said to be *brachymetropic* or *myopic*, the latter being the more ancient name for this state of refraction. A myopic eye cannot focus rays on the retina unless they were originally divergent. On the other hand, an eye which can focus on the retina not simply parallel but even convergent incident rays is said to be *hypermetropic*.[1]

Without the aid of spectacles, a myope cannot focus for distant objects; and so he is at considerable disadvantage as compared with an emmetrope. On the other hand, an hypermetrope has always to exert some accommodation in order to see any actual object distinctly, which frequently results in numerous, sometimes distressing, symptoms of fatigue. Both defects therefore impair the efficiency of vision, and hence DONDERS classified them together under the name *ametropia*.

More often than not these defects are due to abnormal length of the axis of the eye,[2] which is shorter in an hypermetropic than in an emmetropic eye. The matter appears to be closely connected also with the position of the centre of rotation of the eye, which is too far back in a myopic eye and too far forward in an hypermetropic eye. As a general thing there are no abnormal curvatures of the cornea and crystalline lens that can account for ametropia.[3]

In order to ascertain the exact condition of an ametropic eye, it is necessary to determine the range of adjustment that can be produced in its refraction by active muscular effort. For example, if we compare an emmetropic eye which can be accommodated for objects anywhere from an infinite distance to six inches with a very myopic eye whose range is only between six inches and three inches, naturally, it would be inferred at once that the latter has a much narrower margin of accommodation than the former. But suppose now that the myopic eye uses a concave spectacle lens six inches in focus, so as to enable it to see clearly to infinity; this eye has then the same actual range of accommodation as the other, namely from six inches to infinity. The action of the spectacle lens in this illustration is to form a virtual image nearer than the actual object, so that an object six inches away, for instance, appears to be only three inches, and thus

---

[1] ¶The far point of an hypermetropic eye is at a finite distance behind or beyond the eye, that is, its far point is "virtual." (J. P. C. S.)

[2] ¶"Axial ametropia." (J. P. C. S.)

[3] ¶"Curvature ametropia," whereas abnormalities of the indices of refraction of the ocular media are included under what is called "indicial ametropia." (J. P. C. S.)

is brought to the near point where it can be seen distinctly by the myopic eye here supposed.

Accordingly, the interval between the far point and the near point does not afford a method of comparison of the amplitudes of accommodation of two far-sighted eyes; and in order to compare them with each other we must first equalize their refractions by the use of suitable lenses.

If a spectacle glass is not to magnify or reduce the objects viewed through it, its second principal point should coincide with the first nodal point of the eye.[1] This could be accomplished, if it were worth while, by using a thick meniscus lens (see latter part of §9). Let F and N denote the distances of the far point and near point of the eye, and A the distance of the nearest point for which the eye can accommodate when provided with a lens of negative focal length F, all these distances being measured from the first nodal point of the eye; then

$$\frac{1}{A} = \frac{1}{N} - \frac{1}{F}$$

and the amplitude of accommodation, according to DONDERS, is measured by the reciprocal of A.[2]

The amplitude of accommodation, therefore, is measured in units of curvature, that is, in reciprocals of the units of length. The unit of length corresponding to the spectacle numbers that are in vogue at present is the inch, either Paris inch or Prussian inch; and we might call the reciprocal unit a "Zolltel."[3] For instance, an emmetropic eye

---

[1] ¶The statement in the text is not entirely clear: no actual spectacle glasses are used in this way. The condition that the so-called "spectacle magnification" shall be unity requires that the second principal point of the correction glass and the first focal point of the eye shall be coincident; which until quite recently was supposed to be the proper adjustment of the glass in front of the eye; but in modern "Punktal" lenses and similar types of spectacle glasses, this condition is not fundamental and is only approximately satisfied. (J. P. C. S.)

[2] ¶The amplitude of accommodation, as defined by DONDERS, is usually given by the formula

$$A = \frac{1}{p} - \frac{1}{r},$$

where p and r denote the far and near point distances, respectively, both measured from the first principal point of the eye, and A (not the reciprocal of A) denotes the amplitude of accommodation. According to this expression, the amplitude of accommodation of the eye is equal to the refracting power of a thin lens which when placed at the first principal point of the eye would produce by itself an image of the far point at the near point. (J. P. C. S.)

[3] ¶Professor L. D. WELD suggests the term "reciprocal inch." Opticians have long since adopted the "dioptry" for all such purposes, corresponding to the metre as unit of length; and the use of "Kilodioptry," "Hektodioptry," etc., corresponding to millimetre, centimetre, etc., respectively, has also been advocated. It is indicative of the author's singular perspicacity that he recognized immediately the need of units of this kind, as soon as he became familiar with DONDERS' method of measuring the amplitude of accommodation and similar magnitudes. (J. P. C. S.)

with a range of accommodation from infinity to 6 inches, a myopic eye with a range from 6 inches to 3 inches, and an hypermetropic eye with a range from 12 inches behind the eye to 12 inches in front of the eye, all have equal amplitude of accommodation, namely 6 units, because

$$\frac{1}{6} - \frac{1}{\infty} = \frac{1}{3} - \frac{1}{6} = \frac{1}{12} - \left(-\frac{1}{12}\right) = \frac{1}{6}.$$

The amplitude of accommodation continually diminishes with advancing years, at a rate which for emmetropic or nearly emmetropic eyes is approximately proportional to the age, being about 14 dioptries at 10 years,[1] and practically nothing at the age of 65. Loss of the power of accommodation, therefore, occurs naturally in old age, and DONDERS confines the term *presbyopia* to this state. But it should be remarked that from about 50 years of age the far point also recedes from the eye, and an eye that was emmetropic in youth will eventually become hypermetropic, and an eye that was slightly myopic may in the same way get to be emmetropic.

The gradual decrease of the amplitude of accommodation is probably due to an increase of rigidity of the external layers of the crystalline lens, the lens itself becoming less flexible. Moreover, according to the discussion in §10, an increase of the indices of refraction of the outer layers of the lens must produce a decrease of the refracting power of the lens and consequently cause the second focal point of the eye to be moved farther back.

Another thing to be mentioned is that generally the efforts of convergence and accommodation are made simultaneously, and hence quite involuntarily there is some definite connection between the two innervations. Anyone who has not practised the voluntary control of his accommodation finds it much easier to accommodate for distant binocular vision when the axes of the two eyes are parallel and to make the greatest effort of accommodation when the eyes are converged. DONDERS, therefore, differentiates between:

(1) The *absolute amplitude of accommodation*, in which the far point is located with the axes of the two eyes parallel or even divergent, and the near point with the axes as convergent as possible. The near point of accommodation is farther off than the near point of convergence. This is the utmost possible amplitude of accommodation, and in the case of a certain young emmetrope 15 years old was found to be as much as 1/3.69 "Zolltel."

---

[1] ¶The text reads here "$3\!/\!8$ Zolltel" instead of "14 dioptries." (J. P. C. S.)

(2) The *binocular amplitude of accommodation*. In this case the convergence is not made any stronger than is necessary to fixate the point for which the eyes are accommodated. The power of accommodation thus attained is not quite as great as in the first case, the amplitude of binocular accommodation for the same individual being 1/3.9.

(3) The *relative amplitude of accommodation* for a given degree of convergence. For the same individual, with the axes of the eyes parallel, this quantity was only 1/11, reaching its maximum value 1/5.76 for a convergence of 11°, and changing more and more slowly as the convergence increased. At 23° it was 1/6.4; with 38° convergence at the binocular near point, it was 1/9; and at the absolute near point, with 73° convergence, it became zero.

In ophthalmic practice, therefore, it is necessary to choose some definite degree of convergence in order to make comparisons of powers of accommodation, and suitable lenses must be used to try to enable the patient to accommodate with this degree of convergence.

For the determination of the far point, the most appropriate convergence is zero, the eyes being directed to a very distant object. The distance of the far point is directly equal to the focal length of the weakest concave lens in the case of a myopic eye, or of the strongest convex lens in the case of an hypermetropic eye, with which it is possible to see a very distant object with perfect distinctness. For the determination of the near point, DONDERS recommends using a convex lens of such power as will bring this point invariably to about 8 inches from the eye (supposing it to be naturally farther away than that), in order to insure a sufficient effort of accommodation. The effect produced by the lens must, of course, be taken into account in the subsequent calculation.

Printed letters and figures of various sizes serve very well as test objects in measuring the refraction of the eye of an inexperienced patient.[1]

On the whole it is advisable to employ suitable glasses in cases where the eyes have not sufficient accommodation for the occupation of the patient. Presbyopic eyes require a convex lens for reading or writing, and for near objects generally, in order to reduce the size of the blur circles. A stronger glass is needed in the evening or in weak illumination, when the pupil is wide open and the blur circles

---

[1] The following, for example, have been published: *Schriftskalen*, by JAEGER, Jr., of Vienna, 1857; and SNELLEN's *Test types for the determination of the acuteness of vision:* London, WILLIAMS & NORGATE; GERMER BAILLIÈRE of Paris, PETER's of Berlin and GREVEN of Utrecht. In the latter the type are arranged in a graduated scale of sizes and for each size the number of Paris feet is indicated, at which a normal eye should be able to read it. Similar charts have been made also by GIRAUD TEULON (Paris, NACHET).

consequently larger, than is necessary in daylight or with bright illumination. The general rule is to use a lens which will bring the near point within 10 or 12 inches of the eye; except that for very old people, between 70 and 80 years of age, whose visual acuity is considerably reduced it is desirable to bring the image to 8 or 7 inches so as to increase the apparent size of the object.

It is particularly important to prevent myopes from holding the head down to look at near objects and from converging their eyes too much, because the stretching, pulling and distension of the membranes at the back of the eye, which thus result from the increased blood-pressure and muscular strain, soon get worse, and the increased myopia may seriously impair the vision and be dangerous. In the milder degrees of near-sightedness for which the distance of the far point exceeds 5 inches, it is generally permissible to use concave spectacles, and wear them constantly, that have the effect of removing the far point to infinity. This virtually transforms the myopic eye into an emmetropic one. The patient must, however, never hold books, writing, sewing, etc. nearer than 12 inches from the eye. If the eyes are otherwise in good condition, it is possible to read and write without difficulty at this distance; but if it becomes necessary to engage in work requiring closer examination, the patient should employ weaker concave, or perhaps even achromatized prismatic, lenses (the latter being thicker on the side towards the nose), so that very near objects may be seen with less effort of accommodation and convergence.

Near-sighted people who have never worn spectacles must sometimes become accustomed to them gradually, in order to allow the connection between accommodation and convergence to adjust itself to the new conditions. Weaker lenses are provided at first, and after the patient has had some experience with them, stronger ones may be substituted which will completely neutralize the myopia. In the case of shorter ranges of accommodation or of considerably reduced visual acuity, it will usually be found better to use weak lenses for viewing the ordinary near-by objects and to have a lorgnette for seeing at a distance.[1]

In the higher degrees of myopia the eye is usually painful and dangerously affected. There are numerous other considerations that cannot be discussed here, and a competent oculist should by all means be consulted. The general indifference of near-sighted people to the condition of their eyes is responsible for many subsequent disorders and much blindness, and the patient cannot be too earnestly warned against such neglect.

---

[1] ¶Bifocal lenses are now generally employed instead. (L. D. W.)

Hypermetropic eyes require convex glasses. It is a good plan to give a patient of this kind at first a glass that is a little too strong for him, so that he cannot see a distant object distinctly with it until he has learned how to relax the accommodation that he has always been in the habit of using. In proportion as he ceases to exert accommodation, the strength of the lens should be increased. As the amplitude of accommodation diminishes, an hypermetrope requires stronger convex glasses for near vision and weaker lenses for far vision. Thus, by proper choice of spectacles, the very severe disability due to continual strain of accommodation can be entirely relieved, and one of the greatest triumphs, in a practical way, that have been achieved by the new ophthalmology is this simple remedy that can now be used in the most obstinate cases of asthenopia resulting from far-sightedness, which used to be the despair of both patient and oculist.

1855. STELLWAG V. CARION, Die Akkommodationsfehler des Auges. *Wiener Sitzungsber.* XVI. 187.

— CZERMAK. Akkommodationslinien. Ibid. XV. 425, 457.

1856. A. V. GRAEFE, Über *Myopia in distans* nebst Betrachtungen über das Sehen jenseits der Grenzen unserer Akkommodation. *Archiv für Ophthalmol.* II, 1, p. 158-186.

1857. J. J. OPPEL, Über das Sehen durch kleine Öffnungen und das GERAMsche Diaskop. *Jahresber. d. Frankfurter Vereins.* 1856-1857. p. 37-42.

1858. F. C. DONDERS, Winke betreffend den Gebrauch und die Wahl der Brillen. *Archiv für Ophthalmol.* IV, 1, 286-300.

1859. M. MAC-GILLAVRY, *Onderzoekingen over de hoegrootheid der accommodatie.* Dissertat. Utrecht 1858. HENLE u. PFEUFER. *Zeitschrift für ration. Medicin.* (3) VI, 612-613.

1860. F. C. DONDERS, Beiträge zur Kenntnis der Refraktions- und Akkomodationsanomalien. *Archiv für Ophthalmol.* VI, 1. S. 62-105. VI, 2. S. 210-283. VII, 1. p. 155-204. *Verslagen en Mededeelingen der K. Acad.* Amsterdam 1861. p. 159-201. *Jaarlijksch Verslag betrekkelijk het Nederlandsch Gasthuis voor Ooglijders.* I, 63-205. II, 25-68. IV, 1-118.

— C. LANDSBERG, Beschreibung eines neuen Optometers und Ophthalmodiastometers. POGGENDORFFS *Ann.* CX, 435-452. *Polytechn. Zentralbl.* 1860. p. 405-406.

— A. BUROW, Über den Einfluss peripherischer Netzhautpartien auf die Regelung der akkommodativen Bewegungen des Auges. *Archiv für Ophthalm.* VI, 1, 106-110.

1861. CH. AEBY, Die Akkommodationsgeschwindigkeit des menschlichen Auges. HENLE u. PFEUFER. *Zeitschrift.* (3) XI, 300-304.

— GIRAUD TEULON, Des mouvements de décentration latérale de l'appareil cristallin. *C. R.* LII, 383-385. *Inst.* 1861. p. 82. *Cosmos.* XVIII, 284-286.

— H. DOR, Des différences individuelles de la réfraction de l'œil. *J. d. la Physiologie.* XI, XII. *Arch. d. sciences phys.* (2) X, 82-85.

— H. DE BRIEDER, *De stoornissen der accommodatie van het oog.* Dissertat. Utrecht. — *Jaarlijksch Verslag betr. het Niederl. Gasthuis.* II, 69-142.

— V. JAEGER Jr., *Über die Einstellungen des dioptrischen Apparats im menschlichen Auge.* Wien 1861.

— STELLWAG V. CARION, Zur Literatur der Refraktions- und Akkommodationsanomalien. *Zft. d. K. K. Ges. d. Ärzte.* 1861.

1862. DE HAAS, *Geschiedkundig onderzoek omtrent de Hypermetropia en hare gevolgen.* Dissert. Utrecht. — *Jaarlijksch Verslag betr. het Nederl. Gasthuis* III, 157-208.

1863. A. BUROW, Vorläufige Notiz über die Konstruktion eines neuen Optometers. *Archiv für Ophthalmol.* IX. 2, 228-231.

—   A. Burow, *Ein neues Optometer*. Berlin 1863.
—   Idem, *Über die Reihenfolge der Brillenbrennweiten*. Berlin 1864.
—   A. v. Graefe, Ein Optometer. *Deutsche Klinik*. 1863. S. 10.
1864.   F. C. Donders, *On the anomalies of accommodation and refraction of the eye*. London.
         pp. 1–635.
1865.   E. Javal, Une nouvelle règle à calcul. *Ann. d'ocul*. Bruxelles. LIII, 181.
1866.   J. W. Verschoor, Optometers en Optometrie. *Zesde Jaarlijksch Verslag van het
         Nederl. Gasthuis voor Ooglijders*. p. 97–160.

§ 12. Mechanism of Accommodation[1]

The known changes that occur in the different parts of the eye
during the accommodation are as follows:

1. The pupil contracts in accommodation for near vision and
dilates for far vision. This change is readily observed and has long
been known. It is to be observed in every eye which alternates between
near and far vision in the same direction. A lasting contraction of
the pupil due to too long exposure to an excessive degree of illumination
must, however, be avoided.

2. The pupillary margin of the iris and the centre of the anterior
surface of the lens move forward slightly in incipient accommodation
for near vision. In order to observe this, a well-defined distant
fixation point is chosen, and a needle point interposed as the object
for near vision. With one eye occluded, the point of the needle is
brought into exact alignment
with the distant fixation point.
The eye must be kept steadily
focused in this position and not
allowed to wander to one side,
because the success of the experiment depends entirely on
keeping the direction of the eye
unchanged. The observer is
placed so as to look at the cornea
of the subject's eye from one

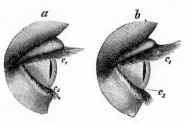

Fig. 59.

side and slightly from behind, where he can just see the black pupil
of the eye protruding about halfway in front of the corneal margin of
the sclerotica when the eye is focused on the distant object. If the
subject then fixes his vision on the nearer object, that is, on the needle
point, the observer will notice immediately that the black oval of the
pupil, and perhaps also a portion of the margin of the iris nearest him,
becomes visible in front of the sclerotica. Fig. 59*a* shows the appearance of the eye for the case of far vision, and Fig. 59*b* its appearance
for near vision. The alteration in the position of the black spot becomes

[1] See also Appendix IV to Part I. G.

most noticeable by watching the width of the bright interval between it and a darker band c_1c_2 that appears on the anterior edge of the cornea. This band is the distorted image of the margin of the sclerotica projecting beyond the iris on that side of the eye as made by the refraction through the cornea. As its inner surface is usually in shadow, it looks darker than the iris, which is illuminated from in front. When accommodation for near vision begins, the interval between this strip c_1c_2 and the dark pupil becomes perceptibly smaller. If the pupillary margin did not move forward, this interval would, on the contrary, become wider in near vision, because the pupil contracts uniformly along all diameters. It would become wider likewise if the forward movement of the pupil occurred as a result of an accidental turning of the subject's eye towards the observer. Therefore, by watching the dark band above mentioned, there is no possibility of any deception. It was pointed out in §3 that the anterior surface of the lens is always in close apposition to the pupil.

3. The anterior surface of the crystalline lens becomes more convex in near vision, less convex for far vision. This fact can be demonstrated by the reflex in the anterior surface of the lens. As in the previous experiment, two well-defined objects serving as fixation points have to be aligned by the eye. The room must be completely dark and, except for a large bright flame, which is adjusted on a level with the eye to one side of the line of sight, no larger or brighter object should be in front of the eye, so as to prevent all disturbing corneal reflections. In

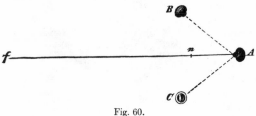

Fig. 60.

Fig. 60, the eye of the subject is supposed to be at A, a cross section of the flame is shown at C, and the nearer and farther points of fixation are designated by n and f, respectively The observer must now adjust his own eye (B) on a level with the eye of the subject and place the lamp so that the angle BAf is about equal to the angle CAf. He moves his eye back and forth in the neighbourhood of B until he catches the reflexes from both surfaces of the lens. These images (Fig. 61, b and c) are not as bright as the reflex from the cornea (a). The image (b) in the anterior surface of the lens is erect and somewhat larger than that in the cornea, but it is usually so faint that it is almost impossible to recognize the exact form of the flame. Its apparent position is far behind the pupil (8 or 12 mm). Consequently,

it vanishes behind the edge of the iris on the slightest movement
of either the observer's eye or of the light. This image will be called
the *first* lens reflex, to distinguish it from the *second*
lens reflex in the posterior surface. The latter (Fig. 61,
c) is inverted and much smaller than the corneal reflex
and the first lens reflex, and therefore it appears as a
bright, fairly well defined little spot. Its apparent position is just beyond the surface of the pupil, about a
millimetre away. Hence, its displacement with respect
to the pupil and the corneal reflex is comparatively

a b c
Fig. 61.

slight when the observer moves his head. When the patient's eye is accommodated for near vision, the first lens reflex becomes considerably
smaller and usually approaches the centre of the pupil. The reduction
in the size of the image may be seen best by using a shield, instead of
a flame, with two openings in it in a vertical line which are both
illuminated from behind. The same result can be obtained by using
a plane horizontal mirror adjusted under a flame so that the flame
and its image in the mirror are like two similar sources of light. Each

of the reflex images in the eye will appear then as a pair of luminous spots,
and the way in which the pair belonging to the anterior surface of the lens
approach each other or separate, according as the eye looks at the near object
or the far object, may be easily and
clearly seen. In Fig. 62, the reflexes for

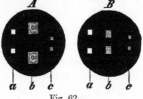

a b c   a b c
Fig. 62.

far vision are illustrated in *A*, and for near vision in *B*; the corneal
reflex is marked *a*, the first lens reflex *b*, and the second lens reflex *c*.
The source of light in these diagrams is supposed to be a pair of rectangular slits illuminated from behind.

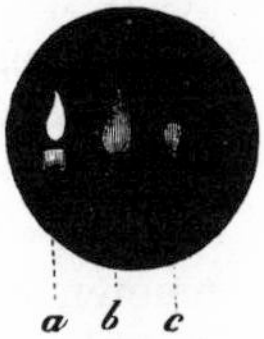

The size of the image of a given object in a convex mirror is
proportional to its radius, and consequently the experiment above
proves that the anterior surface of the crystalline lens becomes more
convex in accommodation for near vision. It is true that a very slight
reduction in the size of the reflex would occur as a result of the refraction of the rays in the cornea if the anterior surface of the lens merely
approached the cornea without altering its convexity, but a simple
calculation is sufficient to show that the reduction in the size of the
mirror image from this cause would be extremely insignificant as
compared with what actually occurs.

4. The reflex in the posterior surface of the lens likewise becomes
somewhat smaller in accommodation for near vision. In order to
verify this, more exact methods of observation have to be employed,

which will be described in a supplement to this section. These methods show that the apparent position of the posterior surface of the lens (as seen through the lens and cornea) is not appreciably altered. As the apparent position of the posterior surface of the lens is but slightly different from its actual position, and as the shifting of the cardinal points of the eye during accommodation, as will be pointed out presently, is of a kind that is calculated to have at least a partly counteracting influence on this apparent position, it may be assumed that the actual position of the posterior surface of the lens is not appreciably altered in accommodation. The shifting of the cardinal points has also a partially counteracting influence on the size of the second lens reflex. However, it may be demonstrated that no assumption as to possible variations of the optical constants is sufficient to account for the amount of reduction in the size of the image in near vision that is actually observed. It may, therefore, be inferred that the posterior surface of the lens also becomes more convex in near vision, but only to a slight extent.

As these observations indicate that, in addition to the changes of curvature, the anterior surface of the lens must become thicker in the middle in near vision; and since its volume cannot alter, it must be also inferred that the equatorial diameter of the lens is shortened.

In the cross section of the anterior portion of the human eye shown in Fig. 63, the cornea and lens are drawn on a 5 to 1 scale from actual measurements of a living eye as made by the author. On the side marked *F*, it shows these structures when accommodated for

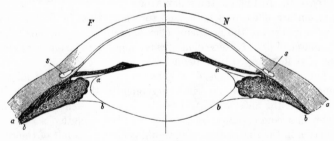

Fig. 63.

distant vision, and on the side *N* for near vision. The ciliary processes in this figure are drawn as if the section passed through the folds of the zonule situated between the processes. This is done so that the relations of the zonule may be seen. The anterior and posterior edges of its folds are marked *aa* and *bb*, respectively.

The effect of the increased convexity of the surface of the lens is to shorten its focal length, its two principal points being shifted forwards at the same time. This is partly due to the forward displacement of the anterior surface of the lens and partly because the increase of curvature of the anterior surface is greater than that of the posterior. Both circumstances conspire to bring rays, coming from the external source of illumination and converging from the cornea on the lens, to a nearer focus than they would have in the far seeing eye. The magnitude of the changes observed in the lens of a living eye seems also to be sufficient to account for the amplitude of accommodation.

No other changes in the ocular media, which could have an effect ôn accommodation, have been observed. In particular, the curvature of the cornea remains entirely unaffected throughout the process. On the other hand, it is conceivable that accommodation for near vision might be aided by an elongation of the eyeball as a whole produced by the simultaneous contraction of all six eye-muscles. However, there is no indication of any such process, nor does it seem to be necessary. Furthermore, it seems to be contrary to the results of the author's experiments as described in § 2, which show that a change of pressure in the eye is accompanied by a change in the convexity of the cornea; whereas no such change in its convexity during accommodation has been observed. As a further objection to this conjecture, it might be pointed out that even a slight continuous pressure on the eye reduces the amount of blood in the vessels of the retina and makes it insensitive to light.

As to the mode by which the deformation of the lens is produced, no one has yet been able to answer this question with certainty. Earlier investigators, like THOMAS YOUNG, supposed that the lens is composed of muscle fibres which was therefore called the *musculus crystallinus*. Even if the fibres of the lens could possibly be considered homologous to muscle fibres, in spite of their entirely different form, no nerve fibres run to the lens. Their presence in such transparent structures as are here under consideration could hardly have escaped observation. Besides, all experiments in which induced electric current has been applied to fresh animal lenses have failed to produce any change in form, though this produces contraction in all known muscular structures. Such experiments were carried out, for example, by CRAMER[1] on the eyes of freshly killed seals and birds. Changes in the form of the lens were obtained as long as the iris and ciliary apparatus were uninjured, but the extirpated lens failed to give them. In collaboration with v. WITTICH, the author has conducted similar experiments on the lenses of freshly killed rabbits and frogs, with the same negative results.

[1] *Het Accommodatievermogen.* p. 58 and 86.

However, CRAMER found that the changes of accommodation could be reproduced on extirpated eyes if an induced current were passed through the anterior portion of the eye. His experiments may be described as follows: A wooden ring of a proper size was placed upon the stage of a microscope having a flat illuminating mirror, and on this ring the eye of a seal (*phoca littorea*), five weeks old, was placed with the cornea downwards. The animal had just been killed by strangulation. The eyeball was freed from muscles, fat and other adjacent parts, and a portion of the sclerotica, choroid and retina carefully removed from the dorsal surface without injury to the vitreous humor. By ingenious adjustment of the microscope and its mirror, CRAMER was able to observe the image of a candle flame, about 35 cm away, clearly depicted on the posterior surface of the vitreous humor when the latter was viewed under a magnification of 80 diameters. As soon as the current of a little electro-magnetic machine was transmitted between the two sides of the cornea, the image became larger and more indistinct. CRAMER then passed a cataract needle through the edge of the cornea, inserting its point through the pupil behind the iris and cut the iris so that it had a radial cleft which passed from its base to the pupil. After this procedure the electric current produced no change in the image. These experiments were not successful when carried out on the eyes of dogs and rabbits, because right after death the pupil becomes very small, and rather strong electric currents cause the lens to become opaque (probably through electrolysis). CRAMER found that the action of electric currents on the eyes of pigeons changed the reflex on the anterior surface of the lens, but not on the cornea. The change of the image on the anterior surface of the lens could be observed better in extirpated eyes from which the cornea had been removed. The increased convexity of the lens continued as long as the current of the induction apparatus was passed through it and disappeared when it stopped. It could not be produced after the iris had been removed.

CRAMER's conclusions were, primarily, that the form of the lens is altered by contractile structures contained in the eye itself; and, moreover, he regarded the iris as the special organ that was chiefly responsible for these changes. He attributed a marked convexity to the iris because he regarded its origin as being on the inner surface of the *musculus ciliaris* farther back than previous anatomists had supposed. According to his assumption, both the circular and radial fibres of the iris contracted simultaneously to produce accommodation of the eye for near vision. Thus the circular fibres would give the radial fibres a fixed point of attachment at their central end, which, being tense, would exert pressure on the parts behind them (edge of lens and vitreous body). The result would be a tendency on the part of the very yielding elastic lens to bulge out through the pupil at the only place where there was no pressure against it, and so to become more convex. The contraction of the pupil in near vision would also be explained as due to the compression of the annular muscle of the pupil necessary to give the radial fibres of the iris a hold at the inner end.

DONDERS called attention to the fact that the elastic tissue on the inner wall of SCHLEMM's canal, to which the periphery of the iris is attached, might have some significance in accommodation. The iris and the ciliary muscle are attached in common to this wall of the canal and the muscle fibres pass backwards to be attached to the choroid. With the choroid as its fixed point, any contraction of this muscle might stretch the elastic tissue in the wall of SCHLEMM's canal and thus draw the base of the iris backwards. As a result, it would be in a more favourable position to exert pressure on the structures lying behind it.

Indeed, it is easy to see that the peripheral parts of the iris must go backwards if the centre of the lens and the pupillary margin of the iris move forwards. For the volume of the aqueous humor contained in the anterior chamber of the eye is constant. If it has to give way in the middle on account of the bulging out of the lens, it will be forced to the sides and consequently push back the peripheral parts of the iris.

CRAMER has remarked that the mode of extension of the anterior chamber in near vision in the case of children may be seen with the naked eye. The author has found that this can be observed also in

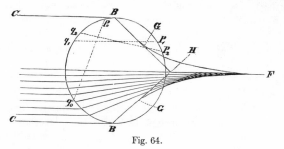

Fig. 64.

adults by means of a special way of illuminating the eye. If the light falls on the eye entirely from the side so that the iris is mostly in shadow, a curved bright band or caustic line can be seen by an observer who adjusts his eye at the proper place on the side opposite the light. In the lower half of Fig. 64 the paths are shown of a pencil of parallel rays refracted at a spherical surface separating air from a medium of the same index of refraction as the aqueous humor. The focus of the central rays is designated by F. The outer rays do not go through this focus, but intersect the adjacent rays and form thus a caustic surface, a meridian section of which is represented by the arc GF. The outermost ray CB is refracted along BH. The caustic curve GF ends at the point G at the middle of the chord in which the straight line BH cuts the circle. Suppose now that planes are passed through the refracting sphere situated like the iris in the aqueous humor. For example, if the straight line q_0P_0 is the trace of a plane perpendicular to the plane of the diagram, its entire anterior surface would be illuminated with light. But if the plane were passed through q_1P_1, part of it would lie in front of the outside refracted ray BG, and be illuminated. The part beyond it would remain dark. If the plane were passed through q_2P_2, it would cut the caustic surface. Here again a part would be light and a part dark, but the boundary between the illuminated and non-illuminated portions would stand out as a bright line corresponding to the line in which the plane q_2P_2 cuts the caustic surface. It may be seen from the figure that, if the portion of the plane, q_2P_2, which cuts the caustic surface, were to move backwards, that is, away from the refracting surface, the bright line would approach the border.

Now this can be observed on the iris when the eye is accommodated for near vision. If the patient's eye is illuminated from the side so that the caustic curve appears at the ciliary margin of the iris, and if he looks alternately at a near and a far object in the same line, the

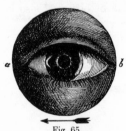

Fig. 65.

caustic curve will be seen to approach the margin of the iris on accommodation for near vision and move away from it in far vision. This illumination of the iris is shown in Fig. 65. The light falls on the eye from the side in the direction of the arrow. The corneal reflection of the light is visible at b on the side towards the light. The caustic curve with its light shining partly through the projecting edge of the sclerotica is seen on the other side at a.

According to the suppositions of CRAMER and DONDERS, the iris and the ciliary muscle produce the change of the form of the lens by increasing the pressure in the vitreous body and on the outer margin of the lens in such fashion that only the centre of its anterior surface behind the pupil is free from the increased pressure. It is possible that the increase in convexity of the anterior surface of the lens which CRAMER noticed first might be explained on this basis.

On the other hand, the change of the shape of the lens, as shown by the writer's measurements, cannot be explained without the aid of some other force. The lens could not become thicker in the middle as a result of the hydrostatic pressure acting on its posterior surface and edge. Such a pressure would tend to cause the equatorial plane of the lens to bulge forwards and, consequently, to make its posterior surface flatter.

An assumption which would appear to avoid this difficulty is that in the passive, far seeing state of the eye the lens is stretched by the zonule attached to its edge. The folds of the zonule pass outwards and backwards from their insertion on the capsule of the lens, thereby forming sheaths for the ciliary processes, and are attached to the posterior extremities of these processes and to the ciliary muscle, where they finally coalesce with the hyaloid membrane, retina and choroid. On contraction, the ciliary muscle could pull the posterior end of the zonule forwards nearer the lens and reduce the tension of the zonule. But the effect of the tense zonule is to exert a pull on the lens along its equatorial diameter, and thus to shorten its axis and make its surfaces flatter. If the pull of the zonule is relaxed in accommodating for near vision, the equatorial diameter of the lens will diminish, and the lens will get thicker in the middle, both surfaces becoming more curved. If the pressure of the iris is superadded, the equatorial plane of the lens will bulge forwards, increasing the curvature of the anterior surface and decreasing that of the posterior surface, so that the latter may be approximately equal to its original amount when the lens is accommodated for far vision.

It would seem that the changes in form of the lens could be explained on this basis. Besides, it is relatively easy to change the form of the lens in dead eyes by cutting the zonule. This would also agree with the fact that the writer has found the thickness of the lens of a live eye adjusted for distant vision less than it ever is in the lens of a dead eye. This difference can hardly be attributed to a swelling of the lenses of cadavers by the absorption of water, since, according to W. KRAUSE's observations, the indices of refraction of the outer, middle and inner layers of the lenses from calves 24 hours after death are exactly the same as directly after death. One would expect a decrease of the index of refraction in consequence of the absorption of water.

In order to give a summary of the probable variations of the optical constants and cardinal points of the eye that occur in accommodation for near vision and, at the same time, to show that the observed changes in the form of the lens are sufficient to account for accommodation, the author has calculated the optical constants for two accommodations of a schematic eye that correspond closely to certain accommodations which he measured. The only difference between the eye as adjusted for far vision and LISTING's schematic eye is that the surfaces of the lens are slightly more to the front, and the lens itself is supposed to be thinner. The indices of refraction of the aqueous and vitreous humors and of the crystalline lens are assumed to have the same values as given by LISTING, namely, 103/77 and 16/11, respectively. Distances are expressed in mm, and the positions of the various points are given by their distances from the vertex of the anterior surface of the cornea. On the assumption that when accommodated for distance this schematic eye can see distinctly at infinity, the axial point of the retina will be 22.231 mm beyond the anterior surface of the cornea. The calculation for the other state of accommodation is based on the assumption that the image of an object 118.85 mm in front of the first focal point of the eye, or 130.09 mm from the vertex of the cornea, is sharply focused on the retina. This agrees with the amplitude of accommodation of a normal eye.

	Accommodation for far vision	Accommodation for near vision
Assumed:		
Radius of curvature of cornea......................	8.0	8.0
Radius of curvature of anterior surface of lens........	10.0	6.0
Radius of curvature of posterior surface of lens........	6.0	5.5
Position of anterior surface of lens..................	3.6	3.2
Position of posterior surface of lens.................	7.2	7.2
Calculated:		
Anterior focal length of cornea......................	23.692	23.692
Posterior focal length of cornea.....................	31.692	31.692
Focal length of lens...............................	43.707	33.785
Distance of anterior principal point of lens from anterior surface......................................	2.1073	1.9745
Distance of posterior principal point of lens from posterior surface......................................	1.2644	1.8100
Distance between the two principal points of lens.......	0.2283	0.2155
Posterior focal length of eye........................	19.875	17.756
Anterior focal length of eye........................	14.858	13.274
Position of the anterior focal point..................	−12.918	−11.241
Position of the first principal point..................	1.9403	2.0330
Position of the second principal point................	2.3563	2.4919
Position of the first nodal point.....................	6.957	6.515
Position of the second nodal point...................	7.373	6.974
Postition of the posterior focal point................	22.231	20.248

Some earlier observers[1] employing less precise methods of investigations were led to suppose that they had found variations of the curva-

[1] J. P. LOBÉ, *Diss. de oculo humano.* Ludg. Batav. 1742. p. 119. — HOME, *Philos. Transact.* 1796. p. 1.

ture of the cornea. Subsequent more accurate measurements of this convexity with the aid of reflex images have shown that it remains entirely unchanged. Such measurements have been made by SENFF,[1] CRAMER[2] and the author himself. These experiments can be made very exactly with the ophthalmometer, inasmuch as a change of 1/200 of the length of the radius may be observed. It would require a change of the radius of the cornea from 6.8 mm to 8 mm to produce by itself a range of accommodation of the eye from 5 inches to infinity. The author's own results have invariably been negative. A very ingenious experiment of THOMAS YOUNG which gives the same result should be mentioned here. He describes it as follows: "From a small botanical microscope I take a double convex lens having a radius and focal length of 0.8 inch, which is fastened in a socket one-fifth of an inch deep; securing its edges with wax, I drop into it a little moderately cold water till it is three-fourths full, and then apply it to my eye, so that the cornea projects into the socket, and is everywhere in contact with the water. Forthwith my eye becomes far-sighted, and the refracting power of the glass lens, which is reduced by water to a focal length of about 1.6 inches, is not sufficient to supply the place of the cornea, which has been disqualified by the superposition of the water; but the addition of another lens, of five inches and a half focus, restores my eye to its natural state, and somewhat more. I then use the optometer, and find now the same inequality in the horizontal and vertical refractions as without the water; and in both azimuths my power of accommodation enables me to focus an object four inches away, as formerly. At first sight, indeed, my accommodation appeared to be a little less than it was, and sufficient only for a range extending from infinity to five inches from the eye; which led me to believe that possibly the cornea did have some slight effect in the natural state; but, reflecting that the artificial cornea was about a tenth of an inch before the place of the natural cornea, I calculated the effect of this difference, and found it exactly sufficient to account for the diminution of the range of vision."

An approximate estimate, at any rate, may be obtained of the amount of the forward displacement of the pupillary margin of the iris in near vision, after having calculated the dimensions and convexity of the cornea and the distance of the pupillary plane from it. In Fig. 66 the cornea is represented by C and its outer edges are marked c and d; and ab is the pupil for far vision. Suppose the observer is so placed with respect to this eye that its entire pupil is just hidden; then cb must be the path of the observer's line of vision in the aqueous humor of the patient's eye. If, when the latter is focused for near vision, the entire pupil becomes just visible in front of the rim of the sclero-

[1] WAGNER, *Handwörterbuch der Physiologie.* Art. Sehen.

[2] *Het Accommodatievermogen der Oogen.* Haarlem 1853. p. 45.

tica, and if its width $\alpha\beta$ is perceived, it must lie in front of the line cb. Yet it must touch this line, as was shown by Fig. 60. Thus the amount of the displacement may be at least approximately found. In the eyes which the writer measured this displacement amounted to 0.36 mm for O. H.'s eye and to 0.44 mm for B. P.'s eye. In case the pupil does not move forwards the whole way in near vision, but, say, only half-way or two-thirds, the amount of forward movement must be estimated, and a calculation made accordingly.

Fig. 66.

The radius of curvature of the anterior surface of the lens may be measured by the aid of the reflex image in it. However, the reflex in this case is too faint and vague for its distance to be measured exactly with the ophthalmometer. If, on the other hand, there is produced a corneal reflex of variable size along with the first lens reflex, the sizes of the two images may be readily compared by the naked eye, and they may be made equal. It is easy to find the size of the corneal image either by measurement or by calculation. For example, the author adjusted two bright flames in a vertical line with each other so as to be reflected in the anterior surface of the lens; and at the same time two other flames, smaller and fainter, were reflected in the cornea, so that their images appeared to be close to the reflexes in the lens, and at the same distance apart. Instead of using a pair of flames, a single flame and its reflected image in a horizontal mirror is more convenient.[1] The reflex images in the anterior surface of the lens for both near and far vision were measured in this way; and it was found that, in eyes with good accommodation, the image in the anterior surface of the lens in near vision is only about 5/9 as large as that in far vision. The image is formed by an optical system composed of a refracting and a reflecting surface; whose focal length may be calculated by equation (8b), §9, from the size of the image and the size and distance of the object; since the above mentioned formula applies to reflecting systems also. The radius of the reflecting surface may be found when the focal length of the compound system has been ascertained. The two focal lengths of the refracting system which lies in front of the reflecting surface will be denoted by f_1, f_2, and the radius of the reflecting surface will be denoted by r, to be reckoned positive or negative according as the mirror is concave or convex, respectively. Hence, if, finally, the distance of the vertex of the reflecting surface from the second principal point of the refracting system is denoted by d, the focal length of the compound reflecting system will be:

$$q = \frac{f_1 f_2 r}{2(f_2 - d)(f_2 - d + r)} \qquad \qquad (1)$$

Now by this formula, q will diminish when d becomes smaller, that is, when the anterior surface of the lens approaches the cornea. But when q becomes smaller, the size of the reflex image of a distant object will also decrease in the same proportion. However, as the change of d amounts to only about 0.4 mm, and that of $(f_2 - d)$ to about 28 mm, and that of $(f_2 - d + r)$ to about 38 mm, the change in q is found to be extremely small and amounts only to about $1/40$ of its total value; whereas the direct observation of the image gives a reduction of about 4/9. It is obvious, therefore, that the reduction in the size of the image is not to be explained as due to the forward movement of the anterior surface of the lens, but must, as a matter of fact, be produced simply by an increase of the curvature of this surface. The following results were obtained in this way by measurements of living eyes:

[1] GRAEFES *Archiv f. Ophth.* Bd. I. Abt. 2. S. 45.

Eye	Radius of curvature of anterior surface of lens		Displacement of the pupil in accommodation
	for far vision	for near vision	for near vision
O. H.	11.9	8.6	0.36
B. P.	8.8	5.9	0.44
J. H.	10.4		

In order to calculate the radius of curvature of the anterior surface of the lens by the above equation, the radius of curvature of the cornea and the distance of the anterior surface of the lens (pupil) from the cornea must both be known. Each of these magnitudes had already been measured in the eyes mentioned above.

The reflex image of a distant object as seen in the posterior surface of the lens likewise changes in size with changes of accommodation of the eye, but to a very slight extent. The writer watched this variation through the ophthalmometer by observing the reflex images in the posterior surface of the lens due to two illuminated apertures in a screen, in a vertical line on one side of the axis of the eye. The cornea reflexes were formed alongside the second lens reflexes, as shown in Fig. 67; where a_0 and a_1 are the two images of the lower light, and b_0 and b_1 of the upper. The images a_1 and b_0 were not superimposed but appeared close together side by side so that they could be distinguished apart. In accommodation for near vision, b_0 shifted a little towards a_0, and a_1 towards b_1; the amount

Fig. 67.

thereof being estimated as equal to half the width of each spot of light; and since the distance between the centres of the apertures in the screen was six times the length of one of them, the reduction of the size of the image was about 1/12 its total size.

Finally, the author tried to determine whether the posterior surface of the lens was also shifted forward in accommodation for near vision. The method employed for this purpose was the same as that used for finding the apparent distance of the posterior surface of the lens from the cornea. With the same arrangement of the apparatus, an examination was made to see whether the reflex in the posterior surface of the lens is altered when the accommodation of the eye is varied without changing the direction of the optic axis. For this purpose, the light and the telescope were placed one on the right and the other on the left, and afterwards interchanged. However, the author was not able to detect any changes of the position of this reflex under these circumstances. The apparent distance of the posterior surface of the lens from the cornea is therefore not appreciably altered by change of accommodation.

From these observations of the reflex image in the posterior surface of the lens and of the apparent place of this surface, what can be inferred as to the real changes of this surface? Its apparent place is certainly very little affected by the refraction through the lens, because this surface is quite close to the posterior nodal point of the lens. Hence, it may be concluded that any possible variations of this apparent position due to changes of the refracting power of the lens in accommodation are negligibly small. For example, in the two schematic eyes whose optical constants were computed in this section by way of illustration, the posterior surface of the lens was apparently shifted forward 0.191 mm in far vision, and 0.113 mm in near vision. Thus, whereas, as a matter of fact, it stayed fixed, yet when the eye was acommodated for near vision, this surface apparently moved backwards 0.078 mm. But this is too small to be perceived. Besides, this calculation is merely useful to show that the movements and their differences are after all very minute, without indicating at all the real sense of the variation in the actual crystalline lens itself, because in this case the separation of the principal points of the lens is an essential consideration, which is certainly smaller in the actual lens than in the schematic homogeneous lens.

All that can be said, therefore, is that the actual position of the posterior surface of the lens is not appreciably altered by the changes incident to acommodation.

In order to ascertain the effect of changes of the ocular media on the reflex image in the posterior surface of the lens, suppose that the reflecting surface were separated from the last refracting surface of the eye by an extremely thin layer of vitreous humor. Under such circumstances, the cardinal points of the refracting system will be the same as the cardinal points of the eye. Let the index of refraction of the vitreous humor be denoted by n; and, also, let the distance of the posterior focal point of the eye from the posterior surface of the lens be denoted by p, and let the distance of this surface from the second nodal point of the eye (measured therefore towards the front of the eye) be denoted by ϵ. In equation (1), which gives the focal length of a combined refracting and reflecting system, the following substitutions have to be made:

$$f_1 = p + \epsilon$$
$$f_2 = n(p + \epsilon)$$
$$f_2 - d = p.$$

Here, therefore, the focal length of the compound system becomes:

$$q = \frac{nr}{2} \cdot \frac{(p+\epsilon)^2}{p(p+r)} \qquad . \qquad . \qquad . \qquad . \qquad . \qquad . \qquad (2)$$

In accommodation for near vision ϵ invariably gets greater because the nodal point of the eye must move forwards with the change of shape of the lens. For this reason, if r and p did not change at all, the value of q and the size of the reflex image must both increase. But in accommodation for near vision p does diminish, which involves a decrease in the value of q as these magnitudes are related in the eye. Differentiating with respect to p, we find:

$$\frac{dq}{dp} = \frac{nr}{2} \cdot \frac{p+\epsilon}{p^2(p+r)^2} \left[pr - (2p+r)\epsilon \right].$$

Only the last factor in this expression, contained in square brackets, can be negative, though in the normal eye it will probably not be so, because ϵ is very small as compared with p and r. Therefore $\frac{dq}{dp}$ will be positive, that is, q and p will both increase or decrease together. In accommodation for near vision, p becomes smaller (if we neglect for the time being the change in ϵ and consider r constant) and therewith both q and the mirror image on the posterior surface of the lens become smaller also. Indeed, it might be supposed that the observed reduction in the size of this image was due to this cause, were it not for the fact that calculation by equation (2) shows that this is not the case. If we take from LISTING's schematic eye the values $p = 14.647$, $\epsilon = 0.3601$, $r = 6$, then p would have to diminish to 10.597 for q to be reduced to 1/12 of its total value. This implies, therefore, that the posterior focal point of the eye has receded to 4 mm in front of the retina, which exceeds the possible variation of the position of this point. But as a part of the reduction in size of the image produced by this means would be counteracted by the forward displacement of the nodal point due to increase of ϵ, as already explained, undoubtedly, the reduction in size of the reflex in the posterior surface of the lens cannot be what it is seen to be unless there is some increase in the curvature of this surface, slight as it may be.

When the values of q for the focal lengths of both of the schematic eyes of this section are computed, the results are 5.6051 for the case of far vision and 5.3562 for the case of near vision, these magnitudes differing from each other by no more than about 1/21 of their average values, whereas the corresponding radii of curvature (6 and 5.5 mm) differ by 1/12. Here the change of the refracting medium partially conceals that of the radius of curvature and makes it appear to be smaller than it really is. The conclusion is that the posterior surface of the lens becomes more curved in accommodation for near vision.

It is important for the mechanism of accommodation to know exactly the point of origin of the iris. In Fig. 3 SCHLEMM's canal with its surrounding area was represented as it appears in very thin sections of the tunics of the eye. A is the cross section of the canal which probably forms an elongated cleft in the living eye accommodated for far vision; C is the cornea, S the sclerotica, D the conjunctiva, B the choroid, E a ciliary process and J the iris. The inner wall of the canal is made up of different tissues. The most posterior portion of this wall at a very evidently consists of the same type of closely interwoven white fibrous tissue as the sclerotica from which it arises. The anterior portion, on the contrary, consists of another type of tissue which is more opaque than fibrous tissue, and consists of fibres which are more sharply defined and are very resistant to the action of acetic acid and potash. Consequently, it may probably be considered elastic tissue. In front this portion of the wall is inserted between the membrane of DESCEMET and the cartilaginous *substantia propria* of the cornea. Behind it is partly attached to the posterior fibrous portion of the wall and partly unites with the fibre bundles of the tensor muscle of the choroid. The choroid is attached only to the posterior half of the inner wall of SCHLEMM's canal at the point where the fibrous and elastic portions unite. However, from the anterior portion of the wall of the canal there originates also a loose network of fibres which exhibit the characteristics of elastic tissue and which are inserted on the periphery of the iris. The mass of fibres which belong to the tensor muscle and the iris seem to arise partly from the wall of the canal, though some seem to pass directly from the choroid to the iris. In the tissue of the ciliary processes a large number of sectioned blood vessels of wide lumen are visible and on their surface towards the vitreous humor is the layer of black pigment.

In order to be convinced of the correctness of the structure of the iris as here stated, it is necessary, on the one hand, to examine thin sections of the dried tunics of the eye, taking into consideration the fact that the process of drying produces much distortion, and that the elastic fibres are very easily torn or broken away from the attachment of the iris when the latter is sepasated from the cornea. On the other hand, it is necessary to examine fresh specimens, in the preparation of which it is best to insert a bristle in SCHLEMM's canal, at the same time carefully avoiding any traction on the iris or the choroid, for thereby the muscle mass which binds these parts together may be given any form at all. If the iris is lifted lightly and laid back on the ciliary processes, the fine elastic threads which pass over from it to the anterior edge of the canal become visible. If the bristle is then pulled forwards, the elasticity of the anterior portion of the canal wall will be evident. If, however, the iris and the choroid are turned forward and the bristle pulled backward, the posterior portion of the wall is seen to be inelastic.

The author regards the method of attachment described above as very important with respect to the backward movement of the lateral portions of the iris in near vision. Thus, if the iris is relaxed, it will be held fast to the inner wall of SCHLEMM's canal by the net-work of elastic fibres extending from *b* to the anterior edge of the canal. If, however, the circular and radial fibres of the iris contract simultaneously, the fibrous mass on the posterior border of the canal provides a sufficiently firm opposition; and hence we may say that the relaxed iris is attached to the anterior, the contracted iris to the posterior edge, of SCHLEMM's canal, which on the average are 0.45 mm apart. In Fig. 63 an attempt has been made to represent the different mode of attachment of the iris in far vision (side *F*) and in near vision (side *N*), SCHLEMM's canal being designated by *s* on both sides of the diagram.

The ciliary processes are another part of the eye, whose actions during accommodation must still be considered. L. FICK[1] has shown that they contract under the influence of an electric current and empty themselves of blood which can readily flow out through quite large vascular channels into the *vasa vorticosa* of the choroid. He assumes that, by this transfer of blood into those portions of the eye which lie behind the partition formed by the lens and the zonule, the hydrostatic pressure will be increased there and diminished in front. Consequently, the centre of the lens will be pushed forwards, producing an increase of curvature of its anterior surface. On the other hand, FICK asserts that as a result, the posterior surface will become flatter. This is not in accordance with the author's observations. J. CZERMAK[2] has also attempted to explain the mechanism of accommodation by supposing there was a swelling of the ciliary processes in addition to the contraction of the iris and the ciliary muscle assumed by CRAMER. This might exert pressure on the border of the lens.

The opinion that the eye-muscles changed the form of the eyeball by their pressure on it, especially elongating it in the direction of the axis of the eye and thus separating the retina farther from the lens, had many notable adherents prior to the discovery of the change in form of the lens. The following facts militate against this view. First, any increase of the hydrostatic pressure in the eye tends to flatten the cornea, as the author has found by measurements with the ophthalmometer. Were this the case, it might have been observed in the living eye. Second, the ophthalmoscope reveals how even a slight pressure with the finger on the eyeball causes the blood vessels of the retina to become smaller in diameter, only permitting an intermittent blood stream to pass through with each beat of the pulse, and finally collapsing entirely. As soon as this intermittent movement (visible pulsation of the arteries) begins,[3] the sensitivity of the retina disappears, probably as a result of insufficient blood supply, and the field of vision becomes entirely dark.

Finally, the experiments of THOMAS YOUNG should be mentioned. These can hardly leave any doubt concerning the fact that not the slightest increase in length of the axis of the eye occurs in near vision. It is possible to touch the surface of the conjunctiva between the eye-lids with a smooth well-polished piece of metal without appreciable discomfort. A smooth iron ring (as of a key) is placed in the inner angle of the eye upon the conjunctiva and is pressed against the inner edge of the orbit. The eye is then turned inwards so that the subject looks at a distant object through the ring and over the bridge of the nose. As a result, the inner border of the cornea comes to lie close to the key, and the possibility of the forward movement of the eyeball in accommodation is thus prevented. Now the ring of a very small key is

[1] J. MÜLLERS *Archiv.* 1853. S. 449.

[2] *Prager Vierteljahrsschr.* XLIII. S. 109.

[3] DONDERS in *Nederl. Lancet.* 1854. Nov. S. 275.

inserted between the eyeball and the bone at the outer angle of the eye. As a result of pressure from this key on the eyeball the retina is stimulated, and a dark impression, which looks at first perhaps like a bright spot, appears in the field of view and, as it were, in front of the bridge of the nose. In YOUNG's own case it extended as far as the place of clearest vision, so that he was able to note that straight lines contained within the boundaries of this pressure image appeared slightly bent. He judged that this was caused by the slight indentation of the sclerotica due to the pressure of the key. Inasmuch as the pressure image appeared at the place of clearest vision, the little key must have touched the posterior side of the eyeball in the region of the yellow spot. Under such circumstances, obviously, no axial elongation of the eye could occur without forcing the key from its position. If, therefore, accommodation were accompanied by an axial elongation of the eye, either it could not have occurred at all, or the key would have had to be forcibly displaced, resulting in an extraordinary increase in the area of the retinal impression on account of the greater indentation of the posterior wall of the eyeball. But nothing like this happened. The eye can accommodate as well as ever, and the retinal impression remains entirely the same during altered accommodation.

THOMAS YOUNG must have had somewhat protuberant eyes, as may also be inferred from other experiments which he describes. When the above experiment was made by the writer, only one edge of the retinal impression extended as far as the place of clearest vision. However, there was no doubt as to the possibility of accommodation and the constancy of the retinal impression.

A direct corollary from this experiment is that the distance of the inner contour of the cornea from the yellow spot or from a point on the posterior wall of the eye a little towards the outside from the yellow spot is absolutely fixed. But it would not be possible for the distance from the cornea to the yellow spot to change without marked asymmetry of the eye, unless the distance from the edge of the cornea changed likewise.

FORBES supposed that in accommodation for near vision the interior of the inner eye was under increased pressure, and that change of form of the lens was due to its different elasticity in different directions on account of the varied form and density of its layers. On the other hand, DE HALDAT could find no variation of the focal length of the optical system of the eye or of extirpated lenses when compressed in water.[1]

There is no other subject in physiological optics about which so many antagonistic opinions have been entertained as concerning the accommodation of the eye. One reason for this is that many of the decisive facts were not discovered until very recently, so that formerly there was much more room for hypotheses. In order to take a rapid survey of these views, instead of following the chronological order, as is done, however, in the bibliography at the end of this section, the various views will be grouped together here, chiefly to show their bearing on each other.

1. *Theories that deny not only the necessity but the existence of any change of the optical system of the eye.* Many naturalists believed that the eyes of human beings and other animals, as distinguished from artifical lenses, were endowed with the faculty of focusing images of objects at different distances all at the same place or approximately so. MAGENDIE[2] maintained that he had verified this in the eyes of white rabbits in which pigment is absent from

---

[1] *Comptes rendus.* XX. p. 61, 458 and 1561.
[2] *Précis élémentaire de Physiologie.* I. p. 73.

the choroid so that the retinal image can be seen through the posterior part of the sclerotica. As a matter of fact, however, the image cannot be seen through the sclerotica well enough defined to observe the slight differences that are involved in accommodation. RITTER,[1] HALDAT,[2] and ADDA[3] corroborated MAGENDIE. HALDAT and ENGEL[4] maintained that it is true for the crystalline lens alone. When the crystalline lens is separated from the humors of the eye and examined in the air, its focal length is extraordinarily short, and, by ordinary optical laws, the distance of an image in it is not markedly different whether the object is at infinity or just 7 inches away. This explains the results obtained by ENGEL.[5]

On the contrary, HUECK,[6] VOLKMANN,[7] GERLING,[8] MAYER[5] and CRAMER,[9] by more accurate experiments, verified the fact that the eyes of human beings and other animals had different focuses for objects at different distances, although theoretically the matter was beyond doubt. TREVIRANUS[10] believed that he could give a theoretical explanation of the supposed fact that the position of the image is independent of the position of the object by assuming for this purpose a special law for the increase in thickness of the lens. His mathematical discussion was refuted by KOHLRAUSCH.[11]

STURM[12] believed he could utilize the fact that the refracting surfaces of the eye are not strictly accurate surfaces of revolution, to explain accommodation for different distances. To begin with, he studied the behaviour of a homocentric bundle of rays refracted at a curved surface which is not a surface of revolution, and found that the rays, instead of being united in a single focal point, have two focal planes. In each of these planes the rays meet in a focal line, the directions of the two focal lines being perpendicular to each other. Thus, if the cross section of the bundle of rays in one focal plane is a short horizontal straight line, it will change through an ellipse with its major axis horizontal into a circle as we proceed towards the other focal plane and then through an ellipse with its major axis vertical into a vertical straight line when the second focal plane is reached. STURM's idea was that between the two focal planes the cross section of the bundle of rays in the eye contracted enough to give clear images. If the luminous point is close to the eye, the two focal planes are at some distance beyond the lens, but as long as the retina lies between them, the images are perhaps distinct enough for vision.

Aberrations of the kind that STURM supposes actually do seem to occur in most human eyes, and the phenomena dependent on them will be described in §14; where, however, it will be shown that the interval between the two focal planes is by no means so important as STURM thinks and that, instead of promoting the clearness of vision, this defect in the eye tends rather to impair it.

[1] GRAEFE und WALTHERS *Journal.* 1832. Bd. VIII. S. 347.

[2] *Comptes rendus.* 1842.

[3] *Ann. d. Ch. et de Phys.* Sér. 3. Tom. XII. p. 94.

[4] J. ENGEL, *Prager Vierteljahrsschr.* 1850. Bd. I. S. 167.

[5] See refutation of above by MAYER, ibid. 1850. Bd. IV. Ausserord. Beilage.

[6] *Diss. de mutationibus oculi internis.* Dorpati 1826. p. 17. — *Die Bewegung der Kristallinse.* Leipzig 1841.

[7] *Neue Beiträge zur Physiol. d. Gesichtssinnes.* 1836. S. 109.

[8] POGGENDORFFS *Ann.* XLVI. 243.

[9] *Het Accommodatievermogen.* Haarlem 1853. S. 9.

[10] *Beiträge zur Anat. u. Physiol. der Sinneswerkzeuge.* 1828. Heft I.

[11] *Über* TREVIRANUS *Ansichten vom deutlichen Sehen in der Nähe und Ferne.* Rinteln 1836.

[12] *Comptes rendus.* XX. 554,761 and 1238. See refutations by CRAHAY, *Bull. de Bruxelles.* XII. 2. 311. BRÜCKE, *Berl. Berichte.* I. 207.

DE LA HIRE[1] insists that there is only one distance of distinct vision, and that so long as an object is not too far from this place one way or the other, it can be seen well enough to be recognized; but there is no accommodation. HALLER[2] was of much the same opinion but supposed that the contraction of the pupil contributed also to diminish the blur circles of near objects. Quite recently the same opinion has been advocated by BESIO.[3]

All these views which deny not only the necessity but even the existence of any internal change in the eye during accommodation may be most easily refuted by the simple fact that an object at a fixed distance from the eye can be seen distinctly or indistinctly at pleasure. Moreover, SCHEINER's experiment which consists in viewing a fixed point through two holes in a card, which can be seen single or double, voluntarily, is another way of disproving them. Lastly, the observations with the ophthalmoscope as mentioned in §11 which enable the changes of the optical image on the retina to be seen objectively is an answer to such opinions.

2. *Opinions which consider the contraction of the pupil as sufficient to account for accommodation in near vision.* SCHEINER[4] discovered that the pupil is contracted in near vision. When the eye is accommodated for distant vision, the blur circles on the retina corresponding to luminous points that are near by can certainly be diminished by a contraction of the pupil. However, a very simple experiment suffices to show that the contraction of the pupil is not enough to enable the eye to accommodate for near objects. All that anybody need to do is to look through a narrow hole that is smaller than the pupil and that acts, so to speak, as an artificial, motionless pupil, in order to verify the fact that even such near objects appear indistinct in far vision, and far objects appear indistinct in near vision. Besides HALLER, who was mentioned above, LEROY,[5] HALL,[6] and MORTON[7] were supporters of this view. OLBERS,[8] DUGES,[9] HUECK and DONDERS,[10] adduced arguments in opposition thereto. J. MILE[11] proposed a curious theory of the result of the contraction of the pupil, but it is likewise disproved by the experiment mentioned above, and he himself afterwards abandoned it.[12] He believed that in far vision the peripheral rays of the cone of light which would cross the optic axis in front of the retina were deflected from it by diffraction at the edge of the pupil and, consequently, did not cross the axis until later. Diffraction of light, however, is not at all a simple deflection of entire rays in this fashion.

3. *Opinions that involve a change of curvature of the cornea.* The first person who supposed he had detected a change of curvature of the cornea appears to have been LOBE.[13] OLBERS[14] does not venture to say definitely as a result of his observations that the convexity increases in near vision. HOME,[15] ENGELFIELD and RAMSDEN, however, claimed to have definitely detected an

[1] *Journal des Sçavans.* 1685. p. 398.

[2] *Elementa Physiologiae.* 1743. Tom. V. p. 516.

[3] *Giorna'e Arcad.* CV. p. 3.

[4] *Oculus.* p. 31.

[5] *Mém. ?. l'Acad. d. Sciences.* 1755. p. 594.

[6] MECKELS *Archiv.* Bd. IV. S. 611.

[7] *American Journal of med. Sciences.* 1831. Nov.

[8] *De oculi mutationibus internis.* Gotting. 1780. p. 13.

[9] *Institut* 1834. No. 73.

[10] RUETE, *Leerboek der Ophthalmologie.* 1846. bl. 110.

[11] MAGENDIE, *Journal de Physiologie.* VI. p. 166.

[12] POGGENDORFFS *Ann.* XLII.

[13] ALBINUS, *Dissert. de oculo humano.* Lugd. Bat. 1742. p. 119.

[14] *De oculi mutat. int.* p. 39.

[15] *Philosoph. Transact.* 1795. p. 13 and 1796. p. 2.

increase of the curvature. A subject who possessed a good power of accommodation was attached to a firm board with a slot in it so that he could not move his head. A little way from the eye, a plate was fastened to the board in which there was a small opening serving as fixation point. On one side of the eye an adjustable microscope, with an ocular micrometer, was also placed on the board, in order to observe the farthermost curvature of the surface of the cornea. In near vision the cornea was supposed to become more convex, so that its centre moved forward 1/800 of an English inch. Measurement of the reflex image in the cornea, carried out later by HOME, gave more doubtful results. Perhaps, in both instances he was deceived by very minute, uniform movements of the head of the subject. No such differences were found by THOMAS YOUNG[1] in the measurements he made of the reflex images in the cornea. Indeed, he completely refuted the hypothesis of alterations in the convexity of the cornea by demonstrating, as described above, that the power of accommodation remained constant even when the eye is under water. HUECK[2] obtained similar results when he repeated HOME'S experiments, but he thought he had ascertained that respiratory movements produced regular to and fro movements of the head, due to inhaling usually in near vision and exhaling in far vision. When he held his breath, the movements of the middle of the cornea ceased entirely or became very irregular. These irregular movements were apparently produced by contractions of the *musculus orbicularis oculi*, as with every contact with the eyelashes the eyeball was drawn back a little. BUROW[3] repeated HOME'S work very painstakingly, but failed to detect any regular movements of the corneal surface. VALENTIN,[4] obtained the same results. SENFF[5] measured the reflex images with a telescope so that his results were not affected by small displacements of the eye; and found that the radius of curvature of the cornea did not change as much as 0.01 Paris line,[6] in a range of accommodation of from 4 to 222 inches. CRAMER[7] also obtained negative results from a measurement of the reflex image in the cornea made with the help of his ophthalmoscope. Such measurements may be very easily and accurately made with the ophthalmometer,[8] and invariably these results as obtained by the author were negative also.

Recent support of the hypothesis that accommodation is effected by a change of curvature of the cornea is to be found in the works of FRIES,[9] VALLÉE[10] and PAPPENHEIM.[11] The latter assumes that the contraction of the iris causes the cornea to become more convex in near vision.

4. *The supposition that accommodation is produced by a shifting of the position of the lens.* This assumption is the oldest, having been proposed by KEPLER,[12] whose theory of vision was the first also to recognize the necessity of accommodation. This hypothesis always has had many adherents among

---

[1] *Philosoph. Transact.* 1801. I. p. 55.

[2] *Die Bewegung der Kristallinse.* S. 40.

[3] *Beiträge zur Physiologie und Physik des menschl. Auges.* Berlin 1842. S. 115.

[4] *Lehrbuch der Physiologie.* 1848. Bd. II. S. 122.

[5] WAGNERS *Handwörterbuch der Physiologie.* Art. Sehen. S. 303.

[6] ¶That is, not as much as about 0.02 mm. (J. P. C. S.)

[7] *Het Accommodatievermogen.* bl. 45.

[8] GRAEFES *Archiv für Ophthalmologie.* Bd. I. Abt. II. S. 24.

[9] *Über den optischen Mittelpunkt im menschl. Auge.* Jena 1839. S. 27.

[10] *C. R. de l'Acad. d. Sciences.* 1847. Oct. p. 501.

[11] *Spezielle Gewebelehre des Auges.* Breslau 1842.

[12] *Dioptrice.* Propos. 64.

whom were SCHEINER,[1] PLEMPIUS,[2] STURM,[3] CONRADI,[4] PORTERFIELD,[5] PLATTNER,[6] JACOBSON,[7] BREWSTER,[8] J. MÜLLER,[9] MOSER,[10] BUROW,[11] RUETE,[12] WILLIAM CLAY WALLACE,[13] and C. WEBER.[14] Most of them considered it probable that voluntary contractions of the ciliary body are able to move the lens to and fro. In order to get around the mathematical difficulty of requiring the lens to execute an impossible displacement in the act of accommodation, they had to resort to the assumption that the focal length of the cornea is greater and that of the lens less than is actually the case. This hypothesis found support in recent times especially by observations of the living eye which demonstrate that the pupil approaches the cornea in near vision. BIDLOO[15] had already observed the increased convexity of the iris in near vision in birds. This was afterwards confirmed for the human eye by HUECK,[16] BUROW[17] and RUETE. C. WEBER showed by a mechanical contrivance that in the case of dogs the anterior surface of the lens moves forward as soon as the anterior portion of the eye is stimulated by an electric current. For this purpose he made a round hole in the centre of the cornea of the eye of a living, opium-narcotized dog; and inserted a little rod in it, until it came in contact with the anterior surface of the lens. The other end of the rod was supported by the shorter arm of a sensitive lever which magnified the forward movement of the anterior surface of the lens.

On the other hand, HANNOVER[18] assumed the possibility of a forward and backward movement of the lens within its capsule, during which process the so-called *Liquor* MORGAGNII would exchange places with it. That there is no such fluid in the normal capsule of the lens, has already been stated.

5. *Hypothesis of change of form of the lens.* This theory, which has triumphed at length was likewise proposed a long time ago and had many defenders even before the actual existence of such changes was known to be a fact.[19] DESCARTES[20] originated this explanation of acommodation; and others

[1] *Oculus.* Oeniponti 1619. Lib. III. p. 163.

[2] *Ophthalmographia.* Lovanii 1648. B. III.

[3] *Dissertatio visionem ex obscurae camerae tenebris illustrans.* Altdorfii 1693. p. 172.

[4] FRORIEPS *Notizen.* Bd. 45.

[5] *On the eye.* Edinburgh 1759. Vol. I. p. 450.

[6] *De motu ligamenti ciliaris.* Lipsiae 1738. p. 5.

[7] *Suppl. ad. Ophthalm.* Copenh. 1821.

[8] *Edinb. Journal of Science.* I. 77. — POGGENDORFFS *Ann.* II. 271.

[9] *Zur vergleichenden Physiologie des Gesichtsinns.* Leipzig 1826. S. 212.

[10] *Repertor. d. Physik.* Berlin 1844. Bd. V. S. 264.

[11] *Beiträge zur Physiol. u. Physik des menschl. Auges.* Berlin 1842.

[12] *Lehrbuch der Ophthalmologie.*

[13] *The accommodation of the eye to distances.* New York 1850.

[14] *Disquisitiones quae ad facultatem oculum accommodandi spectant.* Marburgi 1850. p. 31.

[15] *Observ. de oculis et visu variorum animalium.* Lugd. Bat. 1715.

[16] *Bewegung der Kristallinse.* S. 60.

[17] *Beiträge zur Physiol. usw.* S. 136.

[18] *Bidrag til Øjets Anatomie.* Kjöbenhavn 1850. p. 111.

[19] ¶SCHEINER suspected that, along with some slight elongation of the eyeball, there might also be a concomitant change in the form of the crystalline lens in accommodation. HUYGEN's views on the subject seem never to have been definitely settled in his own mind, and at one time he inclined to think that the act of accommodation was effected by a change of curvature of the lens, but subsequently, in 1670, he returned again to the explanation of a forward movement of the lens as the sole responsible agency for producing this effect. (J. P. C. S.)

[20] CARTESIUS, *Dioptrice.* Lugd. Bat. 1637.

who embraced it were PEMBERTON,[1] CAMPER,[2] HUNTER,[3] YOUNG,[4] PUR-
KINJE,[5] GRAEFE,[6] TH. SMITH,[7] HUECK,[8] STELLWAG VON CARION[9] and FORBES.[10]
Some earlier anatomists, for example, LEEUWENHOEK and PEMBERTON, called
the lens, perhaps for this reason, the *musculus crystallinus,* supposing that its
fibres were contractile. YOUNG inclined to this view on the basis of experiments which, while they seemed to him to be completely convincing, did not
succeed on every eye. If the blurred image of a luminous point is examined
through a fine grill of parallel wires, it is seen to be crossed by dark straight
lines which are shadows of the wires. When YOUNG's own eye was acommodated for distant vision, these lines appeared to be perfectly straight; but
when he looked at near objects, the lines at the sides of the blur circle were
convex outwards. The phenomenon was not changed by putting the eye
under water so as to eliminate the influence of the cornea. The only explanation of the curvature of the previously straight shadows was the change of
curvature of the surfaces of the lens. The pupil should be dilated in order
to perform this experiment. WOLLASTON could not observe the effect
(nor could the author), but KOENIG, another friend of YOUNG's, verified it.
Corroboratively, YOUNG found, by looking through four parallel narrow
vertical slits on his optometer, that the four images of the white horizontal
line intersected at one point when the eye was accommodated for far vision,
but did not do so when it was adjusted for near vision.

The variation of the reflex images in the lens during accommodation were
noted first by MAX LANGENBECK,[11] who drew the correct inference that the
anterior surface of the lens is, therefore, more convex in near vision. His
method of observation, however, was not favourable, because he had the
subject look directly at the flame, and this meant that the observer had to
see the three reflex images very close together, so that the exceptionally
bright corneal image makes it hard to see the other two. Perhaps, this is
the reason why LANGENBECK's observation did not attract the notice of
physiologists. CRAMER observed the same thing; but he improved the method
of observation especially by having the rays of light fall on the eye from one
side while the observer looks into it from the other. He also described an
instrument which he called an *ophthalmoscope,* designed to make the observations more easily and more accurately. This instrument was essentially a
stand to which was attached a microscope with a magnifying power of from
10 to 20, a lamp, cross hairs serving as a fixation mark, and a hollow conical
tube conveniently shaped for the adjustment of the patient's eye. The lamp
is regulated to enable the observer to watch the reflex image in the anterior
surface of the lens in between the other two reflex images when he looks
through the microscope at the pupil of the patient's eye. However, the
essential thing here, which is the reduction of the size of the reflex image in the
anterior surface of the lens, is not so convenient for observation in this way as
the method with the naked eye as described above, in which the object con-

---

[1] *Dissert. de facultate oculi, qua ad diversas distantias se accommodat.* Lugd. Bat. 1719.

[2] *Dissert. physiol. de quibusdam oculi partibus.* Lugd. Bat. 1746. p. 23.

[3] *Philosoph. Transact.* 1794. p. 21.

[4] Ibid. 1801. P. I. p. 53.

[5] *Beobachtungen u. Versuche zur Physiol. d. Sinne.* Berlin 1825.

[6] REILS *Archiv für Physiologie.* Bd. IX. S. 231.

[7] *Philosophical Magazine.* 1833. T. V. 3. No. 13.—SCHMIDTS *Jahrbücher.* 1834.
Bd. I. S. 6.

[8] *Bewegung der Kristallinse.* Leipzig 1841.

[9] *Zeitschrift der k. k. Gesellschaft der Ärzte zu Wien.* 1850. Heft 3 and 4.

[10] *Comptes rendus.* XX. p̌. 61.

[11] *Klinische Beiträge.* Göttingen 1849.

sists of two separated luminous points. The mere shifting of the reflex in the anterior surface of the lens, which can be easily and accurately seen in CRAMER's instrument, is not conclusive by itself on account of the asymmetry of the eye, (of which CRAMER was not then aware), unless a preliminary set of experiments that are easily carried out has shown that this reflex image invariably moves towards the centre of the pupil from any other position.

Without knowledge of the work of either of the last two investigators, and at a time when CRAMER's discovery had been published merely in brief notices[1] by himself and DONDERS, and even before the appearance of DONDERS' great book which was crowned by the Dutch Institute of Sciences, the author had discovered the same facts[2] for himself, and had discovered, besides, the behaviour of the posterior surface of the lens in accommodation,[3] as above related.

Numerous instances in which the eye appeared to accommodate after the removal of the lens in the operation for cataract, were cited to prove that the power of accommodation was not dependent on displacements and changes of form of the lens. However, it should be borne in mind here that patients even with poor accommodation may recognize objects whose images are blurred. The mere fact that a person who can read print with cataract glasses can with the same glasses distinguish people at a distance, window-frames, etc., is no reason at all for supposing that he has the power of accommodation. Anybody can easily verify for himself the fact that when his eye is focused on his finger about a foot away, he can still perceive various details of distant objects. In order to establish the existence of accommodation, the patient must be able with the same glasses to see a given object either distinctly or indistinctly, as he chooses, depending on whether he tries to focus for one distance or another. SZOKALSKY believes that he has actually observed such a case. This particular eye, however, could see objects distinctly at a distance of 17 inches without cataract glasses which is impossible without some substitute for the lens. DONDERS has suggested the use of entoptical phenomena to determine during life whether the lens has been renewed in eyes which have been operated on for cataract.

6. *The supposition that the form of the eyeball changes.* If the retina could be removed farther from the optical system of the eye, that is, if the eyeball could be elongated, this would afford the eye a means of accommodation for near vision. The supporters of this opinion usually have assumed that the form of the eyeball could be changed by pressure exerted on it by the eye muscles, either by the recti alone, or by the obliques alone, or by all acting together, or by the added action of the *orbicularis oculi*. Among these were STURM,[4] LE MOINE,[5] BUFFON,[6] BOERHAVE,[7] MOLINETTI,[8] OLBERS,[9] HAESELER,[10] WALTHER,[11] MONRO,[12] HIMLY,[13]

---

[1] *Tijdschrift der Maatschappij vor Geneeskunde.* 1851. W. 11. bl. 115 and *Nederlandsch Lancet.* 2. Serie. W. 1 bl. 529. 1851-52.

[2] *Monatsberichte der Berliner Akad.* 1853. Feb. S. 137.

[3] GRAEFES *Archiv für Ophthalmologie.* Bd. I. Abt. II. S. 1-74.

[4] *Dissert. de presbyopia et myopia.* Altdorfii 1697.

[5] *Quaestio an obliqui musculi retinam a crystallino removeant.* Parisiis 1743.

[6] *Histoire naturelle.* Paris 1749. T. III. p. 331.

[7] *Praelectiones academ.* Taurini 1755. Vol. III. p. 121.

[8] HALLER, *Elementa Physiologiae.* 1763. T. V. p. 511.

[9] *Dissert. de oculi mutat. int.* Gottingae 1780. §43.

[10] *Betrachtungen über das menschliche Auge.*

[11] *Dissert. de lente crystallina.* § 1.

[12] *Altenburger Annalen f. d. J.* 1801. S. 97.

[13] *Ophthalmologische Beobachtungen und Untersuchungen.* Bremen 1801.

MECKEL,[1] PARROT,[2] POPPE,[3] SCHROEDER VAN DER KOLK,[4] ARNOLD,[5] SERRE,[6] BONNET,[7] HENLE,[8] SZOKALSKY[9] and LISTING.[10] CLAVEL[11] assumed that the eye muscles might not only change the form of the eyeball but also might cause the cornea to become more convex and the lens to be moved forward. The reasons why such a change of the form of the eyeball appears to be improbable have been already stated above.

The various views here considered are the more important of those that have been advanced concerning this intricate subject. Many other modes of explanation have been suggested also, which rightly found less favour. Here v. GRIMM[12] may be mentioned who assumed that the indices of refraction of the ocular media might vary, and WELLER[13] who proposed to explain accommodation not by a change in the eye itself but by a psychic process.

Literature:

1611. KEPLER, *Dioptrice.* Propos. 26.

1619. SCHEINER, *Oculus.* Oeniponti 1619. Lib. III. p. 163.

1637. CARTESIUS, *Dioptrice.* Lugd. Batav

1648. V. F. PLEMPIUS, *Ophthalmographia* Lovanii. B. III.

1685. DE LA HIRE, *Journal des Sçavans.* 1685. p. 398.

1693. STURM, *Dissertatio visionem ex obscurae camerae tenebris illustrans.* Altdorfii, p. 172.

1697. STURM, *Dissert. de presbyopia et myopia.* Altdorfii.

1712. A. F. WALTHER, *Diss. de lente crystallina oculi humani.* Lipsiae. Also in HALLER, *Disput. anat.* Vol. IV.

1715. BIDLOO, *Observationes de oculis et visu variorum animalium.* Lugd. Batav.

1719. PEMBERTON, *Dissert. de facultate oculi, qua ad diversas distantias se accommodat.* Lugd. Batav.

1738. J. J. PLATNER, *De motu ligamenti ciliaris in oculo.* Lipsiae. p. 5.

1742. J. P. LOBÉ (ALBINUS), *Diss. de oculo humano.* Ludg. Batav. p. 119. Also in HALLER, *Disput. anat.* Vol. VII.

1743. HALLER, *Elementa Physiologiae.* T. V. p. 516.

      LE MOINE, *Quaestio an obliqui musculi retinam a crstallino removeant.* Paris.

1746. P. CAMPER, *Dissert. physiologica de quibusdam oculi partibus.* Lugd. Batav. p. 23. Also in HALLER, *Disput. anat.* Vol. IV.

1749. BUFFON, *Histoire naturelle.* Paris. T. III. p. 331.

1755. LE ROY, *Mémoires de l'Acad. de Paris.* 1755. p. 594.

      BOERHAVE, *Praelectiones academicae.* Taurini. Vol. III. p. 121.

1758. v. GRIMM, *Diss. de visu.* Gottingae.

1759. PORTERFIELD, *On the eye.* Edinburgh. Vol. I. p. 450. — *Edinb. med. Essays.* Vol. IV. p. 124.

1763. MOLINETTI in HALLER, *Elementa physiologiae* V. p. 511.

---

[1] CUVIER, *Vorlesungen über vergl. Anat.* Trans. by MECKEL. Leipzig 1809. Bd. II. S. 369.

[2] *Entretiens sur la physique.* Dorpat 1820. T. III. p. 434.

[3] *Die ganze Lehre vom Sehen.* Tübingen 1823. S. 153.

[4] LUCHTMANS *Diss. de mutatione axis oculi.* Traject. ad Rhenum. 1832.

[5] *Untersuchungen über das Auge des Menschen.* Heidelberg 1832. S. 38.

[6] *Bulletin de thérapie.* 1835. T. 8. L. 4.

[7] FRORIEPS *N. Notizen.* 1841. S. 233.

[8] CANSTATTS *Jahresbericht für 1849.* Bd. I. S. 71.

[9] *Archiv ür physiologische Heilkunde.* VII. 1849. 7.—8. Heft.

[10] WAGNERS *Handwörterbuch d. Physiologie.* IV. 498.

[11] *Comptes rendus.* XXXIII. p. 259.

[12] *Dissert. de visu.* Gottingae 1758. See also OLBERS, *de oculi mutationibus internis.* p. 29.

[13] *Diätetik für gesunde und schwache Augen.* Berlin 1821. S. 225.

1783.   OLBERS, *Diss. de oculi mutationibus internis*. Gottingae.
1793.   TH. YOUNG, *Observations on vision. Phil. Trans.* 1793. P. II. p. 169.
1794.   HUNTER, *Phil. Trans.* 1794. p. 21.
1795.   HOME, *Phil. Trans.* 1795. P. I. p. 1. (Accommodation after operation for cataract.)
1796.   HOME, *Phil. Trans.* 1796. P. I. p. 1.
        TH YOUNG, *De corporis humani viribus conservatricibus.* Gottingae. — *Phil. Trans.* 1800, p. 146.
1797.   KLÜGEL in REILS *Archiv.* Bd. II. S. 51. (In answer to HOME.)
1801.   MONRO, *Altenburger Annalen f. d. J.* 1801. S. 97.
        HIMLY, *Ophthalmologische Beobachtungen und Untersuchungen.* Bremen.
        *TH. YOUNG, *On the mechanism of the eye. Phil. Trans.* 1801. P. I. p. 23.* (This is a work of astonishing perspicacity and originality, which was qualified to settle the question as to accommodation even at that time, but, on account of its conciseness, it is often hard to follow, and, moreover, it presupposes the most thorough knowledge of mathematical optics.)
1802.   HOME, *Phil. Trans.* 1802. P. I. p. 1. (Accommodation after operation for cataract.)
        ALBERS, *Beiträge zur Anatomie und Physiologie der Tiere.* Heft I. Bremen.
1804.   GRAEFE in REILS *Archiv für Physiologie.* Bd. IX. S. 231.
1809.   CUVIER, *Vorlesungen über die vergleichende Anatomie,* translated by MECKEL. Leipzig. Bd. II. S. 369.
1811.   WELLS, *Phil. Trans.* 1811. P. II. Also in GILBERTS *Annalen* XLIII. 129 and 141.
1816.   MAGENDIE, *Précis élémentaire de Physiologie* I. p. 73. Paris. Translated by ELSÄSSER. Tübingen 1834. I. 54.
1820.   G. PARROT, *Entretiens sur la physique.* Dorpat. T. III. p. 434.
1821.   JACOBSON, *Suppl. ad Othphalm.* Copenhagen.
        C. H. WELLER, *Diätetik für gesunde und schwache Augen.* Berlin. S. 225.
1823.   J. POPPE, *Die ganze Lehre vom Sehen.* Tübingen. S. 153.
        RUDOLPHI, *Grundriss der Physiologie.* Berlin. Bd. II. Abt. 1. S. 9.
        LEHOT, *Nouvelle théorie de la vision.* Paris.
        PURKINJE, *De examine p' ysiologico organi visus et systematis cutanei.* Vratislaviae. (Discovery of the lens reflex.)
1824.   BREWSTER, *Edinb. Journal of Science* I. p. 77.— POGGENDORFF, *Annalen* II. S. 271.
        SIMONOFF in MAGENDIE, *Journal de Physiologie.* T. IV.
1825.   PURKINJE, *Beobachtungen und Versuche zur Physiol. der Sinne.* Berlin. S. 128.*
1826.   J. MÜLLER, *Zur vergleichenden Physiologie des Gesichtssinns.* Leipzig. S. 212.
        HUECK, *Diss. de mutationibus oculi internis.* Dorpati.
        MILE in MAGENDIE, *Journal de Physiologie* VI. p. 166.
1828.   TREVIRANUS, *Beiträge zur Anatomie und Physiologie der Sinneswerkzeuge des Menschen und der Tiere.* Heft I.
1831.   MORTON in *American Journal of med. Sciences.* 1831. Nov.
1832.   RITTER in GRAEFE u. WALTHERS *Journal.* VIII. S. 347.
        FR. ARNOLD, *Untersuchungen über das Auge des Menschen.* Heidelberg. S. 38.
        G. J. LUCHTMANS, *Diss. de mutatione axis oculi secundum diversam distantiam objecti ejusque causa.* Traject. ad Rhenum.
1833.   TH. SMITH, *Philos. Magazine* V. 3. No. 13. — SCHMIDTS *Jahrbücher der Medizin.* 1834. Bd. I. S. 6.
1834.   DUGÉS, *Institut.* Nr. 73.
1835.   SERRE, *Bulletin de Thérapie.* T. VIII. L. 4.
1836.   VOLKMANN, *Neue Beiträge zur Physiologie des Gesichtssinns.* S. 109.
        R. K. KOHLRAUSCH *über* TREVIRANUS' *Ansichten vom deutlichen Sehen in der Nähe und Ferne.* Rinteln.
1837.   SANSON, *Leçons sur les maladies des yeux,* publiées par BARDINOT et PIGNE. Paris. (Concerning the reflexes of the crystalline lens.)
        MILE in POGGENDORFFS *Annalen* XLII. S. 37 u. 235.

1838. PASQUET in FRORIEPS *Notizen*. Bd. VI. Nr. 2.
1839. J. F. FRIES, *Über den optischen Mittelpunkt im menschlichen Auge, nebst allgemeinen Bemerkungen über die Theorie des Sehens*. Jena. S. 27.
1840. NEUBER in OSANNS *Zeitschrift*. Heft 7–12. S. 42.
1841. HUECK, *Die Bewegung der Kristallinse*.
        BONNET in FRORIEPS *Neue Notizen*. 1841. S. 233.
1842. HALDAT in *Comptes rendus*. 1842.
        ADDA in *Annales de Chimie et de Phys*. Ser. III. T. XII. p. 94.
1842. BUROW, *Beiträge zur Physiol. u. Physik des menschl. Auges*. S. 94–177.*
        S. PAPPENHEIM, *Die spezielle Gewebelehre des Auges*. Breslau.
1844. MOSER, *Repertor. d. Physik* V. S. 364.
1845. STURM, Sur la théorie de la vision. *Comptes rendus*. XX. p. 554, 761, 1238; POGGENDORFFS *Annalen* LXV. 116.
        FORBES, *Comptes rendus*. XX. p. 61; *Institut. No*. 576. p. 15; No. 578. p. 32.
        DE HALDAT, *Comptes rendus*. XX. p 458 and 1561; *Institut*. No. 596. p. 90 (in reply to FORBES.)
1846. DONDERS in RUETE, *Leerboek der Ophthalmologie*. bl. 110.
        H. MEYER in HENLE u. PFEUFFER, *Zeitschrift für rationelle Medizin*. Bd. V. (Origin of the lens reflex.)
        SENFF in R. WAGNERS *Handwörterbuch der Physiologie*, Art. "Sehen" by VOLKMANN. S. 303.
        BESIO, *Giorn. Arcad*. CV. 3; *Institut*. No. 666. p. 338.
        J. G. CRAHAY, *Bulletin de Bruxelles*. XII. 2. 311; *Institut*. No. 644. p. 151.
1847. L. L. VALLÉE, *Comptes rendus*. XXV. p. 501.
1848. VALENTIN, *Lehrbuch der Physiologie*. Bd. II. Abt. 2. S. 12.
        SZOKALSKY in GRIESINGER, *Archiv für physiol. Heilkunde*. VII. S. 694.
1849. MAX. LANGENBECK, *Klinische Beiträge aus dem Gebiete der Chirurgie und Ophthalmologie*. Göttingen.
        DONDERS in *Nederlandsch Lancet*. 1849. bl. 146.
1850. JOS. ENGEL, *Prager Vierteljahrsschrift* XXV. S. 167 and 208.
        H. MAYER, ibid. Bd. XXVIII. Ausserord. Beilage, and Bd. XXXII. S. 92.*
        HENLE in CANSTATTS *Jahresbericht für 1849*. Erlangen. S. 71.
        WILLIAM CLAY WALLACE, *The Accommodation of the eye to distance*. New York.
        C. WEBER, *Nonnullae disquisitiones quae ad facultatem oculum rebus longinquis et propinquis accommodandi spectant*. Marburgi.
        C. STELLWAG VON CARION, *Wiener Zeitschrift der Ges. der Ärzte*. VI. S. 125. 138.
        A. HANNOVER, *Bidrag til Öiets Anatomie, Physiologie og Pathologie*. Kjöbenhavn. p. III.
1851. H. HELMHOLTZ, *Beschreibung eines Augenspiegels zur Untersuchung der Netzhaut im lebenden Auge*. Berlin. S. 37.*
        LISTING in R. WAGNERS *Handwörterbuch der Physiologie*. Art.: Dioptrik des Auges. Bd. IV. S. 498.*
        CRAMER, *Tijdschrift der Maatschappij vor Geneeskunde*. 1851. W. 11. bl. 115; *Nederlandsch Lancet*. Ser. 2. W. 1. bl. 529.
        CLAVEL, *Comptes rendus*. XXXIII. p. 259; *Archives des sciences phys. et natur*. XIX. p. 76.
1852. DONDERS in *Nederl. Lancet*. 1852. Feb. bl. 529.
1853. H. HELMHOLTZ, *Monatsberichte d. Akad. zu Berlin*. Feb. S. 137.
        *A. CRAMER, *Het Accommodatievermogen der Oogen physiologisch toegelicht*. Haarlem. Translated by DODEN. Leer 1855.
        L. and A. FICK in J. MÜLLERS *Archiv für Anat. u. Physiol*. 1853. p. 449.*
1854. DONDERS in *Onderzoekingen gedaan in het Physiologisch Laborat. der Utrechtsche Hoogeschool*. Jaar VI. p. 61.
        J. CZERMAK in *Prager Vierteljahrsschrift* XLIII. S. 109.
1855. *H. HELMHOLTZ, Über die Accommodation des Auges in v. GRAEFE, *Archiv für Ophthalmologie*. Bd. I. Abt. II. S. 1.

Supplement

An experiment by Bahr should be mentioned here with respect to the phenomena connected with the mechanism of accommodation. Accommodated for near vision, he looked at a brightly illuminated rectangle, until a strong after-image had been formed in his eye. He then projected it on a distant surface, changing his accommodation accordingly, and estimated its apparent size thereon. Inasmuch as the size of the image on the retina is proportional to the distance of the retina from the posterior nodal point of the eye, and since the size of the retinal image is the same in both cases, it is possible to calculate from such an experiment how much the distance of the retina from the second nodal point has changed. By his experiments Bahr found a forward displacement of the nodal point amounting to 0.35 mm; whereas, according to the author's calculation as given on page 152, this displacement was 0.4 mm. If, instead, there had been an elongation of the eyeball, the change of distance would have had to be much more considerable; and if such an elongation were the sole basis of accommodation, it would have to amount to 3 mm, which is impossible, as Bahr's experiments also show.

Knapp[1] determined for the eyes of four individuals the positions of the far point and near point and the curvature and position of the cornea and of the surfaces of the lens in accommodation for both far and near vision. According to these data, the accommodation as computed from the changes of curvature of the crystalline lens agrees close enough with the amplitude of accommodation that was actually found; so that any assumption of an elongation of the eye was thus ruled out.

In two cases very favourable for examination in which the lens had been removed in a cataract operation, Donders[2] was convinced that there is no evidence of accommodation in such eyes, though they could see distinctly with the aid of a convex lens placed before them. Nevertheless, in the attempt to see objects near at hand, convergence and contraction of the pupil occurred. If it were possible to elongate the eyeball by means of the pressure of the eye muscles, this would be able to produce a certain amplitude of accommodation even in eyes without the crystalline lens. As a result of all these facts it can no longer be doubted that *an elongation of the eyeball does not occur in accommodation for near vision.*

A much better method than any of those described above for measuring the curvatures of the crystalline lens is to use the ophthal-

[1] *Archiv für Ophthalmol.* IV, 2, p. 1-52.
[2] *On the anomalies of accommodation and refraction.* London. p. 320-321.

mometer in a dark room and to obtain the reflex images by a beam of sunlight; as was done by B. Rosow.

Concerning the muscles that produce the change of form of the lens, it may be observed in the first place that cases have been noticed in which, although the iris ceased to function, entirely satisfactory accommodation occurred. The author himself knew an astronomer, with whom naturally it was easy to perform optical experiments and who was well acquainted with the phenomena concerned in them; and although his iris was completely paralyzed, notwithstanding he was able to accommodate perfectly well. Moreover, A. v. Graefe[1] found that the power of accommodation was entirely normal in the case of a workman after recovery from an injury of his eye which had resulted in the complete separation of the iris.

There is nothing left except the ciliary muscle to which accommodation can be attributed. In this structure a circular layer of fibres has recently been discovered first by van Reeken, and more definitely by H. Mueller and Rouget. These are situated in the angle turned towards the ciliary processes; moreover, they are interwoven with meridional fibres, and in many instances the circular fibres bend so as to continue as meridional fibres. From this anatomical arrangement of the circular fibres it may be inferred in the first place that these elements of the ciliary muscle cannot act except in conjunction with the meridional fibres. Indeed, such an arrangement of muscle fibres is evidently a very favourable one for action on the zonule; for if there were nothing but radial fibres in the muscle, as represented in the old descriptions, the inner corner of the muscle would have been forced in, and the zonule would have been bent convex towards Schlemm's canal (Fig. 63s). The result would be that the zonule would be much less relaxed than in the existing arrangement where any such bending is avoided. The circular fibres of the muscle must pull the corresponding edge of the muscle towards the tip of the ciliary processes and towards the edge of the lens. The effect of this action is to shift the centre of the zonule towards the margin of the lens in the direction of the edges of its folds, without pulling it outwards towards Schlemm's canal.

Whether the circular fibres of the ciliary muscle exert a pressure on the ciliary processes, as H. Mueller supposes, which is transmitted to the edge of the lens, is hard to determine, because we do not know whether the ciliary processes are filled with blood in the living eye so as to be stout enough to exert an appreciable pressure on the lens. Many ophthalmologists consider it very doubtful whether they even touch the lens.

[1] *Archiv für Ophthalmologie.* VII, 2, p. 150–161.

W. HENKE has conjectured that it is only the circular fibres of the ciliary muscle that produce accommodation for near vision, and that it is the contraction of the meridional fibres that restore the accommodation for far vision. Thus he regards the two points of attachment of the meridional fibres of the muscle as fixed, and supposes that it would be curved inwards by the action of the circular fibres, and be stretched straight again, when accommodation relaxes, by active tension, the circular fibres being released. This mode of action seems to the author highly improbable, first, because there are many indications to show that there is no active accommodation for far vision, and also because the fibre layers of the ciliary muscle are too much interwoven, meridional fibres being confounded with circular fibres and *vice versa;* so that separate action of the individual fibres is scarcely to be thought of. The example of the iris which HENKE adduces against this argument is of very doubtful value in the light of recent investigations of the *musculus dilatator iridis.* Besides, in the opinion of the writer, the *ligamentum pectinatum* as an anterior point of attachment and the choroid as a posterior point of attachment for the muscle are much too elastic to permit a considerable action of the muscle, such as HENKE supposes, in a direction that is so disadvantageous. Finally, according to HENKE's description, the external surface of the muscle would have to stand out from the sclerotica in accommodation for near vision and catch hold again in far vision. But it is not very clear where a fluid can come from that could fill the empty space of this cleft, and unless there were something of the kind, the air pressure would prevent the muscle from yielding.

In conclusion, the author sees no reason to modify the theory of the mechanism of accommodation as given above on page 151 which still seems to him to give the most probable explanation. Recent experiments reported by C. VÖLCKERS and V. HENSEN tend to confirm this opinion.

1855. RUETE, De Irideremia congenita. *Progr. acad. Leipzig.* VIRCHOWS *Archiv.* XII, 342.
— VAN REEKEN. Ontleedkundig Onderzoek. van den toestel voor accommodatie van het oog. *Onderzoekingen gedaan in het Physiol. Laborat. der Utrechtsche Hoogeschool,* Jaar. VII, 248–286.
1856. J. P. MAUNOIR, Mémoire sur l'ajustement de l'œil aux différentes distances. *Arch. des sciences phys.* XXXI, 309–316.
— BRETON, Adaptation de la vue aux différentes distances, obtenue par une compression mécanique, exercée sur le globe oculaire. *C. R.* XLIII, 1161-1162. *Inst.* 1856. p. 455. *Cosmos.* IX, 690. X, 29–30.
— GOODSIR, Notice respecting recent discoveries on the adjustment of the eye to distinct vision. *Proc. of Edinb. Soc.* III, 343-345. *Edinb. J.* (2) III, 339-342
1857. STOLTZ, Accommodation artificielle ou mécanique de l'œil à toutes les distances. *C. R.* XLIV, 388-390; 618-620. *Arch. des sciences phys.* XXXV, 139. *Cimento* VI, 154-155. *Cosmos.* X, 320-321.
— BAHR, *De oculi accomodatione experimenta nova. Dissertat.* Berlin.

—   H. Müller, Über einen ringförmigen Muskel am Ciliarkörper. *Archiv für Ophthalm.*
        III, 1, IV, 2.   S. 277-285.

1859.   J. Mannhardt, Bemerkungen über den Akkommodationsmuskel und die Akkom-
        modation. Ibid. IV. 1.   S. 269-285.

—   Ch. Archer, On the adaptation of the human eye to varying distances.*Phil. Mag.*
        (4) XVII, 224-225.

—   Respighi, Sull'accommodamento dell'occhio humano per la visione distinta. *Mem.
        di Bologna.* VIII, 355-389. *Zeitschr. für Chemie.* 1859. S. 10-18.

—   Magni, Dell'addattamento dell'occhio umano alla visione distinta. *Cimento* X,
        12-20.

1860.   J. H. Knapp, Über die Lage und Krümmung der Oberflächen der menschlichen
        Kristallinse und den Einfluss ihrer Veränderungen bei der Akkommodation auf die
        Dioptrik des Auges. *Archiv. für Ophthalmol.* VI, 2, S. 1-52. VII, 2, S. 136-138.

1860.   W. Henke, Der Mechanismus der Akkommodation für Nähe und Ferne. Ibid.
        VI, 2, S. 53-72.

—   L. Happe, *Die Bestimmungen des Sehbereichs und dessen Korrektion, nebst Erläu-
        terungen über den Mechanismus der Akkommodation.* Braunschweig 1860.

1861.   A. v. Graefe, Fall von acquirierter Aniridie als Beitrag zur Akkommodationslehre.
        Archiv für Ophthalmol. VII, 2, S. 150-161.

1863.   O. Becker, Lage und Funktion der Ciliarfortsätze im lebenden Menschenauge.
        Wiener Medic. Jahrbücher. 1863.

1864.   E. Förster, Zur Kenntnis des Akkommodationsmechanismus. *Sitzungsber. d.
        Ophthalmol. Ges. Erlangen,* S. 75-86. *Klinische Monatsbl. für Augenheilk.* Sept.
        to Dec. 1864.

1865.   B. Rosow, Zur Ophthalmometrie. *Archiv für Ophthalmol.* XI, 2, S 129-134.

—   Mandelstam, Zur Ophthalmometrie. Ibid. XI, 2, S. 259-265.

§ 13. Chromatic Aberration in the Eye

It is only approximately correct to suppose that rays of light issuing from a luminous point and entering the eye are reunited in a single focus after traversing the ocular media. We must now examine this affair more closely, with particular reference in this section to the so-called *chromatic aberration;* due to the fact that the different wavelengths of light are unequally refrangible in solid and liquid transparent media. Since the magnitudes of the focal lengths of a curved refracting surface depend on the indices of refraction of the media, it follows that rays of light of different colours, after traversing an optical system of such surfaces, will generally be focused at different points. It is only by means of special combinations of refracting surfaces that the foci for light of different colours can be made to coincide, in which case the optical contrivance may be said to be *achromatic* in a certain sense.

Now the eye is not achromatic, although in ordinary vision the colour dispersion is scarcely noticeable at all. Fraunhofer demonstrated that the optical system of the eye really has different focal lengths for light of different colours in the following way. Observing a prismatic spectrum through an achromatic telescope which had a fine set of cross hairs in the eyepiece, in order to get sharp definition, he found that he had to focus the ocular lens nearer the cross hairs for the violet part of the spectrum than for the red. With the other eye focused on an external object, he viewed the cross hairs in the telescope illuminated by light from one part of the spectrum, and by adjusting the ocular contrived to see both them and the external object distinctly at the same time. Then he measured how much the ocular had to be displaced to get the same adjustment in another part of the spectrum. Thus, having previously measured the chromatic aberration of the ocular itself, he was able to calculate the chromatic aberration of the eye with respect to a pair of colours corresponding to two different places in the spectrum. By these experiments FRAUNHOFER found that an eye which is emmetropic for light corresponding to the *C* line (in the bright red part) of the solar spectrum had to be from 18 to 24 Paris inches[1] nearer the object, in order still to see it distinctly when the object emitted light corresponding to the *G* line (in the violet part) of the solar spectrum, without changing its accommodation.

The author has obtained similar results with his own eyes. Monochromatic light from different parts of a prismatic spectrum was admitted through a fine hole in an opaque screen, and the maximum distance was found for which the small illuminated opening could be seen as a well defined point. The far point of the author's eye was about 8.5 ft for red light and 1.6 ft for violet light; whereas it was only a few inches away for the extreme violet light at the end of the solar spectrum that cannot be seen at all unless the brighter parts of the spectrum are shaded.

In an ordinary rectangular spectrum projected by a prism on a white wall some distance away, the differences of the distances of distinct vision for different colours are strikingly manifest; because, while the red end may appear fairly well in its proper form, the violet end is more or less blurred (and in the author's own case has a sort of swallow-tail shape).

The rather slight chromatic aberration of the human eye as compared with artificial optical instruments is explained by the fact that water and aqueous solutions generally have much less dispersion than glass. Since the indices of refraction of the ocular media are not very different from that of water, it is reasonable to expect that the aqueous and vitreous humors, at least, would have about the same dispersion as that of water. Accordingly, the writer has calculated the dispersion of LISTING's reduced eye, which has a single refracting surface, on the assumption that the light is refracted from air to water. For the rays used by FRAUNHOFER in his experiments, the indices of refraction of water are as follows:

For *C* line (red)   1.331705;

For *G* line (violet)   1.341285.

[1] ¶1 Paris inch = 12 Paris lines = 27.07 mm.   (J. P. C. S.)

The radius of the refracting surface of the reduced eye is 5.1248 mm; and hence the second focal lengths will be found to be 20.574 mm (for red light) and 20.140 mm .(for violet light.) Thus, when the eye is accommodated for parallel red rays, so that the focal point for red light is on the retina, the focal point of the violet rays will be 0.434 mm in front of it; which implies that this is accommodated to see distinctly a source of violet light for a distance of 713 mm away (or about 28 inches). FRAUNHOFER (as stated above) found this distance in his own case to be between 487 and 650 mm; which indicated that the dispersion in an eye made of distilled water would be rather less than it is in the actual human eye. But if it is supposed that the reduced eye is accommodated for a distance of 8.5 ft (2.6 m) in the red, corresponding to the author's experiment with his own eye, the retina would still have to be 0.123 mm beyond the focal point of red light; and at the same time the eye is accommodated for a violet source of light 22 inches away or 560 mm; whereas in the writer's case this latter distance was 19 inches. MATTHIESSEN[1] also calculated from his experiments the interval between the focal points of the human eye for red and violet light and obtained from 0.58 to 0.62 mm; which can be compared with the value 0.434 mm for an eye made of distilled water. MATTHIESSEN's method consisted in measuring the shortest distance at which a ruled glass surface could be seen distinctly when it was illuminated, first, by red light and then by violet light. All these experiments by different methods agree in showing that, so far as chromatic aberration is concerned, the human eye corresponds very closely to an eye of distilled water; the dispersion of the natural eye being if anything a little higher. Perhaps, we might conjecture that, just as the refractivity of the crystalline lens is greater than that of pure water, so also its dispersion is higher.

Certain other experiments in which the colour dispersion of the eye is noticeable may also be described here. Phenomena of this kind are generally much more striking when instead of using white light, a mixture of only two colours is employed that are as different as possible in refrangibility. The best way to obtain this effect is to transmit sunlight through ordinary violet coloured glass, which will absorb the intermediate colours almost entirely and transmit only the extreme red and violet. But if lamplight is used, which is deficient in blue and violet, ordinary blue (cobalt) glass is better, as it filters out also much of the orange, yellow and green and transmits abundantly the extreme red, and blue and violet. A coloured glass of this kind is placed right behind a narrow aperture in a dark screen and illuminated

---

[1] *Comptes rendus.* T. XXIV. p. 875.

from behind by a lamp whose rays after traversing the glass and the hole in the screen enter the observer's eye. Under these circumstances the aperture may be regarded as a luminous point emitting red and violet rays; which will appear differently, depending on the distance for which the observer's eye is accommodated. When it is accommodated for the red rays, the violet light produces a blur circle, and the opening appears as a red point with a violet fringe around it; and *vice versa*. There is an intermediate state of accommodation for which the focus of the violet rays is in front of the retina, and that of the red rays beyond it, in such fashion that the coloured blur circles on the retina are equal in size; and only when this is the case will the source appear to be of the same uniform colour. For this state of accommodation, there might be some light of intermediate colour, say, green, which would be focused at a point on the retina.

Incidentally, this method affords a means of finding with considerable degree of accuracy the distances for which the eye can be accommodated for the intermediate parts of the spectrum; for they are the same as the distances for which the eye can see the mixed red-violet spot as being of uniform colour. The difference of colour at the edges is very easily detected, even by an unpractised observer; and it is much easier to distinguish than the inexactness of a white image. When the eye is accommodated for light of a certain definite frequency for a distance farther than that of the luminous point, the blur circle of the red rays on the retina will be larger than that of the violet, and the spot will appear as a violet disc with a red border; whereas the reverse effect will be observed when the eye is accommodated for a distance less than that of the luminous point. Effects similar to these always occur whenever an object emits two kinds of light of very different frequencies. The phenomena are very striking, for example, in certain experiments on the mixing of spectrum colours which will be subsequently described in the theory of colour mixtures.

With white light there is, of course, also some separation of the component colours, but ordinarily it is hardly noticeable. In this connection, experience shows that a white surface which is farther away than the point of accommodation of the eye, is tinged with a faint blue border; whereas if the object is nearer than the point of accommodation, the border will be a faint reddish yellow. But when the eye is accommodated for the exact distance of the white surface, no such coloured border is seen, unless some opaque obstacle is held close to the eye so as to cover part of the pupil; in which case a coloured border appears along the opaque edge. The border between a white and black field appears yellow when a card is interposed halfway in front of the

pupil from the side of the black portion, and blue when it is interposed from the side of the white portion.

The phenomena of chromatic aberration in the human eye as
above described are easily explained by the fact that the second focal
point for violet light lies in front of that for red. In Fig. 68 the luminous point is supposed to be at A; the first principal plane of the eye is

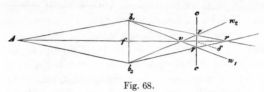

represented by the
straight line b_1b_2; the
points on the optical
axis designated by r
and v are the points
conjugate to A with
respect to the red

Fig. 68.

and violet rays, respectively; the straight line cc represents the plane
where the outside red rays of the cone b_1b_2r intersect the outside
violet rays of the cone b_1b_2v. Obviously, if the retina of the eye is
in front of the plane cc, that is, when the eye is accommodated for
an object farther away than A, it will be illuminated at the boundary
of the cone by red light only, whereas near the axis there will be a
mixture of colours. When the retina coincides with cc, so that the
eye is accommodated for light of intermediate frequency coming from
A, it will be illuminated all over by a uniform mixture of colours.
And when the retina is beyond cc, as will be the case when the accommodation is for a point nearer than A, the edge of the illuminated
area will be violet while the central part will be a mixture of colours.
Now suppose that when the eye is accommodated for A, so that the
retina is at cc, the lower half of the aperture b_1b_2 is covered by an
opaque screen; thereby cutting off all the violet rays beyond b_2v and
fv, all the red rays between b_2r and fr, and, of course, also, the prolongations of these rays. All the violet illumination disappears then
from the part of the retina above the axis, and all the red from the part
below the axis, the result being a small blur circle on the retina which
is red above and violet below, instead of a clear-cut image of the
point A.

If the source at A, instead of being a single luminous point, is a
surface uniformly illuminated with both red and violet light, there will
be formed on the retina simultaneously both a red and a violet image
of this surface, one of which is necessarily blurred. But the blurred
image of a uniform surface looks exactly the same as if it were in
focus, except towards the edge where the blur circles of the separate
points only partially overlap one another, and here the image fades out,
encroaching on the surrounding darkness only so far as the blur
circles of the border points extend. Now if red and violet images of a

luminous area are projected together on the same surface, the central portion of the resultant image where both colours are supposed to have normal brightness will appear as a blended mixture of the two; whereas the border will have that one of the two colours for which the blur circles are larger and for which, therefore, the border of the image encroaches farther on the surrounding parts. If the image of the surface is intercepted in the plane cc where the red and violet blur circles are of the same size, the colours will be uniformly mixed right to the edge. But when the edge of a card is gradually inserted in front of the pupil, the blurred images are partially eclipsed, as we saw in § 11; and these eclipses proceed from opposite sides when one of the blurred images is due to too near accommodation and the other to too far accommodation, as is the case here with the red and violet images. Hence, the congruence of the coloured images ceases, and coloured edges are visible. For red light the surface behaves like an object that is too near the eye, and hence the image in this case disappears from the side opposite to that on which the card is inserted in front of the pupil. With violet light it is just the other way. Hence, if the card is introduced, say, from below, the red surface vanishes from above and the violet from below with a red margin below and a violet margin above. When a small red-violet line is inspected through a narrow slit, the red image can be easily separated entirely from the violet image by moving the slit to and fro in front of the pupil.

When the light emitted by a luminous point is composed not simply of red and violet but of white light of all colours, the intermediate colours are distributed in their natural order between red and violet, and the effects of the chromatic aberration are not so striking as with two colours alone. Instead of a purple field with a violet border, we now have a white field bordered by pale blue, indigo and violet; and the inner part of this border is so nearly white that the border usually appears narrower. And instead of a purple field with a red border, there appears, likewise a white field faintly tinged at the boundary with yellow, orange and red, the pale yellow being hardly discernible against the white background.

The special case when the retina is at the place cc (Fig. 68) where the diameter of the bundle of rays is smallest needs to be considered. Here the blur circles of the red and violet rays are the same size. The green rays corresponding to the middle of the spectrum are united at the point where the axis meets the retina; and the rays of the rest of the colours form small blur circles. The resultant image on the retina ought therefore to be greenish at the centre, with a border of mixed red and violet, that is, purple; but it is not that way at all in the eye. For this particular position of the retina the light corresponding to the brightest colours, yellow and green, is concentrated almost exactly at a point, and the purple border is both too narrow and too faint to be perceived.

All the phenomena above described may be perceived just as in the eye, only exaggerated, in a non-achromatized telescope, provided a higher magnifying power is used than the instrument is intended to have. The real image made by the objective is not caught on a screen, as on the retina of the eye, but is viewed through a magnifying eyepiece. The image in the objective must be magnified, otherwise the coloured border is generally too small to be seen distinctly. In this case, also, when the telescope is focused on a more distant object, a white area will appear to have a red and yellow border; whereas when the telescope is focused on a nearer object, the same area will appear to have a blue border. When the telescope is focused so as to give the sharpest image of the white area, a very narrow purple border is seen. If one half of the object glass is screened, the opposite side of the white area has a blue and yellow border, etc., in perfect analogy to the case of the eye.

In order to calculate the size of the blur circle due to chromatic aberration in the eye, LISTING's reduced eye with water for the refracting medium may be used for this purpose, since, according to FRAUNHOFER's measurements, the dispersion of such an eye would not be very different from that of the human eye. From Fig. 68 we have:

$$\frac{\gamma\gamma}{b_1b_2} = \frac{\delta r}{fr} = \frac{\delta v}{fv},$$

and therefore

$$\gamma\gamma \cdot fr = b_1b_2 \cdot \delta r,$$

By addition,

$$\frac{\gamma\gamma \cdot fv = b_1b_2 \cdot \delta v.}{\gamma\gamma[fr+fv] = b_1b_2 \cdot [\delta r + \delta v]}$$
$$= b_1b_2[fr-fv]$$
$$\gamma\gamma = b_1b_2\frac{fr-fv}{fr+fv}.$$

Taking 4 mm, the mean pupillary diameter in normal eyes, as the length of b_1b_2, and substituting the following values as previously obtained:

$$fr = 20.574 \text{ mm},$$
$$fv = 20.140 \text{ mm};$$

consequently,

$$\gamma\gamma = 0.0426 \text{ mm}.$$

According to the table given in § 11 for the dimensions of blur circles of objects for which the eye is not accommodated, the diameter $\gamma\gamma$ of the blur circle caused by dispersion should be equal to that given by a luminous point 1.5 metres away (or about 5 ft) in an eye accommodated for infinity. This degree of lack of accommodation

would result in a very appreciable confusion of the details in the image
of an object, as may be easily verified by trying the experiment. In
order to understand why the dispersion of white light in the eye
which results in blur circles on the retina of these dimensions does not
actually confuse vision to any sensible extent, not only the size of the
blur circle but the distribution of the light in it has to be taken into
account.

When the eye gets light of a definite frequency emitted from a
point-source, the retina being to one side or the other of the focus of the
bundle of refracted rays, the blur circle on the retina is equally illuminated all over. But if the luminous point emits white light of all sorts
of frequencies, and the retina of the eye is in focus for the brightest
part of the spectrum corresponding to greenish yellow light, there will
be blur circles for the light of other colours, and their diameters will
be greater in proportion as these colours are farther from the middle of
the spectrum. Thus, whereas the centre of the affected area of
the retina is uniformly illuminated by light of all kinds, especially by
the most brilliant and most concentrated kind, the outlying portions
get light only from the extreme parts of the spectrum, which not only
have less intrinsic brilliancy, but are still further enfeebled in their
effects by being spread over a larger area. Theoretically, the image is
infinitely brighter at the centre than anywhere else.

As the law of the luminosity of the different parts of the spectrum
has not yet been mathematically formulated, the calculation will be
made on the assumption that all the colours of the spectrum are equally
bright. Of course, this means that the values found for the illumination
at the borders of the blur circles will be too large; but even so, the calculation will show why the blur circles due to chromatic aberration
produce far less confusion than those of equal size due to imperfect
accommodation.

*Theoretical Distribution of Intensity
in a Blur Circle due to Chromatic Aberration of Light proceeding from a Point-
Source.*

In Fig. 69 the straight line *bb*
represents the principal plane of the
reduced eye of radius *R*; and we may
suppose that the diaphragm which
limits the bundle of rays lies in this

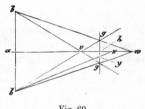

Fig. 69.

plane, as is approximately the case in the natural eye, so that *bb* is a
diameter of the stop, whose radius will be denoted by *b*. The incident
rays are supposed to be parallel; and the focal points of the extreme
violet and extreme red rays are designated by *v* and *w*, respectively.

These extreme rays intersect each other at the two points designated
by g, so that the straight line gg is the diameter of the entire blur circle,
whose centre is at the point designated by h. To get the best image,
the retina should be in the plane gg. Let the index of refraction
corresponding to light from the middle part of the spectrum, that is
focused at h, be denoted by N and put $ah = F$. Then by equation
(3a), §9:

$$F = \frac{NR}{N-1} \quad \cdot \quad \cdot \quad \cdot \quad \cdot \quad \cdot \quad \cdot \quad \text{(1a)}$$

If n denotes the index of refraction for light of some other kind which
is focused at a point x, and if $f = ax$ denotes the focal length for these
rays, then

$$f = \frac{nR}{n-1} \quad \cdot \quad \cdot \quad \cdot \quad \cdot \quad \cdot \quad \cdot \quad \text{(1b)}$$

Let $\rho = hy$ denote the radius of the blur circle due to this kind of light;
then its value will be given by one of the following formulae:

$$\frac{\rho}{b} = \frac{f-F}{f}, \quad \text{or} \quad \frac{\rho}{b} = \frac{F-f}{f},$$

according as $f > F$ (that is $n < N$) or $f < F$ (that is, $n > N$), respectively.
When the above expressions for F and f are substituted, we have, either

$$\frac{\rho}{b} = \frac{N-n}{n(N-1)} \quad \cdot \quad \cdot \quad \cdot \quad \cdot \quad \cdot \quad \cdot \quad \text{(2a)}$$

for $n < N$, or

$$\frac{\rho}{b} = \frac{n-N}{n(N-1)} \quad \cdot \quad \cdot \quad \cdot \quad \cdot \quad \cdot \quad \cdot \quad \text{(2b)}$$

for $n > N$.

Now the intensity H of the illumination on the retina for light of
colour corresponding to the value n of the index of refraction is:

$$H = A\frac{b^2}{\rho^2} \quad \cdot \quad \cdot \quad \cdot \quad \cdot \quad \cdot \quad \cdot \quad \text{(3)}$$

where A denotes the intensity of the incident light over the area bb.
Combining this equation with either equation (2a) or equation (2b), so
as to eliminate b and ρ, we find in both cases:

$$H = A\frac{n^2(N-1)^2}{(n-N)^2} \quad \cdot \quad \cdot \quad \cdot \quad \cdot \quad \cdot \quad \text{(3a)}$$

Now the intensity of illumination J at any point in the blur circle
is:

$$J = \int H dn, \quad \cdot \quad \cdot \quad \cdot \quad \cdot \quad \cdot \quad \cdot \quad \text{(4)}$$

the integral being taken over all values of n included in the given range of colours. In the expression for H, the factor A is really a function of n, but its mathematical form is unknown. The factor n^2 varies very little over the range of the spectrum; and so for practical purposes, the product

$$An^2(N-1)^2 = B$$

may be regarded as constant, which is equivalent to assuming that the brightness of the spectrum is practically uniform throughout its range, varying but little from red to violet. This assumption is really less favourable to our theory than the actual fact. According to equation (4):

$$J = \int \frac{B\,dn}{(N-n)^2}; \qquad \cdot \quad \cdot \quad \cdot \quad \cdot \quad \cdot \quad (4a)$$

the integral being taken between the proper limits of n. However, every point of the blur circle is illuminated by light from both the red and violet ends of the spectrum. Let n_1, n_2 denote the extreme values of the index of refraction for the red light, so that

$$N > n_2 > n_1,$$

and let n_3, n_4 denote the extreme values of the index of refraction for violet light, so that

$$n_4 > n_3 > N.$$

Equation (4a) becomes therefore:

$$\left. \begin{aligned} J &= B \int_{n_1}^{n_2} \frac{dn}{(N-n)^2} + B \int_{n_3}^{n_4} \frac{dn}{(N-n)^2} \\ &= B\left\{ \frac{1}{N-n_2} - \frac{1}{N-n_1} + \frac{1}{N-n_4} - \frac{1}{N-n_3} \right\} \end{aligned} \right\} \qquad \cdot \quad \cdot \quad \cdot \quad (4b)$$

Now if ρ_0 denotes the distance from the centre of the blur circle to the point where the intensity is to be ascertained, this point will be illuminated by light of all colours for which the radii of the blur circles are greater than ρ_0, or between ρ_0 and r. For the less refrangible colours, equation (2a) gives:

$$\frac{1}{N-n} = \frac{1}{N} + \frac{1}{N(N-1)} \cdot \frac{b}{\rho}.$$

Since $\rho = r$ for $n = n_1$, and $\rho = \rho_0$ for $n = n_2$, therefore,

$$\left. \begin{aligned} \frac{1}{N-n_1} &= \frac{1}{N} + \frac{1}{(N-1)N} \cdot \frac{b}{r} \\ \frac{1}{N-n_2} &= \frac{1}{N} + \frac{1}{(N-1)N} \cdot \frac{b}{\rho_0} \end{aligned} \right\} \qquad \cdot \quad \cdot \quad \cdot \quad \cdot \quad (4c)$$

Similarly, with respect to n_3 and n_4, we must employ equation (2b), which may be written:

$$\frac{1}{N-n} = \frac{1}{N} - \frac{1}{N(N-1)}\frac{b}{\rho}.$$

For $n = n_4$ put $\rho = r$, and for $n = n_3$ put $\rho = \rho_0$; accordingly,

$$\left.\begin{array}{l} \dfrac{1}{N-n_4} = \dfrac{1}{N} - \dfrac{1}{N(N-1)}\;\dfrac{b}{r} \\[2mm] \dfrac{1}{N-n_3} = \dfrac{1}{N} - \dfrac{1}{N(N-1)}\cdot\dfrac{b}{\rho_0} \end{array}\right\} \quad . \quad . \quad . \quad . \quad (4d)$$

Substituting in (4b) the values given by (4c) and (4d), we get finally:

$$J = \frac{2B}{N(N-1)}\left\{\frac{b}{\rho_0} - \frac{b}{r}\right\} \quad . \quad . \quad . \quad . \quad (5)$$

The value of J becomes infinite at the center of the blur circle ($\rho_0 = 0$) and vanishes at the border where $\rho_0 = r$.

Calculation of the intensity at the edge of a uniformly illuminated area. The straight line AB in Fig. 70 represents the edge of a luminous

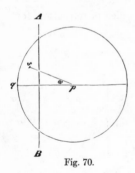

Fig. 70.

surface; and it is assumed that every point of this edge is blurred. Suppose that p is the point where the intensity is to be found, and let $r = pq$ denote the radius of the blur circle. This point p will get light from all those points of the surface that lie within the circle described around p as centre with radius r. Suppose s is one of these points, and put $sp = \rho$, and angle $spq = \omega$. Let J denote the intensity of illumination due to a single blur circle at the distance ρ from its centre. Then the total intensity at the point p will be

$$H = \int\!\!\int J\rho\, d\omega\, d\rho, \quad . \quad . \quad . \quad . \quad . \quad (6)$$

where the double integral must be taken over all parts of the area within the circle described around p. Now suppose that the edge of the illuminated surface is a straight line, and let the distance of the point s from it be denoted by x; then if the centre p of the circle is on this edge,

$$\rho\cos\omega = x,$$

Integrating the expression for H, first, with respect to ω, using the limiting value of the angle ω as given by the last equation, we obtain:

$$H = \int_x^r 2J\rho \text{ arc cos} \left(\frac{x}{\rho}\right) d\rho \quad . \quad . \quad . \quad . \quad (6a)$$

When the blur circles are due to imperfect accommodation, J may be considered as independent of ρ, and in this case:

$$H = J\left[r^2 \text{ arc cos}\left(\frac{x}{r}\right) - x\sqrt{r^2 - x^2} \right] \quad . \quad . \quad . \quad (7)$$

This equation gives, therefore, an expression for the intensity of illumination at a point near the edge of the surface as a function of the distance from the edge. For $x = r$, we get $H = 0$; and for $x = -r$, we have $H = Jr^2\pi$, so that here the intensity is equal to the general intensity of the uniformly illuminated area.

When the blur circles are due to dispersion, the value of J given by equation (5) may be substituted in equation (6a). The result of performing the integration in this case is:

$$H = \frac{2Bb}{N(N-1)} \left\{ r \text{ arc cos}\left(\frac{x}{r}\right) + \frac{x}{r}\sqrt{r^2 - x^2} + x \text{ log nat} \left(\frac{r - \sqrt{r^2 - x^2}}{r + \sqrt{r^2 - x^2}}\right) \right\} (8)$$

For $x = r$, we find (as before) $H = 0$, and for $x = -r$,

$$H = \frac{2Bbr\pi}{N(N-1)};$$

so that the intensity at such a point becomes equal to the constant intensity of the central portions of the surface.

The variations of these functions are represented graphically by the curves in Fig. 71, curve A corresponding to equation (7) and curve B to equation (8). The ordinate H is shown as a function of the abscissa x. The ordinate ba represents the uniform intensity of

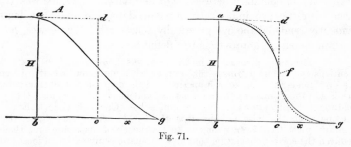

Fig. 71.

illumination of the interior portion of the surface, and the point c shows the position of the edge, so that the dotted line adc would indicate the intensity of an image that was sharply defined at the edge. The diameter of the blur circle of the point c is bg. A striking difference between curve A and curve B is that the latter becomes perpendicular to the x-axis at the point f, corresponding to the actual position of the boundary. That is, for $x \doteq 0$, the derivative

$$\frac{dH}{db} = \frac{2Bb}{N(N-1)} \left\{ \frac{2}{r} \sqrt{r^2 - x^2} + \log \text{ nat } \left[\frac{r - \sqrt{r^2 - x^2}}{r + \sqrt{r^2 - x^2}} \right] \right\} \quad . \quad . \quad . \quad (9)$$

becomes infinite. This sudden drop in intensity enables the eye to recognize the position of the edge, even if some light does extend beyond it. In the case represented by curve A, however, the falling off is more gradual, so that there is nothing to indicate exactly where the edge is.

If it were possible to take into account the diminishing brightness of the colours towards the ends of the spectrum, the curve B would be found to follow more nearly the dotted line drawn adjacent to it. That is, the intensity would approach its normal maximum value more rapidly inside the edge, and would fall off more rapidly outside, than curve B indicates.

It will be clear from these considerations why the distinctness of visual images is so little affected by chromatic aberration. A combination of lenses intended to correct the chromatic aberration of the eye does not produce any appreciable improvement of the visual acuity, according to the writer's experience. A concave flint glass lens of 15.4 mm focal length, taken from the objective of a microscope, was found suitable for this purpose. It was combined with convex crown glass lenses so as to produce a system with a negative focal length of about 2.6 ft; which was adapted for the writer's eye so that he could discern distant objects through it clearly. On looking through this arrangement with half of the pupil covered, no coloured fringes appeared at the boundary between light and dark. The same was true even with the eye imperfectly accommodated; so that the lenses evidently rendered the eye practically achromatic. There was, however, no apparent improvement in definition.

The chromatic aberration in the eye was known to NEWTON, who mentions the coloured fringes that appear when the pupil is half covered.[1] NEWTON made the mistake of supposing that the dispersion of all transparent media is proportional to their refraction; and hence he concluded that an achromatic combination of lenses was impossible. Curiously enough, EULER,[2] starting from the false premise that the eye is achromatic, argued that NEWTON must have been wrong as to his theory of dispersion and thence deduced the correct conclusion that an achromatic combination of lenses was possible. D'ALAMBERT[3] took exception to this reasoning, by pointing out that the chromatic aberration may not necessarily become noticeable in the

[1] *Optics.* Lib. I. P. II. Prop. VIII.

[2] *Journal Encyclop.* 1765. II. p. 146. — *Mém. de l'Acad. de Berlin.* 1747.

[3] *Mém. de l'Acad. de Paris.* 1767. p. 81.

eye, even if it were just as great as it is in glass lenses. DOLLOND,[1] too, argued the same way and asserted that the eye cannot be achromatic, no matter if there are several different refracting media in it; because at every refraction the rays are bent towards the axis. The validity of DOLLOND's reasoning will be manifest when it is remembered that the violet rays are always more refracted than the red rays in going from one medium to another, so that at every refraction in the eye the violet rays must be bent towards the axis more than the red rays. MASKELYNE[2] measured the chromatic aberration of the eye, and found the interval between the focal points to be 0.61 mm corresponding to a visual angle of 15''; whereas a telescope is considered as achromatic when this angle is as much as 57''. JURIN[3] noted the coloured edges of ill-defined objects; and WOLLASTON[4] the peculiar appearance of the prismatic spectrum due to the inability of the eye to accommodate for all colours at once. MOLLWEIDE[5] gave a complete theory of the appearances observed with the pupil half covered, and TOURTUAL discussed fully all the phenomena relating to the subject. The first accurate measurements of the chromatic aberration of the eye were made by FRAUNHOFER[6] with reference to the fixed spectral lines discovered by WOLLASTON and himself; and subsequent measurements were made by MATTHIESSEN.[7]

And yet in spite of all these investigations, many natural philosophers, like FORBES[8] and VALLÉE,[9] continue to cling to the idea that the eye is absolutely perfect and that it is more or less completely achromatic.

1704. J. NEWTON, *Optics.* B. I. P. II. Prop. VIII.*
1747. L. EULER, *Mém. de Berlin.* 1747. p. 285. — 1753. p. 249. — 1754. p. 200.
1767. D'ALEMBERT, *Mém. de l'Acad. de Paris.* 1767. p. 81.*
1789. MASKELYNE. *Phil. Trans.* LXXIX. 256.*
1798. COMPARETTI, *Observationes de coloribus apparentibus.* Patavini.
1801. TH. YOUNG, *Phil. Trans.* 1801. P. I. p. 50.*
1805. MOLLWEIDE in GILBERTS *Annalen.* XVII. 328. u XXX. 220.
1814. *FRAUNHOFER in GILBERTS *Annalen.* LVI. 304. — SCHUHMACHERS *astronom. Abhandlungen.* Altona 1823. Heft II. S. 39.
1826. J. MÜLLER, *Zur vergl. Physiol. des Gesichtssinns.* Leipzig. S. 195. 414.*
1830. *TOURTUAL, Über Chromasie des Auges. MECKELS *Archiv.* 1830. S. 129.*
1837. MILE, POGGENDORFFS *Ann.* XLII. 64.
1847. A. MATTHIESSEN, *Comptes rendus,* XXIV. 875; *Institut.* No. 698. p. 162; POGGENDORFFS *Ann.* LXXI. 578*; FRORIEPS *Notizen.* III. 341; *Archive d. sciences phys. et natur.* V. 221; *Berl. Berichte.* 1847. S. 183.*
       L. L. VALLÉE, *Comptes rendus.* XXIV. 1096; *Berl. Ber.* 1847. S. 184.*
1849. J. D. FORBES, *Proceed. Edinburg Roy. Soc.* Dec. 3. 1849. p. 251; SILLIMAN'S *Journ.* (2) XIII. 413; *Berl. Ber.* 1850. p. 492.*
1852. L. L. VALLÉE, *Comptes rendus.* XXXIV. 321; *Berl. Ber.* 1852. S. 308.*
1853. L. L. VALLÉE, *Sur l'achromatisme de l'œil* C. R. XXXVI. 142-144; 480-482.
1855. CZERMAK, Zur Chromasie des Auges. *Wiener Sitzungsber.* XVII. 563.
1856. A. FICK, Einige Versuche über die chromatische Abweichung des menschlichen Auges. *Archiv für Ophthalm.* II. 2. 70-76.

---

[1] *Philos. Trans.* LXXIX. p. 256.
[2] *Philos. Trans.* LXXIX. 258.
[3] SMITH'S *Optics.* 96.
[4] *Philos. Trans.* 1801. P. I. p. 50.
[5] GILBERTS *Annalen.* XVII. 328. u XXX. 220.
[6] GILBERTS *Annalen.* LVI. 304. — SCHUMACHERS *astronom. Abhandlungen.* Heft II. S. 39.
[7] *Comptes rendus.* XXIV. 875.
[8] *Proc. Roy. Edinb. Soc.* Dec. 3. 1849. p. 251.
[9] *Comptes rendus.* XXIV. 1096. XXXIV. 321.

1862. F. P. Leroux, Expériences destinées à mettre en evidence le défaut d'achromatisme de l'œil. *Ann. de chimie.* 3. LXVI. 173–182. *Cosmos.* XX. 638–639.

— Trouessart, *Défaut d'achromatisme de l'œil. Presse scientifique.* p. 72–74.

Note by A. Gullstrand

With the further development of the theory of optical imagery and of the so-called aberrations, for the sake of accuracy, a distinction should be made between the phenomena that were formerly grouped together under the head of chromatic aberration. Since all the magnitudes that determine the nature of the imagery may have different values for different indices of refraction, the only exact way of describing the phenomena of chromatic aberration, as it is called, is in terms of the *chromatic differences* of these parameters. Along the axis of a centered optical system, for example, we must first take into account the *chromatic difference of focus* and the *chromatic difference of magnification.* By the former is meant the distance between the two focal points due to two different kinds of light; and the latter is proportional to the difference between the primary focal lengths of the system. The difference of magnification cannot be found directly from the difference of focus except in the special case when the position of the second nodal point is independent of the index of refraction, as is the case in the reduced eye, but as is not the case in the human eye. For the same reason, both differences vanish simultaneously in the achromatization of an infinitely thin optical system; but as a rule this does not happen.

The focus difference is what Helmholtz has in mind above in his discussion of the distribution of light within the blur circles. As to the difference of magnification, perhaps it might be neutralized by just the same mechanism as for the focus difference, provided the images are very small. The reason why a bright point is seen without a coloured border, is because, as Helmholtz has proved, the dimensions of the blur circles of light of the longest and shortest wave-lengths are about equal and also because the coloured borders are faint. However, two adjacent bright points cannot produce concentric blur circles at the same time for light of both short and long wave-lengths, since one of them must necessarily lie outside the axis. The centre of the blur circle due to light of short wave-length is nearer the axis for this latter point than that of the blur circle due to light of long wave-length; and hence the two sides of this point cannot be seen in one and the same colour at the same time, on account of the chromatic difference of magnification. Since the chromatic difference of the size of the image is to the size of the image for a given kind of light in the same ratio as the chromatic difference of focal length is to the focal length for the given kind of light, the value of this ratio can be obtained for the reduced eye from HELMHOLTZ's numerical data. In round numbers it is 3 per cent. While it may be somewhat larger than this in the human eye, obviously the image must be fairly large before the chromatic difference of magnification would be noticeable; and considering the distribution of light in the chromatic blur circles, it is hardly to be supposed that this difference is appreciable when it is measured in minutes and is of the same order of magnitude as the angular size of the place of most distinct vision.

The chromatic difference of magnification increases with the size of the image, but at the same time the ability to see the coloured borders diminishes, because they fall on parts of the retina that are farther removed from the place of most distinct vision. Now if this decrease of the visual acuity were proportional to the increase of the width of the coloured border, the phenomena of the chromatic difference of magnification, although physically present on the retina, would not be physiologically revealed by the visible appearance of coloured fringes. This physiological mechanism is adequate to mask the chromatic differences of magnification in the outlying portions of a large retinal image. If, however, the object consists of two bright, narrow lines whose angular separation amounts to 3°, and a point is fixated symmetrically situated between them, the lines will appear more than 5′ nearer together when they are illuminated by violet light than when they are illuminated by red light; this difference being divided equally between both lines, so that each of them appears like an impure spectrum of about 2.5 minutes in apparent width. Without making the statement that the eye is able to distinguish between a spectrum of this kind and a bright line at an angular distance of 1.5° from the point of fixation (because at present exact determinations of this question have not been made and perhaps they would be difficult), it may be noted that there is in the eye a mechanism tending to neutralize the chromatic difference of magnification in the case of objects of this kind.

As the writer has shown by entoptical investigations,[1] considerable chromatic dispersion occurs in the passage of light from the vitreous humor to the retina. The reason of this is that the shadows due to refraction of light in the most curved central portion of the fovea— the entoptical fovea, as the writer has called it—cannot be seen with light of long wave-length, but only with light of short wave-length, and is undoubtedly due to the luteous ingredients in the lymph of the retina. On leaving the vitreous humor, rays belonging to image-points near the axis are refracted in the fovea away from the axis, and since

[1] Die Farbe der Macula centralis retinae. *Arch. f. Ophth.* LXII, 1. S. 1. 1905. Zur Maculafrage. Ibid., LXVI, 1. S. 141. 1907.

this effect is greater for the rays of shorter wave-length, the result is a comparative magnification of the images due to these rays. Just how much this contributes toward neutralizing the effect of the chromatic difference of magnification, it would be difficult to say.

Since the centres of the refracting surfaces of the eye do not all lie on the line of sight, the centre of the exit-pupil of the eye has different positions for light of different wave-lengths. Strictly speaking, therefore, a *chromatic difference of the directions of the lines of sight* in the vitreous humor has to be taken into account. However, this effect is hidden by the unsymmetrical form of the blur circle due to the monochromatic aberrations. This is made manifest by viewing a small artificial source of light through cobalt glass with the eye adjusted for red; the bluish blur circle that most people see appears broader on the temporal than on the nasal side.

§ 14. Monochromatic Aberrations[1]

Besides the inexactness of the image due to unequal refrangibility of light of different frequencies, optical instruments made of glass lenses with spherical surfaces are subject to another kind of aberration, namely, *defects on account of spherical form* or so-called *spherical aberration*. This aberration is due to the fact that, in general, a homocentric bundle of rays even of one homogeneous kind of light after being refracted at curved surfaces will be only approximately homocentric. There are, indeed, certain curved surfaces (aplanatic surfaces) which may, under proper conditions, reunite the rays exactly at one point. They are surfaces of revolution generated, as a rule, by a curve of the fourth degree; though in certain cases, for example, when the point source is at infinity, the genetratrix is an ellipse.[2] Moreover, by a suitable choice of constants (indices of refraction, curvatures and distances apart) it is possible to design centered systems of spherical refracting surfaces in which for a given point on the optical axis the spherical aberration is more or less inappreciable. Systems of this kind are called aplanatic also.[3] Of course, the blurred image of a luminous point on the axis of a centered system of spherical refracting surfaces is symmetrical with respect to the axis. It forms a round spot which is brightest at the centre and fades rapidly in all directions from that point.

[1] See Appendix V at end of Part I.   G.

[2] ¶Or an hyperbola, in case the first medium is more highly refracting than the second. (J. P. C. S.)

[3] ¶This is the original meaning of the term "aplanatism" in geometrical optics; but since the time of ABBE the word has become more restricted and is applied to an optical system which is not only free from spherical aberration along the axis but also satisfies the so-called "sine condition."   (J. P. C. S.)

The monochromatic aberrations in the optical system of the eye are not, like the spherical aberration of glass lenses, symmetrical about an axis. They are much more unsymmetrical and of a kind that is not permissible in well constructed optical instruments. Neither the term "spherical aberration" as applied to spherical surfaces nor the awkward expression "aberration on account of the form of the refracting surface," which is used with respect to other curved refracting surfaces, is sufficiently general to describe this particular fault in the case of the optical system of the eye; and the term that will be used here is *monochromatic aberration*, since this aberration is concerned simply with homogeneous (monochromatic) light, and also in order to distinguish it from the *chromatic aberration*, which was the subject of the preceding section.

The phenomena are as follows:

1. Suppose the object is a very small luminous point (for example, a pinhole in a piece of opaque black paper illuminated from behind), which is situated rather farther from the eye than the greatest distance of accommodation; so that its image on the retina will be indistinct. In place of the bright point, what is seen is not a circular spot, as in the case of a telescope out of focus, but a star-shaped pattern with from four to eight irregular points or rays, which is usually different in the two eyes, and different also for different individuals. Fig. 72, *a* and *b*, show the patterns as they look in the writer's right and left eye, respectively. When blurred images of this kind are produced by white light, the outer edges of the bright parts have a blue border, and the edges towards the center are orange coloured. For most people the vertical dimension of the figure is greater than the horizontal. When the illumination is faint, only the brightest parts of the pattern are visible, and it then appears as a small cluster of spots, one of which is usually more conspicuous than the others. With very intense light, on the other hand, as when the pinhole is illuminated by direct sunlight, the points of the star seem to merge together, while all around it an immense number of exceedingly fine, brilliantly coloured, radiating lines form a sort of corona of much greater extent. The name *hair corona* will be used to distinguish this phenomenon from the star-shaped blurred image.

Fig. 72.

Now as he is watching the star-shaped figure, or the group of spots, in case of feeble illumination, suppose the observer gradually inserts a card from below in front of his eye; then he will see the lower part of the blurred image eclipsed first, which corresponds, of course, to the upper part of the retinal image; and if the card is interposed from above, or from the right or left, the part of the image that disappears first will be the upper part or right or left part, respectively. But the behaviour of the more extended hair corona, produced by very bright illumination, is different. When the pupil is gradually covered from below, the lower part of the central, star-shaped figure disappears as before, but not the lower part of the corona. ·However, the appearance of the corona will be disturbed and altered, and very brilliant diffraction patterns will develop, depending on the reduction and deformation of the pupillary opening. The radiant appearance of stars and distant lights is an example of these phenomena.

2. When the eye is accommodated for a distance greater than that of the luminous point (which may be accomplished in case the source is far away by inserting a weak concave lens before the eye), there appears another kind of star-shaped figure, whose longer dimension is generally horizontal. Fig. 72, *c* and *d*, represent these appearances in the writer's right and left eye, respectively. Now when the pupil is gradually covered from one side, it is the opposite side of the figure that disappears first, and hence the same side of the retinal image. Accordingly, this figure is made by rays that have not yet crossed the axis of the eye. If the cornea is moist with tear-fluid, or has been covered with oil-drops from the MEIBOMian glands by vigourous blinking, the star pattern is usually larger and more irregular and considerably altered by blinking, and when the pupil is covered from one side, the effect is not a simple disappearance of one side of the figure.

3. When the luminous point is situated where the eye can accommodate for it, moderate illumination shows it as a small, round, bright spot without any irregularities. The radiant appearance again becomes evident, however, when the illumination is increased, whatever the state of accommodation. With gradual changes of accommodation, all we find is that the starry pattern which is vertically elongated for shorter accommodation becomes smaller and rounder and then elongates horizontally into a star again, when the distance of accommodation exceeds that of the source of light.

4. When the source of light is a narrow line, the resulting appearance can be found by constructing the blurred starry images for each separate point of the luminous source, which will partly overlap each other. The brighter portions of these figures unite to form stripes, which appear as multiple images of the bright line. Most people see two of them, whereas in certain positions many persons see five or six of these double images.

In order to demonstrate experimentally also the connection between
these double images of lines and the star-shaped images of points, cut
a narrow slit in a piece of black paper, and make a small
pinhole a little way from one end of it, as shown in Fig.
73, *a*. Viewed from a distance, the double images of the
slit will be seen to be just as far apart as the brightest parts
of the star, and to be exactly in line with them, as shown
in Fig. 73, *b*; where, in the blurred image of the bright
point, only the brightest parts of the star-shaped spot in
Fig. 72, *a* are reproduced.

a   *b*

Fig. 73.

An example of this phenomenon is afforded by the
multiple images of the horns of the crescent moon as seen by most
persons. Another illustration is the effect that is occasionally seen at
the edge of a bright area for which the eye is not exactly accommodated. The transition at the edge from light to darkness appears to
be made in two or three stages. Other related phenomena are to be
described later in the theory of irradiation.

5.   In general, the accommodation of the eye
is not the same for horizontal and for vertical lines
at the same distance. Suppose a person looks
intently at a pencil of rays all radiating from one
point, as shown in Fig. 74, the eye being at a suitable distance for easy accommodation. Now it
will be noticed that each of these lines can be seen

Fig. 74.

separately clear and distinct one after another, but only one at a time
can be made to stand out sharp and black, and all the others will

appear more or less blurred. If the
person is accustomed to noting changes
of accommodation in his own eyes, he
will observe that it takes less accommodation to focus the horizontal line distinctly, and more accommodation to
focus the vertical line distinctly. That
is, a vertical line must be held farther
from the eye than a horizontal one, in
order to see them both with equal clearness at the same time. A. FICK saw
vertical lines distinctly at a distance of

Fig 75.

4.6 m, and at the same time horizontal lines at a distance of 3 m.
In the writer's case the distances were 65 cm and 54 cm for horizontal
and vertical lines, respectively.

Consider a white card on which a large number of concentric circles
is drawn very close together but at equal distances apart, as repre-

sented in Fig. 75. When this is inspected at a convenient distance for good accommodation, peculiar radiating sectors will be seen, which on closer examination will be found to be due to the fact that along the brighter radii the black and white lines are sharply differentiated, while in between them are bright grey blurred places where the black lines are fainter. By varying the accommodation a little or the distance of the diagram from the eye, other portions of the figure become clear, and we get an impression as if the sharply defined radii were rapidly rotating. When the card is held fairly close to the eye, and the eye accommodated for a farther distance, some 8 or 10 sectors will be seen with clear-cut lines; and where these join each other, they are nebulous, but it is evident that the black lines of one sector do not harmonize with those of the adjacent sectors. The result is the most interior circles have a queer distorted appearance. Obviously, these phenomena are all due to some sort of asymmetry of the eye. An optical instrument that is symmetrical around its axis may certainly produce a blurred image of a point on the axis; but it would have to be symmetrical and therefore circular.

The next thing to be ascertained is what features of the small, star-shaped, blurred image are permanent and occur regularly in good eyes; and, on the other hand, how it is modified by such transient influences as the presence of tear-fluid and other impurities on the cornea from the lids and eyelashes. A. FICK has shown that these latter effects may be imitated artificially by obtaining the image of a luminous point in a glass lens with a film of water on its surface.

These evanescent phenomena are of rare occurrence in the writer's own eyes. Ordinarily the same patterns as those shown in Fig. 72, which somehow recall the star-shaped structure of the crystalline lens as depicted in Fig. 20, constantly recur. In fact, the author might be persuaded that the most essential characteristics of these star-shaped patterns were due in some way to the irregularities of the crystalline lens, because when the illuminated hole is very close to the eye, the so-called entoptical phenomena, to be described in the next section, become manifest in the blurred image. There also we shall see how the place in the eye can be determined where the little object is that causes this phenomenon. What was found was, that as the distance of the luminous point from the eye was gradually increased, certain alternately bright and dark bands produced by the entoptical image of the crystalline lens were transformed into the bright and dark specks and streamers of the star patterns shown in Fig. 72, *c* and *d*. Sketches illustrating the process were made by YOUNG.[1]

[1] *Philos. Transact.* .1801. I. pl. VI.

As to the second class of phenomena above mentioned, namely, differences of focal length for horizontal and vertical lines, the explanation as yet is not quite so certain. Such effects are of course to be expected wherever light is refracted by surfaces with different curvatures in different directions, or even by spherical surfaces, when the rays are incident obliquely; either of which might occur in the eye. Horizontal and vertical meridian sections of the refracting surfaces of the eye have not quite the same curvature; and, besides, we know that the human eye is not exactly centered, and that the place of direct vision is not on the straight line that comes nearest to meeting the requirements of an axis of the eye.

The focal lengths of YOUNG's eye were quite different in the horizontal and vertical meridians, and he found by experiment that this difference was not in the cornea.[1] Thus, when his eye was immersed in water so as to neutralize almost completely the refraction of the cornea, there was practically the same difference of power of accommodation in the two meridians as before. This fault of the eye can be corrected, as YOUNG likewise remarked, by using spectacles inclined at a certain angle to the axis of the eye; as has been verified by the writer, who found that a weak concave lens could be held before the eye and adjusted at the right angle to enable him to see equally distinctly both horizontal and vertical lines at the same time.

And, lastly, imperfect transparency of the ocular media may also be partly responsible for monochromatic aberrations in the eye. The fibres of the cornea and lens certainly seem to be bound together by another substance of pretty nearly the same index of refraction, so that with moderate illumination these parts appear perfectly homogeneous and transparent. But when they are strongly illuminated by concentrating light on them with a lens, the light reflected from the edges of the elementary parts is strong enough to produce a faint cloudy glow. A part of the light transmitted through them is scattered and must fall on parts of the retina outside the place where the regularly refracted light goes. In fact, when a very brilliant light is seen against a dark background, there is a nebulous white glow over the surroundings, brightest near the light. As soon as the light is cut off, the luminosity of the background vanishes also. It would seem that this phenomenon must be explained by diffused refraction.[2]

The theory of refraction at aspherical surfaces and at spherical surfaces at oblique incidence will not be fully treated here, because, without more accurate information as to the forms of the refracting

---

[1] *Philos. Transact.* 1801. I. p. 40.
[2] HELMHOLTZ in POGGENDORFFS *Ann.* LXXXVI. 509.

surfaces of the eye, it would be of little use for investigations of ocular refractions. It will suffice to examine two cases of this sort of refraction, in which the conditions are mathematically simple.

First, consider the refraction at the vertex of an ellipsoid with unequal axes. Let the axis corresponding to the vertex be represented by the straight line gb, Fig. 76; the luminous point p being supposed to lie on it. The plane of the diagram is a principal section of the ellipsoid and contains therefore another axis gh. Since the normals to the ellipsoid at points in a principal section are also contained in that section, the normals to the curve bch must therefore lie in the plane of the diagram. A ray pc will be refracted at c in a direction lying in the plane through p and the normal at c, that is, in the plane of the diagram, and hence will intersect the axis bg at some point q. This would not be so if the plane of the diagram were not a principal section of the ellipsoid. Draw ad normal to the surface at c; then by the law of refraction

$$\sin \angle\, pcd = n \sin \angle\, acq,$$

where n denotes the relative index of refraction of the two media. So far the condition is the same as for a surface of revolution. The rays

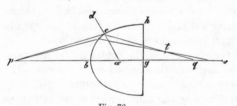

Fig. 76.

that are incident on the surface nearly normally in the vicinity of the vertex b will therefore all be refracted to a point on the axis whose position depends on the radius

of curvature $(r_{,})$ of the curve bch at the point b. When the point p is at infinity, the focal length of the surface in this principal section is equal to $\dfrac{n\,r_{,}}{n-1}$. A perfectly similar expression will be obtained in the same way for rays issuing from p in the other principal section (which is the plane containing bq and the third axis of the ellipsoid), except that the radius of curvature at the vertex of the ellipsoid has a different value $(r_{,,})$ in this principal section; and hence the focal length of the rays in the second principal section is $\dfrac{n\,r_{,,}}{n-1}$. That is, the ray pq will be intersected by those immediately adjacent to it in the plane of the diagram at some point q; but it will be intersected by the adjacent rays lying in a plane perpendicular to that of the diagram, not at the point q, but at some other point s. Now let us suppose that the rays from p all pass through a circular opening perpendicular to the axis pq at b. The cross section of this bundle of rays will be circular at b; but between b and q it will be elliptical with the major axis of the ellipse perpendicular to the plane of the diagram. The ellipse gets smaller and more elongated, the nearer the cross section is to q; and at q the cross section of the bundle of rays is a horizontal straight line perpendicular to the plane of the diagram. Beyond this point the cross section is again an ellipse with its major axis perpendicular to the plane of the diagram, which soon becomes more and more round and is actually circular about midway between q and s; then it becomes an ellipse again with its major axis in the plane of the diagram, which collapses into a vertical line at s. Beyond this point it gradually gets broader again and becomes more and more circular.

The results are similar when a narrow bundle of incident rays encounters a spherical refracting surface obliquely. Suppose that the curve bch in Fig. 76 is the section of a spherical surface and that the straight line pc represents a ray incident on it at a finite angle of incidence. We know (cf. Fig. 32) that rays proceeding in the plane of the diagram and incident on the surface in the immediate vicinity of the point c do not intersect each other in a point on the axis pq after refraction, but at a point off the axis which lies on the caustic surface. Suppose t is this point. Conceive now that the whole figure is rotated around ap as an axis; so that the ray pc will come in succession into the positions of all rays from p that cross the axis at the same angle. The corresponding refracted ray cq will also describe a ray-cone with its vertex at the point q. Consequently, whereas the rays immediately adjacent to pc in the plane of the diagram intersect it at t, those adjacent to it on either side of that plane intersect at it q. Finally, it may be added that other adjacent rays do not intersect pc at all.

Another question to be asked about this subject is, What is the effect of diffraction of light at the edge of the pupil on the monochromatic aberrations? And this suggests a further question as to whether the star-like form of the small blurred patterns may not be due to the minute indentations in the edge of the pupil. In fact, if a luminous point is viewed through an opening smaller than the pupil, the edge of which is not perfectly smooth, a more extensive star-shaped figure will be seen; although, as a rule, such patterns consist rather of very fine hair-like brightly coloured rays, similar to the hair corona of the eye which was described above and which is seen around any brilliant point-source even without using an artificial opening. When the opening is rotated around its centre, the entire corona turns with it; which shows that the effect is due to the contour of the aperture.

The writer could not be sure of perceiving in his own eye the indication of any diffraction of light due to the fine fibrous structure of the crystalline lens. When a small luminous point is observed through a smooth round hole in a metal disc, invariably the whole diffraction pattern turns with the disc. Any features of this pattern that might be due to the fibres of the cornea or lens would necessarily have remained stationary. However, BEER[1] describes diffraction phenomena in his eye which he attributes to a fibrous structure of the ocular media.

Still these diffraction phenomena are essentially differentiated from the appearance of the small blur circles by the circumstance that the latter are eclipsed on one side, without affecting the appearance of the opposite side, when the pupil is screened on one side. On the contrary, when a diffraction pattern is caused by a fine thread or a narrow slit, it never extends merely in one direction, but always in two opposite directions, because every interruption of a wave of light is invariably manifested in opposite, and usually in all, directions. Now the hair-line figures have this very characteristic; as soon as an obstacle begins to encroach upon the pupil, the whole figure becomes more or less altered and distorted.

But apart from the diffraction effects due to irregularities in the contour of the pupil, it should be remembered that the pupil as a whole being a small round opening, may also cause diffraction. Whenever light from a point-source is refracted at one or more surfaces of limited aperture, even if the optical system is otherwise achromatic and aplanatic, the focus of the refracted rays is not a sharply defined point, but a small light pattern, due to diffraction at the edge of the aperture, with alternately bright and dark places, whose form and position depend generally on the size and shape of the aperture. If the aperture is circular, as in the eye and in most optical instruments, the diffraction figure consists of a bright central disc surrounded by several dark and bright rings whose brightness falls off rapidly. Let d denote the diameter of the aperture, r its distance from the image, and l the wavelength of the light; then by both theory and experiment it is found that the diameter of the central bright circle is

$$\delta = 2.440 \, \frac{lr}{d} \cdot$$

If we put $l = 0.0005$ mm (as representing the average value of a wavelength of light) and $r = 20$ mm for the eye, the above formula becomes:

$$\delta = 0.0244 \cdot \frac{1}{d},$$

where the magnitudes are all expressed in millimetres. For the minimum diameter of the pupil ($d = 2$ mm), $\delta = 0.0122$ mm. A blur circle of this size on the retina corresponds to a visual angle of $2'6''$, and is

[1] POGGENDORFFS *Ann.* LXXXIV. 518.

equal to that corresponding to a point 25 metres away, when the eye is accommodated for an infinite distance. Since the smallest visible object consisting of two separate points subtends an angle of about 1′, diffraction effects begin to impair visual acuity when the pupil has its least diameter.

Another instance of monochromatic aberration is found in the streaks of light that appear to proceed upwards and downwards from a bright object when the eyelids are half closed. These are due to refraction by the concave boundaries of the areas of moisture left upon the eyeball by the lids. These curved boundaries act like a small prism of variable angle, or a series of small prisms, and cause considerable deviations in the direction of the incident light.

Measurements made by various physicists as to the inequality of the focal lengths of the eye in the horizontal and vertical meridians indicate that much divergence exists among individuals in this respect. Some observers, as BRÜCKE,[1] fail to detect any difference at all, or obtain conflicting results.

YOUNG reports that his eye will bring to the same focus rays in the vertical meridian diverging from a luminous point 304 mm away and rays in the horizontal meridian from one 213 mm away. In order to express this difference independently of the accommodation distance, he computes the focal length of a cylindrical lens which, used as a spectacle glass, would make the two distances identical, and finds that it would be 700 mm. That is, a convex lens of this focal length with the cylindrical axis horizontal, or a concave one with the cylindrical axis vertical, would have neutralized the defect in his case. The two corresponding distances found by A. FICK for his eyes were 3 m and 4.6 m, respectively, while the writer finds 0.54 m and 0.65 m. These latter figures will be seen to differ in the opposite sense from those of YOUNG, and to be much smaller in amount. Expressed in terms of the focal length of a cylindrical lens, the difference of the two meridians in FICK's case corresponds to a focal length of 8.6 m and in the writer's case to one of 3.19 m. Data of this kind are easily obtained by means of two pins stuck, one vertically and the other horizontally, in a long bar; the observer looks from one end of the bar at one of the pins and adjusts the other at such a distance that both are clearly visible at once.

A. FICK observes that an eye looking casually at anything is usually accommodated for vertical lines. In order to make an approximate calculation of the distance between the two focal planes, let us suppose that LISTING's schematic eye is accommodated for vertical lines; and that the difference of focus in the horizontal and vertical meridians is the same for this eye as it was in each of the three cases cited above. We find that the focal point of rays in the horizontal meridian would be, according to the data of:

TH. YOUNG,   0.422 mm in front of the other;
A. FICK,   0.035 mm beyond the other;
H. HELMHOLTZ, 0.094 mm beyond the other.

It is to be noted that these differences amount to less than the chromatic aberration of the focal points of red and violet rays (0.6 mm). Moreover, they have very little effect on the visual acuity so long as it is simply a question of distinguishing separate lines that all have the same general direction; and they are not detrimental to any extent except when it comes to seeing crossed lines distinctly at the same time.

[1] *Fortschritte der Physik im Jahre* 1845. Bd. I. S. 211.

The multiple images of a point or a line arising from imperfect accommodation had been noted by DE LA HIRE[1] and JURIN,[2] neither of whom, however,
found the correct explanation. Subsequently, YOUNG[3] described and sketched
the form of the blurred figures for various distances of the luminous point;
and expressed the opinion that the star-like shapes might be due to slight
irregularities in the anterior surface of the crystalline lens. HASSENFRATZ[4]
referred to them also and attributed them to the same cause, regarding them
as lines of intersection of two caustic surfaces. PURKINJE[5] describes the
phenomena of multiple images, and also those observed on viewing fine parallel
lines, and constructs the star figure, which he considers as most probably due
to facets of the cornea. PÉCLET[6] notes the multiple images of a bright line,
and ascribes it to peculiarities of the refracting surfaces, as do also NIEDT,[7]
GUÉRARD[8] and FLIEDNER.[9] The last named gives a very complete description
of all these phenomena. TROUESSART[10] thinks that a network must be assumed
to be beyond the refracting surfaces of the eye, and that the multiple images
are produced by its manifold meshes, on the same principle as SCHEINER's
experiment. FICK's[11] view of this matter has been mentioned already. These
same phenomena have been discussed also by AIMÉE[12] and CRANMORE.[13] An
entirely unique theory as to the origin of the multiple images, known to
oculists as *polyopia monophthalmica*, was advanced by STELLWAG VON
CARION.[14] He claims to have observed that the different images are formed by
light polarised in different planes. But this is a mistake; and he was probably
misled by using in his experiments a poorly polished tourmalin crystal with
slightly curved surfaces or striations in the interior. A plate of this kind with
a slightly cylindrical surface, rotated in front of the eye, would bring the
horizontal and vertical rays to a focus alternately, thus eliminating one set of
double images at a time. In order to get rid of the effect of such a fault in the
crystal, it should be placed between the source of light and a small pinhole in a
screen, so that the light is polarised before it comes through the opening. If
now the opening is observed from a sufficient distance to get the star-shaped
figure, it will be found that rotating the tourmalin, and therefore also the
plane of polarisation of the light, does not have the slightest influence on the
double images. Besides, the results said to have been obtained by STELLWAG
are not in accordance with the laws of double refraction. His theory has been
disproved by GUT.[15] STELLWAG's paper includes a summary of the medical
literature on the pathological occurrence of abnormal *diplopia monoph-
tha'mica*.

---

[1] *Accidens de la vue.* p. 400.

[2] SMITH's *Optics.* "Essay on distinct and indistinct vision." p. 156.

[3] *Philos. Transactions.* 1801. I. p. 43. Pl. VI.

[4] *Ann. de Chimie.* 1809. T. LXXII. p. 5.

[5] *Beiträge zur Kenntnis des Sehens.* S. 113—119. *Neue Beiträge z. Kenntnis d. Sehens.* S. 139-146. 173.

[5] *Ann. d. Chimie et d. Phys.* LIV. 379. — POGGENDORFF's *Ann.* XXXIV. 557.

[7] *De dioptricis oculi coloribus ejusque Polyopia.* Dissert. Berolini 1842.

[8] *Institut.* 1845. No. 581. p. 64.

[9] POGGENDORFFS *Ann.* LXXXV. 321. 460. LXXXVI. 336. *Cosmos.* I, 333.

[10] *C. R. de l'Acad. d. sc'ences.* XXXV. 134-136, 398. *Archive de Genève.* XX. 305. *Institut.* 1852. p. 304.

[11] HENLE u. PFEUFFER, *Zeitschrift.* N. Folge V. S. 277.

[12] *Ann. d. Chimie et d. Physique.* LVI. 108. — POGGENDORFFS *Ann.* XXXIII. S. 479.

[13] *Philos. Magazine.* (3) XXXVI, 485.

[14] *Wiener Sitzungsberichte.* VIII. 82. *Denkschriften d. k. k. Akad.* V. 2. p. 172.

[15] *Über Diplopia monophthalmica.* Dissert. Zürich 1854.

The phenomena of diffraction in the eye have been investigated by BAUDRI-MONT,[1] WALLMARK[2] and BEER.[3] The streaks of light, produced by the concave films of tear-fluid when the eyelids are half closed, were noted by MEYER[4] of Leipzig.

YOUNG[5] seems to have been the first to mention the asymmetry of the eye in different meridian planes. He quotes the statement of a Mr. CARY, to the effect that many persons find it necessary to wear their glasses close against the eyes, in order to see well with them. Further observations on the subject were made by AIRY,[6] FISCHER,[7] CHALLIS,[8] HEINEKEN,[9] HAMILTON,[10] SCHNYDER,[11] and, finally, by A. FICK.[12] SCHNYDER employed cylindrical spectacle lenses to correct this defect. A more complete summary of these investigations will be found in FECHNERS *Zentralblatt* for 1853, pp. 73-85; 96-99; 374-379; 558-561.

The question of the spherical aberration of the eye, in the sense in which that term is applied to artificial optical instruments, loses its practical importance as compared with the much more serious defects that have been described. In YOUNG's experiments with his optometer, described in the preceding section, a single thread viewed through four openings appeared as four intersecting lines which did not meet all in one point when the eye was accommodated for near vision. VOLKMANN[13] likewise endeavoured to determine by experiment whether the optical system of the eye shows spherical aberration. Through four small openings in a curved line in a screen, he looked at a needle, which could be set at different distances from the eye. Evidently, if the axial portion of the eye brought the rays to a nearer focus than the peripheral parts, this fact would be proved by getting distinct images through the inner apertures before getting them through the outer apertures, when the needle was moved away from the eye towards the position of distinct vision; and, on the contrary, if the images in the outer holes are seen distinctly before those in the inner holes, it means that the edge rays are brought to a focus first.[14] VOLKMANN's results were different for different individuals. For regular refracting surfaces of revolution these experiments of YOUNG and VOLKMANN would undoubtedly have indicated the nature and magnitude of the spherical aberration of the eye. But in most meridians of the ordinary eye the points of intersection of the refracted rays with the central ray do not form a continuous series at all, so that here the conception of spherical aberration really does not apply.

[1] *C. R. d. l'Acad. d. sc.* XXXIII. 496; *Institut.* No. 931; *Phil. Mag.* (4) II. 575.

[2] POGGENDORFFs *Ann.* LXXXII. 129.

[3] POGGENDORFFs *Ann.* LXXXIV. 518.

[4] POGGENDORFFs *Ann.* LXXXIX. 429.

[5] *Phil. Transact.* 1801. I. p. 39.

[6] *Edinb. Journal of Sc.* XIV. p. 322.

[7] *Berl. Denkschriften* 1818 and 1819. S. 46.

[8] *Transact. of the Cambridge Phil. Soc.* II.: *Phil. Mag.* (3) XXX. 366.

[9] *Phil. Mag.* XXXII. 318.

[10] FRORIEPS *Notizien.* VII. 219.

[11] *Verhandl. d. schweizer. naturf. Ges.* 1848. S. 15; FRORIEPS *Notizen.* X. 346; *Arch. de Genève.* X. 302.

[12] *De errore quodam optico asymmetria bulbi effecto.* Marburgi 1851; HENLE u. PFEUFFER *Zeitschrift.* N. Folge. Bd. II. S. 83.

[13] R. WAGNERS *Handwörterbuch für Physiol.* Article: "Sehen."

[14] ¶See description of "annulus" method of testing for spherical aberration, similar to VOLKMANN's method for the eye, in paper by L. D. WELD in *School Science and Mathematics.* XVIII (1918), 547. (J. P. C. S.)

1694   DE LA HIRE, *Accidens de la vue* in *Mém. de l'Acad. de Paris.* 1694. p. 400.
1738. JURIN, *Essay on distinct and indistinct vision.* p. 156 in R. SMITH'S *Optics.*
1801. TH. YOUNG in *Philos. Transactions for* 1801. I. p. 43.*
1809. HASSENFRATZ, *Ann. de Chimie.* T. LXXII. p. 5.
1818. FISCHER, *Berliner Denkschriften für* 1818 *u.* 1819. S. 46.
1819. PURKINJE, *Beiträge zur Kenntnis des Sehens.* Prag. S. 113-119.*
1824. PÉCLET, *Ann. d. Chimie et d. Phys.* LIV. 379; POGGENDORFFS *Ann.* XXXIV. 557.
       AIMÉE, *Ann. d. Chim. et d. Phys.* LVI. p. 108.
1825. PURKINJE, *Neue Beiträge zur Kenntnis des Sehens.* Berlin. S. 139-146. 173.*
       BREWSTER, *Edinb. Journal of Science.* XIV. p. 322. (Concerning AIRY'S eye).
1842. NIEDT, *De dioptricis oculi coloribus ejusque Polyopia.* Dissert. Berolini.*
1845. GUÉRARD, *Institut.* No. 581. p. 64.
1846. VOLKMANN, Article: "Sehen," in R. WAGNERS *Handwörterbuch für Physiologie.*
1847. CHALLIS in *Philos. Magazine.* (3) XXX. p. 366; *Trans. Cambridge Phil. Soc.* II.
1848. H. MEYER in HENLE u. PFEUFFER, *Zft. für rat. Med.* V. 368.
       HEINEKEN, *Philos. Magazine.* (3) XXXII. p. 318.
       HAMILTON in FRORIEPS *Notizen.* VII. 219.
       SCHNYDER, *Verhandl. d. schweizer. naturf. Gesellsch.* 1848. p. 15.
1849. WALLMARK, *Öfvers af Akad. förhandlingar.* 1849. p. 41; POGGENDORFFS *Ann.*
       LXXXII. 129.
1850. CRANMORE in *Philos. Mag.* (3) XXXVI. p. 485.
       BAUDRIMONT, *Comptes rend. de l'Acad. d. sc.* XXXIII. 496; *Institut.* No. 931; *Philos.*
       Mag. (4) II. 575.
1851. BEER, POGGENDORFFS *Ann.* LXXXIV. S. 518.
       A. FICK, *De errore optico quodam asymmetria bulbi oculi affecto.* Marburg. Summary
       in HENLE u. PFEUFFER, *Zft. für rat. Med.* Neue Folge. II S. 83.
1852. *FLIEDNER, Beobachtungen über Zerstreuungsbilder im Auge, sowie über die Theorie
       des Sehens. POGGENDORFFS *Ann.* LXXXV. 321.* 460.* LXXXVI. 336*; MOIGNO,
       Cosmos. I. 333.
1852. TROUESSART, *Comptes rend. d. l'Acad. d. sc.* XXXV. p. 134-136. 398; *Archive de
       Genève.* XX. 305; *Institut.* 1852. p. 304.
       STELLWAG VON CARION, *Wiener Sitzungsber.* VIII. 82; *Denkschr. d. k. k. Akad.*
       V. 2. S. 172; *Zeitschrift d. Ärzte zu Wien.* 1853. Heft 10 u. 11; FECHNERS *Zentral-*
       blatt. 1854. 281-292.
1853. MEYER (of Leipzig), POGGENDORFFS *Ann.* LXXXIX. 429.
1854. A. FICK in HENLE u. PFEUFFER, *Zft.* N. Folge. V. 277.
       GUT, *Über Diplopia monophthalmica.* Dissert. Zürich.

Supplement

Since the publication of the preceding section, these particular
forms of aberration have been investigated more from the medical
standpoint, especially by DONDERS and KNAPP. The convenient
term *astigmatism* (derived from the Greek στίγμα, a mark, and ἀ
privative, meaning "without focus") has been suggested by WHEW-
ELL to describe these defects. He makes a distinction between
regular and *irregular astigmatism.* The former includes those phenomena described above under No. 5, and in the remainder of the section,
due to the fact that the curvatures of the refracting surfaces of the
eye, especially of the anterior surface of the cornea, are different in
different meridians. On the other hand, *irregular astigmatism,* as
manifested in the phenomena of *polyopia monocularis,* includes those

effects that are produced as the result of the fact that even when the rays all lie in a single meridian plane they do not come to an exact focus.

Apart from those cases in which there are conical protuberances, ulcers, and similar injuries on the surface of the cornea, irregular astigmatism is usually traceable to the crystalline lens, as explained above. The best evidence of this is the fact that eyes without the crystalline lens exhibit no symptoms whatever of *polyopia*, whereas the manifestations of regular astigmatism, especially the linear or oval form of the blur circle, are much more regular and pronounced in such eyes than in normal eyes.

The separate effects due to single sectors of the crystalline lens were carefully investigated by DONDERS, by moving about in front of the eye a small perforated screen so as to let the light go sometimes through one sector of the lens and sometimes through another. His results showed, first, that while each sector of the lens converged the rays approximately to a focus, the focus is not the same for different sectors. And, moreover, the focusing is not quite accurate even for a single sector, the rays near the axis having apparently a longer focal length than those traversing the peripheral parts of the lens. Consequently, in the blur circle due to a single sector of the lens the rays traversing the peripheral portion are more concentrated before arriving at the narrowest section of the bundle, and the central rays are more crowded together beyond this place.

Nearly all human eyes exhibit at least some slight degree of regular astigmatism, which may be measured in a manner similar to that used for determining the amplitude of accommodation. As already explained, in astigmatic eyes the distances of distinct vision are different for lines lying in different azimuths of the field of view (see Fig. 74). If the greatest of these distances of distinct vision is denoted by P, and if, for the same state of accommodation, the least distance is denoted by p, the astigmatism is measured by the difference of the reciprocals of these lengths, that is,

$$As = \frac{1}{p} - \frac{1}{P} .$$

As long as the amount of astigmatism (As) is less than $1/40$,[1] there is no appreciable impairment of visual acuity, but if it exceeds this value, good definition becomes difficult, and cylindrical lenses will be of aid to the patient. The focal length of the cylindrical surface should be equal to the quantity As, and the lens may be either convex

---

[1] ¶The distances are supposed here to be measured in inches. The limiting value of the so-called "physiological astigmatism," as given in the text, is equivalent to one dioptry. (J. P. C. S.)

with the axis of the cylinder parallel to the line that is in focus at the distance P, or concave with the axis of the cylinder perpendicular to that line. The other surface of the lens may be ground spherical (spherocylindrical lens) so as to correct at the same time any ametropia that may need correction.

The best way of ascertaining easily whether there is any astigmatism, the amount of it, and the meridians of greatest and least refraction, is by means of a set of cylindrical lenses. STOKES has proposed the use of an astigmatic lens of variable degree of astigmatism composed of two equal cylindrical lenses in contact. Placed with their cylindrical axes at right angles, the combination is not astigmatic but equivalent to an ordinary spherical lens; but by rotating one of the lenses relatively to the other, the cylindrical axes can be inclined to each other at various angles, so as to increase the amount of astigmatism to its maximum value when the cylindrical axes are parallel.

E. JAVAL has devised a convenient apparatus, made by Messrs. NACHET of Paris, for quick measurement of astigmatism. Two charts each consisting of 24 radial lines are observed through a pair of convex lenses with their optical axes parallel. The charts are adjusted at such a distance that at first only one of the lines can be seen distinctly; and then cylindrical lenses, either single or combined in pairs, and set in circular mountings capable of being rotated, are inserted and adjusted until all the lines in both figures stand out clearly. The cylinders can be rotated around the optical axis so as to bring the cylindrical axes in the right azimuths for most distinct vision for each eye.

Corneal measurements of astigmatic eyes made by DONDERS and KNAPP show that almost invariably regular astigmatism is a case of corneal astigmatism, and that the higher degrees of corneal astigmatism are frequently masked to a slight extent by an opposite astigmatism of the crystalline lens.

The azimuth in which the distance of distinct vision is greatest is, as a rule, nearer the vertical meridian than the horizontal, as, for example, in the cases of both A. FICK and the writer, as above stated; but the contrary condition is also not uncommon, as illustrated by YOUNG's vision in this respect.

1852.   A. MÜLLER, Über das Beschauen der Landschaften mit normaler und abgeänderter Augenstellung. (Supposedly due to astigmatism.) POGGENDORFFS *Ann.* LXXXVI. 147–152. *Cosmos.* I. 336.

1852.   A. BEER, Über den optischen Versuch des Herrn LIBRI. POGGENDORFFS *Ann.* LXXXVII. 115–120.

—   J. HIPPESLEY, Phenomena of light. *Athen.* 1852. p. 1069–1070; 1368.

—   R. W. H. HARDY, Phenomena of light. Ibid. p. 1306.

1853.   FECHNER, Über einige Verschiedenheiten des Sehens in vertikalem und horizontalem
         Sinne nach verschiedenen Beobachtungen. FECHNERS *Zentralblatt*. S. 73-85;
         96-99; 374-379; 558-561.

—   L. L. VALLÉE, Théorie de l'œil. *C. R.* XXXVI. 769-773; 865-867.

—   FLIEDNER, Zur Theorie des Sehens. POGGENDORFFS *Ann.* LXXXVIII, 29-44.

—   H. MEYER, Über die sphärische Abweichung des menschlichen Auges. Ibid.
     LXXXIX. 540-568.

—   BEER, Über den Hof um Kerzenflammen. Ibid. LXXXVIII. 595-597.

—   POWELL, On a peculiarity of vision. *Rep. of Brit. Assoc.* 1852, 2. p. 11.

1854.   J. P. DEPIGNY, Hof um Kerzenflammen. *Arch. des sciences phys.* XXVI. 166-172.

—   J. GUT, Über Doppeltsehen mit einem Auge. HENLE und PFEUFFER, *Zft.* (2) IV.
     395-400.

1855.   Über den Gang der Lichtstrahlen im Auge. *Verhandl. der naturforsch. Ges. in Basel.*
         I. 269-282. *Arch. des sciences phys.* XXXII. 145-146.

—   H. MEYER, Über den die Flamme eines Lichts umgebenden Hof usw. POGGENDORFFS
     Ann. XCVI, 235-262; 603-607; 607-609.

1856.   Idem, Über die Strahlen, die ein leuchtender Punkt im Auge erzeugt. Ibid. XCVII
         233-260. XCVIII, 214-242.

1857.   VAN DER WILLIGEN, Eine Lichterscheinung im Auge. POGGENDORFFS *Ann.* CII.
         175-176.

—   J. TYNDALL in *Phil. Mag.* (4) XI. 332. (An interference phenomenon.)

1858.   G. M. CAVALLIERI, Sulla cagione del redere le stelle e i punti luminosi affetti da
         raggi. *Cimento.* VIII. 321-360.

1860.   F. ZÖLLNER, Beiträge zur Kenntnis der chromatischen und monochromatischen
         Abweichung des menschlichen Auges. POGGENDORFFS *Ann.* CXI. 329-336. *Ann.
         de chimie.* (3) LX. 506-509.

—   WHARTON JONES, Analysis of my sight, with a view to ascertain the focal power of
     my eyes for horizontal and for vertical rays, and to determine whether they possess
     a power of adjustment for different distances. *Proc. of Roy. Soc.* X. 380-385.
     Phil. Mag. (4) XX. 480-483.

1861.   DONDERS, Beiträge zur Kenntnis der Refraktions- und Akkommodationsanomalien.
         Arch. für Ophthalm. VII. 1 S. 155-204.

1862.   J. H. KNAPP, Über die Asymmetrie des Auges in seinen verschiedenen Meridianen.
         Arch. für Ophthalm. VIII, 2 S. 185-241.

—   GIRAUD TEULON, Causes et mécanisme de certains phénomènes de polyopie mono-
     culaire. *C. R.* LIV. 904-906; 1130-1131. *Inst.* 1862. p. 138-139; 173.

—   F. C. DONDERS, *Astigmatismus und zylindrische Gläser.* Berlin.

1863.   B. A. POPE, Beiträge zur Optik des Auges. *Archiv für Ophthalm.* IX, 1 S. 41-63.

—   C. KUGEL, Über die Wirkung schief vor das Auge gestellter sphärischer Brillen-
     gläser beim regelmässigen astigmatismus. Ibid. X, 1 S. 89-96.

—   MIDDELBURG, *De Zidplaats van het Astigmatisme.* Utrecht.

—   PH. H. KNAUTHE, *Über Astigmatismus.* Dissert. Leipzig.

1864.   F. C. DONDERS, Der Sitz des Astigmatismus (nach MIDDELBURGS Resultaten).
         Archiv für Ophthalm. X, 2. S 83-108.

—   J. H. KNAPP, Über die Diagnose des irregulären Astigmatismus. *Monatsbl. für
     Augenheilkunde.* 1864. S. 304-316.

—   DONDERS, *Anomalies of accommodation and refraction.* London. 1864. p. 449—556.

1865.   L. KUGEL, Über die Sehschärfe bei Astigmatikern. *Archiv für Ophthalm.* XI, 1.
         S. 106—113.

—   H. KAISER, Zur Theorie des Astigmatismus. Ibid. XI, 3. S. 186-229.

—   X. GALEZOWSKI, Étude sur la diplopie monophthalmique. *Ann. d'oculistique.* LIV.
     p. 199-208.

1866.   E. JAVAL, Sur le choix des verres cylindriques. *Ann. d'oculist.* LV. p. 5-29.

—   Idem, Histoire et bibliographie de l'astigmatisme. Ibid. LV. p. 105-127.

§ 15. Entoptical Phenomena

Under suitable conditions light falling on the eye may render visible certain objects within the eye itself. These perceptions are called *entoptical*. Ordinarily the small opaque particles suspended in the vitreous or aqueous humors or in the crystalline lens do not cast any visible shadows on the retina and are therefore not noticed. This is because the intensity of the light entering the pupil is generally uniformly distributed over every part of it, and therefore, so far as the illumination of the posterior chamber of the eye is concerned, the entire pupil acts like a luminous surface. But when a source of light is a broad surface, no perceptible shadows are produced unless the opaque object is large or else is very near the screen. Now there are certainly some objects in the eye, particularly the blood vessels of the retina, which fulfil the latter condition by being very close to the sensitive membrane behind them, and which are therefore, in position to cast shadows on the retina. But the areas of the retina lying behind the blood vessels are always thus shaded, so that this is their normal condition, and it is only under special circumstances, to be discussed later, that these shadows become visible.

But at present suppose we consider the tiny, opaque bodies in the transparent ocular media. In order to perceive them, it is necessary to use light from a very small source held close in front of the eye. This source may be the real image of a distant lamp produced by a small convex lens, or the virtual image of the sun or of a flame in a highly polished small metal ball, or the customary small illuminated opening in an opaque screen. The best arrangement is to use a con-

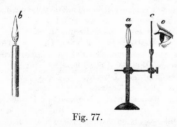

Fig. 77.

vex lens of large aperture and short focus, mounted as shown at *a* in Fig. 77, whereby a reduced image of a flame *b* at some distance in front of it is focused on a small opening in the opaque screen *c*. This results in a wide cone of rays emerging from the opening. The eye at *o*, very close to the opening, looks through it at the broad, uniformly illuminated aperture of the lens, where the objects that are entoptically perceived will appear now with great clearness. If, as in Fig. 78, the luminous point *a* lies between the eye and its anterior focal point *f*, the image of it in the optical system of the eye will be virtual and situated at a point *α* in front of *a*, so that the rays reaching the retina seem to diverge from *α*. A small opaque object *b* that happens to be in the

vitreous humor will then cast on the retina a shadow β, which will
be larger than the obstacle
itself.   If the point a coincides with the first focal
point of the eye, the rays in
the vitreous humor will be
parallel, as shown in Fig. 79,
and then the shadow β will
be of the same size as the

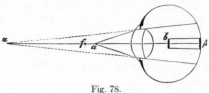

Fig. 78.

obstacle b; whereas if the focal point f is between the eye and the
luminous point a, as in Fig. 80, the image a will lie beyond the retina,
the rays in the vitreous humor being,
therefore, convergent, and in this case
the shadow will be smaller than the
obstacle. Consequently, these entoptical
appearances are magnified in size, the
nearer the eye is to the luminous point;
and *vice versa*.

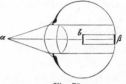

Fig 79.

The area of the retina that is illu-
minated in these experiments is really the blur circle of the luminous
point, and it is within this area that the shadows are cast of the opaque
particles. While these shadows are sufficiently distinct to enable us to
get some idea of the form of the obstacle, they are always somewhat

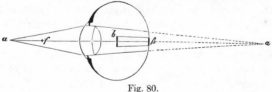

Fig. 80.

blurred. This is because the source of light is not strictly a point but
has a more or less appreciable area, and it is the image of this area as
produced by the optical system of the eye that acts here as the source
so far as the shadow on the retina is concerned, and naturally this
image will always have a certain extent. Now any shadow depending
on a source of light that is not a mere point will have a penumbra where
the illumination of the shadow gradually merges into the general bright
illumination of the environment. Consequently, the distinctness of the
perception of an entoptical phenomenon will be greater in proportion
as the illuminated aperture is smaller, and also in proportion as the
little opaque obstacle that casts the shadow is closer to the retina.
However, of course, a small aperture involves a correspondingly more

intense light for its illumination. And, besides, with a very narrow aperture another phenomenon has to be taken into account that affects the sharpness of delineation of the shadow, namely, the diffraction fringes due to diffraction around the edges of the obstacle consisting of bright and dark bands that appear on the contours of all shadows produced by an extremely small, intense source of light. With ordinary sources of light of larger size these diffraction fringes vanish in the penumbra.

When the position either of the eye or of the luminous point is varied, the shadows of opaque particles at different distances from the retina will be shifted differently, forming new configurations. This effect can be employed, as LISTING showed, to determine the approximate position of a particle within the eye. The entoptical field of view is circumscribed by the round shadow of the iris. As various points of this are observed one after the other, the shadows of all the opaque particles that do not lie in the pupillary plane will be shifted with respect to the contour of the field. This motion of the shadows in the entoptical field is what LISTING called the *relative entoptical parallax*. He counts this parallax as positive when the movement of the shadow is in the same sense as that of the point of fixation, and negative when it is in the contrary sense.[1] Accordingly, for objects in the pupillary plane, the parallax is zero; for objects beyond the pupil, it is positive; and for objects in front of the pupil, it is negative. For objects which are very close to the retina, the movement of the shadow is almost the same as that of the fixation point, so that the shadow seems to follow the fixation point unless the opaque particle is itself actually in motion in the fluid vitreous humor. The shadow on the retina is, of course, on the same side of the eye as the opaque particle; but since an image on the retina is projected in the field of view on the opposite side of the optical axis of the eye, objects that are perceived entoptically always appear to be inverted.

Entoptical phenomena are as follows:

1. The illuminated field is bounded by the shadow of the iris, and is therefore almost round corresponding to the form of the pupil. If there are notches, creases or salients in the edge of the pupil, as is often the case, they will all be duplicated in the entoptical image. Even the dilatation and contraction of the pupil can be observed entoptically, most easily when the other eye is alternately covered and uncovered with the hand. This causes the pupils of both eyes to dilate and contract in unison, which can be easily seen in the similar variation of the size of the entoptical image.

---

[1] ¶That is, positive or negative according as the movement of the eye is "with" or "against" the shadow movement, respectively. (J. P. C. S.)

2. There are usually visible in the entoptical field stripes, cloud-like or more luminous places, and circular areas resembling drops of liquid with bright nuclei, which come and go and move about as the eye is opened and shut. These are due to the moisture secreted by the tear-glands and spread over the surface of the cornea by winking the eyelid. These appearances are depicted in Fig. 81. The spots usually run together, and have an independent downward motion. The stripes are most pronounced near the edge of the eyelid when the lid arrives in front of the pupil, and are due to the thin concave film of moisture stretched from the cornea to the edge of the eyelid. The droplets are probably drawn together by capillary action about particles of dust, mucus, etc. The bright spot in the middle of each droplet seems to be an imperfect optical image of the source of light; for example, if the light comes through a triangular opening, the bright spot is triangular.

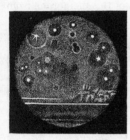 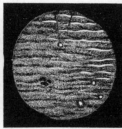 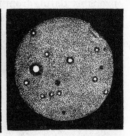

Fig. 81.   Fig. 82.   Fig. 83.

This image appears erect in the entoptical field, while it must be inverted on the retina. The accumulations of liquid on the cornea thus act as small convex lenses, beyond each of which is formed an inverted image of whatever objects lie before it. The fact that these images move downward across the field is evidently due to the actual settling of the viscous masses of mucus which the opening eyelid has just dragged upwards with it.

3. The irregularities on the anterior surface of the cornea after pressing or rubbing the closed eye for a time with the fingers. For from a quarter of an hour to an hour afterwards there appears an indistinct array of wavy or reticulated lines and scattered spots, as shown in Fig. 82. Certain areas, however, may sometimes remain unchanged, thus indicating that the cornea is not quite the same here as elsewhere.

In some cases there are special dark spots and lines, also originating in the cornea, which seem to be permanent and are nearly always the result of some previous inflammation or injury.

4. Various entoptical phenomena originate in the anterior wall of the lens-sac or capsule, or in the anterior portion of the substance of the lens. Four of these are described by LISTING, as follows:

(a) *Pearl specks*, more or less round discs, bright in the centre, with clear-cut dark borders. They look sometimes like little air-bubbles or drops of oil or microscopic crystals (Fig. 83). LISTING believes them to be small particles of mucus in the *liquor Morgagnii*.

(b) *Dark specks*, distinguished from the foregoing by the absence of a bright nucleus and also by their greater diversity of form. They seem to be due to local opacity of the lens or lens capsule (Fig. 84.)

(c) *Bright patches*, usually having a few radiating arms like an irregular star, and located near the middle of the field (Fig. 85). LISTING regards these as the images of umbilicate structures with ridge-like branches or seams in the anterior capsule membrane, probably dating from the pre-natal separation of this membrane from the inner surface of the cornea.

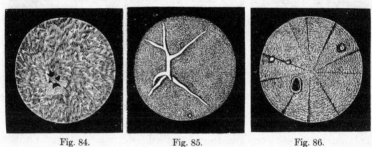

Fig. 84.   Fig. 85.   Fig. 86.

(d) *Dark radiating lines* (Fig. 86), which may be regarded as evidence of radial structure of the lens.

Practically all eyes exhibit one or more of these phenomena; rarely is one found that does not.

5. *Moving objects* in the vitreous humor, commonly called "flying gnats" (*mouches volantes* or *muscae volitantes*). Sometimes these look like strings of pearls or groups of circles with bright nuclei, or irregular masses of minute globules, or faint lines like creases in a transparent membrane. Many of them are close enough to the retina to be visible without any special arrangement, by merely looking at some broad uniformly illuminated background like the bright sky. That these motions are real and not simply apparent is easily proved by holding the head erect and looking towards the sky through a window pane, at the same time noting some fixed mark on the glass; then, as a rule, the entoptical appearances will be seen to move slowly downwards, across the field of view. If the observer glances downwards, and then quickly up again, the floating spots follow the movement of the fixa-

tion point, but they are usually thrown a little higher than this point
and then begin to settle down again. But for a simple downward or
lateral movement of the eye, the case is different, and the object does
not seem to waver over the point of fixation. Moreover, in looking
vertically up or down, these peculiar effects are fairly stationary.
In making such observations there is a strong temptation to try to
look at one of these "gnats" that is near the point of fixation so as to
see it better; which makes it seem to fly away without ever being
overtaken. This curious effect is probably the explanation of the
name *mouches volantes*. This apparent motion is not to be confused
with a real motion, and in order to investigate the latter, it is necessary
to have a steadfast external point of fixation. The best way to compare a movable object of this kind with something which is at rest is
to select a position for the head such that it is possible for the eye to
look vertically either upwards or downwards with comfort, because
in this case the apparent movements of the floating particles cease
almost entirely, and the real movements can be watched. Any one
of the little objects that is out to one side in the field of view can be
brought to the place where it can be seen most distinctly by simply
turning the eye suddenly towards it, and then bringing it slowly back
again.

The various forms of these objects are classified by DONDERS
and DONCAN[1] as follows:

(a) *Rather large, isolated circles*, with bright centres and darker
or paler borders, usually surrounded also by a small halo of light.
They vary from 1/28 to 1/120 mm in diameter and are usually found
from 1/3 to 3 or 4 mm in front of the retina, though they sometimes
occur much nearer the lens. When the eye has been in repose a long
time, there are only a few of these appearances. They become particularly manifest, apparently from below, on a quick upward movement of the eye, coming to a sudden standstill and then sinking slowly
back again. The movements of the darkest of them may be followed
directly for a distance of 1.5 mm, and probably extend much farther.
DONCAN found the lateral movement of these spots, produced by a
sidewise movement of the eye, to be much less; but the writer has not
been able to observe any such difference. By putting his head on one
side, he can make these spots appear to sink just as readily and as
far towards the floor as with the head upright; their actual motions
being, of course, upwards towards the highest corner of the eye.
In the upright position the lateral movements of the spots is certainly
not so great as the vertical, because laterally they participate simply

---

[1] ANDREAS DONCAN, *Dissert. de corporis vitrei struct.* Trajecti ad Rhenum 1854.—
Onderzoekingen gedaan in het physiologisch Laborat. der Utrechsche Hoogeschool. Jaar VI. 171.

in the movements of the point of fixation. There is no conclusive evidence of any movement parallel to the visual axis. In many cases groups of such spots, apparently distinct from each other, are observed to be moving along together and maintaining the same distance apart, as if there were some invisible connection between them. By microscopic examination of carefully prepared specimens of the vitreous humor, DONCAN found that these aggregations correspond to pale cells in this substance not far from the surface that are apparently in process of transformation into mucus (see Fig. 87).

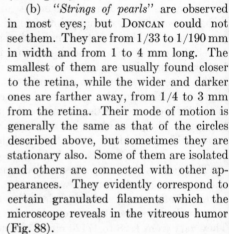

Fig. 87.

Fig. 88.

(b) *"Strings of pearls"* are observed in most eyes; but DONCAN could not see them. They are from 1/33 to 1/190 mm in width and from 1 to 4 mm long. The smallest of them are usually found closer to the retina, while the wider and darker ones are farther away, from 1/4 to 3 mm from the retina. Their mode of motion is generally the same as that of the circles described above, but sometimes they are stationary also. Some of them are isolated and others are connected with other appearances. They evidently correspond to certain granulated filaments which the microscope reveals in the vitreous humor (Fig. 88).

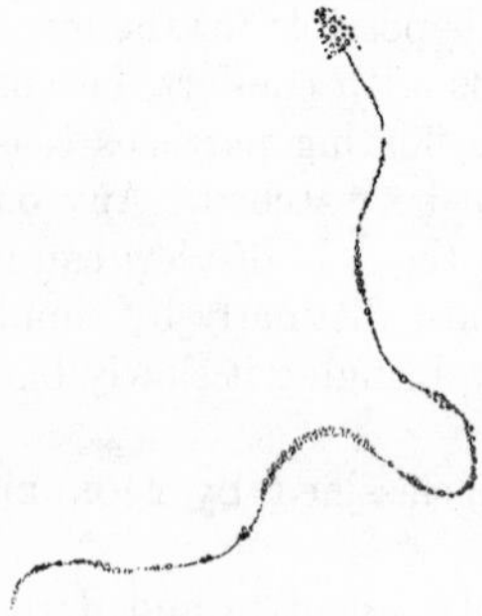

(c) The *clusters of circles* of various sizes, part pale and part dark, which are seen in the microscope as granular aggregations (Fig. 89) and are usually more opaque than the other types, because several particles lie along the line of sight. It is these clusters that most frequently

Fig. 89. Fig. 90.

produce the effect of *mouches volantes* in ordinary vision. It is not unusual for some of them to appear to be suspended in equilibrium near the visual axis; but on moving the eye, they behave after the manner of the "strings of pearls," appearing and passing out of view in the same way, only in greater numbers.

(d) *Folds or wrinkles*, appearing as bright streaks bounded by

rather indistinct dark lines. DONCAN distinguishes two kinds of these
also, namely: very crooked threads or separate, slender bands, very
close together and connected in some invisible way; and an irregularly
curled membrane crumpled in the most diverse fashion, of permanent
shape, and appearing under the microscope as shown in Fig. 90. These
also move like the "string of pearls" and are not more than from 2.5 to
4 mm in front of the retina. Another variety consists of very extended
membranes which are either a very little way beyond the lens or from
2 to 4 mm in front of the retina, none being found between 4 and 10 mm
from the retina. The folds in the former type of membrane are as
broad as 1/23 mm; those in the latter are seldom broader than 1/60 mm.
They appear when the visual axis is moved to one side, but
especially also in case of a swift sudden downward movement. In the
latter case, those lying close to the lens apparently move upwards,
whereas those near the retina drop downwards, so that they are seen
passing each other as they cross the visual axis. Then these wrinkled
membranes get more and more indistinct, without, however, passing
out of the field of view; until, perhaps, on repeating the movement,
they come plainly into view again. DONCAN concludes that these
membranes do not actually move as they appear to do, but that what
is observed is the propagation of the wrinkles which, being formed at
the periphery when the movement of the eye is suddenly terminated,
extend to the other side of the membrane, where they lose their individuality and are less perceptible. The explanation of the opposite
movements of the membrane and the wrinkles in it is that they are on
opposite sides of the centre of rotation of the eye. When the pupil is
dilated by atropin, or if the luminous source is held very near the eye,
so that the field of view is quite wide, it will be found, particularly
with abrupt and vigourous lateral movements of the eye, that other
membranes besides will be revealed in the region immediately beyond
the lens, which usually do not extend as far inwards as the visual axis,
and which terminate here in an irregular or torn edge.

The nature of the movements of the objects suspended in the
vitreous humor leaves little room for doubt that they are small bodies
of less specific gravity than the perfectly fluid medium in which they
are floating. Since they are often to be seen traversing the whole
entoptical field of view, not only horizontally but vertically as well,
so far at least as the writer's own experience goes, and since with
divergent incident light this field is larger than that determined by
the pupil, it appears that the region in which they are floating is
certainly of larger lateral dimensions than the pupil itself. But the
drifting particles seem unable to move in a direction away from the
retina; for even when the visual axis is pointed vertically upwards,

these same objects, which on account of their specific lightness might be expected to rise to the top of the vitreous humor next the lens, are seen to be in motion across the retina, but do not appear to recede from it. Perhaps, the obstacle may be the membranes whose folds are visible in the entoptical field, and which seem to be parallel to the retina. Some particles of this kind appear also to be attached to the hyaloid membrane. DONDERS reports having discovered one in his left eye that was in equilibrium on the visual axis. It may have had a tendency to descend (that is, apparently ascend) from this position, but could not really do so, as if it were tethered to the hyaloid membrane from below by a filament of some kind.

By taking heed of these entoptical phenomena one may learn to recognize individually those peculiar to his own eyes, and he will see then that the same succession of appearances is continually reproduced, and that, according to DONDERS' observations, they remain unaltered for years. Microscopic examination indicates that they are in the nature of debris from the embryonic structure of the vitreous humor. In the embryo, the humor is contained in cells, which are subsequently nearly all transformed into mucus; but some parts of the cell walls and nuclei, or the filaments into which they are resolved, still remain. Just what residue from the structure of the vitreous humor is left in the adult is not quite certain.

We come now to the perception of the blood vessels of the retina. These require somewhat different methods of observation from those employed for the perception of the entoptical objects so far described. What is common to both methods is that the position or width of the shadow of the blood vessels on the rear surface of the retina is something out of the ordinary, and moreover the shadow is kept in continual motion. The three principal methods of observing the blood vessels are as follows:

1. With a convex lens of short focus an intense beam of light (preferably sunlight) is concentrated on a point of the external surface of the sclerotica, as far as possible from the cornea, so as to form a small but exceedingly bright image of the source on the sclerotica.[1] Now when the eye looks at a dark background, the latter will appear illuminated with a reddish yellow glow, and against this will be seen the dark retinal blood vessels ramifying in various directions like the branches of a tree. Fig. 91 shows these blood vessels as they appear after the injection of a suitable stain. As the focus of the lens is moved to and fro over the sclerotica, the branched figure accompanies

[1] The best way to make this experiment nowadays is with the illumination lamps that have been introduced in the practice of ophthalmology. G.

the motion proceeding always "with" the illumination. By such movements the vascular "tree" is more clearly visible than with the light kept stationary on one spot; in which case, indeed, it gradually disappears altogether. However, movement of the appearances is not so essential in this as in other methods of observation. It might be noted that the smaller the bright spot on the sclerotica, the more sharply defined will be also the smaller branches of the vascular figure, so that by a suitable adjustment it is possible to make out even the most minute capillaries. In the centre of the field, corresponding to the point of fixation, there is a place devoid of all blood

Fig. 91.

vessels. The capillaries form a ring of elongated meshes around this area. Both H. MÜLLER and the writer have noticed the peculiar appearance of this spot, quite different from the rest of the fundus of the eye. While the latter is uniformly illuminated (except for the dark, vascular figure), the place of direct vision has more lustre and looks something like shagreened leather. Another thing to be noticed in observing this spot is that when the eye is fixed on some external object, and at the same time the focus of the lens is shifted upwards over the sclerotica, the vascular figure likewise moves upwards, as already stated; but the shagreen lustre has a slight downward displacement towards the point of fixation of the eye. MEISSNER likewise observed by this same method that this place was brighter, and he mentioned a dark crescent-shaped shadow on the edge of it, such as is seen by the second method of observation. But the writer has not been able to see this with light incident through the sclerotica.

In this experiment the light enters the eye through the sclerotica and choroid. The former is translucent; the latter is covered with black pigment, but not so heavily in the back part of the eye as to absorb all the light falling on it. In front, where the eye is lined with the cilary processes, the pigment is more dense, so that when the bright focus of the lens falls on the anterior portion of the sclerotica near the cornea, the retina gets only a relatively feeble illumination. This illuminated place on the eyeball constitutes the source of light, so far as the interior of the eye is concerned; for the sclerotica, being only

translucent, does not produce regular refraction, so that the transmitted rays are scattered from the place of illumination more or less
uniformly in all directions. Whereas in ordinary vision the light that
reaches the retina all comes through the pupil, in these experiments it
comes from a point on one side, and thus the shadows of the blood
vessels in the anterior layers of the retina fall on parts of the sensitive
membrane behind it that are altogether different from the places where
they usually are.

That the vascular figure must have an apparent motion in the same
sense as the focus of the lens can be seen from Fig. 92. Suppose that v

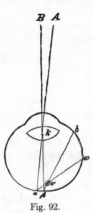

Fig. 92.

indicates the cross section of one of the blood
vessels, and that k designates the position of the
nodal point of the eye. When the focus of the
incident light is at a on the sclerotica, the shadow
of the blood vessel falls at a, and is therefore projected by the eye in the direction aA as a dark
line in the field of view. If the focus is at b, the
shadow falls at β and the dark line appears on
the field at B. That is, as the bright focus moves
from a to b, the figure of the blood vessel apparently shifts in the field of view from A to B, so
that the movement is "with" the movement of the
source. The shagreened area around the centre
of direct vision exhibits the opposite kind of motion,
and hence it is certainly not produced in the
same way as the motion of the shadows of the blood vessels; but the
structure of the yellow spot is not yet well enough understood to
enable us to interpret the reason of this phenomenon. As viewed
against the dark background, the vascular tree appears to encroach
upon the boundary of the shagreened area somewhat on the side
opposite the source of light; above and below it merely touches it; and
on the side towards the light there is an interval between them. The
appearance is as if the light came from one corner of the eye. This
would indicate that the ramifications of the blood vessels are more
towards the front than the layer that by refraction or reflection of the
light is responsible for the shagreened appearance of the central spot;
and hence when the light is incident obliquely, the shadows of the
blood vessels on the rear surface of the retina are not perpendicularly
under the vessels. Consequently, that structure which produces the
shagreened appearance seems to have almost exactly the same extent
as the place in the retina where there are no blood vessels.

2. The second method of observing the vascular system of the
retina is as follows: The observer looks at a dark background and at

the same time moves a brilliant light to and fro a little below or to one side of the eye. Under these circumstances the back-ground presently appears suffused with a pale grey glow, against which may be seen the dark outlines of the vascular figure. It remains visible only so long as the light is kept moving. When the light is moved from right to left, the vertical branches are most distinctly seen; and when it is moved up and down, the horizontal ones are more prominent. As the light moves, the whole vascular figure moves also, but not uniformly in all its parts. MEISSNER very aptly compares its motion with that of an image reflected from the surface of water which is agitated by ripples. Closer examination shows that as the light alternately approaches and recedes from the visual axis, the motion of the vascular figure against the background proceeds in the same sense ("with the light"); but if the light describes an arc about a point on the visual axis, the motion of the figure occurs in the opposite sense ("against the light"). Thus, for example, when the light is held below the eye and moved vertically upwards and downwards, the vascular tree is seen to move likewise upwards and downwards with the light; but if it is moved horizontally from right to left, the figure moves at the same time from left to right, and *vice versa*. The more central branches of the vascular tree do not appear as distinctly outlined in this method as in the other two.

In the centre of the field, corresponding to the point of fixation, is what several observers describe as a bright circular or elliptical disc, a drawing of which as made by BUROW is reproduced in Fig. 93. It is brightest in the middle, while on the edge next the source of light there is a dark, crescent-shaped shadow. H. MÜLLER is unable to see this disc at all, and all that the writer can see is the crescent-shaped shadow on the side of the contour next the light, without any distinct boundary on the opposite side. This central disc also moves when the light is moved, as may be easily verified by fixing the eye on some external point while the experiment is in progress. In the writer's own case the point of fixation always lies on the edge next the light, supposing the crescent-shaped outline is rounded out into a complete bright disc.

Fig. 93

The entire theory of these phenomena has been worked out by H. MÜLLER, and is as follows: The illumination for the interior of the eye in this experiment comes from the bright retinal image of the flame, which is far around on one side of the retina, since the lamp is held at some distance from the centre of the field of view. Being also very near the eye, the lamp forms a fairly large image on the retina, and the amount of light thus diffusely reflected into the vitreous humor is sufficient to stimulate a visual sensation over the entire retina. This mode of illumination, therefore, is similar to that of the first method, but differs from it in the fact that the luminous spot on the eye-wall gets its light directly from in front through the pupil instead of from outside through the sclerotica. Images formed on the peripheral parts of the retina do not make very distinct impressions, and in order to give sufficient light, the image used here must be fairly large. This is the reason why the shadows of the finer blood vessels are not so clear-cut in this as in the preceding method. The mode of motion of the vascular figure is completely explained by MÜLLER's theory. In Fig. 94 the points designated by k and v represent the positions of the

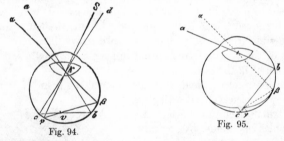

Fig. 94.   Fig. 95.

nodal point of the eye and one of the blood vessels on the retina, respectively. When the source of light is at a, its retinal image falls at b; and the light reflected from b casts a shadow at c of the blood-vessel v. This shadow will be visible in the field of view along the prolongation kd of the straight line connecting the points k and c. Now if the light is moved from a to α, the points b, c and d take the new positions β, γ, and δ, respectively; and hence d is seen to move in the same sense as a. But if a is moved at right angles to the plane of the diagram, the reverse happens. When a lies in front of this plane, b lies behind it, c in front of it, and d behind it. Thus when a is moved out from the plane of the diagram, d moves the other way, in exact accord with the observations.

MÜLLER gives a reasonable explanation of the appearance of the bright central disc with the crescent shadow as being the shadow of the *macula lutea*. Suppose the *macula lutea* is at c in Fig. 95, with the *fovea centralis* at the bottom of it. The point b on the retina is illuminated by the light at a, and the shadow of the elevated edge of the little concavity on the side towards b will fall right in the fovea. The shadow of the whole area as it actually lies on the retina itself will be turned away from the point of fixation and towards the light, and will appear therefore as projected in the field of view away from the light, in agreement with the results of observation. The writer has noticed that when the source of light a is brought nearer the visual axis so that the point b is closer to the fovea c, the crescent shadow appears to have a bright outer margin. This is doubtless due to light which has been reflected to the external surface of the *macula lutea* from behind the retina, as indicated by the dotted line $a\beta\gamma$ in Fig. 95. In cases where the *macula lutea* has less steep sides, no such shadow is visible at all.

3. The third method of observing the retinal blood vessels consists in looking through a narrow aperture at a bright background, like the sky, at the same time moving the aperture rapidly to and fro in front of the pupil. The blood vessels are seen very sharply delineated as dark lines on a bright background, and appear to move in the field of view in the same sense as the aperture moves. In the centre, corresponding to the point of fixation, the non-vascular area is visible, which, so far as the writer is concerned, has a finely granulated appearance and seems to be traversed by a round shadow as the aperture is moved to and fro. With horizontal movements of the aperture, we see the blood vessels that run vertically; and *vice versa*. The same vascular figure may be seen also by looking through a compound microscope with nothing upon the stage, the background being the uniformly bright circular aperture of the diaphragm. When the eye is moved to and fro a little at the ocular, the slender retinal blood vessels appear sharply delineated in the field, particularly those running at right angles to the direction of the motion; whereas the others vanish that are parallel to this direction.

In the first two methods, the light is incident on the retina from an unusual direction, and hence also the shadows of the blood vessels fall upon parts of the retina that are not shaded in normal vision. The shadows therefore constitute an unaccustomed stimulus. On the contrary, in the third method just described the light enters the eye through the pupil in the ordinary way. If the pupil is perfectly free, and the eye is turned towards the bright sky, every point of the pupillary plane may be considered as a source of light sending rays in all directions to the fundus of the eye, just as if the pupil itself were a luminous surface. The result is that the blood vessels of the retina project broad hazy shadows on the parts of the retina immediately behind them, the length of the umbra being only about four or five times the diameter of the blood vessel. According to E. H. WEBER, the diameter of the thickest branch of the *vena centralis* is 0.038 mm; and KÖLLIKER estimates the thickness of the retina at the back of the eye as 0.22 mm. Hence it may be assumed that the umbra of the vascular shadow does not reach the posterior surface of the retina at all. But when the light enters the eye through a narrow aperture in front of the pupil, the shadow of the blood vessel is necessarily smaller and more sharply defined, and since the umbra is longer, parts of the retina that were formerly partially shaded are now completely shaded, while other adjacent parts are not shaded at all.

The reason why we do not perceive the shadow of the vascular system under ordinary visual conditions is because the regions covered by the shadow, being accustomed to the darkness, are less fatigued than the rest of the retina. But as soon as the position or extent of the shadow varies, it falls on fatigued and less sensitive portions, and therefore becomes visible as a feeble illumination; and at the same time the more sensitive areas that are normally in the shadow are exposed to the full light, and therefore more strongly stimulated than usual. This is the reason why sometimes, and especially at the outset of the experiment, the appearance of the vascular figure may be momentarily that of a bright object on a dark background; and, indeed, many persons pay more attention to this bright aspect than to the dark permanent phase. However, when the shadow in our experiments has taken its permanent position, the shaded area begins to recover its sensitivity, whereas the unusual illumination of the parts that are normally in shadow soon fatigues and benumbs them, so that the temporary effect mentioned above rapidly dies away. In order to make it permanent, the shadow must be kept changing from place to place. This is done by moving the source to and fro, so that we continue to see those blood vessels whose shadows are altered thus. These changes of the sensitivity of the retina will be studied more fully in §25.

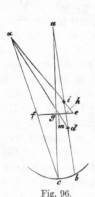

Fig. 96.

LISTING's parallax method is sufficient to enable us to tell whether an object seen entoptically is in front of the pupil or beyond it or perhaps near the retina. In Fig. 96 suppose that the point marked *a* is the image of the luminous point in the optical system of the eye, and that *c* is the position of the fovea on the retina. Let the straight line *fe* represent the plane of the pupil or rather of its image in the crystalline lens; which, however, is almost the same thing. And, finally, let *d* designate the position of some dark object behind the pupil. The shadow of the point *g* where the straight line *ac* crosses the pupil falls on the retina right at the fovea, and hence the point g corresponds to the place in the pupil that is seen in direct (foveal) vision in the entoptical field. The shadow of the object at d is projected on the retina at the point b where the straight line ad meets the retina; and this point b corresponds also to the point h where the straight line ad crosses the pupillary plane; that is, d and h are seen at the same place in the entoptical field. Moreover, if there is another object situated at a point i on the straight line ab, but lying in front of the pupil, it will appear to be at the same place as the object d. But now suppose that either the eye itself or the source of light is displaced, so that some other point in the pupillary plane, for example, the point f, is seen entoptically in direct vision; then the source will lie somewhere on the straight line cf, say, at the point a. Accompanying this movement, the shadows of the objects d and i will shift their apparent positions with respect to the pupil, proceeding from h to m and from h to e, respectively, where m and e designate the points where the straight lines ad and ai cross the plane of the pupil. Thus, in the entoptical field, while the place of direct vision has been shifted from g to f, the image of the object d behind the pupil has been shifted in the same sense from h to m, and that of the object i in front of the pupil has been shifted in the opposite sense from h to e; in other words, using LISTING's mode of expression, the parallax of d is positive and that of i negative. With a little practice, it is always easy to tell whether the entoptical phenomenon in the circular field of view is displaced one way or the other ("with" or "against" the motion of the light), and so to determine on which side of the pupil the object lies.

BREWSTER first proposed a method of measuring more accurately the position of an object suspended in the vitreous humor. Essentially, it depends on using two sources of light and thus obtaining two shadows of the same object. Knowing the distance of the shadows from each other, we can find then the distance of the object from the retina. BREWSTER's arrangement for this purpose consisted in looking through a lens in front of the eye at two flames which were near together. DONDERS changed the details of this method, by causing the eye to look through a pair of apertures in a metal plate, 1.5 mm apart, at a brightly illuminated white area on which the entoptical phenomena appeared to be projected. Then he got the distance between the centres of the two partially overlapping circular images of the pupil, which amounts simply to measuring the diameter of the uncovered portion of one of these discs; and he measured also the distance between the two images of the entoptical object. These two measured distances are in the same ratio to each other as the required distance of the object from the retina is to the apparent distance of the pupil from the retina (18 mm); so that the distance of the object can be easily computed.

DONDERS' procedure was modified by DONCAN merely by making the measurements on the principle of the microscope method *à double vue.* One eye looks through a tiny aperture or through a pair of them towards a small concave mirror illuminated by skylight, while the other eye looks at a card placed at the distance of distinct vision. The size of the entoptical object and the distance between its two images are measured on this card with a pair of dividers, and likewise the distance between corresponding points on the edge of the iris. In order to calculate the real size of the entoptical object from its apparent size, it is necessary to know also the distance of the peep hole from the cornea. It is best to adjust this aperture at the anterior focal point of the eye, that is, 12 mm from the cornea, because then the entoptical shadow is just the same size as the object itself. The apparent size of the object in the field of view as measured by the dividers is in the same ratio to its real size as the distance of the card from the eye is to the anterior focal length of the eye (15 mm). The aperture can be adjusted approximately in the first focal plane of the eye by attaching the metal plate at the end of a little tube of suitable dimensions.

The apparent extent of the movement of the vascular figure in the field of view, as seen by the first of the methods described above, was measured by MÜLLER; the corresponding movement of the luminous focus on the sclerotica being measured at the same time with a pair of dividers. Thence the distance of the blood vessel, that casts the shadow, from the light-senstitive layer of the retina can be found, approximately at any rate, either by geometrical construction or arithmetical computation. A section of the eye, like that in Fig. 92, is drawn in its actual size. Suppose the focus moves to and fro over the

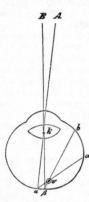

sclerotica between the points marked a and b; and let v designate the position of a blood vessel whose shadow falls at a in the vicinity of the yellow spoⱡ when the focus is at a, so that the blood vessel v whose apparent size is to be measured is on the straight line aa. Let $a\beta$ represent the real movement on the retina which is calculated from the apparent, displacement of the blood vessel in the field of view; where β, therefore, designates the position of the shadow when the focus is at b. The point v where the straight lines aa and $b\beta$ intersect must be the position of the blood vessel, and its distance from the retina can be found by measurement or by calculation. Thus, in several experiments, MÜLLER found for the distances of the blood vessels from the sensitive layer of the retina the following values (given in mm): 0.17; from 0.19 to 0.21; 0.22; from 0.25 to 0.29; and from 0.29 to 0.32. With three other observers he got: 0.19; 0.26; and 0.36mm. By anatomical measurements be found between 0.2 and

Fig. 92.

0.3 mm for the distance of the blood vessels from the layer of rods and cones in the region of the yellow spot; which indicates that the cones are the elements on which the shadows are cast; as other considerations do also, which will be treated in §18.

A Jesuit named DECHALES,[1] who flourished in the seventeenth century, was the first to advance a theory as to the origin of the *mouches volantes*, and to attribute them correctly to shadows of little particles suspended in the eye in the region of the retina. On the other hand, PITCAIRN[2] supposed they were on the retina itself. MORGAGNI[3] thought that they were in all the ocular media, but that those more to the front perhaps could not be seen without using small sources of light. DE LA HIRE[4] was likewise mistaken in supposing that the permanent "gnats" were confined to the retina, and that the flitting ones were in the aqueous humor. An experiment was described by LE CAT[5] which contains in principle the whole method of entoptical investigation, and which consisted in erecting a needle close in front of the eye and observing its inverted shadow in the blur circle of a small source of light. About this same epoch AEPINUS[6] also observed entoptically the shadow of the iris and the contraction and dilatation of the pupil, and gave a correct explanation thereof.

[1] *Cursus seu mundus mathematicus.* Lugduni 1690. T. III. p. 402.

[2] PITCAIRNII *Opera.* Lugd. Bat. p. 203. 206.

[3] *Adversaria anatomica* VI. Anim. LXXV. p. 94. Lugd. Bat. 1722.

[4] *Accidens de la vue.* p. 358.

[5] *Traité des sens.* Rouen 1740. p. 298.

[6] *Novi Comment.* Petropol. Vol. VII. p. 303.

But it was not until 1760[1] that small apertures and strong lenses began to be used for seeing these phenomena distinctly, although even DECHALES was not entirely ignorant of this method.

Long afterwards LISTING[2] and BREWSTER[3] developed a more exact theory of the entoptical phenomena and methods of locating the particles in the eye; and subsequently DONDERS[4] pursued the same study. Then one of his pupils, DONCAN,[5] established the agreement between the entoptical effects and the miscroscopical structure of the vitreous humor; and similar investigations were made by JAGO.[6] In addition to the authors already named, STEIFEN-SAND,[7] MACKENZIE[8] and APPIA[9] described various forms of entoptical objects.

The subjective appearance of the central blood vessels was discovered first by PURKINJE,[10] who showed how to see them by the three methods described above. He obtained them also by stimulating the eye by pressure and congestion of the blood. The significance of the shadow movement which is so important in the theory of these effects was pointed out by GUDDEN.[11] With homocentric light emanating from the pupil or with a focus on the sclerotica, there was apparently no difficulty about the theory of the phenomenon. But MEISSNER[12] showed that the behaviour was different when the light moved inside the eye, which led him to entertain some doubts as to previous explanations. These doubts were confirmed by H. MÜLLER,[13] to whom we are indebted for the theory of this method of experiment as given above. PURKINJE had already observed that there is a bright spot in the centre of the field of view that looks like a little pit or cavity; and BUROW[14] described more accurately the appearance of the yellow spot, but interpreted it as looking more like a protuberance than a little depression; which was due to the former incorrect theory of the experiment that MÜLLER perfected.

1690. DECHALES, *Cursus seu mundus mathematicus.* Lugduni. T. III. p. 402.
1694. DE LA HIRE, *Accidens de la vue* in *Mém. de l'Acad. d. sc.* p. 358.
      PITCAIRNII *Opera.* Lugd. Bat. p. 203. 206.
1722. MORGAGNI *Adversaria anatomica* VI. Anim. LXXV. p. 94. Lugd. Bat.
1740. LE CAT, *Traité des sens.* Rouen. p. 298.
      AEPINUS, *Novi Comment.* Petrop. VII. p. 303.
1760. *Histoire de l'Acad. d. sc. pour l'an 1760.* p. 57.
1819. PURKINJE, *Beiträge zur Kenntnis des Sehens.* S. 89.*
1825. Idem. *Neue Beiträge.* S. 115. 117.*
1842. STEIFENSAND in POGGENDORFFS *Ann.* LV. p. 134*; v. AMMONS *Monatsschrift für Medizin.* I. 203.
1845. *LISTING, *Beitrag zur physiologischen Optik.* Göttingen.*

[1] *Histoire de l'Acad. d. sciences.* 1760. p. 57. Paris 1766.
[2] *Beitrag zur physiologischen Optik.* Göttingen 1845.
[3] *Transactions of the Roy. Soc. of Edinb.* XV. 377.
[4] *Nederl. Lancet.* 1846–47. 2. Serie. D. II. bl. 345. 432. 537.
[5] *De corporis vitrei structura. Dis.* Utrecht 1854; *Onderzoekingen ged. in het Physiol. Laborat. d. Utrechtsche Hoogeschool.* Jaar VI. p. 171.
[6] *Proceed. Roy. Soc.* 18 Jan. 1855.
[7] POGGENDORFFS *Ann.* LV. p. 134; v. AMMONS *Monatschrift f. Med.* I. 203.
[8] *Edinburgh Medical and Surgical Journal.* July 1845.
[9] *De l'oeil vu par lui-même.* Genève 1853.
[10] *Beiträge zur Kenntnis des Sehens.* 1819. S. 89. Neue Beiträge. 1825. S. 115. 117.
[11] J. MÜLLERS *Archiv für Anat. u. Physiol.* 1849. S. 522.
[12] *Beiträge zur Physiologie des Sehorgans.* 1854.
[13] *Verhandl. der med.-physik. Ges. zu Würzburg.* IV. 100. V. Lief. 3.
[14] J. MÜLLERS *Archiv.* 1854. S. 166.

1845. BREWSTER in *Transactions of the Roy. Soc. of Edinb.* XV. 377.
       MACKENZIE, *Edinb. Medical and Surgical Journal.* July 1845.
1846. DONDERS in *Nederlandsch Lancet.* 1846–47. 2. Serie. D. II. bl. 345. 432. 537.
1848. BREWSTER in *Phil. Mag.* XXXII. 1; *Arch.d. sc. phys. et natur. de Genève.* VIII. 299.
1849. GUDDEN in J. MÜLLERS *Archiv.* 1849. S. 522.*
1853. APPIA, *De l'oeil vu par lui-même.* Genève.
1854. *A. DONCAN, *De corporis vitrei structura.* *Dissert.* Trajecti ad Rhenum; *Onder-
       zoekingen ged. in het Physiol. Laborat. d. Utrechtsche Hoogeschool. Jaar* VI. p. 171.
       BUROW in J. MÜLLERS *Archiv.* 1854. S. 166.
1855. JAMES JAGO in *Proceedings of the Roy. Soc.* 18 Jan. 1855.

Supplement

On bright surfaces intermittently illuminated (for example, by moving the hand to and fro in front of the eye, with the fingers spread out) VIERORDT observed a stream movement which he took for the motion of the blood in the retinal vessels; but neither MEISSNER nor the writer could verify this phenomenon as having the appearance of a current flowing between banks; and therefore the writer ventured to doubt VIERORDT's explanation of it. However, he may have been able to see it better and more definitely, and in his case it may have really been a picture of the flow of blood.

Besides, PURKINJE and J. MÜLLER, looking at an extended bright surface, had seen the appearance of bright points in the field of view with a line proceeding from them, which continually reappeared at irregular intervals, always following the same path with the same fairly great velocity. O. N. ROOD has recently observed that this phenomenon can be seen very much better by looking at the sky through a dark blue glass. The way the writer does it is to look at a point in the window-pane so as to see the little moving particles in the eye always at the same place, and so to compare their paths with the vascular figure projected also on the glass.

Now after having repeated these observations, the writer is disposed to believe that they do depend on a movement of the blood in some such way that one of the larger particles gets jammed in one of the narrower vessels. In this case the vessel usually gets comparatively empty on the far side of a particle of this kind, while great numbers of blood corpuscles are congested on the other side. As soon as the obstruction gives way, the whole congregation flows past quickly. This procedure is often witnessed in watching the capillary circulation through a microscope. In the case of the experiment mentioned above, a brighter, more elongated band precedes in the visual field, corresponding to the empty place in the blood vessel beyond the obstruction; and following it, there is a darker shadow which, in the writer's opinion, corresponds to the congested corpuscles.

In the author's right eye this phenomenon is very distinct in two parallel vessels to the left of the point of fixation; and frequently recurs, occasionally in both vessels at the same time. Apparently the motion is upwards, and the figure vanishes by wriggling through a sinuous curve with considerably increased speed. The interesting thing is that in the entoptical image of the vascular figure not only are the two parallel vessels found at the place specified above, but also the S-shaped curve at their junction point leading into a larger ramification of veins; that is, the two methods of observation agree perfectly. Of course, the two blood vessels here mentioned are not the only ones which exhibit this movement, and there are numerous other places in the same eye; but they are farther from the point of fixation, and the appearances are not so characteristic.

Accordingly, the phenomenon here described should be regarded as an optical representation of little obstructions in the circulation of the blood, occurring ordinarily only at certain constricted places of the vascular tract, and only when a rather larger corpuscle tries to get past.

1853.	TROUESSART, Suite des recherches concernant la vision.	*C. R.* XXXVI, 144–146.
1856.	VIERORDT, Wahrnehmung des Blutlaufs den Netzhautgefässen.	*Archiv für physiol. Heilkunde.* 1856.	Heft II.
—	MEISSNER in *Jahresbericht für 1856.* HENLE und PFEUFFER *Zeitschr.* (3) I, 565–566.
1857.	J. JAGO, Ocular spectres, structures and functions as mutual exponents.	*Proc. Roy. Soc.* VIII, 603–610.	*Phil. Mag.* (4) XV, 545–550.
1860.	O. N. ROOD, On a probable means of rendering visible the circulation in the eye.	SILLIMAN's J. (2) XXX, 264–265; 385–386.
1861.	L. REUBEN, On normal quasi-vision of the moving blood-corpuscles within the retina of the human eye.	SILLIMAN's J. (2) XXXI, 325–388; 417.

Note by A. Gullstrand

There are two entoptical phenomena belonging in the domain of the dioptrics of the eye that have this in common, namely, that although no notice was taken of them when they were first discovered, attention has again been directed to both of them.

When a candle flame in an otherwise dark room is brought near the visual axis of the passive eye from the temporal side, often a faint spot of light is seen to move in the opposite direction. This phenomenon was first explained by BECKER[1]; and it has been described again by TSCHERNING[2] who recommends causing a candle flame to pass below the visual axis. Different individuals do not see the spot of light with equal distinctness. The writer cannot succeed in seeing it except under special circumstances; as it is mostly hidden by the vascular figure, and he does not know how to produce the conditions

[1] O. BECKER, Über Wahrnehmung eines Reflexbildes im eigenen Auge. *Wiener Med. Wochenschrift* 1860, S. 670 and 684.

[2] TSCHERNING, *Optique physiologique.* Paris 1898. p. 43.

that are conducive to its apparition. Other people see it so distinctly that they recognize the inverted image of the flame in it. This phenomenon is akin to what is known as the "Lichtfleck" (flare spot) among opticians, due to harmful reflection of light at the refracting surfaces of an optical instrument. So far as twofold reflections are concerned, there is no refracting surface in the eye that needs to be considered except the anterior surface of the cornea, as this is the only surface where there is a sufficient difference between the indices of refraction of the adjacent media. Now calculation shows that light which is reflected again back into the eye from the anterior surface of the cornea, produces an erect image of the flame not far from the retina; which consequently appears to be inverted, so that its apparent displacement must be "against" the motion of the light. The light reflected at the anterior surface of the lens, and then back again at the anterior surface of the cornea, forms an image near the posterior surface of the lens; which must be projected on the retina in a very large blur circle that cannot be differentiated from the diffusely reflected light in the ocular media.

In a dark room most people with dilated pupils discern coloured rings around small sources of light which are particularly distinct against a dark background. The rings comprise the colours of the spectrum, red being on the outside, and the angular diameter of the yellow ring amounting to some 6° or 7°. Artificial light is usually deficient in radiations of short wave-lengths; and under such circumstances the spectrum is not apt to be very distinct beyond the blue-green. On looking through a small hole, the ring vanishes entirely as soon as the hole is centered on the pupil. But when the hole is decentered with respect to the pupil, the instant it reaches the edge of the dilated pupil two tiny spectra flash forth. The straight line joining them passes through the flame—at right angles to the direction in which the hole was moved. Thus, any two parts of the coloured ring at opposite ends of a diameter can be produced at will. The disposition of the colours in the ring is characteristic of an interference-spectrum, and the experiment with the hole shows that the phenomenon is due to a radial grating that comes into action only in the vicinity of the edge of the pupil. But owing to the ray-formed structure of the lens, the fibres of the lens are not exactly radial, and therefore cannot be responsible for any exact ring-shaped type. In confirmation of this, it may be shown that the ring seems to be composed of several small pieces not entirely similar to one another. That the ring is produced by a radial grating, may be proved also by interposing in front of it a piece of opaque paper with a straight edge. For instance, if the paper is inserted from the temporal side with its edge vertical, until only a small segment of the pupil on the nasal side is left exposed, the two sides of the ring are eclipsed, and only the upper and lower parts remain. In this case only a portion of the grating contained in the lens is left uncovered, and this portion contains horizontal fibres together with some that are not quite horizontal. Hence, no parts of the ring can be seen except those for which the tangent is parallel to the direction along which the uncovered fibres lie.

With relaxed accommodation, or under conditions of excitement, the pupil of the eye is often dilated enough to see the coloured ring immediately. But with some persons the experiment with the hole is not successful without artificial dilatation of the pupil unless the other eye is screened; whereas other people still are not able to see the coloured ring at all without a mydriatic. The phenomenon was described and correctly explained by both DONDERS[1] and BEER,[2] and was subsequently investigated more fully by DRUAULT[3] and SALOMONSOHN.[4] The latter, by the way, appended to his paper a summary of the literature on the subject; but he was mistaken in supposing that the coloured rings that occur with glaucoma are produced in the same way. They vanish gradually, and all over at the same time, when a card is interposed in front of the eye, which shows that their origin is due to round or polygonal elements, in the same way that coloured rings are produced by a clouding of the cornea. Their diameter, too, is larger. On the contrary, in cases where the glaucoma has produced the necessary dilatation of the pupil without concomitant cloudiness of the cornea, it sometimes happens that the physiological coloured rings, originating in the lens, become visible, and may be confused with purely glaucomatous phenomena of a similar appearance.

In the same manner, and with the same behaviour with respect to an interposed card, under certain physiological conditions, coloured rings can be seen that are due to some secretion on the surface of the cornea or to some irregular evaporation of moisture there. Many persons habitually see a ring of this sort marking the outer boundary of the light diffused around a bright source; the larger ring originating in the lens being separated from it by a dark gap.

---

[1] See J. H. A. HAFFMANS, Beiträge zur Kenntnis des Glaukoms. *Arch. f. Ophth.* VIII. 2. S. 124. 1862.

[2] BEER, Über den Hof um Kerzenflammen. POGGENDORFFS *Ann.* Bd. 84. S. 518. 1851; Bd. 88. S. 595. 1853.

[3] A. DRUAULT, Sur la production des anneaux colorés autour des flammes. *Arch. d'opht.* 18. p. 312. 1898.

[4] H. SALOMONSOHN, Über Lichtbeugung an Hornhaut und Linse. *Arch. f. Physiologie.* Jahrg. 1898. S. 187.

§ 16. The Illumination of the Eye and the Ophthalmoscope

A part of the light that reaches the retina of the eye is absorbed, especially by the black pigment of the choroid, and another part is diffusely reflected and returns through the pupil and out of the eye altogether. Ordinarily, we are absolutely unaware of this latter portion; so much so, indeed, that the pupil of another person's eye looks entirely black. The explanation of this is to be found mainly in the peculiar refraction conditions in the eye, but to some extent also because, as a matter of fact, comparatively little light is reflected back from most parts of the black fundus of the eye.

According to the principle of the reversibility of the light path, light will traverse precisely the same route through an optical instrument from one end to the other in either direction. Thus, for example, so far as this principle is concerned, it makes no difference which one of a pair of conjugate points is regarded as the source of the light and which one as the image, because in this respect object and image are interchangeable. Suppose, therefore, that the eye is accommodated to focus on the retina an exact image of an external luminous object; and suppose that we regard the illuminated part of the retina as being itself a luminous object: then its image projected by the ocular media will coincide exactly with the external object. In other words, all the light proceeding from the retina through the eye will return punctually to the outside luminous body. In order to get some of this light, an observer would have to insert his eye between the luminous body and the illuminated eye, which, of course, cannot be done without some auxiliary contrivance to prevent the illuminating light from being intercepted.

There is the same difficulty about seeing the light that returns from a person's eye when his eye is accommodated to see distinctly the pupil of the observer's eye. In this case there is an accurate dark image of the pupil of the observer's eye projected on the retina of the other person's eye. Conversely, there is an image of this dark place on the retina projected on the pupil of the observer's eye; so that all the observer can do is to see the reflex of the black of his own eye in the other person's eye.

Thus, under ordinary circumstances, even the parts of the fundus of the eye that reflect light better than the other places, as, for example, the white area where the optic nerve enters the eye and the blood vessels, are not visible to an outside observer. Although the choroid of the eye of an albino is almost devoid of pigment, his pupil will look black too, provided proper precautions are taken to prevent light from getting into the eye through the sclerotica; as can be done by holding a dark screen in front of the eye, with a hole made in it the size of the pupil, so as to enable the observer to see through it.[1]   It is the light that penetrates through the sclerotica that causes the customary red appearance of the pupil of an albino's eye. Similarly, viewed from in front, the object-glass of a *camera obscura*, that is used to project the image of a single light in a dark room, looks black; even if the image is received on a piece of white paper.

But if the illuminated eye is not accommodated exactly either for the luminous object or for the pupil of the observer's eye, it may be possible for the observer to get some of the light returning from the pupil of the other person's eye; and then the pupil will look bright to him.

It is not hard to understand how the observer can get light from all those parts of the retina of another person's eye, that are comprised within the area covered by the blurred image of the pupil of his own eye. Suppose, for a moment, that the pupil of the observer's eye is replaced by a luminous disc whose blurred image in the other person's eye coincided exactly with what was there before. Now in this case rays of light proceed from one or more points of the illuminated disc to all the points of its blurred image. Accordingly, rays of light may come back from all parts of the illuminated area on the retina to the corresponding point or points on the disc; that is, to the place where the observer's pupil is. Thus the observer will see the other person's eye as luminous, whenever the blurred image of his own pupil in that eye partly overlaps the blurred image of a luminous object.

Suppose, therefore, that the observer looks right past the edge of a light, that is screened from his own eye so as not to blind him, into another person's eye; and suppose that this latter eye is accommodated for a point between the two eyes or for a point much farther away than the opposite eye: under these circumstances, the observer will see the pupil of the other eye shining red. The arrangement of this experiment is indicated

Fig. 97.

in the accompanying diagram (Fig. 97); where B represents the observer's eye, S the screen which protects it from the direct rays of the lamp-light shown in plan at A, and C the illuminated eye. The straight line BC is the visual axis of the observer's eye, whereas that of the other eye may have any direction as, for example, along the straight

[1] F. C. DONDERS in *Onderzoekingen gedaan in het Physiologisch Laborat. der Utrechtsche Hoogeschool.* Jaar VI. p. 153. — VAN TRIGT in *Nederlandsch Lancet.* 3. Ser. D. II. bl. 419.

line *Cd*. The experiment is usually successful also without taking
account of the accommodation of the illuminated eye, provided the
observer is far away, or provided the patient looks to one side, as
in Fig. 97; because then the image of the light and that of the pupil
of the observer's eye are projected on the lateral parts of the retina
where the images are generally not clear-cut. The illumination is
brightest when the light falls at the place where the optic nerve
enters the eye, because the light is highly reflected from this white
substance, and also because its translucency is such that it does not
offer any definite surface for the projection of a clear-cut image.

It may be noted that with sufficiently strong illumination enough
light goes through the choroid to the sclerotica to be perceptible when
it is diffusely reflected back again. This light behaves like that of the
blur circle. Hence, with strong illumination, even when the patient's
eye is exactly accommodated for the pupil of the observer's eye, the
luminosity may be feeble, especially if there is not much pigment in
the eye, as was explained above.

The luminosity of the eye can be observed still better, provided
the light from the flame is not permitted to fall directly on the eye,

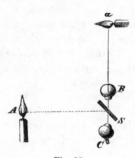

but is reflected on it from a glass plate,
through which the observer can look
into it. In Fig. 98, *A* shows the position of the light and *S* that of the transparent glass plate, which reflects the
light into the eye at *C* as if it came from
a source *a* behind the observer's eye at
B. A small retinal image of the light
is projected on the fundus of the eye
C; thence the light returns towards *a*
and falls again on the surface of the
glass plate, where a part of it is reflected

Fig. 98.

back to the real source at *A;* but another part traverses the plate and
proceeds onward toward the reflected image at *a*. The observer with
his eye at *B* is in a position to intercept these rays, and thus to perceive the luminosity of the eye at *C*. If a small hole is bored in the
plate to enable the observer to see through it, the reflecting surface
may be silvered.

Now although under these circumstances the observer beholds the
illuminated fundus of the eye, as a rule, perhaps, he cannot make out
any of its details, because he is unable to accommodate for the image
of the fundus that is produced by the ocular media. To do this, he
must use appropriate glass lenses. The combination of an illumination
apparatus with glass lenses in this way constitutes an instrument

called an *ophthalmoscope* (or "ocular mirror"), which enables the observer to see distinctly the images on the retina and the details of the retina of another person's eye, and to investigate them.

BRÜCKE called attention to a peculiar advantage which must be afforded by the bacillary layer of rods and cones in the reflection of light from the retina. These elements are small cylinders, 0.030 mm long and 0.0018 mm thick, made of some highly refracting substance. Packed close together like palisades, they constitute the last layer of the retina. The axes of those which cover the retina in the back of the eye are pointed towards the pupil, so that all light that falls on these elements penetrates them nearly parallel to their axes. Now when light, proceeding in a denser medium, arrives at the boundary of a less dense medium at a very large angle of incidence, it is totally reflected there. So we may infer that light which has once been refracted into a retinal rod is mostly retained there, and if it should fall on the curved cylindrical surface anywhere, it is nearly all internally reflected. For example, suppose the index of refraction of the substance of the rods is equal to that of oil (1.47), and the index of refraction of the intervening substance is equal to that of water (1.33); then any rays that make an angle with the surface less than 25° will be totally reflected. But the rays that arrive through the pupil must fall on the rod-walls at angles that are never more than about 8°. If the light has at last reached the farther (outer) end of the rod, and if here part of it is diffusely reflected from the choroid, nearly all of this portion must be sent back again through the same rod. Such light as proceeds in a direction more inclined to the axis, may, of course, succeed in escaping from the rod; but not until it has been repeatedly reflected at the surface of the adjacent rod, will it contrive to get into the vitreous humor. On the other hand, the light that comes back nearly parallel to the axis of the rod suffers only a few total reflections at most, and hence will not have lost much when it emerges. Besides, this light will be directed towards the pupil and will issue through it. This function of the rods appears to be of importance, especially in the case of those animals that have a highly reflecting surface or tapetum instead of the layer of black pigment cells on the choroid. The first effect of it is that the light which was originally incident on the sensitive elements of the retina meets and stimulates them again on the rebound. And, secondly, on its return, it affects only the same elements of the retina or possibly in some measure those right next to them. Thus, the light that arrives at any one place is practically confined to a very minute region of the retina; a circumstance that must have an important bearing on the accuracy of vision. When the retinal image is sufficiently bright, diffusely scattered light of this sort may be noticeable in the field of view. An instance of this was given in the preceding section in the description of the method of observing the vascular figure by moving a light to and fro below the eye. As the basis of the mathematical theory of the luminosity of the eye and the ophthalmoscope, a series of general propositions will now be stated and discussed. The special cases to be considered afterwards are much simplified by formulating these general laws.

I

If two rays of light traverse a system of isotropic media from opposite directions, and if in any one of these media their paths coincide, they must coincide in all the media.

Suppose that the straight line AB in Fig. 99 is the path of the two rays which we know to be common to both of them; and that the first ray, proceeding along the straight line EB, is refracted at B in the direction BA. The other ray, proceeding from A to B along the straight line AB, is likewise refracted at B, say, in the direction $BE_{,}$. First, of all, it must be proved that $E_{,}B$ and EB coincide. Draw DBC normal to the refracting surface at the point B, and put angle $EBD = a$, angle $E_{,}BD = a_{,}$, and angle $ABC = \beta$; and let m and n denote the indices of refraction of the media containing the points E $(E_{,})$ and A, respectively. By the law of refraction, the first ray BA must lie in the plane containing BD and EB; and, moreover,

$$m \sin a = n \sin \beta.$$

Likewise, the second ray $BE_{,}$ must be in the plane determined by BD and AB, that is, in the same plane with BE; and also:

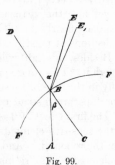

Fig. 99.

$$m \sin a_{,} = n \sin \beta.$$

Consequently, $\sin a = \sin a_{,}$

or $a = a_{,}$,

since the angles here are both acute angles. Hence, the ray $BE_{,}$ coincides with the ray EB, and the two rays pursue the same path in opposite directions as far as this medium extends. At the next refracting surface the same proof applies, and so on throughout the entire system.

Notes: 1. Evidently, the proposition is true also when the light is reflected at a surface.

2. In the case of the eye, if a ray on its way through the vitreous humor coincides with another ray proceeding in the opposite direction in the same medium, the paths of these rays outside the eye coincide also.

3. According to the general enunciation of this proposition, as given here, the case can be supposed in which for certain directions of polarisation and for

certain angles of incidence, the rays might be entirely extinguished by a refraction or reflection. But such circumstances do not occur in the applications of the theorem to the illumination of the eye. The light is incident nearly normally on the refracting surfaces of the eye, and hence any polarisation effects due to either refraction or reflection will be practically negligible. Moreover, the losses of light by reflection and absorption in the eye may be left out of account. It is only where the glass plate reflector is placed very obliquely to the rays of light that there is any considerable loss of light.

There is another corresponding proposition of wide application concerning the intensity of the light that proceeds to and fro over the same path, which, however, may be given here without proof because anybody who is at all familiar with the laws of optics can easily prove it for himself, and because also the principle is not needed for the purposes of the present discussion. This more general rule may be stated as follows.

Suppose light proceeds by any path whatever from a point A to another point B, undergoing any number of reflections or refractions *en route.* Consider a pair of rectangular planes a_1 and a_2 whose line of intersection is along the initial path of the ray at A; and another pair of rectangular planes b_1 and b_2 intersecting along the path of the ray when it comes to B. The components of the vibrations of the aether particles in these two pairs of planes may be imagined. Now suppose that a certain amount of light J leaving the point A in the given direction is polarised in the plane a_1, and that of this light the amount K arrives at the point B polarised in the plane b_1; then it can be proved that, when the light returns over the same path, and the quantity of light J polarised in the plane b_1 proceeds from the point B, the amount of this light that arrives at the point A polarised in the plane a_1 will be equal to K.

Apparently the above proposition is true no matter what happens to the light in the way of single or double refraction, reflection, absorption, ordinary dispersion, and diffraction, provided there is no change of its refrangibility, and provided it does not traverse any magnetic medium that affects the position of the plane of polarisation, as FARADAY found to be the case.

II

In order to see the luminous pupil of another person's eye, the retinal image of the source of light in his eye must overlap the retinal image of the pupil of the observer's eye, at least to some extent.

If the observer is to get light from any part of the retina of another person's eye, it is necessary, in the first place, for this part of the retina to be illuminated by the source of light, so that it must be comprised in the image of the source of light. In the second place, assuming, for the sake of argument, that light proceeds from the pupil of the observer's eye, then by the preceding proposition, it could go just as well to the given part of the retina of the other person's eye as it could come from it; and therefore this part of the retina must likewise be contained in the retinal image of the pupil of the observer's eye, no matter whether this image is clear-cut or blurred.

Notes: 1. This proposition is true not only when the light proceeds directly from the source to the illuminated eye and thence into the observer's eye, but also when any lenses or mirrors are interposed along the way. Incidentally, this fact affords a convenient way of showing experimentally how an ophthalmoscope acts in one's own eye. The light used for illumination is adjusted and the instrument arranged in the same position in front of the observer's eye as it would be in front of the patient's eye; then the part of the field that is bright corresponds to the part of the retina that is illuminated. It is possible to tell whether this bright field is large or small, and whether it is uniformly illuminated or whether there are dark places in it, and how dark they are. Then the source of light is transferred behind the instrument where the observer's eye would naturally be, so that the light shines through the peephole. Whatever is illuminated now in the field of view is comprised in the part of the retina that the observer will be able to see. This is the simplest and easiest way of getting a clear idea of the effects of various combinations of flat and curved mirrors and of convex and concave lenses in ophthalmoscopes; without having to make complicated geometrical constructions that are ofttimes more confusing than helpful to the unintiated.

2. The effect of the mode of illumination described in this section is easily regulated by the above rule. Everyday experience teaches us (as can be proved also by a simple construction of the procedure of the light) that the blurred image of a distant object cannot cover the sharp image of a nearer object that is seen distinctly, but that the blurred image of a near object may cover the sharp image of a more distant one. In the experiment with the perforated mirror the blurred image of the peephole which must be adjusted as near as possible in front of the patient's eye overlaps the image of the more distant source of light which is perhaps sharply in focus. If no mirror is employed, so that the observer looks past the light into the patient's eye, the flame and the observer's eye seem to the patient to be near together, and when his eye is not nicely accommodated for them, their blurred images are fused together. With illumination by a transparent plate of glass, both the image of the light and that of the pupil of the observer's eye may be sharply in focus. The former is seen reflected in the plate and the latter is seen through the plate, so that they come together on each other. Accordingly, it is best for the patient himself to adjust the glass plate so that his eye looks luminous to the observer. All that he has to do is to be careful that the observer's eye appears to be covered by the reflected image of the source of light.

A reciprocity law similar to that given above for light proceeding in opposite ways over the same path may also be formulated for the amount of light transmitted to and fro. In this connection, let us state here, first, the following

Fundamental Law of Photometry.

Suppose a and b are the areas of two tiny elements of surface in a transparent medium at the distance r apart; and let the brightness of the luminous element at a be denoted by H; then the quantity of light received by b will be

$$L = \frac{H.ab \cos \alpha \cos \beta}{r^2}; \qquad \cdot \quad \cdot \quad \cdot \quad \cdot \quad \cdot \qquad (1)$$

where a, β denote the angles made by the normals to a and b, respectively, with the straight line connecting these elements. Similarly, the quantity of light which would proceed from b to a would be the same as before, supposing the brightness of the element b were the same as that of a in the first case.

III

Let n_1, n_2 denote the indices of refraction of the first and last media, respectively, of a centered system of spherical refracting surfaces; and let a and β designate two surface-elements near the axis and perpendicular to it, in the first and last media, respectively. *Assuming that the brightness of the surface-element a is n_1^2H and that of β is n_2^2H, the quantity of light that goes from β to a is equal to that that goes from a to β.*

Not to make the proof more complicated than is necessary for the applications we have here in view, the losses of light due to reflection at the refracting surfaces may be neglected; and it may be also assumed that the rays are all incident on the refracting surfaces at angles so small that the cosine of any such angle may be put equal to unity; although the proposition is true when this is not the case.

1. *Case when β does not coincide with the image of a.*

In Fig. 100 the straight line AC represents the axis of the optical system, with its first and second principal points at F and G, respectively. The element of surface a in the first medium may be represented by a point in the diagram, since it is infinitely small; and the

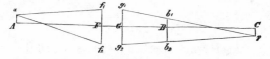

Fig. 100.

image of a in the last medium is designated by γ. Consider the bundle of rays proceeding from a; its cross section in the first principal plane is represented by f_1f_2, and the corresponding cross section in the second principal plane by g_1g_2; so that $g_1g_2 = f_1f_2 = \Phi$, say. The other surface-element β is supposed to be in a plane perpendicular to the axis at the point designated by B; and b_1b_2 represents the cross section of the bundle of rays in this plane. Let A and C designate the feet of the perpendiculars on the axis drawn from the conjugate points a and γ, respectively. According to equation (1), the quantity of light coming from a that falls on f_1f_2 is

$$\frac{n_1^2H \cdot a \cdot \Phi}{AF^2},$$

supposing that the brightness of a is $n_1{}^2H$. The more distant cross sections g_1g_2 and b_1b_2 receive this same amount of light. In the latter section the quantity of light that is delivered to the element β is in the same ratio to the entire quantity of light as the area of β is to that of the cross section b_1b_2; so that if this ratio is denoted by Ξ, the quantity of light that comes from a to β is

$$X = \frac{\Phi}{\Xi} \cdot \frac{n_1{}^2Ha\beta}{AF^2} \quad . \quad . \quad . \quad . \quad . \quad (2)$$

Moreover,

$$\frac{\Phi}{\Xi} = \frac{(g_1g_2)^2}{(b_1b_2)^2} = \frac{CG^2}{BC^2}.$$

Hence, by substitution in equation (2):

$$X = n_1{}^2Ha\beta \, \frac{CG^2}{BC^2 . AF^2}.$$

But by equation (8a) of § 9:

$$\frac{GC}{AF} = \frac{F_2}{AF - F_1},$$

where F_1, F_2 denote the two focal lengths of the optical system; hence

$$X = Ha\beta \cdot \frac{N_1{}^2F_2{}^2}{[AF \cdot F_2 + BG \cdot F_1 - AF \cdot BG]^2} \quad . \quad . \quad (2a)$$

Similarly, for the quantity of light sent from β to a, on the assumption that the brightness of β is $n_2{}^2H$, we obtain:

$$Y = Ha\beta \cdot \frac{n_2{}^2F_1{}^2}{[AF \cdot F_2 + BG \cdot F_1 - AF \cdot BG]^2} \quad . \quad . \quad (2b)$$

Since everything is symmetrical on the two sides, all that is necessary in order to derive this last expression is to substitute Y for X in equation (2a), and to interchange the pairs of magnitudes according to the following scheme:

$$AF \text{ and } BG$$
$$F_1 \text{ and } F_2$$
$$a \text{ and } \beta$$
$$n_1{}^2H \text{ and } n_2{}^2H.$$

Since, by equation (9c) of § 9,

$$n_1F_2 = n_2F_1,$$

we derive from equations (2a) of § 9,

$$X = Y,$$

which was to be proved.

2.   *Case when β coincides with the image of a.*

Suppose first that β coincides with the image of a, in both size and position; in which case also a coincides exactly with the image of β. Accordingly, all light coming from a falls on β, and *vice versa.* In Fig. 100 nothing is changed here except that now we must think of β as being at γ. If the brightness of the element a is $n_1{}^2H$, the total quantity of light which it sends to β is

$$X = n_1{}^2H \frac{a\Phi}{AF^2}; \quad . \quad . \quad . \quad . \quad . \quad (3a)$$

and, similarly, if the brightness of the element β is $n_2{}^2H$, the total quantity of light which it sends to a is

$$Y = n_2{}^2H \frac{\beta\Phi}{GC^2} \quad . \quad . \quad . \quad . \quad . \quad (3b)$$

Now as β here has to be the image of a, according to equation (8b), §9, we must have:

$$\frac{a}{\beta} = \frac{F_2{}^2}{(GC - F_2)^2},$$

since the areas of similar figures are proportional to the squares of their corresponding linear dimensions. Moreover, by equation (8a), § 9:

$$GC - F_2 = \frac{GC.F_1}{AF},$$

and hence:

$$\frac{aF_1{}^2}{AF^2} = \frac{\beta F_2{}^2}{GC^2},$$

But $F_1 : F_2 = n_1 ; n_2$, consequently,

$$\frac{an_1{}^2}{AF^2} = \frac{\beta n_2{}^2}{GC^2} \quad . \quad . \quad . \quad . \quad . \quad (3c)$$

Combining equations (3a), (3b) and (3c), we derive finally the result that $X = Y$, which was to be proved.

Should one of the two elements, a say, be greater than the image of β, then the parts of a that did not belong to the image of β would neither send light to β nor get light from it; and neither X nor Y would be changed on this account, so that the proposition would still be valid.

Notes: 1. The above proof is equally applicable to a centered optical system composed of both refracting and reflecting surfaces.

2. The condition that the two surfaces a, β shall be infinitely small is not essential, provided simply they are not so extended that the cosines of the angles of incidence of the rays at the various refracting surfaces are not very different from unity. For inasmuch as the proposition is true for each pair of infinitesimal portions of the two areas, it applies also to the entire areas.

Suppose the above proposition is applied to the case of the luminosity of the eye, one element of surface being in the retina of the illuminated eye and the other element being formed by the pupil of the observer's eye. If the difference in the indices of refraction of the aqueous and vitreous humors is neglected, and if any arbitrary symmetrical optical system of lenses or mirrors is supposed to be inserted between the two eyes, the proposition is as follows:

IIIa

The quantity of light proceeding from an element of the retina of the illuminated eye and entering the observer's eye is equal to the product of the brightness of the illumination of the retina and the quantity of light which would come from the pupil of the observer's eye and fall on the retina of the illuminated eye, on the supposition that the brightness of illumination of the pupil of the observer's eye were equal to unity.

Suppose the brightness of illumination of the element of the retina by the source of light is denoted by H; and let k denote the amount of light that is sent from the pupil of the observer's eye to the element of the retina on the supposition that the brightness of illumination of the pupil is equal to unity; then, by the proposition which has just been proved, k would likewise be equal to the quantity of light that would proceed from the element of the retina to the pupil of the observer's eye, provided the brightness of illumination of the retinal element were equal to unity. But this latter is not equal to unity but is equal to H; and hence the quantity of light that is actually communicated from the element of the retina to the pupil of the observer's eye is equal to Hk, in agreement therefore with the above statement.

In a sense this proposition is a sort of sequel to proposition II, because the quantitative relations which were lacking in that statement are given here. The proof as first given applied simply to an ophthalmoscope in which the rays of light met the surfaces of the mirrors and lenses at nearly normal incidence, with no appreciable loss of light. But evidently the proposition is true also when the eye is illuminated by oblique reflection from a glass plate, because when the light is not polarised the losses incurred in traversing such a plate from one eye to the other are just as great when the light proceeds through it one way as when it goes through it the opposite way.

IV

When an observer sees a clear-cut image of a luminous object in a symmetrical optical system of lenses and mirrors, then, on the supposition that the losses of light by reflection and refraction are negligible, each place in the image appears just as bright as the corresponding place in the object would appear without the optical instrument; provided the entire pupil of the observer's eye is filled with light coming from one single point of that part of the object. But if this latter condition is not satisfied, the brightness of the optical image is in the same ratio to that of the object seen directly as the area of the part of the pupil of the observer's eye that is filled with light is to the area of the entire pupil.

When the eye sees an object directly and distinctly, or its image in a symmetrical optical system, the eye by itself, or the eye and the optical system together, may be regarded as an optical system that projects an image of the object on the retina. Let a denote the area of a surface-element of the object, and b the area of the corresponding part of the image on the retina. According to proposition III above, the same quantity of light that goes from a to b would go from b to a, provided the brightness of illumination of the retinal element b were equal to $\dfrac{(n_2)^2}{(n_1)^2}H$, where H denotes the brightness of illumination of the element a, supposed to be in a medium of index of refraction n_1, and n_2 denotes the index of refraction of the vitreous humor. The quantity of light that would go from b to a under these circumstances can easily be calculated. If the cross section of the bundle of rays going from a point in b to a point in a as made by the plane of the pupil has an area denoted by q, the quantity of light M going from b to a is equal to that going from b to q, namely,

$$M = \frac{n_2{}^2}{n_1{}^2} H \cdot \frac{qb}{R^2},$$

where R denotes the distance of the pupil of the observer's eye from the retina of the illuminated eye. To be perfectly accurate, q denotes here the cross section of the bundle of rays made by the plane of the exit-pupil of the observer's eye; and R should be measured from this plane. In the above expression for the quantity of light coming to the observer from the illuminated element b there are two magnitudes that depend on the properties of the optical system which is interposed in front of the eye, namely, the cross section q in the pupil of the observer's eye, and the size of the image b on the retina of the other person's eye. But the brightness of this image depends not only on the quantity of light that it receives, but also on the area b over which this light is spread, being inversely proportional to b. If the quantity of light per unit of area is taken as the unit of the intensity of illumination, the intensity J of illumination of the retinal element b is

$$J = \frac{M}{b} = \frac{n_2{}^2}{n_1{}^2} H \cdot \frac{q}{R^2},$$

where now q is the only magnitude that depends on the peculiarity of the artificial optical system. When the eye looks directly at the luminous object, the entire pupil, of cross section Q, is filled with light, and the intensity of illumination of the light coming from b will be

$$J = \frac{n_2^2}{n_1^2} H \cdot \frac{Q}{R^2}.$$

This is the maximum intensity, because q can never be greater than Q. It is the natural brightness of the luminous area. The intensity of illumination of a surface as seen through an optical instrument can never be greater than its natural brightness, and is to the latter always in the ratio of q to Q.

Notes: 1. It is only when the luminous point is infinitesimally small, that its image as seen through an optical instrument, even with the highest magnifying power, extends over an element of the retina that it is no larger than the smallest blur circle, so that therefore it always retains the same size; and only under these circumstances can an optical instrument increase the apparent brightness of an object. This is the explanation of how the stars can be made visible in the day-time by looking at them through a powerful telescope with a large aperture; because the apparent luminosity of the star increases in proportion to the quantity of light coming from it that is brought to a focus by the instrument; whereas the telescope does not increase the brightness of the background of the sky.

2. Moreover, when the blurred image of a uniformly illuminated surface is projected in the eye, the intensity of illumination of the retina can never exceed that obtained by looking at the surface directly without any artificial optical contrivance. The proof of this statement is exactly the same as for the case when the image is not blurred, since proposition III applies equally to clear-cut images and blurred images. Here, likewise, the brightness of illumination is proportional to the cross section made by the plane of the pupil with the bundle of rays that can be sent from the corresponding point of the retina to the illuminated surface.

The author ventures to add that optical constructions of lenses and mirrors frequently trespass against the fundamental laws here stated. Many persons still believe that by concentrating light in the eye or in a microscope, etc., by means of convex lenses or concave mirrors, not only the apparent size of the illuminated surface, but its apparent brightness also, can be magnified. With the increased amount of light that can be obtained by such means there is invariably an accompanying magnification of the image, so that the image is merely bigger, not brighter. There is no optical instrument whatever that can make a luminous surface of any appreciable dimensions appear brighter to the eye than it does to the naked eye. It is just as impossible for an illuminated surface ever to be brighter than the illuminating source.

V

General method of estimating the brightness of illumination of a place in the retina of a person's eye as seen through an ophthalmoscope.

(a) *Case when the loss of light by refraction and reflection is assumed to be negligible.* Let x designate the position of a point at the place in the retina under consideration; the problem is to find out how the bundle of rays proceeds from this point x to the pupil of the patient's eye. According to propositions I and II, some of this light must return to the illuminating object, and some of it must go to the pupil of the observer's eye. Suppose P denotes the area of the pupil of the patient's eye, and p denotes the area of the cross section in this same plane of that part of the bundle of rays which returns to the illuminating object. Moreover, let H denote the brightness of illumination that would exist at the given place on the retina if the patient looked directly at the source of light and focused it on his retina. This magnitude may be called the *normal* brightness of illumination. It depends essentially on the structure of the retina itself, and, of course, also on the brightness of the illuminating object and on the size (P) of the pupil of the patient's eye. When an ophthalmoscope is employed, the actual brightness of illumination of this part of the retina is necessarily less than this; that is, it is equal to

$$\frac{p}{P}H.$$

Now let Q denote the area of the pupil of the observer's eye; and let q denote the area of the cross section in this plane of the part of the bundle of rays coming from x that enters the pupil of the observer's eye; then the brightness of this part of the retina as it looks to the observer is

$$\frac{q \cdot p}{Q \cdot P}H.$$

(b) *Case when there is appreciable loss of light by reflection or refraction.* In all the types of ophthalmoscope hitherto constructed the only one in which there is such a loss of light is in the case of the construction proposed by the author where unsilvered glass plates are used. In this case, and in all similar contrivances, the losses of the bundle of rays going from the eye to the illuminating object are precisely the same as those of the rays that actually go from the light to the eye. Suppose that light of unit intensity proceeds from the source to the illuminated eye, and produces there an illumination a; and that light of the same unit intensity proceeds from the patient's eye to the observer's eye and produces there an intensity β: then the above expression has to be multiplied both by a and β, so that it becomes:

$$\frac{a \cdot \beta \cdot p \cdot q}{P \cdot Q}\,H.$$

This complete reciprocity in the problem of the illumination of the eye as contained in the preceding propositions has enabled us to investigate the brightness of illumination of the images in every case by reducing the matter to the determination of the procedure of a single bundle of rays. Otherwise, the brightness at any particular place on the retina would have had to be found by summation of the effects of all the blur circles superposed there, that are made by the separate points of the source of light. Besides, in the writer's opinion, the subject is made clearer by the method used here. It is easy to follow the route of the rays from a point on the retina separately through each of the comparatively simple optical systems of the ophthalmoscope, one of which is for illumination, and the other for observation; but a complete view of the entire procedure from the source of light to the eye of the spectator is hard to follow, mainly because there is, so to speak, a sort of mosaic made of innumerable blur circles on the retina belonging to the various points in the source of light and in the pupil of the observer's eye.

VI

Method of obtaining a distinct image of the fundus of the eye

The illuminated eye is represented at A in Fig. 101. The image of a point a on the retina is produced at the point designated by b; the location of which will depend on the existing state of accommodation of the illuminated eye. The two arrows drawn through a and b correspond to the sizes of the two figures there. In the illustration the image of the place on the retina is shown magnified and inverted. An observer who, without using glasses or apparatus of any kind, desires to see the image of the retina that is formed at b, must, therefore, adjust his eye at some place C where he is able to accommodate so as to see

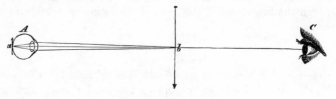

Fig. 101.

the image distinctly. However, under such circumstances, the field of view of the observer, being limited by the pupil of the patient's eye, would be so small that he might not be able to make out anything.

Heretofore two main methods have been employed to render the position of the image at b more convenient for the observer. In one case the image of the retina is virtual and erect, and in the other case it is real and inverted.

A. *Method of erect (virtual) image.*

In this method (Fig. 102) a concave lens B is employed, whose focal length B is less than the distance of the point b. The effect of this is to make the rays converging from A to b again divergent, so that they appear to come from a point d back of the patient's eye. In this figure also the arrows indicate the comparative sizes of the object at a and the images at b and d. Putting $a = Bb$, $\gamma = dB$, then

$$\frac{1}{a} + \frac{1}{\gamma} = \frac{1}{p};$$

where p denotes the negative focal length of the interposed lens. The observer must be able to accommodate for the distance γ if he is to see distinctly the image of the retina at d. The distance a depends on the state of accommodation of the patient's eye and on the distance between A and B. If both a and γ are prescribed, the value of p may be calculated, which gives the power of the lens that must be used to get a distinct image under the given conditions. Thus, if both eyes were accommodated for parallel rays, then $a = \gamma = \infty$, and hence also $p = \infty$, that is, no lens would be necessary at all. Ordinarily, also a lens is not needed to see the more lateral parts of the retina, because

Fig. 102.

they appear to be far away, and the ocular media by themselves can form images of them that are easy for the observer to see. In this mode of observation the image of the retina at d is erect.

As to the magnification, suppose that b were a luminous object whose image would be formed on the retina at a. The rays reversed produce an image of this retinal image, which according to the preceding propositions is congruent with the luminous object at b. Let β denote the size of the luminous object and of the image at d that is equal to it; and let δ denote the size of the image seen by the observer; then

$$\frac{\beta}{\delta} = \frac{a}{\gamma}.$$

If the *apparent size* of the image as seen by the observer is defined to be the ratio of its actual size to its distance from the observer's eye, then when the observer looks through the concave lens the apparent size of the image is

$$\frac{\delta}{\gamma} = \frac{\beta}{a}.$$

The apparent size of the object at b for the eye A is

$$\frac{\beta}{a+q},$$

where q denotes the distance AB. It is therefore rather smaller than the apparent size of the image δ. Now on the supposition that the distance for which the eye A is accommodated is very much greater than q, the latter is negligible in comparison with a, and in this case the apparent size of the luminous object for the eye A is equal to β/a. Thus, with this arrangement, the image of the retina of the patient's eye appears to the observer just as large as, or rather larger than, the corresponding object appears to the patient. Hence, the magnification of the place on the retina of the patient's eye may now be easily found. If the size of the image of β formed on the retina at a is denoted by x, and if the distance of the retina from the second nodal point of the eye is denoted by y, then

$$\frac{x}{\beta} = \frac{y}{a+q}$$

$$\frac{\beta}{\delta} = \frac{a}{\gamma}.$$

Multiplying these equatations, we have:

$$\frac{x}{\delta} = \frac{y \cdot a}{\gamma(a+q)}.$$

In LISTING's schematic eye $y = 15.0072$ mm; and if γ is put equal to 25 cm (which is the so-called distance of distinct vision), we obtain for the magnification:

$$\frac{\delta}{x} = 16.67 \frac{a+q}{a}.$$

Since q is usually very small as compared with a, the magnification may be put equal to $16\frac{2}{3}$.[1]

With this method the line of demarcation of the field of view as determined by the vaguely seen contour of the pupil of the patient's eye is not sharp. For practical purposes the field may be considered as limited by the lines of sight (see §11) drawn from the centre of the pupil of the patient's eye. If these lines are treated as rays of light proceeding from the observer's eye, the part of the retina of the other person's eye that is in the field of view is found to correspond to the blurred image of the centre of the pupil of the observer's eye. When this centre, or rather its image in the concave lens, is at the first focal point of the patient's eye, its blur circle, as was proved in the preceding section on entoptical phenomena, will be of the same size as the pupil of the patient's eye. Usually, however, the observer's eye cannot be as close as this to the patient's eye; and the blur circle corresponding to

---

[1] ¶In the text the distance γ is assumed to be equal to 8 (Prussian) inches; so that the value of the magnification is given as $14\frac{1}{6}$ instead of $16\frac{2}{3}$. (J. P. C. S.)

the field of view is smaller than the pupil of the patient's eye in proportion as the observer is farther way.

B.   *Method of the inverted image (indirect method)*

The other method of enabling an observer to inspect the retina of the eye consists in inserting a convex lens of short focus (from 1 to 3 inches) close in front of the illuminated eye (Fig. 103). As before, let a designate an illuminated place on the retina, and b the position of its image outside the patient's eye A. The rays coming from a fall on the convex lens at B before they are converged to the image at b; and the lens produces an image at d which is nearer and smaller than the image at b, but inverted like b. The observer puts his eye at C, as

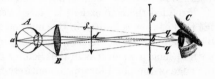

Fig. 103.

far off as necessary to accommodate to see the image. If the distances Bb and Bd are denoted by a and γ, respectively, and if the positive focal length of the lens is denoted by p, then

$$\frac{1}{\gamma} - \frac{1}{a} = \frac{1}{p}.$$

As a is usually very much greater than p, γ is nearly equal to p, but always somewhat smaller.

Let x denote the size of a part of the retina at the point a; and let β and δ denote the sizes of the images at b and d, respectively. Finally, let y denote the distance of the retina from the second nodal point of the eye, and q denote the distance of the first principal point of the lens from the first nodal point of the eye; then

$$\frac{x}{\beta} = \frac{y}{a+q},$$

$$\frac{\beta}{\delta} = \frac{a}{\gamma}.$$

Multiplying these two equations, we get:

$$\frac{x}{\delta} = \frac{y \cdot a}{\gamma \cdot (a+q)} = \frac{y \cdot (a+p)}{p(a+q)}.$$

As a rule, the lens B is adjusted with its focal point at the centre of the pupil of the illuminated eye A, in which case p and q are nearly the same; and hence the magnification is

$$\frac{\delta}{x} = \frac{p}{y}.$$

Employing the value of y in LISTING's schematic eye, the image δ is found to be magnified 2, 3 or 4 times according as the focal length of the convex lens is 30, 45 or 60 mm, respectively. This is the actual magnification of the real image of the retina. The magnification for the observer is

$$\frac{p}{yc} \times 25,$$

where c denotes the distance Cd in centimeters; the conventional distance of distinct vision being taken as 25 cm.

Provided the convex lens is placed very close to the patient's eye, the field of view is limited in this method by the pupil of this eye. But the farther away the lens is, the more magnified the pupil becomes, until at length when it is in the vicinity of the focal plane of the lens, the edge of the pupil disappears entirely from the field, and the extent of the field then is determined merely by the aperture of the lens. Here also, as in the preceding method, the extent of the field can be found by treating the lines of sight of the observer's eye as if they were rays of light. The lens B forms an image of the centre of the pupil of the observer's eye somewhere near its focal point, that is, approximately in the pupillary plane of the patient's eye; and thence the lines of sight diverge to the fundus of this eye. These lines intersect at or near the anterior nodal point of this eye, depending on the adjustment of the lens B; and therefore they proceed through the patient's eye practically without being refracted, as indicated by the dotted lines in Fig. 103. If u and v denote the aperture of the lens B and the diameter of the portion of the retina that is in the field, respectively, then

$$\frac{v}{y} = \frac{u}{p}.$$

With such small lenses the aperture may very well be made equal to half the focal length, that is, $u = p/2$; and hence, in this case:

$$v = \tfrac{1}{2}y = 7\tfrac{1}{2} \text{ mm.}$$

Accordingly, under such circumstances a larger field is commanded than is practicable by the first method, without artificial dilatation of the pupil by atropin.

VII

Illumination system of the ophthalmoscope

The eye may be illuminated in any of the three ways mentioned above, that is, directly by a light or by an opaque mirror with a hole in it or by a transparent unsilvered plate of glass used as a mirror.

If the eye is illuminated without any mirror at all, the image of the retina has to be inverted to be seen distinctly, and it takes considerable skill. Indeed, this method is not to be recommended unless there is no other instrument at hand except a simple convex lens of short focus. The procedure is as follows. The observer, protected by a screen from the direct light of the lamp, as shown in Fig. 97, looks right past this light in the other person's eye, and holds a convex lens of from 2 to 4 inches focus in front of this eye, as in Fig. 103. In order to find the correct adjustment, the lens is placed at first close in front of the eye, and then gradually brought back from it until the pupil is so magnified that its edges disappear behind the edges of the lens. A real inverted image of the retina is seen then at *d* (Fig. 103). In order to determine the brightness of illumination of this image, the first thing to do is to trace the bundle of rays that proceeds from the point *a* of the retina, according to the directions given under proposition V above. These rays are converged by the ocular media towards the point *b*, and then by the lens to the point *d*. Beyond *d* the bundle of rays is divergent and wide enough by the time it gets to *qq* for the rays to fill the pupil of the observer's eye completely; which means that the place on the retina of the illuminated eye can be seen in its entire actual degree of brightness. This "actual" brightness and the "normal" (greatest possible) brightness are in the same ratio to each other as the part of the bundle of rays *qq* that returns to the source of light is to the entire bundle of rays (see Prop. V). Now if the source of light is large enough and properly adjusted, it takes comparatively few rays to return past the light and fill the pupil of the observer's eye completely; and in this case the "actual brightness," of the place *a* on the retina is not much less than the "normal brightness," and the apparent brightness for the observer is equal to the "actual brightness."

The illumination of the eye *A* by an opaque mirror with a hole in it (Fig. 104) is far more convenient for observation. In the diagram, *A* and *B* are the eyes of patient and observer, respectively; *C* is the convex lens and *SS* is a perforated mirror. The image of the point *a* on the retina is focused at *d* and viewed by the observer through the hole in the mirror. Only a small portion of all the rays coming from *a* goes through the hole in the mirror. The rest are reflected and may return to the source of light. The mirror *SS* may be concave (RUETE), plane (COCCIUS), or convex (ZEHENDER). Moreover, a convex lens *L* can be interposed between the mirror and the source, as shown in the figure. Evidently, by this method the brightness of the illumination may be nearly normal (see Prop. V).

When the pupil of the eye *A* is in the focal plane of the lens *C*, the field of view depends on the size of the lens, as found above. How much of the retina can be illuminated? Since all the light the observer gets passes through the lens, it is evident that the illuminated part of the retina cannot exceed the blurred image of the lens; and this blurred image itself, as was shown in VI above, corresponds to the observer's field of view. This image, in all its parts, will have its maximum brightness when light goes from every place in the lens to every place in the pupil. This condition will be satisfied, provided the pupil of the illuminated eye is equal to or less than the image of the mirror SS (or of the lens L) that is made by the lens C somewhere near the pupil, and provided light goes from every point of the mirror (except, of course, where the hole is bored) to every part of the lens C. But the latter requires that the lens shall be situated at the image of the source D in the mirror, and that the size of the lens must be equal to that of this image or less than it.

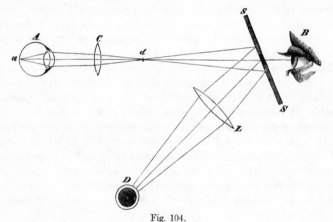

Fig. 104.

To give an example of such constructions, suppose that we wish to get a 4-fold magnification with the ophthalmoscope, and that, consequently, a lens C of 60 mm focus is employed with an aperture of 30 mm. The mirror S, which may be a concave glass with a hole in it, must be placed so far from the image d that the observer can accommodate for it, that is, about 150 mm away. In this case, therefore, the distance of S from C would be 210 mm. By equation (14b), §9, the image of the mirror in the lens will be 60/150 or 2/5 of its own size. As this image is to be of the same size as the pupil of the illuminated eye, which with artificial dilatation may have a diameter of 10 mm, the diameter of the mirror should be 25 mm.

The focal length of the mirror is determined by the condition that it has to produce an image of the light-source that covers the lens C. The diameter of the flame of a large ARGAND burner is about 15 mm. If the diameters of the lens and flame are taken as 30 mm and 15 mm, respectively, and if these values are substituted for β_1 and β_2 in equation (14b), §9, and if also $f_1 = CS = 210$ mm; the focal length of the mirror comes out to be $F = 70$ mm; and the distance of the source from the mirror must be 105 mm.

In case one prefers to use a plane mirror and a convex lens, as in Fig. 104, instead of a concave mirror, the sum of the distances of the two lenses L and C from the centre of the mirror must be used in the above calculation, instead of the distance of the mirror from the lens C.

When the mirror and lens are in two separate parts which the operator holds in position, of course, it is not possible to keep them adjusted at exactly the distance calculated by the formula; and in fact good images can be had with fairly large variations from the correct distance. However, it is well for the observer to know, at any rate, the best conditions for holding his instrument.

The conditions are more unfavourable when the observation has to be made with a perforated mirror and a concave lens; as represented in Fig. 105, where, as before, A and B designate the two eyes and S the mirror. Suppose that a denotes the fraction of the cone of rays that comes into the observer's eye from the point a on the retina of the other eye; and that $(1-a)$, therefore, is the other

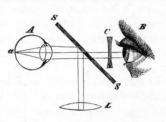

Fig. 105.

part of this light that is reflected by the mirror to the source of illumination. Under these circumstances, the actual brightness of this part of the retina, according to proposition V above, will be $H(1-a)$, where H denotes the "normal" brightness there. As before, let J denote the area of the apparent pupil of the patient's eye (A), and let R denote the corresponding magnitude in the observer's eye; also, let g denote the distance between the two apparent pupils, and h the distance for which the eye A is accommodated; then the cross section of the part of the bundle of rays that enters the observer's eye is

$$aJ \cdot \frac{(h-g)^2}{h^2}.$$

Generally, this cross section will be smaller than R. The brightness as it appears to the observer in this case will be

$$H \cdot a(1-a)\frac{J \cdot (h-g)^2}{Rh^2}.$$

For $a = 1/2$, the expression $a(1-a)$ has its greatest value; and hence the best arrangement, so far as brightness is concerned, is when half of the rays go to the observer's eye and the other half are reflected back. In this case the brightness attains the value

$$\tfrac{1}{4}H \cdot \frac{J \cdot (h-g)^2}{Rh^2}.$$

A large source of light placed near the eye is used to get as great a field as possible in the illuminated eye; or a convex lens placed at L can be used for this purpose. If the image of the source in this lens covers the pupil completely, the entire blurred image of the lens L in the eye A will be illuminated.

The illumination by means of a transparent glass plate in the convex lens method gives only one quarter of the brightness that can be gotten with a silvered mirror with a hole in it. On the other hand, this mode of illumination in the concave lens method is sometimes superior. For example, suppose that the mirror SS in Fig. 105 is not silvered and has no hole in it, but is just a plate of glass or several plates put together. Along every ray incident on the mirror, a certain portion of light a will be transmitted through it, and another portion $(1-a)$ will be reflected from it. The brightness of the light reflected from the mirror is equal to $H(1-a)$, where H denotes the "normal" brightness of the retina at a, for the case of light incident directly on it. The cross section of the bundle of rays emitted from a at the place where they enter the eye B is

$$J\frac{(h-g)^2}{h^2}.$$

Since only the portion a of the light goes through the plate (or plates), the brightness as seen by the observer is

$$H \cdot a(1-a)\frac{J \cdot (h-g)^2}{R \cdot h^2}.$$

which also has its maximum value for $a = 1/2$, in which case it becomes

$$\tfrac{1}{4}H \cdot \frac{J \cdot (h-g)^2}{R \cdot h^2},$$

provided

$$R < \frac{J(h-g)^2}{h^2}.$$

This condition will usually be satisfied for normal eyes, because, as a rule, the pupil J of the illuminated eye will be smaller than the pupil R of the observer's eye. When the pupil J is artificially dilated with atropin, this will not be the case, and then the apparent brightness is simply $H/4$. The method of observation with a mirror with a hole in it is better in this last case, because then the brightness is given by the above expression, provided

$$R < a \cdot \frac{J(h-g)^2}{h^2}$$

and

$$a = \tfrac{1}{2}$$

When normal eyes are examined without the use of atropin, the same brightness might be obtained by means of both methods of illumination, provided the pupils of the two eyes did not alter their sizes. But the silvered mirror reflects on the whole more light into the illuminated eye and causes the pupil to contract more; so that under these circumstances the transparent mirror may give a larger field of view and a greater brightness. Besides, it illuminates the visible surface of the retina uniformly, whereas the blurred image of the hole in the other type of mirror has the effect of a shadow, so that the illumination is greater at some places than at others. And, lastly, in case of the unsilvered mirror the corneal reflex is less troublesome, because the light reflected from the mirror is more or less polarised, and on being reflected from the cornea without change of polarisation, most of it fails to get through the transparent glass plate or plates.

In order that the unsilvered mirror shall reflect as much as half of the incident light, it may consist of a single glass plate or of several such plates put together, only the mirror must be inclined at a suitable angle depending on the number of plates. For one plate the proper angle of incidence is 70°, for three plates it is 60°, and for four plates it is 56°.

Various types of ophthalmoscopes

1. HELMHOLTZ's ophthalmoscope with reflecting glass plates and concave lenses; shown in section and actual size in Fig. 106; and as seen from in front, half-size, in Fig. 107. The illustrations include an improvement in the original construction, which was added by the instrument-maker REKOSS and which consists in two rotatable discs containing the requisite concave lenses. The three glass plates constituting the mirror are designated by *aa*. These form the sloping face of a rectangular prism box, the bottom of which is a right triangle, as seen in section in Fig. 106. The two perpendicular sides of this hollow prism are made of metal plates, covered on the inside with black velvet to absorb the light as much as possible. The smaller one of the metal plates is fastened to the frame of the instrument in such fashion that it can be rotated around the optical axis; and there is an opening in it corresponding to this axis. The glass plates are held against the prismatic box by a rectangular frame; and the frame itself is fastened to the triangular base of the prism by two screws *ee*. The glass plates are inclined to the optical axis of the instrument at an angle of 56°.

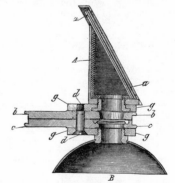

Fig. 106.

Moreover, two discs *bb* and *cc* turn around an axis *dd* inserted in the metal frame *gg*; and each of these discs has five circular openings, four of which contain concave lenses of from 6 to 13 inches focus; the fifth opening being left empty. These openings, one after the other, can be turned into the optical axis of the instrument; and thus the observer with his eye in the hollow eyepiece B may look through each of them in turn and through the glass plates aa. As shown in Fig. 106, the empty opening of the disc bb, and one of the openings with a lens in it belonging to the disc cc, are in position for the observer. The latter can therefore use any one of the eight lenses by itself or any combination of a pair of them. To keep the discs in place, each of them has little notches around the circumference which catch in the ends of two springs h.

Fig. 107.

Of all the forms of ophthalmoscope with movable mirror, this original type still seems to the writer the best for examination of the eye with a concave lens, that is, with high magnification, without artificial dilatation of the pupil, and particularly in cases where the eye is very sensitive to light. The reasons for this opinion are the same as those given above in the theory of illumination by transparent glass plates. When a healthy eye is inspected through this instrument, it can stand the illumination for hours at a time without being blinded. The author himself has often showed his retina to twenty students in succession and not felt any discomfort; whereas with a silvered mirror the patient cannot bear the illumination for five minutes without being blinded by it. And therefore for most physiological experiments the writer prefers this type of instrument to other forms. On the other hand, for clinical purposes a larger field and more brightness with less magnification are generally desirable; and so for observations of that kind the silvered mirror with a hole in it, and combinations of convex lenses, are usually employed.

In using the ophthalmoscope above described, the observer stands or sits right in front of the patient, with a bright lamp at his side. A screen is adjusted to shade the patient's face. First, the observer takes the ophthalmoscope, and, before looking through it, focuses it about at the right place in front of the patient's face, turning it until the bright reflex from the glass plates falls on the eye. Then he looks through the instrument and sees the redly illuminated retina. Supposing he cannot at once accommodate his eye for the finer details of the retina, with the forefinger of the hand that is holding the instrument he turns one of the discs containing the lenses until he finds the proper concave lens for his purpose. In case the illumination of the retina vanishes, all that is necessary is to watch the reflex of the mirror in the patient's face and bring it back on to the eye.

2. Ruete's ophthalmoscope, with perforated concave mirror, mounted on a stand, as shown in Fig. 108. On a round wooden base a hollow upright a supports a round wooden rod b that fits in a, and that can be raised or lowered, and fastened at any height by a spring on its lower end. A semi-circular brass holder c rests on top of this rod, and can be raised or lowered with it, and turned to one side or the other. In this contrivance is inserted a concave mirror d with a hole through it in the centre. The diameter of the mirror is about 8 cm, and its focal length about 27 cm. By means of screws which can be tightened or loosened the mirror can be turned around its horizontal diameter at any inclination. In the middle of the vertical rod a there are two wooden collars e and f which may be turned around a, and each of which carries

a horizontal arm.
On the arm *g* a
black screen is sup-
ported whose duty
is partly to cut off
the light of the
lamp from the ob-
server, and partly
also, if necessary,
to cut down the
light reflected from
the mirror into the
illuminated eye;
which can be done
by shading a por-
tion of the mirror
by the screen. The
arm *h*, which is a
foot long and grad-
uated in inches,
carries two up-
rights *i* and *k* which
can be shoved

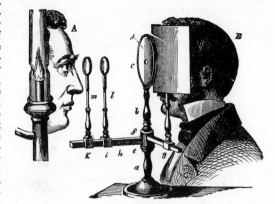

Fig. 108.

either way on the horizontal arm. These uprights are supports of lenses,
convex or concave, according to circumstances, which can be adjusted at
the right height; the business of the lenses being to produce a distinct image of
the fundus of the patient's eye (*A*) for the observer (*B*) to see. The illustration shows how it is done.

The instrument is not well adapted for observations with concave lenses,
which in clinical practice at any rate are perhaps used less frequently; because
the two eyes cannot be brought close enough together to see more than a very
small field. On the other hand, the instrument seems to be very convenient
for clinical observations with convex lenses; especially if an assistant is present
to adjust the patient's head so that his pupil is at the focus of the light. By
using a second convex (ocular) lens (which, however, should perhaps be
inserted behind the mirror), a sort of little telescope can be constructed which
will give a higher magnification. The brightness is very great with this instrument; but it does not permit of observing the image formed on the retina.

3. EPKENS' ophthalmoscope, with plane perforated mirror, mounted on a
stand; as modified by DONDERS and VAN TRIGT. The complete instrument is
shown in plan in Fig. 109, and in elevation in Fig. 110. The mirror *D*, shown
by itself in Fig. 111, is a silvered plate of glass with the silvering removed at
the centre, making a hole of about the diameter of the pupil. Subsequently,
DONDERS had a hole made in the mirror, as in COCCIUS' method, so as to
prevent the light coming to the observer from being diminished by reflection.
The mirror is mounted inside of a cubical box *EE* and can be turned by the
screw *F*. The eye to be examined is adjusted at *N*, and the observer's eye
opposite to it at *O*. Here there is a disc with a set of lenses similar to that
added to the HELMHOLTZ instrument by REKOSS. The lenses used by DON-
DERS were three convex lenses of focal lengths 20, 8 and 4 cm, and three concave lenses of focal lengths 16, 10 and 6 cm.

In EPKENS' original instrument the cubical box was connected with a
conical tube, and a lamp placed at the end of it where the micrometer *M*
is now. If necessary, a convex lens may be inserted in the end of the tube with
its focal point not far from the lamp, so that for any one looking in the instru-

ment the entire surface of the lens appears luminous, and thus a larger area of the retina is illuminated. The entire apparatus attached to the upright rod A can be adjusted at the proper level. A circular disc, painted black to cut off superfluous light from the lamp, is inserted at K; and a piece of oilcloth LL is suspended on the lower side of the instrument from the bar Z, to hide the observer's face from that of the patient.

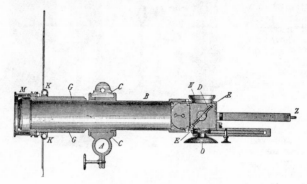

Fig. 109.

However, as it was difficult to examine patients for the correct movements of their eyes, the apparatus was made more flexible by DONDERS and VAN TRIGT. The tube was contrived so that it could be turned in a ring C; and the box EE could be turned around the axis determined by the screws b and c. The lamp was separated from the instrument. At the end of the tube G a micrometer gauge was inserted, the opposite points of which were imaged in

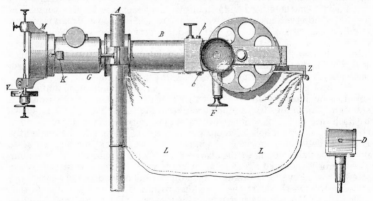

Fig. 110. Fig. 111.

the patient's eye when it was accommodated properly. Accordingly, the micrometer could be moved by means of the tube G which slides over the tube B. By turning the micrometer screw V, the distance between the points can be altered and measured. If n denotes their distance apart and x their distance from the anterior nodal point of the patient's eye, then the distance between the images of these points on the retina is

$$y = \frac{n}{x} \times 15 \text{ mm,}$$

where the distance of the posterior nodal point from the retina is put equal to 15 mm.

By inserting a drawing device in the opening at O such as is used in microscopes, and marking on it the intervals between the two micrometer points and the positions of the blood vessels, etc., on the retina, the real dimensions of these, and of similar details on the retina, may be ascertained.

Subsequently, DONDERS inserted another micrometer, this time in the tube B, to be used with near-sighted eyes. In the mouth of this tube he also fitted a conical attachment for the reception of a convex lens of larger diameter; enabling the observer to obtain a more widely illuminated field in the eye in examinations with pupils dilated by belladonna.

The instrument is intended especially for examination of the retina with a concave lens. Besides being convenient and easy to use, it is very accurate and reliable for investigating and measuring retinal images and the more minute details in the fundus of the eye. SAEMANN's portable ophthalmoscope is similar in construction. Imagine that the tube of EPKENS' instrument has shrunk until it is just a mere offset in the side of the box, and that the solid stand is removed, and, finally, that, instead of the disc with the lenses, a device is used for holding one lens at a time; the result will be SAEMANN's ophthalmoscope.

4. COCCIUS' portable ophthalmoscope (Fig. 112), in which a plane silvered mirror with a hole in it is employed, and a lens for illumination. The side of the small rectangular mirror is about 3 cm long; and the diameter of the central hole is less than half a centimetre. The edge of the hole on the side of the illuminated eye is beveled a little. The mirror is fastened to a thin brass plate which is attached beneath to the upright rod b. The lens ordinarily used is about 5 inches in focus, but it can be removed and another lens substituted if desirable. Its position with regard to the mirror can be firmly secured by screwing up the handle e until it clamps the horizontal arm d that carries the upright support for the lens. The instrument can be taken apart and put away in a little box. Like RUETE, COCCIUS used a concave lens

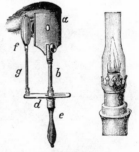

Fig. 112.

as well as a convex lens between the mirror and the lamp. But the concave lens is disadvantageous on account of the reflex, and subsequently several concave lenses were provided which could be shoved in on the back side of the mirror as needed. This ophthalmoscope is very useful for oculists on account of its compactness and transportability. The examination can be made conveniently either with convex lens as in RUETE's instrument or with concave ens as in EPKENS'.

5. ZEHENDER's portable ophthalmoscope, with convex perforated metallic mirror and lens for illumination, with holder similar to that of COCCIUS. The only essential difference between this instrument and the one just described is that a convex metallic mirror of about 6 inches radius is used here instead of a plane glass mirror. By adjusting the convex lens nearer to the convex mirror or farther from it, the focal length of the reflecting system can be varied according to circumstances. Another real advantage, in the author's opinion, is in having a metallic mirror, so that the rim of the peep-hole is thin and black

and smooth. In using a perforated mirror and a concave lens to obtain the maximum brightness only half of the bundle of rays coming from a point on the retina can enter the observer's eye, unless the pupil of the illuminated eye is more than twice as large in area as that of the observer's eye; as the writer has proved. Hence, as a rule, part of the pupil of the observer's eye is necessarily covered by the edge of the hole in the mirror, so that a part of this edge is right in front of his eye. Consequently, it is a good thing to avoid having anything in this edge that might reflect light, and this is accomplished with ZEHENDER's metallic mirror much better than with COCCIUS' glass mirror.

6. MEYERSTEIN's prism ophthalmoscope. In place of a metallic mirror a rectangular prism is used in this instrument, the light being reflected from the hypotenuse face. The observer looks through a hole in the prism.

Subsequently, MEYERSTEIN used an illumination lens in conjunction with the perforated prism, a small telescope being inserted between the prism and the observer's eye. Eventually, to reduce the cost, the prism was replaced by a perforated mirror. The writer believes also that the use of the prism proved to have more disadvantages than advantages. There is an attachment by which the whole apparatus can be fastened to the border of the patient's eye; together with an arm in two links that carries a wax candle for illumination. Since the patient's eye is completely screened from external light, the instrument can be used in a brightly lighted room. By inserting or removing the ocular lens of the little telescope, the optical system can be adapted to emmetropic or ametropic eyes.

7. ULRICH's ophthalmoscope. In this instrument the essential features of RUETE's apparatus are combined on a portable tube which has a lateral attachment for holding the light used for illumination.

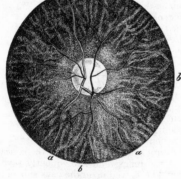

The following results of observation of normal eyes with the ophthalmoscope may be mentioned. With strong illumination (with silvered mirror and convex lens) the fundus of the eye appears red; except where the optic nerve enters, and there it is bright white. The blood vessels of the retina, originating from the centre of the white optic nerve, are conspicuously prominent on the red background. The arteries can be distinguished by their lighter red colour and by a stronger light reflex from their surface. In between the blood vessels the fundus of the eye appears in some places bright red and elsewhere brown, depending on the amount of pigment. Often the blood vessels of the choroid can be discerned, as illustrated in Fig. 113, especially in the more peripheral parts. The picture shows the appearance of the optic nerve. Branches of the retinal artery are indicated by *aaa*, and of the retinal vein by *bbb*; and between them can be seen the much wider blood vessels of the choroid. The latter are not always equally clear. In most eyes the pigment layer over these vessels is so thin that they stand out in contrast to the more highly pigmented intermediate places.

Fig. 113.

With increased illumination there is no very striking change in the appearance of the fundus of the eye except at the place where the optic nerve enters. Apparently, at this place a relatively large amount of light gets through the pigment layer of the choroid, and being reflected from the sclerotica, comes back again. The experiment described in §10 by which the image on the retina can be seen in the inner angle of the eye, and also the entoptical appearance of the choroid figure as seen by light that penetrates the sclerotica, show that right much light can get through the coatings of the eye. This portion of the returning light, due to reflection in the choroid and sclerotica, may be fairly uniform all over the fundus of the eye, even when the brightness of the retina itself varies considerably.

On the other hand, with weaker illumination (with glass plates), the parts of the fundus of the eye in the vicinity of the optic nerve are particularly bright, the brightness diminishing uniformly from here out towards the periphery of the retina. But the place of direct vision is especially conspicuous by its lack of brightness and a more yellowish colour than that of the immediate surroundings; which is not the case with high illumination. The reason may be that with feeble illumination the amount of light that goes back and forth through the pigment layer is scarcely noticeable, and so the perceptible reflex is due mainly to the parts of the retina, especially its blood vessels, that are missing in the yellow spot. In both modes of observation this latter place appears as a tiny bright spot transversely oval in shape. COCCIUS, who discovered it, attributed the appearance to the reflex from the sides of the foveal indentation; and DONDERS afterwards proved directly that this little reflex of light is at the place of direct vision. For this experiment a plane mirror has to be used with a concave lens behind it (DONDERS-EPKENS or HELMHOLTZ). The fixation mark may be a lamp-flame or the micrometer tips in DONDERS apparatus. The eye to be examined is directed towards the image of this object in the mirror, pains being taken to see that it can accommodate for it so as to see distinctly some definite point of the object. Under these circumstances the observer sees a perfectly sharply delineated inverted image of the object focused on the retina of the other person's eye and the reflex of the fovea at the place where the image is most clear-cut. In case this reflex is too faint to be seen at first, it can easily be found by making the subject turn his eye first to one part of the fixation-target and then to another; and the tiny reflex will move about on the retina in response to these minute motions of the eye.

For testing the exactness of the retinal image, the micrometer device is useful which DONDERS added to EPKENS' ophthalmoscope. The author uses for this purpose in his instrument a horizontal thread in front of the light as object of fixation; because with this opththalmoscope the several reflecting surfaces produce multiple images of a narrow vertical line. When the illuminated eye is sharply focused on the object, the image on the retina also is very neat. With any variation of accommodation it becomes vague. Indeed, a delicate object is not at all necessary to observe the variation of the image with varying accommodation. Provided the eye in question is not near-sighted, it is sufficient to watch the retinal image of a distant light while the patient accommodates for far or near vision in the same line of sight. With accommodation for far vision, the image of the distant light also appears distinct; but with accommodation for near vision, it gets hazy. Usually at the same time the details of the retina vanish also unless the observer, with the help of his own accommodation, can follow the new position of the image; and then he has to use another concave lens to be sure that a blurred image of the distant light is projected on the distinctly visible retina. The experiment may be varied too by causing the patient to fixate a distant object permanently, while the light itself is brought near the eye, enabling the observer to verify that the image of the near light is blurred.

From the most ancient times the brilliant appearance in the dark of the eyes of certain animals, as, for example, dogs and cats, had been observed.[1] In many creatures a portion of the fundus of the eyeball, covered with thin fibres or lamellae, has no pigment and presents an iridescent appearance. This is called a tapetum, which under favourable circumstances is easily visible. An old idea that was widely prevalent was that such eyes were indeed self-luminous, the luminosity being developed by the animals themselves, especially when they were excited; and so there was a disposition to attribute this alleged development of light to the action of the nervous system. This ocular luminosity in the case of animals is most striking in a dark room when light coming from behind the observer goes close past his head to the eye of the animal; and for this very reason the actually incident light might often be hidden from the spectator. The eyes of white rabbits that are devoid of pigment and of albinos generally ought to shine in the same way by internal light. PREVOST[2] was the first to show that the so-called shining of animal eyes never occurred in complete darkness and is not produced either arbitrarily or by emotion, but is invariably due to reflection of incident light. GRUITHUISEN[3] found the same result independently and showed that the tapetum, together with a certain "extraordinary refraction" in the crystalline lens, is responsible for the phenomenon. He saw this glow even in the eyes of dead creatures. These facts were verified by RUDOLPHI,[4] J. MÜLLER,[5] ESSER,[6] TIEDEMANN[7] and HASSENSTEIN.[8] It was RUDOLPHI who pointed out that it is necessary to look in the eye in a particular direction to get this luminous effect. ESSER gave the right explanation of the origin of the colour as being due to seeing variously coloured parts of the retina through the pupil. Lastly, HASSENSTEIN found that the glow occurred when the eye was compressed in the direction of its axis, and conjectured that it is also produced arbitrarily by living creatures who possess an ability of contracting the axis of the eye. Thus, the luminosity was admitted to be a reflex phenomenon, but the conditions of its shining or not were not made clear.

In the case of the human eye, the luminosity had not been noticed formerly except in rare kinds of disease, particularly in connection with swellings in the fundus of the eye. BEHR[9] observed it even when the iris was gone, and found that the observer had to look in the diseased eye in a direction almost parallel with the incident rays. This is the fundamental condition in BRÜCKE's method of observing the luminosity of the eye. The ocular glow when the iris is absent is striking, because the illumination of the retina is much greater in such cases; and, besides, the power of accommodation of the eye is lost.

Finally, W. CUMMING[10] and BRÜCKE[11], independently of each other, discovered the way of making healthy human eyes appear luminous, the observer looking almost parallel to the incident light. BRÜCKE had already used the

[1] ¶See, for example, PLINY, Book XI, Chap. 55. (J. P. C. S.)

[2] *Biblioth. britannique.* 1810. T. 45.

[3] *Beiträge zur Physiognosie und Eautognosie.* S. 199.

[4] *Lehrbuch der Physiologie.* I. 197.

[5] *Zur vergleichenden Physiologie d. Gesichtssinns.* Leipzig 1826. S. 49. — *Handbuch d. Physiologie.* 4. Aufl. I. 89.

[6] KASTNERS *Archiv für die gesamte Naturlehre.* Bd. VIII. S. 399.

[7] *Lehrbuch der Physiologie.* S. 509.

[8] *De luce ex quorundam animalium oculis prodeunte atque de tapeto lucido.* Jena 1836.

[9] HECKERS *Annalen.* 1839. I. S. 373.

[10] *Medico-chirurgical Transactions.* XXIX. p. 284.

[11] J. MÜLLERS *Archiv für Anat. u. Physiologie.* 1847. S. 225.

same method previously in studying animal eyes that had a tapetum. WHAR-
TON JONES[1] states that about the same time BABBAGE had showed him a
silvered glass mirror with a bit of the silver removed, intended for throwing
light into the eye and looking through the aperture. This device suggests
immediately COCCIUS' ophthalmoscope; but as BABBAGE does not appear to
have used any lenses in conjunction with his mirror, the most that can be said
about his procedure is that he was able to obtain some notion of the parts
of the retina in an unusual way. Probably, this is why he did not publish an
account of his contrivance at the time.

The other aspect of the question, that is, why the parts of the retina, even
when they are illuminated, as, for example, in animal eyes with a tapetum
and in eyes of albinos, cannot be recognized by the observer, has frequently
been discussed. As long ago as the beginning of the eighteenth century,
MÉRY[2] noticed in the case of a cat immersed in water that the eyes were not
only luminous, but the blood vessels of the retina could be discerned. LA
HIRE[3] gave the correct explanation of this latter fact. He was aware that the
refraction of the rays had to be altered in order to make the eye appear luminous, but he did not know how to give any more complete explanation. The
same was true of KUSSMAUL,[4] who shows that the retina will be bright and
recognizable, provided both the cornea and lens are removed, or provided
some of the vitreous humor is taken out so as to shorten the axis of the eye.

So far as the author is aware, he was the first[5] to make clear the connection between the directions of the entering and outgoing rays, and to discover
the real reason of the blackness of the pupil, and hence also the principle of
the construction of the ophthalmoscope. For illumination he used plane
unsilvered glass plates, and for studying the retina a concave lens. On the
other hand, TH. RUETE was the first to use a perforated mirror and the
method of observation with a convex lens. The new instrument quickly
assumed extraordinary importance in ophthalmology, and consequently a
great number of different types of ophthalmoscope were designed, the most
characteristic of which have been described. But no essentially new principles for the illumination or investigation of the retina are contained in any
of these constructions.

The theory of the illumination of the eye and of the ophthalmoscope as
given above by the author has not been modified in any essential respect.
The improvements which STELLWAG VON CARION has endeavoured to make
in it are not improvements in the author's opinion. This ophthalmologist,
sincerely desirous of employing the principles of physics in his own science,
was led into errors by the fundamentally incorrect ideas as to the intensity
of illumination and brightness that were 'current in previous works on these
subjects.

1704. MÉRY in *Annales de l'Académie des sciences*.   1704.
1709. LA HIRE, ibid.   1709.
1810. PREVOST in *Bibliothèque britannique*.   XLV.
    GRUITHUISEN, *Beiträge zur Physiognosie und Eautognosie*.   S. 199.
    RUDOLPHI, *Physiologie*.   I. 197.
1826. J. MÜLLER, *Zur vergleichenden Physiologie des Gesichtssinns*. Leipzig S. 49.
    ESSER in KASTNERS *Archiv für die gesamte Naturlehre*. VIII. 399.

[1] *Archives générales de Médecine*.   1854. II.

[2] *Annales de l'Acad. d. sc.*   1704.

[3] Ibid.   1709.

[4] *Die Farbenerscheinungen im Grunde des menschlichen Auges*. Heidelberg 1845.

[5] H. HELMHOLTZ, *Beschreibung eines Augenspiegels zur Beobachtung der Netzhaut im
lebenden Auge*. Berlin 1851. Also in VIERORDTs *Archiv für Physiol. Heilkunde*. II. 827.
(See also English translation by T. H. SHASTID, Chicago, 1916.—J. P. C. S.)

1836. HASSENSTEIN, *De luce ex quorundam animalium oculis prodeunte atque de tapeto lucido.* Jenae.

1839. BEHR in HECKERS *Annälen.* Bd. 1. S. 373.

1844. E. BRÜCKE, Über die physiologische Bedeutung der stabförmigen Körperchen. J. MÜLLERS *Archiv für Anatomie und Physiologie.* 1833. S. 444.*

1845. E. BRÜCKE, Anatomische Untersuchung über die sogenannten leuchtenden Augen bei den Wirbeltieren. Ibid. 1847. S. 387.*

KUSSMAUL, *Die Farbenerscheinungen im Grunde des menschlichen Auges.* Heidelberg.

1846. W. CUMMING in *Medico-chirurgical Transactions.* XXIX. 284.

1847. E. BRÜCKE, Über das Leuchten der menschlichen Augen, in J. MÜLLERS *Archiv.* 1847. S. 225* u. 479.*

1851. H. HELMHOLTZ, *Beschreibung eines Augenspiegels zur Untersuchung der Netzhaut im lebenden Auge.* Berlin.

1852. TH. RUETE, *Der Augenspiegel und das Optometer.* Göttingen.

H. HELMHOLTZ, Über eine neue einfachste Form des Augenspiegels, in VIERORDTS *Archiv für physiologische Heilkunde.* II. 827.

FOLLIN in *Archives générales de Médecine.* 1852. July.

A. COCCIUS, *Über die Ernährungsweise der Hornhaut.* Leipzig.

FROEBELIUS, *Mediz. Zeitung Russlands.* 1852. No. 46.

1853 A COCCIUS, *Über die Anwendung des Augenspiegels nebst Angabe eines neuen Instruments.* Leipzig.*

A. C. VAN TRIGT, *Dissertatio de Speculo oculi.* Utrecht.—*Nederlandsch Lancet.* Ser. 3. Dl. II. 430. In German with notes by SCHAUENBURG.1854.

H. A. O. SAEMANN, *De speculo oculi.* Regiomonti.

R. ULRICH, Beschreibung eines neuen Augenspiegels in HENLE u. PFEUFFERS *Zeitschrift für rationelle Medizin.* Neue Folge. IV. 175.*

MEYERSTEIN, Beschreibung eines neuen Augenspiegels. Ibid. S. 310.

FOLLIN et NACHET, *Mém de la Société de Chirurgie.* 1853. III.

SPENCER WELLS, *Medical Times.* Sept. 1853.

1854. DONDERS, *Verbeteringen van den oogspiegel, in Onderzoekingen gedaan in het Physiologisch Laboratorium der Utrechtsche Hoogeschool.* Jaar VI. bl. 131* u. 153.*

ANAGNOSTAKIS, *Essai sur l'exploration de la ré ine et des milieux de l'oeil sur le vivant au moyen d'un nouvel ophtalmoscope.* Paris 1854. (A perforated concave mirror.) Also in *Annales d'oculistique.* Feb. and March 1854.

STELLWAG VON CARION, *Theorie der Augenspiegel.* Wien.*

G. A. LEONHARD, *De variis oculorum speculis illorumque usu.* Leipzig.

TH. RUETE, *Bildliche Darstellung der Krankheiten des menschlichen Auges.* Leipzig. Numbers 1 and 2; also under the title: *Physikalische Untersuchung des Auges* S. 23-27.*

W. ZEHENDER, Über die Beleuchtung des innern Auges mit spezieller Berücksichtigung eines nach eigener Angabe konstruierten Augenspiegels, in GRAEFES *Archiv für Ophthalmologie.* I. 1. S. 121.*

1855. LIEBREICH, ibid. I. 2. S. 348.

STELLWAG VON CARION, *Zeitschrift der Ärzte zu Wien.* XI. S. 65.*

Supplement

The form of ophthalmoscope that has finally been most generally adopted by ophthalmologists is one that resembles most the COCCIUS or ZEHENDER instrument described above, except that, instead of a plane or convex mirror in conjunction with a convex lens for illumination as used in those constructions, a concave mirror, 1 inch in diameter and of 5 or 6 inches focus, without any convex lens, has been substituted. The mirror is sometimes made of metal, having the advantage of a better aperture with sharp, non-reflecting rim; or else it is silvered on glass with a hole in the centre. In the latter arrangement the surface of the mirror is better protected against injury. But it has a disadvantage, especially in the method of observation with erect image; because the edge between the reflecting surface and the aperture cannot be made as small and sharp as with a metal mirror.

Coccius' method of observing the fundus of one's own eye is described in the second part of this work. Any perforated mirror will do for this purpose, but a convex mirror is best. Another autophthalmoscope, by which the left eye examines the illuminated retina of the right eye, has been described by F. Heymann. Light enters the right eye through a hole in a plane mirror; and the left eye looking towards the hole in the mirror sees the reflected image of the right eye. In front of the right eye, as in Ruete's ophthalmoscope, a convex lens (of about 2 1/4 inches focus) is placed with its focal point in the pupil of that eye. This lens produces an inverted image of the retina at its focus. Behind this image there is a reflecting rectangular prism which deflects the rays towards the perforated mirror. Two other convex lenses, one between prism and mirror, and the other in front of the left eye, form a kind of little bent telescope; through which the left eye sees the image of the retina of the right eye, and which also makes it impossible for both eyes to be accommodated for the hole in the mirror at the same time. In order to vary the position of the place on the retina that is under observation, Heymann inserts also in front of the observing eye a prism spectacle glass of variable power, whose refracting edge can be turned in different directions.

Giraud Teulon's binocular ophthalmoscope is described in the third part of this book.

1855. E. Jaeger, *Beiträge zur Pathologie des Auges mit Abbildungen in Farbendruck.* Wien.
—   Idem, Ergebnisse der Untersuchung des menschlichen Auges mit dem Augenspiegel. *Wien. Ber.* XV. 319-344.
1856. Casterani, Ophthalmoscope. *Cosmos.* VIII. 612.
—   W. Zehender, Über die Beleuchtung des innern Auges durch heterozentrische Glasspiegel. *Archiv. für Ophthalm.* II. 2 S. 103-130.
1857. J. Porro, La lunette panfocale, employée comme ophthalmoscope. *C. R.* XLV. 103 to 104. *Cosmos.* XI. 96-97.
—   A. Burow, Über Konstruktion heterozentrischer Augenspiegel und deren Anwendung. *Archiv für Ophthalm.* III. 2, S. 68-80.
—   Schneller, Ein Mikrometer am Augenspiegel. Ibid. III. 2. S. 121-186.
       R. Liebreich, *De l'examen de l'oeil au moyen de l'ophthalmoscope.* Bruxelles (From Mackenzie's translation of the *Traité pratique des maladies des yeux.*)
1859. A. Zander, *Der Augenspiegel, seine Formen und sein Gebrauch.* Leipzig and Heidelberg.
1861. O. Becker, Über die Wahrnehmung eines Reflexbildes im eigenem Auge. *Wiener Med. Wochenschrift* 1860. S. 670-672; 684-688. (Image of posterior surface of lens reflected in cornea.)

1863. BUROW Jr., Notiz betreffend die Beobachtung des eigenen Augenhintergrundes. *Archiv für Ophthalmol.* IX. 1 S. 155–160.

1863. F. HEYMANN, *Die Autoskopie des Auges.* Leipzig.

—   R. LIEBREICH, *Atlas der Ophthalmoskopie.* Berlin. Hirschwald.

1864. C. SCHWEIGGER, *Vorlesungen über den Gebrauch des Augenspiegels.* Berlin.

—   A. COCCIUS, Beschreibung eines Okulars zum Augenspiegel. *Archiv für Ophthalm.* X. 1. S. 123–147.

—   R. SCHIRMER, Über das ophthalmoskopische Bild der Macula lutea. Ibid. X. 1. S. 148–151.

—   WINTRICH, Über die Benutzung des zweckmässig abgeblendeten zerstreuten Tageslichts zur Oto-, Ophthalmo- und Laryngoskopie. *Erlanger Medic. Neuigkeiten.* 1864. 9 April.

Note by A. Gullstrand

"Die von mir aufgestellte Theorie des Augenleuchtens und der Augenspiel hat keine wesentlichen Veränderungen erfahren." These words of HELMHOLTZ are still true today. Undoubtedly, the construction of the instrument has been essentially improved and its region of application essentially extended. The ophthalmologist who uses the ophthalmoscope every day not only for the most subtle diagnoses of diseased conditions of the fundus of the eye, but also for investigating the ocular media, and, in various ways, for finding the refraction of the eye, knows best how to estimate HELMHOLTZ's immortal service to mankind.

This is not the place to describe these methods and their results; but the solution of one problem may be mentioned briefly which could not have been even proposed at the time when the ophthalmoscope was invented. The *photography of the fundus of the eye*, which, thanks to the sensitiveness of modern dry plates, is no longer impracticable, affords useful results at present which we owe chiefly to the work of DIMMER[1] in this field. The main difficulty to be overcome was to get rid of the corneal reflex of the source of light. Since one part of the pupil is used for the light that illuminates the fundus of the eye and another part for the passage of the light that is diffusely reflected from the fundus, the external incident light that is reflected from the cornea may be suitably intercepted. On similar principles THORNER[2] has constructed a stationary reflex-free ophthalmoscope, and WOLFF[3] has constructed a portable electric ophthalmoscope. Both of them have photographed the fundus of the eye.

---

[1] FR. DIMMER, *Die Photographie des Augenhintergrundes.* Wiesbaden 1907.

[2] W. THORNER, *Die Theorie des Augenspiegels und die Photographie des Augenhintergrundes.* Berlin 1903.

[3] H. WOLFF, Zur Photographie des menschlichen Augenhintergrundes. *Arch. für Augenheilk.* LIX. S. 115. 1908.

Appendices to Part I

by

A. Gullstrand

I. Optical Imagery

When HELMHOLTZ's original contributions were published on the Dioptrics of the Eye, the characteristic conception of optical imagery that was current at that time assumed that rays of light emanating at a point were reassembled approximately at another point, and that thus a certain point of the image was associated with a definite point of the object. This conception continues to be very widespread at the present time, although it cannot be reconciled with actual facts as now known. It was well understood that in no single instance were rays of light emanating from a point on the axis of a centered optical system completely reunited at one point, but that an aberration occurs or an error, depending partly on the different refrangibility of rays of different wave-lengths, the so-called chromatic aberration, but manifesting itself also in case of monochromatic light, and known then as the spherical aberration because it depends on the form of the refracting surface and because formerly only spherical surfaces were used. Students of optics were aware also that a point of an object which was at a considerable distance from the axis of the instrument was not reproduced as a point, since the corresponding bundle of refracted rays is astigmatic; and they had the formulae for calculating this astigmatism. The constitution of an oblique bundle of refracted rays and its lack of homocentricity continued, however, to be just as unknown as the general laws of optical imagery themselves; since they took account only of those rays proceeding from a point of the object which were in the meridian plane and in a plane perpendicular to this plane, although such rays constitute an exceedingly small portion of the total rays concerned in the optical effect. Thus finding it impossible to investigate the actual imagery in this way, and without knowledge of the general laws, they invented a system, whereby ABBE, for example, omitting all reference to the actual facts in the case of refraction of light, sought to ascertain the purely mathematical conditions of the imagery of one space in another in such manner that every point and every straight line in one region were reproduced by a corresponding point and a corresponding straight line in the other region.[1] These conditions were in harmony with the known laws of optical imagery in the case of an infinitely small object situated on the axis of a centered system provided with an infinitely narrow stop. The theory of collinear imagery applied to objects of finite extent and stops with finite apertures, which is the basis of the expositions still to be found in modern text-books, constitutes therefore an essentially arbitrary extension of the region of validity of these laws, inasmuch as a system of fictions had to be introduced in place of the real undiscovered laws. Of course, the realities can be represented as aberrations or deviations from the ideal relations of collinear correspondence provided we remember always that the ideal cannot be realized; but in making use of fictions there is the continual and serious danger of overstepping the border between what is true and what is nearly true. This one thing alone might show the advantage of a direct study of the facts themselves as soon as such a study had become possible through the ascertainment of the laws in question.

The reason why the laws of actual optical imagery have been, so to speak, summoned to life by the requirements of physiological optics is due partly to the fact that by means of trigonometrical calculations, tedious to be sure but easy to perform, it has been possible for the optical engineer to get closer to the realities of his problem. Thus, thanks to the labours of such, men as ABBE and his school, technical optics has attained its present splendid development; whereas with the scientific means available a comprehensive grasp of the intricate relations in the case of the imagery in the eye has been actually impossible.

The necessary reorganization of the theory of optical imagery could not be interwoven with the most recent investigations because the latter had been worked out principally in two dimensions, whereas the general imagery-problem is ·three-dimensional. Ever since the general investigations of STURM[2] and HAMILTON,[3] it sufficed to determine the constitution of a bundle of rays in terms of magnitudes of the first and second order, without, however, keeping in mind the

---

[1] ¶See J. C. MAXWELL, On the General Laws of Optical Instruments. *Quart. Journ. Pure and Appl. Math.*, II, 1858, 233–246; also MAXWELL's Scientific Papers, I., 271-285. (J. P. C. S.)

[2] CH. STURM, Mémoire sur l'optique. *Journ. de Math. pures et appliquées.* 1838. — Mémoire sur la théorie de la vision. *Comptes rendus de l'Acad. des sc.* t. XX. 1845.

[3] W. R. HAMILTON, Theory of systems of rays. *Transactions of the Royal Ir. Acad.*, vol. XV. 1828. *Supplements* in vol. XVI. Part 1. 1830; vol. XVI. Part 2. 1831; vol. XVII. 1837.

conditions of validity of the laws that were ascertained by use of these magnitudes. STURM discovered that all the rays of a bundle go approximately through two mutually perpendicular focal lines, provided the aperture of the bundle is infinitesimal as compared with the distance of the focal lines from the stop and from each other. But in oblique incidence of light in optical instruments the latter condition is not even approximately the case, and in the case of the eye the so-called astigmatic difference is as a rule less than the diameter of the pupil; so that as a matter of fact the notion of these focal lines is fundamentally false. Hence, to begin with, it was necessary to make a thorough study of a bundle of optical rays in general and to discuss the special cases in detail taking account of magnitudes of the third[1] and fourth[2] orders, and not merely of the first and second orders, as was customary heretofore; and in place of the notion of the focal lines to substitute a knowledge of the precise geometrical magnitudes that determine the form of the caustic surface together with the position, dimensions and form of the narrowest section of the bundle of rays. In case of the peculiar complicated structure of a bundle of rays refracted into the eye, a special investigation was necessary of the so-called circular points (umbilics)[3] of the refracting surfaces and the corresponding bundles of normals. However, the aberration in the eye as ascertained by a study carried out in this way was found to be so great, and the blur circles on the retina even with the best focusing turned out to be so large, that the role in the imagery assigned to the narrowest cross section of the bundle cannot possibly be correct. This can easily be shown by taking a double convex lens of wide aperture and using it to focus on a screen the image of the filament of an incandescent lamp. The sharpest image of the filament is obtained when the lens is focused so that the image appears to be surrounded by a veil; whereas the image is decidedly inferior when the lens is focused so that the veil disappears, although in the latter case the image is produced by using the narrowest section of the ray-bundle. This shows that the light-distribution inside the section of the ray-bundle is of primary importance, whereas the dimensions of the section are of secondary importance. In place of the approximate measures of the dimensions of the narrowest cross sections as found by series-development, it was all the more necessary to substitute the precise geometrical magnitudes that determine the form of the caustic surface; because it is the section of this surface that controls the distribution of the light

[1] A. GULLSTRAND, Beitrag zur Theorie des Astigmatismus. *Skand. Arch. f. Physiol.* Bd. II. 1890. S. 269.

[2] Idem, Allgemeine Theorie der monochromatischen Aberrationen und ihre nächsten Ergebnisse für die Ophthalmologie. *Nova Acta Reg. Soc. Sc. Ups. Ser.* III. 1890.

[3] A. GULLSTRAND, Zur Kenntnis der Kreispunkte. *Acta Mathematica.* 29. 1904.

within the section of the ray-bundle. Another point necessarily connected with the matter just mentioned involves a revision of the conception of the function of the stop. The main business of the stop, according to the old view, was to cut out the rays, and hence it had to be considered as infinitely narrow, which is a fiction with no reality at all; because with an infinitely narrow stop diffraction-phenomena would completely mask the image-appearances. Least of all can this fiction be employed in the case of the eye, where it becomes ridiculous in consequence of the actual size of the stop. Inasmuch as the problem requires us to postulate a stop of arbitrary size, the only exact means of investigating the effect of the stop is by the method of optical projection through the centre of the stop.

These were the main considerations that led to the investigation of optical imagery[1] by ascertaining the fundamental equation from which the general laws thereof are derived. Since the medium of the crystalline lens of the eye is not homogeneous, the laws of optical imagery in heterogeneous media[2] had finally to be studied also before the optical imagery in the eye could be made a subject of thorough investigation.

At present the writer will endeavour to give here only such portions of the theory of optical imagery as are required to comprehend the imagery in the eye, but in order not to obscure the results by mathematical intricacies the analytical processes will be entirely omitted. Those details can be found in the contributions to which reference has been made and, so far as some of the simpler questions are concerned, partly also in other articles[3] where the writer has taken pains to make the subject as clear as possible for such readers as are not acquainted with infinitesimal or differential geometry.

General Laws. In the mathematical theory of the laws of optical imagery two experimental facts are necessary and sufficient, namely, the rectilinear propagation of light in isotropic media and the general law of refraction. From the latter, by mathematical deduction, it can be proved, that through each point on any ray of an originally homocentric bundle of rays a surface can be constructed which cuts all the

[1] Idem, Die reelle optische Abbildung. *Kungl. Sv. Vet. Akad. Handl.* Bd. XLI. No. 3. 1906.
[2] Idem, Die optische Abbildung in heterogenen Medien und die Dioptrik der Kristallinse des Menschen. Ibid. Bd. XLIII. No. 2. 1908.
[3] Die Konstitution des im Auge gebrochenen Strahlenbündels. *Arch. f. Ophth.* LIII, 2. 1901. S. 105 — Über Astigmatismus, Koma und Aberration. *Ann. d. Physik.* 4. Folge. 18. 1905. S. 941. — Tatsachen und Fiktionen in der Lehre von der optischen Abbildung. *Arch. f. Optik.* I. 1907. S. 2.

rays orthogonally, and also that the optical length along any ray between two such surfaces is the same for all the rays of the bundle. If the lengths of the different portions of the ray-path in each medium are multiplied by the corresponding values of the index of refraction, what is meant by the optical length along the ray is the sum of these products.[1] In this form the general law of refraction is found to be valid also for anisotropic or "heterogeneous" media, where we have curved paths of light, so-called trajectories, instead of rays; and where the optical length is expressed as a definite integral. In either case the surfaces which are drawn at right angles to the directions of propagation of the light are commonly called wave surfaces, whose normals in the case of isotropic media are identical with the rays of light, but in anisotropic media of continuously variable index are tangent to the trajectories along which the light is propagated. In general, therefore, the investigation of the convergence of the rays amounts to an investigation of the constitution of a bundle of normals to the wave surface, which in turn depends on the form of the surface in question. However, except in a few simple and practically unimportant cases these surfaces cannot be represented by useful algebraic equations, and thus it becomes necessary to investigate the surface in the immediate vicinity of some selected point, and the bundle of rays in immediate proximity to a certain special ray. The bundle of rays which emanates from a point of the object contains one ray which in the stop-space goes through the centre of the stop, and which is therefore called the *chief ray* of the bundle. Thus, the totality of these chief rays, each proceeding from one point of the object, constitutes a homocentric (or monocentric) bundle of rays in the medium where the stop is, which behaves exactly as if the light radiated from the centre of the stop. Precisely as we have to investigate a bundle of rays in the immediate vicinity of a selected ray, so also the imagery of an object can be studied only in the immediate vicinity of a selected object-point. The chief ray belonging to this selected object-point is called the *central ray* or *guide-ray*. The laws of optical imagery are found by investigating the central bundle of object-rays and the bundle of chief rays in the immediate vicinity of the guide-ray, and also by investigating the bundle of contiguous object-rays in the immediate vicinity of the chief rays in question; and are called the *laws of the first order* or of a higher order according as they are obtained by one or more derivations (or differentiations) from the general law of refraction. By reason of the complexity of the problem only the laws of the first order are applicable in the general case, so that when

---

[1] ¶See Volume II, §19. (J. P. C. S.)

the object is an extended one the formulae in question have to be applied to as many arbitrarily selected guide-rays as are necessary in order to obtain a correct idea of the imagery that is involved.

The laws of the first order in regard to convergence of rays are derived from the *general constitution of a bundle of optical rays* by employing STURM's formulae; which enable us to find the magnitudes that determine the wave surface of the bundle of refracted rays, provided the refracting surface and the bundle of incident rays are given. A characteristic property of a bundle of optical rays considered as normals to the wave surface is, that, in general, any given ray of the bundle will be intersected by contiguous rays in one point (which is a singular or special case) or else in two separate points (which is the rule). Thus along any particular ray chosen at random, the bundle of rays is ordinarily *astigmatic* and has therefore two *focal points* (or image points)[1]; whereas in case the two focal points are identical, the bundle of rays is said to be *anastigmatic* along this ray. Designating one of these points as the *primary focal point*, we may speak of the plane containing the contiguous rays that meet the given ray in this point as the *primary principal section* of the bundle of rays with respect to the ray in question; and of the line perpendicular to the primary principal section at the primary focal point as the *primary focal line*. Similarly, contiguous rays lying in the secondary principal section of the bundle with respect to the given ray, that is, in the section perpendicular to the primary principal section, will meet this ray in the *secondary focal point*; and the *secondary focal line* will be a line perpendicular to the *secondary principal section* at the secondary focal point. Thus in a bundle of rays which is astigmatic with respect to a certain ray the contiguous rays that meet this ray are all contained in one or other of the two principal sections; whereas if the astigmatism vanishes along this ray, so that the two focal points are coincident, all the contiguous rays (neglecting magnitudes of order higher than the first) will intersect the ray in question.

[1] ¶The only satisfactory rendering of the German word "*Fokalpunkte*" is "focal point," as meaning simply a point of intersection of a lot of rays of a bundle. Thus, any pair of so-called "conjugate" points is in this sense a pair of "focal" points. But "the focal points of an optical system" (for which the Germans have the special word *Brennpunkten*) are not even a pair of conjugate points. If we call these latter (as is done to some extent in the translation) the "principal focal points" (*Hauptbrennpunkten*), there is again a possibility of confusion with the "principal points" (*Hauptpunkten*) of the system; which, however, could be avoided by calling them the "unit points," as some English writers do. The reader must be on his guard to distinguish between all these terms, as employed in the text; and also between similar expressions, as, for example, "focal distance" (*Fokalabstand*) and "focal length" (*Brennweite*). The term "focal planes" may be used to mean simply a pair of conjugate planes or to refer to the principal focal planes of the system; etc. (J. P. C. S.)

As a rule, both the focal points and the principal sections vary from one ray to another, and the loci of the first and second focal points are two surfaces called the first and second *caustic surfaces*, respectively; sometimes referred to also as the two sheets of the caustic surface. As a result of this structure of the ray-bundle, a convergence of all the rays at one point is to be regarded as a singular event, so that as a rule the idea of *ray-convergence is concerned only with contiguous rays and occurs only on the caustic surfaces*. If a line is drawn on a surface which cuts a bundle of rays, the totality of rays which meet this line constitutes what is called a *ray-surface* (or ruled surface). The way to study such a surface is along some particular ray just as in the study of a bundle of rays; and it follows that the plane containing this ray which is tangent to the ruled surface either revolves continuously through 180° as we proceed along the ray from infinity in one direction to infinity in the other, or else the tangent-plane remains stationary. In the former case the ruled surface is called a *skew surface* or *"scroll"* with respect to the given ray; and the tangent-plane at the first focal point coincides with the second principal section with respect to the ray, and *vice versa;* and therefore the two focal lines of any given ray will ordinarily be tangent to every skew surface that contains this ray. However, when the tangent-plane to a ruled surface remains the same at every point along the ray, this plane coincides with one of the principal sections with respect to this ray; and contiguous rays of the ruled surface (neglecting magnitudes of order higher than the first) will intersect the ray at its focal points. Thus, since the ruled surface has a focal point along the given ray, it is what may be called a *focal ruled surface* (or a *developable surface* or *"torse"*) with respect to this ray. At the focal point itself the tangent-plane is indeterminate, and therefore every plane containing the given ray is tangent to the ruled surface; and hence also the two focal lines of the ray will in general be tangent to the developable surfaces that contain the ray in question. If a bundle of rays is anastigmatic along a certain ray, every ruled surface containing this ray will be developable or focal with respect to it; and any arbitrary pair of mutually rectangular lines perpendicular to the ray at its focal point may be regarded as the focal lines. Thus, it follows that the general constitution of a real bundle of optical rays is defined by the fact that *the focal lines of any ray, at right angles to each other and also to the ray, are tangent to every ruled surface containing that ray.* Inasmuch as the so-called *focal plane* perpendicular to the given ray at one of its focal points will intersect a ruled surface in a line which may have any curvature, it is obvious at once that in order for this line to be considered as the focal line at this place, the stop-opening must be dimin-

ished until the line in question becomes so short that it is indistinguishable from a piece of any other curved line. The general constitution
of a bundle of optical rays may be defined also by the fact that the
two focal lines with respect to any given ray are intersected by all the
contiguous rays (disregarding infinitesimal aberrations of order higher
than the first); but this statement requires an explicit definition of
what is meant by a contiguous ray. Draw the ray corresponding to a
point on the ruled surface at a finite distance from the given ray,
and do the same thing for points nearer and nearer the given ray; then
ultimately the distance between the point and the given ray will
vanish entirely, and the ray corresponding to this point will be contiguous to the given ray. But this definition will be fundamentally
misunderstood if the conclusion is deduced that all the rays of a
narrow bundle of finite width go approximately through two STURM
focal lines.

Since (neglecting infinitesimals of order higher than the first) all
the contiguous rays of a bundle of rays which is anastigmatic along a
certain ray meet this ray in the focal point, there occurs in this case a
perfect ray-convergence of the first order; and the focal point is the optical
reproduction or image of the point where the light originates. Hence,
in case of a stop of finite aperture, the optical imagery cannot be said
to be due to the fact that all the rays coming from an object-point go
approximately through the image-point, but merely to the fact that
contiguous rays intersect at this point, so that the concentration of the
light here is infinitely great as compared with that at a point at a finite
distance from this spot. The imagery supposed in the first case above
is indeed mathematically correct for an infinitely narrow bundle of
rays, but since it is physically impossible on account of diffraction
effects to produce an optical image by such means, this imagery represents merely an ideal dreamed of in olden times; whereas the latter
case mentioned above describes exactly the actual process as it takes
place. If the reality here appears to be little different from the ideal,
the explanation is to be found in the circumstance that both in the
eye and likewise on the photographic plate shades of brightness are of
more importance than absolute brightness.

The criterion of actual *optical imagery* is just this perfect ray-
convergence of the first order. As is evident from the foregoing, this
convergence of the rays is susceptible of mathematical investigation
only along definite rays. The rays chosen for this purpose are the chief
rays defined above. Assuming that the chief ray corresponding
to each point of the surface of the object has been constructed
and traced through the optical system by trigonometrical calculation, and that somewhere in the path of the light a screen is

interposed, we shall obtain on it a *punctual correspondence* with the object by means of *optical projection*, since every point on the screen where a chief ray arrives is the optical projection of the point of the object where this ray originates, and the centre of the stop is to be regarded as the centre of projection. Thus, the optical projection is a mathematical conception which, however, may be illustrated physically by means of any optical system with a very brilliant object, provided the screen is adjusted so that the image is not sharply focused on it; since to every bright point of the object corresponds a bright spot of light on the screen, and as the opening of the stop is made smaller and smaller, the image will become less and less hazy. A special case of general optical projection is realized in the pinhole camera; wherein, generally speaking, every point where a chief ray meets the surface of a screen adjusted arbitrarily is the optical projection of the corresponding point of the object; and every section in which the screen cuts a ruled surface composed of chief rays is the optical projection of a corresponding line on the surface of the object; such that the ratio of the lengths of corresponding line-elements, in case they are both perpendicular to the chief ray in question, represents the so-called *coefficient of linear projection.* Similarly, an optical projection can be produced by means of a bundle of rays emanating from a point of an object. This can be shown physically by stretching a wire at any part of an optical system of wide aperture in the path of a beam of light proceeding from a luminous point, and observing the shadow that is formed on a screen set up in one of the media. If the wire is placed in the medium where the point-source itself is situated and revolved around the chief ray until its shadow on the screen is tangent to one of the principal sections of the bundle along the chief ray, the ruled surface indicated by the wire in this position is a focal or developable surface with respect to the chief ray in both the object-space and the screen-space; since every ruled surface in the object-space is to be considered here as having a focal point coinciding with the luminous point itself. In this particular case the coefficient of linear projection can be replaced by the *coefficient of angular projection*; which is the ratio of the infinitely small angles subtended at the focal points of the developable surfaces by an element of the line projected on the screen and the corresponding element of the wire.

Since anastigmatic convergence of the rays occurs generally only along singular (or extraordinary) chief rays, a punctual optical imagery, characterized by the fact that the separate points of the surface of an object are reproduced as points in perfect ray-convergence of the first order, is for a fixed position of the centre of the stop a mathematical impossibility; and if there is really any such thing as a general optical imagery, it is simply a question as to the imagery of single lines. *The condition of the optical imagery of lines requires that (neglecting infinitesimals of order higher than the first) all rays contiguous to the chief rays proceeding from the various points of the object-line shall meet the optical projection of this line.* Since in this imagery there is no other punctual correspondence except that obtained by optical projection, and since the rays emanating from a point of the object-line meet the corresponding image-line in different points, obviously the ratio of the lengths of corresponding elements of these lines depends simply on the optical projection; whereas the *magnification-ratio* of the optical imagery is the ratio of the lengths of the corresponding elements of the lines which meet the image-line and object-line perpendicularly; that is, the ratio of the orthogonal trajectories of image-line and object-line, assuming that object-surface and image-surface are both perpendicular to the chief ray. Thus, the magnification-ratio is identical with the coefficient of linear projection of the orthogonal trajectories, supposing these latter could in general be projected into each other.

The fact that there is a general imagery of lines as above explained is proved by the writer's fundamental equation of optical imagery; and the laws thereof result as a consequence. These *general laws of optical imagery*, except for the case of grazing incidence of the chief rays, and also except when there are peaks and edges at the points of incidence, apply without reservation to any optical system with isotropic media of either constant or continuously variable index of refraction; and may be formulated as follows:

At every point where the chief ray makes a finite angle with the surface of an object there are two intersecting lines on the surface, inclined to each other at a finite angle, which will be reproduced in the image-space by perfect ray-convergence of the first order, the image-surface being different for each system of lines.

The tangents to the imageable lines lie entirely in the planes normal to those ruled surfaces which in the image-space are in contact with the principal sections of the bundle of refracted rays. The tangents to the image-lines themselves lie in the same principal sections taken in opposite order.

There is no other imagery with perfect ray-convergence of the first order. The only points of the system of imageable lines that are reproduced by points are the singular points. Singular points in these systems occur only when the bundle of rays after refraction in the image-space is anastigmatic along the chief ray; in which case the two image-surfaces have a point of contact.

The magnification can be expressed only by means of the ratio of the distances of the image-lines to the distances of the corresponding lines on

*the surface of the object. However, at the singular points the first term of
the magnification is given by the ratio of the length of an element of the
image-line to that of the corresponding object-line; and in case of a line
composed of singular points the magnification is represented by the ratio
of the length of the image-line to that of the object-line.*

*The product obtained by multiplying the relative index of refraction of
the optical system by both the coefficient of angular projection and the
coefficient of magnification is invariably equal to unity.*

*The magnification-ratio at each point and the directions of the tangents
to the imageable lines are independent of the position of the stop on the
chief ray.*

*As a rule imageries cannot be combined or compounded. If a dif-
ferent medium is chosen for the image-space, the imageable lines will be
altered thereby. The same thing happens when the distance between the
object-point and the optical system is varied.*

*Imageries are absolutely reversible. When the procedure of the rays is
reversed, the original image-lines represent one system of imageable lines
lying on the surface in question, whereas the tangents to the corresponding
original imageable lines lie in the respective principal sections of the
bundle of refracted rays.*

The optical imagery of the character thus described is a mathematical conception, postulating a fixed position of the centre of the
stop and monochromatic light. In the application of the theory to
actual physical combinations, it should be borne in mind therefore
that, strictly speaking, any point in the plane of the stop can be taken
at pleasure as centre of the stop, which will be discussed more in detail
presently as to its important practical bearings. In case of compound
light the *chromatic differences* also have to be taken into account
besides. The latter concern not simply the magnitudes obtained by
trigonometrical calculation that determine the path of the guide-ray,
but also the positions of the image-lines, their orientation, and that of
the imageable lines, and, finally, also the magnification-ratios; all
these magnitudes, according to the circumstances of the case, being
calculated for different kinds of light. STURM's formulae, which have
been extended to include certain singular cases hitherto left out of
account, are of service here, and in addition certain other formulae
derived by the writer.

If along a guide-ray the plane of incidence is a principal normal
plane of the refracting surface, and each successive plane of incidence
is either identical with the preceding plane of refraction or perpendicular to it, the imageries can be compounded, because the tangents to the
imageable lines and to the image-lines lie everywhere in the plane of
refraction and in the plane containing the guide-ray which is perpen-

dicular to this plane, respectively. The so-called *singly asymmetrical systems* characterized by the existence of a plane of symmetry represent a special case under this head that is of practical importance. Although in the general case, where there is no such plane, and the optical system is said therefore to be *doubly asymmetrical*, only the imagery-laws of the first order are applicable, complete laws of the second order have been deduced by the writer in case of the systems first named. Moreover, if the guide-ray is the line of intersection of two planes of symmetry of the optical system, the latter is said to be a *symmetrical system*; and under such circumstances we know also the laws of the third order along the guide-ray which were found originally by SEYDEL in the special case of a centered system consisting of spherical surfaces. Moreover, in singly asymmetrical systems, and even to a greater extent in symmetrical systems, the laws of the first order are considerably simplified. Again, if the optical system is comprised of surfaces of revolution having a common axis which passes through the centre of the stop, and if the surface of the object is likewise symmetrical with respect to the axis, or if it is a plane perpendicular to the axis, the case is that of a *system of revolution*. Systems of this description, of which a centered system of spherical surfaces is a particular case, have a practical importance beyond all others; for which also the imagery-laws become much simplified. Thus since the plane determined by the chief ray and the principal axis is always a plane of symmetry, one pair of corresponding lines of object and image must always be in this plane and the other pair perpendicular to it; and, consequently, image-lines and imageable lines are always parallel circles and meridians; and moreover the imageries can be compounded along every chief ray.

The practical bearing of this mode of classifying the systems will be apparent on comparing the imagery in the case of an ordinary magnifying glass and a bicylindrical lens. In the latter case the laws of a symmetrical system are applicable along the axis, and of a singly asymmetrical system along a guide-ray lying in one of the two planes of symmetry; whereas for any other guide-ray only the general laws in case of double asymmetry are valid. But in case of an ordinary magnifying glass, supposing that the pupil of the eye is on the axis of the lens, the special laws for a system of revolution are applicable along the axis, whereas along any other chief ray the laws are those of a singly asymmetrical system with certain special simplifications due to the properties of surfaces of revolution.

Optical Imagery in a System of Revolution. The simpler laws that apply to an optical system which is symmetrical around an axis may be obtained by elementary methods and suffice for an explanation of the

imagery in the case of the eye. The primary principal section of a
bundle of rays emanating from a point of the object is the *meridian
plane* determined by the chief ray and the axis of revolution; whereas
the secondary principal section is the *equatorial plane* perpendicular to
the former and also containing the chief ray. Since the ruled surfaces
which are tangent to these planes in the object-space have this same
relation in each successive medium, and are therefore focal throughout
the system, the bundle of refracted rays may be ascertained by investigating these developable surfaces. The fact that also the entire image-
process can be discovered by the study of these two ruled surfaces,
follows at once from the general laws of optical imagery given above;
for without them all that is really known in this case is the effect of the
rays which happen to lie in these two ruled surfaces, and which constitute an exceedingly small portion of the total quantity of rays that
are concerned in the imagery.

In Fig. 114 the straight line AC is supposed to be the prolongation
of the chief ray which is incident
at the point A, whereas BC is the
prolongation of another ray lying
in the meridian plane and belonging to the same bundle; and AO
and BO are the corresponding
normals to the refracting surface.

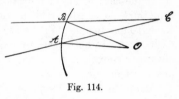

Fig. 114.

The angles of incidence CAO and CBO are denoted by i and $i+\omega$
respectively; and therefore

$$\angle AOB + i = \angle ACB + i + \omega,$$

and hence

$$\omega = \angle AOB - \angle ACB.$$

Now if the point B is taken closer and closer to the point A until
BC represents a ray contiguous to the chief ray, AC becomes finally
the primary focal distance τ of the bundle of incident rays measured
from A, and AO the radius $\rho_\prime$ of the primary principal curvature of the
refracting surface, and $\angle AOB = \dfrac{AB}{\rho_\prime}$, $\angle ACB = \dfrac{AB\cos i}{\tau}$. Thus when
AB is infinitely small,

$$\frac{\omega}{AB} = \frac{1}{\rho_\prime} - \frac{\cos i}{\tau},$$

and, similarly, if i', ω', τ' have analogous meanings for the bundle of
refracted rays,

$$\frac{\omega'}{AB} = \frac{1}{\rho_\prime} - \frac{\cos i'}{\tau'}.$$

Since

$$\sin (i+\omega) = \sin i \cos \omega + \sin \omega \cos i,$$

and since the angle ω becomes infinitely small along with the arc AB, so that ultimately $\cos\omega = 1$ and $\sin\omega = \omega$, after multiplying both sides by the value n of the index of refraction of the first medium and at the same time dividing by AB, the identity above may be written in the following form:

$$\frac{n \sin (i+\omega) - n \sin i}{AB} = n \cos i \, \frac{\omega}{AB} = n \cos i \left(\frac{1}{\rho'} - \frac{\cos i}{\tau} \right).$$

Similarly, if n' denotes the index of refraction of the second medium,

$$\frac{n' \sin (i'+\omega') - n' \sin i'}{AB} = n' \cos i' \left(\frac{1}{\rho'} - \frac{\cos i'}{\tau'} \right).$$

Since, according to the law of refraction, the left-hand members of these two equations are equal to each other, we obtain:

$$\frac{n' \cos^2 i'}{\tau'} = \frac{n \cos^2 i}{\tau} + \frac{n' \cos i' - n \cos i}{\rho'} \quad \cdot \quad \cdot \quad \cdot \quad \cdot \quad A_1$$

If the case is one of reflection instead of refraction, precisely the same method can be used provided we put $n' = -n$, since then also the left-hand members of the two identities above will still be equal to each other. In both cases the magnitudes denoted by τ, τ' and ρ' are always to be reckoned positive in one and the same direction from the point of incidence.

Again, in Fig. 115 suppose that B designates the position of the secondary focal point of the bundle of incident rays, represented here as lying on the prolongation of the chief ray; and let O in this diagram

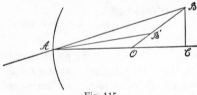

mark the position of the centre of the secondary principal curvature of the refracting surface situated on the normal drawn to the surface through the incidence-point A; and suppose the entire figure is revolved around the

Fig. 115.

line OB as axis. As this rotation starts, the point A is carried to an adjacent point of the refracting surface lying in the equatorial plane, and the normal to the surface at this point will be contiguous to the normal AO and will therefore meet it in the point O. Similarly, the ray which falls on the surface here will be contiguous to the chief ray AB and will meet it in the point B. But since a ray in the equatorial plane contiguous to the refracted chief ray must be contained in the same plane as the corresponding incident ray and normal, it must intersect the line OB at a point B', which is therefore the secondary focal point of the bundle of rays situated on the refracted chief ray AB'.

Accordingly, if s, s' denote the distances of the secondary focal points before and after refraction, both measured from the incidence-point A, and if ρ'' denotes the radius of the secondary principal curvature of the refracting surface with respect to this same point, and finally, if BC is drawn perpendicular to the normal AO, we may write:

$$\frac{BC}{OC} = \frac{s \sin i}{s \cos i - \rho''} = \tan \angle BOC$$

and consequently

$$\frac{n \sin i}{\rho'' \tan \angle BOC} = \frac{n \cos i}{\rho''} - \frac{n}{s}.$$

Since a similar equation is obtained for the bundle of refracted rays, and since, according to the law of refraction, the left-hand members of the two equations are equal to each other, we obtain finally

$$\frac{n'}{s'} = \frac{n}{s} + \frac{n' \cos i' - n \cos i}{\rho''} \qquad . \quad . \quad . \quad . \quad . \quad A_2$$

The same remarks that were made above with respect to formula A_1 concerning the special case of reflection and the positive directions of the linear magnitudes apply here also. As is obvious from the way they were derived, both formulae are valid not merely for a system of revolution but in any case where one of the principal sections of the bundle of incident rays and a principal normal section of the refracting or reflecting surface coincide with the plane of incidence. Ordinarily as the formulae show, the bundle of refracted rays is astigmatic, and hence in a system of revolution, except under special circumstances, the two image-surfaces are tangent to each other only at the place where the axis meets them, and consequently the axial object-point is the only point that is reproduced by a point.

For this latter point $\cos i = \cos i' = 1$ and $\rho' = \rho''$ and accordingly the two formulæ A reduce to the first of formulae (3), § 9, in the HELMHOLTZ text; where the focal distances for the incident and refracted rays are measured in opposite directions conformably to the old custom, the radius of curvature of the refracting surface being reckoned always as positive.

However, for any point of the object not on the axis *two different imageries* are to be taken into account; and therefore we may designate the imagery of the parallel of latitude determined by the primary focal point of the bundle of refracted rays as the *primary imagery*.

The magnification-ratios corresponding to the two imageries may be obtained as follows: Let p, q, p', q' denote the distances from the incidence-point of the primary and secondary focal points of the bundle of incident chief rays and the corresponding bundle of refracted rays, respectively. In Fig. 116 the straight line ACD is supposed to represent the prolongation of one of the incident chief rays; whereon

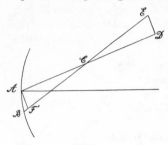

the points C and D designate the primary focal points of the bundle of chief rays and the bundle of rays belonging to the given point of the object, respectively. Draw DE perpendicular to the chief ray AD, and mark on it a point E, and suppose that BE is the chief ray which goes through E. Draw AF perpendicular to ACD and meeting BCE in the point designated by F. Then

Fig. 116.

$$\frac{AF}{DE} = \frac{AC}{CD} = \frac{p}{\tau - p}.$$

Now if the point E is taken infinitely near the focal point D, so that BE and AD are two contiguous chief rays, the point B may be considered as lying on the tangent to the refracting surface, and hence the angle BAF will be equal to the angle of incidence. If the length DE is denoted by β, then

$$AB = \frac{\beta p}{(\tau - p) \cos i},$$

and hence, multiplying both sides by $n \cos^2 i \left(\dfrac{1}{\tau} - \dfrac{1}{p} \right)$, we may write:

$$AB \cdot n \cos^2 i \left(\frac{1}{\tau} - \frac{1}{p} \right) = -\frac{n \cos i \, \beta}{\tau}.$$

An analogous relation connecting the bundle of refracted chief rays and the bundle of refracted rays corresponding to the given point of the object may be obtained in precisely the same way; and by applying formula A_1 to each of the two bundles of rays, it will be seen that the left-hand sides of the two equations are equal; whence it follows that

$$K_1 = \frac{n \cos i \, \tau'}{n' \cos i' \, \tau} \quad \cdot \quad \cdot \quad \cdot \quad \cdot \quad \cdot \quad \text{B}_1$$

where the symbol K_1 denotes the *primary magnification-ratio*.

Similarly, for the *secondary magnification-ratio*, we shall find:

$$K_2 = \frac{ns'}{n's} \quad \cdot \quad \cdot \quad \cdot \quad \cdot \quad \cdot \quad \cdot \quad \text{B}_2$$

since, in case Fig. 116 represents the equatorial section, the chief ray of the bundle of incident rays would have to coincide with the normal to the section of the refracting surface made by the equatorial plane,

and instead of multiplying by the expression given above, the factor
here would be

$$n\left(\frac{1}{s}-\frac{1}{q}\right).$$

In the particular case when $\tau = \tau' = 0$, in Fig. 116 $AF = \beta$ and
therefore $K_1 = \dfrac{\cos i'}{\cos i}$. For $s = s' = 0$, it is evident at once that $K_2 = 1$.

Since formulae A are addition-formulae containing the products of
the reciprocals of the focal distances and the corresponding values of
the index of refraction, it is convenient to reckon directly in terms of
these functions. Thus, the quotient of the focal distance from any
point by the index of refraction is called the *reduced focal distance* with
respect to that point. The focal distance is reckoned positive when we
proceed from the origin of the measurement to the focal point in the
direction that is called the positive direction; and the reciprocal of
this distance, which is therefore equal to one of the principal curvatures
of the wave surface, is a measure of the convergence of the bundle of
rays in the given principal section at the point taken as origin. Hence,
the value obtained by multiplying the reciprocal of the focal distance
by the index of refraction is called the *reduced convergence*. Employing
this idea, we may write equations A and B for both imageries as follows:

$$\kappa^2 B = A + \kappa D, \qquad \kappa KB = A \quad . \quad . \quad . \quad . \quad . \quad \text{C}$$

Here the magnitudes denoted by A and B are the reduced convergences of the bundles of incident and refracted rays, respectively; i.e.,
$A = \dfrac{n}{\tau}$, $B = \dfrac{n'}{\tau'}$, or $A = \dfrac{n}{s}$, $B = \dfrac{n'}{s'}$, according as the formulae relate to the
primary or secondary imagery, respectively. The magnitude denoted
by κ is the value of the magnification-ratio at the point of incidence
and is equal to $\dfrac{\cos i'}{\cos i}$ or to 1; whereas K denotes the primary or secondary magnification-ratio at the given focal point. The magnitude
denoted by D is the *refracting power* of the surface at the point of
incidence and is given by one of the following expressions, namely:

$$\frac{n'\cos i' - n\cos i}{\rho'\cos i'\cos i} \quad \text{or} \quad \frac{n'\cos i' - n\cos i}{\rho''},$$

according as it refers to the case of the primary or secondary imagery,
respectively.

It is easy to prove that *formulae* C *are likewise true when the reduced
convergences are measured from any pair of points which are conjugate to
each other with respect to the imagery in question.* If κ_1 denotes the value
of the magnification-ratio for this pair of conjugate points, and if the

reduced convergences at these points measured from the point of
$_0$incidence are denoted by A_0, B_0, then, besides equations C, we have
also the pair of similar equations:

$$\kappa^2 B_0 = A_0 + \kappa D, \qquad \kappa\kappa_1 B_0 = A_0$$

and by subtraction we obtain:

$$\kappa^2 (B_0 - B) = A_0 - A.$$

Moreover, if A_1, B_1 denote the reduced convergences at this same
pair of points for the bundle of rays determined by A, B, then

$$\frac{1}{B_1} = \frac{1}{B} - \frac{1}{B_0}, \qquad \frac{1}{A_1} = \frac{1}{A} - \frac{1}{A_0},$$

and therefore also

$$B_1 = \frac{BB_0}{B_0 - B}, \qquad A_1 = \frac{AA_0}{A_0 - A} = \frac{\kappa KB.\kappa\kappa_1 B_0}{\kappa^2 (B_0 - B)}$$

consequently,

$$\kappa_1 K B_1 = A_1.$$

On the other hand, eliminating A or A_0, we obtain

$$\kappa - K = \frac{D}{B}, \qquad \kappa - \kappa_1 = \frac{D}{B_0},$$

respectively; and by subtraction

$$\kappa_1 - K = D\left(\frac{1}{B} - \frac{1}{B_0}\right) = \frac{D}{B_1},$$

wherein, by substituting the value $\dfrac{A_1}{\kappa_1 B_1}$ for K, the following result is
obtained:

$$\kappa_1^2 B_1 = A_1 + \kappa_1 D.$$

In order to find the resultant imagery of one of the two imageable
systems of lines that is produced by two successive refractions, suppose, to begin with, that the positions have been determined of each
pair of focal points in the second and third media corresponding to a
point of the object in the first medium; and let κ_1, κ_2 denote the magnification-ratios for the imagery of the given object-lines in the second
medium and for the imagery of these image-lines in the third medium,
respectively; and, finally, let D_1, D_2 denote the refracting powers of
the two surfaces with respect to the given imagery. Then if A, B
denote the reduced convergences of any bundle of rays measured at
the given object-point in the first medium and at the corresponding
focal point in the last medium, respectively, the following pair of
values will be found for the reduced convergence at the conjugate
point in the second medium:

$$\frac{A}{\kappa_1^2}+\frac{D_1}{\kappa_1}=\kappa_2^2\,B-\kappa_2 D_2,$$

whence, by writing

$$\kappa=\kappa_1\kappa_2, \qquad D=\frac{D_1}{\kappa_2}+\kappa_1 D_2$$

the general equation of the focal distances for the combination of the imageries by two refractions assumes the same form as in case of a single refraction, namely

$$\kappa^2 B=A+\kappa D.$$

Moreover, if K_1, K_2 denote the magnification-ratios for the two surfaces at the focal points of the bundle of rays, the reduced convergence measured in the second medium is given also by the following pair of values:

$$\kappa_2 K_2 B=\frac{A}{\kappa_1 K_1}$$

and hence putting $K=K_1\,K_2$, we obtain:

$$\kappa K B=A.$$

This procedure can be repeated indefinitely. In general, therefore, if for the pair of conjugate points at which the reduced convergences are measured the magnification-ratio with respect to the imagery due to the first n surfaces is denoted by k_n, and if the refracting power of the optical system composed of the first n surfaces is denoted by $\mathfrak{D}_n$, then

$$k_n=\kappa_1\kappa_2\kappa_3 \ldots \kappa_n=\Pi\kappa,$$

and the formula found above for the refracting power of two surfaces may be written in the following form:

$$k_2\mathfrak{D}_2-k_1\mathfrak{D}_1=\frac{k_2^2 D_2}{\kappa_2}.$$

In the case of n surfaces, therefore, we obtain by summation:

$$k_n\mathfrak{D}_n=\frac{k_1^2 D_1}{\kappa_1}+\frac{k_2^2 D_2}{\kappa_2}+ \ldots +\frac{k_n^2 D_n}{\kappa_n}=\sum\frac{k^2 D}{\kappa}.$$

The range of validity of the general image-equations,

$$\kappa^2 B=A+\kappa D, \qquad \kappa K B=A$$

which are applicable along any chief ray in a system of revolution may therefore be extended to any number of media, provided κ denotes the magnification-ratio for a pair of points conjugate to each other with respect to the given imagery, A and B the reduced convergences of a bundle of rays with respect to these points, and K the magnification-ratio with respect to the focal points determined by A and B, and provided also that for the compound system consisting of n components

$$D = \frac{1}{\kappa} \sum \frac{k^2 D}{\kappa}$$

in which this sum contains one term for each component system.

The angular magnification may be also found by means of these formulae. This term denotes the ratio of the angles subtended at two conjugate points by the distance between a pair of image-lines and the distance between the corresponding pair of imageable lines. Consequently, if the indices of refraction are denoted by n, n', and the elementary arcs of the orthogonal trajectories of the lines which are imaged in each other are denoted by β,β', the angular magnification-ratio with respect to the pair of points, for which the lateral magnification-ratio (as it is called in order to distinguish it from the other) has the value κ, is given by the ratio of the two angles, $\dfrac{\beta' B}{n'}$ and $\dfrac{\beta A}{n}$ and hence is equal to $\dfrac{nKB}{n'A}$, which is the same as $\dfrac{n}{n'\kappa}$. The continued product of the angular magnification-ratio, the lateral magnification-ratio and the relative index of refraction is therefore invariably equal to unity. Just as we employ the term reduced distance, it is convenient to introduce here the idea of the *reduced angular magnification-ratio as being equal to* $\dfrac{KB}{A}$, *i.e., equal to the reciprocal of the lateral magnification-ratio.*

Putting $B = 0$ in the general image-equations, we find that the reduced distance of the *first principal focal point* is equal to $-\dfrac{1}{\kappa D}$; and similarly, putting $A = 0$, we get for the reduced distance of the *second principal focal point* $\dfrac{\kappa}{D}$. Again, putting $K = 1$, we find for the reduced distances of the *first and second principal points*[1] $\dfrac{\kappa - 1}{\kappa D}$ and $\dfrac{\kappa - 1}{D}$, respectively. Accordingly, by subtracting the latter values from the former, the reduced distances of the first principal focal point from the first principal point and of the second principal focal point from the second principal point are found to be $-\dfrac{1}{D}$ and $\dfrac{1}{D}$, respectively. Thus,

---

[1] ¶It would seem advantageous to call the principal points in this case the "unit points" ($K = 1$), as is done by some English writers.   (J. P. C. S.)

the *refracting power* may be defined, perfectly generally, as *the reciprocal of the quotient of the second principal focal length by the corresponding index of refraction*.

When *the image-equations are referred to the principal points*, they take the form

$$B = A + D, \qquad KB = A,$$

which expressed in words are equivalent to the following statements: *When rays of light traverse an optical system, the value of the reduced convergence increases by an amount equal to the refracting power of the system*; and *the lateral magnification-ratio is equal to the quotient of the reduced distances of the focal point from the principal point for the corresponding bundles of refracted and incident rays*; whereas the reduced angular magnification-ratio at the principal points themselves is equal to unity. These latter formulae are just as general as the others, and have the advantage of exhibiting clearly the essence of optical imagery; whereas, on the other hand, they have the disadvantage of necessitating a troublesome transformation in applying them to a so-called telescopic or afocal system (which is a better term), characterized by the condition $D = 0$; while the general image-equations are applicable in the form in which they are given.

If in the image-equations referred to the principal points the condition is imposed of equal (unreduced) convergences of the corresponding bundles of incident and refracted rays, the result is that

$$\frac{B}{n'} = \frac{A}{n} = \frac{D}{n' - n}, \qquad K = \frac{n}{n'}$$

and the focal points of the bundle are in this case identical with LISTING's nodal points; the (unreduced) angular magnification at these points being equal to unity. But since the properties ascribed to the nodal points have no reality for rays of finite inclinations except for a system consisting of a single spherical surface, as is too obvious to need explanation, the image-equations referred to these points are of little service, because by means of the reduced angular magnification-ratio the image-equations referred to the principal points secure precisely the advantages that the nodal-point equations are supposed to possess.

On the other hand, in numerous instances the *image-equations referred to the principal focal points* are of real utility. These equations may be obtained either directly from the expressions found above for the distances of the principal focal points from any pair of conjugate points or as follows: If, first B, and then A, is eliminated from the general image-equations, the latter may be expressed in a form which is very useful for certain problems, namely:

$$D = A\left(\frac{1}{K} - \frac{1}{\kappa}\right) = B(\kappa - K),$$

These formulae are applicable, for example, when one of the pair of conjugate points at which the magnification-ratio is equal to κ is situated at infinity, that is, when either $\kappa = 0$ or $\frac{1}{\kappa} = 0$. Thus, if the reduced convergences of a bundle of rays measured at the first and second principal focal points of an optical system are denoted by L and L', respectively, the following equations are found:

$$KD = L, \qquad KL' = -D.$$

Consequently,

$$LL' = -D^2, \qquad \frac{L}{L'} = -K^2,$$

where K, as usual, denotes the magnification-ratio at the focal points of the bundles of rays whose reduced convergences are L, L'.

If in case of the *combination of two systems* it is desired to find the refracting power $\mathfrak{D}$ of the compound system directly and the positions of the principal points without pursuing the method given above, the necessary formulae for this purpose can be obtained as follows: Suppose the first system is defined by its refracting power D_1 and a pair of conjugate points for which the magnification-ratio is κ_1; and also the second system is defined similarly by its refracting power D_2 and a pair of conjugate points for which the magnification-ratio is κ_2; and let the reduced distance (that is, the distance divided by the corresponding index of refraction) of the first one of the last mentioned pair of points from the second one of the pair named first be denoted by δ. Moreover, let A_1, B_1, K_1 and A_2, B_2, K_2 denote the reduced convergences of a bundle of rays and the magnification-ratios for the first and second members of the system, respectively. Then by the definition given above the refracting power of the compound system is equal to $\frac{D_1}{K_2} + K_1 D_2$.

By eliminating A_1 and B_2 from the general image-equations we get

$$K_1 = \kappa_1 - \frac{D_1}{B_1}, \qquad \frac{1}{K_2} = \frac{1}{\kappa_2} + \frac{D_2}{A_2}$$

and since

$$\frac{1}{B_1} - \frac{1}{A_2} = \delta,$$

we find:

$$\mathfrak{D} = \frac{D_1}{K_2} + K_1 D_2 = \frac{D_1}{\kappa_2} + \kappa_1 D_2 - \delta D_1 D_2.$$

This expression enables us to compute the refracting power of the compound system in terms of the magnitudes that define the two component systems, and, for $\delta = 0$, it reduces to the expression which was obtained previously for this condition. Let the reduced distances of the first and second principal points (or "unit points") of the compound system as measured from the first one of the pair of conjugate points of the first system and from the second one of the pair of conjugate points of the second system be denoted by H, H', that is, put $H = \dfrac{1}{A_1}$, $H' = \dfrac{1}{B_2}$. We have here the condition that $K_1 K_2 = 1$ and hence

$$\kappa_1 - \frac{D_1}{B_1} = \frac{1}{\kappa_2} + \frac{D_2}{A_2}.$$

If we substitute on the left-hand side of this equation the expression for A_2 in terms of B_1, and on the right-hand side the expression for B_1 in terms of A_2, the equation may be transformed as follows:

$$B_1 \left(\delta D_2 + \kappa_1 - \frac{1}{\kappa_2} \right) = D_1 + D_2 = -A_2 \left(\delta D_1 + \frac{1}{\kappa_2} - \kappa_1 \right).$$

Then by substituting the expression for B_1 in terms of A_1 and that for A_2 in terms of B_2, the following result may be found:

$$\frac{A_1}{\kappa_1} \left(\delta D_2 + \kappa_1 - \frac{1}{\kappa_2} \right) = \mathfrak{D} = -\kappa_2 B_2 \left(\delta D_1 + \frac{1}{\kappa_2} - \kappa_1 \right).$$

Hence, *the general formulae for the combination of two systems are*:

$$\mathfrak{D} = \frac{D_1}{\kappa_2} + \kappa_1 D_2 - \delta D_1 D_2,$$

$$H = \frac{1}{\kappa_1 \mathfrak{D}} \left(\delta D_2 + \kappa_1 - \frac{1}{\kappa_2} \right),$$

$$H' = -\frac{\kappa_2}{\mathfrak{D}} \left(\delta D_1 + \frac{1}{\kappa_2} - \kappa_1 \right).$$

In case the *two component systems are referred to their* principal points (or "unit points"), by putting $\kappa_1 = \kappa_2 = 1$, we obtain:

$$\mathfrak{D} = D_1 + D_2 - \delta D_1 D_2 \qquad H = \frac{\delta D_2}{\mathfrak{D}} \qquad H' = -\frac{\delta D_1}{\mathfrak{D}}.$$

If *one of the component systems is afocal*, then $D_1 = 0$ or $D_2 = 0$, according as it is the first or second system, respectively; and if the other system is referred to its principal points (or "unit points"), that is, if $\kappa_2 = 1$ or $\kappa_1 = 1$, then either

$$\mathfrak{D} = \kappa_1 D_2, \qquad H = \frac{\delta}{\kappa_1^2} + \frac{\kappa_1 - 1}{\kappa_1^2 D_2}, \qquad H' = \frac{\kappa_1 - 1}{\kappa_1 D_2}$$

or

$$\mathfrak{D} = \frac{D_1}{\kappa_2}, \qquad H = \frac{\kappa_2 - 1}{D_1}, \qquad H' = -\kappa_2^2 \delta + \frac{\kappa_2(\kappa_2 - 1)}{D_1}.$$

And, finally, if *both component systems are afocal*, by substituting in the expression for δ the value of B_1 in terms of A_1 and that of A_2 in terms of B_2, we find:

$$\frac{1}{\kappa_1\kappa_2 B_2} = \frac{\kappa_1\kappa_2}{A_1} - \frac{\kappa_2\delta}{\kappa_1}$$

whereas the magnification-ratio has everywhere the constant value

$$K = \kappa_1\kappa_2.$$

For example, in the case of a plane parallel plate or of a prism traversed by the chief ray along the path of minimum deviation, for each of the two imageries $\kappa_1\kappa_2 = 1$, and consequently

$$\frac{1}{B_2} = \frac{1}{A_1} - \frac{\delta}{\kappa_1{}^2}.$$

If the plate or prism is surrounded by air and if the angles of incidence and refraction at the first surface are denoted by i, i', then for the bundle of emergent rays:

$$\frac{1}{B_2} = \frac{1}{A_1} - \frac{\delta \cos^2 i}{\cos^2 i'} \quad \text{or} \quad \frac{1}{B_2} = \frac{1}{A_1} - \delta.$$

Thus, if the plane of refraction is assumed to be the primary principal section, and if the light were originally homocentric, the distance of the first focal point from the second will be

$$\delta \cdot \frac{\cos^2 i' - \cos^2 i}{\cos^2 i'}.$$

This focal segment, being therefore independent of the position of the radiant point-source, is a measure of the actual astigmatism of the system. Evidently, it is negligible only in case the path of light inside the plate or prism is vanishingly small as compared with the distance of the source.

In physiological optics it is convenient to have available formulae for the *combination of three optical systems*; which, by using the above general methods, may be obtained as follows: Let D_1, D_2, D_3 denote the refracting powers of the component systems and $\mathfrak{D}$ that of the compound system; and let δ_1, δ_2 denote the reduced distances of the first principal ("unit") point of one system from the second principal ("unit") point of the preceding system. In the first place, let us determine the positions of the points conjugate to the principal ("unit") points of the second system in the first and last media. We have:

$$A_1 + D_1 = \frac{1}{\delta_1}, \qquad B_3 = D_3 - \frac{1}{\delta_2},$$

$$\frac{\kappa_1}{\delta^1} = A_1, \qquad \kappa_3 B_3 = -\frac{1}{\delta_2}$$

and moreover

$$\kappa_1 = 1 - \delta_1 D_1, \qquad \kappa_2 = 1, \qquad \kappa_3 = \frac{1}{1 - \delta_2 D_3};$$

whence we obtain the following general formula for the refracting power:

$$\mathfrak{D} = D_1(1 - \delta_2 D_3) + D_2(1 - \delta_1 D_1)\ (1 - \delta_2 D_3) + D_3(1 - \delta_1 D)_1.$$

The reduced distances of the principal ("unit") points of the compound system measured from the two conjugate points found in the first and last media are, as was proved above,

$$\frac{\kappa - 1}{\kappa \mathfrak{D}} \quad \text{or} \quad \frac{\kappa - 1}{\mathfrak{D}},$$

where κ is written in place of $\kappa_1 \kappa_3$; and hence for the reduced distances H, H' of the principal ("unit") points of the compound system from the first principal ("unit") point of the first system and from the second principal ("unit") point of the second system, respectively, we obtain finally:

$$H = \frac{1}{A_1} + \frac{\kappa - 1}{\kappa \mathfrak{D}} = \frac{\delta_1}{1 - \delta_1 D_1} + \frac{\delta_2 D_3 - \delta_1 D_1}{\mathfrak{D}(1 - \delta_1 D_1)}$$

$$H' = \frac{1}{B_3} + \frac{\kappa - 1}{\mathfrak{D}} = -\frac{\delta_2}{1 - \delta_2 D_3} + \frac{\delta_2 D_3 - \delta_1 D_1}{\mathfrak{D}(1 - \delta_2 D_3)}.$$

If the compound system is symmetrical with respect to the middle component, then, since $\delta_2 = \delta_1$ and $D_3 = D_1$, we have:

$$\mathfrak{D} = 2D_1(1 - \delta_1 D_1) + D_2(1 - \delta_1 D_1)^2,$$

$$H = -H' = \frac{\delta_1}{1 - \delta_1 D_1}.$$

So far as *choice of signs* is concerned, the image-equations for the case of a single surface were derived on the general assumption that the distances of the focal points and centre of curvature of the refracting or reflecting surface from the point of incidence were counted positive in one and the same direction, and that a positive sign for the magnification-ratio means "erect" (or "sympathetic") imagery. Moreover, since in case of reflection, the sign of the index of refraction has to be reversed, and in compound systems the positive direction must be consistent throughout, it is best to define this direction with reference to the way the light travels in the object-space. If we choose here the direction which corresponds to the motion of the light, then since at every reflection both the positive direction with respect to the motion of the light and the sign of the index of refraction are reversed, a positive sign of the reduced convergence implies that the rays in that case are convergent. A positive sign of the refracting power means that the system acts as a convergent system. The reduced distance from one point to another will always be positive provided in passing from the former to the latter the direction of the light is followed. Hence, we have the *following general rules*. That direction anywhere along the chief ray is always the positive direction which corresponds to the way the light goes in the object-space. The indices of refraction of the media which are traversed by the light after an odd number of reflections are to be reckoned as negative. The distance from one point to another is positive if we proceed from the first point to the second by going in the positive direction; and the radius of curvature is the distance measured from a point of the surface to the centre of curvature. Finally, the magnification-ratio is positive when, looking along the given chief ray in the positive direction, we see the lines imaged in each other lying on one and the same side of this ray.

The reduced convergence and refracting power may be measured in terms of any suitable unit. But in ophthalmology the *dioptry*[1] has become established as the unit of the refracting power of a lens; being defined as the refracting power of a lens surrounded by air whose focal length is one metre. Accordingly, it is advisable to adopt this unit generally, and therefore to define it as follows: *The dioptry is the unit of the reciprocal value of a length (the principal focal length or conjugate focal distance) divided by the corresponding index of refraction; the distance in question being expressed in terms of the metre as the unit of length.*[2]

The simple and convenient mode of exhibiting all the laws of imagery in the case of a system of revolution in a form that is applicable along any chief ray, which as a special case may coincide with the axis of revolution itself, was made possible by introducing the ideas of reduced convergence and refracting power. However, it can readily be seen that the general image-equations, in spite of their different form, are identical with equations (7) and (7d) as given in § 9 in the original text of this book; while equations (7b) and (7c) are easily recognizable also in the form used above. On the other hand, in the above discussion no special importance was attached to the equations referred to the nodal points. The reason of this was because, as already stated, so far as rays of finite slope are concerned, the essential characteristic of the nodal points has no reality except for the case of a single spherical surface. In accordance with the view that

[1] ¶Spelled also *dioptre* (French; also an English usage) and *diopter* (American). The origin of the word is the same as that of *dioptrics*. Essentially, the *dioptry* is simply a unit of curvature, that is, it is merely a geometrical magnitude. (J. P. C. S.)

[2] A. GULLSTRAND, Über die Bedeutung der Dioptrie. *Arch. f. Ophth.* Bd. XLIX, 1. S. 46. 1899. It should be noted that in this paper the coefficient k used for afocal systems denotes the reduced angular magnification-ratio.

the imagery of an object of finite dimensions might be considered as approximately similar to that of the central portion, the geometrical constructions may enable us to visualize the relations of the conjugate points to each other and to the cardinal points. But if we insist on sticking to what is actually the case, this method is no longer justifiable, because the laws on which the construction depends are not valid except for the fiction of rays which are inclined at infinitesimal angles, and therefore such constructions often create false notions. Neither the nodal points nor the principal ("unit") planes or principal focal planes, whose characteristic properties are likewise due to the fiction of rays inclined at infinitesimal angles, afford any advantage in showing what actually takes place, and so these ideas also have been cast aside here as so much useless ballast. The same is true in regard to the geometrical constructions alluded to, and even the diagrams (Figs. 114-116). employed above in obtaining the image-equations for the case of a single surface were intended merely to spare the reader the otherwise unavoidable differential calculus.

There is no fiction anywhere at all in the preceding treatment. It is always a question of precise geometrical magnitudes and, so far as the magnification is concerned, of coefficients and ratios expressly defined as limiting values. This is the distinction that must be made between the idea of reduced convergence and the ideas of the optical divergence of rays and the optical inclination of a ray,[1] which have no validity except for the fiction of rays inclined at infinitesimal angles.

The opposite way was pursued by ABBE and his school[2] in their treatment of the laws of optical imagery, for they proceeded to derive the theory of collinear imagery from simple geometrical assumptions without reference to the phenomena of refraction and reflection of light. But since we do not have collinear imagery except for the fiction of infinitely narrow bundles of rays and for an exceedingly small element of the surface of the object on the axis of a system of revolution, whereas new fictions have to be introduced along other chief rays, collinear imagery is found to be simply an unattainable ideal when once the general laws of imagery have been ascertained. If it is alleged that in many modern optical instruments the reality does not fall very far short of this ideal, the explanation is due to an accumulation of mathematical singularities in the construction. We must be on our guard against supposing that it is possible to attain this ideal exactly, and certainly we have no right at all to assume that it represents the kind of imagery that occurs in the case of the eye.

---

[1] H. v. HELMHOLTZ, *Handbuch der physiologischen Optik*, 2. Auflage, Hamburg and Leipzig 1896. S. 66, 71.

[2] S. CZAPSKI, *Grundzüge der Theorie der optischen Instrumente nach* ABBE. 2. Auflage, Leipzig 1904.

In *applying the imagery-laws* it must be kept steadily in view that all that they tell us is the positions of the focal points and the magnification-ratios along the chief ray under consideration. Therefore, in *investigating the image formed on a screen* the effects due to an arbitrary choice of the chief ray need to be specially considered. As part of the system of revolution, the surface of the screen itself must either be a transversal plane perpendicular to the axis, as is generally the case, or a surface of revolution around the same axis as that of the instrument; and, moreover, only such rays coming from points of the object as cross the axis can act as chief rays. In case the image-point corresponding to the axial object-point lies on the screen, the two image-surfaces will be tangent to the screen at that point. Along a chief ray going through the centre of the stop, which proceeds from a point of the object at a finite distance but not far from the axis, the bundle of rays will be astigmatic. But if the size of the stop is finite, and provided the ratio between the distance of the object-point from the axis and the diameter of the stop does not exceed a certain magnitude, the same bundle of rays will be anastigmatic along another ray going through the stop. The anastigmatic image-points arising in this way and corresponding to object-points which are not far from the axis lie on a surface which is tangent to the screen at its axial point. Practically, we never have to deal with the image of a mathematical point; and hence within a certain finite region surrounding the axial image-point, whose extent depends on the size of the stop, the image on the screen is practically indistinguishable from that which would be due to an actual point-to-point reproduction. Evidently, the extent of this region will be greater and greater in proportion as the curvatures of the two image-surfaces are more and more nearly alike and coincide more nearly with the curvature of the screen. Now when we investigate a bundle of rays proceeding from a point which is immediately adjacent to the part of the surface of the object that corresponds to this region, it appears that it cannot have an image-point on the screen unless it lies along a ray which meets the axis but passes eccentrically through the stop; and therefore only one of the two systems of imageable lines on the surface of the object will be reproduced in the corresponding zone of the screen. In case of a plane screen, generally it is the system of meridian lines that is reproduced in this zone by positive optical systems, because in an ordinary optical system of spherical surfaces the concave sides of the image-surfaces are generally turned towards the instrument, the primary image-surface being nearer the system than the secondary. But in the part of the screen beyond this zone there is no image-point along any ray at all, so that here the image is formed simply by optical projection.

In accordance with the process just described, it is easy to show, *e.g.* by using a simple photographic landscape lens, that in the central region of the ground-glass screen focused to get the sharpest image of the axial point of the object, all the points and lines of the object will be reproduced with equal sharpness; whereas in a surrounding zone lines of the object in a meridian plane show up better than others; and beyond this region the definition is about like that which can be obtained with a pinhole camera.

When we investigate in this way the image of a figure consisting of radiating (meridian) lines and parallel (concentric) circles, centered with respect to the axis and placed at right angles thereto, it appears that for a small stop the position of ·a circle in the image will vary with the position of the stop on the axis, and that if the object-circles are at equal distances apart, they will not be equally spaced in the image. This experiment proves that the magnification-ratio along the axis, which is independent of the position of the stop, does not generally give the magnification of the image, but simply the limiting value which it approaches more and more nearly as the size of the object is steadily diminished. Hence the image of the system of parallel circles is not similar to the object; whereas, by virtue of the characteristic properties of a system of revolution, the meridian lines do give an image that is similar to the object, even when the screen is moved out of focus, so that the entire image is formed by optical projection. As the size of the object is diminished, the lack of similarity in the image of the parallel circles becomes less and less, until it disappears entirely at the instant when the object collapses into a point on the axis. Owing to the degree of accuracy demanded by the investigation, it is always necessary to calculate trigonometrically a greater or less number of chief rays in order to ascertain where they cross the screen; and then the image-equations will enable us to find the focal points where the chief rays intersect the two image-surfaces. The values of the secondary magnification-ratios can usually be found directly from the position of the secondary focal point, because, owing to the similarity between object and image in case of the meridian lines, this ratio is equal to the ratio of the distance of the focal point from the axis to that of the object-point. But the values of the primary magnification-ratios have to be obtained from the image-equations. However, since the focal points generally will not lie on the screen, linear projection coefficients have to be employed to investigate the image. Now in a system of revolution not only the imageable lines and the corresponding image-lines but their orthogonal trajectories coincide with the meridian lines and parallel circles, so that these trajectories can be projected into each other also. Let us therefore distinguish here between the *primary linear projection coefficient* for projection of the meridian lines and the *secondary linear projection coefficient* for projection of the parallel circles. Just as in the case of the secondary magnification-ratio, the secondary linear projection coefficient may be defined as the ratio between the distances from the axis of the points where the given chief ray meets the screen and the surface of the object. But the primary linear projection coefficient is found as follows: Let δ' denote the reduced distance of the screen from the first focal point as measured along the chief ray; and let $\mathfrak{B}$ denote the reduced convergence of the bundle of chief rays at this point. Then the distance of an adjacent chief ray from the focal point is to its distance from the point where the first ray crosses the screen in the same ratio as the distances of the two points from the point of intersection of the two rays are to each other, *i.e.*, as $\dfrac{1}{\mathfrak{B}}\left(\dfrac{1}{\mathfrak{B}}-\delta'\right)$, and therefore $1-\delta'\mathfrak{B}$ is the linear projection coëfficient at the two points. Consequently, the *primary linear projection coefficient* for the corresponding object-point is

$$C_1 = K_1(1-\delta'\mathfrak{B});$$

and a similar formula defines the second of these coefficients. The application of this formula implies that the bundle of chief rays has been traced into the image-space, and that the ordinary image-equations have been employed for this purpose. The actual linear magnification in the projection depends on the inclinations of the surfaces of the object and screen to the chief ray. If w, w' denote the angles between the chief ray and the normals to these surfaces, the limiting value of this magnification is equal to $C_1 \dfrac{\cos w}{\cos w'}$. For the projection of parallel circles this limiting value is equal to the secondary linear projection coefficient.

The imagery-laws of the first order here treated apply also in general to singly asymmetrical systems. However, in such systems the magnification-ratios and the linear projection coefficients must be calculated in the same way as in case of the primary magnification-ratio and primary linear projection coefficient in a system of revolution. The plane of symmetry, which in a singly asymmetrical system is not a meridian plane at all, is called the *tangential plane*; and the plane perpendicular to it is called the *sagittal plane*. The formulae for the imagery along the axis in *symmetrical systems* may be found from the formulae for singly asymmetrical systems by putting the cosine of the

angles of incidence and refraction equal to unity throughout. In order
to distinguish the imageries in the two planes of symmetry, one of these
planes is called arbitrarily the primary plane and the other the secondary plane. In a system of revolution the equations obtained in this
way for the imagery along the axis are independent of the orientation
of the plane of symmetry.

Imagery-Laws of Higher Order. The imagery laws of *second order*
completely developed for singly asymmetrical systems lead to formulae
which, for example, in the case of systems of revolution, enable us to
ascertain the inclinations of the image-surfaces along a chief ray and
the asymmetry-value of the first magnification-ratio. The latter
magnitude tells how much this ratio varies from one chief ray to
another adjacent chief ray. Other formulae are expressions for the
asymmetry-values of the bundle of rays and afford information as to
degree of convergence of the rays. The general, doubly asymmetrical
bundle of rays is defined by four magnitudes of this kind; whereas the
singly asymmetrical bundle of rays which occurs in systems of revolution is characterized by two asymmetry values.

Proceeding from one ray to the next in the plane of symmetry of a
singly asymmetrical bundle of rays, we find that the primary focal
points (or image points) all lie on the section of the primary caustic
surface that envelops the rays. This section which may be called the
τ-curve is the line $\tau F' \tau$ in Fig. 117 where F', F'' designate the two
focal points lying on the ray $O F' F''$. The rays which proceed in the

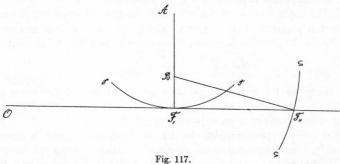

Fig. 117.

plane of the diagram are to be constructed therefore as tangents to
this curve, and hence the curved line which passes through O and
intersects all the rays orthogonally will be a section of the wave-surface
with respect to this point. If the secondary focal point is marked on

each ray, the locus of these points will be a curved line, the so-called
s-curve, indicated in the diagram as $sF_{,,}s$, which for a finite magnitude
of the astigmatic difference $F_,F_{,,}$ always cuts the ray at a finite angle.
The radius of curvature $AF_,$ of the τ-curve, denoted by R, is called the
direct asymmetry-value of the bundle along the ray $OF_,F_{,,}$. On the
other hand, if the normal is drawn to the s-curve at $F_{,,}$ meeting the
primary focal plane at B, the distance $BF_,$ of this point from the
primary focal point, denoted by S, is called the *transverse asymmetry-
value*. According to their definitions, the signs of the magnitudes R, S
depend on the choice of the positive direction. Therefore, in the case
represented in the figure, they are both positive provided the upward
direction is defined as positive. In a system of revolution it is a good
plan to consider the distance of an object-point from the axis always
as positive, and throughout the entire system to treat as positive the
direction of any line drawn in this same direction perpendicular to the
chief ray. The signs of the astigmatic difference (or distance between
the two focal points) and the angle θ which the δ-curve makes with the
secondary focal plane are defined by the equations

$$E = s - \tau, \qquad S = -E \tan \theta.$$

When the asymmetry-values have the same sign, the form of the
primary caustic surface at the focal point is saddle-shaped, because
the centre of curvature of the section made by the primary focal
plane is at the point where the line $AF_,$ meets the tangent drawn to
the s-curve at $F_{,,}$. Now since the curvature of this section is equal to
$-\dfrac{S}{E_2}$, it increases with increasing values of S so that the saddle-shape
becomes more and more tubular or gutter-shape.

If the angle u between the ray $OF_,F_{,,}$ and an adjacent ray is considered as positive when we reach this ray by starting at O and proceeding in the positive direction, we can write the following identities:

$$R = -\frac{d\tau}{du}, \qquad S = -\frac{ds}{du},$$

and therefore the asymmetry-values are the limits of the rates of
change of the focal distances measured from the wave-surface in
passing from one ray to an adjacent ray.

For a first approximation, the degree of ray-convergence is determined by the magnitudes of the asymmetry-values. When it is necessary to have more exact knowledge about this, these values can be
calculated along several rays; for along each ray there is a point on the
τ-curve where the two curvatures of the primary caustic surface can
be found, besides another point on the s-curve where the inclination of
this curve can be ascertained. The latter curve throughout is a

cuspidal edge, as is evident from the fact that the meridian plane is a plane of symmetry. Hence, the curve in which the secondary caustic surface is cut by the secondary principal plane has a cusp at the secondary focal point, where the two branches of the curve are tangent to each other and to the ray $OF,F,.$.

Picturing these relations as deviations or aberrations of the separate rays, we can say that in an astigmatic bundle of rays the distance of the point of intersection of a ray with the primary focal plane, belonging to the chief ray, from the corresponding primary focal line represents the primary lateral deviation of the ray. The secondary lateral deviation is defined similarly with respect to the secondary focal line. Thus, the *primary and secondary lateral deviations* are equal to

$$-\frac{u^2}{2}R - \frac{v^2}{2}S \quad \text{and} \quad -uvS,$$

respectively, where v denotes the angle which the ray makes with the meridian plane. However, these formulae are approximately correct only for infinitely small angles and give merely the deviations that depend on the second power of the angle of inclination. Consequently, they are inserted here not to be used, but simply in order to show the connection between the asymmetry-values that represent exact magnitudes and the ordinary conception of deviations.

Let us employ here the symbol s to denote the length of an arc of the curve made by the intersection of the meridian plane with the wave-surface, and at the same time also introduce the following other symbols, namely,

$$D, = \frac{1}{\tau}, \qquad D,, = \frac{1}{s}, \qquad \frac{dD,}{ds} = U, \qquad \frac{dD,,}{ds} = W;$$

then generally:

$$U = \frac{R}{\tau^3}, \qquad W = \frac{S}{\tau s^2}.$$

The magnitudes U, W, called the *direct and transverse curvature-asymmetries*, respectively, which accordingly are the rates of change of the principal curvatures of the surface from one point to a contiguous point, are not to be employed for the wave-surface but for the various refracting or reflecting surfaces of the system. If in Fig. 117 the straight line $OF,F,,$ is supposed to represent the normal to a refracting surface of a system of revolution, the s-curve would have to be a straight line coinciding with the axis, since in a surface of revolution the centre of curvature in the secondary principal section lies on the axis of revolution itself. Therefore for a surface of revolution, and for the bundle of chief rays of a system of revolution whose wave-surface is a surface of revolution, the magnitudes denoted by W and S are given by the formulae $W = -\dfrac{(\rho'' - \rho')\,\tan\theta}{\rho'\,\rho''^2}$ and $S = -(q-p)\tan\theta$, where θ denotes the angle between the normal to the surface or the chief ray of the bundle and a transversal plane perpendicular to the axis.

If the bundle of rays is anastigmatic along a certain ray, the two caustic surfaces are in contact with each other at the focal point. The radius of curvature of the τ-curve is the same as in the anastigmatic bundle of rays, and the curvature of the s-line is found from the transverse asymmetry-value by means of the expression

$$-\frac{R-2S}{S^2}.$$

In the case shown in Fig. 118 $(R-2S)$ has therefore the same sign as R. When the two asymmetry-values have the same sign, the focal points

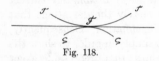

Fig. 118.

of a consecutive ray lie both on the same side of the focal plane at F, and the intersection of the two caustic surfaces with this focal plane is a curve which has a cusp at the focal point common to both surfaces. The tangents to the two branches of the curve which come together in the cusp make with each other the angle whose trigonometrical tangent is

$$\frac{2\sqrt{RS}}{R-S}.$$

Since in the cases that ordinarily occur the direct asymmetry-value exceeds the transverse value, this angle whose bisector lies in the plane of symmetry is an acute angle, and consequently the cross-section of the bundle of rays is a characteristic figure similar to an arrowhead.

If the calculation is carried a step further by another differentiation, the *imagery-laws of third order* are derived; which give, for example, formulae that enable us to find in a system of revolution the curvatures of the image-surfaces at the point of intersection with the axis, together with the distortion-value of the primary magnification-ratio and the coefficient of variation of the asymmetry-value. The latter is the differential coefficient of the asymmetry-value for a consecutive chief ray with respect to the distance of the object-point from the axis, supposing this distance to become gradually less and less; and accordingly the direct asymmetry-value is always three times the limit of the transverse asymmetry-value. Again, the distortion-value is the variation of the primary magnification-ratio depending on the second power of the angle of inclination, which is obtained by passing to a consecutive chief ray. Moreover, the *value of the aberration* along the axis is obtained.

The wave-surface corresponding to the axial object-point is evidently a surface of revolution; which must be true likewise concerning the primary caustic surface; whereas the secondary caustic surface is represented by a piece of the axis of revolution itself. Moreover, since the axis is a line of symmetry, the section of the primary caustic surface made by a meridian plane must have a cusp at the primary focal point where the axis is tangent to it, and where the radius of curvature must be zero, since the asymmetry-values vanish here. If the axis of revolution with which the s-line coincides here is represented by the straight line OF in Fig. 119, and if the curve AFB is the locus of the centres of curvature of points lying on the τ-curve (*i.e.*, if AFB is the evolute of the τ-curve), the so-called *aberration-value* denoted by A is equal to the radius of curvature of the curve AFB at the focal point F, and the lateral deviation depending on the third power of the angle of inclination of the ray is equal to $-\dfrac{u^3 A}{6}$. According to the convention as to the sign of the radius of curvature, a positive value of A, commonly spoken of as positive "spherical aberration," indicates that

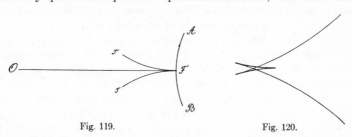

Fig. 119.   Fig. 120.

the cusp of the τ-curve points along the positive direction. When the "spherical aberration is corrected," the τ-curve has at least three cusps, and under certain circumstances even more; but, though it might be mathematically possible to make them all collapse into a single point, this cannot be practically achieved. A case of this sort is exhibited in Fig. 120, for which the aberration-value at the axial focal point is positive. Along the adjacent rays both the direct and transverse asymmetry-values are found to be positive, as is evident in the first case from the curvature of the τ-curve; and in the second case because, the primary caustic surface being a surface of revolution, the curvature of the section made by a plane perpendicular to the axis is negative.

Along the rays which are tangent to the τ-curve at the two symmetrical cusps the direct asymmetry-value is equal to zero. For rays of greater slope this function is negative, whereas the transverse asymmetry-value continues positive until it vanishes for the ray which is tangent to the τ-curve at the point on the axis where the two branches intersect. The lateral deviation continues negative so long as the slope of the ray has not attained the slope of the tangent to the τ-curve that passes through the axial focal point; thereafter for rays of greater slope it is positive. Accordingly, if aberration means the same thing as deviation of rays, we can speak of "corrected spherical aberration" only for a definite ray-slope. Since the rays with slope-angles smaller than this are in the same relation to each other as in case of "positive spherical aberration," the diagram Fig. 120 represents the case which in the phraseology of optical engineering is that of "corrected spherical aberration with positive zones" for the aperture corresponding to the critical slope-angle above mentioned.

These notions are not sufficient for the exactitude required in physiological optics. If the rays are drawn which are tangent to the τ-curve at the two cusps which point away from the focal point, a conical surface will be generated by revolving these lines around the axis, and a similar conical surface corresponds to it in the stop-space. The section of this surface made by a plane perpendicular to the· axis will be a curve $U = 0$ or $R = 0$, according as we have the wave-surface in mind or the corresponding bundle of refracted rays, respectively; while along every ray intersecting this curve the direct asymmetry-value in the image-space is equal to zero. The diameter of this curve, together with the diameter and position of the cuspidal edge of the caustic surface generated by the two cusps during the revolution may be readily calculated for a given system, and may be found experimentally for a system whose elements are not given. For example, all that is necessary in this case is to observe the curves of the caustic surface projected on a screen perpendicular to the axis while the screen is adjusted until the curves in question are no longer visible. In case the curve corresponding to the last cross section of the caustic surface does not coincide with the contour of the cross section of the bundle or rays, it represents the cuspidal edge mentioned above, and if the stop-opening is diminished until the contour and edge coincide, the diameter of the stop then will be the diameter of the curve $R = 0$. However, the degree of ray-convergence inside this curve depends on the distance of the edge from the focal point and varies inversely as this distance. Again, with respect to rays that intersect the plane of the stop outside this region, the curve $W = 0$ or $S = 0$ constructed in similar way controls this case. Along those rays crossing this curve

which meet the axis at the place in the image-space where the two
branches of the τ-curve come together, the refraction is anastigmatic;
and hence at this point there is complete ray-convergence of the first
order along an infinite number of rays. Finally, the lateral deviation
of the edge-ray affords a measure of what the writer calls the *total
peripheral aberration*. The necessity of keeping these ideas separate
and distinct can be readily seen from the fact that, in the typical case
of the "corrected spherical aberration" represented in Fig. 120, the
aberration-value is positive along the axis, whereas it is negative for
rays corresponding to the curve $R = 0$; while the total peripheral
aberration will be positive or negative according to the size of the stop.
The total peripheral aberration is considered positive when the edge-
rays behave as in ordinary positive aberration, *i.e.*, when the lateral
deviation is negative.

If an astigmatic bundle of rays has two planes of symmetry, it is
said to be a *symmetrical astigmatic bundle* along the ray corresponding
to the line of intersection of these planes; and is defined by four
aberration-values A_1, G_1, G_2, A_2; the *direct* and *transverse aberrations*
in the primary principal section being measured by A_1 and G_2, respectively; while A_2 and G_1 have similar meanings with respect to the
secondary principal section. If the intercepts on the line of symmetry
are denoted by s_1, s_2, and if the angles between this line and the
projections of a ray on the two principal sections are denoted by w_1,
w_2, then

$$A_1 = -\frac{d^2 s_1}{d w_1{}^2}, \quad G_1 = -\frac{d^2 s_1}{d w_2{}^2}, \quad G_2 = -\frac{d^2 s_2}{d w_1{}^2}, \quad A_2 = -\frac{d^2 s_2}{d w_2{}^2},$$

and there exists the general relation

$$G_1 - G_2 = s_2 - s_1 .$$

The primary and secondary surfaces have cuspidal edges which cut
orthogonally the primary and secondary principal sections, respectively. The direct aberration-values have the same geometrical
meaning with respect to the curved sections as in the case of a system
of revolution. The curvatures of the edges of the first and second
caustic surfaces are

$$-\frac{G_2}{(s_2 - s_1)^2} \quad \text{and} \quad -\frac{G_1}{(s_2 - s_1)^2} ,$$

respectively; and hence it follows that both edges cannot be straight
at the same time. Although it is mathematically possible for the
caustic surfaces of a bundle of rays to collapse into actual focal lines, it
appears therefore that a bundle of rays constructed on the type of

STURM's conoid is a mathematical impossibility. If the astigmatism

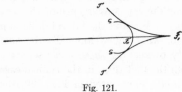

Fig. 121.

is sufficiently minute compared with the diameter of the stop and the amount of aberration, there will be two rays along which the astigmatism is abolished. The relation between the τ-curve and the s-curve in the principal section containing these rays is shown in Fig. 121. In the other principal section the τ-curve has a cusp at $F_{\cdot\cdot}$, and the curvature of the s-curve is finite at the point $F_{\cdot}$. If the astigmatism along the line of symmetry is continually diminished, the two anastigmatic focal points on the τ-curve approach nearer and nearer to the cusp, and the curvature of the s-curve gets greater and greater, and finally becomes infinite at the moment when these two points coincide with the two focal points into a single point. In the *symmetrical anastigmatic bundle of rays* thus obtained the s-curve therefore also has a cusp, and the radius of curvature of its evolute at the focal point is

$$\frac{4G^3}{(A-3G)^2}.$$

Of the various categories of these bundles of rays, that one for which all the aberration-values have the same sign, and in which the transverse aberration is numerically less than the direct aberration in both principal sections, is of special importance in physiological optics. Under these circumstances both caustic surfaces lie on the same side of the focal plane. The primary surface whose sections made by the principal sections constitute the τ-curve has no edges, and its section made by a plane parallel to the focal plane is a closed curve at finite distance from the focal point which has finite curvature everywhere; whereas the secondary surface always has two edges corresponding to the s-curve which meet in the focal point, and may have also two other edges besides. The latter is what happens in case the differences A_1-3G and A_2-3G have the same sign. (In the anastigmatic bundle of rays, as results from the relation given above, the two transverse aberration-values coincide.)

The greater the difference A_1-A_2, called the *astigmatism of the aberration*, the more pronounced becomes the phenomenon of astigmatism, varying in degree with the size of the stop, since the position of the cross section of the bundle that is most suitable for the imagery depends on the size of the stop and the direct aberration. But in proportion as the astigmatism of the aberration is less prominent, the better is the determination of the kind of ray-convergence by means of the difference $A_1 + A_2 - 6G$, which is a measure of the *diagonal astigmatism of the aberration*. The four edges that we have here on the secondary caustic surface, and that go through the cusps, necessitate eight cusps in a section of this surface parallel to the focal plane, arranged in one of the two typical forms shown in Fig. 122; which, particularly in the second type, involve similar indentations in the section of the bundle of rays. When $A_1 = A_2 = 3G$, the wave-surface has perfect contact of fourth order with a surface of revolution or may be itself a surface of this description. In the latter case the secondary caustic surface collapses on the axis of revolua surface of this description. In the latter case the secondary caustic surface collapses on the axis of revolution; whereas in the other case it involves a greater number of edges depending on the aberration-values of higher order arranged according to the same scheme and a greater number of similar indentations of the cross section of the bundle of rays.

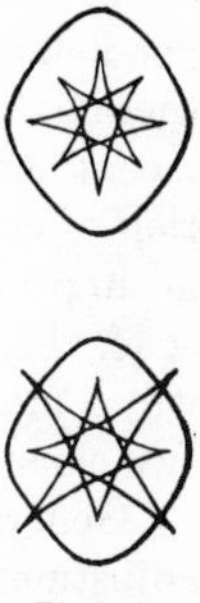

Fig 122.

Corresponding to the aberration-values are the four *coefficients of flattening* ("Abflachungswerte") on the wave-surface denoted by Φ_1, Ω_1, Ω_2, Φ_2, of which Φ_1, Ω_2 are the measures of the *direct and transverse flattening* in the primary and secondary principal sections, respectively, while Φ_2, Ω_1 have the same meanings for the secondary principal section. The connections between these magnitudes and the principal curvatures D_1, D_2 are exhibited in the following equations:

$$A_1 = \frac{\Phi_1}{D_1^4}, \quad G_1 = \frac{\Omega_1}{D_1^2 D_2^2}, \quad G_2 = \frac{\Omega_2}{D_1^2 D_2^2}, \quad A_2 = \frac{\Phi_2}{D_2^4}, \quad \Omega_1 - \Omega_2 = D_1 D_2 (D_1 - D_2) ;$$

and moreover

$$\Phi_1 = \frac{d^2 D_1}{ds_1^2}, \quad \Omega_1 = \frac{d^2 D_1}{ds_2^2}, \quad \Omega_2 = \frac{d^2 D_2}{ds_1^2}, \quad \Phi_2 = \frac{d^2 D_2}{ds_2^2} ;$$

where s_1, s_2 denote the lengths of arcs of the primary and secondary principal sections of the surface, respectively.

However, the coefficients of flattening have to be used merely for characterizing the refracting surfaces of a system, whereas the bundles of rays are defined by means of the aberration-values. Hence, in a system of revolution the coefficient of flattening Φ at the vertex of each surface must be known in order to calculate the aberration along the axis.

In cases where a caustic surface has multiple curves of intersection with a screen, a multiple imagery of the corresponding system of lines is produced, as follows from the general imagery-laws. Particularly easy to produce is a double imagery of lines in the symmetrically astigmatic bundle of rays with large aberration-values; because for certain positions of the screen there are two parallel sections of the caustic surface in the plane of the screen, which are not curved too much. But even in systems of revolutions where the caustic surface of the axial bundle makes a circular section with a plane screen perpendicular to the axis, a double imagery of a short line intersecting the axis may be obtained, since the section corresponding to an adjacent chief ray has approximately the same form; and on the supposition of circles corresponding to the different points of the object-line, an impression is produced of two parallel lines, with an intervening space, however, which is brighter than the surroundings. In the same way a multiple imagery may be the result of the edges occurring in the two caustic surfaces of a symmetrically anastigmatic bundle of rays.

Generally, therefore, different imageries correspond to different adjustments of the screen; and what position of the screen is best will depend on the accidental nature of the object to be reproduced and the requirements as to definition or distinctness of the image. For the axial point of the image in a system of revolution, the narrowest cross section of the bundle of rays, as derived from the aberration-value and the size of the stop, at all events does not possess the importance formerly ascribed to it. In general it can be said that the greater the requirement as to reproduction of minute detail, the nearer the screen must be adjusted to the cusp of the caustic surface. The mistiness due to blur-circles which increases with the distance of the screen from the place of the narrowest cross section determines therefore the limit of efficiency of the optical system; that is, according to the degree of ray-convergence.

In the above description[1] of the most important phenomena of *the monochromatic aberrations* entirely in terms of mathematically exact magnitudes there was no room for the proofs; for these the reader must be referred to the writer's works already mentioned. The bridge between this theory and the current method of representing the aberration in a system of revolution has been indicated above. The deviations depending on the asymmetry-value are found usually in books on geometrical optics under the name *coma*, but these phenomena for chief rays of finite slope have hitherto not been correctly treated in such works.

---

[1] See a somewhat more detailed description as follows: Die Konstitution des im Auge gebrochenen Strahlenbundels, *Arch. f. Ophthalmologie.* Bd. LIII, 2. 1901. S. 185.

II.   Procedure of the Rays in the Eye

Imagery-Laws of First Order

1. The Cornea

Anterior Surface of Cornea. During the time that has passed since the first ophthalmometer was made by HELMHOLTZ, there have been great advances and essential improvements in the ophthalmometry of the anterior surface of the cornea. This physiological method of research has been a blessing to practical ophthalmology and to mankind. Every busy oculist uses it daily at the present time. However, convenient as this method is nowadays, the results obtained by it are not due to the improvements. The credit for the method was, and still is, due to HELMHOLTZ; although to others, and mainly to JAVAL and SCHJÖTZ, belongs the credit of bringing the method into ordinary ophthalmological practice. As might be supposed, the necessary adaptations of the method to such uses involved sacrifices in some directions, and even today the scientific investigator finds it advantageous to return to HELMHOLTZ's original construction for the more precise measurements.

The principle of the ophthalmometer is essentially the same as that of the astronomical instrument known as a heliometer. Its plan is to measure a mobile object by shifting the reading or collimation to the object itself. This is effected by bringing in contact two optical images of the object, which involves a "doubling" or duplex mechanism and a collimation device. These mechanisms are both united in the adjustable plane-parallel glass plates in HELMHOLTZ's ophthalmometer. The disadvantage of this construction is noticeable only in two directions. The necessary readjustments and repeated readings, together with the calculations or interpolations in case a numerical table is employed, take a troublesome amount of time; and the arrangements for investigating other normal sections besides the horizontal are too clumsy or inconvenient for the instrument to come into general extensive use. Suggestions of changes in the construction were soon forthcoming. COCCIUS[1] made the calculations and repeated readings unnecessary by using a constant "doubling" device, consisting partly of the glass plates and partly

[1] A. COCCIUS, *Über den Mechanismus der Akkommodation des menschlichen Auges.* Leipzig 1867. *Ophthalmometrie und Spannungsmessung am kranken Auge.* Leipzig 1872.

of a double-refracting calcspar prism, and produced the collimation
by varying the size of the object. When HELMHOLTZ's plates are used,
it is equivalent to dividing the objective in two parts, and hence also
the exit-pupil of the telescope is divided in the same way; but with the
double-refracting prism the exit-pupil of the instrument is undivided,
and the two double images can be viewed through every point of the
exit-pupil. (The exit-pupil is the image of the object-glass in the
ocular, which can be seen as a bright disc by pointing the telescope
to the sky, and looking along the axis from a point in front of the
ocular at the distance of distinct vision.)

Of these two methods of "doubling," namely, with exit-pupil
divided and undivided, the former has this disadvantage, that, in
case the focusing is not perfectly sharp, there is an apparent displacement of the double images with respect to each other in a direction
perpendicular to the line of separation. If, as in HELMHOLTZ's instrument, the line of separation is in the plane of "doubling," although
it is true the accuracy of the measurement will not be affected, still
a difference of height or level may be erroneously inferred; which will
be mentioned again farther on. On the other hand, all the existing
constructions with undivided exit-pupil have the disadvantage of
chromatic dispersion, which is absent in the case of the plane parallel
plates.

For measuring the curvature of the cornea in different normal
sections, MIDDELBURG[1] used a large ring on which the lights could
be oriented in various meridians; whereas WOINOW[2] and HELM-
HOLTZ[3] employed a mirror-arrangement which made it possible to
have a stationary source of light. None of these devices was well
adapted for obtaining collimation by variation of the size of the object.
But the numerous readings that had to be made with the ophthalmometer and the laborious calculations were avoided by LANDOLT[4] in an
instrument called at first a diplometer, in which the glass plates
were replaced by prisms, and the collimation was produced by displacing the prisms along the axis of the instrument.

Originally, flames were used for the object in ophthalmometric
measurements. But just as soon as these were replaced by the diffused
light reflected from white surfaces, the very modifications could be
introduced that made possible the beneficient use of ophthalmometry

[1] Der Sitz des Astigmatismus (nach MIDDELBURG). A letter from F. C. DONDERS to
A. v. GRAEFE. *Arch. f. Ophth.* X, 2. 1864. S. 83.

[2] M. WOINOW, *Ophthalmometrie.* Wien 1871.

[3] H. v. HELMHOLTZ, *Handbuch der Physiologischen Optik.* 2. Aufl. Hamburg and
Leipzig 1896.

[4] E. LANDOLT, L'ophthalmomètre, *Compte rendu et mémoires du congrès international de
Genève.* 1878.

in clinical practice. JAVAL and SCHJÖTZ[1] used for the object a pair
of diffusely illuminated white areas, which could be displaced on a
circular arc with its centre in the eye of the patient. The arc could
be rotated around the axis of the instrument. With this apparatus
the investigation of any normal section was just as easy as that of the
horizontal meridian. The collimation was easily made by adjusting
the relative positions of the white areas. The advantages of constant
"doubling" without dividing the exit-pupil were completely realized
by using a WOLLASTON prism. And various details of practical construction were contrived to facilitate the manipulation of the instrument.

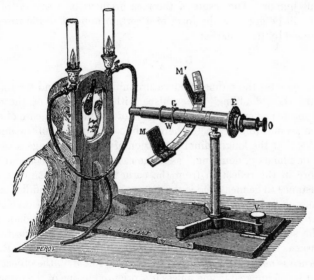

Fig. 123.

The original model of the ophthalmometer of JAVAL and SCHJÖTZ
had the external appearance shown in Fig. 123. A notch at *E* and a
pin at *G* serve as sights for adjusting the instrument. The WOLLASTON
prism is inserted at *W* between two convex lenses, one of which makes
the light parallel that comes from the reflex image in the cornea,
while the other acts as object-glass of an astronomical telescope.
The two white areas or *"mires"* are shown at *M* and *M′*. Their actual
appearance is illustrated in Fig. 124 in which the distance indicated

[1] JAVAL et SCHJÖTZ, Un ophthalmomètre pratique. *Transactions of the international
medical Congress*. VIII. Session. London 1881. III. p. 30. *Annales d'oculistique*. LXXXVI.
1881. p. 5.

by D represents the size of the object, the collimation being made with reference to the lines ab and cd. The steps or graduations on one

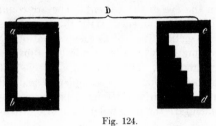

Fig. 124.

of the white areas are calculated so that when the images overlap, each step corresponds to one dioptry of cornea-refraction, supposing there were no difference between the index of refraction of the cornea and that of the aqueous humor. The result of the measurement of a section of the cornea will be given in the form of a certain number of dioptries D, determined by the equation

$$D = \frac{1000}{\rho}(n-1)$$

where ρ denotes the radius of curvature in millimetres and $n = 1.3375$.

Since the "doubling" takes place without division of the exit-pupil, and hence apparent displacements of the images in case of such division are not to be expected here, a difference of level of the images indicates that the longitudinal dimension of the reflex image does not lie in the plane of "doubling," as is the case with the object, and that therefore in the reflection from the cornea a rotation has occurred. The distance to be measured is the distance between the middles of the two lines ab and cd in Fig. 124. If the cornea is a surface of revolution around the axis of the instrument, this line will be a meridian line, and the same thing is true with respect to its image as reflected in the cornea, and hence there cannot be a difference of level. But if the cornea is astigmatic, with two planes of symmetry, the object-line will not be an imageable line unless it is oriented in one of the principal sections of the cornea; so that the image-line lies also in the same principal section, and a difference of level is again excluded. But if the object-line is between the two principal sections, the reflected image is formed by optical projection. The best way to understand what takes place here is to draw from the two ends of the object-line two lines perpendicular to the principal sections of the cornea, which will make a rectangle whose diagonal is the object-line itself, and whose sides are imageable lines. The two dimensions of this rectangle in the image reflected in the cornea are determined by the two magnification-ratios that are approximately inversely proportional to the refracting powers of the principal sections of the cornea; so that the reflected image is a rectangle whose sides are indeed oriented correctly but are of different lengths relative to each other; which means that the diagonal of this rectangle is not in the same plane as that of the object. Consequently, its extremities which are to be collimated in the measurement cannot both be brought at the same time in the plane of "doubling," and hence there is a difference of level. The mathematical meaning of this proof is, that in optical projection the inclination to a principal section of a line which does not lie therein is varied when the coefficients of projection for lines which are in the two principal sections have different values; and that when the distance apart of image-lines corresponding to the two imageries is neglected, these coefficients are the same as the magnification-ratios. The proof is strictly valid only for a very small object-line. The exact proof for the size that is employed cannot be given without taking account of the laws of optical projection of higher order. When there is considerable asymmetry in the structure of the cornea, the relations that exist are quite a complicated problem; but if there is a plane of symmetry, it is certain that the difference of level will not vanish except for this plane and the one perpendicular to it, provided the axis of the instrument is in the plane of symmetry.

Easy location of the principal sections, as shown in the regular cases by absence of difference of level, convenient collimation mechanism, and direct reading of the result,—these are the principal advantages of the ophthalmometer of JAVAL and SCHJÖTZ, which, along with the handy form of the entire instrument, have resulted in the employment of the methods of ophthalmometry in ophthalmological practice.

However, these modifications of HELMHOLTZ's original construction are not without disadvantages. The amount of doubling is nearly 3 mm. On the supposition that the investigation is made in a plane of symmetry, this is a measure that depends on the angle between a pair of normals in this plane drawn to the surface of the cornea at points which are about 3 mm apart, a measure that does not give the radius of curvature exactly. Moreover, this measure is not perfectly precise except for a definite value, namely, 45 dioptries, because this is the value for which the instrument is calibrated; but the arc itself is graduated by calculations based on the laws of imagery of the first order that are not entirely permissible for the size of object that is used. Thus errors are introduced depending on the construction, and they are very difficult to eliminate. It is true these errors are not sufficiently great to affect the value of the instrument as it is used in the practice of ophthalmology, but for certain finer physiological researches they limit always the applicability of the results obtained by measurement. Besides, there are other possible errors due to focusing and collimating. With respect to the former, the distance for which the graduations on the scale are calculated can be obtained only by sharp focusing on the cross-hairs; nor does the "doubling," which is the basis of the calculation, correspond to the real "doubling" unless the focusing is sharp. These errors due to faulty focusing are cumulative. For instance, if the image formed by the object-glass is between it and the cross-hairs, so that the instrument is therefore too far away from the patient's eye, supposing that the "doubling" remains invariable, the object will have to be made larger to give a reflected image of unchanged size. The collimation occurs at a point on the axis. Now if the path of the light is traced backwards from this point, the chief ray lies along the axis at first until it comes to the cemented surface of the WOLLASTON prism where it is split in two rays. The two chief rays which meet the image reflected in the cornea in the two points that are to be collimated diverge, therefore, from the apparent place of this point, and the "doubling" increases with the distance of the instrument from the patient's eye; so that the object must be made greater still than if the "doubling" did not depend on the distance. In order to avoid these errors as much as possible, a very sharp focusing on the cross-hairs is necessary, and if the measurements are to be very precise, it will be well always not to forget HELMHOLTZ's advice[1], to regulate the focusing by parallax displacements of the eye of the observer— which means however that the aperture of the ocular must be sufficiently large.

With regard to the collimation error, the effect of the chromatic dispersion of the prism tends to make it worse, because the edges to be collimated have coloured borders whose appearance is affected by the intensity and composition of the illumination that is used. Modern instruments have transparent *mires* and incandescent electric lights, whereby bright reflected images are obtained without very disturbing coloured borders; as this light is relatively poor in rays of short wavelength, so that the spectrum appears shorter also. This disadvantage can be still further reduced by using coloured glasses. Another thing that influences the amount of the collimation errors is the form of the figure to be collimated, which has undergone numerous modifications since the first model of the instrument. The first improvement was with respect to the collimation for adjusting the level of the images, and consisted in providing the white *mires* with a black line lying in the plane of the "doubling." This serves the purpose in a very satisfactory way, since the line appears continuous without any break in it when

[1] As given by JAVAL, Contribution à l'ophthalmométrie. *Annales d'oculistique.* LXXXVII. 1882. p. 213.

the two images are exactly in level, and since the eye has a remarkable power of detecting a very small displacement of the two parts of this line with respect to each other. On the whole, a similar contrivance is best also for the collimation in making the measurements. The purpose of the steps on the *mire* is to have a convenient way of reading the amount of astigmatism. The best way to do this is to make the adjustment for the first principal section by using a certain one of the *mires* always for this purpose, and then in the other principal section to collimate by displacing the other *mire*. Therefore, at the beginning of the measurement the latter one must always be brought to the zero-point of the scale corresponding to symmetrical adjustment of the *mires* for correct collimation and for the average value of the curvature of the cornea. When the investigation is finished, the curvature in the first principal section is read off by the position of the first *mire*, and the degree and sign of the corneal astigmatism by the position of the second *mire*. On a scale where an interval of 1° corresponds to a dioptry, the zero-point, for example, can be taken on the left-hand part of the arc at 22° from the axis, and a scale can be added reading to 10° in both directions. Then the point on the right-hand part of the arc which is symmetrical to the zero-point will be marked by the number 44. With such an arrangement of the scale the steps on the *mires* are superfluous, and therefore the forms of the figures to be collimated can be constructed solely with a view to the sharpest collimation.

It almost goes without saying that the errors of measurement with modern ophthalmometers, even in the case of long practice and highest skill on the part of the observer, are not to be lightly estimated. The collimation error, indeed, with the instruments now in use, ought not to be more than 1/4 dioptry, and may be rather less when the figures to be collimated are advantageously constructed. But the focusing error, which depends in great measure on the skill of the observer and the repose of the patient, will not be certainly below this value except under the most favourable circumstances; so that as a usual thing the possible error may be estimated at between 1/4 and 1/2 dioptry. While these errors are comparatively unimportant for purposes of ordinary practice, they cannot be left out of account in the more precise measurements of corneal astigmatism or in the measurements of the radius at several points in one and the same principal section.

In case of the measurement just mentioned the large "doubling" comes also into consideration. When we try to get rid of this disadvantage by using a prism with half the "doubling," the collimation errors will be doubled.

In addition to the ophthalmometer of JAVAL and SCHJÖTZ, which was modified in some ways in the new model of 1889[1], a few other types will be briefly mentioned here. The instrument-maker KAGE-NAAR of Utrecht employed a biprism construction instead of the WOLLASTON prism; and consequently his ophthalmometer has a divided exit-pupil, the line of separation being vertical and lying in the "doubling" plane. The result is there are no difficulties about levelling the reflex images, but the apparent displacements that are possible with divided exit-pupil have an effect on the final result, which therefore is subject here to an additional source of error. On the other hand, while the HELMHOLTZ plates are retained in the ophthalmometer of LEROY and DUBOIS,[2] the "doubling" in this instrument is constant; and thus *ceteris paribus* the focusing error is reduced, although, otherwise, the difficulty as to contact-adjustment of the two images mentioned above militates against the practical use of the instrument. The most perfect construction from a theoretical standpoint is represented by the SUTCLIFFE ophthalmometer.[3] The exit-pupil is divided here too—indeed divided into five parts—but the apparent displacements thus produced are ingeniously utilized as a check on the sharpness of the focusing. Two mutually perpendicular normal sections are measured simultaneously, as the observer sees three images. In investigating the vertical and horizontal meridians the central part of the exit-pupil produces one image; a second image is due to the upper and lower parts; whereas the third image is formed in the same way by the right and left parts. The apparent displacements that occur in case of error in focusing are accompanied by a "doubling" of the two images last mentioned, which will not disappear until the focusing is right. The "doubling" in the two mutually perpendicular meridian planes of the instrument is variable, the object itself being fixed and having a form very favourable for exact collimation. Thus, while errors of both focusing and collimation appear to be reduced to a minimum, perhaps the greatest advantage of all is to be found in the fact that here the correct collimation in both principal sections is checked by a glance. The measurement of corneal astigmatism as thus obtained is far more reliable, inasmuch as the ordinary method of determination may involve a summation of the errors of two successive focusings, and consequently a bigger error may be made in comparison with the degree of the

[1] SULZER, Description de l'ophthalmomètre JAVAL et SCHJÖTZ. Modèle 1889 in *Mémoires d'ophthalmométrie* par E. JAVAL. Paris 1890.

[2] C. J. A. LEROY et R. DUBOIS, Un nouvel ophthalmomètre pratique. *Annales d'oculistique*. XCIX. 1888. p. 123.

[3] J. H. SUTCLIFFE, One-position ophthalmometry. *The optician and photographic trades review*. XXXIII. 1907. Supplement p. 8.

physiological corneal astigmatism; whereas in this new method such is not the case. Practical experience with this instrument in the Upsala clinic has completely demonstrated its superiority for investigating corneal astigmatism.

However, the great advantage of finding the astigmatism by a single measurement may be obtained also with the ordinary ophthalmometer, because, as the writer has pointed out,[1] this can be ascertained from the contact-difference (*Denivellation*) in a plane making an angle of 45° with the principal sections. For this purpose all that is needed is to make one of the white *mires* in the ordinary ophthalmometer adjustable in a plane at right angles to the plane of "doubling" and to add a corresponding scale. The scale interval corresponding to one dioptry must be half as great as that of the scale in the plane of the collimation-figure which is calibrated for measurement of the radii.

These methods enable us to find simultaneously the radii that are to be compared with each other. The only way to do this, when the problem consists in ascertaining the radii at different points in one and the same principal section, is by photographing the reflex image in the cornea. Such measurements, it must be admitted, take much time and require also special apparatus made for the purpose. Consequently, they are not suitable for the general run of practice, but on the other hand they give a resultant accuracy that previously could not be obtained in any other way. In this method the writer[2] used an object which gave the radius at seven points in one and the same principal section at the same time. The corresponding parts of the object were computed so that their reflex images in a spherical surface all had the same size, for example, about 2/3 mm for a radius of 7.8 mm.

After this concise description of the means that are employed nowadays of investigating in numerous ways the form of the anterior surface of the cornea, let us pass on to a summary of the results. HELMHOLTZ was perfectly justified by the knowledge of geometrical optics in his day in regarding the form of the non-astigmatic cornea as elliptical, because the dioptric behaviour of an ellipsoid was known, but the asymmetry values that are characteristic of the dioptric behaviour of any surface whatever were not known. Accordingly, as soon as the asymmetry of the cornea with respect to the visual axis had been established, there was nothing better to do than to

---

[1] A. GULLSTRAND, En praktisk metod att bestämma hornhinnans astigmatism genom den s. k. denivelleringen af de oftalmometriska bilderna. *Nordisk Oftalmologisk Tidskrift.* 1889.

[2] Photographisch-ophthalmometrische und klinische Untersuchungen über die Hornhautrefraktion. *Kungl. Sv. Vet. Akad. Handl.* 1896. Bd. 28.

calculate by means of it the constants of the ellipsoid in question. HELMHOLTZ's own statement,[1] that the "representation of the form of the cornea by an ellipsoid is for the time being a fairly close approximation," is still true today, although subsequent investigations have shown that a different view gives a better approximation.

BLIX,[2] by an entirely peculiar ophthalmometric method of his own, whose greatest advantage, however, lies in the determination of the situations of the ocular refracting surfaces, and which therefore will not be described until later, was the first to demonstrate that the form of the cornea is considerably different from that of an ellipsoid. As was pointed out by AUBERT[3] at the time, these differences may be most simply expressed by saying that in a central "optical zone" the variations of curvature are less, whereas in the rest of the cornea they are greater, than they would have to be if the curvature were elliptical. The curvature of the optical zone, which corresponds roughly to the diameter of a pupil of medium size, is approximately spherical, or at any rate the accuracy that is attainable in ophthalmometric measurements is not high enough to enable us to compute the constants of an ellipsoid that might represent its variation from a spherical form. The form of the cornea has been better ascertained from the researches of SULZER[4] and ERIKSEN,[5] who have supplied us with a considerable mass of data to show that the flattening of the cornea out toward the periphery not only is frequently asymmetrical both horizontally and vertically, but is also in most instances more rapid in the latter meridian than in the former. On the other hand, SULZER's conclusions from this last fact concerning the variation of the astigmatism of the eye with the size of the pupil are due to the erroneous idea that there could be any such thing as astigmatism of an annular zone of the cornea, which is mathematically impossible. And ERIKSEN's views about the astigmatism at various places in the cornea are simply mathematical consequences of the flattening out toward the periphery.

Qualitatively, these researches of SULZER and ERIKSEN are convincing, because the results given above follow from a comparison of the flattening in different directions. But, quantitatively, they are

[1] *Handbuch d. phys. Opt.* 2. Auflage. S. 17.

[2] M. BLIX, Oftalmometriska studier. *Upsala Läkareförenings Förhandlingar.* XV. 1880. S. 349.

[3] H. AUBERT, Nähert sich die Hornhautkrümmung am meisten der einer Ellipse? PFLÜGERS *Arch. f. d. ges. Physiologie.* XXXV. 1885. Die Genauigkeit der Ophthalmometermessungen. Ibid. XLIX. 1891.

[4] La forme de la cornée humaine et son influence sur la vision. *Arch. d'Ophth.* XI. 1891. p. 419. XII. 1892. p. 32.

[5] *Hornhindemaalinger.* Aarhus 1893.

not satisfactory to the same degree, because measurements with an ophthalmometer merely give the angle between two elements of the cornea separated by an interval depending on the amount of "doubling" in the instrument, whereas the measurements were made for smaller angular steps. With the ophthalmometer of JAVAL and SCHJÖTZ the angle measured in case of normal corneal curvature, with the "doubling" usually employed, is more than 20°. If the measurements are repeated at intervals of 5° in the direction of fixation, the reflex image of one of the *mires* in the next four measurements is still inside the part of the surface measured first, and the assumption that these five measurements have given the curvature at five different places is therefore not justifiable. This comment, however, is less applicable to ERIKSEN's researches, because in his work the amount of "doubling" was only 1 mm. The mathematical utilization of the form of the cornea as thus found for investigating the refraction of the rays depends, however, on the assumption that in each successive measurement one end of the object is reflected from the same place on the cornea as the opposite end in the preceding measurement. This requirement, together with the use of sufficiently small surface-elements in the measurements, has heretofore not been fulfilled except in the photographic methods of the writer.

The disc shown in Fig. 125 was employed as object, which was made in such manner that the intervals between one circle and the next were proportional to the radii of the corresponding surface-elements. It was photographed for five different lines of fixation, namely, when the eye was directed right toward the objective, and when the line of fixation was turned into the four principal directions, such that the most peripheral surface-element measured in the central adjustment coincided precisely with the most

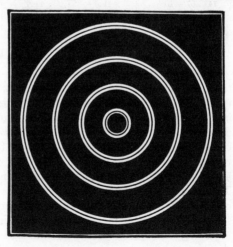

Fig. 125.

central element measured in the peripheral adjustment. The photograph was measured on a dividing engine with a microscope, the readings being corrected by the periodic errors of the screw, as carefully ascertained. The precision of the measurements, checked by numerous trials, was obtained by dividing the rings in two parts as shown in the figure, since the cross-hairs could be sharply set on the bright space in the photographic negative without difficulty. The angles between the normals to the cornea at the different places used for reflection and the normals parallel to the visual axis were known from the construction of the apparatus; and the corresponding radius was found by measurement, since it was considered as belonging to that point where the normal made equal angles with the normals at the two extreme points of the element to be measured. As result of these investigations, the writer obtained the complete measurement and calculation of a typical normal cornea, some data of which are herewith subjoined.

Angle corresponding to the normal at the centre of the measured element	VERTICAL		HORIZONTAL	
	Upwards	Downwards	Inwards	Outwards
38° 55′ 30″	. . . .	28.5	27.9	32.3
34° 3′ 50″	41.7	36.6	28.4	38.8
29° 14′ 20″	35.2	40.2	37.4	41.2
24° 24′ 50″	37.7	41.2	40.9	43.6
19° 33′ 10″	39.8	42.2	42.5	43.5
14° 37′ 10″	41.7	43.4	42.8	44.0
9° 41′ 10″	42.8	43.8	43.5	43.8
4° 49′ 30″	43.3	43.6	43.8	43.4
0° 0′ 0″	44.5		44.2	

The radii of curvature here are calculated in dioptries by assuming the value 1.3375 for the index of refraction, as is usual in ophthalmometry. A graphical representation of the results of this table is given in Fig. 126 after the method used by ERIKSEN; which shows very distinctly the comparatively slight variation of the radius of the cornea in the central portions and the rapid flattening in the peripheral regions, together with the asymmetry both vertically and horizontally and the flattening that begins nearer the centre in the vertical section. The irregularities of the curves are due to the unavoidable errors of observation, irrespective of the method, and dependent on the fact that, as a matter of fact, the first refracting surface of the dioptric system of the eye is not the anterior surface of the cornea but the fluid layer resting on it which is responsible for the reflex images employed in the ophthalmometric investigation. In the photographic method, doubtless, it would not be difficult to smooth out these irregularities by exact mathematical methods, since seven measurements are always taken at once, and by virtue of the construction of the disc the various errors cannot amount to anything more than

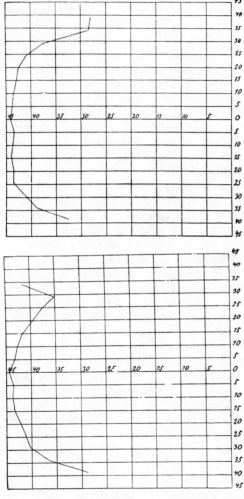

Fig. 126.

that one of the radii of two adjacent elements comes out just as much too large as the other is too small. But this mathematical labour would scarcely be worth while, for, although the curvature asymmetry of the cornea at the point of incidence of the effective chief ray in the ocular imagery might thus be determined, this value would be of little further use until we knew more than we do at present about the form of the lenticular surfaces.

We must not omit to mention here that MATTHIESSEN[1] endeavoured to compare the curvature of the horizontal section as obtained above with that of an ellipse. The writer had assembled in a table the coördinates of all the points of the cornea employed in the reflection, and from these coördinates MATTHIESSEN computed the tangential ellipses. Now if the curvature were elliptical, the ellipses thus obtained ought to have coincided approximately with one another. But the semi-axes majores of these ellipses vary from 14.46 to 8.62, although the first measurement on the nasal side and the two first on the temporal side were left out of account—and hence the central part of the optical zone was not considered. In the writer's opinion therefore the agreement is not satisfactory, but at the same time he can endorse MATTHIESSEN's conclusion, that from the rest of the 15 coordinates there is a basis for making an ellipse in the horizontal section of the cornea which agrees fairly well with the average values of the measurements of other workers. All that can be concluded from this is, that, in vision with a pupil of medium size, the assumption of a spherical shape for the utilized part of the cornea is provisionally the best approximation; and in cases where the excentric parts of the cornea are predominantly effective (as in certain investigations of the lens constants) the ellipse may continue to be considered as a better approximation than any similar hypothesis.

Moreover, the curves exhibited in Fig. 126 represent the qualitative results obtained by SULZER and ERIKSEN most faithfully, as might have been expected from the fact that these diagrams are derived from a typically normal cornea, while the researches of those writers relate to a large number of eyes. Another thing in common is that the starting point corresponds to the line of fixation of the patient when he looks right into the objective of the instrument. The point designated by zero in the preceding table is therefore the point of the cornea for which the normal is parallel to the line of sight (_Visierlinie_); and since this is always the origin in modern clinical ophthalmometry, it may be called the _ophthalmometric axial point_.

Starting from this point, the _form of the normal cornea_ can be described by saying that there is a central optical zone where the curvature is approximately spherical, and which extends horizontally about 4 mm, and somewhat less than this vertically, and is decentrated

[1] L. MATTHIESSEN, Über aplanatischen Brechung und Spiegelung in Oberflächen zweiter Ordnung und die Hornhautrefraktion. PFLÜGERS _Arch. f. d. ges. Physiologie._ XCI. 1902. S. 295.

outwards and usually also a little downwards; and that the peripheral parts are considerably flattened, decidedly more so on the nasal side than on the temporal, and usually more so upwards than downwards.

Out from the ophthalmometric axial point the pupil also is decentrated outwards and usually a little downwards, corresponding indeed in extent very nearly to the decentration of the optical zone, so that in the most typically regular eyes the latter can be considered as approximately centered with respect to the pupil. Accordingly, in ascertaining the centering of the refracting surfaces of the eye, the best procedure is to take the normal to the cornea which goes through the centre of the pupil as being the *optical axis of the eye*. Strictly speaking, the eye has no optical axis, because the refracting surfaces are not exactly centered; but a line has to be chosen that satisfies the requirements of such an axis approximately. The orientation of this axis is easily found, by placing a perforated round white disc at the objective of the ophthalmometer or of a telescope, whose reflex image is adjusted concentrically to the pupil by motion of the patient's eye; and then all that remains to be done in order to obtain the required data is to adjust the fixation mark.

However, more important for the dioptrics of the cornea than this measurement is the *angle of incidence of the line of sight*, and the orientation of its plane of incidence. The special significance of the line of sight, which with respect to the imagery-laws of the first order is the chief ray of the bundle of effective rays in distinct vision, and which proceeds from the point of fixation to the apparent centre of the pupil, consists partly in the fact that for the actual convergence of rays in the eye it has the same *role* as in the fictitious collinear imagery is ascribed to the visual axis (*Gesichtslinie*) that passes through the anterior nodal point; because its orientation can be exactly ascertained. Practically, indeed, it is quite immaterial whether we speak of the line of sight (*Visierlinie*), line of fixation (*Blicklinie*) or visual axis, so far as inclination to the optical axis is concerned, because the differences between these angles are below the limit of the possible errors. But since the position of the line of sight can be accurately found, whereas that of the visual axis cannot, it is better generally to reckon only with the former, as was first pointed out by BLIX.[1] The angle of incidence thereof was measured by LEROY[2], and afterwards by the writer.[3] The most accurate results are obtained with the HELMHOLTZ ophthalmometer, by placing the fixation mark on the

[1] Loc. cit.

[2] De la Kératoscopie ou de la forme de la surface cornéenne, déduite des images apparentes réfléchies par elle. *Arch. d'ophth.* IV. 1884.

[3] Loc. cit. *Skand. Arch. f. Phys.* II. 1890.

prolongation of the axis of the instrument and adjusting a small source
of light so that the reflex image is seen in the centre of the pupil.
By rotating the plate-carriage on the ophthalmometer until the source
of light lies in the plane of "doubling," and by turning the plates
until the double images of the source each coincide with an edge of
the doubled pupil, the proper adjustment of the source of light can
be made. In this delicate experiment it often appears that the angle
of incidence depends on the size of the pupil, and hence this angle
should be ascertained always for a medium size of pupil of 4 mm.
The quotient of the distance of the light-source from the axis of the
ophthalmometer by the distance between the vertex of the cornea and
the plane passed through the source perpendicular to the axis is equal
to twice the tangent of the required angle of incidence. By similar
centering of the reflex image of a round white disc this angle can be
found without an ophthalmometer. In normal eyes the writer has
found it to vary from 0° to 6°, and sometimes he has obtained negative
values; in which case, therefore, the source of light had to be shifted
towards the nose from the axis of the instrument. The angle between
the plane of incidence and the horizontal plane may amount to as
much as 30° in perfectly normal eyes, and it usually extends in the
direction from above inwards to below outwards when in the perfectly
normal eye there occurs a perceptible deviation from the horizontal.
For very small values of the angle of incidence, generally every orientation of the plane of incidence is possible. The angle between the line
of sight and the optical axis is always larger than the angle of incidence, and as a rule is rather more than half as much again. Thus,
if P, P' in Fig. 127 designate the real and apparent positions, respectively, of the centre of the pupil, and if u denotes the angle between the
line of sight and the optical axis and i the angle of incidence, then

$$\sin u : \sin i = \rho : (\rho - d),$$

where d denotes the apparent depth of the anterior chamber of the
eye, and ρ denotes the radius of curvature of the optical zone of the
cornea. For small angles the value found is sufficiently accurate
when the angles themselves are substituted for their sines; and for
an apparent depth of the anterior chamber of 3 mm and a radius of
7.8 mm, the ratio is 1.625. It may be remarked that the first of the
measurements given by HELMHOLTZ at the end of §3 for the position
of the centre of the pupil with respect to the axis of the cornea, as
determined by the constants of the ellipse, shows complete agreement
between this axis and the optical axis which is assumed here, within
the limits of the errors of observation; while the differences that
occur in the other two measurements are not greater than can be

explained by the asymmetry of the horizontal section of the cornea
and the consequent deviation from the elliptical form.

Accordingly, it would seem to be justifiable to employ the angle
of incidence of the line of sight and the inclination of this line to the
optical axis, both of which angles
can be easily measured at present
with the usual apparatus, instead
of the angle a between the visual
axis and the axis of the corneal
ellipse, which HELMHOLTZ uses.
The angle which HELMHOLTZ[1] calls
β, and which in the literature of
physiological optics is sometimes
denoted by a and sometimes by γ,
is the angle between the line of
fixation and the normal to the
cornea that goes through the centre
of the optical zone of the cornea.

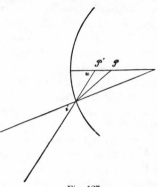

Fig. 127.

This angle is entirely without significance for the dioptrics of the eye.

With respect to the *curvature of the optical zone of the cornea*, in
consequence of what has been stated above concerning the accuracy
of measurements with modern ophthalmometers, we may attach
comparatively high value to the old investigations, which have been
compiled by DONDERS.[2] For 110 adult men the average value was
7.858 mm, the maximum and minimum values being 8.396 and 7.28.
For 46 women the corresponding values were 7.799, 8.487 and 7.115.
From these numbers HELMHOLTZ derived the schematic value 7.829.
Much more extensive numerical data are available for modern ophthalmometry. STEIGER[3] found the average value of the corneal refraction of
1916 eyes to be 43.03 dioptries, corresponding to a radius of 7.843 mm.
SULZER[4] takes the average value as 43.7 dioptries, corresponding to
a radius of 7.723 mm. The discrepancy here can easily be accounted
for by the unavoidable personal equation. In view of the fact that the
third decimal figure is uncertain, and since SULZER's material was
not as extensive as STEIGER's, perhaps the nearest approach to the
truth is to estimate the *ophthalmometric average value of the radius of
curvature of the optical zone of the cornea* at 7.8 mm; and, on the basis
of DONDERS' numerical results as given above, to put the physiological
limits at 7 and 8.5 mm—numerical values which may henceforth be

[1] *Handbuch d. phys. Opt.* 2. Auflage. S. 19.

[2] F. C. DONDERS, *On the anomalies of accommodation and refraction.* London 1864.

[3] ADOLF STEIGER, *Beiträge zur Physiologie und Pathologie der Hornhautrefraktion.*
Wiesbaden 1895.

[4] Loc. cit.

generally assumed and which are not inconsistent with exact investigations. So far as the limiting values are concerned, the lower one may be surpassed in microphthalmos and in keratoconus, and the upper one in flattening of the cornea in post-operative pressure or after ulcerations; but under all circumstances these limits are likely to be wide enough for physiological relations. From STEIGER's results the variations are found to lie between 7.5 and 8.1 mm in at least about 80% of the cases, since in 88.5% the refraction was found to be between 41.25 and 45 dioptries. The *sexual difference of corneal curvature* as indicated by the above data of DONDERS was established by the larger material of STEIGER (mean value for boys and girls 42.89 and 43.15 dioptries, respectively). His investigations indicate that the cornea becomes flatter with advancing years; but it is doubtful whether the material was sufficient to decide this question. However, his measurements prove that there is a connection between the radius of the cornea and the distance of the pupil; just as a similar connection between this radius and the size of the body and the circumference of the head is indicated by the investigations of BOURGEOIS and TSCHERNING,[1] since a larger anthropometrical measure implies a larger mean value for the radius of the cornea.

However, although the curvature of the optical zone of the cornea is nearly spherical both vertically and horizontally, this is not the case with the zone as a whole. For the normal condition is an appreciable astigmatism. This *physiological corneal astigmatism* was definitely ascertained by the ophthalmometric measurements carried out first by NORDENSON.[2] Concordant results of various investigators show that its average value amounts to between 0.50 and 0.75 dptr, and that the section of least curvature is not very far from the horizontal direction or the longitudinal extent of the eye-slit. As evidence thereof STEIGER's figures may be used. He found a mean value of 0.78 dptr in 3170 eyes. But when the eyes were left out of account that had an astigmatism of more than 2.0 dptr, which are always to be regarded as pathological cases, he obtained with 3073 eyes an average value of 0.70 dptr, and in two-thirds of these the corneal astigmatism was between 0.50 and 1.0 dptr, and in nearly seven-eighths of them between 0.25 and 1.25 dptr. In 89.4% of the eyes the direction of the section of least curvature was horizontal.

A *change of corneal astigmatism with the age* of the patient has been

[1] Recherches sur les relations qui existent entre la courbure de la cornée, la circonférence de la tête et la taille. *Ann. d'oculistique.* XCVI. 1886.

[2] E. NORDENSON, Recherches ophthalmométriques sur l'astigmatisme de la cornée chez les écoliers de sept à vingt ans. Ibid. XC. 1883.

certainly shown by the researches of Schön,[1] Steiger and Pfalz.[2] The astigmatism is said to be *with the rule* or *against the rule*, according as the section of least curvature makes an angle not greater than 30° with the horizontal or vertical planes, respectively, or coincides with one or the other of these planes (also referred to sometimes in the literature of the subject as "As. rectus" or "As. perversus" and "direct astigmatism" or "inverse astigmatism"). It is found that, *with advancing years the physiological astigmatism with the rule decreases, whereas the percentage of cases with corneal astigmatism against the rule increases.* Connected with this variation is an increase of the number of cases in which the principal meridians of the astigmatism are not the horizontal and vertical planes. This is also easily explained, since static influences, which with distinct astigmatism were not sufficient to produce an appreciable change in the form of the cornea, are necessarily more and more in evidence with steadily diminishing astigmatism.

The geometrical surface that represents the form of the optical zone of the cornea when its curvature may be regarded as spherical both horizontally and vertically is a toric surface. This is a surface generated by the revolution of the arc of a circle about an axis in its plane, or, according to the geometrical definition, is the enveloping surface of a sphere whose centre moves along a circle.

According to a general law of the theory of curved surfaces, known as Dupin's theorem, the form of any section of the anterior surface of the cornea made by a plane perpendicular to the axis and infinitely close to the ophthalmometric axial point is elliptical; and the axes of the ellipse are to each other as the square roots of the radii of principal curvature, so that the vertical axis is the axis minor in normal physiological astigmatism. But if we suppose a number of such sections of the cornea to be made in succession, the form of each curve being ascertained by the ratio between its horizontal and vertical diameters, on account of the marked flattening that occurs in the vertical section of the cornea, the contour of these slices will be found to be such that the deeper we go, the less this ratio becomes. It is still problematical as to what is the depth when this ratio is unity. But that it does occur before we come to the base of the cornea, can be seen from the coördinates calculated for the case illustrated by the curves above (which is the only case so far for which such a calculation can be made). From the table in question it is sufficient to give here three points in each direction as follows:

[1] W. Schön, Die Akkommodationsüberanstrengung usw. *Arch. f. Ophth.* XXXIII. 1. 1887.

[2] G. Pfalz, Über Astigmatismus perversus — eine erworbene Refraktionsanomalie. *Zeitschr. f. Augenheilkunde.* III. 1900.

Nasal		Temporal		Upwards		Downwards	
x	y	x	y	x	y	x	y
0.860	3.556	0.831	3.483	0.905	3.680	0.856	3.541
1.231	4.218	1.168	4.084	1.298	4.383	1.201	4.157
1.792	5.048	1.579	4.692	1.680	4.948	1.636	4.801

In this table x denotes the depth of the section from the ophthalmometric axial point, and y denotes the distance of the point on the surface from the ophthalmometric axis. If the 12 points are constructed, it is found that, for a given value of x the values of y are larger upwards than inwards, and larger downwards than outwards; and hence that the vertical diameter of the section is greater than its horizontal diameter. However, this is on the assumption that the outer portion of the eyeball is similar in form. Hence, from the more considerable flattening of the normal cornea vertically, it follows that a section of the outer portion of the eyeball just behind the cornea and perpendicular to the line of sight must have a longer diameter vertically than horizontally. It appears, moreover, that if the cornea were not under the influence of external forces, its natural form would have to show astigmatism against the rule. How the actual form of the cornea comes to be different from this natural form, is exactly what might be expected from the action of external forces due to the pressure of the eyelids. Since this pressure is exerted only upwards and downwards, and by reason of the structure of the lid-slit must be stronger in the former than in the latter direction, it must produce a flattening corresponding to the surface of contact, which affects only the vertical section, and must be more pronounced above than below. The compression from above downwards must also result in a direct astigmatism (astigmatism with the rule) of the optical zone. That this mechanism is sufficient from a qualitative point of view to account for the form of the cornea, is evident because the surface of contact with the eyeball, anyhow so far as the upper lid is concerned, extends over the cornèa. This is true too, though not to the same extent, with respect to the lower lid, because most people habitually look downwards below the horizontal plane.

Several facts can be adduced to show that this mechanism is quantitatively sufficient also. First, the difference between the actual and natural forms of the cornea means an exceedingly slight deformation, which might perhaps be produced by the interaction of the forces due to the pressure of the eyelids and the effective processes in the genesis of the form of the cornea. However, in the second place, it is easy to show in the ophthalmometric investigation that any increment of these forces produces a sudden deformation, the astigmatism being considerably augmented by pinching the lids together, accompanied by a pronounced vertical asymmetry of the cornea with increased flattening. And in abnormal cases like keratoconus, the effect of these external forces comes out in the most striking way, as shown by the fact, which the writer could demonstrate, that it is typical to find a large amount of direct astigmatism (that is, astigmatism with the rule) at the vertex of the cornea, together with a marked vertical asymmetry, involving decentration of the vertex downwards and greater flattening upwards, as has been observed in most cases.[1] In very old age the coatings of the eyeball become more rigid, and the eyelid pressure diminishes, the general tone of the tissue being reduced and the fatty matter in the socket drying up. Hence, the difference between the actual and natural forms of the cornea must get slighter, and accordingly we find STEIGER's statistics show a considerable increase of cases of very old persons with inverse corneal astigmatism or astigmatism against the rule. Lastly, with increase of pressure the action of the eyelid pressure must give way against the pressure from within tending to make the cornea assume its natural form; and the clinical investigations of MARTIN[2] and PFALZ,[3] together with the laboratory researches of EISSEN,[4] have demonstrated that increase of pressure in the normal eye is accompanied by corneal astigmatism against the rule. Thus it appears that where the action of the eyelid pressure is promoted, there will be an increase, and where it is excluded, there will be a decrease, of the deformation, which differentiates the actual form of the cornea from its natural form corresponding to the shape of the outer portion of the eyeball. The writer thinks it is fair to conclude that the pressure of the eyelids, or the resistance that is offered by them to the dilatation of the eyeball, is the explanation of the normal direct astigmatism of the optical zone, and likewise of the excess of the peripheral flattening in the vertical section, and of the normal vertical asymmetry of this flattening.

The calculation of the form of the cornea from the ophthalmometer measurements is made as follows: In Fig. 128 the straight line *AEF* represents the ophthalmometric axis, and the straight line *DGE* shows the path of a ray proceeding from a point of the object, which,

[1] Ett fall af keratoconus med tydlig pulsation af hornhinnan. *Nord. Ophth. Tidskr.* IV. 1892. S. 142.

[2] G. MARTIN, Études d'ophthalmométrie clinique. *Ann. d'oculistique.* XCIII. 1885. p. 223.

[3] G. PFALZ, Ophthalmometrische Untersuchungen über Kornealastigmatismus. *Arch. f. Ophth.* XXXI. 1 1885. S. 201.

[4] W. EISSEN, Hornhautkrümmung bei erhöhtem intraokularem Druck. Ibid. XXXIII. 2. 1888. S. 1.

after reflection at the cornea, goes to the ophthalmometer in the

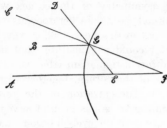

direction GB. The normal to the cornea at the reflecting point G is CGF, which is inclined to the axis at an angle $\varphi = CFA$. In HELMHOLTZ'S ophthalmometer or an instrument with similar "doubling" device the straight lines BG and AF are parallel. Consequently, the angle of incidence is equal to φ and the

Fig. 128.

angle $DEA = 2\varphi$. With other instruments the line BG makes a small angle with the axis, which, however, for the ratio between the distance of the ophthalmometer and the radius of the cornea, and with the limitations in other ways to the precision of the measurements, may be neglected. The same thing is true with respect to the distance of the point E from the cornea. Thus, either the angle 2φ is obtained directly in degrees by measuring the angular distance of the object-point from the axis of the instrument, or tan 2φ is found by dividing the linear distance of this point from the axis by the distance from the cornea of the transversal plane in which the point lies. In this way the angle φ corresponding to a given object-point is ascertained accurately enough. Referring now to Fig. 129, let the ophthalmometric axis again be represented by the straight

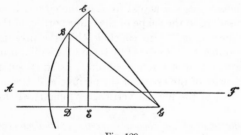

line AF, and suppose that the light from two different object-points is reflected from the cornea at the two points B, C, at which the normals are BG, CG intersecting in the point

Fig. 129.

G. The smaller the arc BC, the more nearly will the point G coincide with the centre of curvature of this element of the cornea; and ultimately the distance $BG = CG$ will be equal to the radius of curvature ρ. Let D and E designate the feet of the perpendiculars dropped from B and C, respectively, on the straight line drawn through G parallel to the axis; and let the distance of B and C from the axis be denoted by y_1, y_2, respectively; then

$$BD = \rho \sin \varphi_1, \qquad CE = \rho \sin \varphi_2,$$

and, since $CE - BD = y_2 - y_1$, the following *general formula for calculating the radius of curvature* is obtained:

$$\rho = \frac{y_2 - y_1}{\sin \varphi_2 - \sin \varphi_1},$$

where $y_2 - y_1$ is given by the value of the "doubling," and the angles φ_1, φ_2 are known by the positions of the object-points. In the special case, when these points are symmetrically situated with respect to the axis of the ophthalmometer, so that $\varphi_2 = -\varphi_1$, the formula may be put in the form given by HELMHOLTZ,[1] namely

$$\rho = \frac{\beta}{2 \sin\left(\dfrac{1}{2} \arctan \dfrac{b}{2a}\right)},$$

where β denotes the value of the "doubling," b the distance apart of the object-points collimated in the reflex image, and a the distance from the cornea of the line joining these points. The smaller the angles are, the more nearly is this formula equivalent to the approximate formula

$$\rho = \frac{2a\beta}{b} \quad \text{or} \quad D = kb,$$

which in the last form, where k denotes the constant of the ophthalmometer, is the fundamental formula in modern ophthalmometry.

In making measurements for different visual directions each new direction must be chosen so that one of the points of the cornea used for reflection in the preceding measurement is utilized in the next determination; as otherwise the measurements are not adapted for calculating the form of the cornea. In this secondary position of fixation a number of radii and corresponding values of the angle φ with respect to the secondary axis are obtained from the measurement. These angles are computed first by adding the amount of rotation of the line of fixation to the angle φ as measured from the ophthalmometric axis of the cornea, and then the values of y with respect to this axis can be found from the general formula. From the relations

$$GD = \rho \cos \varphi_1, \qquad GE = \rho \cos\varphi_2, \qquad GD - GE = x_2 - x_1,$$

which are obvious from the diagram (Fig. 129), the values of x may be found by means of the formula

$$x_2 - x_1 = \rho(\cos \varphi_1 - \cos \varphi_2),$$

and thus as the result of the calculation we have obtained the co-

[1] *Handbuch d. phys. Opt.* 2. Aufl. S. 16.

ordinates of the points of the cornea used for reflection the inclinations of the normals at these points and the radii of curvature of the arcs of the measured normal section that are comprised between them. These data are sufficient, and also necessary, in order to investigate by trigonometrical calculation the influence of the cornea on the aberration.

Heretofore, the exact calculation of the form of a cornea has been performed only by the photographic-ophthalmometric investigation. However, the method is essentially equivalent to a series of corresponding measurements that can be made with the HELMHOLTZ ophthalmometer. JAVAL's ophthalmometer can also be adapted to the same purpose by different methods. A method of this kind which is unobjectionable in principle has been proposed by BRUDZEWSKI[1] and by BASLINI.[2] But the calculation of the results is wrong in the case of both of them; for the former employs a relation between the normal and the radius of curvature that is applicable only to a surface of the second degree, and the latter calculates the values of x by a formula that is true only for a circle. If the form of the cornea is to be calculated by means of relations that are true for an ellipsoid, undoubtedly the best way is to go about it regularly and to calculate the constants of the ellipsoid by the method given by HELMHOLTZ.[3]

The rule stated above for calculating the astigmatism from the amount of "Denivellation" (or difference of level in the double image) in a meridian inclined to the principal section at an angle of 45°, is obtained as follows. One of the principal sections of the cornea having been ascertained, the arc of the ophthalmometer is turned through half a right angle, and then the collimation is made, and the "Denivellation" compensated by adjusting one of the *mires* in the direction perpendicular to the plane of "doubling." The collimated points are then the extremities of a line whose optical projection at the focus of the ophthalmometer lies in the plane of doubling. With the degree of accuracy that can be obtained by the instrument, it is permissible to neglect the interval between this focus and the two focal points of the bundle of reflected rays that do not lie exactly in the same plane. Hence, as follows from the formula on page 290, the projection-coefficients for the two principal sections are equal to the corresponding magnification-ratios; and these latter are to each other inversely as the refracting powers in the two principal sections,

---

[1] K. v. BRUDZEWSKI, Beitrag zur Dioptrik des Auges. *Arch. f. Augenheilk.* XL. 1900. S. 296.

[2] C. BASLINI, Recherches ophthalmométriques. *Arch. d'ophth.* XXIV. 1904. p. 565.

[3] *Handbuch der phys. Optik*, 2. Aufl. S. 17.

since

$$K_1D_1 = K_2D_2 = L,$$

where K and D denote the magnification-ratio and refracting power, respectively, and L denotes the convergence of the bundle of incident rays with respect to the focus of the reflecting surface of the cornea. The tangent of the angle between the projected line and the first principal section is equal to $\frac{K_2}{K_1}\tan \omega$, where ω denotes the angle between the corresponding object-line and the same principal section. Since the tangent of the former angle is equal to unity, it follows that $\tan \omega = \frac{D_2}{D_1}$, and hence

$$\tan (\omega - 45^0) = \frac{D_2 - D_1}{D_2 + D_1} = \frac{c}{b},$$

where c denotes the adjustment that has to be made to compensate the "Denivellation", and b denotes the length of the projected object line as found by the collimation. By EULER's theorem, employing the constant of the ophthalmometer, we may write: $\frac{1}{2} (D_1 + D_2) = kb$ and thus we obtain finally the following mathematical statement of the rule above mentioned:

$$D_2 - D_1 = 2kc.$$

This formula is thus approximate to the same extent as those generally employed in modern ophthalmometry. The errors involved therein are, however, of no consequence in the measurement of astigmatism and do not need to be taken into account until it is necessary to calculate the absolute value of the refraction of the cornea.

The corneal substance. Disregarding the layer of fluid over the anterior surface of the cornea, which in the dioptrics of the eye can be considered as an infinitely thin film bounded by concentric surfaces, and consequently without influence on the ray-procedure; the corneal tissue constitutes the first ocular refracting medium. After ABBE's modern refractometer method had been introduced, the *index of refraction of the cornea* was measured by AUBERT and MATTHIESSEN[1] and found to be 1.377 for the eye of a man fifty years of age, and 1.3721 for that of a child two days old. LOHNSTEIN[2] obtained by calculation from the indices of refraction of the component parts a value intermediate between the two just mentioned. MATTHIESSEN's[3] final

---

[1] H. AUBERT, *Grundzüge der physiologischen Optik.* Leipzig 1876.

[2] TH. LOHNSTEIN, Über den Brechungsindex der menschlichen Hornhaut. *Arch. f. d. ges. Physiologie.* LXVI. 1897.

[3] L. MATTHIESSEN, *Die neueren Fortschritte in unserer Kenntnis von dem optischen Baue des Auges der Wirbeltiere.* Hamburg 1891.

comparison of results gave the value 1.3763, and since the fourth decimal is always doubtful, 1.376 may be taken as the best schematic value.

Heretofore, no one except BLIX[1] has measured *the thickness of the cornea* in the living eye by an unobjectionable method. His ophthal-

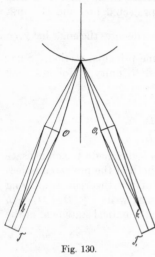

Fig. 130.

mometer consists of two microscopes, T, T_1 arranged according to the plan of Fig. 130 with their objectives at O, O_1. In place of the ocular of the second microscope there is a brightly illuminated diaphragm b whose image is produced at the point where the two axes meet. The observer looks through the other microscope and focuses it on this point by means of the cross-hairs at b; and hence he cannot see a sharp image of the diaphragm unless the apparent place either of the principal point or of the centre of curvature of a reflecting surface is at the point of junction of the axes. The microscopes may be adjusted in two ways, partly by moving them along the bisector of the angle between their axes without disturbing their mutual relation to each other, and partly by moving them simultaneously and equally along their axes without changing the point of junction. The latter mechanism is used for measuring a radius of curvature, and the former for measuring the interval between two reflecting surfaces. Thus, the thickness of the cornea is measured by two successive adjustments in which the reflex image, first, in the anterior, and then in the posterior, surface of the cornea is sharply focused. The displacement of the instrument is equal then to the apparent thickness, and the actual thickness is obtained by exact calculations without using approximate formulae. With ten eyes BLIX found thicknesses varying from 0.482 to 0.668 mm. Leaving out the eyes which had these extreme values, the limits were 0.506 and 0.576. These measurements corresponded partly to the vertex as defined by the minimum radius of the cornea, partly to the ophthalmometric axial point, and partly to points that were 20° inwards and outwards from the points first named.

[1] Loc. cit.

The fact that BLIX was able without difficulty to observe the reflex image in the posterior surface of the cornea and utilize it in measuring the thickness of the cornea, whereas HELMHOLTZ[1] had tried in vain to see this image, was due to the high magnifying power of the microscope, which was necessary in order to see the image separate from the more luminous image in the anterior surface. With the methods of illumination available nowadays there are no difficulties at all about obtaining reflex images from the posterior surface of such clarity that the thickness of the cornea can be determined by the same method as is used for the thickness of the lens. In order to get reflex images as sharp and bright as possible, a source of light must be used with the greatest possible specific intensity. On account of its convenience of adjustment, the incandescent filament of the NERNST lamp (see p. 470) is the only kind of light to be considered, since neither sunlight nor the electric arclight is satisfactory for the purpose, and all other sources of light have much less specific intensity. The lamp should be attached at one end of a closed tube, which has an adjustable slit at the other end, and in the middle of which there is a lens system that can be decentered at pleasure. This lens system is for the purpose of focusing a sharp image of the filament of the lamp on the rear side of the slit. With the slit wide open and the eye protected by a dark glass, the sharp focusing is found by parallax displacements of the eye. By rotating and moving the lamp, and also by decentering the lens system in a direction perpendicular to the length of the slit, it is not difficult to focus the image of the filament right in the middle of the aperture of the slit. The slit mechanism should be the so-called bilateral arrangement with both edges simultaneously adjustable. The tube as a whole should be capable of rotation around its axis and attached to a stand. This source of light gives a luminous line of variable intensity, which in its specific intensity is far superior to all other sources of light that can be conveniently employed for ophthalmometry. For brevity we shall call it hereafter the ophthalmometric NERNST lamp.

For measuring the thickness of the cornea by the method given by HELMHOLTZ as illustrated in Fig. 50, the writer uses two of these lamps with vertical slits placed one exactly above the other in such fashion that the horizontal plane through the vertex of the cornea passes midway between the two slits. With proper intensity of light and a good telescope magnifying twenty times, the reflex images even at the thinnest place are extraordinarily clear when the angle of incidence is about 25°. A small incandescent lamp with a straight vertical filament was used for the source of light whose reflex image in

[1] Über die Akkommodation des Auges. *Arch. f. Ophth.* I, 2. 1855. S. 1.

the anterior surface of the cornea was to be collimated with the
reflex image of the ophthalmometric NERNST lamp in the posterior
surface. The angle was measured with an instrument similar to a
theodolite fastened above the head of the patient, its vertical axis
ending downwards in a point. The precise orientation of the vertex
of the cornea on the prolongation of this axis was achieved by focusing
the telescope, which was capable of rotation around a horizontal axis,
first, on this point, and then on the image reflected in the cornea.

The experiment is easy to make when the angular distance vertically between the middle points of the two slits is 12°, in which case
the element of the cornea that is used is so small that the imaginary
reflex image of the vertical line determined by the two ends of the slit
can be regarded as a straight line. The ophthalmometric NERNST
lamps and the telescope were adjusted each at an angle of 25° from the
zero position of the telescope of the theodolite, and by a preliminary
trial the direction of fixation was found for which the angle of incidence
was practically the same when the positions of lamp and telescope were
interchanged, because with this adjustment the optical axis of the
eye does not differ much from the zero position of the telescope of the
theodolite. The basis of the calculations was the average results of
measurements made on different days in both adjustments. By this
arrangement the reflex image in the posterior surface is seen at the
place where the normal to the anterior surface crosses the posterior
surface, and the calculation is very simple. Since this normal is
common to both surfaces, it is the line or axis of centres of the cornea,
and since it coincides with the zero position of the theodolite, the
measurement gives the angular distance ω of the lamp from this line,
and the angle of incidence is $\frac{1}{2}$ $(25° + \omega)$. The procedure of the rays
is the same as in Fig. 127 where the posterior surface of the cornea
takes the place of the pupil of the eye. Having first calculated the
angle of refraction i', we can find the angle u', between the line of
centres and the ray refracted at the anterior surface, and hence the
thickness d for the given value of the radius ρ of the anterior surface,
by means of the following formulae:

$$25^0 - i = u' - i' \qquad \sin u' : \sin i' = \rho : (\rho - d).$$

The eyes of two individuals were measured by the writer with the
utmost pains, and the values 0.46 and 0.51 were obtained; corrobo-
rating very exactly the results found by BLIX. After BLIX had observed the image reflected in the posterior surface of the cornea,
TSCHERNING[1] succeeded in making it visible with a small incandescent

---

[1] *Optique physiologique.* Paris 1898.

lamp. In one case also he tried to measure the thickness of the cornea, and obtained a result of 1.15 mm. This may have been due to errors in his method, which was not nearly so accurate, and to the small specific intensity of this source of light. From measurements in the living eye, *the schematic value of the thickness of the cornea* in the optical zone may be taken therefore, as BLIX proposed, as being about 0.5 mm.

Measurements with dead eyes have given very discrepant results, the values for the vertex varying between 0.4 and 1.0,[1] and sometimes even exceeding this latter value. This may be due in part to a *post mortem* swelling, and partly also to the method of measurement. In some instances the writer has removed entirely the healthy cornea of a freshly enucleated eye and measured the thinnest place in it with the ordinary micrometer screw used for measuring thicknesses, with the contact surfaces reduced to a diameter of 1/2 mm. The values obtained in this way were between 0.4 and 0.6 mm.

By using the arrangement above described, *the radius of the posterior surface* can be measured in the same way as the radii of the lens surfaces, whereas a direct measurement with the ophthalmometer does not prove satisfactory. With the HELMHOLTZ type of instrument the writer finds that generally he cannot see the reflex images in the posterior surfaces of the cornea, because they are masked by the rays that are diffusely refracted at the edge of the plates. The slits are adjusted horizontally, and the reflex images of the straight horizontal filaments of two incandescent lamps are so focused that each reflex image is the prolongation of one of the reflex images in the posterior surface of the cornea due to the ophthalmometric NERNST lamp. The object represented by the vertical distance between the two incandescent lamps is reproduced then by an image reflected in the anterior surface of the cornea which is equal to the reflex image in the posterior surface corresponding to the vertical distance between the two slits. Just as in measuring the thickness, the fixation mark is so adjusted that the line of centres of the two surfaces of the cornea coincides with the zero position of the telescope of the theodolite, and the angular distances of the observing telescope and NERNST lamps are equal. What has to be measured are the sizes and distances of the two objects, together with their angular distances from the line of centres; these magnitudes for the NERNST lamps and the incandescent lamps being denoted here by b, a, u and b_0, a_0, u_0, respectively. Since for the reflection at the anterior surface of the cornea the angle of

[1] MERKEL in *Handb. d. ges. Augenheilk.* v. GRAEFE u. SÄMISCH. I. Leipzig 1874. S. 44-45.

incidence is equal to u or $\frac{1}{2}(u+u_0)$, the ratio ϵ of the two reflex images β, β_0 is found by the relation

$$\frac{\beta_0}{\beta}=\frac{ab_0 \cos u}{a_0b \cos \frac{1}{2}(u+u_0)},$$

which follows from the general formula $K=\dfrac{L}{D}$ for the secondary imagery, provided the distances of the object are reckoned from the principal focus of the corneal mirror. But the ratio of the sizes of the two reflex images of the object represented by the NERNST lamps is equal to the inverse ratio of the reflecting powers of the two reflecting systems in question, since for both reflections the value of L here may be considered the same without sensible error. The reflecting power of the anterior surface of the cornea with respect to the secondary imagery is

$$-\frac{2 \cos u}{\rho_1},$$

where ρ_1 denotes the radius of curvature of this surface in the vertical section; whereas the power of the reflecting system which produces the reflex image in the posterior surface of the cornea, as found by the formula on page 285 is

$$2D_1(1-\delta_1D_1)+D_2(1-\delta_1D_1)^2,$$

where D_1 denotes the refracting power of the anterior surface of the cornea with respect to the secondary imagery, and D_2 denotes the reflecting power of the posterior surface for the same imagery. If the radius of curvature of the vertical section of the posterior surface is denoted by ρ_2, and if n denotes the index of refraction of the corneal substance, then

$$D_1=\frac{n \cos i'-\cos i}{\rho_1}, \qquad D_2=-\frac{2n \cos u'}{\rho_2};$$

the angles being denoted just as above in the determination of the thickness of the cornea.

If the point of incidence on the posterior surface of the cornea is designated by P in Fig. 127, then P' will be the first principal point of the reflecting system with respect to the secondary imagery; and δ_1 denotes the reduced distance of P from the point of incidence on the anterior surface, whereas H denotes the distance of P' from this point of incidence. From the formula on page 285 we get

$$1-\delta_1D_1=\frac{\delta_1}{H},$$

and since in Fig. 127 evidently

$$n\delta_1:H=\sin u:\sin u',$$

therefore
$$1 - \delta_1 D_1 = \frac{\sin u}{n \sin u'}.$$

Hence, putting ϵ equal to the ratio of the dimensions of the two reflex images of the NERNST lamps, we obtain

$$\epsilon = -\frac{2 \cos u}{\rho_1} : \frac{2 \sin u}{n \sin u'} \left\{ \frac{n \cos i' - \cos i}{\rho_1} - \frac{\sin u}{\rho_2 \tan u'} \right\}.$$

From the final formula

$$\frac{\rho_1}{\rho_2} = \frac{\tan u' \, (n \cos i' - \cos i)}{\sin u} + \frac{n \sin u' \tan u'}{\epsilon \sin u \tan u},$$

where $\epsilon = \dfrac{\beta_0}{\beta}$ as found by measurement, the writer has obtained the values 1.1822 and 1.1811 in the two cases mentioned above. On the assumption that the ratio of the radii of curvature of the horizontal sections of the anterior and posterior surfaces is the same, these values give, for the schematic radius 7.8 mm of the anterior surface, the value 6.6 mm for the radius of the posterior surface.

These investigations with reflex images in the posterior surface were also carried out by the writer for angles of incidence up to 40°, in which case the observation is more easily made. With a little practice, however, the observation is sufficiently successful for the given value $u = 25°$. Smaller angles are better because the asymmetry values, on which the lack of similarity between object and image depends, become greater with increasing angles of incidence, tending therefore to vitiate the validity of the imagery-laws of the first order, although the formula is exact for any value of the angle of incidence. After the observer's eye has become sufficiently adapted to the room illuminated only by the ophthalmometric NERNST lamp, the reflex images are seen instantly as soon as the objective of the telescope is fixated; and whenever they become indistinct, it is a good plan each time to make the patient look again in this direction, and then turn his eye gradually towards the fixation mark. The correct adjustment of the incandescent lamp can be regulated best by suddenly shutting off the current and then focusing it at the instant of re-illumination.

A vast amount of work is involved in investigating the line of centres, and the writer did not have time to make the complete measurements and computations except in the two cases above mentioned. In both instances the good agreement of the results not only with each other but also with the very accurate researches of BLIX so far as the thickness is concerned, and with TSCHERNING'S[1]

[1] LAGRANGE et VALUDE, *Encyclopédie française d'ophthalmologie.* III. p. 109. Paris 1904.

latest value of 6.5 mm for the radius of the posterior surface, would perhaps seem to indicate their adequacy also. However, owing to the discrepancy that exists between too small a schematic value of the corneal refraction and the results of anatomical measurements of the length of the eyeball—a matter to be considered presently in detail— further investigations were deemed desirable. The writer therefore has measured four other eyes of different individuals by an approximate method, assuming the line of centres to be a line inclined to the line of sight (*Visierlinie*) at an angle of 6°, and using in the calculation the value of the angle as obtained for the case when the thickness of the cornea was found to be 0.46 mm. Now a discussion of the formulae proves that for a given value of ϵ the ratio $\dfrac{\rho_1}{\rho_2}$ will be greater in proportion as the cornea is thicker; therefore the value of the radius of the posterior surface found by this approximate method cannot be too small. In this way the following values of $\dfrac{\rho_1}{\rho_2}$ were found: 1.1864, 1.1734, 1.1486, and 1.1427. For the schematic value 7.8 mm for the radius of the anterior surface, these numbers give values of the radius of the posterior surface between 6.57 and 6.83 mm. Hence, *the ophthalmometric mean value of the radius of the posterior surface of the optical zone of the cornea* can hardly be greater than 6.7 mm, which is the value that is hereafter assumed by the writer.

However, the ophthalmometric mean values of the radii of curvature of the optical zone cannot be used without further consideration for *calculating the ray procedure* by means of the imagery laws of the first order. In a calculation of this kind the curvatures that are involved are those at places where the line of sight (*Visierlinie*) is incident on the temporal side of the ophthalmometric axial point. The radius of the anterior surface must needs be somewhat less at such a point than the ophthalmometric mean value for the whole zone—all the more so because the latter value was found by measurements in which the one point of the cornea used for reflection is at the edge of the optical zone and therefore has probably turned out rather too large. On the other hand, on account of the greater flattening of the anterior surface in the vertical section, the ratio $\dfrac{\rho_1}{\rho_2}$ may be here somewhat larger than in the horizontal section; and, besides, it must prove to be greater in case the measurement was not made exactly along the line of centres. Therefore, in calculating the ray procedure a radius of the anterior surface should be used that is somewhat smaller, and a radius of the posterior surface that is somewhat larger, than the schematic values of these magnitudes for the optical zone. Since the difference at the point of incidence of the line of sight and at the vertex of the optical zone cannot be calculated, there is no other alternative in calculating the ray procedure except to identify the curvatures at these two points in advance. For the reasons assigned, the writer assumes for *the schematic values of the radii of curvature at the vertices of the optical zone of the cornea in this calculation the data* 7.7 *and* 6.8 mm.

The index of refraction of the aqueous humor must be known in order to ascertain the cornea system. Previously, the value given by HELMHOLTZ (p. 107) has been quite generally accepted and the numerous refractometer measurements which have been made since (which have been collected by FREYTAG[1]) show scarcely greater variations from this value than are shown by the variations of the values in the case of distilled water. Although more recent investigations tend to give rather lower values, there hardly appears to be any sufficient reason as yet for modifying HELMHOLTZ's schematic value beyond merely discarding the figure in the fourth decimal place as not being at all certain. Similarly, while recent measurements of the index of refraction of the vitreous humor have given a value which in the fourth decimal place is one or two units less than that of the aqueous humor, it may be regarded as practically identical with the latter. The writer assumes therefore for both indices the *schematic value* 1.336.

The constants of the cornea system. If the radii and thickness of the cornea are denoted by ρ_1, ρ_2 and d, respectively (all expressed in metres), and if the indices of refraction of the cornea and the aqueous humor are denoted by n_1, n_2, then from the general formulae for the combination of two optical systems, namely,

$$D_c = D_1 + D_2 - \delta D_1 D_2 , \qquad H_c = \frac{\delta D_2}{D_c}, \qquad H_c' = -\frac{\delta D_1}{D_c},$$

where

$$D_1 = \frac{n_1 - 1}{\rho_1}, \qquad D_2 = \frac{n_2 - n_1}{\rho_2}, \qquad \delta = \frac{d}{n_1},$$

the following numerical results may now be calculated:

Refracting power D_c........................ = 43.053 dptr
Position of the first principal point 1000 H_c.... = −0.0496 mm
Position of the second principal point
   1000 $(d + n_2 H_c')$........................ = −0.0506 mm

[1] G. FREYTAG, *Vergleichende Untersuchungen über die Brechungsindizes der Linse und der flüssigen Augenmedien des Menschen und höherer Tiere in verschiedenen Lebensaltern.* Wiesbaden 1907.

where the vertex of the anterior surface of the cornea is taken as the origin or zero point. The values of the focal lengths are 23.227 and 31.031 mm.

2. The Lens

Unless a BLIX ophthalmometer is available, HELMHOLTZ's method of ascertaining *the positions of the surfaces of the crystalline lens* is still today the best method. The lamps and fixation mark may be connected with a rectilinear scale (HELMHOLTZ[1]) or with a graduated arc (TSCHERNING[2]); or the angles can be read off as in the previous investigation of the posterior surface of the cornea. The advantage of the latter arrangement is that the ophthalmometric NERNST lamps can be used, which are not convenient for adjustment along a straight or curved scale. (TSCHERNING calls the instrument he uses for this purpose an "ophthalmophakometer.")

For measuring the depth of the anterior chamber of the eye, DONDERS[3] uses a so-called corneal microscope which was focused first on the anterior surface of the cornea (made visible with calomel so as to get the exact focus) and then on the edge of the pupil; the apparent position of the pupil being thus found by the change of focus. Perhaps more reliable results can be obtained by the method of MANDELSTAM and SCHÖLER[4] worked out under HELMHOLTZ's supervision, which was used by REICH.[5] An unsilvered plate of glass acting as a mirror is interposed between the microscope and the cornea so as to reflect the light along the axis of the microscope into the eye. The image of the lamp reflected in the anterior surface of the cornea can be shifted by optical means until it is sharply in line with the edge of the pupil. The position of the reflex image as found by calculation will be the apparent place of the pupil. In these methods, as also in that of HELMHOLTZ, what is measured is the distance of the edge of the iris from the anterior surface of the cornea.

Doubtless, BLIX's method described above, which to a certain extent is connected with the one just mentioned, is the most accurate that has been used at all. It determines the distance of the anterior surface of the lens. This distance can be obtained also by HELMHOLTZ's method for measuring the distance of the posterior surface of the lens, as this is a general method of finding the apparent position of a re-

[1] *Handbuch d. phys. Opt.* 2. Aufl. S. 103.

[2] Loc. cit.

[3] Instrument pour mesurer la profondeur de la chambre antérieure et la courbure de la cornée. *Congrès de Londres. Compte rendu.* 1872. p. 209.

[4] L. MANDELSTAM und H. SCHÖLER, Eine neue Methode zur Bestimmung der optischen Konstanten des Auges. *Arch. f. Ophth.* XVIII, 1. 1872. S. 155.

[5] M. REICH, Resultate einiger ophthalmometrischer und mikrooptometrischer Messungen. Ibid. XX, 1. 1874. S. 207.

flecting surface. However, it should be noted that, although this plan gives exceedingly accurate results for the measurement of the thickness of the cornea owing to its smallness, the determination of the position of the surface of the lens is quite a different matter, because the distance between the points where the ray enters and leaves the cornea is too considerable to permit the intervening piece of the cornea to be regarded as the portion of a sphere. Perhaps, therefore, for such measurements as these we ought to calculate an osculating ellipse based on the radii as measured at these places and at the point where the axis used in the measurement meets the cornea; and to employ this curve for trigonometrical calculation of the position of the surface in question. On the other hand, the errors due to neglecting the refraction at the posterior surface of the cornea are of quite secondary importance. In these measurements TSCHERNING adjusts two lamps in a plane which contains the axis of the telescope and determines the axis of the system by observing the reflex images of the lamps in the cornea and in the given surface of the lens, which should appear to be all in a straight line. In the calculation the cornea is regarded as spherical, apparently without observing HELMHOLTZ's precaution of repeating the measurement by changing the direction of the incident light without altering the angle of incidence. Concerning this method, therefore, perhaps it should be said that, while the investigation is certainly much simpler, the results are not so reliable.

There are two other methods of investigating the depth of the anterior chamber, mainly intended for clinical use, namely, that of HEGG[1] with a stereoscopic instrument and variable pointer and that of GRÖNHOLM[2] with CZERMAK's orthoscope, which latter is merely for approximate measurements.

The following values of the distance between the pupillary plane and the vertex of the cornea were obtained by the original method of HELMHOLTZ:

HELMHOLTZ [See §3.]..............4.024	3.597	3.739	
KNAPP[3].........................3.692	3.707	3.477	3.579
ADAMÜK and WOINOW[4].............3.998	3.237	2.900	3.633

[1] E. HEGG, Eine neue Methode zur Messung der Tiefe der vorderen Augenkammer. *Arch. f. Augenheilkunde.* XLIV. Erg.-Heft. 1901. S. 84.

[2] V. GRÖNHOLM, Eine einfache Methode die Tiefe der vorderen Augenkammer zu messen. *Skand. Arch. f. Physiologie.* XIV. 1903. S. 235.

[3] J. H. KNAPP, Über die Lage und Krümmung der Oberflächen der menschlichen Kristallinse und den Einfluss ihrer Veränderungen bei der Akkommodation auf die Dioptrik des Auges. *Arch. f. Ophth.* VI, 2. 1860. S. 1.

[4] E. ADAMÜK und M. WOINOW, Zur Frage über die Akkommodation der Presbyopen. Ibid. XVI, 1. 1870. S. 141.

whereas v. REUSS[1] consistently got smaller values which evidently cannot be taken into account along with the above. The mean of the preceding is 3.598. In two instances values of 3.921 and 3.651 were found by the method of MANDELSTAM and SCHÖLER; and for three different individuals values of 3.639, 3.708 and 3.652 were obtained by REICH; so that this method gives a mean value of 3.714 mm. The emmetropic eyes investigated by BLIX gave a mean value of 3.515, but it should be noted that only one of the five eyes was measured at the vertex of the cornea, all the others being measured at the point where the line of sight (*Visierlinie*) meets the cornea, so that the true mean value must be a little larger, and probably is more nearly equal to that found by HELMHOLTZ's method.

The results of these investigations justify the assumption of *the schematic value of* 3.6 mm *for the distance between the anterior surfaces of the cornea and crystalline lens*. This was the value that HELMHOLTZ[2] took in his schematic eye, and it has been quite generally adopted. The mean values obtained by STADFELDT[3] and AWERBACH[4] by TSCHERNING's approximate method are: STADFELDT from measurements of 10 eyes, 3.81; AWERBACH, for 15 emmetropic eyes, 3.4; for 28 hypermetropic eyes, 3.5; and for 43 myopic eyes, 3.6.

The determination of the position of the posterior surface of the lens gives its *thickness*. The results of measurements made under HELMHOLTZ's supervision are:

HELMHOLTZ[5] [See p. 112.]............3.414   3.801   3.555
KNAPP 3.920   3.848   3.776   3.622
ADAMÜK and WOINOW..............3.202   3.963   3.944   3.567

the mean value being 3.692 mm. The results of MANDELSTAM and SCHÖLER together with those of REICH give the mean value 3.787 mm; the mean of STADFELDT's measurements is 3.63; and AWERBACH obtained 3.89, 3.94 and 3.88 for emmetropia, hypermetropia and myopia, respectively.

The value that HELMHOLTZ took for his schematic eye was 3.6 mm. According to the numbers given above, on the assumption that the methods of measurements were absolutely accurate, this value should be from 0.1 to 0.2 mm greater. But if the sources of error are taken into account, depending on the asymmetrical flattening of the cornea,

---

[1] A. v. REUSS, Untersuchungen über die optischen Konstanten ametropischer Augen. Ibid. XXIII, 4. 1877. S. 183.

[2] *Handbuch d. phys. Opt.* 2. Aufl.

[3] A. STADFELDT, *Den menneskelige linses optiske konstanter.* Kopenhagen 1898.

[4] M. AWERBACH, Zur Dioptrik der Augen bei verschiedenen Refraktionen. (Russian.) *Inaug.-Diss. Moskau* 1900. Reviewed in *Jahresber. ü. d. Leist. u. Fortschr. i. G. d. Ophthalmologie.* XXXI. S. 652.

on the unknown form of the anterior surface of the lens, and on using
a total index for the index of refraction of the lens, there can be no
doubt that HELMHOLTZ's number is within the possible limits of error.
Moreover, the lens gets larger and larger as years go on, and according
to all measurements of the dead lens that have been made hitherto the
thickness increases but never decreases. Also the difference between
the thickness of the unaccommodated lens in the living eye and that
of the dead lens is found to be less with advancing years. For these
reasons, and finally, because, owing to various individual variations
of the lens substance that begin to be very manifest soon after the age
of youth, the schematic value should apply to a youthful eye. The
latter should be taken rather less than the mean value. Hence, the
writer concludes that with the present available material of investigation there is no good ground for changing *the schematic value of the
thickness of the unaccommodated lens* as assumed by HELMHOLTZ,
that is, 3.6 mm.

Curvatures of the Surfaces of the Lens. The same conclusion has
been reached also concerning the radii of curvature of the two surfaces
of the lens. The variations between the mean values of these dimensions and the schematic values as assumed by HELMHOLTZ are comprised within the limits of the errors that are involved in the methods
of measurement. It would seem therefore to be unnecessary to give
here the actual figures. It is sufficient to say that investigations by
TSCHERNING's method have yielded similar results, mean values
according to STADFELDT being 10.9 and 6.0 mm, and according to
AWERBACH 10.4 and 6.1 mm. The schematic values of the radii of
curvature of the surfaces of the lens as used by HELMHOLTZ are 10 and
6 mm; and apparently they are still the best values to take for this
purpose.

In the earlier measurements of the curvatures of the surfaces of
the lens, sometimes HELMHOLTZ's original method was employed
and sometimes also the reflex images, obtained by using sunlight,[1]
or the DRUMMOND lime-light,[2] were measured directly with a HELM-
HOLTZ ophthalmometer. The ophthalmometric NERNST lamps are
peculiarly adapted for the more recent methods. For an accurate
computation of the radius from the results found by measurements,
all that is necessary is to use the method given above for finding the
curvature of the posterior surface of the cornea. The formula given by

[1] B. Rosow, Zur Ophthalmometrie. A. d. physiol. Labor. des Herrn Prof. HELMHOLTZ.
Arch. f. Ophth. XI, 2. S. 129.

[2] v. REUSS, loc cit.

HELMHOLTZ,[1] which is applicable for infinitesimal angles of incidence, enables us to obtain an approximate value. The writer's own calculations as performed by the first of these methods, like those of other investigators, indicate no reason for changing HELMHOLTZ's schematic values of the distance or curvatures of the surfaces of the lens.

The measurements of SAUNTE[2] made in TSCHERNING's laboratory are peculiar. Diffused light obtained from an electric arc lamp was employed in a quite complicated arrangement of apparatus. Since there was an angle between the incident light and the ophthalmometric axis just as in the method of measuring the posterior surface of the cornea described above, SAUNTE called his method a "decentrated ophthalmometry." But in spite of the oblique incidence, formulae are used in the calculation that are applicable only for perpendicular incidence, and hence the results are not easily assessed.

TSCHERNING's method as used by STADFELDT and AWERBACH amounts to finding the apparent position of the centre of curvature in a manner similar to that for finding the place of the surface. Thus, a line of centres having been determined, the light is allowed to enter the eye in the direction of the ophthalmometric axis, at a certain angle with the line of centres; and all that is necessary is to measure the angle of incidence and calculate by trigonometry the position of the centre of curvature. However, fairly large angles are required, and in the calculation the surfaces are regarded as spherical, and hence only approximate values can be found in this way, with errors that cannot be estimated. TSCHERNING himself has pointed out the uncertainty in the results due to the feeble specific intensity of the light-source used in the experiment, and intimated that the method was not free from objections. Perhaps, therefore, the differences between the values obtained by STADFELDT and AWERBACH and the schematic values are within the limits of possible errors.

The form of the surfaces of the lens in the living eye has been minutely investigated by BESIO[3] by TSCHERNING's method. He discovered such a pronounced flattening towards the periphery that it certainly cannot be accounted for as due to possible error. On the other hand, on account of the approximate method of calculation, the results in a quantitative sense are probably less trustworthy. According to him, the osculating surface of the second degree was hyperbolic for the anterior surface and parabolic for the posterior surface of the lens. By investigations of the dead lens, with proper

[1] *Handbuch*, 2. Aufl. S. 144.

[2] O. H. SAUNTE, *Linsemaalinger (Linsenmessungen)*. Odense 1905.

[3] E. BESIO, La forme du cristallin humain. *Journal de physiologie et de pathologie générale*. III. 1901. pp. 547, 761, 783.

precautions and use of exact methods of calculation, the fact of the flattening towards the periphery was positively confirmed by DALÉN,[1] although with respect to the anterior surface of the lens HOLTH[2] had obtained a contrary result.

In experimenting with the reflex image in the anterior surface of the lens it has been frequently noticed that for slight movements of the patient's eye the image executes slight movements also but with remarkably high speed, as if there were hollows or furrows on the surface. However, as the reflected light is not due entirely to the anterior surface of the lens, as is indicated by the diffused form of the reflex image, but is reflected partly also from the adjacent layers, it is not possible to draw any conclusions from this phenomenon as to the form of the surface itself.

The substance of the lens, as shown by refractometric investigations, consists of a medium of variable index of refraction. Physiological measurements indicate very clearly that during childhood and until puberty the variation of the index is continuous throughout the lens. However, towards the end of the second decade of life, perhaps usually a little later, light reflexes begin to be manifest; implying a discontinuity in the variation of the index of refraction. With movements of the source of light, these granular appearances or *"Kernbildchen"* (as they were called by HESS[3] who described them first in the eyes of human beings) behave as if they had their origin in a continuous surface. Consequently, in order to investigate the dioptrics of the lens, we need to know the laws of optical imagery not simply for media of continuously variable index of refraction, but also when there are such discontinuities in the variation of the index as may be considered as amounting to surfaces separating two different media of variable index of refraction. Now while we do not know enough about these surfaces of discontinuity[4] to apply to them the laws above mentioned, at the same time, so far as the imagery produced by the surfaces of the lens is concerned, these laws are absolutely requisite, because the ordinary formulae are not applicable to this imagery when the light goes obliquely through the lens. The problem was attacked by

[1] ALBIN DALÉN, Ophthalmometrische Messungen an der toten menschlichen Kristallinse. *Mitt. a. d. Augenklinik d. Carol. Med. Chir. Inst. z. Stockholm,* 1905.

[2] S. HOLTH, Études ophthalmométriques sur l'œil humain après la mort. IX. *Congr. intern. d'ophth. d'Utrecht. Compte rendu.* 1899. S. 386.

[3] C. HESS, Über Linsenbildchen, die durch Spiegelung am Kerne der normalen Linse entstehen. *Arch. f. Augenheilk.* LI. 1905. p. 375.

[4] The idea of discontinuity relates here solely to the mathematical function of the variation of the index and not at all to the manner in which the space is occupied by the substance of the lens.

L. HERMANN[1] and L. MATTHIESSEN,[2] who derived differential equations for the ray-convergence from the formulae for homogeneous media by proceeding to the limit. Now this method is not justifiable unless the same mathematical process has not been employed already in developing the original formulae; and consequently, the differential equations thus obtained for the ray-convergence in a meridian section and for the aberration are not correct. Moreover, these investigations did not include the magnification-ratios. Hence all that was known of the required laws was the differential equation for the ray-convergence along the axis of a system of revolution, as obtained first by LIPPICH,[3] and the differential equation for the ray-convergence in the equatorial section, as derived by HERMANN for an optical system of concentric layers, and by MATTHIESSEN for a system of revolution. In addition, an approximate law of the increase of the index of refraction as found by MATTHIESSEN[4] has been used for integration, just as if it were mathematically exact, leading therefore again to erroneous results.

In obtaining the laws in question, it is evident that the general fundamental equation of optical imagery, and the general laws derived from it (p. 270) for any optical system whatsoever, cannot be employed unless the variation of the index of refraction of the media in it is continuous. When there is a plane of symmetry, the differential equations are simplified and are applicable then to the meridian plane of a system of revolution. In this case we obtain by integration the same equations as were found for homogeneous media, namely,

$$\kappa^2 B = A + \kappa D, \qquad \kappa K B = A,$$

where the refracting power is given by a definite integral corresponding to the summation formula. In addition to the complete laws of the first order, the investigation has led also to formulae for calculating the aberration. At the surface of the lens where the light passes between two media one of which has a variable index of refraction, the refracting power has the same value for the second imagery as if the two media were homogeneous, but not for the first imagery; and, moreover, the formula for calculating the imagery along the axis is different.

It appears from a study of the ray-convergence in the eye for the case of a point-source of light that the wave surface of the bundle

---

[1] L. HERMANN, Über Brechung bei schiefer Inzidenz mit besonderer Berücksichtigung des Auges. *Arch. f. d. ges. Physiol.* XXVII. 1882. S. 291.

[2] L. MATTHIESSEN, Über den schiefen Durchgang unendlich dünner Strahlenbündel durch die Kristallinse des Auges. Ibid. XXXII. 1883. S. 97.

[3] In a review in *Zeitschr. f. Math. u. Phys.* XXIII. 1878. Hist.-Lit. Abt. S. 63.

[4] *Grundriss der Dioptrik geschichteter Linsensysteme.* Leipzig. 1877.

of refracted rays in the eye is not a surface of revolution at all, but may be considered as having complete contact of the fourth order with such a surface. The star figures seen as radiating lines around the luminous point are due to a definite peculiarity of the wave surface characterized by a wave-like procedure of the line in which the wave surface is cut by a co-axial cylinder. Since the genesis of this form of wave surface has been shown (p. 192) to be due to the passage of light through the lens, the necessary mathematical consequence is that either the lens-surfaces themselves or the *iso-indicial surfaces* of the substance of the lens must have such a form. These latter surfaces, each of which is the locus of points where the index of refraction has one and the same value, constitute therefore a system of surfaces having complete contact of the fourth order with a system of revolution; and consequently it is this system which must be the basis of the investigation.

If the lens is supposed to be composed of a medium of continuously variable index of refraction, this is not perfectly true except for the youthful lens which shows no sign of discontinuity; whereas in case of the riper lens it is just about as accurate as the physiological data heretofore available will permit. The mathematical methods of dealing with the dioptrics of surfaces of discontinuity have been worked out.

The substance of the lens constitutes an optical system which for investigating the dioptrics of the lens is combined in the ordinary way with the systems represented by the surfaces of the lens; and which will be referred to as the *core of the lens*, as proposed by MATTHIESSEN. It is to be regarded, therefore, as a system of revolution of continuously variable index of refraction; and, for complete information as to the dioptrics of the lens, all that remains to be done is to find the law of the variation of the index. Since the total variation of the index of refraction of the crystalline lens as well as the thickness of the lens and the diameter of the pupil are relatively small as compared with the focal length, this law can be expressed in the form of a series, provided refractometer investigations show that the series is convergent. The point where the index of refraction has its greatest value may be considered as the centre of the lens, and taken as the origin of a system of coördinates whose x-axis lies along the axis of revolution and is reckoned as positive towards the retina. If μ_0 denotes the value of the index of refraction at the centre of the lens, and μ its value at the point x, y, the general form of the *indicial equation* including powers of x, y as high as the fourth is as follows:

$$\mu_0 - \mu = \frac{1}{2}(m\,x^2 + n\,y^2) + \frac{1}{6}(M\,x^3 + 3Nx\,y^2) + \frac{1}{24}(p_m x^4 + 6p_0 x^2 y^2 + p_n y^4),$$

since in a system of revolution the coefficients of the missing terms in the series vanish. If only the first two terms are retained, the equation reduces to one of the second degree; and the corresponding *indicial curve*, that is found by plotting the distances measured from the centre of the lens along a diameter as abscissae and the indices of refraction as ordinates, turns out to be a parabola. A series of investigations, carried out by MATTHIESSEN and his successors on the crystalline lenses of the eyes of human beings and other animals, indicates that the indicial curve is approximately parabolic in form, although the osculating curve of the second degree may also be an ellipse of great eccentricity. This result in itself is a complete justification of the propriety of expressing the indicial equation in the form of a series, because it converges rapidly; and it shows also that the indicial equation of the second degree is a first approximation that may be employed so long as it does not conflict with mathematical or physical realities. However, further mathematical study reveals that there are some conflicts of this kind. MATTHIESSEN could not formulate a single indicial equation for the nucleus of the lens, but had to assign to each half of it a special function, according to which the iso-indicial surfaces of one system had a single intersection with those of the other, although in the diagrammatic figure of a meridian plane[1] the points of intersection were arbitrarily rounded off. But this is equivalent to a surface of discontinuity passing through the centre of the lens, which would necessarily give a reflex, and whose existence may be positively denied on the basis of the absolute absence of any anatomical evidence for it. It is true that the most recent measurements of the index of refraction[2] might be compatible with a single indicial equation of the second degree for the case of a symmetrical, accommodating lens, and with one of the third degree for an asymmetrical lens. But this would involve such a great increase in the thickness of the lens for accommodation that it may be definitely ruled out. Hence it appears to be unavoidable for the dioptrics of the nucleus of the lens to include in the indicial equation all the terms of the fourth degree. Another indicial equation, due to MAXWELL, and obtained by developing the reciprocal of the index of refraction in a series of powers, is essentially nothing more than an interesting problem of geometrical optics without physiological reality. When terms of higher powers than the second are neglected, it reduces to MATTHIESSEN's formula.

MATTHIESSEN's parabolic indicial curve, which was used also

---

[1] Loc. cit. *Grundriss usw.* S. 198.
[2] FREYTAG, loc. cit.

by Monoyer[1] in the latest investigation of this subject, is typically analogous to Sturm's focal lines of the general bundle of optical rays, both approximations originating by discarding terms higher than the second and being applied beyond the limits where they are valid. The law of the total index given by Matthiessen affords a perfect illustration of the unfortunate influence that the focal lines have exerted in geometrical optics. Mathematical investigation shows that in general the total index varies with every change of the shape of the lens, and hence cannot be calculated at all from the values of the index of refraction at the centre of the lens and in the outside cortical layer. Matthiessen's law, that the total index is just as much greater than the index at the centre of the lens as the latter is greater than that of the outside cortex, might indeed be correct, provided the indicial surfaces were geometrically similar to each other in strict mathematical sense, and provided that the only possible changes in the form of the lens were such as to preserve this characteristic unchanged. Obviously, from what has been stated above, this singular condition in the human eye is ruled out.

The next problem, therefore, is to determine the seven constants of the indicial equation as given above. From measurements of the index of refraction, considering at the same time the limits of accuracy of these methods, not more than three equations can be obtained for this purpose, since we may consider that we know accurately enough the values of the index at the centre of the lens, at its poles, and in the equator. Two additional equations are derived from the values of the radii of curvature of the surfaces of the lens, since there is very great probability for the assumption that the curvatures of adjacent iso-indicial surfaces are equal. From a physiological source one other equation may be obtained, by calculating the refracting power of the lens-core from the loss of refracting power of the eye when the lens has been extracted. However, one more equation still is necessary, and for that Matthiessen's parabolic law can be used provided it is restricted to the axis of the lens, especially as from the investigation on which it is based this law may be considered as correct so long as it does not conflict with the actual facts. Hence the writer has obtained the needful seventh equation by assuming a parabolic indicial curve along the axis for which the constant p_m is equal to zero. However, here he has made a special investigation to prove that a variation from this law along the axis even to an extent that we know would

[1] Monoyer, La théorie des systèmes stratifiés. *Société française d'ophthalmologie. Congrès de* 1908. Paris. The method is a variation of that of Matthiessen, and, like it, does not give any unique indicial equation.

be out of the question is essentially without any influence. For each case the results have been put in such form that if future investigations should give a value of p_m different from zero, the constants of the indicial equation may be obtained directly by substituting this value.

On account of the slow variation of the index of refraction in the vicinity of the centre of the lens, the position of the centre of the lens can only be found approximately. The change of form of the anterior surface of the lens is so considerable during accommodation that the lens itself becomes very nearly symmetrical in shape, probably involving a marked increase in the thickness of the two portions of the lens on each side of the centre. Moreover, after the appearance of sclerosis of the core of the lens, the latter is found usually a little nearer the anterior than the posterior surface. From such considerations the writer has estimated the distance of the centre of the lens from the anterior and posterior surfaces as having the values 1.7 and 1.9 mm, respectively. However, so far as the dioptrics of the lens is concerned, these distances may be considered as being equal.

Concerning the indices of refraction, measurements made prior to the introduction of the refractometer are of no value. Recent measurements with this instrument yield numerical results varying from 1.38 to 1.39 for the outside cortex and from 1.40 to 1.42 at the centre of the lens. Undoubtedly, the most reliable results are those of FREYTAG[1] who carried out numerous measurements with careful regard for the necessary precautions. His determinations have therefore been taken by the writer for the schematic values. From table III of his measurements for eyes of human beings up to 30 years of age the following are the mean values of the index of the superficial layer of the lens:

Anterior Vertex	Equator	Posterior Vertex
1.387	1.375	1.385

and for the same class of eyes table IX gives the mean value of the index for the

Centre of the lens: 1.406.

The difference between the values of the index at the vertices and at the equator, as here established has very great significance for the dioptrics of the lens, and, incidentally, it is this very difference that makes it possible to formulate an indicial equation of the second degree like MATTHIESSEN's for the accommodating lens. The difference between the values found for the two vertices is perhaps of less importance, since, in the first place, this difference has very little effect on the dioptric equations, secondly, it is small, and, thirdly,

---

[1] Loc. cit.

the *post mortem* drying up that takes place in the eye produces a change in its fluid that renders the result in this respect rather less certain. Accordingly, the writer assumes for the index of the two vertices of the lens the mean value of 1.386 as the schematic value. The index at the equator cannot be used in the calculation until the distance of the layer in question from the centre of the lens is known; and since no measurements of this distance seem to have been made, the writer employs the above result by assigning the schematic index 1.376 to the points whose coördinates are $x = 0$, $y = \pm 4.2$; which implies that the mean value of 1.375 given above belongs to a point in the equator estimated as being a little towards the periphery.

The refracting power of the core lens and the total index of the lens would follow from the schematic values thus defined, provided MAT-THIESSEN's law of the total index were correct. But as this is not the case, the only thing left to do is to ascertain the value in question by direct investigation. Moreover, the variation of the total index with every change in the form of the lens makes its determination illusory, no matter whether this is done by direct measurement on the dead lens according to HELMHOLTZ's method (as illustrated by Fig. 49) or whether BERLIN's[1] method is used by comparing the lens with and without accommodation in the living eye. On the other hand, the striking difference between the values 1.4519, 1.4414 as found by HELMHOLTZ (p. 110) and the values 1.4260 to 1.4434 as given by STADFELDT[2] may possibly be explained by this change of the total index, together with such sources of error as are unavoidable on account of *post mortem* variations of the physical index of refraction; especially as a variable factor is introduced by the mode of fastening the lens in the experiment, which must affect the value of the total index. Indeed, it would seem to be extremely doubtful whether the total index of the unaccommodated lens in the living eye can be found at all with the dead lens, inasmuch as all the passive relations and particularly the distribution of the tension of the zonule between the various groups of fibres require to be exactly reproduced.

It is quite certain, therefore, that there is no other way of ascertaining the refracting power of the lens and the total index except in the living eye; and the only method that is left is to calculate it from the loss of refraction that the eye suffers when the lens is extracted. This matter was actually within the province of ophthalmology during the past twenty years when it was quite the fashion to treat myopia by

[1] E. BERLIN, Über eine Bestimmung des totalindex der Linse am lebenden Auge. *Arch. f. Ophth.* XLIII. 1897. S. 28?.

[2] Loc. cit.

an operation in which the crystalline lens was extracted. It developed from a comparison of the correction of the eye before and after the operation, that HELMHOLTZ's schematic eye does not represent the actual relations close enough, the total index of the lens being too great and the axial length of the eyeball too short.

In this calculation of the total index, the refraction of the eye before and after removal of the lens may be determined, as BJERKE[1] did, with respect to the apparent position of the optical centre of the lens; in which case the loss of refraction is directly proportional to the refracting power of the lens, and the approximation which consists in using an optical centre in place of the principal points of the lens has no effect on the accuracy that is obtainable by the calculation. The best way to perform the calculation is as follows. The general image-equations referred to the principal points of the cornea are

$$B = A + D_c , \qquad KB = A.$$

Let δ denote the reduced distance of the optical centre of the lens from the posterior principal point of the cornea; κ the magnification-ratio at the optical centre; and x the apparent position of this centre with respect to the anterior surface of the cornea. Then substituting $\dfrac{1}{\kappa - H_c}$, $\dfrac{1}{\delta}$ and κ for A, B and K, respectively, we obtain:

$$\kappa = 1 - \delta D_c , \qquad x = \frac{\delta}{\kappa} + H_c.$$

Now since the distances of the optical centre from the two surfaces of the lens are proportional to the radii of curvature, the schematic values as above defined give:

$$\delta = \frac{0.05 + 3.6 + 2.25}{1.336} \text{ mm}$$

$$\kappa = 0.80987 \qquad x = 5.4 \text{ mm.}$$

Let D_c, D_l, and D denote the refracting powers of cornea, lens, and eye as a whole; then the general formula for the combination of two systems is

$$D = D_c + \kappa D_l.$$

Let A, B denote the reduced convergences for a distinct image in the eye before the lens is removed, measured at the apparent place of the optical centre of the lens; and let A_0, B_0 denote the reduced convergences for a distinct image after removal of the lens, with respect to the actual position of the optical centre of the lens; so that

$$\kappa^2 B = A + \kappa D , \qquad \kappa^2 B_0 = A_0 + \kappa D_c.$$

[1] K. BJERKE, Über die Veränderung der Refraktion und Sehschärfe nach Entfernung der Linse. II. *Arch. f. Ophth.* LV. 2. 1903. S. 191.

Since the values of the left-hand sides of the two equations are identical, we have:

$$A_0 - A = \kappa^2 D_l.$$

It is pretty well ascertained that most eyes that have been operated on for cataract require a correction glass of between 10 and 11 dptr; and from this fact the value of A_0 can be calculated. Previous attempts to harmonize this fact with data for a schematic eye have not been successful and have resulted in obtaining an augmented optical effect of the correction glasses used for the calculation, by assuming a great distance between the glass and the vertex of the cornea. For example, TREUTLER[1] places the posterior vertex of the correction glass at a distance of 13 mm from the vertex of the cornea, and estimates the distance of the second principal point of the glass as being 1.5 mm from the glass surface. Thus, using the mean value of the correction, he obtains the value 80.735 mm for the distance of the virtual far point of the aphakic eye from the vertex of the cornea, corresponding therefore to a value $A_0 = 13.27$ dptr.

This value is certainly rather too high, because in making an accurate measurement of the refraction of the eye the distance between the glass and the eye is taken as small as possible, and since, too, in most clinics the eyelashes of those who are operated on for cataract are removed. Nevertheless, if this value is used here by the writer, it is because he considers it as being an outside upper limit.

It is not permissible simply to put $A = 0$ in calculating the refracting power of the crystalline lens, as is usually done, because, in the first place, the normal refraction of the eye as ascertained by trial-case glasses is not emmetropic at the age when most cataracts are extracted, and, secondly, owing to the aberration, this method does not give the value along the axis that is to be used in the imagery-laws of the first order. Whereas the aberration in the eye as a whole amounts to a difference of at least 1 dptr between the latter value and the value obtained by the ordinary method of refraction, the same difference may not exist in case of the eye that has been operated on for cataract. Indeed, the writer has proved ophthalmometrically that that part of the cornea, which ordinarily remains uncovered by the lid and has to be considered when the pupil has a fairly large size, is responsible for a slight positive aberration; as has been confirmed also by the ophthalmoscope in a case of spontaneous reabsorption of the lens. But after the cataract operation there occurs a pronounced flattening of the vertical section of the cornea, which has an effect on

[1] Einige Bemerkungen zu den schematischen Augen. *Klin. Monatsbl. f. Augenheilk.* XL. 1902. S. 1.

the aberration in such fashion that the refraction of the operated eye as found by the trial-case method gives a value that is extremely likely to be the refraction along the axis. Consequently, while the value of A_0 is not influenced by the aberration, that of A is equal to the sum of the mean value of the refraction at the average age of the person who undergoes the cataract operation and the amount of the difference due to aberration between the measured refraction and the exact refraction along the axis. By assuming the schematic value $A = 0.75$ dptr, perhaps the writer may have chosen a lower limit for it. Hence, the value of 19.1 dptr for the refracting power of the crystalline lens as obtained by the formula above can certainly not be too small. Since the refracting powers of the two surfaces of the lens are 5 and 8.33 dptr, the approximate schematic value of the refracting power of the core lens comes out to be 6 dptr as a probable upper limit. Now in the calculation of a schematic eye with this small value for the refracting power of the lens, it appears that it is only with this upper limit that the axial length of the eye is found to be in agreement with the results of anatomical measurements; and hence the writer uses it also as the basis of the calculation of the indicial equation. Let x_1, x_2 denote the abscissae of the two vertices of the lens; μ_1, μ_2 and ρ_1, ρ_2 the indices of refraction and the radii of curvature, respectively, at these points; μ_0, μ_3 the indices of refraction at the points whose coördinates are $x = 0$, $y = +4.2$, and $x = 0$, $y = -4.2$; and D the approximate value of the refracting power of the core lens. Taking the millimetre as unit of length, the writer has therefore used the following numerical values in the calculation:

$$x_1 = -1.7 \qquad x_2 = 1.9 \qquad \rho_1 = 10 \qquad \rho_2 = -6 \qquad D = 0.006$$
$$\mu_0 = 1.406 \qquad \mu_1 = \mu_2 = 1.386 \qquad \mu_3 = 1.376.$$

For $p_m = 0$, these numbers give the following values of the constants of the indicial equation:

$m = 0.012537$	$n = 0.0010475$
$M = -0.0023004$	$N = 0.00011470$
$p_o = 0.0011150$	$p_n = 0.0016012$

It should be remarked that these constants are not mere numerical values, but are magnitudes with physical dimensions, and hence vary in value with the choice of the unit of length. Since the linear magnitudes are expressed here in millimetres, the unit of refracting power, reduced convergence, etc., is equal to a thousand dioptries (Kilodioptry).

By means of the indicial equation, the writer has constructed the sections of the iso-indicial surfaces made by a meridian plane, by

calculating a sufficient number of coördinates for values of the index
of refraction equal to 1.386 and 1.404.   The outer
curve (Fig. 131), therefore, does not coincide with
the surface of the lens, but has a contact of the
second order with it at the vertices only.   The
parabolic law of the variation of the index of refraction along the axis is shown by the fact that the
difference between the value of the index at the
centre of the lens and that on the outer curve is
ten times as great as the same difference for the
inner curve.

   The following are the exact values obtained
for the refracting power (D_k) of the core lens and
the positions of its principal points:

   $D_k = 0.005985$ $H = 0.22921$ $H' = 0.25752,$ Fig. 131.

the reduced distances H, H' being reckoned from the centre of the lens.
As compared with previous estimates, the total index has the remarkably low value of 1.4085.   As long as the exact image-equations in heterogeneous media were unknown, the fictitious total index was the only
method of representing this imagery at all.   But now that the core lens
has become a definite dioptric conception, perhaps the best way to
understand its effect is in terms of the *equivalent core lens;* which is to
be understood here as a lens having the same index of refraction as
that at the centre of the crystalline lens and suspended in a medium
with the same index of refraction as that at the vertices of the crystalline lens; its refracting power and the positions of its principal points
being identical with those of the real core lens.   Moreover, the refracting power of the equivalent core lens is divided between the two
surfaces in the same ratio as it is divided in the real core lens between
the two portions of the substance of the lens on opposite sides of the
centre.   The advantage of using the equivalent core lens is because,
so far as the imagery-laws of the first order are concerned, the entire
lens system then has precisely the optical characteristics of the actual
crystalline lens; whereas, on the contrary, the total index gives a
wrong position for the principal points of the lens.   The radii and
thickness of the equivalent core lens, expressed in millimetres, are
found to have the following values:

   $r_1 = 7.9108$ $r_2 = -5.7605$ $d = 2.4187;$

and if the distance of the anterior surface of the equivalent core lens
from the anterior vertex of the lens is 0.5460 mm, the principal points
of the equivalent core lens coincide with those of the real core lens.

Employing the formulae on page 285 for the combination of three component systems, we find therefore the following data for the crystalline lens as a whole:

$$D_l = 19.1107 \qquad 1000n_2H_l = 2.07792 \text{ mm} \qquad 1000n_2H' = -1.39317 \text{ mm},$$

where H, H' denote here, as usual, the reduced distances of the principal points of the lens from the corresponding surfaces.

In the schematic eye it is best to consider the lenticular system as a system of revolution, just as also the surfaces of the cornea are represented as being surfaces of revolution, although the physiological form is not astigmatic. It is extremely probable that the latter is the case with the lens also. For the astigmatism of the entire system, that is, the total physiological astigmatism of the normal eye, does not amount to that of the cornea by itself, which implies that there must be an opposite lenticular astigmatism. As was explained above, ophthalmometric investigations of the cornea show that a section near the base of the cornea made by a plane perpendicular to the ophthalmometric axis is oblong in shape with its longer diameter vertical. And yet it is hardly conceivable that this is the case unless the whole anterior part of the eyeball has a similar shape, so that certain static conditions are thus involved that are calculated to produce an opposite lenticular astigmatism, which would be a natural result both of a corresponding oblong shape of the lens and of a feebler curvature in the vertical section due to greater tension of the zonule. However, due to the sources of error inherent in the methods, previous attempts at measuring lenticular astigmatism in the living eye cannot claim to be very reliable. Generally speaking, the measurements indicated a direct astigmatism of the anterior surface of the lens and an inverse astigmatism of the posterior surface; a result which by itself would seem to indicate pretty clearly its probable dependence on the sources of error that are involved in the unequal flattening of the cornea in different directions and on the decentration of the refracting surfaces. It should be added that an astigmatic refraction in the core lens may be involved in the form of the iso-indicial surfaces, without having to assume that the surfaces of the lens are astigmatic.

3. The Optical System of the Eye

For the compound system composed of the cornea and the lens the expression

$$1000n_2\delta = 0.0506 + 3.6 + 1000n_2H_l$$

has to be substituted in the general formulae, and thus for the eye as a whole we obtain:

$$D = 58.636, \qquad 1000\,H = 1.3975, \qquad 100\,n_2H' = -4.2061,$$

which are therefore the fundamental constants of the schematic eye. The complete data, as based on the calculation of the equivalent core lens, are collected in the following table. The numerical results of that calculation were obtained only to three places of decimals, and, consequently, there may be a difference as compared with the numbers given above amounting to as much as one unit in the last decimal place.

Schematic Eye, Accommodation Relaxed

Index of refraction of cornea......................	1.376	
" " " " aqueous and vitreous humors...	1.336	
" " " " the lens.....................	1.386	
" " " " the equivalent core lens........	1.406	
Position of anterior surface of cornea...............	0.	
" " posterior " " "	0.5	mm
" " anterior " " lens...............	3.6	
" " " " " equivalent core lens....	4.146	"
" " posterior " " " "....	6.565	"
" " " " " lens.................	7.2	"
Radius of anterior surface of cornea...............	7.7	"
" " posterior " " cornea...............	6.8	"
" " anterior " " lens.................	10.0	"
" " " " " equivalent core lens.....	7.911	"
" " posterior " " core lens.............	−5.76	"
" " " " " lens.................	−6.0	"
Refracting power of anterior surface of cornea.......	48.83	dptr
" " " posterior " " "	−5.88	"
" " " anterior " " lens.........	5.0	"
" " " equivalent core lens.............	5.985	"
" " " posterior surface of lens.........	8.33	"

Cornea System

Refracting power.............................	43.05	dptr
Position of first principal point...................	−0.0496	mm
" " second principal point................	−0.0506	"
First focal length.............................	−23.227	"
Second focal length...........................	31.031	"

Lens System

Refracting power.............................	19.11	dptr
Position of first principal point.................	5.678	mm
" " second principal point...............	5.808	"
Focal length.................................	69.908	"

Complete System of Eye

Refracting power........................... 58.64 dptr
Position of the first principal point.............. 1.348 mm
    "   "   " second principal point........... 1.602 "
    "   "   " first focal point................. −15.707 "
    "   "   " second focal point............... 24.387 "
First focal length............................ −17.055 "
Second focal length....................... 22.785 "
Position of the retinal fovea.................... 24.0 "
Hypermetropia along the axis.................. 1.0 dptr

The refraction-state as found by investigating such an eye as this would be that of emmetropia as will be shown presently in discussing the aberration. A section of the schematic eye is represented by Fig. 132 in which the surfaces are regarded as spherical.

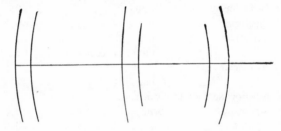

Fig. 132.

From the foregoing explanation it follows that the axial length of the schematic eye is determined by the refraction of the cornea and the mean refraction of the aphakic eye. The greater the refracting power of the cornea and the average hypermetropia of the aphakic eye, the shorter will be the axial length of the schematic eye. By taking account of the difference between the radii of curvature of the cornea at the vertex of the optical zone and the mean radius of curvature of this zone, the value of the refracting power of the cornea given above is the greatest value that is compatible with the preceding metrical results. The same thing is true as to the basis of the calculation by which the hypermetropia of the aphakic eye was found. Obviously, therefore, the length of the axis of the schematic eye cannot be made shorter without doing violence to the facts of the case. It is true that if the lens is removed from the schematic eye, it is 0.1 dioptry more hypermetropic than it should be according to TREUTLER's requirements. Moreover, the axial length of 24 mm is just inside the limits which he thinks are established by measurements of the dead eye. Without attaching undue importance to these measurements, the writer believes however, that he is almost forced to conclude that they would make it very unlikely that the axial length of the schematic eye is greater than 24 mm. According to MAUTHNER,[1] measurements on dead eyes give more values around 25 mm, which would be a good agreement, allowing 1 mm for the thickness of the sclerotica and choroid. However, on the other hand, lower values have been found in numerous measurements. But in estimating measurements of this kind it should be borne in mind that the length of the eye is diminished by *post mortem* changes; nor is it probable that it could be brought back to its original length by artificial restoration of the intraocular pressure that exists in the living eye, since, by virtue of their anatomical structure, a *post mortem* increase of thickness of the cornea and sclerotica may be accompanied by a contraction of the interior of the eyeball.

The remarkably low refracting power of the lens of the schematic eye is a necessary mathematical consequence of the change of refraction that occurs when the lens is removed. Taking account of the effect of aberration, it cannot be greater in the unaccommodated eye than has been found above. The mathematical connection that has been shown to exist between the total index of the lens and its shape enables us for the first time to calculate a schematic eye that is not contrary to any ascertained fact; whereas so small a value for the refracting power of the lens is, on the assumption of the validity of MATTHIESSEN's law, hopelessly at variance with the results of measurements of the index of refraction, and, besides, would not be sufficient for the low total index in the accommodating eye. If by elongating the axis of the schematic eye to a length of 30.98 mm it were made myopic to such a degree that it would be emmetropic if the lens were removed, the myopia along the axis would be 13.16 dptr at the first principal point, and the far point would be 74.58 mm in front of the vertex of the cornea. A glass of 16.7 dptr would be required to correct this myopia, with its second principal point, according to TREUTLER, 14.5 mm in front of the vertex of the cornea, not taking account of the effect of aberration. However, if the latter is taken into consideration, the glass required would have to be about 18 dptr, which agrees perfectly with the results of clinical investigation.

But if it is thus absolutely necessary to take the aberration into account in the exact schematic eye, on the other hand, it may be desirable to calculate a simplified schematic eye, wherein, neglecting the divergent effect of the posterior surface of the cornea, we may assume that the lens is homogeneous, and the entire system free from aberration. But as the fiction of a homogeneous lens is in itself so different

---

[1] L. MAUTHNER, *Vorlesungen über die optischen Fehler des Auges.* Wien 1876. S. 422.

from the actual relations that the positions of the principal points of
the lens cannot be exactly located, we may as well take advantage of
the fiction by assuming the position of the optical centre of the lens.
If the calculation is to be performed anyhow with the incorrect positions of the principal points, there is no sense in taking account of the
distance of these points from each other. The equivalent surface of
the cornea to be used in a simplified schematic eye of this kind has a
radius of curvature which agrees very closely with the schematic radius
of the optical zone as found by the ophthalmometer, and hence this
value has been assumed. By retaining only three decimals in the value
of the total index of the lens, the following values have been found for
a simplified schematic eye; the assumed values (except in case of the
total index of the lens) being the same as in HELMHOLTZ's latest
schematic eye,[1] provided the figures in the last two decimal places are
discarded in the value of the radius of curvature of the cornea and in
the last decimal place in the value of the index of refraction of the
aqueous and vitreous humors. (HELMHOLTZ's data therefor are 1.4371,
7.829 and 1.3365, respectively.) The lens in the calculation is an infinitely thin lens with the vertices of its two surfaces at the optical
centre of the crystalline lens of the eye.

Simplified Schematic Eye

Data assumed

Index of refraction of the aqueous and vitreous humors	1.336	
" " " " " lens.....................	1.413	
Radius of curvature of the equivalent surface of cornea	7.8	mm
" " " " " anterior surface of lens....	10.0	"
" " " " " posterior surface of lens...	−6.0	"
Position of optical centre of lens....................	5.85	"

Calculated values

Refracting power of cornea.......................	43.08	dptr
" " " lens..........................	20.53	"
" " " optical system of eye...........	59.74	"
First focal length of the cornea....................	−23.214	mm
Second focal length of the cornea..................	31.014	"
Focal length of lens..............................	65.065	"
First focal length of eye..........................	−16.740	"
Second focal length of eye........................	22.365	"
Position of first principal point....................	1.505	"
" " second principal point..................	1.631	"
" " first focal point........................	−15.235	"
" " second focal point......................	23.996	"

[1] *Handbuch d. phys. Opt.* 2. Aufl. S. 140.

A *reduced eye* corresponding to the exact schematic eye and having an index of refraction of 4/3 would have a radius of curvature of 5.7 mm.

According to the accuracy demanded in any given case, one or the other of these models can be employed. With regard to the simplified schematic eye, it should be expressly noted that, due to neglect of the aberration, the total index of the lens is greater than its actual behaviour indicates, as its value in the exact schematic eye is only 1.4085; and, consequently, this latter eye should be used in case it is desired to trace the rays through the lens exactly. In the simplified schematic eye it may be said that we are never concerned with calculating the refraction at the single surfaces of the lens, but the lens is always to be treated as a single unresolvable optical system.

In the schematic eye both the decentration of the refracting surfaces and the obliquity of the line of sight (*Visierlinie*) are left out of account entirely, because the decentration is doubtful in amount, and moreover seems to be variable in extent. As we have already seen that the anterior surface of the cornea does not have any exact vertical plane of symmetry, obviously, the reflex images of infinitely large objects cannot determine any precise centering of the optical system. However, in HELMHOLTZ's experiment illustrated in Fig. 51 the effect of the asymetry of the cornea is eliminated as far as possible by basing it on the osculating ellipse, and there would seem to be hardly any doubt as to the fact that this experiment proves that the lens is decentered with respect to the axis of this ellipse. But since, by virtue of the asymmetrical structure of the cornea, it is not certainly established that the calculated axis of the ellipse is a normal to the cornea, it is not proved by the experiment that the axis of the lens does not in general coincide with the normal to the cornea that passes through the centre of the pupil. Investigations carried out by TSCHERNING's[1] method afford just as little proof of this. If, in observing the reflex images in the surfaces of the lens, the axis of the telescope and two lights, preferably ophthalmometric NERNST lamps, are adjusted all in one vertical plane, then, supposing there was a vertical plane of symmetry, a position of the eye can be found for which all six reflex images would be seen lying in one straight line. But generally this is not the case. When the patient's eye looks right into the telescope, the reflex images in the anterior surface of the lens are on the nasal side of the reflex images in the cornea, and those in the posterior surface of the lens are on the temporal side. If then the look is directed in towards the nose, in most cases, first, the reflex images in the posterior surface of the lens turn into line with the reflex images in the anterior surface

---

[1] Beiträge zur Dioptrik des Auges. *Zeitschr. f. Physiol. u. Psychol. d. Sinnesorgane.* III. 1892. S. 429 and elsewhere.

of the lens, and, last of all, the latter come in line with the reflex images in the cornea. This experiment shows that as a matter of fact the optical system as a whole has no vertical plane of symmetry (as had been previously ascertained in other ways by ophthalmometric investigations of the cornea); and, provided the surfaces were accurately spherical, or in case the experiment could be performed for very small angles of incidence, it would show that the axis of the lens does not coincide with a normal to the cornea, but passes on the nasal side of the centre of curvature of the cornea. Now in reality very large angles of incidence have to be used to perform this experiment with any success, because indeed it is generally necessary to dilate the pupil artificially, and then we have no right to assume that it is only the optical zone of the cornea that is concerned in the phenomenon. On the contrary, the uneven peripheral flattening in different directions is a factor; and therefore the experiments are not convincing. The same thing applies to the investigation of the vertical decentration where the lights are adjusted in a horizontal plane containing the axis of the telescope. With typically normal eyes the look has to be lifted a little above this plane in order to bring the various reflex images in line with each other.

Accordingly, with respect to the decentration of the refracting surfaces, all that can be said is that the optical system has no axis of symmetry, and that the optical axis of the lens, meaning thereby a common normal to the two surfaces of the lens, meets the cornea in a point that lies outwards and generally a little downwards from the ophthalmometric axial point; as is the case also with the normal to the cornea which passes through the centre of the pupil of medium size. But the fact that this normal, which was defined above as the *optical axis of the eye*, does not coincide with the optical axis of the lens, is so far not proved. Although, obviously, small deviations are extremely likely, they cannot be used in calculations, especially as they have not yet been definitely proved to exist. Investigations of the eye with a luminous point (see below) prove that, if present, they do not affect the imagery in the eye.

Practically, therefore, the only decentration that needs to be considered is that due to the inclination of the line of sight to the optical axis of the eye, which can also be determined by the decentration of the pupil with respect to the ophthalmometric axis of the cornea. In order to find experimentally the position of this axis, we must, as pointed out above, employ a pupil of medium size, preferably 4 mm produced by illumination. For although the apparent centre of the pupil does not seem to vary for small changes of the diameter, very considerable differences occur with greater variations of the diameter.

Thus, in one case where the investigation was made with a HELMHOLTZ ophthalmometer by the method described on page 315, the writer found for the angle between the line of sight and the optical axis 6.5° with maximum pupil and 2.7° with minimum pupil; and hence, on the supposition of a spherical cornea, the displacement of the centre of the pupil towards the nose, occurring during the contraction, would amount to 0.28 mm. However, part of this displacement may be really due to the asymmetrical flattening of the cornea in the horizontal meridian; and, besides, a difference as large as this is perhaps exceptional. By another, but not so sensitive method, HUMMELSHEIM[1] found that the pupil contracted concentrically.

Point-to-point correspondence of object and image occurs in a very narrow region in the vicinity of the axis of the optical system; and the structure of the retina corresponds to this fact in the most perfect manner, since it is adapted for distinct imagery only in a very small part of it. Hence, the excellence of *the peripheral imagery in the eye* is a matter of secondary importance. If, as a first approximation, the optical system is considered as a centered system of revolution, the two image-surfaces are surfaces of revolution concave towards the forward side, the first of which, whereon are focused the image lines of parallel circles, is nearer the optical apparatus than the second on which the radial or meridian lines are reproduced. Since YOUNG's[2] time various investigators have endeavoured to construct these image-surfaces by calculation or to compute the astigmatism for the peripheral imagery, generally obtaining results in which the retina is close to the image-surfaces or between them. However, until the precise form of the posterior surface of the lens is ascertained, not much value, if any, can be attached to such calculations. The effect of the lamination of the lens on this astigmatism was calculated by HERMANN;[3] who found that the lamination tended to reduce the astigmatism. But this conclusion is due partly to his assumptions and partly to the fact that the differential equations which he used for the primary imagery are not correct. Computation of the schematic lens with variable index of refraction as given above shows that, for a ray incident at the centre of the anterior surface of the lens at an angle of 25°, and on the assumption that the posterior surface is parabolic, the astigmatism is greater than in a homogeneous lens with the corresponding total index. Of the methods of direct investigation of the peripheral imagery on the retina, the one that gives the least trustworthy results is by observing the image of a source of light through the sclera, as can be

[1] Pupillenstudien, *Arch. f. Augenh.* LVII. S. 33. 1907.

[2] TH. YOUNG, On the mechanism of the eye. *Philos. Transactions*, 1801.

[3] Loc. cit.

done when the light enters sideways in the protruding eye. The measurement of the refraction with the ophthalmoscope by the method of the erect image also cannot compare with the skiascopic method, which has perhaps given the most reliable results so far. By this method DRUAULT[1] found that the retina is probably between the two image surfaces, and that the second surface is beyond it and nearer than the first.

Since the line of sight makes a finite angle with the optical axis, the imagery in the *fovea centralis* of the retina, strictly speaking, belongs to the region of the periphery. However, the resulting astigmatism for an angle of 5° amounts only to about one-tenth of a dioptry, as the writer has shown by calculation with HELMHOLTZ's schematic eye.[2] (TSCHERNING has calculated this astigmatism for different angles and finds much higher values, partly due to using a wrong formula, and apparently due also to his having confused these angles with the angles of incidence. From the formulae on page 277, it can be seen that the ratio of the refracting power of the first imagery to that of the second imagery is equal to $1 : \cos i \cos i'$. But this ratio by itself does not give the astigmatism, because in the primary imagery the principal points do not coincide with the point of incidence. TSCHERNING,[3] however, has not only used $1 : \cos^2 i$ in place of the correct ratio, but has also neglected the distances of the refracting surfaces from each other and from the corresponding principal points; which, together with the confusion of the angles, is responsible for the erroneous results.)

III. Refraction of the Eye

What is meant by the refraction of the eye is its focusing as dependent on the length of the axis and the refracting power of the optical system. This name has become firmly established, but it is not altogether a happy designation, inasmuch as it suggests merely one of the factors of optical focusing, whereas the different states of refraction are generally dependent on variability of the other factor also. It is found to be a great advantage in optical problems to reckon all distances as positive in a certain definite direction—otherwise, the necessary changes of sign are apt to lead to errors. And so on the basis of

---

[1] Astigmatisme des rayons pénétrant obliquement dans l'œil. Application de la skiaskopie. *Arch. d'ophth.* XX. 1900. p. 21.

[2] Loc. cit., *Skand. Arch. f. Physiol.* II.

[3] Loc. cit., *Encyclopédie française d'ophthalmologie.* III. p. 185.

this principle, in dealing with the subject of the refraction of the eye either distances measured in the direction in which the light goes must be counted as positive, as is usual in other parts of optics, or conversely. The latter method commonly prevailed until HESS[1] first introduced a theoretically more correct mode of treatment. Thus, according to him, the far-point distance and the near-point distance are both negative when these points are real. The disadvantage of this method for the physician who is not trained in physics, and who therefore has to acquire this mode of view, is too slight to be compared with the simplifications that are gained thereby; and so the writer will follow HESS's method, with the conviction that these advantages will be appreciated by oculists and ophthalmologists.

The focusing of the eye is measured by the convergence of the bundle of rays that falls on it when the image is sharply in focus on the retina; and the only other question that has to be decided is at what point this convergence is to be measured. On account of the simpler form of the image-equations as referred to the principal points, the first principal point of the eye is particularly suitable for this purpose. Thus, in the general equation

$$B = A + D,$$

A denotes the refraction of the eye expressed in dioptries, D the refracting power of the optical system, and $\frac{1}{B} = b$ the reduced distance of the retina from the posterior principal point, which may be called the *reduced length of the axis;* whereas $a = \frac{1}{A}$ denotes the distance from the anterior principal point of the point that is exactly in focus. However, for practical reasons, it is desirable to measure the convergence of the bundle of incident rays also at the place where the spectacle lens is worn or, more accurately, at the second principal point of this glass. If g denotes the distance of the first principal point of the eye from the second principal point of the glass, whereby g is always positive, and if A_g denotes the convergence of the bundle of incident rays at the glass, then

$$\frac{1}{A_g} = \frac{1}{A} + g, \qquad A_g = \frac{A}{1 + gA}, \qquad A = \frac{A_g}{1 - gA_g}.$$

In these expressions g is hardly ever more than 15 mm, and A and A_g usually do not exceed 20 dptr. Practically, therefore, the error

---

[1] C. HESS, Die Refraktion und akkommodation des menschlichen Auges und ihre Anomalien. Leipzig 1902. A separate volume in GRAEFE-SAEMISCH, *Handb. d. Augenheilk.* 2. Aufl. II. T. XII. Kap.

due to neglecting the product g^2A^2 or $g^2A_g^2$ will be of no consequence. and the useful approximate formulae

$$A_g = A(1 - gA), \qquad A = A_g(1 + gA_g)$$

will be accurate enough. HESS calls A_g the *correction value* of the refraction; and hence the above relations may be expressed by saying, *the difference between the refraction and the correction value is numerically equal to $gA\%$ or $gA_g\%$, provided the distance g is given in centimetres; the correction value being always algebraically less than the refraction.* In ophthalmological literature correction value and refraction are sometimes called also "spectacle refraction" and "principal point refraction," respectively. Thus, in myopia the spectacle refraction is numerically greater than the principal point refraction, whereas in hypermetropia it is just the reverse.

Since the act of accommodation consists essentially in a change of the optical focusing of the eye, innumerable states of refraction are comprised within the limits determined by the far point and the near point. If the distances of far point and near point from the first principal point of the eye are denoted by r and p, and if the corresponding convergences are denoted by R and P, respectively, the eye may have every refraction between these values. The difference

$$R - P$$

is the amplitude of accommodation; the refracting power of the optical system being increased, but the refraction itself being diminished by accommodation. However, when we speak simply of the refraction of the eye, it is understood that we refer to its *static* refraction, when it is focused for the far point, and when accommodation, therefore, is relaxed. But if accommodation is exerted, there is a *dynamic* state of refraction, which has its smallest limiting value when the eye is focused for the near point.

Ametropia differs from *emmetropia* in the fact that for the former the refraction has a finite value, this value being positive for *hypermetropia* and negative for *myopia*. The spectacle refraction is the power of the glass that will make an ametropic eye emmetropic; whence is derived also the name correction-value.

As a general rule, the refraction must be determined by *combination of the eye with an optical instrument*. Let D_0, D and D_t denote the refracting powers of the optical instrument, the optical system of the eye, and the compound system, respectively; and let δ denote the distance (or in case the eye is immersed in a fluid, the reduced distance) of the anterior principal point of the eye from the posterior principal point of the optical system which is to be combined with it. Then the data of the compound system can be found by the formulae:

$$D_t = D_0 + D - \delta D_0 D, \qquad H_t = \frac{\delta D}{D_t}, \qquad H_t' = -\frac{\delta D_0}{D_t}.$$

Now if, generally, the convergences of the artificial system (or the reduced convergences, if this system is not surrounded by air) at its principal points are denoted by $A_0 = \dfrac{1}{a_0}$ and $B_0 = \dfrac{1}{b_0}$; and if A, B, a, b, and A_t, B_t, a_t, b_t have similar meanings for the eye and the compound system, respectively, the distances being all reduced distances; then B_0 denotes the refraction of the eye measured at the second principal point of the artificial system, and the principal point refraction is obtained from the expression:

$$A = \frac{A_0 + D_0}{1 - \delta(A_0 + D_0)}.$$

Hence, provided the distance of the object is so great that we may put $A_0 = 0$ (as is the case in ordinary spectacle fitting), D_0 denotes the correction value. In case of other combinations we get certain simplifications for special values of δ. If both A_0 and δ vanish, then the principal point refraction is equal to D_0. For $\delta = \dfrac{1}{D_0}$ we find

$$A = -D_0^2 \left(\frac{1}{D_0} + \frac{1}{A_0} \right) = -\frac{D_0^2}{L_0},$$

where L_0 denotes the reduced convergence measured at the anterior focal point of the artificial system; the equation being therefore identical with the general focal point equation. We obtain the same equation for the correction value of the ametropia when $\delta = \dfrac{1}{D_0} + g$. Hence, for a given value of D_0, the distance of the first focal point of the artificial system from the object is in these cases proportional to the refraction or to the correction value of the ametropia.

The size of the retinal image is given by the two general equations

$$KB = A, \qquad KD = L;$$

the distinct images in the *fovea centralis* being small enough for us to substitute here the ratio of the linear magnitudes of image and object in place of the magnification-ratios (which actually represent only the limiting values). Let a, β denote the linear sizes of object and image for the naked eye; then if the reduced *principal point angle* (ω_h) and the reduced *focal point angle* (ω_f) are defined to be the angles equal to $a A$ and $a L$, respectively, the following expressions will be obtained:

$$\frac{\beta}{\omega_h} = b, \qquad \frac{\beta}{\omega_f} = \frac{1}{D};$$

which are better adapted for the case when the object is very far away, because then the magnification-ratio tends to become infinitely small. (In air the reduced angles are the same as the angles themselves, but they are employed here in order that the formulae may be applicable at once to vision under water.) These formulae state that *the ratio of the size of the retinal image to the focal point angle depends simply on the refracting power of the optical system, whereas its ratio to the principal point angle involves only the reduced length of the axis of the eye.* In employing them it should be noted that, by the definition of the angles, they are negative in the case of a real object, and the resulting negative sign of β simply means that the image on the retina is inverted. The visual angle formerly used which has its vertex at the anterior nodal point of the eye is not so well adapted for precise purposes; and indeed the use of the nodal points in physiological optics is rather unfortunate anyhow, because there is no real advantage in them, and, on the other hand, they are conducive to much that is imaginary.

When the eye is used in conjunction with an artificial optical system, the size of the image on the retina can be ascertained by the effect which this system produces on the magnitudes of the principal point angle and the focal point angle; that is, by investigating *the magnifying power of an optical system used in conjunction with the eye.* But here the question as to the absolute magnifying power of the instrument must be kept distinctly separate from that of the individual magnifying power. The capability of the instrument itself is measured by the absolute magnifying power, since this magnitude has nothing whatever to do with the eye; whereas the individual magnifying power differs from the absolute magnifying power simply because it does take into account the idiosyncrasies of the eye in question. If a_0, β_0 denote the sizes of object and image with respect to the optical instrument, then

$$\omega_h = \beta_0 A, \qquad \beta_0 = \frac{a_0 A_0}{B_0}, \qquad B_0 = A_0 + D_0 = \frac{A}{1 + \delta A};$$

and hence by eliminating A_0, B_0, we find:

$$-\frac{\omega_h}{a_0} = D_0 - A(1 - \delta D_0).$$

An optical instrument used in conjunction with the eye performs best when the accommodation is entirely relaxed. Only beginners, and especially young people, accommodate unnecessarily in using an optical instrument. Moreover, since the emmetropic eye is to be regarded as normal, we must put $A = 0$ in the above formula in order to obtain the *absolute magnifying power of an instrument.* Accordingly, the absolute magnifying power is measured by the refracting power, and hence is expressed best by this value in dioptries. However, most people who work with optical instruments do not know what refracting power means, and so in order to get an abstract number without any dimensions, it is customary to multiply this value by the conventional "distance of distinct vision," namely 0.25 m. Thus, the refracting power in dioptries is four times as great as the conventional value of the magnifying power. The idea of the distance of distinct vision goes back to the time when it did not occur to people that the eye could be focused for infinity; and for this very reason it is an extremely unfortunate expression, because even nowadays an optician may be led to suppose that when an instrument is in action the image must be formed at this conventional distance from the eye. It is singular that ABBE,[1] who perceived the necessity of the notion of the absolute magnifying power of a lens system,—and called it "die vergrössernde Kraft"— was obliged to think of it in terms of a definite distance of the instrument from the eye, because at that time the distance of distinct vision was regarded as being something real. As a matter of fact, it is nothing more than simply a conventional distance of projection. When, employing this conventional mode of speech, we say that the magnification number of an instrument is n, all that we mean is that its refracting power is $4n$ dioptries; and hence an emmetropic eye, using this instrument without exerting any accommodation, obtains a retinal image of the object that is n times as large as it would be if the object was viewed by the eye alone at a distance of 25 cm from its anterior principal point; the reduced length of the eye not having been altered by the accommodation that is required in this latter instance.

In the case of an afocal instrument like the telescope, the absolute magnifying power cannot be obtained by the above formula. But it can be found immediately from the fact that in such types of instruments the values of the magnification-ratio are the same everywhere; and, consequently, an afocal instrument is completely determined as soon as we know the positions of a pair of conjugate points and the corresponding magnification-ratio. The reciprocal of this ratio is the reduced angular magnification-ratio; and if the latter is denoted by k, then

$$k = \frac{\omega_h}{a_0 A_0} \,,$$

where the reduced convergence A_0 is measured from the point on the axis of the instrument that is conjugate to the anterior principal point

[1] ERNST ABBE, *Gesammelte Abhandlungen.* I. Jena 1904. S. 445.

of the eye. For an emmetropic eye the object is at infinity when the instrument is afocal. In this case the distance apart of the two points just mentioned is infinitesimal as compared with the distance of the object, and hence the number k gives the absolute magnifying power of the focal system.

The *individual magnifying power* in the various cases is to be found from the general formula above. With an ordinary magnifying glass, for example, both δ and D_0 are positive; and hence $1 - \delta D_0$ is positive also, provided the posterior focal point of the glass is beyond the anterior principal point of the eye. Under such circumstances, the individual magnifying power is less than the absolute magnifying power for an hypermetropic eye, and greater for a myopic eye; and assuming that the reduced length of the eye is constant, the individual magnifying power increases with accommodation. Exactly the reverse is the case when the anterior focal point of the magnifying glass is nearer the glass than the first principal point of the eye; and if these two points coincide, the individual magnifying power and the absolute magnifying power are equal, no matter what the state of refraction of the eye is. If we put

$$\Delta = \delta - \frac{1}{D_0},$$

where Δ denotes, therefore, the reduced distance of the anterior principal point of the eye from the posterior focal point of the optical instrument, the following equation is obtained:

$$-\frac{\omega_h}{a_0} = D_0 (1 + \Delta A),$$

which is the same in form as that given by ABBE.[1] It shows that what was stated above in regard to a magnifying glass is true likewise for any optical system—for example, in case of a compound microscope for which D_0 is negative, and where δ may be negative for an instrument of low power; differences of magnifying power as above given being numerical differences.

Hence, the individual magnifying power as given by this formula is expressed in dioptries, since, after all, the scientific measure of magnifying power must be a measure of refracting power. In order to obtain an abstract number, this value must be multiplied either by the conventional distance of projection or by the distance which would be best for viewing the object in question by the naked eye, in each case the distance being given in metres. The first of these numerical values would not contribute anything useful, because nobody who is not

[1] Loc. cit.

already familiar with refracting power will be interested in individual magnifying power; but the latter number does give an expression for what may be termed the *individual effective power* of the magnifying instrument. Inasmuch as the displacement of the posterior principal point of the eye during accommodation is too slight to be taken in account, the individual magnifying power of an optical instrument as found by using the principal point angle is sufficient for obtaining the individual effective power; because the latter measure involves a comparison between two different states of accommodation, and the size of the retinal image is always proportional to the principal point angle, no matter what the accommodation may be.

Hence, *the essential facts concerning the magnifying power of an optical instrument used in conjunction with the eye* may be summed up as follows:

The expression

$$sD_0(1+\Delta A),$$

gives generally the individual magnifying power of the instrument in dioptries, provided we put s equal to the number 1; and for $A=0$, it gives also the absolute magnifying power. If, on the other hand, we put s equal to the value in metres of the distance of distinct vision in case of the given individual (counting this distance as positive), the above expression gives the number representing the individual effective power; and for $s=0.25$ m, which is the conventional distance of projection, and for $A=0$, it gives the number that expresses the conventional magnifying power of the instrument. Again, if we put s equal to the distance of the first principal point of the eye from the object, the above expression is identical with that of ESCHRICHT and PANUM[1], which is erroneously referred to the nodal point angle. A positive value for the expression means magnification without apparent inversion. Moreover, it should be noted that the method of derivation throughout implicitly assumes that the images are very small, and hence the formula applies only to the size of the image that is seen distinctly when the eye is stationary. There is really no difference between this formula and that of ABBE who used the tangent of the angle instead of the angle itself. However, nothing is gained by doing this, because, so far as we are concerned with the actual imagery, we have no right to substitute the magnitudes of object and image in place of the magnification-ratio unless the field is so circumscribed that the difference between angle and tangent is negligible. The contrary assumption is due to a fiction of the imagery's being collinear according to ABBE's notion.

[1] P. L. PANUM, Die scheinbare Grösse der gesehenen Objekte. *Arch. f. Ophth.* V, 1. 1859. S. 1.

The peculiar contrivance of the organ of vision, with a very narrow field of distinct vision, which, however, may be shifted from place to place, is responsible for the circumstance that in inspecting an extended object the real factor after all is not the size of the image on the retina but the amount of the requisite angular movement of the eye. And hence when we come to consider *the magnification of an extended object,* we must employ the angle at the centre of rotation of the eye in place of the principal point angle, that is, the angle subtended at the centre of rotation by the image as seen in the instrument. And here we must keep in mind the fact that the values as given by the imagery-laws of the first order are merely approximate.

Again, when we wish to *compare the sizes of the retinal images in different eyes,* evidently, the principal point angles, cannot be employed, because the reduced length of the axis of the eye is not the same for different degrees of refraction. However, we know from ophthalmometric investigations that the differences that occur in the optical system of the eye are not connected with the state of refraction; and hence the focal point angle does afford a measure of the size of the retinal image that—at least in case of so-called axial ametropia—is independent of the refraction, and consequently is best suited for the purpose here. The refracting power of the optical system of the eye is equal to the ratio between the focal point angle and the size of the retinal image; but it is not practicable to compare the sizes of the retinal images in two different eyes unless the refracting power has the same value for both eyes. For most eyes this seems to be approximately the case, and such cases of ametropia as show no sign of any difference of this kind are included under what is known as *axial ametropia,* as distinguished from *curvature ametropia,* which is the name given to those forms of ametropia in which the length of the axis of the eye is normal. However, both in axially-ametropic eyes and in emmetropic eyes different values of the refracting power do occur, as we know from v. Reuss's[1] investigations. Hence the size of the retinal image as measured by the focal point angle represents merely its probable value, and the best we can obtain at present.

Finally, *in comparing the visual acuity before and after removing the crystalline lens of the eye,* the angle to be used (as Bjerke[2] found) is *the angle whose vertex is situated at the apparent place of the optical centre of the lens.* (With the degree of accuracy that is attainable in making this comparison it is quite permissible to use here the simplified schematic eye.) If this angle is denoted by ω', and if the magnification-

[1] Loc cit.
[2] Loc. cit.

ratio at this optical centre is denoted by κ, then

$$\omega' = \beta_0 A' = \kappa \beta B',$$

where A', B' are the reduced convergences. Now since $\kappa B'$ has the same value before and after the extraction of the lens, this must be true also with respect to the ratio $\dfrac{\omega'}{\beta}$.

The derivation of the formulae is precisely the same for the other angles as for the principal point angle; and hence the three following expressions,

$$-\frac{\omega_n}{a_0} = -\frac{A_n A_0}{B_0} = D_0 - A_n(1 - \delta_n D_0) = D_0(1 + \Delta_n A_n)$$

are quite general, where ω_n denotes the angle which the image as seen in the optical instrument subtends at the point designated here by N; A_n denotes the refraction of the eye as measured at this point; and δ_n, Δ_n denote the distances of N from the second principal point and from the second focal point of the optical instrument, respectively.

Thus we are in the position to investigate now the variations of the visual acuity as dependent both on the ametropia and on its correction. The visual acuity of the eye is partly a measure of the sensitivity and efficiency of the retina itself; and consequently must be measured by some method which enables us to compare the sizes of the retinal image in different eyes. The principle of it consists, therefore, in ascertaining the smallest actual value of the focal point angle when accommodation is entirely relaxed (far point focusing). But the visual acuity is partly also a measure of the capacity of the individual eye, entirely apart from its state of accommodation; and from this aspect it must be measured by the smallest actual value of the principal point angle. The former measure is called the *absolute visual acuity*; and the latter *the natural visual acuity*, as directly ascertained, therefore, by finding the least value of the principal point angle for the unaided eye. In both of these measurements the retinal image is the smallest image possible, and for one and the same eye this smallest image is the same in both cases. Now the visual acuity is inversely proportional to the "angle of distinctness" or resolving power of the eye; and since for a given value of β we have always

$$\frac{\omega_h}{\omega_f} = \frac{B}{D},$$

we derive the following formula for the absolute visual acuity (S) in terms of the natural visual acuity (S_n):

$$S = S_n\left(1 + \frac{A}{D}\right).$$

If L denotes the correction-value measured at the anterior focal point of the eye, then since

$$\frac{1}{A} = \frac{1}{L} - \frac{1}{D},$$

the formula above may be expressed also in terms of L instead of A, as follows:

$$S_n = S\left(1 - \frac{L}{D}\right).$$

If f denotes the numerical value of the anterior focal length of the eye in centimetres, the preceding formulae may be stated in words, thus: *The absolute visual acuity is found by adding to the natural visual acuity $f\%$ for every dioptry of ametropia; and the natural visual acuity is found by subtracting from the absolute visual acuity $f\%$ for every dioptry of the correction-value at the anterior focal point of the eye.* However, in using these rules it must be remembered that for a myopic eye both the ametropia and the correction-value are negative, and hence algebraic addition is equivalent to arithmetical subtraction, and *vice versa*. The formulae show how axial ametropia affects the natural visual acuity In a case of pure curvature ametropia, in which the reduced length of the axis of the eye is normal, the natural visual acuity is independent of the ametropia. On the other hand, for the same sensitivity of the retina, the absolute visual acuity, as in the case of curvature-anomalies of an emmetropic eye, is inversely proportional to the refracting power of the optical system of the eye.

If in measuring the visual acuity of the eye by the aid of an auxiliary optical instrument the vertex of the "angle of distinctness" used in the determination is taken at the anterior principal point of the interposed optical system, and if the apparent value of the visual acuity as thus found is called *the relative visual acuity* and denoted by S_r; the ratio of S_r to S is equal to $\dfrac{\omega_f}{a_0 A_0}$, and the ratio of S_r to S_n is equal to $\dfrac{\omega_h}{a_0 A_0}$; and hence these ratios may be obtained immediately from the above formulae. From the equations

$$S_r = S \cdot \frac{L}{B_0} = S_n \cdot \frac{A}{B_0}$$

we derive:

$$S_r = S\,(1 + \delta_f L) = S_n\,(1 + \delta A),$$

where δ_f denotes the distance of the anterior focal point of the eye from the posterior principal point of the auxiliary optical system. In the ordinary determination with a spectacle glass this interval is so slight that it is negligible for the degree of precision with which the visual acuity can be measured; and the same thing applies also to the difference between the value of L and the correction value as found in this case. For $\delta_f = 0$, the relative visual acuity of the unaccommodated eye is equal to the absolute visual acuity; and hence, with sufficient accuracy for practical purposes, we may say that *the absolute visual acuity is obtained immediately by making the measurement with a spectacle glass that abolishes accommodation;* and also that the ratio between the natural and the absolute visual acuity is the same as that between the correction value and the ametropia. According to the above, the distance at which the vision is tested is a matter of no consequence whatever; but the shorter this distance, the more powerful must be the instrument employed, and the more perfect must be the fulfilment of the condition that the distance from the anterior principal point of the instrument shall be the basis of the measurement of the visual acuity, and that its posterior principal point shall coincide with the anterior focal point of the eye.

Moreover, the formulae show that *the relative visual acuity of the unaccommodated eye is to the natural visual acuity generally in the same ratio as the ametropia is to the correction value measured at the posterior principal point of the auxiliary system;* the latter value being the same as the refracting power of the auxiliary system only when the object is very far away. But for a great distance of the object,

$$(1+\delta A)\,(1-\delta D_0) = 1,$$

and hence

$$S_n = S_r\,(1-\delta D_0).$$

Consequently, if the interval δ is given in centimetres, we can say that *the natural visual acuity generally may be found from the relative visual acuity as determined with a distant object by subtracting from it $\delta\%$ for every dioptry of the power of the glass employed,* no matter whether the eye accommodates or not.

Instead of using the angle ω_h which is concerned in the measurement of the natural visual acuity, suppose we employ the angle ω' with its vertex at the apparent place of the optical centre of the crystalline lens. Then, applying the formula above, we get the ratio of the relative *visual acuity after extraction of the transparent crystalline lens to that found before its extraction,* namely:

$$\frac{1-\delta' D'}{1-\delta' D''},$$

where δ' denotes the distance of the apparent place of the optical centre from the posterior principal point of the auxiliary system, and D', D''

denote the refracting powers of the spectacle lenses used before the operation and afterwards, respectively. The same result is obtained, rather more circuitously, by comparing the absolute visual acuity of the eye without the crystalline lens to that of the eye with it, this ratio being equal to $D:D_c$.

When the eye is combined with an optical instrument in such manner that the posterior principal point of the instrument and the anterior focal point of the eye are united, it is possible to *calculate the change in the length of the eyeball corresponding to a given value of the axial ametropia.* According to the formulae on page 361, the refracting power of the compound system in this case is equal to that of the eye alone, and the anterior focal point of the system as a whole coincides with the anterior principal point of the auxiliary system. Since the focal lengths are not altered by inserting the latter system in this way, the reduced displacement of the posterior focal point is

$$H_t' = -\frac{D_0}{D^2};$$

and if the correction value is D_0, the posterior focal point lies on the retina of the eye. According as the basis of the calculation is the exact or simplified schematic eye, it follows that the length of the axially ametropic eye differs from that of the emmetropic eye by 0.389 or 0.374 mm, respectively, for every dioptry of the correction value. The same result is obtained by using the general focal point equation.

When the eye is combined with an instrument whose posterior focal point coincides with the anterior principal point of the eye or with its anterior focal point, the natural visual acuity in the former case, or the absolute visual acuity of the unaccommodated eye in the latter case, is obtained by measuring the angle $a_0 D_0$; as follows immediately from the formula

$$\omega_n = -a_0 D_0 (1 + \Delta_n A_n),$$

since in both cases $\Delta = 0$. Since, as was shown above, the refraction in the first instance, and the correction value in the second, is proportional to the distance of the anterior focal point of the auxiliary system from the object, these combinations have frequently been used in the construction of optometers.

In measuring the refraction of the eye, besides an auxiliary optical instrument, an indicator is needed or some means of telling whether the image in the eye is sharp or not. The best means will always be a measurement of the visual acuity that is under the control of the investigator and independent of the patient's opinion. The division of the pupil into separate parts would afford another indicator for the existence of blur circles; these parts being employed, simultaneously or in succession, for optical projection, unless the accuracy of the result is impaired by the aberration-behaviour of the normal eye. Here may be mentioned the indicators based on the experiments of SCHEINER and MILE; together also with the method recently proposed by HOLTH[1] under the name of Kinescopia. If the connection between the size of the pupil and the ocular aberration were such that the laws of the first order were applicable, the theory of this latter process would be contained in the value of the linear projection coefficient (page 290), since the question involves the optical projection on the retina of a hole held in front of the eye. In this case the magnitude denoted by κ in the formula

$$C = \kappa \, (1 - \delta' \mathfrak{B})$$

is the magnification-ratio at the point conjugate to the hole with respect to the optical system of the eye; whereas δ' denotes the reduced distance of the retina from this point, and $\mathfrak{B}$ the reduced convergence of the bundle of object-rays measured at the same place. A positive value of C here indicates an optical projection in the direct sense (homonymous), that is, a crossed monocular diplopia in SCHEINER's experiment and an apparent movement opposite ("against") the real movement in MILE's experiment. Putting

$$\Delta' = \frac{1}{\mathfrak{B}} - \delta' \, ,$$

where Δ' denotes the reduced distance of the image-point that is conjugate to the object-point as measured from the retina, we may write the preceding formula as follows:

$$C = \kappa \mathfrak{B} \Delta' = \frac{\mathfrak{A} \Delta'}{K},$$

where K denotes the magnification-ratio at this image point, and $\mathfrak{A}$ is the convergence of the bundle of object-rays as measured at the place where the hole is. Hence, it follows that C does not change sign when the sign of κ changes in consequence of a shifting of the hole along the axis of the eye past its anterior focal point.

The same formulae give also the *size of the blur circle* in so far as this can be obtained by the laws of the first order; but the results are to be considered as being merely approximations to the real facts in the case when the pupil is small and the focusing error quite large. Under these circumstances $\mathfrak{A}$ and $\mathfrak{B}$ denote the reduced convergences of the bundle of object-rays as measured at the *entrance-pupil* before

---

[1] S. HOLTH, Nouveau procédé pour déterminer la réfraction oculaire. *Ann. d'Oculistique.* CXXXI. 1904. p. 1.

refraction and at the *exit-pupil* after refraction, respectively. The centre of the entrance-pupil is the apparent position of the pupil of the eye and the centre of the exit-pupil is the point conjugate to the centre of the entrance-pupil with respect to the optical system of the eye; and κ denotes the magnification-ratio for this pair of conjugate points. If the (static or dynamic) refraction of the eye as measured at the entrance-pupil is denoted by $\Re$, then

$$\frac{\kappa^2}{\delta'} = \kappa D + \Re, \qquad \kappa^2 \mathfrak{B} = \kappa D + \mathfrak{A}, \qquad \frac{\kappa K}{\delta'} = \Re, \qquad KD = L \, ;$$

consequently,

$$\kappa^2 \left(\frac{1}{\delta'} - \mathfrak{B} \right) = \Re - \mathfrak{A}, \qquad \frac{\delta' \Re}{\kappa} = \frac{L}{D} \, ;$$

and hence

$$C = \frac{\delta'(\Re - \mathfrak{A})}{\kappa} = \frac{L}{D} \left(1 - \frac{\mathfrak{A}}{\Re} \right) \, ;$$

where C denotes the ratio of the diameter of the blur circle to the diameter of the entrance-pupil, and δ' denotes the reduced distance of the retina from the exit-pupil. Neglecting in this formula the distance between the entrance-pupil and the anterior principal point of the eye and also the difference between the size of the pupil and that of the entrance-pupil, we may put $\kappa = 1$ and consider δ' as representing the reduced length of the axis of the eye. The approximate formula derived in this way was obtained by SALZMANN[1] for the general case, and by NAGEL[2] for the special case when $\mathfrak{A} = 0$. GLEICHEN,[3] using the magnification-ratio for the pupil, has shown that the latter formula holds exactly.

The laws of imagery and optical projection of the first order are not sufficient for investigating *blurred vision*. For with a pupil of medium size the aberration of the eye is such that focusing errors amounting to several dioptries are not enough to prevent the existence of curves formed by the intersection of the caustic surface with the retina, involving a single or multiple imagery of lines; whereas, on the other hand, even with the sharpest focusing, blur circles of considerable magnitude occur. With a smaller pupil phenomena of diffraction have play. Due to the first circumstance, the exact investigation of the *depth of focus* of the eye, CZERMAK's so-called accommodation-line,

---

[1] M. SALZMANN, Das Sehen in Zerstreuungskreisen. *Arch. f. Ophth.* XXXIX. 2. 1893. S. 83.

[2] A. NAGEL, Die Anomalien der Refraktion und Akkommodation des Auges. *Handb. d. ges. Augenheilk. von* GRAEFE und SAEMISCH. Bd. VI. Kap. X. 1880. S. 457.

[3] A. GLEICHEN, *Einführung in die medizinische Optik.* Leipzig 1904. S. 117. And: Über die Zerstreuungsfiguren im menschlichen Auge. *Arch. f. Optik.* I. 1908. S. 211.

proves to be a very complicated mathematical problem. These aberrations explain also the influence of practice in trying to interpret the image-patterns made by other sections of the caustic surface, as SALZMAN[1] has emphasized. This practice also is particularly important for explaining the peculiar ability of reading in the case of high uncorrected hypermetropia; although the ratio between the size of the blur circle and the size of the indistinct image has something to do with it also.

In general, *for the optical projection on the retina of objects that are not seen distinctly,* the linear projection coefficient C_0 may be found from the fact that the reduced angular magnification-ratio at the pupil is equal to the reciprocal of the linear magnification-ratio:

$$C_0 = \frac{\delta' \mathfrak{A}}{\kappa}.$$

When the object is real and has to be adjusted near the eye to be seen distinctly, both $\mathfrak{A}$ and C_0 are negative, whereas C and $\mathfrak{R} - \mathfrak{A}$ are positive. Hence, for this case:

$$Q = -\frac{C}{C_0} \qquad O = -\mathfrak{A},$$

where Q and O are the numerical values in question. The general formula

$$\frac{C}{C_0} = \frac{\mathfrak{R} - \mathfrak{A}}{\mathfrak{A}}$$

may then be put in the form:

$$Q = 1 + \frac{\mathfrak{R}}{O}.$$

Let p denote the diameter of the entrance-pupil and o the linear size of the object; then $\dfrac{pQ}{o}$ is the ratio of the diameter of the blur circle to the linear size of the image projected on the retina. It follows at once from the formula that Q diminishes as O increases, provided $\mathfrak{R}$ is positive; whereas when this latter magnitude is negative, the case is just opposite. This agrees with the fact that when an object approaches an hypermetropic eye, the size of the blurred image on the retina increases faster than the diameter of the blur circle; while with a myopic eye it is the other way. This explains how an hypermetrope, of say, 8 dptr can read fine print 5 cm away from his unaided eye. However, the fact that hypermetropia is really more unfavourable than other states

---

[1] M. SALZMANN, Das Sehen in Zerstreuungkreisen. *Arch. f. Ophth.* XL, 5. 1894. S. 102.

of refraction, can readily be understood by observing that for a positive value of the refraction, even when the object is nearest, Q is greater than unity; whereas for emmetropia, Q always has the value unity; and this value is not reached in myopia as long as the object is too near the eye to be seen distinctly. This particular effect of the state of refraction is illustrated best by taking an object whose length is equal to the diameter of the entrance-pupil. Then Q denotes the ratio between the diameter of the blur circle and the size of the image, and the sign of $(Q-1)$ tells whether the blur circles corresponding to the two ends of the object overlap or not. Evidently, they do in hypermetropia; but in emmetropia these two blur circles touch each other; and in myopia there is a space between them. It is apparent, therefore, that emmetropic refraction, and still more myopic refraction, is more favourable for the kind of reading here spoken of than hypermetropic refraction; and that the hypermetrope gets the best results by disregarding his error of refraction and accommodating as much as possible. This is exactly what he does, in the effort to reduce the size of the blur circle, not so much by changing the optical focus as by the accompanying contraction of the pupil. Emmetropes and myopes might therefore be able to read in this way even better than hypermetropes, provided they were able to contract the pupil to the same extent as uncorrected hypermetropes, and had, like the latter, practised the art from childhood.

However, for the size of pupil here under consideration the quality of the image produced by optical projection may not be gauged by the size of the blur circle, because *diffraction* at the edge of the pupil influences the distribution of light inside this circle.[1] It is easy to be convinced of this by using a stenopaic opening. By making himself ametropic with a high power glass in front of his eye and looking through a hole held opposite the centre of the pupil between the glass and the eye, a person may see, even with a 2 mm hole, but better still with a 1 mm hole, a concentration of light on the border of the blur circle corresponding to a small luminous point-source. That this is a diffraction-effect, and not due, say, to aberration of the glass, is shown partly by the fact that the phenomenon persists with larger opening, and partly also because the effect of the aberration would be just the opposite. Being a matter of diffraction, the inference cannot be drawn that the shadow cone corresponding to a black point on a white surface is analogous to the cone of light for the luminous point. The exact investigation of the effect of diffraction in a case of this sort would be a very difficult mathematical exercise. However, it is clear that it

---

[1] Accordingly, there would be no practical result in discussing the case when $C+C_0=K$, however interesting it might be from the geometrical point of view.

does distribute some light in the region of the shadow cone, and hence also does have some influence on the size of the shadow circle and the shadow distribution.

Since in the optical projection in the eye the apparent size of the object is increased by the blur circles, obviously, the magnification in the correction of high hypermetropia by convex glasses is less noticeable than the opposite effect in the correction of high myopia by concave glasses; and in the latter case the correction is not so advantageous, especially if on account of poor visual acuity small retinal images cannot be appreciated anyhow.

Chromatic resolution of the blur circles affords a method of investigating them that is comparatively unaffected by the aberration and diffraction. In the formula on page 371 Δ' has different values for different colours; and therefore when the focusing is sharp for a colour of short wave-length there must be a blur circle for a colour of long wave-length, and *vice versa*; and these blur circles must be seen more and more distinctly in proportion as the light consists of a mixture of two colours of long and short wave-lengths. A cobalt glass of sufficiently saturated colour illuminated by an ordinary candle flame affords practically a very useful light-mixture for this purpose. A very good indicator of the imagery, as described by HELMHOLTZ on page 176, is afforded also by observing the coloured edge of a hole placed in front of the source of light.

DONDERS' *method of finding the refraction* is still for the time being superior to all others. It consists in connecting the eye with various glasses, and using the visual acuity test with object far away as indicator of the focusing. The process therefore gives both the correction-value and the absolute visual acuity, the strongest positive or weakest negative lens being found for which the visual acuity of the eye is greatest. The advantages of this method consist in the objective control made possible by the visual acuity test and in the relaxation of the accommodation, which according to experience is easier for most people with spectacles and a distant object than when they have to look into an instrument. It would take us too far to enter here into the details of this method or of the other methods of optometry. It may be merely remarked in this connection, that just as a great distance of the object is favourable to relaxation of accommodation, similarly a short distance stimulates this power. Thus while DONDERS' method is best for finding the far point, *the determination of the near point* necessary for obtaining the amplitude of accommodation is best made by direct measurement, after having shifted it by inserting a suitable lens before the eye to a distance that is convenient for measuring.

Numerous investigations have established the fact that *the physiological refraction of the eye* at birth is hypermetropic. The contrary data of JAEGER,[1] as HESS[2] and ELSCHNIG[3] have shown, are due to the fact that in his measurements the pupil was not dilated artificially, and that the refraction of babes is essentially diminished by accommodation, temporarily anyhow. Congenital hypermetropia, amounting on the average to 2 dioptries according to STRAUB'S[4] findings, decreases even in childhood, so that from school-age upwards the normal state of refraction is emmetropia or very feeble hypermetropia, returning again after fifty years of age to something like that of infancy and approximately reaching this state at a very advanced age. STRAUB is of the opinion that the greatest part of the hypermetropia continues throughout the entire life, being masked by a tonic of the ciliary muscle; but the material in support of this view is perhaps hardly sufficient to establish its correctness.

The change of refraction that occurs in earliest childhood is the result of the change of the length of the eyeball and of the optical system in growth. As to the optical system, the radius of curvature of the cornea is indeed rather smaller in the infant than in the adult—the values are around 7.0 mm. But the chief difference is in the lens, whose form is nearly spherical, and which therefore must have a very high total index of refraction. The attainment of approximately emmetropic refraction by the vast majority of eyes would evidently imply a regulating mechanism operating in growth. Thus we know that in hypermetropia efforts of accommodation are necessarily of much longer duration than in other states of refraction, and that in continuous accommodation a force is at work which with the growth of the eye tends to lower the refraction. By the tension of the choroid produced by the contraction of the ciliary muscle, a statical moment is always brought into play which might have some effect on the growth of the axis of the eyeball, and whereby the change of form of the lens in accommodation may undoubtedly have some influence during growth on the arrangement of the iso-indicial surfaces, and accordingly also on the total index. It is quite possible that other regulating forces, as yet unknown, may be present also.

The recurrence of hypermetropia in extreme old age is explained partly by the change of form due to the increased resistance of the

[1] ED. V. JAEGER, *Über die Einstellungen des dioptrischen Apparates im menschlichen Auge.* Wien 1861.

[2] Loc. cit. S. 284.

[3] Bemerkungen über die Refraktion der Neugeborenen. *Zeitschr. f. Augenheilk.* XI. 1904. S. 10.

[4] M. STRAUB, Die normale Refraktion des menschlichen Auges. *Zeitschr. f. Physiol. d. Sinnesorg.* XXV. 1901. S. 78. — Über die Ätiologie der Brechungsanomalien des Auges und den Ursprung der Emmetropie. *Arch. f. Ophth.* LXX. 1. 1909. S. 130.

coating of the eyeball and the decreased pressure of the surrounding tissue, as established by ophthalmometric investigation of the cornea; but partly also by senile changes in the crystalline lens. Whether the first of these causes produces a measurable increase in the radius of the cornea, perhaps, as remarked above, cannot yet be positively asserted; but there is hardly any doubt that it might be responsible for shortening the length of the ocular axis a few tenths of a millimetre. The other influence may cause a reduction of the total index, not only by augmenting the cortical index but also by changing the form of the iso-indicial surfaces of the crystalline lens. Last of all, the effect of the senile contraction of the pupil has to be considered also, which with normal aberration must produce at least some slight increase of the refraction; because an eye that was emmetropic with a pupil of medium size would have to show hypermetropia amounting to 1 dptr with an infinitely small pupil.

The change of the lens, that is senile in its last stage, begins in earliest childhood. This is connected with the fact that the lens is a closed epithelium structure with no outlet for discharge; in which indeed, throughout the whole life a constant influx occurs, as is shown by the investigations of PRIESTLEY SMITH.[1] This change is manifested in the living eye by a steady increase of fluorescence[2] that is perceptible without difficulty by suitable arrangements. Another sign of it is the appearance of reflex images on the periphery of the lens core known as HESS's "Kernbildschen"; indicating a surface of discontinuity in the variation of the index, which might constitute, so to speak, the boundary between a core and a cortical layer. And, finally, this process in the lens is shown by an increasingly diffused reflection of the light and by a colour of the light reflected from the core, which with advancing years gets more and more yellow; frequently too by a doubling of the PURKINJE image reflected in the posterior surface of the lens, when this image is being observed in a direction that borders on the equator of the lens core. Correspondingly in the dead lens, along with the steady increase of dimensions, there is found also a progressive sclerosis of the central portions and differentiating of the core. Functionally, this change in the lens is manifested by a progressive *decrease of the amplitude of accommodation* which begins as soon as this magnitude can be measured. The following are the numerical values as given by DONDERS[3] in his fundamental researches:

---

[1] The growth of the crystalline lens. *Brit. Med. Journ.* I. 1883. S. 112.

[2] A. GULLSTRAND, Die Farbe der Macula centralis retinae. *Arch. f. Ophth.* LXII, 1. S. 43.

[3] Loc. cit.

Age in years	Amplitude of accommodation in dioptries
10	14
15	12
20	10
25	8.5
30	7
35	5.5
40	4.5
45	3.5
50	2.5
55	1.75
60	1
65	0.5
70	0.25

However, in considering these numbers it should be borne in mind that the method employed gives the limit of perceptibility of the smallest blur circle, and hence the measurement as made depends on the focus depth and is affected by the size of the pupil. Perhaps, therefore, the senile decrease of amplitude of accommodation may proceed rather more suddenly than the table indicates, and for every 5 years after the age of forty it may be estimated at 1 dptr with sufficient accuracy.

Presbyopia is the recession of the near point beyond the conventional distance of distinct vision, which means here a distance of 22 cm according to the earlier value that was assigned to this arbitrary measure. (In calculating magnifying power the value of 25 cm was taken by the followers of ABBE as the measure of the distance of distinct vision.) In the case of an emmetropic eye presbyopia begins after forty years of age. But from a practical standpoint the customary size of the pupil has much to do with this matter. This magnitude is very often affected by an illness that has lowered the general vitality or by a neurasthenic condition; and thus owing to an increase in the size of the pupil there is a development, familiar to every ophthalmologist, of sudden presbyopia in an emmetrope fifty years old. Corresponding to the idea of presbyopia, the corrected ametrope usually becomes presbyopic at the same age as the emmetrope, but the uncorrected hypermetrope become presbyopic sooner, and the uncorrected myope later or perhaps never.

It would lead us too far at the present stage of this science to take up more in detail *the anomalies of refraction*. Its enormous development since the appearance of the first edition of this treatise is apparent when it is recalled that there for the first time in a supplement the difference between hypermetropia and presbyopia was noticed. DONDERS'[1] great

[1] Loc. cit. Translated in German by O. BECKER: *Die Anomalien der Refraktion und Akkommodation des Auges.* Wien 1866.

work was followed by books by MAUTHNER,[1] NAGEL[2] and LANDOLT;[3] and the entire subject was essentially revised by HESS[4] by employing the exact dioptry-idea, and its treatment elevated to the requirements of the time.

Hypermetropia is congenital in the typical cases and comes under the head of axial ametropia. In its higher degrees it is to be regarded as a structural hindrance, frequently accompanied by other structural faults such as astigmatism, asymmetry, abnormal form of the papilla, etc.; whereas in its milder form it should perhaps be explained as some anomaly of growth. Of all the unusual (or atypical) forms of hypermetropia the most frequent by far is that which occurs after extraction of the crystalline lens, which is also the most remarkable example of a curvature ametropia.

On the other hand, typical *myopia* is an acquired anomaly, belonging, however, like typical hypermetropia under the head of axial ametropia. The mildest degrees of myopia, as of hypermetropia, are probably due to some simple growth anomaly, whereas its highest manifestations are undoubtedly symptoms of disease. Just as to a certain extent the line between growth anomaly and diseased condition is arbitrary, so also the opinions of ophthalmologists are not at all unanimous as to the degree of myopia that is most common. The original cause of it is known to be a disposition, either constitutional or acquired by weakness of some kind, and the effect of over-exertion with close work. The disposition is generally attributed to too much yielding of the coating of the eyeball, but possibly too the static relations in growth may have something to do with it, similar to the predisposition of *dolichocephali* or long-headed folks. As to how and why over-exertion with close work is injurious, there has come to be a wide diversity of opinion. The view that accommodation has a tendency to increase the intraocular pressure to which ophthalmologists nowadays attribute the prejudice against complete correction of myopia on the part of the laity and many factory workers, has been upset by careful investigations. Moreover, the idea that the convergence necessary for close work should bear the blame, can hardly be any longer maintained in those cases where convergence is normal and effected without any abnormal strain of the external muscles of the eye. On the other hand, it is evident that a steady fixation involving exertion

---

[1] Loc. cit. *Vorlesungen über die optischen Fehler des Auges.* Wien 1876.

[2] Loc. cit. *Die Anomalien der Refraktion und Akkommodation des Auges.* In *Handb. d. ges. Augenheilk. von* GRAEFE und SAEMISCH. Bd. VI. X. Kap. 1880.

[3] E. LANDOLT, *La réfraction et l'accommodation de l'oeil.* In *Traité compl. d'ophth.* par WECKER et LANDOLT. T. III. Paris 1887.

[4] Loc. cit. *Die Refraktion und Akkommodation des menschlic̣ en Auges und ihre Anomalien.* Leipzig 1902, and in *Handb. von* GRAEFE und SAEMISCH. 2. Aufl. II. T. XII. Kap.

on the part of all the external muscles, together with the customary knitting of the eyebrows as in sickness, may have a tendency to elongate the axis of the eye. And supposing the steady accommodation that goes on in the hypermetropic eye of a child is a process of regulation inducing emmetropic refraction, may it not likewise be probable that an excessive accommodation strain tends to promote myopia? Certainly, clinical experience testifies to a comparatively frequent conjunction between myopia and those conditions dating back to childhood, which, due to poor visual acuity, require the work to be brought excessively close to the eye; such as lamellar cataract, corneal specks, astigmatism, abnormal decentration, cases where the accommodation by means of the accompanying contraction of the pupil improves vision disproportionately, and is for that very reason apt to be used excessively.

However, while opinions may differ as to the manner of the effect of "near work," the necessity of trying to prevent unnecessarily strenuous "near work" is recognized to be one way of combatting the spread of myopia, as is attempted, for instance, in the modern system of school-hygiene. The glorious victory which Sweden has won by this method is a tribute to WIDMARK's[1] classification. By abandoning Gothic type and the so-called German handwriting, Germany might probably no longer enjoy the unenviable distinction of being known as "Myopia-land."

From what has been said it is evident that the supposition, especially prevalent among uncorrected myopes, that myopia is a sort of adaptation to the needs of civilization, is completely mistaken, since, rather than identifying civilization with close work, myopes are to be considered as people who have to pay for civilization by being disabled.

Cases of unusual or *atypical myopia*, coming under the category of curvature ametropia, occur with abnormal form of the cornea and of the lens surfaces. In the same class, though strictly speaking representing "indicial myopia," belongs the myopia that is found in connection with senile changes of the lens in advanced age, and likewise the temporary myopia discovered first by HIRSCHBERG[2] in case of diabetes, by MOAURO[3] in case of jaundice, and by SCHIECK[4] in case of sleeping sickness; whereas the temporary myopia occurring in case of iritis,

---

[1] J. WIDMARK, Über die Abnahme der Kurzsichtigkeit in den höheren Knabenschulen Schwedens. *Mitt. a. d. Augenklinik d. Carol. Med.-Chir. Inst. zu Stockholm.* X Heft. 1909. S. 41.

[2] J. HIRSCHBERG, Diabetische Kurzsichtigkeit. *Centralblatt f. prakt. Augenh.* XIV. 1890. S. 7.

[3] G. MOAURO, Di alcune alterazioni oculari in malattie epatiche. *Lavori della clin. oculist. di Napoli.* III. 1893. S. 100.

[4] F. SCHIECK, Über temporäre Myopie. *Klin. Monatsbl. f. Augenh.* XLV. 1907. S. 40.

regarded by SCHAPRINGER[1] as an indicial myopia, may be explained by tension of the zonula fibres in case of swelling of the ciliary processes. Senile myopia is always accompanied by a characteristic variation of the aberration and is due to an increase of the total index of the lens. An increase of the core index may tend in this direction, but myopia is possible even without such a change, because with progressive sclerosis the form of the iso-indicial surfaces may be changed. The final stage, known as "false lenticonus," consists in the loosening of the transparent core from the cortical substance or in a cataract formation usually proceeding with pronounced core-sclerosis. The tendency to cataract in diabetes renders it likely that cases of permanent myopia in connection with diabetes among old people are similar. MOAURO and SCHAPRINGER connected temporary myopia with increase of index of the aqueous humor, but as HESS[2] has shown, this is impossible. It might be more reasonable to attribute it to a variation of the index of the substance of the lens caused by a change of composition of the surrounding fluid, because this is the explanation also of temporary hypermetropia as observed in case of diabetes. Thus if the new surfaces corresponding to the change of index do not coincide with the iso-indicial surfaces, the arrangement of the latter will be changed, and the total index for the individual difference in the procedure of the iso-indicial surfaces may be raised thereby as well as lowered.

Astigmatism cannot be included under ametropia proper, because it does not imply a peculiar focusing fault but rather an image fault that defies exact focusing. Whereas in the case of ametropia in the strict sense it is possible to speak of a single image in the *fovea centralis*, this is no longer permissible with astigmatism, but the two imageries have to be kept separate. In the former case there is a certain point-to-point correspondence between object and image, but not so in the latter case. Only those lines are reproduced that are parallel to the principal sections when the latter are planes of symmetry, which however may not be at right angles to each other; but the image-lines on the retina are perpendicular. With astigmatism of sufficient amount its existence can therefore be established even in the most regular cases, and the orientation of the principal sections can be found, by making the patient name the two meridian lines of a circle, as marked on a chart, that are seen distinctly with different focusing, no matter whether the change of focus is produced by accommodation or by lenses from the trial case. However, in the ordinary degrees of this trouble

[1] A. SCHAPRINGER, The proximate cause of the transient form of myopia associated with iritis. *Amer. Journ. of ophth.* X. 1893. p. 399.

[2] Loc. cit. S. 341.

the shortness of the focal length as compared with the amount of the
aberration is such that for normal size of pupil the relations are much
more complicated, because different sections of the caustic surface cause
the imageable lines to lie in different directions for different focusings
or produce a double image.   The only way, therefore, to find the
directions of the object lines corresponding to the principal sections is
to contrive in such fashion that the entire focal interval (as measured
by the astigmatic difference) shall lie in front of the retina and at the
same time coincide with the edge of the caustic surface; so that the
rear edge, being its only line of section, is all that can affect the retina,
as follows from Fig. 121.   This form of the caustic surface shows the
erroneousness of the prevalent opinion that the amount of astigmatism
can be found by using the fan-shaped chart with the meridian lines.
This can only be done by using the visual acuity as indicator, since it is
the maximum visual acuity—and not just merely the "normal" acuity
—that corresponds to the proper correction of astigmatism.   Astigmatism is so common and so often complicated with abnormal decentration of the eye that there is perhaps no other scientific investigation
that has a greater claim on scientists than a conscientious measurement
of refraction and visual acuity.

The limit of the normal astigmatism of the eye probably should be
given as 0.5 dptr, the direct form being more common in youth and
the inverse form ("against the rule") in more advanced life.   Consequently, an inverse astigmatism of 0.5 dptr in youth is to be regarded
as a pathological symptom.   Clinical experience shows that such a
condition may be harder for the patient than a direct astigmatism
amounting to 1 dptr or more.

In the typical cases of abnormal astigmatism the trouble is congenital and evidently dependent on static conditions in the development and growth of the eye.   Acquired astigmatism (except that
beginning in old age and the inverse astigmatism due to increase of
pressure in glaucoma) occurs generally after illnesses and operations
through the cornea.

IV.   The Mechanism of Accommodation

For a dioptric study of the accommodating lens it is necessary
to know the nature of the changes in the form of its surfaces and of the
increase of its thickness.   The other changes which have been shown
to be associated with accommodation are of less importance for the

dioptrics of the accommodating lens than for the mechanical processes of accommodation.

In order to begin the discussion of the problem of the mechanism of accommodation from the optical standpoint, supposing the change of focus of the eye due to the variations above mentioned is known, we have now merely to ascertain the data of the accommodating schematic eye that corresponds to the schematic eye as previously found. However, owing to the difficulties involved in the decentration of the refracting surfaces, and to lack of knowledge as to the form of the peripheral parts of the surfaces of the lens, the requisite data are not sufficiently well known at present. There have been plenty of researches on these subjects, but, so far as the forward displacement of the anterior pole of the lens and the change of curvature of the anterior surface are concerned, the results can be considered as only partially reliable. On the basis of the earlier work,[1] HELMHOLTZ selected the schematic values 0.4 and 6 mm for the change in position of the anterior pole of the lens and the radius of the anterior surface of the lens, respectively, in the accommodating eye; the amount of the optical change of focus being found by calculation. However, the change of focus as found by observation should be greater than appears from this calculation, as up to this time no investigator has found that the radius was reduced to one-half the size, and HELMHOLTZ's accommodating schematic eye shows a change of refracting power amounting to only 6.5 dioptries. The recent investigations of TSCHERNING and BESIO[2] agree very well with these values, provided the relative change of curvature is considered, and allowance is made for the sources of error incident to the methods of investigation. In the cases which TSCHERNING studied, instead of a forward displacement of the anterior surface of the lens, he found a backward movement of the posterior surface, resulting in an increase of 0.3 mm in the thickness of the lens. He attributed this to individual differences, at the same time pointing out that the determination of the position of the surfaces of the lens is not very accurate. In this connection it may be remarked that the results of such measurements are decidedly more certain when HELMHOLTZ's precautions are followed; which consist in repeating the experiment after exchanging the positions of the telescope and the source of light. Furthermore, the cornea must not be regarded as a spherical surface.

The writer also has obtained similar results. He had the opportunity of examining repeatedly, over a long period of time, an intelligent

[1] See the works already mentioned of KNAPP, ADAMÜK and WOINOW, MANDELSTAM and SCHÖLER, REICH, together with compilation in 2nd edition of *Handb. d. phys. Opt.*, S. 147.

[2] Loc. cit. Compiled by TSCHERNING, loc. cit. *Encycl. fr. d'ophth.* T. III. p. 266.

young man, nineteen years old, who was an unusually good marksman and who could fixate well. The determination of the depth of the anterior chamber was made by HELMHOLTZ's method. The radius of the anterior surface of the lens was measured directly with his ophthalmometer, using an ophthalmometric NERNST lamp. The calculation was made by the exact formulae applicable to imagery obtained with an oblique illumination. Values between 0.3 and 0.4 mm were found for the displacement of the pole of the lens when the eye was accommodated for a needle placed 10 cm from the cornea. Results between 10.34 and 10.42 mm were found for the radius of the anterior surface of the lens with relaxed accommodation; and between 5.5 and 5.9 mm. in case of accommodation for a point 10 cm away. The closer agreement of the figures for the anterior surface of the passive lens as compared with the results for the accommodating lens might be taken to show how accurate the measurements were; or it might indicate also the difficulties of exact accommodation in the region of the near point. For this reason the smaller value probably is the more correct.

Hitherto, nothing has been definitely known concerning a change of position of the posterior surface of the lens during accommodation. To be sure, experiments have often indicated a slight movement one way or the other, but the methods used have not been exact enough to exclude the possibility of this result's being due to inherent sources of error, even if the lens itself were actually homogeneous. As a matter of fact, the properties of the heterogeneous medium constitute additional sources of error, inasmuch as the configuration of the iso-indicial surfaces is altered by the change of form of the lens, as shown, for example, by a variation of the total index. Now this would not be of so much importance provided the investigation of the posterior surface of the lens could be made by studying the procedure of rays along the axis, because then it would be easier to apply a correction. But inasmuch as obliquely falling light has to be used, the necessary means for the correction are lacking as long as the exact form of the anterior surface of the lens in both the passive and the accommodating eye is unknown. Besides, owing to the concomitant contraction of the pupil in accommodation, it is often impossible to examine reflex images in the posterior surface of the lens with the axis of the eye maintained in the same direction as it was adjusted for the images in the anterior surface (unless the result is vitiated by an artificial dilatation of the pupil entirely beyond the limits of strictly physiological conditions). And, moreover, the centering of the eye is influenced by accommodation. In view of these sources of error, it is not surprising that quite different results have been obtained for the variation of curvature of the posterior surface of the lens in accommodation. KNAPP, who was one of the earlier investigators, found a difference of from 0.5 to 1.5 mm between the radius of the passive lens and that of the accommodating lens. In the case measured by Tscherning, the radius of the posterior surface of the lens was diminished from 5.7 to only 5.3 mm by accommodation, whereas the corresponding values of the radius of the anterior surface were 9.7 and 5.4 mm, respectively. Besio's results, on the other hand, differed by 1.0 mm.

Taking into account the above sources of error, the only definite conclusion that can be drawn from these investigations is, that *as yet there is no proof of a change of position of the posterior surface of the lens in accommodation*, and that *the curvature of the posterior surface of the lens increases in accommodation, though to a very slight extent.*

By an original method of his own, Gertz[1] has recently come to the same conclusion. He investigated the conditions under which the spot of light mentioned on page 223 appeared as a sharp image, that is, the secondary catadioptric image in the eye. To be sure, owing to the unavoidable oblique incidence of the light in this experiment, there are probable sources of error due to astigmatism that render the method useless for this purpose; but otherwise it is adapted for checking schematic eyes. Gertz also drew no conclusions in regard to this matter, but he found that in this particular case the posterior pole of the lens exhibited no noticeable axial movement during accomodation, and that the curvature of the posterior surface of the lens increased by the generally accepted amount during accommodation. Inasmuch as the question here is simply one of the comparison of the results of different investigations on one and the same eye, under the influence of similar sources of error, perhaps these errors should in the main counteract each other, and the result be correct.

In trying to construct a schematic accommodating lens, it appears to be best to represent the relations as they exist when the power of accommodation is greatest, that is, in youth before the appearance of surfaces of discontinuity or cleavage in the lens. Accordingly, the writer has chosen the focusing for a point approximately 10 cm distant from the cornea. With reference to his numerical results above mentioned, he has likewise assumed that the radius of curvature of the anterior surface of the lens becomes reduced in accommodation from 10 to 5.33 mm. But the value 0.4 mm, taken by Helmholtz for the amount of displacement of the anterior pole of the lens in accommodation, has been retained. Owing to the very small value that must be ascribed to the change of form of the posterior surface of the lens in accommodation, the curvature of this surface in the accommodating

[1] H. Gertz, Über das sekundäre katadioptrische Bild des Auges. *Skand. Arch. f. Physiol.* XXII. 1909, S. 299.

eye is largely a matter of choice. The selection of a symmetrical form seems to be justified, because the schematic eye is intended to have maximum accommodation, and, as far as can be determined from the measurements, the lens approaches this form as closely as possible during accommodation. The accommodative change of curvature of the posterior surface of the lens as here assumed is between the values found by HELMHOLTZ and his pupils, on the one hand; but it is also between the values found by TSCHERNING and his pupils, on the other hand; and in each instance is nearer the value found by the teacher. But as to the reliability of this datum, all that can be said is that with our present knowledge it is not possible to be more accurate. The choice of the definite value 5.33 for the radius of curvature was made, because this number gives the value of the total index that corresponds to MATTHIESSEN's law, and so makes it possible to give a mathematical proof of the law. At the same time, the discrepancy between it and the value obtained by the writer's measurement is no more than might be due to the sources of error of the methods. Since the anterior surface of the lens is subjected to a greater change in accommodation than the posterior surface, it may be supposed that in the axial enlargement the portion of the lens lying in front of the point of maximum index undergoes more variation than the portion beyond it. Consequently, a symmetrical structure of the accommodating lens is probable also for this reason. The refracting power of the lens may be calculated in the usual way from the optical focusing, the data of the corneal system, and the length of the passive schematic eye. By using an optical centre for the lens that is to be calculated, an approximate value of about 33 dioptries is obtained. The refracting power of each surface of the lens is 9.375 dptr. Now since the refracting power of the core lens which comes into the calculation must be somewhat greater than its exact value, and since the sum of the refracting powers of the individual systems again exceeds the total refracting power, the approximate value of 15 dptr is found for the refracting power of the core lens to be used in the calculation. In addition to these data, the other two equations needed for finding the indicial equation of the accommodating lens are dependent on the two conditions, that during the change of form, (1) there is no compression at the centre of the lens, and (2) that the volume included within the largest closed indicial surface remains unaltered. These conditions are due to the fact that the forces operative in accommodation are too feeble to produce by compression any appreciable alteration of the volume or the indices of refraction of the various parts.

Accordingly, the data to be used in the calculation of the accommodating schematic lens are:

$$-x_1 = x_2 = 2, \cdot \qquad \rho_1 = -\rho_2 = 5.333\ldots, \qquad D = 0.015,$$

which give the following constants for the indicial equation:

$$m = 0.0025031, \qquad n = 0.0023443,$$

$$p_m = 0.0224907, \qquad p_o = 0.0021085, \qquad p_n = 0.0008399.$$

Owing to the symmetrical structure, the coefficients M and N are both equal to zero. Exactly as in the case of the unaccommodated eye, these results have been used by the writer to calculate a number of coördinates of the points of intersection of a meridian plane with the iso-indicial surfaces corresponding to the values 1.386 and 1.404 for the indices of refraction. The results are exhibited by the curves in Fig. 134; and for the sake of comparison, the corresponding curves for the unaccommodated lens are reproduced in Fig. 133. The outlines of the surfaces of the lens as shown in these diagrams have been constructed by making them parabolic as far as possible towards the equator; but the connecting branches have been put in arbitrarily and estimated so as to fulfill the condition that the volume contained between the surfaces of the lens and the greatest closed indicial surface should remain unaltered during the change of shape   The writer particularly wishes to emphasize the fact that these figures are entirely accurate only with respect to the iso-indicial surfaces and only on the assumption of the symmetrical structure of the core lens for maximum accommodation. Their purpose is to represent the optical mechanism of accommodation objectively so far as this question is concerned with the imagery laws of the first order along the axis, and to illustrate diagramatically the relationship of this optical mechanism to the dynamics of the accommodative changes of the lens. With respect to the first of these objects, it should be noted that a slight difference of curvature, such as might well be present in many an eye if sufficient weight were attached to the ophthalmometric measurements, would make N have

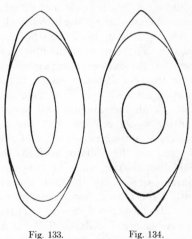

Fig. 133.   Fig. 134.

only a very small value. The effect of this on the form of the iso-indicial surfaces would be hardly noticeable; as can be readily seen, even without calculation, by considering that the comparatively high bending of the unaccommodated lens does not produce any more asymmetry in the arrangement of the iso-indicial surfaces than is shown in Fig. 133. Again, as to the connection between the optical mechanism and the dynamics of accommodation, this will be discussed more at length presently; but here attention is directed simply to the fact that, if, in accordance with BESIO's researches, the peripheral parts of the anterior surface of the lens are flatter than those of the posterior surface, the result might be an asymmetry of the external form of the lens without any asymmetry of the core lens.

A comparison of the distribution of the iso-indicial surfaces in the passive and in the accommodating lens shows at once that the shifting of the individual parts in the direction of the axis during increase of thickness of the lens is greatest in the equatorial plane, and that here the parts lying nearer the axis of the lens are shifted more than those nearer the equator. The mathematical investigation shows that this latter condition is an expression of the alteration of the total index with the change of shape of the lens. As this might have been postulated *a priori* from the anatomical structure of the lens, the conclusion is that the change of the total index accompanying accommodation is necessarily connected with the anatomical structure.

In order to understand this relationship, it is simply necessary to remember that the lens fibres are attached both anteriorly and posteriorly, describing in their course arcs which are convex toward the equator. When the points of attachment of the fibres are separated from one another by the increase of thickness of the lens, the arches must be spread, involving the greatest amount of dislocation of particles in the parts of the fibres farthest from the points of attachment. If the lens were always symmetrical, a centripetal shifting would have to occur at the equator. If the point of maximum centripetal shifting on each lens fibre were determined, and a surface passed through all these points, this surface of maximum accommodative shifting would coincide with the equatorial plane. But since the passive lens is asymmetrical, and the change of shape is particularly marked on the anterior surface, the surface of maximum accommodative shifting must be concave towards the front. This conclusion, drawn entirely from the anatomical structure of the lens with respect to its asymmetrical accommodative change of shape, may also be deduced directly from the figures given above, as a result of mathematical analysis. The slight change of form of the posterior surface of the lens demonstrates that the points of attachment of the lens fibres adjacent to this surface must, on the average, be less separated from one another during accommodation than those of the fibres lying on the anterior surface. Since, on the whole, the fibres of the posterior surface have their points of attachment situated more towards the periphery on the anterior surface, and towards the centre on the posterior surface, and as these conditions are reversed in the case of the fibres of the anterior surface, the distance of the posterior pole of the lens from the anterior point of attachment of the *Zonula Zinnii* must be relatively less changed during accommodation than the distance of the anterior pole from the posterior point of attachment. As a result, the shifting at the anterior point of attachment must occur in a direction approximately corresponding to a tangent to the surface. Consequently, it follows from the anatomical structure of the lens, that *the increase of curvature of the anterior surface of the lens during the accommodative change of form is accompanied by an axipetal shifting of the anterior point of attachment of the zonule.* As may be deduced from the figures given above, mathematical investigation demonstrates the presence of a corresponding shifting in those parts of the largest closed iso-indicial surface that are nearest to the point of attachment.

As the surface of maximum accommodative shifting contains cross or slightly oblique sections of the lens fibres, the rapidity of the centripetal movement of these sections during accommodation must be greater at a point nearer the axis than in the vicinity of the equator. If, for example, a centripetal movement of 0.1 mm occurs 4 mm from the axis, the superficial area of the fibrous cross sections contained within the circle of radius 4 mm is equal to 0.8π square millimetres; and exactly the same area of fibrous cross sections would be contained in the circle of radius 2 mm for a centripetal movement of 0.2 mm. It is true, this mechanism might be impeded by the fact that the fibres lying nearer the axis would be cut obliquely by the surface of maximum shifting in the passive state and perpendicularly during accommodation, provided the centripetal movement could occur to a sufficient extent. But in order to compensate the suggested difference of centripetal shifting, the oblique section must make an angle of 60° with the perpendicular section; and this is manifestly impossible. Another consequence, therefore, of the anatomical structure of the lens is that the equatorial diameters of the smaller iso-indicial surfaces must be proportionately more shortened in accommodation than those of the larger. But according to the mathematical investigation, this is an expression of an increase of the total index; and hence *the increase in total index during accommodation,* as proved by physiological-optical investigations, *may be deduced directly from the anatomical structure of the lens.* The so-called S-shaped curvature of the lens fibres is inferred from the fact that the projection of such a fibre on the equatorial plane is not a straight line; and the reason why in this discussion of the anatomical structure of the lens the possibility of a change in this curvature has not been mentioned, is because the only thing that could modify it would be radially directed elevations and depressions. This is a necessity due to the mode of attachment of the lens fibres in rows, so that any mutual shifting of the individual fibres at these points is impossible. On the other hand, it follows again from the anatomical arrangement of the lens fibres, that during the accommodative change of form, such elevations and depressions must either originate in the iso-indicial surfaces or must be reversed there, if they are already present. Else, they would undergo a reduction of superficial area during accommodation. This might perhaps be possible if the lens were composed of freely movable particles; but is actually impossible because the capability of movement is restricted by the arrangement of the fibres. However, a necessary mathematical consequence of this accommodative change of the iso-indicial surfaces is the variation of the star-shaped appearance of a luminous point.

A slight increase of the index at any given point may result from the interpenetration of individual fibres between others, even though the physical indices of the individual fibres are not altered. This explains why the smaller iso-indicial surface shown in the diagrams is apparently a little nearer the anterior pole of the lens during accommodation, because the superficial extent of that portion of it which is nearest the axis is augmented by the forward displacement, and this must involve an interpenetration of fibres from the central region.

Thus, the dioptric investigation of the lens in accommodation has resulted in finding out the accommodative variations that occur in the substance of the lens. At the same time, it appears that these changes, which for convenience may be grouped together under the name of the *intracapsular mechanism of accommodation*, are not only in complete agreement with the anatomical structure of the lens, but also establish and explain the casual connection between this structure and the variation of the total index of the lens as proved by the change of refraction that occurs when the lens is removed or during the process of accommodation.

The necessary data for the calculation of the schematic accommodating lens, that is, the refracting power of the core lens and the positions of the principal points, in terms of the millimetre as unit of length, are:

$$D_k = 0.01496, \qquad -H = H' = 0.012566,$$

the distances being measured from the centre of the lens, as in the case of the lens of the unaccommodated eye. In finding the *equivalent core lens*, it develops that a mathematically exact equivalent is not possible, because the principal points of the real core lens are too far apart.

The values

$$r_1 = -r_2 = d = 2.6551,$$

corresponding to the maximum possible interval between the principal points of the equivalent core lens, are, however, exact enough for the schematic lens, since the difference between these intervals in the real core lens and the equivalent core lens does not amount to as much as 0.007 mm. The combination of the three component systems of the lens gives the following data for the entire system, in terms of the metre as unit of length:

$$D_l = 33.055, \qquad\qquad 1000n_2H_l = -1000n_2H_l' = 1.9419.$$

These are the values that are obtained with the real core lens; whereas for the equivalent core lens they become 33.056 and 1.9449, respectively.

The total index is 1.426 in the exact schematic eye; and is 1.424 in the simplified schematic eye when the distance between the principal points is neglected.

The table on the following page exhibits the data, side by side, of the exact schematic eye and the simplified schematic eye, as calculated by the writer on the basis of the equivalent core lens, both for relaxed accommodation and for maximum accommodation. The refracting powers are expressed in dioptries and the linear dimensions in millimetres.

Although the exact schematic eye in the passive state has an hypermetropia of one dioptry along the axis, so as to represent the actual normal emmetropic eye, this effect of aberration cannot be taken in account in the case of the accommodating eye, because the amount of aberration under these circumstances has never yet been ascertained. However, owing to the pupillary contraction that is concomitant with accommodation, the influence of any residual aberration that might be present would certainly be considerably reduced. On the other hand, however, a necessary result of the same pupillary contraction is to draw the practical near point of the schematic eye rather nearer the eye than the exact near point, because the depth of focus has to be added in.

It should be noted with regard to the simplified schematic eye, that the difference between the total index of its lens and that of the lens of the exact schematic eye as given above is due to the fact that, instead of the principal points of the lens, an optical centre is assumed, and because in the passive state the effect of aberration is left out of account.

SCHEMATIC EYE

	Exact		Simplified	
	Accommodation relaxed	Maximum accommodation	Accommodation relaxed	Maximum accommodation
Refractive Index				
Cornea............................	1.376	1.376		
Aqueous humor and vitreous body....	1.336	1.336	1.336	1.336
Lens.............................	1.386	1.386	1.413	1.424
Equivalent core lens................	1.406	1.406		
Position				
Anterior surface of cornea...........	0	0	0	0
Posterior surface of cornea..........	0.5	0.5		
Anterior surface of lens.............	3.6	3.2		
Anterior surface of equiv. core lens ...	4.146	3.8725		
Posterior surface of equiv. core lens...	6.565	6.5275		
Posterior surface of lens............	7.2	7.2		
Optical centre of lens...............			5.85	5.2
Radius of curvature				
Anterior surface of cornea...........	7.7	7.7		
Posterior surface of cornea..........	6.8	6.8		
Equivalent surface of cornea........			7.8	7.8
Anterior surface of lens.............	10.0	5.33..	10.0	5.33..
Anterior surface of equiv. core lens ...	7.911	2.655		
Posterior surface of equiv. core lens...	− 5.76	− 2.655		
Posterior surface of lens............	− 6.0	− 5.33..	− 6.0	− 5.33..
Refracting Power				
Anterior surface of cornea...........	48.83	48.83		
Posterior surface of cornea..........	− 5.88	− 5.88		
Equivalent surface of cornea........			43.08	43.08
Anterior surface of lens.............	5.0	9.375	7.7	16.5
Core lens..........................	5.985	14.96		
Posterior surface of lens............	8.33..	9.375	12.833.	16.5
Corneal System				
Refracting power...................	43.05	43.05	43.08	43.08
Position of first principal point.......	− 0.0496	− 0.0496	0	0
Position of second principal point.....	− 0.0506	− 0.0506	0	0
First focal length..................	−23.227	−23.227	−23.214	−23.214
Second focal length................	31.031	31.031	31.014	31.014
Lens System				
Refracting power...................	19.11	33.06	20.53	33.0
Position of first principal point.......	5.678	5.145	5.85	.5.2
Position of second principal point.....	5.808	5.255	5.85	5.2
Focal length......................	69.908	40.416	65.065	40.485
Complete optical system of eye				
Refracting power...................	58.64	70.57	59.74	70.54
Position of first principal point.......	1.348	1.772	1.505	1.821
Position of second principal point.....	1.602	2.086	1.631	2.025
Position of first focal point..........	−15.707	−12.397	−15.235	−12.355
Position of second focal point........	24.387	21.016	23.996	20.963
First focal length..................	−17.055	−14.169	−16.740	−14.176
Second focal length................	22.785	18.930	22.365	18.938
Position of Fovea centralis..........	24.0	24.0	24.0	24.0
Axial refraction....................	− 1.0	− 9.6	0	− 9.7
Position of near point..............		−102.3		−100.8

It would be idle to make a comparison here with previous schematic eyes that have been proposed; because although these schemes are frequently based on the refracting power of the lens as found by the change of refraction after extraction of the lens, the connection between the change of shape of the lens and the amount of accommodation is usually left entirely out of consideration. The reason of this was evidently because it was not possible to construct a schematic eye corresponding to the facts without knowing the dioptrics of hetero-geneous media. Merely with respect to the values of the refracting power, it should be noted that they cannot be compared directly with the data of TSCHERNING and his pupils, because the latter did not always employ the scientific idea of refracting power, and magnitudes as expressed in terms of the dioptry are not commensurable.

A comparison of the lens system of the exact schematic eye in the passive state and for maximum accommodation, as given in Fig. 135, indicates, schematically of course, the intracapsular mechanism of accommodation that was proved above.

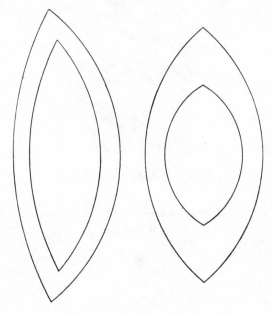

Fig. 135.

While this mechanism is well known for the eyes of very young people, the best we can do in the case of the lens of people of middle age or older is to get an approximate idea of it, because the form of the surfaces of discontinuity in the lens is unknown. As long as the lens shows a small axial cleft, as is the case with the eyes of children (see the schematic drawing of BABUCHIN, Fig. 136), the intracapsular mechanism will probably remain unaltered, since this cleft must be shortened by the tension of the zonule, and its meridional section must assume the form of either a small cross or of a radial cleft. If the central portions become more homogeneous with advancing age, the mutability of form in the centre of the lens begins to decrease, so that the maximum change of curvature of the surfaces of the lens cannot produce the same increase of the total index. Hence it follows that the amplitude of accommodation begins to decrease before the change of curvature of the surfaces of the lens influences the changes in the core. As soon as the central portion becomes less mobile, strains must arise during the changes of shape, and these lead to the formation of surfaces of discontinuity. This is proved by the doubling of the

Fig. 136.

reflex image that occurs in the posterior surface of the lens, as recently described by ZEEMAN.[1] This phenomenon, as was stated above, may be observed in many senile lenses by looking in a direction nearly along the equator of the core, but it was erroneously attributed by ZEEMAN himself to a supposed posterior lenticonus. The investigations of ADAMÜK and WOINOW[2] have shown that the change of curvature of the surfaces of the lens, at least of the anterior surface, is finally checked by increase of sclerosis of the core.

---

[1] W. P. C. ZEEMAN, Über die Form der hinteren Linsenfläche. *Klin. Monatsbl. f. Augenheilk.* XLVI. 1908. S. 83.
[2] Loc. cit.

In the investigation of the *extracapsular mechanism of accommodation* it is well first to review the known facts that have been ascertained for the human eye.

Next to the *change of curvature of the surfaces of the lens* and the *increase of thickness of the lens*, HELMHOLTZ attached most importance to the *contraction of the pupil* accompanying accommodation. It has been a question of debate whether this phenomenon is associated with accommodation or with convergence of the lines of vision. Concerning this, clinical observations on eyes in which accommodation was completely paralysed as a result of diphtheria have shown, that contraction of the pupil occurs in convergence, and that accommodative contraction of the pupil may be unhampered when convergence is absent. It seems most probable that the three innervations are associated with one another and are released by the impulse for clear vision of near objects. (Simply because the pupil becomes contracted by mechanical means when the anterior chamber is drained is no reason for inferring, as TSCHERNING does, that the contraction of the pupil in accommodation is produced by mechanical means.) The function of the contraction of the pupil during accommodation is to be seen in the increase of the depth of focus, since the changes of accommodation requisite for seeing near objects are essentially diminished by the increased depth. This has nothing to do with aberration, as will be shown further on. What advantages this contraction of the pupil offers, might have been better understood before the invention of spectacles, because in those days it afforded the only recourse against normal presbyopia.

The best way at present to observe the *changes in the form of the anterior chamber* during accommodation is with the binocular magnifying glass invented by CZAPSKI. The experiments described by HELMHOLTZ do not always give positive results, for reasons presently to be discussed. In the stereoscopic image obtained with the instrument above mentioned, it is easy to establish definitely not only the protrusion of the central parts, but also (at least in the case of young people with sufficient accommodation) the recession of the periphery. The latter effect is a necessary consequence of the former, since the volume of fluid contained within the anterior chamber cannot be reduced by flowing over into the posterior chamber on account of the physiological adherence of the iris to the anterior surface of the lens capsule. But the periphery of the iris does not move as much as the centre, because the fluid that escapes from the central region takes up in the periphery a space of larger diameter and consequently of less thickness. This does not indicate that the mechanism of the peri-

pheral increase of depth of the anterior chamber assumed by HELM-
HOLTZ may not function, but simply that it might be superfluous for
this particular purpose. That his mechanism is certainly not sufficient,
is demonstrated by one of ULBRICH's cases,[1] in which there was a small
hole in the iris covered by a thin membrane which was invaginated
during accommodation. As the decrease in capacity of the anterior
chamber produced by the protrusion of the central part of its posterior
wall is compensated by the recession of the peripheral portions of the
iris, a dilatation of the pupil must result if the superficial area of the
iris remains the same; or, to express it differently, *the mechanical effect
on the iris of the change of form of the lens during accommodation is to
widen the pupil.* In confirmation of this, sudden traumatic decrease
of space in the anterior chamber results either in the tearing loose of
the iris from its attachment or in its prolapse, if it has had time to
relax.

*The contraction of the entrance-pupil in accommodation does not take
place concentrically.* This was demonstrated in the early days of ophthalmometry, both by KNAPP[2] and by ADAMÜK and WOINOW,[3] whose
work was done under the direction of HELMHOLTZ. They found that
there was invariably a shifting of the centre of the pupil to the nasal
side during accommodation. As the ophthalmometer was set up on
the axis of the osculating ellipse in these observations, so that the
centre of the entrance-pupil was on the nasal side of this axis, this
eccentrical contraction of the entrance-pupil could not be attributed
to the asymmetry of the cornea; but there might be a very great probability that the anatomical pupil behaved in the same way. Even if
this were not the case, it is easy to understand how the entrance-pupil
must show a decentration with respect to the line of sight. For, of two
rays parallel to the line of sight directed towards the nasal and temporal ends of the horizontal diameter of the entrance-pupil, the former
meets the cornea at a greater angle of incidence than the latter. The
apparent shifting due to refraction increases with the size of the angle
of incidence and with the distance of the point of incidence from the
plane of the pupil. Owing to the oblique incidence of the line of sight
and on account of the asymmetry of the cornea, both the angle of
incidence and the distance of the point of incidence from the pupillary
plane will vary asymmetrically with changes in the size of the pupil;
which is the same as saying that the entrance-pupil cannot expand and

---

[1] H. ULBRICH, Zur Lehre von der intraokulären Flüssigkeitsströmung. *Ber. über die*
34. *Vers. d. Ophth. Ges.* Heidelberg 1907. S. 105.

[2] Loc. cit.

[3] Loc. cit.

contract concentrically, if this is what happens in case of the anatomical pupil. In confirmation of this, the angle of incidence of the line of sight varies with the size of the pupil, as was noted above. The same condition occurs in contraction of the pupil during accommodation, as the writer has verified by special investigations.

For a definite line of sight, accommodation is often accompanied by a *change of the direction of the optical axis of the eye.* If the experiment, described by HELMHOLTZ in connection with Fig. 60, is performed with an ophthalmometric NERNST lamp with vertical slit, the lamp, however, being placed far enough back for the light to fall on the inner surface of the sclera in front of the point of origin of the iris, the small spot of light will be observed to be rather farther back in accommodation than it is with accommodation relaxed; provided the eye is made to look past a needle-point fixed 10 cm away at a more distant point, and provided also the subject understands that, whether he is fixating on the distant point or on the needle, he must get a sharp image. It is impossible to follow the movement, because the eye executes lateral movements during the change of focus, but the change in position of the bright spot may be gauged by its altered distance from the corneal limbus. There is a slight movement of the eye towards the temporal side during accommodation. This motion, along with the shifting of the pupil in the nasal direction, may clear up the confusion that in many instances renders it difficult to harmonize the results of HELMHOLTZ's two experiments concerning the change of shape of the anterior chamber during accommodation.

A partial explanation of these experiments may be found by the laws of imagery of the first order. If one tried to explain the phenomenon on the basis of the erroneous notion of the meaning of the nodal points, exactly the opposite conditions would have to be present. For the nodal points move forward during accommodation, and then the line of sight makes a smaller angle with the optical axis of the eye. Consequently, the eye would have to move towards the nasal side if the line of sight were unaltered. But not only observation itself, but exact mathematical investigation of the procedure of the line of sight, shows that what happens is the reverse of this. Suppose the abscissae of the principal points of the optical system of the cornea are denoted by h_c, h_c' and those of the optical system of the whole eye by h, h'; and the corresponding refracting powers by D_c and D, respectively. Moreover, let d, p, p' denote the abscissae of the centres of the pupil of the eye, the entrance-pupil, and the exit-pupil, respectively; and let κ denote the magnification-ratio with respect to the entrance-pupil and exit-pupil. Finally, let n denote the index of refraction of the acqueous and vitreous humors. Then the positions of the pupils and the magnification-ratio can be found by the following formulae:

$$\frac{n}{d-h_c'}=\frac{1}{p-h_c}+D_c, \quad \frac{n}{p'-h'}=\frac{1}{p-h}+D, \quad \kappa=\frac{p'-h'}{n(p-h)}.$$

The distance of the fovea (denoted by l) being projected from the axis, the angle between the line of sight and the optical axis is found by using the reduced coefficient of angular projection. As this is equal to the reciprocal of the magnification-ratio, that angle is directly proportional to $\dfrac{\kappa}{l-p'}$, the value of which in the exact schematic eye is 44.67 with relaxed accommodation, and 45.25 for maximum accommodation; and in the simplified schematic eye 44.7 with relaxed accommodation, and 45.1 for maximum accommodation. Thus, in accommodation there is an increase of the angle between the line of sight and the optical axis, and, consequently, for a constant line of sight there must be a movement of the eye towards the outside in accommodation. However, the amount of this movement might not be sufficient for it to be perceived in the manner mentioned. On the other hand, in the accommodative changes of the asymmetry-values along the line of sight, to which we shall refer again in the proper chapter, lies the cause of a movement of the eye which may be added to that just discussed.

In case of a strong innervation of accommodation the tension of the zonule is diminished, and a decentration of the lens occurs in the direction of gravity. Coccius[1] had described the oscillations of the image in the posterior surface of the lens; and Tscherning[2] had noted a downward displacement of this image. Neither of them, however, understood the real cause of the phenomenon. The oscillations were supposed to be due to action of the "Musculus tensor choroideae," and the connection between the displacement and gravity was not discovered. A strictly scientific explanation and definite solution of this problem was given first by Hess.[3] In the case of a small granular spot in his lens, he verified an entoptical parallactic movement of it towards the pupil, by exertion of maximum accommodation. A very small hole, set up 12 mm in front of the eye, served as the source of illumination. With vigourous effort of accommodation, towards the end of the

[1] A. Coccius, Über die vollständige Wirkung des Tensor chorioideae. *Ber. d. VII. intern. Ophth.-Kongr.* Heidelberg 1888. S. 197.

[2] Théorie des changements optiques de l'œil pendant l'accommodation. *Arch .de physiol.* VII, 1. 1895. p. 181.

[3] C. Hess, Über einige bisher nicht gekannte Ortsveränderungen der menschlichen Linse während der Akkommodation. *Ber. über die XXV. Vers. d. Ophth. Ges. Heidelberg* 1896. S. 41. Also: Arbeiten aus dem Gebiete der Akkommodationslehre. *Arch. f. Ophth.* XLII, 1. S. 288 and 2. S. 80. XLIII, 3. S. 477.

time when the pupil was contracting, the spot on the lens as seen entoptically had an upward displacement in the blur circle. Now this displacement invariably occurred in a direction opposite to that of gravity,
no matter how the head was held, provided the pupillary plane was
vertical, whereas, when the pupillary plane was horizontal, without
changing the position of the far point, there was an increase of the
amplitude of accommodation when the head was bent forwards, and
a decrease when it was bent backwards. The first experiments proved
that with strong accommodation, the spot on the lens was displaced
with respect to the pupil in the direction of gravity; and the last
experiment showed that this is the case with the entire lens.   That
the entire lens sunk in the first experiment, was shown objectively
by the opacities present in the lens. HESS went on to show that, when
a powerful effort of accommodation is being made, the lens shakes
with movements of the eye (indeed, in many people the iris can be
seen to share this trembling); and that both the sinking of the lens
sagittally in the frontal plane and its trembling are increased by the
use of eserin. If the eserin drops are instilled after dilatation of the
pupil by homatropin, the process of accommodation can be observed
through the large pupil in the early stages of the action of the eserin.
In the reflex images in the lens the appearance is quite different; only
the one in the posterior surface appears to tremble and it either sinks
by itself or more than the reflex image in the anterior surface. HESS
pointed out that the lens may sink down without any dislocation of
the reflex image in the anterior surface, because the apparent position
of the centre of curvature may be relatively unaffected by the movement. That the sinking of the lens must actually occur in just this
manner, is a consequence of the anatomical structure of the zonule,
as will be explained below. HESS[1] has also shown that sinking of the
anterior surface of the lens may be observed by means of the marking
of the epithelium, which is visible with the CZAPSKI magnifying glasses,
inside the reflex image in this surface, and also that the anterior surface
shares in the trembling in cases where there are little isolated points
on it that can be watched.

For strong, arbitrary accommodation, the results of the entoptical
measurement of the sinking of the lens were from 0.3 to 0.35 mm. If
the head were turned from the right to the left shoulder, the accommodating lens was shifted by twice this amount, and under strong influence of esserin by almost 1 mm. When the head is moved downwards from above, the lens was displaced forwards 0.15 mm. The

[1] Beobachtungen über den Akkommodationsvorgang. *Klin. Monatsbl. f. Augenheilk.*
XLII. 1904. S. 1.

earlier measurements have been confirmed by HEINE[1] by measuring the apparent shifting of visible objects that occurs with decentration and the parallax of the reflex images in the posterior surface of the lens and in the cornea.

The mobility of the lens under great strain of accommodation proves unequivocally that there is *no difference of pressure* on its two surfaces in the accommodating eye; whereas in the passive state a slight difference of pressure is possible corresponding to the tension of the zonule. Any increase of pressure in the vitreous body and in the anterior chamber due to accommodation is excluded *a priori* by reason of the viscosity of the fluids. For in order for the tension of the choroid to produce an increase of pressure during the act of accommodation, the suprachoroidal space would have to be replenished without hindrance. Also, according to the investigations of HESS and HEINE[2] referred to above, no *increase of pressure* can be observed. In the case of a freshly enucleated child's eye, HEINE[3] succeeded in verifying an earlier observation of BEER which showed that the mechanism of accommodation goes right on unhindered by a fenestrated sclera and without the slightest movement of the drops of vitreous humor that had welled up through the openings of the sclera.

Direct observations as to *the movement of the ciliary processes* in accommodation cannot be made, of course, on the normal uninjured eye, though they may be made in many instances following an iridectomy or in traumatic or congenital irideremia. With the use of eserin, HESS[4] verified a forward movement of the ciliary processes in iridectomised eyes in which they moved out in front of the equatorial plane of the lens. And in a case of congenital irideremia, GROSSMANN[5] succeeded by means of eserin in seeing ciliary processes that were before invisible, but he conceived the shifting as taking place in a direction towards the axis of the eye, and not towards the cornea. The difference is not of fundamental importance for the mechanism of accommodation and might perhaps be due to an anomalous topography of the ciliary muscle in GROSSMANN's case, or to the fact that an iridectomy, which extends far enough peripherally to make the ciliary processes visible, must involve the origin of the iris in the ciliary body, so as to affect

[1] L. HEINE, Akkommodative Ortsveränderungen der Linse. *Ber. über die XXVI. Vers. d. Ophth. Ges. Heildelberg* 1897. S. 20.

[2] C. HESS und L. HEINE, Arbeiten aus dem Gebiete der Akkommodationslehre. *Arch. f. Ophth.* XLVI, 2. S. 243.

[3] Ein Versuch über Akkommodation und intraokularen Druck am überlebenden Kinderauge. *Arch. f. Ophth.* LX, 3. 1905. S. 448.

[4] Loc. cit. Die Refraktion und Akkommodation usw. S. 222.

[5] KARL GROSSMANN, The mechanism of accommodation in man. *Ophth. Review.* XXIII. 1904. p. 1.

the mechanical movement of the ciliary processes by the operation. (In GROSSMANN's case the trembling began after the administration of the eserin drops, and the changes in form of the lens during accommodation could be confirmed. An excessive increase of thickness and an unusual shortening of the equatorial diameter of the lens, together with a displacement of it upwards and inwards, however, cause one to wonder whether the lens and zonule were normal. The lens showed granular opacities at both poles.)

The *edge of the lens* has been observed to become broader in the iridectomised eye during accommodation and after the administration of drops of eserin, but no definite conclusions can be drawn from this fact. Up to the present time, nothing positive is known as to a decrease in the equatorial diameter of the normal lens during accommodation. According to HESS, the margin of the lens in an eye treated with atropin usually appears as a delicate wavy irregular line; whereas, after the introduction of eserin drops, the line is regular and more like a circle. Low swellings and tent-like protuberances, which may be seen in the eye, treated with atropin in the region of the point where the zonule fibres are attached to the capsule, may disappear or become less prominent after the infusion of eserin.

Except for CZERMAK's *phosphene of accommodation*, all the changes during accommodation that have been observed in the living eye have now been duly considered. The phosphene may be due to a mechanical stimulation of the retina on account of the sudden decrease in the tension of the choroid in rare and especially sensitive eyes.

The *dynamics of the contraction of the ciliary muscle* was explained to a very great extent by the investigations of HENSEN and VÖLCKERS.[1] Inasmuch as most of the muscle fibres (the meridional bundle) run almost parallel to the sclera, the most important question is, whether the contraction wave passes from the posterior end forwards or from the anterior end backwards. It has been demonstrated that, if a needle is inserted at the equator of the eyeball of a dog, electrical stimulation of the ciliary muscle causes the outer end of the needle to move backwards, and that there is no place where the needle can be inserted that makes it move forwards. The inference is that the contraction of the ciliary muscle causes the anterior portion of the choroid to move forwards, and that no point of the choroid moves backwards during contraction. The forward movement of the inner coats of the eye may also be observed through a window in the sclera. On the other hand, if all the cornea is removed except a peripheral border 2 mm wide, electrical stimulation of the ciliary muscle is accompanied by a back-

[1] V. HENSEN und C. VÖLCKERS, *Experimentaluntersuchung über den Mechanismus der Akkommodation*. Kiel 1868.

ward movement of this border, thus indicating that what is known in anatomy as the anterior point of origin of the muscle behaves physiologically as such. Moreover, the relaxation of the zonule on contraction of the ciliary muscle is definitely established. The mechanism of accommodation of a dog is different in some respects from that in man. Thus, HESS and HEINE[1] showed that the contraction of the ciliary muscle produces only a slight change of the optical focusing of the eye. Consequently, HEINE's[2] microscopic examination of specimens fixed in the act of accommodation, first for doves and then for monkeys,[3] constitutes a valuable addition to our sources of information. The latter investigation illustrates in the most clear-cut manner the function of the muscular fibres which are attached to the strictly meridional bundles and which in the anterior inner portion have a more radial course. Were it not for them, the increase of thickness of the muscle during contraction would result in a component acting towards the centre of the eyeball; whereas the attachment of this bundle to the inner surface of the meridional bundles of fibres causes the resultant of the shortening and thickening to act on the inner surface of the ciliary body in the direction of the tangent to it. In the first case, a cross section of the muscle would have a radial direction, but, in the actual anatomical arrangement of the muscle bundle, the line that cuts orthogonally the fibres which are in a meridional section, is represented by a circle as a first approximation, with its centre in the vicinity of SCHLEMM's canal. The component corresponding to the increase of thickness coincides at every point with the tangent to this circle, which in turn, except for the most posterior and thinnest parts of the muscle, forms everywhere an acute angle with the inner surface of the ciliary body. Another thing to be noted here is that the full increase of thickness is towards the inner side, because the sclera lies in contact with the outer surface, and that its effect is increased by its concave shape. If a ring-shaped portion of the ciliary body can be imagined, the diameter of this ring must be diminished by a movement forwards and inwards, and the ring must become correspondingly thicker, even if·none of the fibres in it are thickened. Hence, the total action of the meridional and radial fibres, which indeed form one common system, is to produce a relatively *uniform displacement of the inner surface of the ciliary body in the direction of its tangent*; whereas, if there were nothing but meridional fibres, the posterior portion would

[1] Loc. cit. *Arch. f. Ophth.* 1898.

[2] Mikroskopische Fixierung des Akkommodationsaktes. *Ber. über die XXVI. Vers. d. Ophth. Ges. Heidelberg* 1897. — Physiologisch-anatomische Untersuchungen über die Akkommodation des Vogelauges. *Arch. f. Ophth.* XLV. 3. 1898. S. 469.

[3] Die Anatomie des akkommodierten Auges. Ibid. XLIX, 1. 1899. S. 1.

be shifted more than the anterior, and the effect would necessarily be offset by the increase in thickness. These relations, which are a mathematical necessity of the anatomical structure of the ciliary muscle, are illustrated in Figs. 137 and 138, reproduced from HEINE. That the circular fibres, if present, will act in harmony with the others, is what might be expected. Inasmuch as they lie on the inner anterior angle, their contraction can only produce a component at this place directed towards the axis; which will cause a rotation of the resultant in the same sense as the tangents to the meridional fibres will have to be rotated in order to become parallel to the tangent to the inner surface of the ciliary body. Whether this muscle exists or not, is therefore of secondary importance. The bundles

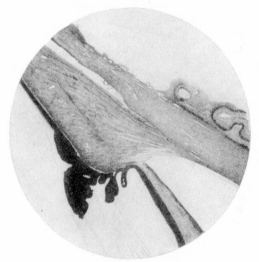

Fig. 137.
Ciliary muscle not contracted.

of the main mass of the muscle do not lie exactly in the meridional plane, but are interlaced and bend back both at their posterior end in the choroid and at the anterior inner angle. Thus, the impression of a circular muscle may be gained much more readily when the fibres are not stretched. In accordance with this, many more oblique sections are to be seen in the ciliary body during accommodation than when it has been treated with atropin. The illustrations also show the opening of SCHLEMM's canal and the widening of the angle of the anterior chamber during accommodation. Since the most anterior radial fibres insert on the inner side of the canal, this action on the canal is as easy to understand as the combined action of the circular and radial fibres. To just how great an extent the enlargement of the anterior chamber is produced by the contraction of the ciliary muscle, cannot be readily explained at the present time, inasmuch as the tension of the iris during the act of accommodation, as proved by UL-BRICH's case, must act in the same direction.

Very recently HESS[1] published new results of comprehensive studies of the mechanism of accommodation. These have shown, in the first place, that accommodation in reptiles and birds takes place in an essentially different way; for the peripheral portions of the anterior surface of the lens are flattened by the pressure of the intrinsic musculature on the part of that surface in front of the equator, whereas the

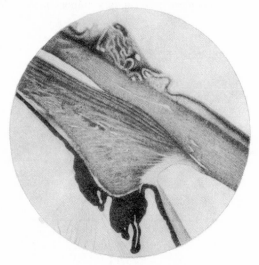

Fig. 138.
Ciliary muscle contracted

portions around the anterior pole become more highly curved, so that in the enucleated eye an accommodative increase of pressure takes place. The shifting forward of the anterior portion of the choroid can be easily seen for some time after enucleation by cutting the eyeball in half along the equatorial plane and watching the movement from behind; it occurs in a manner similar to that found in mammals.

[1] C. HESS, Untersuchungen zur vergleichenden Physiologie und Morphologie des Akkommodationsvorganges. *Arch. f. Augenheilk.* LXII. 1909. S. 345. — Vergleichende Untersuchungen über den Einfluss der Akkommodation auf den Augendruck in der Wirbeltierreihe. Ibid. LXIII. 1909. S. 88. — Also, from personal communications to the writer presumably to be published before the appearance of the first volume of the third edition of HELMHOLTZ's *Phys. Opt.*

At last HESS succeeded also in fixating the act of accommodation in the human eye, with two patients just before death, by using eserin in one eye and atropin in the other. In one case, the eyes were enucleated ninety minutes after death and hardened for eighteen hours in formalin. In the other case, they were enucleated twelve hours after death and studied fresh. After sectioning in the equatorial plane, it was shown, by observation and measurements from the side of the vitreous humor, that both the diameter of the lens and the diameter of the ring formed by the summits of the ciliary processes were smaller, and the notching of the edge of the lens less noticeable, in the eye treated with eserin than in that treated with atropin.

The form of the lens is influenced by the ciliary muscle through the medium of the *zonule*. The fibres of the latter arise over the entire inner surface of the ciliary body as far as the *ora serrata*, so that they appear to cross through it, because the bundles passing to the anterior and posterior surfaces of the lens alternate. As a rule those going to the anterior surface, originate more to the back and in the depressions between the cilliary processes, while those going to the posterior surface of the lens and to the equator arise more to the front and on the summits of the processes. As a result of this arrangement, the bundles of the zonule passing to the anterior surface of the lens, during the contraction of the ciliary muscle, make greater excursions on the average in their long direction than the others do, because, whereas the former lie in the direction of the movement, the latter make an angle with it. This condition is particularly clearly illustrated in Fig. 139 reproduced from RETZIUS. Indeed, it is possible to decide by this figure that the bundles arising farthest forward and passing to the posterior insertion point on the lens are not noticeably relaxed by the contraction of the ciliary muscle, but merely act in a new direction; whereas when the bundles attached to the anterior surface of the lens are relaxed, the points of insertion on the capsule of the lens can move in the direction of their tangents to an extent which must be approximately as much as the movement of the posterior portion of the inner surface of the ciliary body.

What change of form the anterior surface of the lens will undergo on relaxation of the anterior fibres of the zonule, no one can say *a priori*, except that it is certain that the curvature of the central portions must increase. But whether the entire form tends then to become more spherical or hyperbolical, defies conjecture at the present time. It is a fact that a closed elastic membrane containing such a large volume of an incompressible, freely mobile substance that it does not get limp even while it is still spherical, tends to return to the form of a sphere after each deformation. But these conditions do not occur at all in the case of the lens, as is shown by the form of a young person's lens when it is freed from its attachments. This being the state of affairs, when the anterior fibres of the zonule are relaxed, the form of the anterior surface of the lens depends on the size of the surface and the elasticity of the capsule of the lens, and on the distribution of tension in it, which can neither be calculated nor estimated. Hence, it is indeed quite possible that the peripheral portions of the anterior surface do become flatter in accommodation, as BESIO[1] thought he had proved;

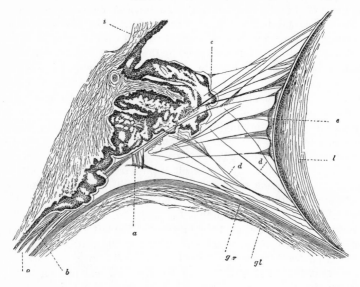

FIG. 139 (reproduced from RETZIUS).

l, lens—*gl*, vitreous humor—*gr*, anterior boundary layer—*o*, orbicular space—*i*, iris root—*a*, short, strong fibrous attachments of the posterior ligament of the zonule—*b*, fibres of the zonule arising behind from the hyaloid membrane—*c*, fibres of the zonule arising anteriorly from the ciliary processes—*d*, fibres of the zonule arising from the ciliary processes which cross the ligaments of the zonule and partly attach to them—*e*, space between the capsule of the lens and the pericapsular membrane.

although in the writer's opinion it cannot be considered as proved, because the approximate methods of calculation may involve considerable sources of error, and the methods of measurement were not very accurate anyhow. Moreover, his measurements appear to have been made on eyes dilated with cocaine, which might influence the mechanics of contraction of the ciliary muscle even if the amplitude of accommodation were not reduced.

[1] Loc. cit.

Since during contraction of the ciliary muscle the fibres of the zonule passing to the anterior surface of the capsule are relatively more relaxed than the others, the useful surface of attachment on both the lens and the ciliary body continually shrinks, because it contracts to the equatorial and posterior points of attachment on the lens and to the anterior parts of the ciliary body. It is just this mechanism which the writer has tried to represent schematically in an intentionally exaggerated way in the contours of the lens surfaces in Figs. 133 and 134. The indicated change of accommodation would correspond to a complete relaxation of the fibres of the zonule proceeding to the anterior surface of the lens and to a forward shifting of the ciliary points of attachment of the other fibres. The writer does not suppose that the lens has just this form in maximum accommodation. For if the relaxation of those fibres is not complete, the result of the mechanism may very well be a somewhat bent form; and if the fibres passing to the equator of the lens are already appreciably relaxed, a decrease in the equatorial diameter may occur. Perhaps, too, the equatorial portions of the lens should be more rounded in both the relaxed and contracted condition of the zonule than is shown in the figures, because the fibres of the zonule are inserted superficially on the lens. But that the bundles proceeding from the anterior portion of the ciliary body to the equator and to the posterior surface of the capsule, are the last to be relaxed, may be inferred from the mode of the sinking and trembling of the lens under maximum effort of accommodation. For this is the only reason why during these motions the lens turns around an axis that passes approximately through the centre of curvature of the anterior surface, so that the reflex image in this surface is practically motionless. This means, for example, that part of the margin of the lens which approaches the optical axis during the displacement of the lens must be inclined forwards by an accurately functioning mechanism; and there is no other mechanism except the tension of the fibres above mentioned that could function in this way. This implies that these fibres are the least relaxed.

Thus, anatomical and physiological investigations prove beyond doubt, that, *with contraction of the ciliary muscle, the ciliary point of origin of the fibres of the zonule, particularly of those going to the anterior surface of the lens, is displaced towards the lens in the direction of the bundle; until, when the contraction is greatest, there is a relaxation of the zonule; and that this contraction is accompanied by an increase of the thickness of the lens and of the curvatures of its surfaces, especially of the anterior surface.* Since the relaxation of the zonule does not begin until the contraction is greatest, it must be kept under tension during normal contraction by an axipetal movement of the points of insertion on the lens, especially of those on the anterior surface. Since there is only one force present which can maintain this tension, namely, the elasticity of the lens capsule, *the extracapsular portion of the mechanism of accommodation consists essentially in an axipetal movement of the points of attachment of the zonule on the lens, especially on the anterior surface, this movement being due to the elasticity of the lens capsule.*

The dioptric investigation of the process of accommodation has shown that an *intracapsular mechanism of accommodation* is a mathematically necessary consequence of the change of form and of the increase of refracting power. Also, in accordance with the histological structure of the lens, it demands *an axipetal movement of the portions of the substance of the lens that are nearest to the points of attachment of the zonule, particularly on the anterior surface, and that are contained within the greatest closed iso-indicial surface.*

Moreover, taking into consideration that there are no known facts which could in any way refute this mechanism (see the discussion of TSCHERNING's theory presently), it is doubtful whether there is a more complete chain of proof in all the medical sciences. Modern investigations have established that the theory of the mechanism of accommodation remains unchanged, in all essential features, just as HELMHOLTZ, by a real inspiration of genius, considering the state of knowledge of that time, conceived it.

In the light of the modern theory of antagonistic action, what is known as *double antagonism* is of particular physiological interest. The form of the lens is determined by two antagonistic elastic forces; and at the same time the muscular force and the stronger of the two elastic forces act antagonistically. Now it is readily seen that this arrangement is beautifully adapted to protect the lens from the action of too strong external forces and from sudden variations of these forces. The force that produces the change of form of the lens in accommodation is the weakest of the three that are present in the system, and, like all elastic forces, constantly diminishes during the development of its effect, so that the movement terminates without any jerk, and the potential energy accumulated can never exceed a certain maximum amount dependent on the elasticity of the zonule. This effect is promoted still more by the fact that, with increasing contraction of the ciliary muscle, the elastic resistance of the choroid is reduced by its stretching. In the relaxation of accommodation, the greatest force in producing the change of form depends then on the elasticity of the choroid, and this force diminishes steadily during the movement, and at the same time the resistance of the lens capsule is

continually increased by dilatation. The advantages of this arrangement may be easily demonstrated by
mechanical models. For example, one of
them is shown in Fig. 140. The two
springs are united by a cord which
represents the zonule. The upper one
represents the lens, its shortening corresponding to the change of form during
accommodation, and its force indicating
the elasticity of the lens capsule. The
lower spring illustrates the elasticity
of the choroid, and the tension of the
chord passing over the pulley, produced
by putting weights in the pan, corresponds to the force of the contracting

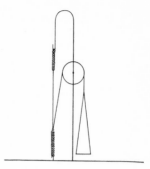

Fig. 140.

ciliary muscle. The upper spring must be the weaker of the two, and
must not be stretched enough for the connecting cord ever to get
slack when the pan reaches the level of the table. Obviously, the
upper spring cannot be injured by suddenly throwing the heaviest
weights into the pan, nor is it in the least danger from a sudden removal of the weights, provided the height of the fall is not too great
and the lower spring not too strong. On the other hand, supposing we
wished to illustrate a fictitious mechanism of accommodation where
the accommodative change of form would be produced by muscular
action and the recovery by the elasticity of the lens capsule, the pan
should be hung directly from the lower end of the upper spring; and
then the elongation of the spring would correspond to the change of
form of the lens in accommodation. In this arrangement the spring
might be injured by a sudden addition of heavy weights. Of course,
this could be avoided by suitable adjustment of the height of fall, and
in this way it might be possible for the lens of a young person to be
protected by this fictitious mechanism of accommodation. However,
this means of protection would fail with decrease of ability of the
lens to change its form, which could be represented by exchanging the
spring for a more brittle one. Every strong tendency to accommodation would result in a jerk on the structure of the lens, any sudden
heavy loading of the pan would produce a breaking of the spring.
When it is realized that opacities can originate in a previously entirely
transparent lens of an older person as a result of an insignificant
mechanical force, such as slight draining of the chamber in an iridectomy, one is disposed not to underestimate the *protective arrangement*
provided by the *double antagonism of the forces acting in accommodation.*

Since the contraction of the ciliary muscle is accompanied by a change of form of the lens merely until, in consequence of the shifting of the parts of the lens, this change reaches its maximum extent, whereas the muscle itself, as we know from the pupillary contraction and the trembling that occurs in the end, may be contracted beyond this point; therefore only a part of the contraction of the ciliary muscle is *manifest*, the rest is *latent*. According to HESS, the transition begins when the actual near point is reached, whereas, during the latent contraction of the ciliary muscle, there is merely a small apparent displacement of the near point further towards the eye, which depends on the concomitant contraction of the pupil.[1] Consequently, an accommodation of two dioptries, at an age when this is all the power of accommodation available, does not make any higher demands on the ciliary muscle than the same amount of accommodation at a younger age. This is a very important fact for the symptomatology of presbyopia; but in connection with it the contraction of the pupil due to latent contraction of the ciliary muscle, especially if the habitual size of the pupil is not very small, is another factor to be taken into account, because this by itself often decoys an uncorrected presbyope into trying to accommodate beyond his strength. HESS called attention to another important consequence of the mechanism of accommodation, namely, that we have the right to conclude from a normal amplitude of accommodation that the action of the ciliary muscle is normal also, because a paresis of the ciliary muscle does not become apparent until the restriction of movement extends to the region of manifest contraction. So far as physiological optics is concerned, this fact is significant as showing, as was remarked before, that TSCHERNING's opinion, as to the performance of the ciliary muscle not being impaired by cocaine, cannot be proved by its effect on the amplitude of accommodation, and therefore is without any basis at present.

There has been quite a lot of discussion in ophthalmological literature of an astigmatic accommodation. Without going into this subject in detail, it may simply be stated that no known facts indicate the possibility of a voluntary change of astigmatism by accommodation or by the practice of astigmatic accommodation. However, it may be possible that the normal inverse lenticular astigmatism or the lenticular astigmatism that is present in the higher degrees of ocular

---

[1] ¶The *physical* or *manifest near point* (what is usually meant by the "near point of the eye") is the point that is conjugate to the point where the optical axis meets the retina when the surfaces of the crystalline lens are most curved, the zonule being relaxed. The *physiological* or *latent near point* (whose position cannot be ascertained by any method at present available) is the point on the optical axis for which the eye would be focused when the ciliary muscle is contracted to its utmost power, supposing there were no limit to the effort of the crystalline lens to become spherical. (J. P. C. S.)

astigmatism may be altered to some slight extent by the accommodative change of form of the lens. But there is no sufficient evidence to show that this actually happens. Owing to the frequent occurrence of vertical asymmetry of the eye, whereby the apparent amount of astigmatism may change with the size of the pupil, it would probably be very difficult to obtain the data necessary to prove that anything of this sort does take place.

After what has been stated in the preceding argument, an exhaustive criticism of the various hypotheses that have been proposed since HELMHOLTZ's discovery of the mechanism of accommodation might seem to be superfluous, because they all presuppose a tension of the zonule during accommodation, and therefore have been actually refuted by HESS's investigations. Hypotheses have been framed by MANNHARDT,[1] SCHÖN[2] and TSCHERNING; and TSCHERNING's theory has stirred up so much controversy and been responsible for so many contributions to the literature of the psychology of science (in the broadest sense of the word), that a brief discussion of it seems to be advisable. As it has already passed through two essentially different phases and appears now to be about to enter a third, the best plan is to take up the first and better known of these phases first; and for that purpose let us consider TSCHERNING's own presentation of his theory as given in his text-book on Physiological Optics, which has been referred to above. The hypothesis consists essentially of three propositions, namely, (1) the assumption that accommodation consists in a temporary formation of a "lenticonus anterior," (2) the assumption that the tension of the zonule produces a structure of this kind, and (3) the assumption that the tension of the anterior fibres of the zonule may be produced by the contraction of the ciliary muscle.

The basis of the first assumption is the argument, that the aberration of the eye during accommodation varies in sign, that the refracting power increases more at the centre of the pupil than it does at the periphery, and that the distortion of the reflex images in the anterior surface of the lens is correspondingly altered by accommodation. But the aberration was investigated by unreliable methods. The writer has shown that the aberroscope does not give the aberration but a distortion value. The distribution of the light in the blur circle as described in TSCHERNING's experiment with the luminous point is such that by the nature of the caustic surface it could not possibly be due to aberration, although it might be an interference phenomenon of

---

[1] J. MANNHARDT, Bemerkungen über den Akkommodationsmuskel und die Akkommodation. *Arch. f. Ophth.* IV, 1. 1858. S. 269.

[2] W. SCHÖN, Zur Ätiologie des Glaukoms. *Arch. f. Ophth.* XXXI, 4. 1885. S. 1; and in other publications.

the kind described above. Finally, all that the experiments with
YOUNG's optometer give is the peripheral total aberration; which is
true also with respect to the skiascopic phenomena[1] which were subsequently included. The latter experiments do not give constant
results, because in many cases the change of the skiascopic aberration
phenomena cannot be observed at all in accommodation; and HESS,
for instance, got a negative result in his investigation with YOUNG's
optometer. Consequently, all that can be concluded is that in many
cases the peripheral total aberration of the eye decreases during
accommodation, and that this phenomenon is unessential so far as the
mechanism of accommodation is concerned. (For further information
on this subject, see the proper chapter below.) The writer's own
experience all goes to show that the phenomenon of the distortion of
the reflex images in the anterior surface of the lens cannot be seen with
sufficient clearness unless the pupil has been treated with cocaine, and,
in the first place, this gives no information concerning normal accommodation. In the second place, this distortion is changed without
alteration of the flattening of the reflecting surface by a change of its
curvature and of its distance from the cornea; and hence even when the
angles of incidence were very small, a calculation would be necessary to
determine whether the change of the distortion indicated a change of
the "Abflachungswert" of the surface. In the third place, such large
angles of incidence are necessary to verify this phenomenon, that the
asymmetrical flattening of the cornea cannot be left out of consideration, and this makes the calculation certainly quite complicated.

TSCHERNING's first assumption, therefore, was entirely without
foundation, although let it be stated once more that there are no
proofs of its impossibility. It was used for a false conclusion. Under
the title of "The Author's Theory of Accommodation," TSCHERNING
says that the "hypothesis" of HELMHOLTZ appears to be no longer
tenable; at least he himself cannot see how such a mechanism can
produce a flattening of certain parts of the lens and at the same time
an increase of curvature of other parts. The only conclusion that can
really be drawn from this statement is, that the cause of this lack of
comprehension must be sought either in the "hypothesis" of HELM-
HOLTZ or in TSCHERNING himself. HELMHOLTZ's own words are:[2]
"Stretched elastic membranes which contain an invariable volume of
an incompressible fluid and which are attached by a circular margin,
as the zonule is to the choroid, tend to approach the form of a segment

---

[1] Le Mécanisme de l'accommodation. *IX. Congr. internat. d'Utrecht. Compte rendu.*
Amsterdam 1900. p. 244.

[2] *Handbuch der Phys. Opt.* 2. Aufl. S. 138.

of a sphere in proportion as its tension increases. In the relaxed state, as is the case in near vision, the anterior surface of the lens is curved forwards in front of the flat curvature of the anterior ridges of the zonule. In the stretched state, as in far vision, this occurs to a much less extent. However, the radius of curvature of the anterior surface of the lens which is about 10 mm is always a little less than that of the zonular arching, which may be estimated at about 14 mm." Thus, he states that the entire curvature made up of the zonule and the anterior capsule of the lens must approach the spherical form when the zonule is contracted. In the supposititious final state when the spherical form was attained, the anterior surface of the lens would be, therefore, a segment of a sphere with a radius of about 14 mm. To infer from this that the anterior surface of the lens, as it bulges forwards with a decrease of tension in accommodation, is obliged to approach the form of a sphere, or that an increase of curvature can be produced by the increase of tension, involves conceptions that are incompatible with the mathematical knowledge of a HELMHOLTZ. Nowhere at all in his writings can the author find any intimation as to the probable form of the surfaces of the lens in the state of accommodation. This is not very surprising because, as already stated, there is no way of either calculating this form or of estimating it. All that can be said about it is HELMHOLTZ's own statement concerning the increase of curvature of the surfaces and of the thickness of the lens. As to the distribution of the increase of curvature over the various parts of the surface, and as to the possibility of a peripheral flattening during this process, nothing is stated; nor can anything be deduced from the relaxation of the zonule.

TSCHERNING's second assumption (that the result of the tension of the zonule is the formation of a "lenticonus anterior") is again simply a false conclusion which he made from experiments that prove that in the extirpated lenses of animals a traction exerted on the zonule may have this effect. Crucial experiments were carried out by EINTHOVEN,[1] HESS[2] and DALÉN.[3] EINTHOVEN exposed the lens and zonule of a calf's eye from above, and found that by pulling with two forceps at opposite ends of a diameter, he could make the curvature of the anterior surface of the lens increase or decrease, according as he pulled more backwards or forwards, respectively. HESS's experiments were made on the freshly enucleated eye of an ape, from which a portion of the sclera was removed without injuring the choroid, and the cornea

---

[1] W. EINTHOVEN, Die Akkommodation des menschlichen Auges. *Ergebnisse der Physiologie.* I, 2. 1902. S. 680.

[2] Loc cit. *Klin. Monatsbl. f. Augenheilk.* 1904.

[3] Loc. cit.

and iris taken away; and he showed that a pull on the zonule produced a decrease of the curvature of the anterior surface of the lens. DALÉN experimented with the dead eye of a human being in which the lens had been laid bare by removing the cornea and iris with special precautions; and he verified ophthalmometrically that there was an increase of the anterior surface of the lens after severing the zonule.

The third assumption (that a tension of the anterior fibres of the zonule may be produced by the contraction of the ciliary muscle) is based on ideas of the anatomy of the ciliary body that are not clearly enough expressed, but that seem to point to the conclusion that there is an innermost muscle layer, which by its contraction would pull the anterior inner end of the ciliary body backwards. These are notions that have no objectively demonstrable connection with the known anatomy of the ciliary body. The subjective connection is concerned with the fibres inserted on the inner side of SCHLEMM's canal.

In Fig. 141, reproduced from TSCHERNING, he has shown the first phase of his idea of the mechanism of accommodation. It may be of

Fig. 141.

some interest to know that the writer has shown that such a mechanism of accommodation is mathematically impossible unless the total index decreases in accommodation. TSCHERNING's assumption that for an accommodation of 7.5 dioptries the radius of the anterior surface of the lens might be reduced to 4.8 mm (which in itself is in startling contrast to the results obtained in all previous ophthalmometric measurements) would not be enough, because the radius would have to be even smaller.

The second phase of TSCHERNING's ideas on this subject appears in the work above cited published in the *Encyclopédie française d'ophthalmologie*. The real difference here is that the decrease of depth of the anterior chamber in accommodation, previously proved beyond a doubt by the more accurate methods of HELMHOLTZ, MANDELSTAM and SCHÖLER, and BLIX, is now admitted to be a fact, in consequence of its having been observed in BESIO's researches even with the less accurate methods of the Sorbonne Laboratory. Now, therefore, he represents the process of accommodation as shown in Fig. 142 (reproduced from this work) in which the continuous line indicates the contour of the lens at rest and the dotted line that of the lens with an accommodation of 7 dptr. It would be idle to discuss the new anatomical conceptions, which enable him to derive this accommodation form of the lens from the passive shape by a tension of the anterior fibres of the zonule. Here we shall merely emphasize the fact that, leaving out of account the sources of error in the method, BESIO's researches support TSCHERNING's first assumption (as we designated it above) for the case of an eye that is *under the influence of cocaine*.

The third phase of TSCHERNING's ideas is indicated in the *Thomas Young Oration* before the *Optical Society* in London in 1907.[1] The part with which we are concerned reads: "v. PFLUGK has recently succeeded in fixing the dead lens in its accommodative shape; he has found that the posterior surface frequently becomes a little concave in its peripheral parts. This concavity increases during accommodation. One of my pupils, Dr. ZEEMAN, has since observed this concavity in the living eye."

VON PFLUGK's experiments[2] consisted in freezing the lens with liquid carbonic acid. However, the value of such experiments for purposes of demonstration should not be very highly estimated, since the action of forces developed by the freezing cannot be overlooked. FISCHER[3] too has shown that the freezing method may give rise to accidental changes of form of the lens; and, besides, the mechanism of accommodation of the eye of a bird is essentially different from that of the human eye, as shown by HESS's investigations mentioned above. ZEEMAN's report, alluded to above, merely proves the presence of the surface of discontinuity. The existence of a posteriorly directed concavity on the posterior

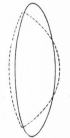

Fig. 142.

surface of the lens can be proved only when two images are seen moving in opposite directions, as has been observed by the writer in the case of true lenticonus posterior.

---

[1] *The development of the science of physiological optics in the nineteenth century.* Reprint from *The optician and photographic trade journal.* Nov. 1, 8 and 15. 1907.

[2] *Über die Akkommodation des Auges der Taube.* Wiesbaden 1906.

[3] F. FISCHER, Über Fixierung der Linsenform mittels der Gefriermethode. *Arch. f. Augenheilk.* LVI. 1907. S. 342.

V.   The Monochromatic Aberrations of the Eye[1]

It is not practicable to obtain an actually homocentric bundle of rays by refraction in an optical system except in certain quite singular cases, in which invariably the rays must emanate originally from a point on the axis of a system of revolution.   Thus, so far as real optical imagery is concerned, this requirement has no significance whatever.   However, this fact was not fully realized for a long time; and until the constitution of the general bundle of optical rays was known more in detail, the only description that could be given of it was in terms of the deviations or so-called aberrations of a ray from the ideal procedure of rays that were homocentric.   According as magnitudes of different orders were included in the computation, various values were obtained for the aberrations of a ray, each representing, as we know now, certain geometrical relations that are characteristic of the bundle of rays.   In this way we may speak of monochromatic aberrations of a certain order.   For example, *astigmatism* is an aberration of the first order, and the *asymmetry-values* are aberrations of the second order.   But at present what is meant by *monochromatic aberration* in the restricted sense usually includes simply aberrations of order higher than the first—and so does not include astigmatism.   The term *aberration* by itself is applied specially to the aberrations of the third order defined by the aberration-values mentioned in a previous section. In physiological optics this is the best term to employ for the deviations or aberrations of order higher than the third.   In technical optics they are also called zonal errors with respect to the axis of a system of revolution.

The fact that the line of sight is not normal to the cornea involves a slight degree of inverse astigmatism in the eye, which, little as it is, tends to compensate the normal direct corneal astigmatism.   At the same time, there are finite asymmetry-values along the line of sight, and hence after refraction in the eye the bundle of rays is singly asymmetrical with respect to the ray corresponding to the line of sight. However, along another ray, as shown by investigations with a luminous point, the bundle of refracted rays is anastigmatic and without asymmetry.   This is the important ray for the imagery, because the convergence along it is of higher order; and consequently, *as a matter of fact, the asymmetry-values of the bundle of rays refracted in the eye are equal to zero.*   But between this state characteristic of the best formed eyes and those degrees of *pathological asymmetry* which may cause a considerable lowering of visual acuity or a bad sort of asthenopia,

¶See experimental investigation by A. AMES, Jr., and C. A. PROCTOR, Dioptrics of the eye, *Jour. Opt. Soc. Amer.*, 5, 1921, 22-84.   (J. P. C. S.)

there are all possible intermediate stages. The methods of studying the asymmetry are both subjective and objective; and as the former are the same as those used for studying the aberration, they will be considered first in the following discussion. The objective methods are ophthalmoscopic; and therefore treatment of this subject will be confined here to the investigation of the asymmetry of the cornea and pathological decentration.

Obviously, sufficient data would be obtained by making a complete ophthalmometric investigation of the anterior surface of the cornea, together with a determination of the position of the optical axis of the eye (in both cases by methods fully described above); but on account of the labour involved, this is practically out of the question. Very good data can be obtained by finding the position of the optical axis and making the ophthalmometric measurements in four directions symmetrically taken in the two principal sections at angles of 10° to the line of sight. However, the majority of cases of pathological or of unusually high physiological asymmetry are found incidentally by the ophthalmologist during the determination of the refraction of the eye; and, therefore, a simpler method of getting the required data is needed. This is supplied by using keratoscopy instead of keratometry.

In keratoscopy the form of the cornea is estimated by the distortion of the reflex image. Now experience proves that this judgment is most reliable when, in the absence of any deformation of the cornea, the reflex image is a square. Accordingly, the target whose reflex image is to be observed in the cornea is made by the writer in the form represented in Fig. 143. When it is held at the right distance or attached at the end of a properly focused telescope, its image in a spherical mirror consists of four squares, each separated from the next by a dis-

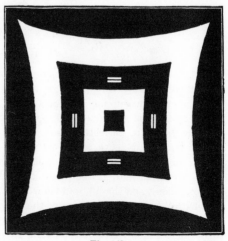

Fig. 143.

tance equal to the length of the side of the central square. If the form of the reflecting surface differs from that of a sphere, the image will be correspondingly deformed, in such fashion that the intervals between the sides are proportional to the radii of curvature of the corresponding elements of the surface. The patient looks, first, straight into the objective of the telescope; and then in four other directions in succession, above and below, and to the right and the left, as determined in each instance by a fixation-mark. For each of the four peripheral adjustments the two points of the cornea that correspond to the reflexes of the middle points of the sides of the two interior figures must be exactly the same as corresponded to the middle points of the sides of the two outer figures when the eye was looking straight in the objective of the telescope. Thus, for the two planes in which the eye looks, the keratoscope gives exactly the same data as the photographic method of keratometry described above.

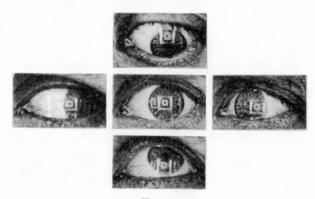

Fig. 144.

Fig. 144 shows the appearance of the reflex images in a typically normal cornea, the same cornea, in fact, as the one for which the ophthalmometric measurements were given in Appendix II. The central image approximately covers the optical zone of the cornea; and the squares there are perfectly regular, except that the top line, being shaded by the lids, is therefore not visible. The image is midway between the upper and lower margins of the cornea, but appreciably nearer the inner margin than the outer. With a magnifying glass one can see plainly, on the plate anyhow, that the pupil is displaced laterally with respect to the centre of the image. The two images in the upper and lower parts of the cornea are symmetrical with respect to each other, and indicate a considerable flattening of the cornea, becoming more marked towards the periphery. In both of them, but particularly in the lower one, the oblique angles show that the cornea in these places is not symmetrical with respect to the vertical median line of the reflex image, but that the vertex of the cornea, that is, the optical zone, is situated on the outside of the ophthalmometric axial point. In accordance with this, the two side images show the normal horizontal asymmetry with decidedly more flattening. These images are fairly symmetrical with respect to the horizontal median line, and yet they seem to indicate in some measure, especially the outer one, the slight vertical physiological asymmetry that was found by the ophthalmometric measurements. The pupil is situated symmetrically with respect to the horizontal median line in each of the side images.

Although, therefore, in this instance a distinct vertical asymmetry is not established, yet there are other eyes which seem to be perfectly normal in their functioning, but in which the keratoscopic images are considerably different from this type. If the notion of asymmetry and decentration is referred to the ophthalmometric axial point, *eyes that are perfectly normal from a clinical standpoint may be classified in three groups*, as follows:

1. In the most regular cases, normal horizontal asymmetry only.

2. In the less regular cases, a combination of vertical and horizontal asymmetry, so as to give the appearance of a normal asymmetry in an oblique direction.

3. In more irregular cases, normal asymmetry in the horizontal meridian of the cornea, combined with pronounced abnormal asymmetry in the vertical meridian, but with vertical decentration of the pupil in the direction of least flattening.

Just as the transition from the second to the third group is a gradual one, so also there is no sharp line of demarcation between the latter and the pathological region. There are cases, for example, which with vertical asymmetry and compensating decentration of pupil show symptoms of asthenopia which can be made to disappear by corresponding correction of the inverse total astigmatism that is ordinarily present. Vertical asymmetry of the cornea with opposite decentration of the pupil may more certainly be regarded as pathological. According to the writer's experience this condition is invariably accompanied by asthenopia or some other symptoms of illness or by myopia.

The best way is to consider the pathological cases as a special kind of anomaly of refraction called *asymmetry* or *decentration*. In the first place, then, this will include pathological *vertical asymmetry* as manifested either by opposite decentration of the pupil or by an inverse total astigmatism and sometimes by an unusually big difference between the corneal astigmatism and the total astigmatism. Frequently, without thorough investigation, these cases are mistaken for a mild myopia that does not disappear until the inverse astigmatism, which is sometimes hard to discover, has been corrected; and that is the explanation of the name "latent" inverse astigmatism. Tscherning's eye (which will be referred to again) shows an unusually high vertical asymmetry which certainly is on the border of the pathological region, if not beyond it, and must be considered as abnormal.

In the second place, there is also an abnormal *horizontal asymmetry*. In rare instances it occurs as an increase of the normal asymmetry, but this is not very troublesome and does not have to be corrected except with large pupil. In other cases, particularly with myopia, there may be more flattening of the cornea on the outside than on the inside; or the investigation of the peripheral refraction by the ophthalmoscope and skiascope indicates a difference of several dioptries, when the eye looks first in a nasal direction and then equally far in a temporal direction.

In the cases mentioned the bundle of rays refracted in the eye may be singly asymmetrical, which is generally the way it is; so that usually with proper correction good visual acuity can be obtained. But this is not so often the case with what is known as *oblique asymmetry*, because the bundle of refracted rays then is apt to be doubly asymmetrical. Accordingly, the caustic surface is not so favourable in form, and the visual acuity is lowered. The existence of an astigmatism whose principal sections make angles of from 35° to 55° with the horizontal plane usually indicates some oblique asymmetry, just as is indicated in ophthalmometric measurements of the cornea when the two meridians for which the "Denivellation" vanishes are not at right angles to each other; or as is shown by a marked difference between the principal sections of the corneal astigmatism and of the total astigmatism.

Although the keratoscope enables us to find merely the corneal asymmetry and the decentration of the pupil, it is a good way of finding an asymmetry of the bundle of rays refracted in the eye. When the asymmetry is very great, the entire eye is affected by the deformation, as shown by ophthalmoscopic investigation of the papilla of the optic nerve. In the typically normal cases the latter is symmetrical around the horizontal line; whereas in abnormal vertical asymmetry and in oblique asymmetry very often there is a corresponding deformation of the optic nerve (ultimately with conical structure downwards or obliquely). The perverse structure of the papilla usually means an abnormal horizontal asymmetry that can be found by the ophthalmoscopic and skiascopic investigation above mentioned.

Thus, while the asymmetry of the bundle of rays refracted in the eye is to be considered practically as a pathological effect, the *aberration* of the bundle is a physiological condition. Indeed, this is something that we might have known in the beginning, because the absence of aberration is an unusual state of affairs, which would be of no use for the eye. Owing to the size of the pupil, the faults of higher order are bound to be of such importance that the aberration along the axis will certainly be a minor matter. Thus, the investigation of the aberration involves a thorough knowledge of the constitution of a wide-angle bundle of rays. The best way is to make a direct investigation of the section of the bundle made by a plane screen, because there the lines of intersection of the caustic surface come out clearly, and enable us to ascertain its form. Fortunately, the retina itself is an excellent screen for this purpose. The only drawback is that the method is subjective and dependent on the patient's powers of observation. Consequently, it is not adapted for use with a large number of subjects. The bundle or rays is created by looking at a small, bright, luminous point. The different cross sections of it are brought on the retina by changing the optical focusing of the eye with the aid of spectacle glasses. The complete exploration of the caustic surface in this way is what the writer calls the method of *subjective stigmatoscopy*, as distinguished from the aimless investigations with a luminous point that are described in the literature.

The necessary mathematical relations having been ascertained, this was the only method that enabled the writer to explore the constitution of the bundle of rays refracted in the eye. And, in fact, now that this constitution is known, there is no other method of showing completely what it is. The reason for this is the extraordinarily complicated form of the caustic surface. Not only are there three cusps in its meridian section, as shown in Fig. 120, but the form of the curve steadily varies as the meridian section is revolved around the axis, in such fashion that the distance of the two symmetrical cusps from the axis becomes alternately a maximum and a minimum. Corresponding to these greatest and least distances of the cusps, the cuspidal edges of the secondary caustic surface are so contrived that, with respect to this alternation, there is a certain analogy with what is known as diagonal astigmatism of the aberration; but with this difference, namely, that whereas there are only two maxima and minima in this effect, the number is greater in the eye. It can be seen from Fig. 145 that the form of the section of the caustic surface is quite complicated even in the case of diagonal astigmatism of the aberration; as this illustration represents the cross section of such a bundle of rays as obtained by a certain form of bicylindrical lens.[1] The meridian sections for which the aberration has its maximum value correspond to the four points of the star-shaped figure; while the bright diagonal lines indicate the sections of the secondary caustic surface where it is bent

---

[1] A. GULLSTRAND, Demonstration eines Instrumentes zur Erzeugung von Strahlengebilden um leuchtende Punkte. *Ber. ü. d. XXX. Vers. d. Ophth. Gesellsch. Heidelberg* 1902.

over at the edges. By screening off a part of the lens, it may be demonstrated that the former are due to rays of light that have already crossed the axis, whereas the latter are made by rays that cross the axis beyond the place where they are intercepted by the screen.

Fig. 145.

Now by subjective stigmatoscopy we find that the bundle of rays refracted in the eye shows precisely the same characteristics as those just described, except that the starry points and the intermediate bright flecks are more numerous and not always arranged perfectly regularly. Just as in HELMHOLTZ's description, when a portion of the pupil of the eye is screened off by the partial interposition of an opaque card, the starry rays that are seen around a bright point vanish first on the same side as that on which the pupil is covered. Since the image of the star pattern appears exactly opposite to the actual inverted arrangement of the blurred image as projected on the retina, the rays of the star are due to rays of light which have crossed each other before getting to the retina. Chromatic effects, such as HELMHOLTZ used, enable us to show this; cobalt glass being particularly suited for the purpose, because it makes the central bright point look purple, while the rays of the star are blue. These star-points, as HELMHOLTZ states, are visible with a sufficiently bright luminous point even when the eye is focused most sharply, provided the pupil is not excessively contracted by the illumination in the room. In a complete investigation by the method of stigmatoscopy, the luminous point is 4 metres away, and its diameter is 2 mm. Accommodation being entirely relaxed, amyopia of 4 dptr is produced at first by the aid of a suitable spectacle glass. The refraction of the compound system is steadily increased, a half dioptry at a time, by changing the glass. Initially, a bright blur circle will be seen, which, perhaps, may appear to be punctuated by brighter points, but which does not admit of any distinct separation into brighter and darker portions. As the far point begins to recede, the first thing that is noticed in the way of change of appearance is the development of a more or less uniformly bright point in the centre, around which the rays of the star begin to be visible; corresponding to the section of the bundle of rays that is shown by HELMHOLTZ in Fig. 72, *b*. The illustration in Fig. 72, *a*, which represents the image seen by HELMHOLTZ in his right eye, is not so well suited to show the simplest case, because it indicates a vertical asymmetry in that eye (possibly due to some small opacity in the lens), which makes it a little hard to explain. Indeed, the drawings Fig. 72, *b*, *d*, that relate to the left eye, do not indicate an eye that is one of the most regular in its structure, but they are sufficiently typical to be used for demonstration. In the best formed eyes the star figure has eight points, and its fundamental form is that of a vertical cross with diagonal rays, one of which however, may be split in two. Evidently, HELMHOLTZ's figure may be explained as a variant of this form in case of an oblique cross. If by increasing the refraction the far point of the reinforced eye is made to recede farther and farther, until at last it becomes virtual, a darker centre surrounded by a brighter serrated line will be seen. With bigger pupil these serrations appear to lengthen out into rays of the star. When the pupil is partly covered, the serrations vanish on the opposite side. Viewed through cobalt glass they are red, implying therefore that they are due to rays of light which have reached the retina before intersecting the central ray. These star-patterns are more numerous than in the ordinary star-figure. The orientation is certainly different from that of the ordinary star-figure, because there are no rays in these patterns in the directions where they are clearly perceived in the ordinary star-figure. When the pupil is artificially dilated, there is a certain focusing for which both kinds of star-patterns may be seen together, and the alternation verified. The serrations lengthened into rays are to be seen in HELMHOLTZ's diagram Fig. 72 *d*, where the dark centre is plainly visible, and where, too, the writer's statement about orientation can be verified. The fact that the number of serrations in HELMHOLTZ's case is less in this section of the bundle of rays than in that shown in Fig. 72 *b*, is due to the fact that he got the different sections of the bundle, not by using different spectacle lenses, but by varying the distance of the luminous point. For instance, when this point is brought closer to the eye the visual angle which it subtends is so large that the star-points next one another merge together.

The cross section of a bundle of rays with diagonally astigmatic aberration, as represented in Fig. 145, exhibits not only the rays corresponding to the ordinary ocular star-figure but also the corners between the rays corresponding to the serrated line that contain the brighter, radially directed spots of light. A cross section of this sort is obtained with a wave surface which has four planes of symmetry, and which is represented by a certain equation of the fourth degree. By varying the bicylindrical combination used in producing this figure, the symmetry may be destroyed and very complicated effects obtained. However, if the equation of the wave surface is one of the eighth degree of corresponding form, and if there are eight planes of symmetry, there will be eight rays in the star-figure and eight indentations with brighter, radial medians, instead of the four corners shown in the figure. And if the symmetry about the eight planes is not perfect, there will be apparent irregularities in the arrangement of the rays and indentations due to the complicated form of the caustic surface. In the organ of vision the contrasts are heightened, because the minimum that is perceptible is lowered in the vicinity of a brightly illuminated point of the retina, which owing to the brighter central parts, must have the effect of making the indentations appear as serrations. When this is taken into consideration, it is not difficult to understand that the appearance of the star-patterns in the eye does not at all imply real irregularities, such as might be produced by edges or cusps in the refracting surfaces themselves or by discontinuities in the variation of the index of the crystalline lens; but that the phenomenon is just as regular as any effect that is dependent on an equation of the eighth degree or higher degree.

A characteristic feature of the wave surface of a bundle of rays of this sort, as found by mathematical investigation, is that out towards the periphery the flattening is different in different meridian sections; the result being that there are just as many minima corresponding to the rays of the star as there are maxima corresponding to the indentations. A cylindrical surface whose axis coincides with the axial ray will cut the wave surface in a line which, when the cylinder is unrolled on a plane, has a sinuous form; the sinuosity being more pronounced in proportion as the section is farther from the centre. This means that the wave surface contains ridges and valleys running radially along it and getting shallower in towards the centre. We might speak of them as "creases" ("Faltenbildungen"), provided the term is used by way of analogy without being taken too literally. Now there is nothing that can be responsible for this idiosyncrasy of the wave surface except a similar peculiarity of the refracting surfaces of the crystalline lens or of the iso-indicial surfaces, because the star-figure around a luminous point disappears when the lens is removed from the eye. This form ought to be manifested in the surfaces of the lens by jerky movements of the reflex images during movements of the eye. As a matter of fact such twitchings are often perceived in the reflexes in the anterior surface of the lens. But so far as the writer has been able to discover, this phenomenon occurs only at the periphery of the lens, and this would not be sufficient for the explanation of the "creases." Besides, the reflex image in question is produced not simply by the anterior surface of the lens, but also in the most anterior portions of the lens substance. This is why it is so vague. The only other hypothesis left, is that the forms of the iso-indicial surfaces of the lens correspond to that of the wave surface. Taking into account the anatomical structure of the lens, we reach the same conclusion from the study of the dioptrics of the lens. During the accommodative change of form of the lens, the iso-indicial surfaces must contain constant volumes; and hence for the different focusings of the eye their superficial areas must be different, supposing they are surfaces of revolution. But this would not be possible unless either the particles of the lens were perfectly mobile, or the substance of the lens had considerable elasticity. Now since neither of these is the fact, the different forms assumed by the iso-indicial surfaces cannot be surfaces of revolution; which means that the change of form must be accompanied by the production of "creases" or by the variation of such "creases." Owing to the concomitant contraction of the pupil in accommodation, a variation such as that just mentioned is difficult to investigate in a perfectly satisfactory manner. However, in case of accommodation that occurs in the first stage of the action of eserin on a pupil that is dilated by homatropin, it is easy to verify the fact that there is some change of this nature.

The fact that the star-figure is due to the iso-indicial surfaces of the lens and their variations during accommodation, plainly shows that this particular peculiarity of these surfaces is influenced by the tension of the zonule. That the effect cannot depend on the anatomical structure of the lens, which in its embryonic stage has the shape of a three-point star, is shown both by the number and by the disposition of these points; whereas in the most regular cases the star-image itself consists of eight rays, its fundamental form being that of a cross with diagonal rays. On the other hand, in the mechanism by which the lens is suspended there is an anatomical contrivance that must produce alternate maximum and minimum tensions of the zonule in the different meridian planes, not simply because the mechanical relations for the ciliary processes are different from those for their interstices, but also because these relations must be modified by the way the fibres of the zonule cross each other in proceeding to the anterior and posterior sides of the capsule of the lens. It is true, the number of these maxima and minima is much greater than the number of rays in the star-pattern. But since the tension for the various maxima cannot be mathematically and precisely the same, the lines of force will have to merge together towards the centre. The star-figure illustrates the same thing. With a larger pupil, the rays of the star are often seen to separate from each other at a certain distance from the bright nucleus. As the lens is composed of fibres, the peculiar form of the iso-indicial surfaces ought to be manifested by a corresponding characteristic arrangement of these elements. Now it is even probable that with steady growth of the lens the anatomical arrangement of the fibres is affected by the tensions that occur, and thus the stellar appearance seen on the anterior surface of the lens by oblique illumination may represent this structure as acquired under the influence of the tension of the zonule. The best way to observe this starry form is with dilated pupil, by the same sort of experiment as was used for inspecting the reflex image in the anterior surface of the lens, where the light was concentrated on this surface by a convex lens. This figure indicates real discontinuities in the variation of the index; but without a very complicated mathematical study, it can hardly be regarded as conclusive on this point, inasmuch as the "creases" in the iso-indicial surfaces certainly seem to be qualified to produce the reflex phenomenon in question.

Owing to the property of the wave surface of the bundle of rays refracted in the eye which has just been proved, it is a mathematical impossibility for any cross section to cut the caustic surface in a smooth curve in the form of a circle concentric with the pupil. On the contrary, this section must be serrated everywhere or must consist of separate isolated points. Accordingly, the serrated curve described above is a section of the caustic surface, and the concentration of light at the centre that is seen at the beginning of the stigmatoscopic investigation is the vertex or cusp of the same surface. Now this means that the aberration along the axis is positive, because the cusp points in the direction in which the light goes. Pursuing farther the stigmatoscopic investigation with dilated pupil, by steadily increasing the hypermetropia of the reinforced eye, we find that in the last section of the bundle of rays where the line of intersection of the caustic surface can still be seen, it does not coincide with the boundary line. The inference is that a meridian section of the caustic surface has three cusps, like the curve drawn in Fig. 120, where the serrations that are the last to be seen in the stigmatoscopic investigation of the given meridian plane are represented by the two symmetrical cusps. By measuring the difference of refraction between this section of the bundle and that which contains the cusp lying on the axis, the distance between the two sections can be found. In the writer's own case this difference is 4 dptr, and apparently this value is never exceeded. A higher value is frequently obtained with persons who are less expert, probably due to their inability to relax the accommodation completely. The diameter of the line $R = 0$ corresponding to the symmetrical cusps of Fig. 120 is measured by the diaphragm held in front of the eye. The serrated curve in the section of the caustic surface nearest the refracting system can be made to coincide in this way with the boundary line of the cross section of the bundle of rays. By this means the writer has obtained a diameter of 4 mm. Let d denote this diameter, D the difference of refraction to be used in the calculation, f the posterior focal length of the eye, and n the index of refraction of the vitreous humor; then the aberration-value is found by the formula:

$$A = \frac{8\,f^4\,D}{1000\,nd^2},$$

the distances being expressed in millimetres and the value of D in dioptries. For $f = 20$ mm and $n = 4/3$ (as in DONDERS' reduced eye), the formula gives 240 mm for the aberration-value; whereas on the assumption that the refracting surface is spherical, the calculated aberration-value for this eye is 540 mm. The amount of the aberration-value found in the living eye proves at once that the bundle of refracted rays acquires a positive aberration in traversing the crystalline lens. This could be demonstrated by HELMHOLTZ's schematic eye; because by giving the surfaces of the lens in this eye a form such that the lens itself does not contribute to the aberration one way or the other, with spherical cornea and emmetropic focusing the value found for the aberration is 162 mm. Hence the writer infers that the variable index of refraction of the lens has little effect on the refraction of paraxial rays in the eye, and that, consequently, the chief significance of this peculiarity of the lens is probably in connection with the change of form of the lens in accommodation and possibly also for peripheral vision. This reasoning is completely sustained by the dioptrics of the lens; which likewise indicates that the lamellar structure of the lens is merely in the interest of the change of form in accommodation, since, as was proved above, the effect of this structure is to augment the astigmatism of an oblique bundle of rays.

Again, if the posterior focal length of the exact schematic eye and the index of refraction of the vitreous humor are substituted in the formula above, the aberration-value thus obtained is 403.5 mm. Now if the aberration-value of the exact schematic eye with the real core-lens is calculated by the writer's formulae, it is found to be

$$A = 691.17 + 75854 \ \Phi_1 - 7511.5 \ \Phi_2 + 6113.9 \ \Phi_3 - 3264.4 \ \Phi_4,$$

where the symbols Φ are used to denote the "Abflachungswerte" of the four refracting surfaces; each of them being found by the equation

$$\Phi = -\frac{3\epsilon^2}{\rho^3},$$

where ρ denotes the radius of curvature, and ϵ is the eccentricity of the surface of the second degree that has contact of the fourth order with the refracting surface in question. When this value calculated for the exact schematic eye is compared with the result 403.5 mm, as obtained in the investigation of the living eye by using the focal length of the schematic eye and the index of refraction of the vitreous humor, it should not be overlooked that the formula by which the latter value was computed is merely approximate, because the effect of the aberration-values of higher order cannot be taken into account. However, since there is in this case a curve $R = 0$, these values must be negative. Hence, the aberration-value calculated for the living eye from the results of the investigation is too small; but how much too small, cannot be estimated at present by investigations. However, in the calculation of the schematic eye, HELMHOLTZ's ellipsoid was used for the corneal refraction, so that even in the schematic eye the calculated value is smaller and, consequently, the effect of negative aberration-values of higher order is taken into account. Suppose, therefore, that the error due to the above cause is compensated by the fact just stated; then if the surfaces of the lens are considered as parabolic; and if the value of the eccentricity of the cornea, as calculated by MATTHIESSEN (as above stated) from the writer's measurements of the cornea, namely, the value $\epsilon = 0.551$, is employed, the aberration-value turns out to be 476.16 mm. As a matter of fact, the surfaces of the lens are probably flatter towards the periphery than the paraboloid; and the peripheral increase of thickness of the cornea may indicate a positive value of Φ for the posterior surface of the cornea, which would lower the calculated aberration-value still more. If these latter considerations are taken into account, the agreement between the value calculated for the exact schematic eye and that found by the investigation of the living eye could not be better.

This result is all the more important because it proves the correctness of using MATTHIESSEN's law along the axis of the lens. The greatest part of the aberration, as calculation shows, originates in the lens and depends on the value of p_n. Now this coefficient can be made smaller by assuming an hyperbolic indicial curve along the axis, but this is contrary to the result of all refractometer measurements. On the other hand, an increase of the value of p_n would result in still greater positive aberration in the schematic eye, which, according to the above, must certainly appear very unlikely.

The region of the pupil enclosed by the curve $R = 0$ is what the writer has called the *optical zone* of the pupil. The name seems to be all the more appropriate because the region coincides approximately with that comprised by the optical zone of the cornea. Within this area the aberration of the normal eye is invariably positive. This can be shown by finding the refraction of the eye at the different parts of the pupil. Everywhere it is less than it is at the centre; and the difference increases out from the centre along any meridian section, more rapidly at first, and then rather more gradually, until it amounts to 4 dioptries at the boundary line. However, in this connection it must be kept in mind that, according to ordinary usage, myopic refraction is negative, and that what is meant by the refraction at a point of the pupil is the state of refraction that the eye would have if an infinitely small stop were situated at this place. This refraction is determined, therefore, by the distance of the point of intersection of the given ray with adjacent rays, not with the axis. Inside the optical zone, along every ray except the axis, there is astigmatism, because the meridional focal distance is shorter than the equatorial. If a meridian section is followed beyond the border of the optical zone, the astigmatism steadily diminishes along the rays meeting this curve and vanishes entirely for the ray that is tangent to the caustic surface at the place where it crosses the axis. Leaving out of account the so-called "creases" in the wave surface, the totality of all such rays for the dilated pupil forms a conical surface with its vertex on the axis. And since along each one of these rays there is a perfect ray-convergence of the first order, the convergence of the rays on the axis at the vertex of the cone is extraordinarily good, and consequently this point in a cross section of the bundle of rays stands out sharply from its surroundings. In vision with a wide pupil it is this point, therefore, that serves for the imagery, the eye being focused for the cross section here indicated. By subjective stigmatoscopy it is easy to prove that with dilated pupil the sharp focusing is for a cross section of the bundle nearer the refracting system than is the case for a pupil of moderate size. Thus in the former case when the eye is accommodated as sharply as possible for the luminous point, the only star-points that are visible around it are such as appear red through cobalt glass and vanish from the opposite side when the pupil is partly screened. But when the far point is brought closer to the eye by means of a convex lens, the result is that with sharp accommodation and with a pupil of moderate size the ordinary star-figure is seen. When, with dilated pupil, the far point is brought so near the eye that the cusp of the caustic is visible, the section of the part of the caustic that is bent over will be seen at the same time, appearing along its boundary as a clear, serrated, bright ring.

In order to make this explanation of the convergence of the rays more intelligible, the writer has had to leave out of account the peculiarity of the bundle of rays that is due to the "creases of the wave surface." This feature involves a difference of the aberration-value in different meridian planes. However, in this method of investigation the measured aberration is its maximum value. The writer has not succeeded in finding any way of measuring the minimum value; and for the present it must suffice to know that in the corresponding meridian planes the aberration-value is smaller, and the point of best convergence of rays lies farther away from the refracting system. The distance of this point from the cusp of the caustic surface is correspondingly smaller, and a ray that goes through it will meet the pupil in a point closer to its centre, and therefore this point of the bundle of rays is used for sharp imagery when the size of the pupil does not surpass that of the optical zone. But there seems to be no reason why, with a pupil of the smallest size, the focusing may not be made for a cross section of the bundle that is still nearer the cusp of the caustic surface.

In the stigmatoscopic investigation, the difference of refraction between the point of most advantageous convergence of the rays and the cusp of the caustic surface may be measured. In this way the writer obtains a difference of 1.5 dioptries, which gives, therefore, the degree of hypermetropia along the axis of an emmetropic eye for pupil of moderate size. But the measurements do not give results that are very accurate; and so in the schematic eye the writer has used the value one dioptry, which is certainly not too large. The difference between the optical focusings of the eye for a pupil of moderate size and for one as large as possible can be satisfactorily obtained in the above manner. In many instances, but not always, the result of clinical investigation by DONDERS' method of refraction may reveal a slight myopia of the emmetropic eye when the pupil is dilated. The simple explanation is that the visual acuity is reduced by the large pupil.

Evidently, from what has been said above, all that can be implied when we speak of the aberration of the eye is the maximum value of this magnitude as it occurs in the particular meridian section under consideration at the time. By more exact methods of investigation, we find that usually there is an astigmatism of this aberration as manifested by an oblique oval form of the section of the caustic surface made by the retina, which is seen also in HELMHOLTZ's Fig. 72 *d*. This means that even when the visual acuity is maximum there is not complete absence of astigmatism along the central ray. Practically, however, this is of entirely secondary importance. In the bundle of rays that falls on the retina of the writer's right eye no traces can be detected of the horizontal asymmetry due to oblique incidence of the line of sight; and hence the asymmetry-values vanish, not indeed along the ray passing through the centre of the anatomical pupil, but along the ray that goes through the centre of the exit-pupil. The ray that is tangent to the cusp of the caustic surface is the controlling ray so far as the imagery is concerned; and, according to the above system of nomenclature, may be called, therefore, the *central ray*. The point where it crosses the plane of the pupil may be named the *optical centre* of the pupil. In the writer's own case this optical centre is in the vertical diameter of the exit-pupil, and the vertical line that divides the pupil in half is a line of symmetry with sufficient accuracy for practical purposes. This is not the case with the horizontal line. For even with the ordinary star-figure seen around a luminous point a vertical asymmetry may be recognized, the ascending rays appearing shorter than the descending ones. With reference to a vertical asymmetry, suppose the upward direction is taken as positive. Accordingly, there is a direct negative asymmetry of the bundle of refracted rays along the ray that goes through the centre of the pupil, which means that *the optical centre of the pupil is above the anatomical centre*. In the absence of a vertical decentration of the pupil with respect to the ophthalmometric axial point, this statement might have been made *a priori*, provided the asymmetrical flattening of the vertical section of the cornea is not compensated by some mechanism operating in the opposite sense. In keratoscopy and ophthalmometry the ophthalmometric axial point is the point of reference. Similarly, in stigmatoscopy the optical centre of the pupil is the point of reference for what is called the "decentration." Thus the vertical asymmetry that has just been found may be spoken of as a downward decentration of the pupil. This normal vertical decentration may occur to any extent, until the optical centre is at the border of a pupil of medium size or even beyond it, in which case the limit of the physiological region is exceeded. TSCHERNING's drawings of the appearances in his eye[1] indicate a vertical decentration of this nature, which undoubtedly is in the neighbourhood of this limit and is certainly abnormally great.

[1] Loc. cit. *Encyclopédie Française d'ophthalmologie*. T. III. p. 207.

Besides this decentration of the pupil, a decentration of the optical zone has also to be taken into account. The former is computed from the relative upward and downward extent of the star-points that are visible in the section of the bundle of rays that contains the cusp of the caustic surface; and the latter is calculated from the difference of refraction when the different parts of the edge of the caustic surface corresponding to the curve $R = 0$ are focused. Thus, in the writer's eye there is a difference of one dioptry between the upper and lower parts of this edge; and in the right eye the calculated decentration of the optical zone amounts to one-eighth of a millimetre downwards and is about the same as the decentration of the pupil in the same direction, which for a diameter of 6 mm has the value of one-seventh of a millimetre.

The writer has not been able by stigmatoscopic investigations to trace the transition from this physiological decentration of the optical zone to the pathological decentration, because these experiments require quite considerable practice and involve much waste of time. Where there is vertical asymmetry of the cornea and contrary decentration of the pupil, it is extremely likely that the pupil would exhibit also the opposite decentration with respect to its optical centre, and that with a pupil of medium size the curve $R = 0$ would not be a closed curve, that is, there would be no optical zone. In the case of TSCHERNING's eye, with a pupil of the size for which he has drawn the blurred patterns, a closed curve $R = 0$ is already lacking; and there is no indication in these drawings that there usually is an optical zone in the pupil. If the vertical asymmetry of the cornea of an eye of this kind should be augmented, the effect of the increase of flattening of the cornea towards the periphery would be to make the direct asymmetry-value in the vertical direction increase more along a ray in the vertical plane of symmetry that passed through the lower part of it. The influence of the aberration under these circumstances as compared with that of the asymmetry would be relegated still more in the background, and the result would be a better convergence of the rays along a ray going through the lower part of the pupil. The upward decentration in an eye of this kind would therefore impair the convergence of the rays, since in TSCHERNING's eye, as the drawings show, the asymmetry-values are negative.

In the normal eye, inside the positive zone, *the aberration is positive even with powerful accommodation*. This is proved by the fact that when the luminous point is moved up in the vicinity of the near point of the eye and fixated, the first thing that is seen is the line of intersection of the focal surface, and it is not until still greater effort of accommodation is exerted that this first appearance is transformed into the star-figure or into the sharp image obtained with undilated pupil. Mathematical investigation of the dioptrics of the core lens shows that there is an accommodative decrease of the value of p_n to such an extent that if this were the only factor that affected the aberration-value during accommodation, the latter would have to be reduced to about two-thirds of its original value. However, the writer has not succeeded in verifying this variation by subjective stigmatoscopy in a perfectly satisfactory way, because the concomitant contraction of the pupil hinders the investigation unless mydriatics are used, and the phenomena with pupil dilated either by cocaine or by homatropin after treatment with eserin do not seem to be unique as to their interpretation.

The physiological importance of the constitution of the bundle of rays refracted in the normal eye as ascertained in the above fashion can be properly estimated only in the light of the general laws of optical imagery. The magnitude of the blur circles as represented by the star-points that are visible around a luminous point would, for instance, completely prevent getting an imagery of the same quality as obtained by the visual acuity of the normal eye, if the blur circles were as important for the imagery as they are supposed to be. Instead of them, what we actually have are the sections of the caustic surface, and therefore any conflict between the degree of visual acuity and the structure of the bundle of rays is cleared up at once. Another matter which likewise receives a satisfactory explanation is the ability of considerably enhancing the visual acuity by practice for different optical focusing or for different degrees of congenital or artificial astigmatism; which is a well known fact of clinical experience. For just as long as sections of the caustic surface continue to fall on the retina, there is always a question of imagery of some kind, and the strain experienced by trying to read with faulty cylindrical correction is simply an expression of the greater difficulty of construing sections of the caustic surface that have an extraordinary form and are less suited for maximum visual acuity. Hence in near work the strain might be felt more because the particular form of the section of the caustic surface, along with the chromatic aberration, might be the controlling factor in the continual changes of accommodative focusing. The mere fact that the cross sections of the bundle of rays on the retina have different appearances, depending on the degree of accommodation, may constitute a factor of this kind.

The magnitude of the aberration is of fundamental importance also for comprehending the constitution of the bundle of rays refracted in the eye in the ordinary cases of astigmatism, because it requires an astigmatism of more than four dioptries in order that sections of the two caustic surfaces may not fall on the retina at the same time.

Thus in the most important practical cases of astigmatism the caustic surfaces are of the type shown in Fig. 121, where there are two rays going through the pupil of medium size along which there is no astig-

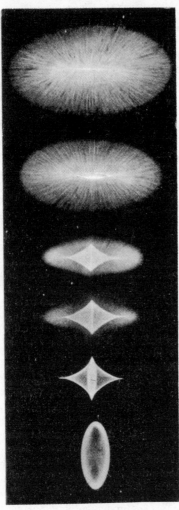

Fig. 146.

matism. The sections of a bundle of this sort are shown in Fig. 146, which is a photograph[1] made with a telephoto-lens, the different cross sections being focused on the plate by varying the distances of the parts of the lens; and hence the dimensions of the sections relative to each other are not correct. The phenomena in the astigmatic eye are similar, as can be verified by using cylindrical glasses. The only difference is in a cleavage of the blurred figures depending on the "creases" of the wave surface. As to the arrow-head effects, seen in two opposite points in the fourth cross section in Fig. 146, where the two anastigmatic focal points are, the same phenomenon is easily verified in the stigmatoscopic investigation of the artificially astigmatic eye. With abnormal vertical asymmetry and not too high a degree of astigmatism, there is always a point of this kind on the caustic surface; and in TSCHERNING's drawings of the cross sections of the bundle of rays refracted in his eye this point is easily recognized. The artificial astigmatism affords a means of eliminating the influence of accommodation in the stigmatoscopic measurement of the aberration, but that is a matter that cannot be discussed here.

Objective stigmatoscopy (as the writer ventures to call it) is the most

[1] For which the writer is indebted to Mr. A. ODENCRANTS, candidate for the degree of doctor of philosophy.

important of all the other methods of investigating the aberration of
the eye. The slit in the ophthalmometric NERNST lamp is replaced by a
small hole; in front of which at an angle of 45° a cover-glass is set up
vertically. The size of the latter is such that no light falls on its edges.
The reflex image in the glass plate of the portion of the incandescent
filament seen in the hole makes a very bright luminous point, which can
be made to coincide with the pupil of the experimenter's eye. Then
when the reflected light is projected into the pupil of the patient's eye
at a distance of from 30 to 50 cm, the observer can investigate the convergence of the rays by moving his head in different directions. Suppose that the eye under examination is able to fixate sharply the reflex
image of the luminous point with this arrangement of apparatus; then
during fixation an image is formed on the retina which, with the diffuse
reflection due to the distribution of light in it, may to a certain extent
be regarded as a punctual image of the source of light of the bundle
of rays to be investigated. For a distance as great as 50 cm the cross
sections of the bundle of rays are of such magnitudes that the size
of the pupil of the observer's eye does not enter into the problem at all.
With his eye properly centered he looks into the patient's eye, whose
pupil is supposed to be of the ordinary medium size in a dark room.
At its centre he will see a bright luminous point, in many instances surrounded indeed by a perceptible star-figure. This point, which owing
to the brightness appears more yellowish, is surrounded by a darker,
that is, a more reddish looking, zone, which in turn is surrounded by
a brighter, more yellowish ring. According to the size of the pupil,
this bright annular zone extends to the margin of the pupil or is surrounded again by a darker, more reddish zone. Now suppose the
observer moves his eye, say, in the horizontal direction; the central
bright point in the pupil of the patient's eye will execute a movement in
the same direction, but the vertical parts of the bright annular zone
will be displaced in the opposite direction. This shows that along the
central ray the rays converge behind the pupil of the observer's eye;
but that the rays that meet the pupil of the patient's eye where the
bright ring is seen are intersected by adjacent rays at places in front
of the pupil of the observer's eye. In other words, the aberration is
positive. Hence, when a luminous point is sharply fixated, a cross
section of the bundle of rays that is in front of the cusp of the caustic
surface is focused on the retina of the patient's eye. So far as physiological relations are concerned, the writer has found not a single exception to this behaviour. Apart from subjective stigmatoscopy, this
is the only method of investigating the aberration within the optical
zone. However, it cannot be used for finding the cuspidal edge of the
caustic surface, because the image on the retina is not good enough

for this purpose. For the objective investigation of the refraction and astigmatism and of the pathological forms of asymmetry and aberration, it is superior to any other method. But it would take us too far to go here into the details of these investigations. It is what may be called a delicate, skiascopic method, but it is really much more than this, since it is a way of investigating the refraction at the fovea itself. Moreover, so far as the asymmetry and aberration are concerned, in the skiascopic method the size of the light-source, the distance between the observer's pupil and its reflex image, and the hole in the mirror are all just so many sources of error that make the phenomena uncertain and affect the accuracy of the conclusions derived from them. Consequently, in its results the method of objective stigmatoscopy is distinctly different from that of skiascopy, although the technique of the latter may be regarded as being a less precise modification of that of the former. But the method of objective stigmatoscopy absolutely requires a thin unsilvered mirror and a specific brightness such as cannot be obtained without the NERNST lamp or an arclight.

In cases of abnormal asymmetry or of negative peripheral total aberration (the latter of which not unfrequently leads to formation of cataract), the different states of refraction of the eye along different rays going through the pupil can be shown without difficulty by ophthalmoscopic measurement of refraction by the method of the erect image. However, in this determination the measurement must be made in a tiny portion at right angles to the meridian section in which the variation of refraction is being investigated, and the diameter of the peephole of the ophthalmoscope may not be more than from 1.5 to 2 mm. In finding the refraction through different parts of the pupil another matter that is important is not to let the peephole be dislocated with respect to the pupil of the observer's eye. The astigmatism that arises and the change of form of the papilla that is caused by it may have the same result. When the refraction varies, the radial principal section is always subject to a greater change of refracting power; and so the rule is, that, if for a displacement of the mirror with respect to the pupil of the patient's eye the papilla appears to be relatively more extended in the direction of the displacement, an increase of refracting power is indicated; and *vice versa*. It is true, this method of showing the physiological aberration does not always succeed. This is undoubtedly because the place of greatest refracting power is so little removed from the centre; and the transversal asymmetry, which, unlike the direct asymmetry, does not vanish here, is conducive to indistinctness. On the other hand, it can often be shown that this indistinctness increases at first with decentration of the hole in the mirror, and then decreases, as the constitution of the bundle of refracted rays demands. With well dilated pupil the relative extension of the diameter of the papilla parallel to the direction of the displacement of the hole in the mirror, that is characteristic of positive aberration, can very often be observed.

Other methods are based on SCHEINER's experiment, which is the principle of YOUNG's optometer and TSCHERNING's aberroscope. The results obtained with this last instrument have much to do with TSCHERNING's theories; and therefore it might be worth while to give some space to its discussion. The instrument consists of two systems of perpendicular opaque lines ruled on the flat side of a planoconvex lens, which is held in front of the eye, from 10 to 20 cm away, and towards a luminous point. The shadows of the lines are seen in the blur circle produced by the artificial myopia. TSCHERNING argues that the aberration of the bundle of rays refracted in the eye is positive or negative according as the curvature of the lines is concave towards the centre or convex, respectively. However, evidently the phenomenon here is one of optical projection. The writer has shown that while it does depend in some measure on the aberration, it involves also another magnitude that cannot be calculated in the living eye. Moreover, the aberration on which the curvature of the lines in the aberroscope depends is not that which is characteristic of the bundle of rays used in vision, but is the aberration that has been imparted to the bundle of rays by the refraction in the glass lens, which is all the more significant in this case, because the aberration generally changes with the convergence of the bundle of incident rays.

That TSCHERNING's interpretation of the phenomena observed with the aberroscope is mathematically impossible, the writer has shown in the following way that anybody can understand. Consider the reduced eye, and suppose that the bundle of rays that issues from the lens of the aberroscope is free from aberration; then the shadows of the ruled lines as formed on the refracting surface will be simple curved lines, lying in planes that intersect each other in the image of the luminous point made by the planoconvex lens. But in order that these shadows should form straight lines on the retina, these planes would have to pass through the image of the luminous point in the eye, on the supposition that the bundle of rays was free from aberration after being refracted through the eye. Now this is impossible unless the image-point in the lens is at the centre of curvature of the refracting surface of the reduced eye.

What is actually found in the investigation with the aberroscope is the sign of the distortion-value for the optical projection, on the assumption that the eye is a system of revolution. Provided there is no refracting surface between the lines to be projected and the screen, that is, between the ruled lines on the aberroscope and the retina, it is true that the sign of this magnitude does depend simply on the sign of the aberration; and, consequently, there would be no objection to the conclusions derived from investigations with the aberroscope, provided the instrument was set up in the vitreous humor! However, there is another factor besides an intervening refracting surface between the lattice of lines and the screen; and this factor cannot be calculated in the optical system of the eye, because the laws concerning it are not known for heterogeneous media. But it does depend on the distance of the lattice; and when this distance is considerable, it is appreciably affected by the aberration of the lens of the aberroscope. Thus, the value of the distortion whose sign is found by the aberroscope contains two terms, one of which depends on the aberration; and the sign of this term changes when the image of the luminous point falls beyond the retina, whereas the sign of the other term does not change. Consequently, the sign of the aberration of the bundle of rays refracted in the eye can be obtained by the investigation with the aberroscope, provided the curvature of the shadows changes sign according as the image of the luminous point falls on one side of the retina or on the other. Now, as a matter of fact, this does happen as a rule with the normal eye, and therefore the normal positive aberration may be established in this way, but not in the way TSCHERNING explains it. On the other hand, the aberroscope, like YOUNG's optometer in this respect, is by no means sensitive enough to bring out the real complicated form of the caustic surface, because, on the whole, no conclusion can be drawn from the curvature of the shadow-lines in the peripheral parts of the blur circle. Perhaps, it might be exceedingly well adapted for diagnosis of abnormal asymmetry, because it tells the sign of the transversal asymmetry, provided the sign of the curvature of the central shadow-line does not change when the image of the luminous point crosses from one side of the retina to the other.

The change of sign of the aberration during accommodation as reported by TSCHERNING has not thus far been proved by investigations with the aberroscope. Undoubtedly, as the writer himself has shown, the curvature of the shadow-lines can be seen to diminish during accommodation. But a change of this kind is bound to occur to some extent from the displacement of the image of the luminous point that is in front of the retina. It may be due partly also to the variation of the component of the distortion-value that is independent of the aberration-value. In order to show that the aberration varies during accommodation, it is absolutely necessary to prove first, by the method given above, that there is positive aberration in the case of emmetropic refraction (which means, of course, that the eye is properly

corrected); and then to cause accommodation by using more and more
concave glasses, with corresponding variation of the original correction; the aberroscope being placed directly in front of the correction-
glass. Now if during accommodation under these circumstances the
following appearances should take place in the order named: shadow-
lines convex towards the centre, then the point of light, and finally
shadow-lines curved the other way, meanwhile nothing being altered
with respect to the correction of the eye and the distance of the
aberroscope;—then, and only then, could the investigation with this
instrument be said to prove that the normal positive aberration becomes negative during accommodation. However, in spite of the publication of the necessary mode of arrangement of the experiment[1], no
such proof has been adduced.

By an experiment with the luminous point also, TSCHERNING
thinks he has shown that the aberration changes sign during accommodation. His method consists in comparing the appearance of the
blur circle when the eye is made myopic by accommodation with
its appearance when the eye is made myopic to the same extent by
means of a convex lens. In the first case he finds a peripheral bright
line parallel to the boundary line. However, owing to the peculiarity
of the caustic surface due to the so-called "creases" in it, it is a mathematical impossibility for a negative aberration to produce a blur circle
with the appearance noted by TSCHERNING. But in the same way a
serrated section of the caustic surface should have been found beyond
the axial focal point (such as occurs in the relaxed eye in front of this
place), as proved, in one way, by the appearance of the bent-over
part of the caustic surface that is seen when the pupil is dilated.
On the other hand, as was mentioned above, the same appearance
of the blur circle can be obtained as in accommodation by imitating,
not simply the accommodative change of refraction, but also concomitant pupillary contraction, and combining the convex lens with
a correspondingly small hole. Any one conversant with the phenomena
of diffraction will recognize immediately the nature of the dark line
that is seen between the bright zone and the boundary line. TSCHER-
NING's experiment might perhaps be used as a popular illustration of
the phenomenon of diffraction. As was explained above, subjective
stigmatoscopy, employed as a scientific method, demonstrates a positive aberration inside the optical zone even with the most powerful
accommodation. And, therefore, the accommodative contraction of
the pupil cannot be for the purpose of diminishing the effect of the
aberration, since this effect is not troublesome even when accommodation is relaxed, although it decreases anyhow during accommodation.

[1] Loc. cit. *Arch. f. Ophth.* LIII, 2. 1901. S. 239.

The skiaskopic investigation shows that in many instances a change of sign occurs in the peripheral aberration during accommodation. Owing to the inherent sources of error in the method, this result cannot be said to be absolutely certain. But if it is established, it seems to be an expression of the change of aberration due to the accommodative change of form of the core-lens; because the latter must probably be accompanied by corresponding variations of the higher derivatives of the indicial equation, and these in turn affect the peripheral total aberration.

During accommodation the asymmetry-values along the line of sight may vary, involving also a variation of the angle between the central ray and the line of sight, although this variation cannot be calculated. However, the central ray alone is responsible for the direction of the optical axis, and, so far as the monochromatic aberrations are concerned, its role is the same as that of the line of sight when the aberrations are left out of account. Obviously, therefore, in consequence of what has been said, there may be an *accommodative change of the direction of the optical axis*, such as is actually observed.

HELMHOLTZ's famous dictum, that the monochromatic aberrations of the eye are such as would not be tolerated in any good optical instrument, is sometimes construed to mean that the eye is a very badly constructed optical affair—which HELMHOLTZ never said and certainly did not mean. But another question that this statement raises is whether these aberrations are not serviceable and what is their purpose. First of all, it should be noted, as HELMHOLTZ pointed out, that a limit is imposed by diffraction to the physical sharpness of the image.

The phenomena of the diffraction of light present exceedingly complicated mathematical problems that cannot be solved very exactly except in special cases. The so-called FRAUNHOFER diffraction phenomena illustrate what is meant here. These are the effects that are observed when light goes through a round aperture on the supposition that the source of light and the screen are both infinitely distant. The latter condition is satisfied by adjusting an optical system beyond the aperture so that its focal plane acts as the screen plane. Under these circumstances, a luminous point is reproduced as a bright disc surrounded by alternately bright and dark rings. The border of the central bright disc, whose brightness fades towards the edge, is at the first minimum of light as represented by the smallest dark ring. Let φ denote the angular distance of this minimum from the axis; then

$$\sin \varphi = 1.22 \frac{\lambda}{2R},$$

where λ denotes the wave-length of the light and R denotes the radius of the circular aperture. The angle is so small that it is sufficiently accurate to substitute the angle itself in place of its sine. Hence, if φ is expressed in minutes, the formula becomes

$$\varphi = \frac{1.22}{R} \cdot \frac{\lambda}{0.00058}.$$

Therefore, for light of wave-length 0.00058 mm, the formula is:

$$\varphi = \frac{1.22'}{R},$$

where R is expressed in millimetres. According to the above, the angular diameter of the projection of the bright central disc on the infinitely distant object-plane is equal to 2φ. However, owing to the way the brightness fades out towards the edge, two points do not have to be at this angular distance from each other to be seen separately. Half of it is supposed to be enough for the purpose; and so the angle φ is the conventional measure of the *resolving power* of the instrument. No matter how much the refraction of the rays may be improved in the optical instrument on the other side of the aperture, and no matter how much the image in the focal plane may be magnified, the limit of efficiency is determined by the resolving power, entirely independently of all these devices.

This calculation is applicable at once to all optical systems that are focused for infinity, provided the stop is in front of the first refracting surface or coincides with its contour. It applies, therefore, to the reduced eye, in which the pupil coincides with the refracting surface. In the human eye, where the pupil is beyond the cornea, all we can get is an approximate value of the resolving power, by substituting in the formula the radius of the entrance-pupil. Of course, λ denotes the wave-length of the light in air; and the indices of refraction of the aqueous humor and vitreous humor are not involved in any way, because the value of φ is based on a projection in the object-space. The question is properly treated by SCHUSTER[1] and GLEICHEN,[2] but both DRUDE[3] and POCKELS[4] base the calculation on the wave-lengths in the aqueous and vitreous humors. POCKELS uses light of wave-length 0.00057 mm in his calculation, and finds $2\varphi = \frac{1}{R} \cdot 144''$. The formula given by HELMHOLTZ on page 196 applies to the reduced eye. By substituting in this formula

[1] ARTHUR SCHUSTER, *An introduction to the theory of optics.* London 1904.

[2] A. GLEICHEN, *Einführung in die medizinische Optik.* Leipzig 1904.

[3] PAUL DRUDE, *Lehrbuch der Optik.* Leipzig 1906.

[4] A. WINKELMANN, *Handbuch der Physik.* 2. Aufl. 6. Bd. Leipzig 1906. S. 1075.

$$2\varphi, \lambda, 2R \quad \text{for} \quad \frac{n\delta}{r}, nl, d, \text{ respectively,}$$

the formula given above will be obtained. The reason why HELM-HOLTZ's formula contains the index of refraction, is because it does not give the angular size of the apparent bright area in the object-space, but the actual size of it on the retina; which is obtained by using the wave-length of the light in the refracting medium. It is true that HELMHOLTZ calculated the size of the disc on the retina by putting $\lambda = l$ instead of $\lambda = nl$; but in calculating the angular size in the object-space, he put $2\varphi = \frac{\delta}{r}$ instead of $2\varphi = \frac{n\delta}{r}$, as can be seen from his numbers; so that the final result of the calculation is correct. Evidently, it was just an oversight in setting down the figures. The results found by DRUDE and POCKELS can be obtained by substituting in HELM-HOLTZ's formula the wave-length of the light in the refracting medium, without taking into account the fact that for the projection of the retinal image of the bright disc in the object-space the index of refraction has to be used again.

The general formula, therefore, has to be used for the *resolving power* of the eye. For an entrance-pupil 2 mm in diameter and for yellow light of wave-length 0.00058 mm the value of this angle is found to be 1.22'; and for blue-green light of wave-length 0.0005 mm, 1.05'; while a distant luminous point has twice this apparent size. The angular measure of the resolving power is directly proportional to the wave-length and inversely proportional to the diameter of the entrance-pupil. Hence, for an entrance-pupil of 3 mm it is 0.82' or 0.7' for the wave-lengths selected above. Owing to the distribution of light in the solar spectrum and still more in the spectra of artificial sources of light, the former number is the one to be used for a comparison with the visual acuity of the eye. If in this comparison account is taken of the fact that, on account of the conventional definition of the resolving power, the angular measure was rather too small than too large, the result is that *the limit of the visual capacity of the eye as imposed by diffraction, as far as it can be calculated, is attained by the visual acuity of the normal eye with a pupil of the size corresponding to a good illumination.*

Thus, we see again that the complicated aberrations of higher order that are present in the eye and the astonishingly large positive aberration within the optical zone do not impair the visual acuity with a pupil of the size mentioned. However, the dioptrics of the crystalline lens tells us that the former aberration is due entirely, and the latter in large measure, to the fact that the lens is composed of a hetero-

geneous medium. The great advantage of such a medium is the elevation of the total index that takes place in accommodation, which denotes a change of optical focusing that is out of proportion to the change
of form, and unattainable with homogeneous media *caeteris paribus*.
The monochromatic aberrations are the necessary evil for obtaining
this advantage; and even if the convergence of the rays is not so good
as it might be, the clearness of the image in good illumination is still
above the limit of the capacity of the eye as imposed by the laws of
diffraction. Hence, the monochromatic aberrations are a witness for
the perfection of the eye, if what is meant by the perfection of an optical
instrument is good convergence of rays to the degree that is needed
to obtain the greatest useful sharpness of image; anything in excess
of this being sacrificed in order to gain some other end.

VI.   Ophthalmoscopy[1]

Ophthalmoscopy in the widest meaning of the word includes all
the dioptrical methods of investigating the various parts of the eye;
but in its narrower sense as meaning the observation of the fundus
of the eye, ophthalmoscopy has always been a subject of the greatest
interest for physiology ever since HELMHOLTZ's invention of the ophthalmoscope. It deserves to be ranked highest of all the dioptrical
methods as being the most beneficial and having the greatest practical
importance.

The *theory of the illumination of the eye* was expressed by HELM
HOLTZ in his famous Proposition II (p. 231) as follows: "If the pupil of
the patient's eye is to appear luminous, the image of the source of light
on his retina must either wholly or partly overlap the image of the
observer's pupil."   Now what is meant here is an indistinct image
composed of blur circles; and yet the statement is not absolutely
correct, because the projection of the light-source or of the pupil of
the observer in the pupil of the patient's eye, as it is produced in
certain ophthalmoscopic methods, is, strictly speaking, not a question
of an image on the retina at all or even of an indistinct image.   By
introducing the idea of the so-called region of radiation of an optical
system, a statement can be formulated which will include all cases.
The fundus of the eye must be illuminated in order to emit light.   Consequently, there is always an *illumination system*, which extends from

[1] ¶This article on "Ophthalmoscopy" was not included in the original appendices in
the first volume of the third edition of *The Treatise on Physiological Optics*. It is taken from
Professor GULLSTRAND's book entitled *Einführung in die Methoden der Dioptrik des Auges
des Menschen* (Leipzig, 1911), pp. 55-90. (J. P. C. S.)

the source of light to the fundus of the patient's eye, and for which the contour of the source of light is to be regarded as the aperture stop. On the other hand, the *ophthalmoscopic system* proper, or the *observation system*, extends from the fundus of the patient's eye to the entrance-pupil of the observer's eye. Now evidently, *the condition of illumination of the eye is that part of the fundus of the patient's eye shall be at the same time in the radiation region of the illumination system and in that of the observation system.*

Moreover, a necessary *condition of ophthalmoscopy* is that in the observation system an optical image of the fundus of the patient's eye shall be cast at a distance for which the observer's eye can be accommodated. Experience alone can decide whether, with a certain disposition of apparatus, the fulfilment of these two fundamental conditions is also sufficient to enable details of the fundus to be seen. For some requirements, either as to sharpness and magnification of the image or as to brightness and extent of field, the above conditions are not enough, and another condition has to be imposed whereby the harmful light in the patient's eye due to regular or diffused reflection must not be permitted to enter the observation system. The methods in which this latter condition is likewise satisfied will be called the methods of ophthalmoscopy without reflex (or reflex-free ophthalmoscopy) as distinguished from all the other methods of simple ophthalmoscopy.

For *simple ophthalmoscopy with erect image*, in case the eyes of both patient and observer are emmetropic, nothing more is needed in the way of instruments than an object-stand and a candle. The source of light is adjusted to one side of the patient's eye and moved downwards until no direct light any longer falls on the iris of this eye. The glass plate used for the mirror is held by the operator in a vertical plane in front of the eye, and as near it as possible, and turned until the light reflected from it falls on the pupil. Placing the pupil of his corresponding eye on the line joining the centre of the pupil of the patient and the middle of the virtual image of the flame in the mirror, without using his accommodation, the investigator beholds the details of the fundus of the eye as a small, brightly enough illuminated spot. By changing the adjustment of the mirror, with corresponding movements of his own head, or by varying the direction in which the patient looks, the observer can cause this spot to traverse the fundus of the eye to suit himself, although of course it takes practice to do it properly. The essential disadvantage connected with this simplest method of ophthalmoscopy *with transparent mirror* is the small field of the illumination system, whereas its feeble brightness is of secondary importance. In the dim illumination of the room by the weak source of light the pupils of both patient and observer are dilated, and the small amount of light reflected into the eye produces very little contraction of the pupil of the patient. However, the intensity of illumination on the retina of his eye in the central part of the luminous area is proportional to the square of the diameter of the pupil, because, for emmetropic focusing, the useful exit-pupil is equal to the entire exit-pupil, provided the least width of the source of light is not less than the diameter of the exit-pupil of the eye. Moreover, supposing both eyes are emmetropically adjusted, the pupil of the observation system in the intervening medium between the two eyes is the smaller of the entrance-pupils, and the solid angle subtended by the useful exit-pupil at the fovea of the patient's eye is proportional to the square of its diameter. Hence, unless the pupil of the observer's eye is smaller than that of the patient, the intensity of illumination in the fovea of the observer is proportional to the fourth power of the diameter of the pupil of the patient's eye. Besides, the reflex from the cornea is so feeble that the blur circle which it makes in the observer's eye does not interfere with seeing, because the details of the fundus can be seen through it, so to speak. The result is that for physiological relations the brightness is generally completely sufficient, provided in investigating the fovea the image of the source of light does not fall on the centre of this region; which usually causes such a contraction of the patient's pupil that the apparent brightness of the fundus becomes too small in comparison with the brightness of the blur circle due to the corneal reflex. Hence, ordinarily, nothing is gained by increasing the specific brightness of the virtual image of the light-source in the mirror, because the brightness of the image reflected from the cornea increases in the same ratio. HELMHOLTZ advised for this purpose making the light fall more obliquely on the plate, or using several plates, but this method was not a practical success. With a large angle of incidence it is not so easy to protect the iris of the patient's eye from direct light, and light coming directly in this eye has an unfavourable effect on the size of the pupil. Besides, when the iris is illuminated directly, the brightness needed to recognize detail in the fundus is different from what it has to be otherwise, and this interferes with the observation. On the other hand, when more plates are used, the diffusely reflected light gets to be of more importance; for it is not an easy matter to keep the six glass surfaces of HELMHOLTZ's ophthalmoscope clean and free from dust. The field of the illumination system increases with the solid angle subtended by the source of light in the pupil of the patient's eye, and hence it is larger with a larger source of light, and when it is placed as near the mirror as possible. But it should be noted that this involves also an increase of brightness of the blur circle in the observer's eye due to the reflex image in the cornea, and it will not be so easy to see through it. This is all the more true when an image of the source of light is projected in the patient's eye with a convex lens, as HELMHOLTZ proposed.

For the reasons above mentioned, the *opaque mirror with a peep-hole* is considered better for direct ophthalmoscopy by the method of the erect image. Since the central hole in the mirror has the same effect in the illumination system as a screen casting a shadow, whereas in the observation system it acts like a pupil or window, the connections here are rather complicated. However, on the one hand, the pupil of the observer's eye through which very little light enters, and which is enlarged by closing the other eye, is usually big enough not to be the pupil of the observation system; and, on the other hand, the window-effect of the aperture in the mirror may be disregarded, because, as the method is employed in practice, this effect is compensated by continual movements of mirror, head and eye. Practically, therefore, the hole in the mirror and the pupil of the patient's eye do not enter into the calculation except as apertures in the observation system. In order to calculate the field of the observation system, suppose that *CD* in Fig. 147 represents the diameter of the hole in the mirror, and *AB* the

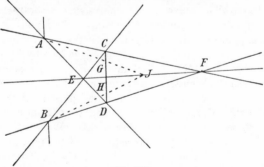

Fig. 147.

diameter of the entrance-pupil of the patient's eye, in a pair of parallel planes perpendicular to the axis of the observation system at the centres of these apertures. The entire or total field of the observation system is defined then by the angle $AEB = v$, and the unshaded (*unvignettierte*) field by the angle $AFB = \omega$. Putting $CD = l$, $AB = p$, and d equal to the interval between the two apertures, we find for the tangents of the angles made by the lines BC and AC with the perpendicular drawn from C to AB the following expressions:

$$\tan\frac{v}{2} = \frac{p+l}{2d}, \qquad \tan\frac{\omega}{2} = \frac{p-l}{2d}.$$

However, these angles are so small that they can be substituted here in place of their tangents; consequently,

$$v = \frac{p+l}{d}, \qquad \omega = \frac{p-l}{d}.$$

With the degree of accuracy attainable by the laws of the first order, there would be no sense in using here a more exact schematic eye than the reduced eye; and hence AB is its own image after refraction in the dioptric system of the eye, and all we have to do is to determine the points conjugate to E and F. Suppose that the light proceeds from F towards AB, and let the distances of E and F from AB be denoted by e and f; so that

$$-e = \frac{pd}{p+l}, \qquad -f = \frac{pd}{p-l}.$$

Let D denote the refracting power of the optical system of the reduced eye whose principal points coincide at the middle of AB; consequently, the reduced distances of the points conjugate to E and F are found from the equations:

$$\frac{1}{e'} = D + \frac{1}{e}, \qquad \frac{1}{f'} = D + \frac{1}{f}.$$

Now the lines drawn from these points to the ends of AB determine the complete field on the retina and the unshaded (unvignetted) field. Hence, if the angular diameters of these fields are denoted by V and Ω, and if the reduced length of the eye is denoted by b, we may write the following expressions for the *extent of the field of the observation system*:

$$V = p\left(1 - \frac{b}{e'}\right) = p(1-bD) + b \cdot \frac{p+l}{d},$$

$$\Omega = p\left(1 - \frac{b}{f'}\right) = p(1-bD) + b \cdot \frac{p-l}{d}.$$

Like all similar formulae, these equations may be used with any system of units, provided the reciprocal of the refracting power is measured in terms of the same unit of length as the other linear magnitudes. Thus if D is given in dioptries, the unit of length is the metre.

The point F lies always in front of the anterior focal point of the eye or beyond the pupil, whereas the point E may be on either side of the focal point or at it. Thus, while f is invariably positive, e may be finite or infinite, positive or negative. Consequently, the formulae show that, as long as $f' > b$, the unshaded field is smaller when the axis of the eye is longer. When we investigate the illumination system, we shall find that f is always greater than b Moreover, it appears that the complete field in all eyes is equal to the size of the pupil, provided the point E is at the anterior focal point of the eye. When E is nearer the eye than this, the complete field is larger, and *vice versa*. In either case the difference between the diameters of field and pupil is proportional to the length of the axis of the eye. If A denotes the refraction of the eye, then

$$1-bD=bA\;;$$

consequently, $\dfrac{V}{b}=v+pA,$ $\dfrac{\Omega}{b}=\omega+pA,$

where the expressions on the left-hand sides of these equations are the principal point angles corresponding to the field-diameters. That is, they are the measures of the *angular diameters of the field*. Now, obviously from what has been stated, these angles are always positive, although for an hypermetropic eye it may happen that $l>p$. There-fore, other things being equal, the angular diameter of the field in-variably increases with increase of refraction of the eye, and con-sequently is greater in hypermetropia than in myopia. The value of v or of ω for the emmetropic eye may be taken as the criterion, and will be designated therefore as the *characteristic angular diameter of the field*. It can be found exactly by using the formulae above containing the trigonometrical tangents. After all, however, the results of this investigation of the ophthalmoscopic field are to be regarded only as approximate, since they have been obtained by using simply the laws of the first order. Moreover, they have been derived on the assump-tion that the window-effect of the pupil of the observer's eye is com-pensated by movements of the head. By combination of these move-ments with displacements of the mirror and corresponding rotations of the observer's eye, a displacement of the field is produced on the fundus of the eye which amounts to a considerable addition to the re-gion that can be seen. Now in order for these movements to have the most effect, the three apertures of the observation system should be as near together as possible. Moreover, not only the unshaded field but the entire field becomes larger when the interval between the mirror and the patient's eye is diminished, as appears from the formulae above. Hence, evidently, in the investigation with erect image, a good ophthalmoscope should be made in such a way as to enable the observer to get so close to the patient's eye that their foreheads come in contact during the investigation. For the same reason, as was pointed out above, the corresponding eyes of observer and patient should always be used in ophthalmoscopy with erect image, that is, either the right eyes of both individuals or the left eyes.

In order to produce an image of the fundus, for any arbitrary state of refraction of the patient's eye, at a place where it can be seen distinctly by the eye of any observer who desires to investigate it, it must be possible to insert conveniently lenses of many different powers behind the hole in the mirror, as they may be needed. But when the mirror is very close to the patient's eye it will be inclined to the axis of the observation system, and an oblique position of the lens usually involves astigmatism and a consequent impairment of the image. In order to avoid this, we must always count on a finite distance between the lens and the hole in the mirror, and therefore the lens-aperture must have a diameter big enough not to involve any so-called window-action. Suppose D_l denotes the refracting power of the interposed lens, which may be considered here as infinitely thin; and m denotes the reduced distance of the first principal point of the observer's eye from the optical centre of the lens (designated by M). The observer's eye is supposed to be accommodated for distinct vision at a certain point O on the axis of the observation system. The refracting power of his eye for this focusing may be denoted here by D. Let $a = \dfrac{1}{A}$ denote the reduced distance of the point O from the first principal point of the observer's eye; and, moreover, let $\dfrac{1}{A_m}$ denote the reduced distance of this same point O from the point M. Now at the same time the patient's eye is accommodated to see distinctly a point O', where O, O' designate, therefore, a pair of conjugate points on the axis of the interposed lens. The symbols m', D', A', A'_m, etc., have the same meanings with respect to the patient's eye as the symbols m, D, A, A_m, etc., respectively, have with respect to the observer's eye.

The refracting power of the lens is equal to $A_m + A'_m$. It may be assumed here with sufficient accuracy that the anterior focal point of the observer's eye coincides with the optical centre of the lens, and hence $A_m = L$, where L denotes the reduced focal point convergence of the bundle of rays incident on the observer's eye. Hence *the refracting power of the lens of the observation system* can be put equal to the sum $(A'_m + L)$.

In order to study *the magnifying power in ophthalmoscopy by the method of the erect image*, we have the following general formula (as on p. 364):

$$-\frac{\omega_m}{a_0} = D_0(1 + \Delta_m A_m),$$

where D_0 denotes the refracting power of the compound optical system composed of the lens and the patient's eye, and Δ_m denotes the distance of the point M from the anterior focal point of this system. And if in this formula the values

$$D_0 = (1 - m_0'D_l), \qquad \Delta_m = \frac{m' \, D'}{D_0} - \frac{1}{D_0} = \frac{m_0'D'}{D_0}$$

are substituted for D_0 and Δ_m, we obtain:

$$-\frac{\omega_m}{a_0} = D_0 + m_0'D'A_m = D'(1 - m_0'A'_m).$$

Since for emmetropic focusing of the observer's eye the angle ω_m is equal to the principal point angle, this formula gives the *absolute magnifying power*, which, on the supposition of such focusing, is equal to D_0. Since m'_0 is always positive, the magnifying power is greater when the patient's eye is myopic than when it is hypermetropic; and, generally, the magnifying power diminishes as the refraction of the patient's eye becomes greater. Estimating the refracting power of the optical system of the eye roughly at 60 dptr, and assuming m'_0 equal to 1 cm, we may say, in the conventional mode of reckoning, that in emmetropia the magnifying power is 15-fold; and $N\%$ greater or smaller in myopia or hypermetropia, respectively, where N denotes the numerical value of A'_m. Thus, in the cases that occur in practice the magnification number varies between 13 and 18.

On the above assumption of the coincidence of the optical centre of the lens and the anterior focal point of the observer's eye, ω_m denotes the focal point angle. Hence, with relaxed accommodation the size of the retinal image in the observer's eye is independent of the axial length of the eye; and

$$-\frac{D'}{D}(1 - m_0'A'_m)$$

denotes the *magnification-ratio* for the imagery of the retina of the patient's eye on the retina of the observer's eye.

Since

$$\omega_f' = a_0D', \qquad \frac{\omega_m'}{\omega_f'} = 1 - m_0'A'_m$$

the general expression for the magnifying power may be written in the form

$$\omega_m = - \omega_m';$$

where the negative sign is due to the fact that the two eyes are looking in opposite directions, and because no change of sign is to be made in the equations defining the angles ω.

The following two expressions for the individual magnifying power are obtained by using the principal point angle:

$$-\frac{\omega_h}{a_0} = D'(1-m_0'A'_m)(1+mA) = B' \cdot \frac{1+m\,A}{1+m'A'};$$

the latter of which shows in the simplest way the effect of the accommodation of the two eyes and the action of any astigmatism that may be present in the patient's eye. Evidently, the magnifying power is reduced by accommodation on the part of the observer and increased by accommodation on the part of the patient; although the variation of the refracting power of the lens in the observation system needed to compensate accommodation is in the same direction in both cases. Moreover, for investigating the fundus of an astigmatic eye the refracting power of the lens is so chosen that by using accommodation the imageable lines of both systems of imagery can be seen distinctly in succession. Hence, both A and A' must have different values for the two principal sections; for the condition that (A'_m+A_m) shall remain constant, is satisfied by accommodation on the part of the observer. Imposing this condition, and denoting the magnification-ratio $-\frac{\omega_h}{\omega'_h}$ by K_1 or by K_2 according as A' is equal to A'_1 or A'_2, respectively, a fairly complicated expression is obtained for the distortion due to astigmatism, as measured by the ratio $\frac{K_1}{K_2}$; in which the distortion depends not only on the astigmatism but also on the refraction states of the two eyes. However, in actual practice the numerical values of expressions of the type mA are so small as compared with unity that, where simply the imagery-laws of the first order are used, it is justifiable to neglect the higher powers of these products. Hence the following *approximate formula of the astigmatic distortion*, which is obtained in this way, is sufficiently accurate for practical purposes:

$$\frac{K_1}{K_2} = 1 - (m'+m)(A'_1-A'_2) \cdot$$

Since a smaller value of the refraction of the eye means a higher refracting power for it, the magnifying power is greater in that one of the principal sections, which is the more highly refracting. In case the observer has not the necessary power of accommodation, then instead of one of the images, or instead of both of them if he selects an intermediate focus, there will be an optical projection; for which the image of the centre of projection in the medium between the first principal point of the observer's eye and the lens must be substituted instead of this principal point. Accordingly, m here denotes the distance of this image of the centre of projection from the optical centre of the lens used; and A denotes the convergence of the bundle of object-rays as measured at this same point. By the same process as before the same formula is obtained; and hence all that is necessary is to substitute the given value in place of m in the approximate formula above. However, it should be observed that in this approximation the difference between the distance of the centre of projection and that of its image from the optical centre of the lens is neglected in the product obtained by multiplying by the refraction. The hole in the mirror for all ordinary sizes that are used acts as the centre of projection; and so its distance from the lens, counted negatively, has to be substituted for m, and $m' + m = d$. The distortion is found to be less than in the ordinary investigation.

The astigmatic distortion thus found applies only to magnification of detail, with which the movement of the observer's eye has nothing to do. Usually, however, the distortion is estimated by the apparent form of the papilla, for which vision with the mobile eye is required. In this case the centre of rotation of the eye is to be taken as centre of projection; which amounts roughly to increasing the magnitude $(m' + m)$ in the approximate formula by about 1 cm, in order to obtain an expression for the apparent distortion.

The intensity of the light in the observation system is measured by the solid angle subtended by the exit-pupil of this system; the intensity of illumination on the retina of the observer's eye being equal to this intensity multiplied by the specific intensity of the light of the illuminated retina of the patient's eye. Having constructed the image of the hole in the mirror as cast by the optical system of the patient's eye, from the extremities of a diameter of this image draw a pair of lines to the opposite ends of the parallel diameter of the pupil, intersecting on the axis at the point defined by f' on page 447. Now since $f' > b$, this point lies behind the retina, and hence the image of the hole in the mirror subtends at the retina a smaller solid angle than the pupil. Moreover, as in ophthalmoscopy the retina of the observer's eye is imaged on that of the patient's eye, the image of the hole in the mirror is the entrance-pupil.

Using the reduced eye as being accurate enough for this investigation, we find for the solid angle subtended by the exit-pupil the following value:

$$\frac{\pi p_n^2 B^2}{4n^2},$$

where n denotes the index of refraction of the vitreous humor, and p_n is *the diameter of the useful pupil of the eye*, the latter magnitude being

defined as follows: The useful pupil is the projection on the pupil of
the image of the hole in the mirror, as formed by the lens of the observation system, from the point, on which the observer's eye is focused,
as the centre of projection; and its diameter is given by the equation:

$$p_n : \frac{1}{A} = \frac{l}{1-(m'-d)D_l} : \left(\frac{1}{A_m} + \frac{m'-d}{1-(m'-d)D_l} \right) = l : \frac{1-(m'-d)A'_m}{A_m} \, .$$

It follows that

$$p_n = l \cdot \frac{1-mA_m}{1-(m'-d)A'_m} \, ;$$

and hence the useful pupil of the eye is greatest when the observer is
hypermetropic and the patient myopic. Substituting the value

$$B = D \cdot \frac{1-m_0 A_m}{1-mA_m}$$

in the expression for the solid angle subtended by the exit-pupil, we
may write this expression as follows:

$$\frac{\pi l^2 D^2}{4n^2} \left\{ \frac{1-m_0 A_m}{1-(m'-d)A'_m} \right\}^2 .$$

Accordingly, in case the optical centre of the lens is at the anterior
focal point of the observer's eye, the intensity of illumination on the
retina of this eye depends simply on the refraction of the patient's
eye.

In *the illumination system* let us try, first, to estimate the mutual
influence on each other of the hole in the mirror and the pupil of the
patient's eye, apart from the source of light. As was shown above, the
complete shadow between the points conjugate to F and E in Fig. 147
due to the hole in the mirror extends into the medium beyond the optical system of the patient's eye. Hence, the first point must necessarily be beyond the retina, if the central part of the field is to be
illuminated. It is true this is not absolutely necessary, because it is
possible that the observation system is not centered. Since the dark
spot on the fundus of the eye made by the shadow is always central
around the axis of the observation system, it is extremely disturbing in
its effect. Therefore, perhaps not so much in the actual practice of
ophthalmoscopy, but certainly for ophthalmoscopy with a centered
observation system, the condition $f' > b$, as formulated above, has to be
satisfied. Now this is equivalent to saying that the hole in the mirror
shall be the pupil of the observation system; and therefore it defines
also the greatest diameter that this opening can have for a centered
observation system. In order to obtain a practically useful expression,
all that is necessary is to project the hole on the pupil from the point

on which the eye is focused. Thus, for *the condition as to the size of the hole in the mirror*, the following formula is obtained:

$$l < p(1+dA).$$

If this condition is not satisfied, then, as stated above, the observation system will have to be decentered. This is accomplished by decentering the mirror until it no longer acts as a perforated mirror, but merely transmits to the eye the light reflected from one side of the hole. This method of using the perforated mirror comes therefore under the head of ophthalmoscopy with an unperforated mirror, and will be considered when we come to treat of that subject.

Supposing, however, the above condition is satisfied, the values of ω and Ω for *the extent of the field as seen through the hole in the mirror and the pupil without being shaded off*, are obtained in the same way as in the observation system. But beyond these limits, except for such shading off of the field as is due to the position and size of the actual source of light, the shading off of the field occurs in the reverse sense, with brightness gradually increasing out towards the periphery.

There does not have to be any other shading than this in the field of the illumination system. Any window-action of the source of light itself can be obviated by casting an image of the source right on the fundus of the eye. In this case the shading off of the field in the illumination system and in the observation system being in opposite sense, the brightness of the ophthalmoscopic image is very uniform, provided the specific brightness of the source of light is itself uniform. Theoretically, by projecting an image of the source of light in the pupil or near by it, a larger field can be obtained without any shading besides. But, practically, nothing is gained in this way in simple ophthalmoscopy, because the investigation is hampered by greatly augmented corneal reflex, apart from the complication of the instrumental arrangements. In order to enlarge the field, practically, therefore, there is no other choice except to produce an image of the light at some other place; which must be done at the cost of further shading off of the field. It would lead too far to attempt here a complete investigation of this matter; for since the contour of the source of light is to be considered as a stop, there are two apertures and a central screen that are involved, and for such a case the general formulae are rather complicated. Here, therefore, it will be sufficient to examine merely the questions that are of practical importance. Let the diameter of the image of the source of light in the mirror be denoted by q, and let the distance of this image from the mirror be denoted by c, this latter magnitude being reckoned as positive when the mirror is between the pupil of the eye and the image in question.

In the first place, with regard to the mutual action on each other of the image of the source of light and the hole in the mirror, the condition will be imposed, as before, that there is no complete shadow on the fundus of the eye. This condition amounts to saying that the angle subtended by the image of the source of light at the point for which the eye is focused is greater than that subtended at this same point by the hole in the mirror. Let the symbol $|K|$ be employed to denote the numerical value of any magnitude denoted by K; then we may write:

$$q : \left| \frac{1}{A} + c + d \right| > l : \left| \frac{1}{A} + d \right|,$$

that is,

$$q > l \cdot \left| \frac{1 + (c+d)A}{1 + dA} \right| .$$

Neglecting powers of dA higher than the first and magnitudes of similar order of smallness as compared with unity, we derive the following approximate formula:

$$q > l \cdot |1 + cA| ;$$

which gives, therefore, accurately enough *the condition as to the size of the image of the source of light.* Unless this condition is satisfied, there will be again a dark spot in the centre of the ophthalmoscopic field. But it is different from that described above in this way, namely, that with rotations of the mirror around an axis passing through the centre of the hole, without decentering the observation system, this spot undergoes displacements in the field of this system, and consequently is not so disturbing as the other spot was. However, since it is liable to cause confusion, it is best to satisfy the condition above.

The characteristic angular size of the field that is not shaded off by the mutual action of the hole in the mirror and the source of light is found by the method used above, and is equal to $\dfrac{q-l}{c}$. According as the numerical value of this magnitude does or does not exceed ω, the extent of the central unshaded field in the emmetropic eye is measured by the angle ω or by the other angle, respectively.

The entire *angular measure of the field of the illumination system* is obtained in the same way as that of the observation system. If the characteristic angular size of the field is denoted by w, and if the linear dimension of the field on the retina is denoted by W, then

$$w = \frac{p+q}{c+d}, \qquad BW = w + pA.$$

Using corresponding symbols λ, Λ to denote the extent of the outer borders of the field that is not shaded off by the mutual action of the source of light and the pupil, we obtain corresponding formulæ, namely:

$$\lambda = \frac{p-q}{c+d}, \qquad B\Lambda = \lambda + pA.$$

The *intensity of the light of the illumination system* depends on the area P_n of the useful pupil, the intensity of illumination on the retina being equal to

$$eP_nB^2,$$

where e denotes the specific intensity of the source of light. In order to find the useful pupil, the image of the source of light and the hole in the mirror must be projected on the pupil from the point of fixation of the eye as centre of projection. According as the projection of the image of the source of light is smaller or greater than the pupil, the area of the projection of the hole in the mirror must be subtracted from the area of the former or from that of the latter, respectively. Accordingly, P_n is the same as the smaller of the two values given by the following expressions;

$$P'_n = \frac{\pi}{4}\left\{p^2 - \frac{l^2}{(1+dA)^2}\right\}, \qquad P''_n = \frac{\pi}{4}\left\{\frac{q^2}{[1+(c+d)A]^2} - \frac{l^2}{(1+dA)^2}\right\}.$$

By auxiliary optical appliances the position and size of the image of the source of light in the mirror can be arbitrarily modified. But as one of the prime factors in the practical employment of the simple ophthalmoscope is the unhampered movement of the mirror, any combination of it with lenses, which (entirely aside from limitations of space) requires complicated manipulation for changing the direction of the incident light, is ruled out in advance. It is only in certain electrical forms of ophthalmoscope when the lamp and mirror are rigidly connected that such combinations as are referred to here are really practical. Generally speaking, therefore, *the form of the mirror* is the only optical method of influencing the image of the source of light. If it is a question of getting the largest possible field with the best possible brightness, evidently the lamp and mirror should be as near together as possible. Now the ratio $\frac{q}{c} = K'$ depends merely on the size of the source of light and its distance, and not on the form of the mirror, since, in both the tangential and the sagittal imagery, the principal points coincide at the surface of the mirror. Hence, starting with the value of K' that is practicable, we must see how the field and the intensity of the light are altered when c is varied. The simplest method to use for this purpose is that of differentiation; although the

process will be illustrated without this by the aid of Fig. 147. Treating
K' as constant, and hence $q \cdot dc = c \cdot dq$, we find by differentiation:

$$\frac{dw}{dc} = \frac{K'd-p}{(c+d)^2}, \qquad \frac{d\lambda}{dc} = -\frac{K'd+p}{(c+d)^2};$$

where the value of K' is negative when c is negative, because the sign
of q is always regarded as positive. As to the size of the entire field,
c and w always have the same sign, as the image of the light source
must never be between mirror and pupil on account of the prevalence
of light reflected from the cornea. Hence, according as the value of
the differential coefficient is positive or negative, the numerical values
of c and w either both increase or decrease together, or as one increases
the other decreases, respectively. But when c is negative, and therefore
K' is negative too, the differential coefficient is negative; and when
c and K' are positive, the sign of the differential coefficient will be the
same as that of the magnitude $(K'd-p)$. Since $|K'|$ and $\frac{p}{d}$ denote
the angular diameters of the source of light and the pupil, respectively,
as measured at the centre of the hole in the mirror, evidently, starting
with a very concave mirror which is supposed to get flatter and flatter
until it is plane and then more and more convex, the entire field of
illumination will continually diminish, provided the angle subtended by
the source of light at the centre of the hole in the mirror is smaller than
the angle subtended by the pupil; whereas in the opposite case the field
is least when c becomes infinite, and begins to increase again when the
image of the source of light is virtual and comes nearer to the mirror.
With regard to the part of the field that is not shaded off by the source
of light and the pupil, the only cases of any practical importance are
those for which $(q-p)$ is positive and Λ and λ have the same sign.
Under these circumstances, the signs of λ and c are opposite, so that,
according as the differential coefficient is positive or negative, the
numerical values of λ and c vary in opposite directions or in the same
direction, respectively. When c is positive, the differential coefficient
is negative; and when c is negative, the sign of the differential coefficient
is opposite to that of $(K'd+p)$. The result is, that, provided the source
of light subtends a greater angle at the centre of the hole in the mirror
than the pupil, the part of the field that is not shaded off by the source
of light and the pupil gets smaller and smaller when the form of the
mirror is varied as described above; whereas in the opposite case, in
the region $q>p$, $\lambda\Lambda>0$, the field increases when the image of the source
of light is real, reaches its maximum value when c is infinite, and
thereafter diminishes when the image becomes virtual. Both when
the image of the source of light is real and when it is virtual, there is a

certain point, when the image approaches the mirror, for which the entire field is shaded by the mutual action of the source of light and the pupil on each other. Thus, putting $\Lambda = 0$, we obtain:

$$c = \frac{p(1+dA)}{K'-pA},$$

in which the value of K' is negative when c is negative. For emmetropia these points coincide with the points where the image of the source of light has been reduced, by bringing it nearer to the mirror, until it has the same size as the pupil; but for cases of decided ametropia there may be considerable departures from this rule, as the formula indicates.

The effect of the form of the mirror on the field of illumination may be illustrated by the aid of Fig. 147, as was mentioned above. For instance, suppose AB represents a real image of the source of light, and CD represents the pupil; the light proceeding from right to left, so that the point J in the diagram may be regarded as the centre of the hole in the mirror. Then by varying the form of the mirror, AB may be displaced farther to the left, without, however, altering the angle AJB. In this case it is plain that the angle $AEB = w$ decreases, and the angle $AFB = \lambda$ increases; whereas if the point F were on the other side of J, the angle λ would decrease also when the interval between the mirror and the image increased. In the latter case, $-K' > \dfrac{p}{d}$; but the opposite case is the one shown in the figure. These conclusions apply to the case when the image is real. When the image of the source of light is virtual, the point J will be between AB and CD, and everything happens in this case in similar fashion.

The conclusions can be summarized as follows: For $|K'| > \dfrac{p}{d}$, a real image of the source of light, for every reason, is better for the size of the field than an infinitely distant image, and the latter is better than a virtual image. On the other hand, for $|K'| < \dfrac{p}{d}$, both a real image and a virtual image are better for the total size of the field, but worse for the portion that is not shaded off by the pupil and the source of light, than an infinitely distant image. Since in the practice of simple ophthalmoscopy by the method of the erect image the technical difficulties are augmented by reduction of the size of the pupil, and since there is no trouble about realizing the condition $|K'| > \dfrac{p}{d}$ with small pupil, usually *the concave mirror is more advantageous* when the size of the field of the illumination system is kept in view. However, the curvature of the mirror must not be increased too much, because the disturbing effect of the corneal reflex will interfere in this case. The more of the light coming from the mirror that is intercepted by the pupil, the greater will be the portion of the flux of light, as determined by the dimensions of the source and of the mirror, that succeeds in entering the eye. Hence the quantity of light penetrating the eye increases with increase of curvature of the concave mirror, and this causes the pupil to contract; all the more because in the larger field the macula region is more exposed to the illumination. Now since the total amount of light falling on the retina passes through the pupil, the proportion of the intensity of illumination on the fundus of the eye to the density of the light on the cornea and lens is never favourable when the curvature of the mirror is increased; that is, the diffusely reflected light coming from these media is always a disturbance. The result is that for general use the radius of the mirror should not be less than about 15 cm. Of course, this limit is merely a fact of experience in agreement with the size of the pupil. If the pupil is dilated—as is usually the case in ophthalmological experiments in physiological laboratories and clinics—a more curved mirror may be used without disadvantage. But in practice the curvature mentioned above is found to be rather too high. It should be remarked too, that, owing to the astigmatism produced by reflection at oblique incidence, the size of the field has to be calculated separately in tangential and sagittal directions.

In working with a mirror of this kind, with the ordinary sources of light, usually the field obtained is bright enough and of sufficient size for finding pathological variations, as long as the macula region is not under investigation. The corneal reflex, which for the other parts of the fundus does not hinder seeing, being more central here, is essentially more disturbing; because also the pupil is more contracted by reason of the stronger illumination of the centre of the retina. In many instances, therefore, it is not possible to investigate this region with this mirror without artificial dilatation of the pupil. Frequently the purpose is achieved by not attempting to have a big field and using a *plane mirror* and a small source of light.

The intensity of illumination in the central part of the field, as shown by the formulae given above, does not depend on the form of the mirror, provided the source of light is not so small that $P''_n < P'_n$. But if the latter is the case, the intensity for an emmetropic eye has precisely the same value for either a convex or a concave mirror of same radius. Hence, the common notion that a convex mirror involves weak intensity of light is true only with respect to the quantity of light that enters the eye.

The size of the mirror should be such that the field of the illumination system can be brought by a single rotation around an axis through the hole in the mirror to the farthest edge of the field of the observation system, without the mirror's intercepting the flow of light. For an emmetropic eye this means that the surface of the mirror should extend above and below the hole for a distance equal to the diameter of the pupil; rather more than this towards the temporal side, and somewhat less on the nasal side. With a round mirror therefore a diameter of 20 mm is ample, and should never be exceeded. A smaller diameter would be better, because less superfluous light would fall on the iris. *The size of the hole* with reference to the condition derived above should be made as small as possible with respect to the practical applicability of the mirror, and under no circumstances should be more than 2 mm in diameter. The chief thing is to reduce as much as possible the detrimental space between the illumination system and the observation system. Hence the perforated hole in the glass mirror should be as thin as possible and cylindrical. A dull black surface on the inside of the hole is a matter of very great importance. Even in the best ophthalmoscopes a little reflex image of the source of light originates here, whose blur circle tends to obscure the ophthalmoscopic image. When the black surface is poor, the light from the blur circle may be strong enough to hinder the observation in case of a small pupil. They have tried to avoid this trouble by scratching off the silver from the mirror instead of boring a hole through the glass; and in fact this method reduces the detrimental space to a minimum. But a mirror of this sort has to be kept scrupulously clean on both sides, which takes a lot of time to use it for one thing; and, besides, there are technical difficulties as to its rear side. Quite recently PRIESTLEY SMITH[1] has proposed cementing another glass on the rear side, which makes it easier to keep clean. How such a mirror works with the method of erect image, has not yet been ascertained by practical experience.

Simple ophthalmoscopy with unperforated mirror is of no value as an independent method. Thus since the mirror must be at one side, its edge past which the observer has to look and the visible portion of the edge of the pupil act like windows, by which there is a one-sided shading off of the field. Besides, it amounts to having to look always eccentrically through the pupil where the convergence of the rays is not so good as at the centre. But this method is used all the time in cases where in the ordinary investigation the pupil is so contracted that the condition as to the size of the hole in the mirror is not satisfied. Hence, as has been stated above, the mirror must be decentered and the per-

[1] A new simple ophthalmoscope. *Ophthalmic Rev.*, XXIX. 1910. p. 33.

forated mirror employed, therefore, as if it were not perforated. One advantage of it is that the edge of the mirror may be conveniently adjusted in any direction of the line of sight. This method is very frequently used for investigating the macula region with contracted pupil. We can tell when we are using it, because the movements of the mirror that are needed for it are automatic, on account of the fact that the macula region can be seen in an eccentric part of the blur circle of the hole in the mirror, but not in the central part.

Simple Ophthalmoscopy by the Method of the Inverted Image

If an image of the pupil of the observer is projected by a convex lens in the pupil of the patient's eye, an inverted image of the fundus of the latter eye will be formed between the lens and the observer's eye; and if the fundus is illuminated, the observer, by using his accommodation or with the aid of a suitable lens, can see the image distinctly. The advantage which this method has over that of the erect image is in the possibility of getting a larger field. As this means that more light must be sent in the eye, the unsilvered mirror used with ordinary source of light is not to be considered. For practical reasons, we may likewise leave out of consideration the case of illumination with unperforated, opaque mirror, in which both mirror and light are placed to one side. On the other hand, both of these methods of illumination may be advantageously used in reflex-free ophthalmoscopy, and therefore they will be discussed presently. With illumination by *perforated mirror* there are four apertures in the *observation system,* namely, the lens of the ophthalmoscope, the hole in the mirror and the two pupils. The window-action of the pupil of the observer's eye is to all intents and purposes practically neutralized by the continuous movements of his eye and of the mirror. Hence, this aperture may be left out of account in determining the field, and the hole in the mirror is to be regarded therefore as being the entrance-pupil of the observer's eye. Now if an image of this latter aperture is projected by the lens of the ophthalmoscope in the entrance-pupil of the patient's eye, evidently a part of this pupil will not be covered by the optical image. For as no light leaves the hole in the mirror, its optical image is that of an opaque screen. Therefore, either the image of this hole must be smaller than the pupil of the patient or else it must be decentered with respect to it. The result is that the hole in the mirror must act as a pupil of the observation system. In those ophthalmoscopic methods in which an image of the entrance-pupil of the observer's eye is formed in that of the patient's eye, the symbol K was used to denote the magnification-ratio for this imagery; and, therefore, let the same notation be used here for the imagery of the hole in the mirror. Since the lens of the ophthalmoscope produces an inverted image of this hole, K is negative, and the diameter of the image is $-Kl$, where as above l denotes the diameter of the hole. Moreover, let D_0 denote the refracting power of the lens of the ophthalmoscope and L_0 its diameter; then since the distance between the lens and the entrance-pupil of the patient's eye is equal to $\dfrac{1-K}{D_0}$, the *angular dimensions of the characteristic field* will be given as follows:

$$\tan\frac{v}{2} = \frac{D_0(L_0 - Kl)}{2(1-K)}, \qquad \tan\frac{\omega}{2} = \frac{D_0(L_0 + Kl)}{2(1-K)}.$$

However, Kl being very small as compared with L_0, the shading off of the field as represented by the difference in the values of these two angles is practically of no importance at all; and hence the *aperture angle* ω_0 for the observation system may be defined by the equation:

$$\tan\frac{\omega_0}{2} = \frac{D_0 L_0}{2(1-K)};$$

the aperture itself being given by the number

$$\frac{D_0 L_0}{1-K}.$$

In ophthalmoscopy by the method of the inverted image, the mirror does not have to be inclined to the axis of the correction lens inserted in front of the observer's eye, but the lens is placed close to the back of the mirror. Hence, in calculating the *magnifying power* (p. 362) in the observation system it is sufficiently accurate to consider the hole as being where the lens is. In practical work the entire field cannot always be utilized. Similarly, the hole in the mirror is not invariably imaged in the pupil of the patient's eye; so that the magnifying power will be calculated here for any adjustment whatever. The point in the observer's eye or in the patient's eye that is designated by M is to be regarded as the centre of the hole in the mirror or of the image of this hole made by the lens, respectively. Accordingly,

$$\omega_m = -K\omega_m';$$

and hence substituting the principal point angle, just as was done in case of the erect image, we find:

$$-\frac{\omega_h}{a_0} = KB' \cdot \frac{1+mA}{1+m'A'} = KD'(1 - m_0'A'_m)(1+mA).$$

The *absolute magnifying power*, therefore, for $m' = 0$, as is approximately realized in the ordinary way of working, is equal to KB'; being inversely proportional to the axial length of the patient's eye. Generally, the magnifying power in this case is independent of the accommodation of the observer's eye, provided the change of focusing in the observation system which it causes is not compensated by change of the state of accommodation of the patient's eye, but by a change of the correction lens. Varying the distance m' on the same assumption, the distance of the lens from the observer's eye being kept constant, we find that when the lens is so close to the observer's eye that m' is negative, the magnifying power is greater when the patient's eye is axially hypermetropic than when it is emmetropic, but less when his eye is axially myopic. When the distance between lens and eye is increased, the magnifying power is unaltered for an emmetropic eye, but increases for a myopic eye, and decreases for an hypermetropic eye. When $m'_0 = 0$, the image of the hole in the mirror is at the anterior focal point of the patient's eye, and then the magnifying power is independent of the axial length of his eye, its absolute value being equal to KD'. But if the distance between lens and eye is increased still more, the magnifying power will be greatest in case of a myopic eye, and least in case of an hypermetropic eye.

The reason why these results are different from the prevalent opinion on the subject is that most people are thinking chiefly of the size of the image made by the ophthalmoscopic lens, whereas the real criterion is the angle subtended by this image.

If, when the interval between the lens and the patient's eye is increased, the change of optical focus of the observation system is compensated by change of accommodation of the observer's eye, the variations of magnifying power are qualitatively the same as before; but the point for which the magnifying power is independent of the axial length of the patient's eye has a different position. According to the general law of optical imagery, the condition for seeing the fundus of the eye distinctly is

$$\frac{A_m}{K^2} = \frac{D_{00}}{K} - A'_m,$$

where D_{00} denotes the refracting power of the system composed of the lens of the ophthalmoscope and the correction glass. By means of this equation and the relations formerly given between A and A_m and between A' and A'_m, A can be eliminated from the factor $(1 + mA)$. The resulting expression is fairly complicated; but if, just as in the case of the erect image, the higher powers of the products of the type

mA are neglected, the following *approximate formula* will be obtained by development in series:

$$-\frac{\omega_h}{a_0} = KB'\left\{ 1 + KmD_{00} - (m' + K^2m)A' \right\}$$

$$= KD'\left\{ 1 + KmD_{00} - (m_0' + K^2m)A' \right\}$$

Accordingly, when one and the same correction lens is used, the magnifying power is the same for different axially ametropic eyes, provided the image of the hole in the mirror is situated at a place between the patient's eye and its anterior focal point and at a distance from the latter equal to K^2m. Practically, therefore, this place is not far from the focal point, because K^2 is seldom more than $1/9$.

Suppose the patient's eye is astigmatic, the refractions in the first and second principal sections being denoted by A'_1 and A'_2, respectively; and let K_1 and K_2 be the values of the ratio $\frac{\omega_h}{\omega'_h}$ when the patient's eye is focused for the imageable lines of the primary and secondary systems of imagery, respectively. The following *approximate formula for the astigmatic distortion* is obtained by series-development:

$$\frac{K_1}{K_2} = 1 - (m' + K^2m)(A_1' - A_2').$$

If, in place of either imagery, or in place of both of them, there is an optical projection, the same formulae as in the case of the erect image are similarly obtained; but now m denotes the distance of the image of the centre of projection from the optical centre of the correction lens. But in ophthalmoscopy with inverted image the hole in the mirror is too big to act as centre of projection, and the magnifying power is so slight that even the form of the papilla is recognized with the immobile eye. Since, therefore, the pupil is the centre of projection, in making the calculation with the reduced eye, m has the same value, whether it is a case of an optical image or of an optical projection. It is evident from the approximate formula that the astigmatic distortion when the lens of the ophthalmoscope is far from the patient's eye proceeds in the same way as with the erect image, but when the lens is near the eye, the reverse relation occurs. Practically, the focusing for which there is no astigmatic distortion cannot be distinguished from the adjustment for which the image of the hole in the mirror lies in the pupil of the patient's eye. From the fact that, for $m' = 0$, the absolute magnifying power is independent of the refracting power of the optical system of the patient's eye, it might be inferred that with this focusing there was no astigmatic distortion. But this is not mathematically true, as can be seen by considering what is meant by absolute magnifying power which supposes an emmetropic adjustment of the observer's eye. Hence, for $m' = 0$, the astigmatic distortion would not be abolished, unless the observer used a different correction glass in passing from one imagery to the other, so as to keep the adjustment emmetropic.

In the same way as with erect image and on the same assumption, namely, that the optical centre of the correction lens is at the anterior focal point of the observer's eye, *the magnification-ratio* for the image of the retina of the patient's eye on that of the observer is given by the expression

$$- \frac{KD'}{D}(1 - m_0'A'_m).$$

The intensity of the light in the observation system is obtained from the same formulae as for ophthalmoscopy with erect image, by equating to zero the distance $(m' - d)$ of the hole in the mirror from the correction lens. If the value found for p_n is not less than the diameter of the entrance pupil, the latter must be used instead of p_n.

In *the illumination system* the *condition* $-Kl < p$ *for the size of the hole* has been formulated already. If it is not satisfied, a decentration is necessary, whereby the pupil of the patient's eye is covered only by a part of the image of the hole in the mirror. The only case that will be considered here is that of the centered system for which the illumination system produces at the centre of the pupil of the eye the image of a screen that casts a shadow; so that, as a matter of fact, the aperture under these circumstances is an annular one. The other apertures that have to be taken into account are the lens of the ophthalmoscope and the contour of the source of light; the mirror itself being of such size that it has no influence on the radiation region. As in the investigation of the erect image, let q denote the diameter of the image of the source of light as made by the lens of the ophthalmoscope in the medium in front of the eye; and let c denote its distance from the image of the hole in the mirror, the sign of this distance being reckoned in the same way here as in the previous investigation. Moreover, let K' denote the angular diameter of the source of light as measured at the centre of the hole in the mirror, and put $\frac{q}{c} = K''$. By means of the angular magnification-ratio we get then $K'' = -\frac{K'}{K}$. Provided the effect of the aperture of the lens of the ophthalmoscope is not involved, the same formulae can be used here as in case of the erect image; m' being substituted for d and K'' for K', and the value $-Kl$ being used instead of l. *The condition as to the image of the source of light,* namely,

$$q > -Kl \mid 1+cA \mid ,$$

without which a complete shadow of the hole in the mirror is visible on the ophthalmoscopic image, is in this case absolutely valid for $m' = 0$. When this condition is satisfied, the area of the *useful pupil P_n* is equal to the smaller of the following two expressions:

$$P_n' = \frac{\pi}{4}(p^2 - K^2 l^2), \qquad P_n'' = \frac{\pi}{4} \left\{ \frac{q^2}{(1+cA)^2} - K^2 l^2 \right\} ;$$

and the *angular magnitudes of the characteristic field* are

$$w = \frac{p+q}{c}, \qquad \lambda = \frac{p+q}{c}.$$

If D_s denotes the reflecting power of the mirror and A_s the reduced convergence of the bundle of rays that is incident on it, all that is necessary for determining the best *form of the mirror* for the case when $m' = 0$ is to use the formula:

$$-\frac{K^2}{c} = KD_0 + D_s + A_s,$$

where the desired numerical value of c is substituted first with a positive sign and then with a negative sign, since the value of q is the same in both cases. In this way two values D_{s1} and D_{s2} will be obtained which depend on each other according to the relation:

$$D_{s1} + D_{s2} = -2(KD_0 + A_s).$$

Therefore, supposing that in actual practice the image of the hole in the mirror is always in the pupil of the patient's eye, there would be two equally advantageous forms of mirror to be selected. But since, for reasons to be explained presently, the value of m' is very often negative, the form of mirror to be taken is that one of the two that is most advantageous in this case. In precisely the same way as in ophthalmoscopy with erect image, it follows that, according as m' is positive or negative, a negative or positive value of c, respectively, will be more advantageous for the field of the illumination system. Thus, concave mirrors of such power, that the image of the source of light formed by them falls between the mirror and the focus of the ophthalmoscopic lens, are excluded from being chosen, because $(-KD_0 + A)$ gives the maximum reflecting power of the mirror. With a mirror having this reflecting power, the image of the source of light is thrown on the retina of the emmetropic eye, and there is no shading off of any part of the whole field. However, this latter advantage is usually offset by the fact that none of the available sources of light are of sufficient uniformity of brightness. It is better, therefore, to choose a somewhat larger focal length for the mirror, which will reduce the shaded part of the field, but increase the unshaded part. If in this way the decrease of c were allowed to go on until $q = p$, the unshaded field in the emmetropic eye would be contracted until it vanished entirely. Now since ophthalmoscopy with inverted image is not so much for the purpose of investigating detail as for the purpose of general survey of the image, this behaviour would manifest itself as a decrease of the intensity of light. In order to avoid this dimming of light, the best thing to do is not to reduce the curvature of the mirror any more than is just enough not to detect in the image any lack of uniformity of the source of light, even in the highest degrees of myopia. What this limit is depends on the peculiarity of the source of light and can be ascertained by experiment only. Besides, different investigators prefer different sources of light and different distances; and therefore it is easy to see that radii of curvature between about 60 and 30 cm can be used. Other things being equal, a longer focal length gives a bigger field, but a smaller portion that is unshaded; which gives the impression of less intensity of light. This is clearer still when a plane mirror is used.

By bringing the source of light nearer the mirror and at the same time protecting the patient's eye from the light, it is easy to illuminate the unshaded part of the field of the observation system. However, in practical experience, without artificial dilatation of the pupil, this causes the pupil to contract, and the corneal reflex becomes so annoying that it is better to give up this big field, and to place the source of light near the patient's eye, as in the method with erect image. But then every part of the field of observation can be illuminated by slight movements of the mirror.

The diameter of the hole in the mirror is usually controlled by the magnifying power to be used, and should be so chosen that the condition as to the size of the hole is satisfied in most cases, but it must not be made smaller than this. Since in general it is not advisable to use a stronger magnifying power than $K = -\dfrac{1}{3}$, unless the pupil is artificially dilated, the hole should ordinarily be 4 mm in diameter. This affords the advantage of more intensity of light in the observation system, and usually produces a big enough pupil, when the other eye is closed, for a hole of this size to be used. On the other hand, particularly if a smaller magnifying power in the observation system is sufficient, the condition as to the size of the hole may be satisfied even with very small pupil. But, in general, if a higher magnification is desired, the hole in the mirror must be smaller. The diameter of the mirror should be so great that the image of the pupil of the patient's eye is completely covered by the reflecting surface, and consequently it must be 30 mm at least. Unless this condition is satisfied, part of the light in the illumination system is lost.

In *performing the investigation* we always begin with a shorter distance between the lens and the patient's eye, in order to extend the field of the observation system by increasing this distance. If in this way we have contrived so that none of the edge of the iris is visible, the focusing has practically been found for which the image of the hole in the mirror lies in the pupil of the patient's eye.

However, when the pupil is small this focusing means a steady hand on the part of the observer, together also with a certain docility on the part of the patient, because slight movements of the patient's eye are enough to darken the field entirely, and then the right focus has to be found all over again in the same way as before. For these reasons, beginners especially, and more experienced practitioners too, when the patient is not an easy subject, frequently prefer the less delicate focusing with the lens not so far away, and choose also the more favourable form of mirror mentioned above for which the value of m' is negative. Along with these variations of the distance of the lens of the ophthalmoscope, the distance of the image of the fundus of the patient's eye is likewise altered. This involves a change of focus of the eye to get sufficient magnification of the ophthalmoscopic image. Now in order that this change of focus may not have to be too great, *the refracting power of the lens of the ophthalmoscope* must not be too great. On the other hand, it should not be so small that the hand holding it cannot be supported against the patient's brow. Perhaps, the lower limit demanded by this consideration, which is about 14 dptr, is the best value to use. The lens may have a diameter of 50 mm with advantage.

In numerous instances it is impossible to investigate the macula region by simple ophthalmoscopy. Indeed when the pupil has a minimum size, the method is hardly possible at all. We always get the impression that the real trouble is with the corneal reflex. Before passing to the consideration of ophthalmoscopy without reflexes, let us therefore investigate first the possibility of *abolishing the corneal reflex* only. Obviously, it is only when we have disposed of methods that fulfil this condition that we can decide whether this necessary requirement in the case of ophthalmoscopy without reflexes is likewise sufficient.

The optical system to be studied now is that in which the rays are reflected at the anterior surface of the cornea, and which extends from the medium where the source of light is situated to the entrance-pupil of the observer's eye—the so-called *first catadioptric system*. Supposing it is the case of the ordinary method with *erect* image, the simplest way is to investigate the form of the region of radiation in the medium where the light travels after having been reflected at the mirror and before being reflected at the cornea. For this purpose only two apertures need to be considered, namely, that of the mirror itself and that of the hole in the mirror. The first of these belongs to the medium in question, and the image of the latter in this medium is the image of the hole that is reflected in the cornea. By drawing, therefore, all the straight lines that pass through the aperture of the mirror and through the corneal reflex of the hole, the maximum region of radiation will be constructed for the first catadioptric system in the medium in question. If some other opening, as, for example, the rim of the correction lens or the pupil of the observer's eye should act here as a window, all the effect it would have would be to restrict somewhat this region of radiation. Now it is clear that, in order to abolish the corneal reflex, all that is necessary is to shift the image of the source of light in the mirror outside this region of radiation; for if none of the lines in this region passes through the image of the source of light, no ray lying therein can go through the system and through the hole in the mirror into the observer's eye. When a transparent unperforated mirror is used, the corneal reflex of the pupil of the observer's eye or of the rim of the correction glass (if present) takes the place of the corneal reflex of the hole in the mirror. But there is also another way of getting rid of the corneal reflex with a hole in the mirror. Since this hole casts a shadow, all that we have to do is to adjust the source of light so that the full shadow of the hole covers its reflected image in the cornea. The apex of the umbra is found from the equation

$$\frac{x}{l} = \frac{x+c}{q}.$$

If here x is put equal to the distance of the centre of curvature of the cornea from the hole in the mirror, then for a given value of c the value is found which q cannot exceed if the image of the hole reflected in the cornea is to be inside the umbra. A practical way of making this adjustment is by moving the source of light farther away. Whether the umbra has been extended far enough by this means, can be told by the disappearance of the corneal reflex when the cornea is expressly illuminated for this purpose. We may therefore either see past the corneal reflex or cause it to vanish when it lies right in the way. Although both the field and the intensity are very small, in many cases it is possible in this way to see the small reflex from the fovea, when it is not possible to do so in the ordinary investigation. However, a sufficient intensity can be obtained with the NERNST *slit lamp*, which the writer designed originally for use in ophthalmometry, and which is consequently known also as the ophthalmometric NERNST lamp. It consists of a closed tube, at one end of which the lamp is inserted; a lens-system being used to form an image of the little incandescent filament in a slit at the other end of the tube, so that this illuminated slit is to be regarded as the source of light. With a vertical slit a bright enough image is obtained by this arrangement, and in most cases the macula region can be investigated without dilating the pupil. Of course, the field becomes smaller as the pupil is more contracted; but even when a pupil is contracted by treatment with eserin, it is possible by this method to see a small field in the fovea. When the distance between slit and mirror is too great, the condition as to the size of the image of the source of light is not satisfied; but a central dark spot will be seen in the illuminated field, which moves in conformity with the movements of the mirror. However, by using a concave mirror with a radius of about 15 cm, a slit from 12 to 15 cm away from it, and an angle of incidence of approximately 45°, this spot will usually disappear. The reason why this is so with a source of light almost linear in form is due to the fact that the bundle of rays after being reflected is not only astigmatic, but has a fairly high asymmetry-value. With this adjustment, after refraction of the light into the optical system of the eye, the second focal point falls on the retina or very near it, provided the refraction of the eye is very anomalous; and owing to the asymmetry the width of the bundle of rays at the first focal point is finite. If this investigation is performed with dilated pupil, it constitutes a diagnostical method which is more delicate than any previous method of this sort. The illuminated field here is very bright and large enough to be investigated conveniently. Besides, owing to the abolition of the corneal reflex, the investigator is enabled to use the central part of the pupil of the patient's eye in the observation system; which would otherwise be impossible, because the corneal reflex here compels the observer to make a movement to one side. Hence, in the ordinary investigation of the macula region by the method of erect image, the observer is always forced to use the more unfavourable part of the pupil for the optical imagery in the observation system; whereas with this method of *simple central ophthalmoscopy* the resolving power of the optical system of the eye is essentially greater, thereby permitting much finer details to be perceived.

The only disadvantage of this method of investigation with un-dilated pupil is the small field. In order to get rid of the corneal reflex when it is desired to obtain a larger field with a smaller pupil, an image of the source of light has to be formed near the narrowest part of the region of radiation of the catadioptric system, that is, near the image of the hole reflected in the cornea, or near the pupil of the observer. This is accomplished by combining a suitable aplanatic convex lens with a plane parallel plate of glass and using the NERNST slit lamp as source of light. If the distance of the lens from the plate of glass used as a mirror is correctly measured, an image of the slit may be produced in the pupillary plane of the patient's eye. It is found also that the corneal reflex may be abolished without difficulty by small movements of this ophthalmoscope, and that the size of the illuminated field is quite large; but very little can be seen in this field due to the hindrance of foreign light. It is not hard to understand that the cause of this obscurity is light that is reflected diffusely in the cornea and in the crystalline lens. All that is necessary in order to see this is to separate the eye and mirror a little. This experiment shows that, when more is required with respect to the extent of the field of the illumination system, it is not enough merely to abolish the corneal reflex, but that *the light diffusely reflected in the cornea and in the crystalline lens must be warded off also.*

However, provided we are content to have a smaller field, the following is a very useful method also: A lens of refracting power about 30 dptr and not more than 10 mm in diameter, combined with a plane mirror perforated by a hole 2 mm in diameter, makes a very suitable instrument for investigating the macula without dilating the pupil. With a horizontal slit a concave mirror may also be used, either by itself or in combination with a convex lens, depending on the curvature of the mirror.

Moreover, in the method of *the inverted image,* the corneal reflex may be abolished without difficulty, provided a suitable aplanatic ophthalmoscope-lens is available, such as can be had nowadays. In order to construct the region of radiation of the first catadioptric system in the medium where the light travels before it is reflected at the cornea, the lens of the ophthalmoscope and the image reflected in the cornea must be considered as the apertures; because, after being reflected from the cornea of the patient's eye, the light must pass through the lens of the ophthalmoscope before entering the pupil of the observer's eye as a corneal reflex. The maximum extent of the radiation space includes all the straight lines that can be drawn through these two apertures. Now if the image of the pupil of the patient's eye made by the lens of the ophthalmoscope falls outside this region of radiation, obviously, this maximum region of radiation will be thereby reduced to zero; because, although the light reflected from the cornea may get through the lens of the ophthalmoscope, it cannot enter the pupil of the observer's eye; and therefore not a single ray of light can traverse the system from the first medium to the last. In the practical employment of simple ophthalmoscopy by the method of the inverted image, where an aplanatic ophthalmoscopic lens is used to get rid of the corneal reflex, the observer must be careful to look towards a point near the edge of the lens, so as to prevent the image of the lens as reflected in the cornea from covering the entire pupil. Under these circumstances, provided the lens is held at the right distance from the patient's eye, by simply decentering it slightly towards the line of fixation of the patient's eye, the corneal reflex will be seen to disappear. Now when this experiment is tried with a very small pupil, it is found that the image of the fundus of the eye is obscured again by foreign light; which goes to prove that for considerable extent of the illuminated field the light diffusely reflected in the cornea and crystalline lens has to be excluded when the pupil is small. As the concentration of light in a beam is inversely proportional to the cross section thereof, in general, the diffusely reflected light gets to be more and more important in proportion as the illuminated area of the retina is larger, as compared with the part of the pupil used in the illumination system.

The necessary and sufficient condition for excluding the light diffusely reflected in the cornea and crystalline lens may be most simply formulated by saying, that *no part of the cornea or crystalline lens of the patient's eye shall be at once in the region of radiation of the illumination system and also in that of the observation system.*

If the exclusion of all the light reflected from the patient's eye, including not only that which is regularly reflected from the surfaces of separation of the ocular media but also that which is diffusely reflected in the cornea and crystalline lens, is the absolute requirement for what is called here *ophthalmoscopy without reflex,* this condition is equivalent to that which has just been stated. For if no part of the anterior surface of the cornea on which the light falls is in the region of radiation of the observation system, no ray of light proceeding from the illuminated area of this surface can come into the pupil of the observer's eye. The same thing is true with respect to the other reflecting surfaces, so that as a matter of fact there is no region of radiation in all three catadioptric systems. But if a small portion of the cornea lies in both regions of radiation, all that this may involve is that a narrow peripheral border of the ophthalmoscopic field will appear dim; whereas, when the corneal reflex is not excluded, the whole image may be invisible. Consequently, another condition must be that, when there is a region of radiation, the source of light must be outside it at least in the first catadioptric system, and preferably in all three of these systems. In accordance therewith the writer has formulated the *condition of ophthalmoscopy without reflex*, as follows:

While a part of the fundus of the patient's eye must be situated in the region of radiation of the illumination system and in that of the observation system at the same time, this must not be the case with any portion of the cornea or crystalline lens; and, moreover, in the three catadioptric systems, the source of light must be outside the region of radiation, if there is such a region.

In this statement it is to be noted that the illumination system contains the source of light as one of the apertures, whereas the three catadioptric systems extend in this direction only to the medium of the source of light.

The most advantageous way of realizing this condition in the case of *central ophthalmoscopy without reflex* is shown in the diagram (Fig. 148),

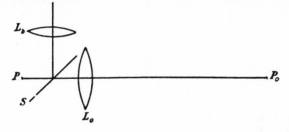

Fig. 148.

where P and P_0 designate the centres of the entrance-pupils of the eyes of patient and observer, respectively, L_0 represents the lens of the ophthalmoscope, and L_b a lens belonging to the illumination system, and S indicates a thin parallel plate of glass inclined at an angle of 45°. The two points P and P_0 are a pair of conjugate axial points with respect to the lens L_0. First, it must be shown how this arrangement can satisfy the conditions of absence of reflex. To begin with the first catadioptric system, disregarding the pupil of the patient's eye, suppose that the maximum region of radiation of this system is constructed in the medium of the source of light. As there are only two apertures in this region of radiation, namely, the openings of the two lenses, and since the opening of lens L_b already lies in the medium of the source of light, all that remains to be done is to find the image of the opening of the lens L_0 for which the light goes first through the transparent mirror S and is reflected then from the cornea and from this mirror in succession, so as to pass finally through the lens L_b. The image of the lens L_0 as thus found will represent the smallest cross section of the region of radiation of the first catadioptric system. It is situated in the vicinity of the image of the pupil of the patient's eye which is made by the lens L_b. If this pupil is dilated as much as possible, there will be place enough here for a source of light, which will be therefore inside the maximum region of radiation of the illumination system as determined by the pupil of the patient's eye and the lens L_b, but which will lie outside the region of radiation of the first catadioptric system. The region of radiation of the third catadioptric system is found in the same way; whereas for investigating the second catadioptric system it is better to take into account the pupil of the patient's eye, from the start. Since its image is to be formed at the centre of the pupil of the patient's eye, the same is true also with respect to the images of the two pupils made by the lens L_b in the medium of the source of light; the image first mentioned being situated on the anterior surface of the lens and consequently coinciding with the image reflected in this surface. Actual calculation[1] based on the exact schematic eye gives the following result:—Take the refracting power of each of the two lenses to be 14 dptr, and the diameter of each to be 50 mm. Consider the mirror S as being at first infinitely thin, and suppose that the lenses are combined with it in such fashion that one of the lenses is the image of the other as reflected in the mirror. Moreover, assume that the diameters of the entrance-pupils of the eyes of both patient and observer are 6 mm, and that an image of the observer's pupil, reduced one-third in size, is formed in the patient's pupil. Then provided a central portion in the plane of the entrance-pupil of the patient's eye about 2.4 mm in diameter is shielded from the light, *no light regularly reflected from the three reflecting surfaces of the eye* will enter the pupil of the observer's eye. In the region of the radiation of the first and third catadioptric systems the pupil of the observer's eye was not taken into account; hence, in general, light regularly reflected from the cornea and from the posterior surface of the crystalline lens will not arrive at the lens L_0.

But in order also to keep *the light that is diffusely reflected* by the cornea and the crystalline lens far from the image in the ophthalmoscope, the place must be essentially restricted where the image of the source of light is formed in the entrance-pupil of the patient's eye. For this purpose the regions of radiation of the observation system and the illumination system, both of which are contracted in the patient's eye, need to be separated so far apart from each other, that

[1] Die reflexlose Ophthalmoskopie. *Arch. f. Augenheilk.* LXVIII, S. 101, 1911.

a point either on the posterior surface of the crystalline lens or on the anterior surface of the cornea will be in the free space between the two regions of radiation. The best way to see this is by constructing these regions of radiation in the medium lying between the mirror S and the cornea. If the patient's eye is emmetropic, and the illuminated portion of the fundus is entirely within the visible field of the ophthalmoscope, the boundary lines of the section of these regions of radiation made by a meridian plane, four for each region, are parallel to each other, as shown in Fig. 149. P'_0 is the image of the pupil of

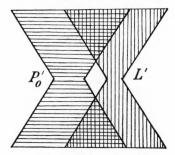

Fig. 149.

the observer's eye, and its centre is at the centre of the entrance-pupil of the patient's eye; while L' represents a small image of the source of light lying in the outer part of this pupil. The radiation regions of the observation system and the illumination system are indicated by horizontal and vertical lines, respectively. It is immediately obvious that the condition stated above, namely, that no portion of the cornea or of the crystalline lens may be at the same time within the regions of radiation of both systems, amounts to saying that both the anterior surface of the cornea and the aerial image of the posterior surface of the crystalline lens must intersect the free rhombic section. Now the distance of the vertex of the cornea is about 3 mm, and that of the aerial image of the posterior vertex of the crystalline lens about 4 mm. from the aerial image of the anterior vertex of the crystalline lens, In calculating the region of radiation of the catadioptric system, supposing also that the entrance-pupil is considered as being at the aerial image of the anterior pole of the crystalline lens, it may easily be shown, on the other hand, that a displacement backwards amounting to 0.5 mm, which is not far from what actually occurs with dilated pupil, will have no perceptible effect on the region of radiation. If the angle at the vertex of the unshaded rhombic figure in the diagram is denoted by ω, and if the width (in mm) of the open space between the two regions P'_0 and L' is denoted by a, all that is required in order to keep the light that is diffusely reflected in the ocular media far away from the image in the ophthalmoscope is to satisfy the condition

$$\tan\frac{\omega}{2}=\frac{a}{7}.$$

In central ophthalmoscopy without reflex it is always possible to use stops to cut out the portions of the fields of the illumination system and observation system that are shaded (*vignettierten*) and to make the two fields overlap each other. Consequently, with suitable instruments the angle ω as determined by the equation above is the same as the angle previously denoted by this symbol, which gives the characteristic angular dimensions of the unshaded field in the observation system, and which therefore may be called the *aperture angle* of an instrument of this kind.

If the width of the space available for the image of the source of light is supposed to be not more than 1 mm, the value of a for a wide open pupil is 2 mm, which means that $\omega = 31°50'$. Thus, under favourable circumstances, in central ophthalmscopy without reflex, we can get an unshaded field, free from obscurity, of from 5 to 6 times the diameter of the papilla, although the diameters of the two lenses would have to be a little larger than they were in the calculation mentioned above.

Since the intensity of illumination on the fundus of the patient's eye is directly proportional to the area of the image of the source of light and to the specific intensity of the light, besides sunlight and electric arclight, the light of the NERNST slit lamp is the only light that can be employed for the small space that is necessary for the image of the source of light.

For the purpose of obtaining higher magnification in the observation system, a stop acting as entrance-pupil of an instrument on the order of an astronomical telescope and having its image in the entrance-pupil of the observer's eye at the point P_0 may take the place of the latter. In this case, according to the definition previously given, K will denote the magnification-ratio with respect to the entrance-pupil of the observer's eye and its image lying in the plane of the entrance-pupil of the patient's eye; and $\omega_h = -K\omega_h'$, where K is positive in sign, meaning therefore that the image in the ophthalmoscope itself is erect. In order to have sufficient brightness with more magnification, the field, which anyhow should not be excessive, may be curtailed, so as to get more space for the image of the source of light and for the image of the entrance-pupil of the telescopic lens in the entrance-pupil of the patient's eye. The diameter of this latter lens may be as much as 10 mm, and, by proper choice of the refracting power and position of the lens L_b, the magnification of the image of the source of light may be increased also at the same time.

An indispensable requirement in all cases is that the images of the stop of the observation system and source of light in the entrance-pupil of the patient's eye shall be sufficiently free from aberrations. This has been achieved in the new *aplanatic ophthalmoscope lenses* as calculated from the writer's data by Dr. v. ROHR and manufactured by ZEISS; the aplanatism being obtained by using an aspherical surface.

It would take too much space to describe the construction in detail and to explain how it is necessary to prevent any bad effect from light that goes through the mirror S without being reflected. Experience shows that with an aperture-angle of 20°, giving therefore a field 3 or 4 times the diameter of the papilla, a magnification can be used of $K = 2$; so that with the larger image correspondingly more detail is visible, whereas previously it was impossible to gain anything with a magnification higher than that of the ordinary erect image. Apparently this is not the limit of the available magnification, but it is probably not more than $K = 3$.

The writer is confident, from certain special experiments, that by using more extended sources of light there is use for the *perforated opaque mirror* in central ophthalmoscopy. But owing to the unavoidable shading off of the field this method is essentially inferior to that with the unsilvered mirror; and hence it will not be discussed more particularly.

Eccentrical (or "acentral") *ophthalmoscopy without reflex*, where there is no longer any attempt to produce an image of the pupil of the observer's eye or of the special stop of the observation system at the centre of the entrance-pupil of the patient's eye, may be easily realized by increasing the distance a; as follows from the foregoing investigation. Thus, in general, a field is obtained that is relatively larger in comparison with the size of the pupil; and this advantage is useful in two ways, namely, either for obtaining *large ophthalmoscopic images for comprehensive survey*, or as affording a method of *ophthalmoscopy without reflex for case of small pupil*. However, a simpler method, to be described below, can be used with advantage for both of these purposes.

If an *opaque* mirror is used for eccentrical ophthalmoscopy without reflex, it is best to adjust it to one side, and not to perforate it. With this arrangement it is easy to fulfil the condition of freedom from reflex, because the mirror, which acts in the illumination system as a stop and in the observation system as a screen, to a certain extent automatically separates the two regions of radiation. This method has been worked out with much success by DIMMER[1] in *photographing the fundus of the eye;* and is used likewise in THORNER's[2] stationary ophthalmoscope. In both methods an image of a stop in the observation system is formed in the entrance-pupil of the patient's eye. But whereas in the first method an image of the source of light is formed in the other part of this pupil, in the latter method there is at this place an image of a stop that belongs to the illumination system. In DIMMER's method the distance *a* is large enough to shut off also the diffusely reflected light, but this does not seem to be the case with THORNER's ophthalmoscope, so far as the crystalline lens is concerned. However, here this light is not so harmful, because the part of the pupil affected by the illumination system is comparatively large. In WOLFF's[3] method of ophthalmoscopy without reflex there is no image of a stop in the observation system in the pupil of the patient's eye, and the observation system is separated from the illumination system by the screening of the mirror. By their methods also both THORNER and WOLFF have made photographs of the fundus of the eye. WOLFF's electrical ophthalmoscope is intended for clinical use and is employed for investigating with the ordinary erect image, but it has the disadvantage of requiring the pupil to have a certain diameter.

All methods of ophthalmoscopy without reflex in which an opaque mirror is adjusted to one side give a one-sided shading off of the field, and are disadvantageous in this way.

In THORNER's[4] latest method of ophthalmoscopy without reflex, he employs a means of simple ophthalmoscopy which is due orginally to SCHULTÉN,[5] and in which the lens of the ophthalmoscope is replaced by a concave mirror belonging to both the observation system and the illumination system. Here only a small source of light is needed, with its image in the mirror formed near the entrance-pupil of the eye or of the telescopic lens, in order to fulfil the conditions of ophthalmoscopy without reflex. Besides some inconveniences of a technical nature, the disadvantages of the method, such as astigmatism and lack of symmetry in the bundle of rays used in the imagery, are due to the unavoidable obliquity of the mirror. A glass mirror silvered on the back gives double images, the fainter one perhaps being comparatively

[1] FR. DIMMER, *Die Photographie des Augenhintergrundes.* Wiesbaden 1907.

[2] W. THORNER, *Die Theorie des Augenspiegels und die Photographie des Augenhintergrundes.* Berlin 1903.

[3] H. WOLFF, Zur Photographie des menschlichen Augenhintergrundes. *Arch. f. Augenheilkunde.* LIX. S. 115. 1908.

[4] W. THORNER, Ein reflexloser Handaugenspiegel. *Zft. f. Augenheilkunde.* XXVI. S. 1. 1910.

[5] SCHULTÉN, Beobachtungen des Augenhintergrundes bei hochgradiger Vergrösserung. *Arch. f. Anat. u. Physiol.* 1883. S. 285.

harmless usually, and yet for certain effects necessarily in the way; and other mirrors are too delicate to be used in practical ophthalmoscopy.

Stereoscopic ophthalmoscopy without reflex occupies an intermediate place between central and eccentrical (or acentral) ophthalmoscopy; because in order to obtain the maximum stereoscopic effect, the images of the two stops of the observation systems must be close to the ends of a diameter of the entrance-pupil of the patient's eye; which means that the axis of symmetry of the two systems shall be centrally situated. If these stops are the entrance-pupils of two telescopic lenses, and if their images are formed in the entrance-pupils of the two eyes of the observer, the condition of correct stereoscopic effect is, that the magnification-ratio for this imagery of the distance between the eyes shall have the same sign, as for the imagery of the pupils. Hence, the astronomical telescope cannot be used, but the telescopic lenses must be made on the order of the terrestrial or prism telescope, in which the image of the fundus as presented to the eyes is inverted. The image of the slit may be vertical and midway between the images of the two stops, or horizontal and above or below these images. Assuming that the magnification-ratio for the images of the entrance-pupils of the telescopic lenses in the entrance-pupil of the patient's eye is $-1/3$, it is advisable to take the distance between the centres of the stops at 16 mm, the diameter of each stop being 6 mm. The distance might perhaps be made greater, but then the instrument could be used only for a pupil of maximum size. On the other hand, there is not much advantage in getting a greater stereoscopic effect than can be obtained in this way. The magnification $K = -1$ may be used with advantage.

THORNER's stationary ophthalmoscope mentioned above was used also for stereoscopic ophthalmoscopy, by halving again the half of the pupil intended for the observation system. Aside from other drawbacks of this method, the maximum stereoscopic effect is not obtained in this arrangement.

The apparatus for ophthalmoscopy without reflex is fairly elaborate, due principally to the separation of the observation system from the illumination system, which is necessary in order to avoid the reflex images in the lens of the ophthalmoscope. But if these reflex images can be tolerated, the apparatus can be essentially simplified. As a matter of fact, with a small source of light, these images are not very much in the way. Besides, as distinguished from the images reflected at the surfaces of the ocular media, they can be made to fall in front of any part of the fundus of the patient's eye. Thus, provided the magnification is not excessive, the advantages of ophthalmoscopy without reflex can be obtained in this way. Consequently, those methods in which the condition of ophthalmoscopy without reflex as formulated above is fulfilled, although reflections of light are tolerated in the lens of the ophthalmoscope, may be called the methods of *simplified ophthalmoscopy without reflex*. If it is simply a question of magnification of the ordinary inverted image, nothing more is needed in a method of this kind than the aplanatic lens of the ophthalmoscope and the author's *electric hand-ophthalmoscope*, in which the image of the filament of an incandescent lamp is produced in a slit near the ophthalmoscope hole containing the necessary correction lens and at a variable distance from it; the illumination tube with the source of light being far enough away to protect the observer's vision from being injured by the heat. In using this mirror with the technique of the ordinary inverted image, it is best to start with undilated pupil and a distance of from 4 to 5 mm between slit and hole, looking a little to the nasal side in order to see macula and papilla at the same time. When, with pupil undilated, the macula is in the field of the ophthalmoscope, the hole should always be between the visual axis of the patient's eye and the slit; for which purpose the illumination tube can be rotated about the optical axis of the correction lens. The lens of the ophthalmoscope with its most curved surface towards the observer is held at first right in front of the patient's eye, in which case reddish light is visible on the temporal edge of the pupil. If this should not be so, either the distance between the lens of the ophthalmoscope and the eye of the observer is to be increased, or the distance between hole and slit diminished. The reddish light being kept steadily in view, and pains being taken to see that the two small images reflected in the lens are as nearly as possible in line with each other, the distance between the lens and the patient's eye is then increased. At the right distance the field is fully illuminated and free from reflex, provided the lens is moved in the nasal direction as far as possible with fully illuminated field. If any obscurity should appear, it is a sign that the distance *a* has been made too short. If owing to the smallness of the pupil it cannot be increased, often the unobscured part of the field can be used without further adjustment. Obviously, the light that obscures the macula region of the image originates in the cornea, while the region of the papilla gets the light that is diffusely reflected in the crystalline lens. Now the distance of the lens of the ophthalmoscope can be varied in both directions, within certain limits, without danger of introducing regularly reflected light. Hence, unless the pupil is abnormally small, the region of the macula can be seen free from obscurity by increasing the distance a little between the lens and the patient's eye; and the region of the papilla in the same way by slightly diminishing this distance. But with the smallest pupil the field is necessarily limited.

However, since the source of light is to one side, this contraction of the field does not have to take place concentrically; but a rectangular stop can be used in conjunction with the lens of the ophthalmoscope, which contracts the field, about one-third on the average, in the direction at right angles to the linear extent of the source of light, without producing any contraction parallel to it. In this way, with a pupillary diameter as small as 2 mm, and with a magnification $K = -1/3$, an aperture angle of 30° may be utilized; giving therefore a visible field free from obscurity that is at least 5 times the diameter of the papilla. And if the aperture angle is reduced by the rectangular stop to one-third the size in one direction, the macula can still be investigated; in fact even when the pupil is contracted by treatment with eserin, although not without difficulty. However, as a rule, one should never try to see the macula in the centre of the field, with undilated pupil. For the condition of cutting off the light that is reflected regularly at the cornea is that the image of the source of light shall be inside the entrance-pupil of the patient's eye, but outside the image of the lens of the ophthalmoscope as reflected in the cornea; which cannot be achieved with small pupil and central direction of sight.

In order with dilated pupil to obtain a larger image for inspection by this method, all that is necessary is to increase the diameter of the lens of the ophthalmoscope without altering its refracting power. How far we can go in this way cannot be determined in advance, owing to technical considerations. With such lenses as have been manufactured already, a field about 7 times the diameter of the papilla has been obtained.

The simplified method of ophthalmoscopy without reflex is well adapted for *demonstration ophthalmoscopes*. All that is necessary for this purpose is to fasten the ophthalmoscope and the lens on a stand, the field being adjusted to another stand, which is so arranged that the image of the slit is formed in the proper part of the pupil, according to the rules given above. But when a stand is used, the advantages of this arrangement should be utilized, by substituting in place of the hole in the mirror, which acts always as a window-opening (*Luke*), the entrance-pupil of a telescopic lens whose exit-pupil is in the entrance-pupil of the observer's eye. Moreover, in order to be able to increase the magnification, it is a good plan to substitute the NERNST lamp for the little incandescent lamp; either the slit being adjusted in similar fashion to the arrangement in the electrical hand ophthalmoscope, or a virtual image of it near the entrance-pupil of the telescopic lens being produced with a transparent mirror. When the NERNST lamp is used, particularly in the first way, a magnification of $K = 1$ is a convenient value, with no risk of getting any disturbing effects from reflexes in the lens. Whether in central ophthalmoscopy by this method even higher magnifications may not be preferable, cannot be stated in advance; as the reflexes are more troublesome with increase of magnification. On the other hand, this method requires less expensive apparatus than the one described above.

Stereoscopic ophthalmoscopy may also be advantageously used in the simplified method without reflex; and with a stationary instrument the magnification may be as much as $K = 1$. With somewhat lower magnification a suitable binocular telescopic lens can be used without a stand, in combination with the illumination tube of the author's electrical ophthalmoscope and the aplanatic lens. By suitable alteration Giraud-Teulon's[1] binocular ophthalmoscope, which in its original form was hardly adapted for stereoscopy, may also be converted into a practically very useful instrument with illumination tube and the aplanatic lens of the ophthalmoscope. Fraenkel's[2] modification of it lacks only the illumination tube and the proper lens. However, the principle employed by Giraud-Teulon, of bringing the two visual axes close to each other by double reflection, can never be free from window-action, and therefore a binocular telescopic lens is always preferable.

[1] Described in Vol. III.

[2] Fr. Fraenkel, Demonstration eines binokularen Augenspiegels. *Ber. über d. 36. Vers. d. Ophth. Ges. Heildelberg* 1910. S. 314.

Helmholtz's Treatise

on

PHYSIOLOGICAL OPTICS

Translated from the Third German Edition

Edited by

James P. C. Southall

Formerly Professor of Physics in Columbia University

Volume II

Handbuch

der

Physiologischen Optik

von

H. von Helmholtz.

Dritte Auflage

ergänzt und herausgegeben in Gemeinschaft mit

Prof. Dr. A. Gullstrand und **Prof. Dr. J. von Kries**
Upsala Freiburg

von

Professor Dr. W. Nagel (†)
Rostock

Zweiter Band

Mit 80 Abbildungen im Text und 3 Tafeln

Die Lehre von den Gesichtsempfindungen

herausgegeben von Prof. Dr. **W. Nagel** und Prof. Dr. **J. v. Kries**

Hamburg und Leipzig

Verlag von Leopold Voss

1911.

Table of Contents of Volume II

Appendix by W. Nagel

Adaptation, Twilight Vision, and the Duplicity Theory

Appendix by v. Kries

EDITOR'S NOTE

The new material in this volume comprises three Notes specially prepared for the English translation by Professor v. KRIES, a chapter at the end contributed by Dr. CHRISTINE LADD-FRANKLIN, and a partial bibliography of works relating to the sensations of vision, which have appeared in the interval since the publication of the third German edition. A Table of Corrigenda for Volume I has been appended. The coloured plates for this edition were made in Germany.

As stated in the Preface, in the preparation of Part II of this work, the Editor has received much assistance from Professors HENRY LAURENS (§§17, 18, 18A and Appendices of W. NAGEL and v. KRIES), M. DRESBACH (§§22, 23, 24 and 25), and L. T. TROLAND and E. J. WALL (§§19, 20, and 21). Miss TOWNSEND and Mr. TRELEAVEN have aided him in reading the proof.

JAMES P. C. SOUTHALL

Department of Physics,
Columbia University,
New York, N.Y.
October 1, 1924.

PART SECOND

The Theory of the Sensations of Vision

§17. Stimulation of the Organ of Vision

The nervous system of the body is acted on by external agents of various kinds, which produce changes in the state of the nerves. These changes may sometimes be detected by auxiliary apparatus, for example, by studying the electrical reactions; but they are also manifested by their actions on other parts of the body with which the nerves are connected. The change of state of the so-called *motor nerves* is accompanied by contractions of corresponding muscles. Under the same circumstances, other nerves, known as *sensory nerves*, excite sensations in the brain which is the organ of consciousness of the body. Now in the case of the motor nerves, no matter how diverse the external action may be—tearing, crushing, cutting, burning, eroding, shocking by electricity,—the invariable result is the contraction of the corresponding muscle, the only difference being one of degree. Therefore, apart from their qualitative differences, these various influences, so far as their relation to the motor nerves are concerned, are called *stimuli*. Quantitatively, we speak of a stimulus as being strong or weak according to the amount of twitching that is produced. The resulting alteration of the state of the nerve due to a stimulus is called *stimulation* or excitation. Similarly, the ability of the stimulated nerve to make the muscle contract is known as its *excitability*. The latter is affected by mortification and by external influences of many kinds.

The sensory nerves may be analyzed in the same way. External agencies, which acting on a motor nerve would cause contraction of the muscle, have another peculiar sort of effect on a sensory nerve and give rise to a sensation, provided the nerve is alive and not disconnected with the brain. But there is undoubtedly an essential difference here, because there are qualitative differences in the sensation corresponding to qualitative differences in the stimulus. But although different stimuli cause different sensations, still their effects are invariably sensations, that is, invariably actions of a kind that do not occur otherwise and are peculiar to the living body. Accordingly, the abstract conception of stimuli and stimulation as used first with reference to the motor nerves has been transferred likewise to the sensory nerves. Thus, the external agencies which acting on the sensory nerves excite sensations are also called *stimuli*, and the change itself that takes place in the nerve is said to be a *stimulation*.

The state of stimulation that may originate at any part of a nerve fibre through the action of stimuli is always conducted to all other parts of the nerve fibre. This is manifested partly by a difference in the electrical actions and also by its effect on other organic structures (muscles, brain, glands, etc.) with which the nerve is connected. What occurs is a contraction of the muscle, or a sensation, or increased glandular secretion, etc. Conduction of the stimulation is never impeded unless the nervous structure has been seriously damaged by mechanical or chemical actions or by coagulation of the nervous tissue in death. Thus, an uninjured nerve fibre possesses not only *excitability* or the capacity of being stimulated everywhere, but *conductivity* also. A separation of these two characteristics has not yet been conclusively demonstrated.[1] Moreover, thus far there are no known differences in the structure and function of the sensory and motor fibres, that might not be attributed to differences in their connection with other organic systems. The fibres themselves seem to be indifferent and to have no other office except to be conductors; transmitting the stimulation either to a muscle, in which case they are motor nerves, or to the sensitive parts of the brain, in which case they are sensory nerves.

According to their quality human sensations fall into five groups corresponding to the so-called *five senses*. The qualities of the sensations cannot be compared with each other unless they belong to the same group. For example, we can compare two different sensations of the sense of sight as to intensity and colour, but we cannot compare either of them with a sound or a smell.

As far as it has been possible to test it, physiological experience shows that *the only sensations that can be produced by stimulation of a single sensory nerve fibre are such as belong in the group of qualities of a single definite sense;* and that *every stimulus which is capable of exciting this nerve fibre at all arouses sensations of this particular sense.* A complete experimental proof of the statement is not possible except with nerve fibres that are collected together in special stems separate from all fibres of the other senses, as in the *nervus opticus* of the sense of sight, in the *nervus acusticus* of the sense of hearing, in the *nervus olfactorius* of the sense of smell, and in the posterior spinal roots of the sense of touch. If different kinds of stimuli act on these nerves different sensations arise, but the sensations are always such as belong to the group of qualities of that particular sense. On the other hand, in the case of fibres that run along the same nerve with those of another quality (for example, gustatory fibres mixed with tactile in

---

[1] ¶See E. D. ADRIAN, Conduction in peripheral nerve and in the central nervous system. *Brain,* **41,** (1918), 23–47. Idem, The recovery process of excitable tissues. *Jour. Physiol.,* **54,** 1920, 1–31; **55,** 1921, 193–225.—R. S. LILLIE, Transmission of physiological influence in protoplasmic systems, especially nerve. *Physiol. Rev.,* **2,** (1922), 1–37.—K. LUCAS. *The conduction of the nervous impulse* (London and New York, 1917). (H. L.)

the tongue in the *nervus glossopharyngeus* and *nervus lingualis*) there is at least a probability of the same sort of thing, since we find that in morbid conditions there is sometimes an isolated paralysis of the gustatory sensations alone without paralysis of the tactile sensations, or *vice versa*; and because also no other tactile nerves have the faculty of exciting gustatory sensations.

Light sensations belong to the *sense of sight*. They can all be compared as to intensity and colour. That part of the nervous system where sensations of this nature can be excited is what J. MÜLLER called the *visual substance*, or, as it is also sometimes called, the *nervous mechanism of vision*. It comprises the retina, the optic nerve, and a part of the brain that is still not exactly defined where the radical fibres of the optic nerve lie. No other nervous mechanism in the body can produce a sensation of light, that is, a sensation of the same quality as that of the mechanism of vision, although the vibrations of the luminiferous aether may also be perceived by the tactile nerves. However the quality of the sensation of radiant heat is entirely different from the sensation of light. It is the same way with aerial vibrations which the auditory nerve perceives as sound, whereas at the same time they excite in the skin a tactile sensation of buzzing. Similarly, vinegar tastes sour on the tongue; but smarts when it touches a raw place on the skin or a delicate mucous membrane like the conjunctiva of the eye.

On the other hand, there are many other kinds of stimuli besides the vibrations of the luminiferous aether which may excite the organ of vision. Mechanical forces and electrical currents possess the power of stimulating all the nervous mechanisms of the body. But when these stimuli act on the optic nerve, they always excite sensations of vision, and never any other kinds of sensation like that of sound or of smell. If at the same time they excite tactile sensations, we must suppose that this is because there are likewise special tactile nerves in the eye and perhaps even in the optic nerve itself (as in all internal parts of the body). These tactile sensations due to pressure on the eye or electrical action are distinct from the simultaneous sensation of light in still another way also; because whereas the former are perceived at the place of the stimulation, the latter are misconstrued as bright objects in the field of view. This question will be considered again in connection with a more detailed description of the mechanical stimulation of the eye.[1]

----

[1] ¶A stimulus that can arouse a specific sensation is commonly said to be "adequate" or "inadequate," according as it does or does not excite the sensation under ordinary circumstances. Thus, for instance, objective light is an adequate stimulus for the eye, but pressure on the eyeball is an inadequate one. (J. P. C. S.)

As all the other organs of sense behave similarly, it may be said that the nature of a sensation depends primarily on the peculiar characteristics of the (receptor) nervous mechanism; the characteristics of the perceived object being only a secondary consideration. A sensation must belong to the group of qualities associated with a certain one of the senses; but what particular sense this is, does not depend at all on the external object, but simply on the nature of the nerve that is stimulated. But the quality of the sensation that is aroused does depend on the nature of the external object that excites it. Whether the sun's rays will be perceived as light or heat, is simply a question of whether they are perceived by the optic nerve or by the cutaneous nerves. But whether they will be perceived as light that is red or blue, and dim or bright, or as heat that is mild or intense, depends both on the nature of the radiation and on the condition of the nerve. The quality of the sensation is thus in no way identical with the quality of the object by which it is aroused. Physically, it is merely an *effect* of the external quality on a particular nervous apparatus. The quality of the sensation is, so to speak, merely a *symbol* for our imagination, a sort of earmark of objective quality.

The first and most important means of stimulating the optic nerve is by *objective light*; because this stimulus acts on the optic nerve far more frequently and continuously than any others. Thus the chief method of perception of external objects is through sensations of the visual mechanism that are aroused by objective light. Accordingly it is not necessary to assume a particular, specific relation or homogeneity between the objective light and the nervous agency of the optic nerve, as was generally supposed by earlier philosophers and physiologists. For the optic nerve is not the only nerve that may be stimulated by objective light (because this is true also of the skin nerves), nor is objective light the only stimulus for the optic nerve. The reason why it is the most common, and therefore the most important, is simply because the optic nerve and the retina are so situated at the back of the eye that while it is easy for light to penetrate to them, they are much more inaccessible to mechanical and electrical actions. This excessive frequency and importance of stimulation by objective light led people to give the name *light* to those aetherial vibrations that are capable of exciting the sensation of light. Properly speaking, the word should be used only in this latter sense, that is, to denote the sensation that is produced by this means. Solar radiation includes *"sunlight"* and *"sunheat,"* depending on the different sensations it excites. As long as man did not ponder over the nature of his sensations, it was natural for him to transfer the qualities of his sensations directly to the external objects, and so to suppose that the rays of the sun were of two kinds corresponding to his two sensations. Besides, at first he knew nothing about the solar radiations except what his sensations told him. He noticed that some radiations, which, like the rays of the sun, contain a preponderance of waves of higher frequencies, affect the eye much more than they do the skin; while others, containing a preponderance of waves of lower frequencies, act on the skin but hardly affect the eye at all. Naturally, the two agencies were considered as objectively separate. In very recent years careful investigation of the phenomena of radiation with respect to their properties that are independent of the nervous mechanism, has shown that the only difference between the so-called light rays and heat rays is in the frequency of the vibrations. And thus in this instance at least physics has succeeded in freeing itself from entanglement with the subjective sensations that were so long confused with the objective causes. The detailed description of objective light as a means of stimulation of the retina will be given in the next chapter.

The phenomena resulting from *mechanical stimulation* of the organ of vision differ according to the extent of the stimulus. In case of a sudden blow on the eye there is a sensation of light which appears and disappears with lightning speed, and which may be very bright and extend over the entire visual field. As opposed to old-fashioned incorrect views of this phenomenon, it may be pointed out here that when this happens in the dark, no trace of light in the injured eye can be seen by another person; no matter how strong the subjective flash may be. And it is impossible to discern any real object in the outside world by virtue of this subjective illumination of the dark field.[1]

The effect of local pressure is easier to investigate. If somewhere at the edge of the orbit a blunt point, like the finger nail, for example, is pressed against the eyeball, it produces a luminous effect, or so-called *pressure-image* or *phosphene*. It is seen in that part of the field that corresponds to the place affected on the retina. Thus when the pressure is exerted from above, the bright spot appears on the lower edge of the field; and when it is exerted at the external angle of the eye, it appears to be on the nasal side of the field. Similarly, when the pressure is exerted from below or at the inner angle, the light seems to be above or on the outside part of the field, respectively. If the object that exerts the pressure is not large, the phenomenon usually has a bright centre surrounded by a dark ring and by an outer bright one. To the

[1] Concerning a legal action in which it was alleged that a man standing at a window received a blow on the eye, and was able to recognize his assailant in the glow of light that was caused thereby, see J. MÜLLER, *Arch. f. Anat.*, 1834, page 140.

writer it is brightest when the pressure is exerted at or near the equator of the eye where the sclerotica is thinnest. The pressure-image appears then on the edge of the dark visual field as a bright arc, nearly semi-circular in form. Under these conditions it is quite far from the point of fixation, that is, from the place in the field corresponding to foveal vision. It coincides, therefore, with the region where objects lie that are not seen distinctly when the eyes are open. However, with some practice in indirect vision, particularly when conspicuous bright objects happen to be at the apparent place of the pressure-image, it is possible to notice that figures in the vicinity of the pressure-image are distorted, due to the curved hollow form of the sclerotica and retina. Often too they are dark in spots. But the pressure-image can be brought nearer the point of fixation by turning the eye far inwards and at the same time pressing on it from the outside; or *vice versa*. The image then is somewhat fainter, because the posterior surface of the sclerotica offers more resistance to pressure. Certain individuals are able to bring the pressure-image to the place of direct vision simply by pressing at the outer angle. THOMAS YOUNG could do this; and although the writer cannot quite succeed at it, the pressure-image comes so near the point of fixation that images of external objects disappear at its centre. The pressure-image is represented in Fig. 1 of Plate I as it looks to the author when a sheet of white paper is placed against the face between the eye and nose, the eye turned inwards as far as possible, and pressure exerted with a blunt instrument on the outer edge of the orbit. The nasal side is at N, and the image consists of a dark spot traversed by a bright vertical band. When the pressure is exerted at the right level, there is a horizontal continuation of the dark spot, the tip of which reaches the point of fixation at a. Moreover, somewhere near the place where the optic nerve enters there is an indistinct shadow b. How the place where the optic nerve enters the eye may be recognized in the field of view, will be explained in §18. PURKINJE observed and depicted a system of fine parallel curved lines extending between the dark pressure-image and the point of fixation. The author sees them best (but not in the way they are represented in PURKINJE's drawing) when the corresponding place in the field of view is very bright.

On the other hand, in the dark visual field there is a bright yellowish circular area within which there is sometimes a dark spot or a dark ring. A dim light is also seen at the entrance of the optic nerve, so that the appearance is similar to that shown in Fig. 1, Plate I, provided the light and dark portions of the drawing are supposed to be transposed. But the author has not been able to detect in the dark field the continuation extending towards the yellow spot.

The phenomena are again different when a moderate uniform pressure is exerted on the eyeball for a longer space of time; for example, by pressing it from in front either with the soft part of the hand or by the tips of the fingers of one hand. In a short space very brilliant and variable luminous patterns will appear in the visual field, which execute curious and fantastic movements, frequently not unlike the most gorgeous kaleidoscopic figures that are shown nowadays by electric projection. PURKINJE has studied these phenomena very carefully, and accurately described and represented them. They seem to have had a high degree of regularity for him. The background generally consisted of fine quadrangles in regular array, on which there were either stars with eight rays, or dark or bright rhombs with vertical and horizontal diagonals; and the patterns were surrounded by alternately bright and dark bands. In the author's own experience there is no such regularity in the figures. The background of the visual field is usually finely patterned at first, but in the most manifold way and in very different colours. Frequently, it is as if the field were strewn with fine leaves or covered with moss; then presently they look like bright brownish-yellow quadrangles everywhere with fine line patterns; and at last they usually develop in the form of dark lines on a brownish-yellow background. Sometimes they assume very complex star-shaped figures, and sometimes they are in the form of an inextricable labyrinth or maze, which seems to be waving or flowing continually. There are often bright blue or red sparks in certain parts of the field which may last for a considerable time. If, when the phenomenon is at its maximum, the pressure is released, without letting extraneous light enter the eye, the play of figures proceeds for a long time still, gradually getting darker until it ceases entirely. But if the eye is opened as the pressure is released, and directed towards a bright object, there is absolute darkness at first; and then gradually single bright objects shining brilliantly begin to be manifest in the middle of the field. For instance, in the writer's own case, separate sheets of white paper appear in their true form but of dazzling brightness, and superposed on them are the remnants of the previous patterns, the dark places in them now showing bright. The abnormal brightness gradually fades away just as the pressure-images do before the eye when it is shut. But the eye on which the pressure was exerted is for a longer time still different from the other eye; because the field looks more violet to it, whereas it looks yellowish to the unpressed eye. VIERORDT and LAIBLIN maintain that with continuous pressure on the eye they have seen the ramifications of the blood-vessels on the retina, red on a dark ground; but the writer has tried in vain to obtain this effect. Moreover, VIERORDT frequently saw the retinal vessels in this way with a bright blue colouring. Both observers witnessed, as STEINBACH and PURKINJE had done before, a network of vessels with blood circulating in them. PURKINJE supposed they were the retinal arteries; but as the appearance was visible along with the previously mentioned blood-vessels of the retina, LAIBLIN concluded from his observations that the circulation which was perceived here must belong "to another layer of the retina, more to the outside, and containing more blood-vessels." In the pressure-images of the eye, except for occasional sudden flashes of the familiar vascular figure of the retina, neither MEISSNER nor the writer himself has ever succeeded in seeing anything similar to a network of vessels. The flowing movement of the labyrinthine system of lines during the last stages of the phenomenon has no similarity at all to a network of vessels.[1] As to the theory of these phenomena, it seems from DONDERS's investigations with the ophthalmoscope that the effect of pressure on the eye is undoubtedly to produce changes in the blood-vessels of the retina, so that the veins begin to pulsate and finally become entirely emptied of blood. This was seen in several cases. The restless and constantly shifting images produced by sustained pressure on the eye might be compared to the sensation of ants running over the skin, such as occurs in limbs that have "gone to sleep" when the nerves have been pressed on for some time. When pressure is exerted on the nerves in the thigh, the foot and lower leg very soon lose the capacity of feeling contact with external objects. Accompanying it there is an intense tingling sensation in the numbed parts of the skin; which in similar fashion soon arouses variable excitements of the sensitive nerve fibres, such as are manifested by the delicate moving figures in the visual field during corresponding states of the retina. On releasing the pressure, the ability of perceiving external objects returns, and the first movements of the foot are often painful; whereas in the case of the eye, the outside light is blinding in its power.

Another phenomenon apparently connected with mechanical stimulation of the retina, consists of certain spots of light that are visible to sensitive eyes in the dark field when they have just executed a quick movement. These are represented in Fig. 2, Plate I, as they look in the field of view of the writer's eyes, when they have been

[1] In my own case (says NAGEL) there is regularly a dense net-work of bright lines on a dark ground when I close one eye almost tight for at least 20 minutes, whether the eye is pressed or not. The bright lines exhibit a *rapid* flowing or flickering, which is very clear. For several minutes at first the phenomenon does not appear and then develops gradually. After a half hour or an hour it is so distinct that it is disturbing when one tries to read with the other eye. The flowing image is most conspicuous when both eyes are closed. Far from being *absent* in the fovea, this flowing is particularly clear there.—N.

moved to the left in the direction of the arrow. The spots marked L and R are the appearances in the left eye and right eye, respectively. The effect is less developed in the eye that turns inwards (the right eye in this case) than in the one that turns outwards. It occurs with the writer only in the morning; either on waking or as a result of indisposition; but other observers, for example, PURKINJE and CZERMAK[1] perceived these spots in the dark at any time of day as fiery rings or half-rings. Their distance from the point of fixation is such than an observer who is familiar with the phenomenon of the so-called blind spot (which will be described later) can infer that they are situated where the optic nerve enters. Therefore, a probable explanation of their origin is that, with sudden motions of the eye, the optic nerve being set in motion along with the eyeball is stretched at the place where it comes into the eye. When PURKINJE[2] turned his eye far inwards, he saw a steady ring of light where the optic nerve enters, surrounded by concentric bright bands towards the middle of the field; but in the writer's case the phenomena are never anything but momentary. If the experiment is tried with the eye open in front of a uniformly illuminated white surface, dark spots corresponding to the entrance of the optic nerve make their appearance when the eye is turned far to one side. They are produced more easily by turning the eye inwards, as was observed by CZERMAK, and have a regular circular form when the eye is turned outwards. In the reddish field produced by closing the eyelids and illuminating them from outside, these dark spots appear blue. In the writer's own case, the dark spots show traces of the same luminous appearances that are visible in the dark field; but CZERMAK insists that with him the latter phenomenon is not a negative reproduction of the former. Here also the stimulated nerve-fibres seem to lose their sensibility to external stimuli on account of the pull on them. The fibres which are here stimulated must be those whose ends are in the immediate neighbourhood of the optic nerve, because the place where the optic nerve enters is itself not sensitive to light, and hence it cannot be supposed that any fibres capable of light sensation end at that place and are responsible for a sensation of light at this very spot. And, finally, the *accommodation phosphene* seen by PURKINJE[3] and CZERMAK[4] has to be considered here. When a person looks out of a window with his eyes fixed on something very near, and then suddenly accommodates for distant vision, a fairly

---

[1] *Physiologische Studien.* Abteilung I. § 5. S. 42 u. Abt. II. S. 32. — *Wiener Sitzungsber.* XII. S. 322 u. XV. 454.

[2] *Beiträge zur Kenntnis des Sehens.* S. 78.

[3] *Zur Physiologie der Sinne.* Bd. I. 126. II. 115.

[4] *Wiener Sitzungsber.* XXVII. 78.

small luminous border will be seen near the periphery of the field of view, which, having the form of a closed ring, flashes out at the instant when accommodation is consciously relaxed. PURKINJE observed the phenomenon also when uniform pressure on the eye was suddenly released. The writer himself has never seen it. CZERMAK thinks the reason of it is because at the instant when the tension of the ciliary muscle ceases, the relaxed zonule is again stretched, while the lens is still shortened radially; which results in a sudden stretching of the outermost edge of the retina where it is attached to the zonule.

When the writer exerts his accommodation and looks towards an uniformly illuminated white surface, there is a shadowy spot at the point of fixation. It shades off brown at the edge, perhaps with brown or bright violet lines radiating from it in various directions. The field of view then usually gets dark rapidly, with net-like designs and parts of the blood-vessels appearing dark against a white background. Everything vanishes when the accommodation is relaxed. PURKINJE describes the brown spot, but says that its centre is white. In this same category belongs an elliptical and spotted luminous effect seen by PURKINJE[1] in the dark visual field when pressure on the eyelids was suddenly released. In order to produce this phenomenon, it was necessary to expose the eye to light a little while in advance. The writer himself cannot see it.

Dogs show no sign of pain when the exposed optic nerve is cut and pulled; but the same kinds of injury to a cutaneous nerve of equal size produces the most intense agony. The human eye sometimes has to be extirpated on account of cancer. In such cases when the optic nerve itself has not degenerated, large masses of light are said to be perceived at the moment the optic nerve is severed,[2] accompanied by somewhat greater pain than is caused by cutting the adjacent parts. It is hardly reasonable to suppose that the severance of the optic nerve would be entirely devoid of pain like that perceived by the tactile nerves. All the other large nerve trunks have their *nervi nervorum*, that is, particularly sensitive fibres which belong to them just as much as to all the rest of the internal parts of the body and which mediate their local sensibility.[3] It can be shown that such *nervi nervorum* are sent from the posterior sensory roots to the anterior roots of the spinal nerves, through which motor fibres alone leave the cord. If the ulnar nerve is struck at the elbow joint, there is a sensation

---

[1] *Zur Physiologie der Sinne.* II. 78.

[2] TOURTUAL in J. MÜLLER, *Handbuch der Physiologie.* Koblenz 1840. Bd. II. S. 259.

[3] ¶The various sensations mediated by the "tactile" nerves, of which HELMHOLTZ writes, have been divided into protopathic, epicritic and deep. See any standard textbook of Physiology. (H. L.)

of pain referred to the region of distribution of the nerve in the fourth and fifth finger, as well as another localized at the place struck, which is more unpleasant than that resulting when the skin alone is stimulated. This must be referred to the nerves of the nerve trunk. In the same way when the eyeball is pressed at the outer angle, the pain of the pressure is felt locally by means of the sensory nerves of this region, and the light that is seen is supposed to be in the region of the bridge of the nose. Something of a similar nature may happen when the optic nerve trunk is stimulated.

That the optic nerve and the retina, both capable of being stimulated by so delicate an agency as light, are tolerably insensitive to the roughest mechanical maltreatment, that is, have no sensation of pain, has seemed a remarkable paradox. The explanation, however, is simple, because the quality of all sensations of the optic nerve belongs to the group of light sensations. The sensibility is not lacking, but the *form* of the sensation is different from that usually associated with this particular kind of stimulus.

Light sensations due to *internal conditions* are very varied. There are a number of luminous phenomena, occurring in all diseased conditions of the eye or of the entire body, that may take up the whole field or may be localized in it. In the latter case they take sometimes the form of irregular spots and sometimes fantastic figures of men or animals, etc. Mechanical causes often participate in these effects, as, for example, increased blood-pressure in the vessels or humors of the eye. Thus, on releasing the eye from uniform pressure, parts of the vascular figure often flash out; and sometimes, after violent exertion separate pulsating parts, maybe larger portions, of the vascular figure are visible.[1] In other cases there may be a sort of chemical stimulation due to altered condition of the blood, for example, by narcotic poisoning. Finally, many of these phenomena also may be explained as due to a spread of a state of excitation within the central part from other parts of the nervous system to the origin of the optic nerve. When the state of excitation in a stimulated sensory nerve is imparted to another that is not acted on by the stimulus at all, we call it an associated sensation. For example, looking at large bright surfaces, such as sunlit snow, causes many persons to feel a simultaneous tickling in the nose. The sound of certain scraping or squeaking noises makes a cold chill run down the back. Apparently, such associated sensations may occur also in the visual apparatus when other sensory nerves are

---

[1] PURKINJE, *Zur Physiologie der Sinne.* I. 134. II. 115. 118. — *Subjektive Erscheinungen nach Wirkung der Digitalis* II. 120.

stimulated, *e.g.*, by intestinal worms in children or by retained faeces, retarded circulation and other abnormal conditions in hypochondriacs. The origin of peculiar fantastic shapes or luminous images associated with the appearance of familiar external objects is due apparently to a similar transference of the state of excitation from the part of the brain that is active in the formation of ideas to the visual apparatus. These have been noted by many observers who state that while they were seeing them they were thoroughly aware of their subjective nature.[1] Certain individuals, for example, GOETHE and J. MÜLLER, could indeed see similar phenomena at any time by simply closing their eyes and remaining for a long time in darkness.

As a matter of fact, the field of vision of a healthy human being is never entirely free from appearances of this kind which have been called the *chaotic light* or *luminous dust of the dark visual field*.[2] It plays such an important part in many phenomena, like after-images, for example, that we shall call it the *self-light* or *intrinsic light* of the retina. When the eyes are closed, and the dark field is attentively examined, often at first after-images of external objects that were previously visible will still be perceived (as to their origin, see §§24 and 25 below). This effect is soon superseded by an irregular feebly illuminated field with numerous fluctuating spots of light, often similar in appearance to the small branches of the blood-vessels or to scattered stems of moss and leaves, which may be transformed into fantastic figures, as is reported by many observers. A quite common appearance seems to be what GOETHE describes as floating cloud-ribbons (*"wandelnde Nebel-streifen"*). PURKINJE speaks of them as "broad streamers, more or less curved, with black intervals between them, which sometimes move in concentric circles towards the centre of the field, to become lost there, or maybe to disintegrate into floating curls, or to revolve as curved radii of circles around this place; the movements being so sluggish that ordinarily it takes eight seconds for a streamer to complete its performance and vanish out of sight." The author's experience is that they generally look like two sets of circular waves gradually blending together towards their centre from both sides of the point of fixation. The position of this centre for each eye seems to correspond to the place of entrance of the optic nerve; and the movement is synchronous with the respiratory movements. One of PURKINJE's eyes being weaker

---

[1] Cases of this sort are summarized by J. MÜLLER, *Über phantastische Gesichtserschei-nungen*. Koblenz, 1826, page 20.

[2] ¶"The completely dark-adapted eye when sheltered from all external stimuli gives a sensation which is variously described as the light chaos, the intrinsic light of the retina, and so on. HERING calls this sensation 'mean grey'." J. H. PARSONS, *An introduction to the study of colour vision*. 1915, p. 251. (J. P. C. S.)

than the other, he could not see these floating clouds except in his right eye. The background of the visual field, on which these phenomena are projected is never entirely black; and alternate fluctuations of bright and dark are visible there, frequently occurring in rhythm with the movements of respiration; as observed by both J. MULLER[1] and the writer. Moreover, with every movement of the eyes or eyelids, and with every change of accommodation, there are accompanying variations of this "luminous dust." The shapes that are assumed are very curious, especially when one happens to be in a strange place that is perfectly dark, as, for instance, in an unlighted hallway where it is necessary to grope one's way; because then these imaginary figures are apt to be mistaken for real objects. Under such circumstances PURKINJE noticed that every unexpected contact and every uncertain movement produced instantaneous oscillations of the eye which were accompanied by gossamer clouds of light and other luminous appearances, such as may easily have been the origin of many ghost stories.

After strenuous exercise and when the body is overheated, PURKINJE[2] noticed a faint glow of light glimmering in his dark field, like the last expiring flickers of a flame of alcohol burning on the top of a table. Upon closer examination he detected countless tiny little points of light darting to and fro and leaving little trails of light behind them. He got a similar effect when he closed his right eye and strained to see with his other weak eye.

Another important fact is, that after a person has lost one of his eyes, or in case the optic nerves and eyes have degenerated and cease to function, he may still have subjective sensations of light.[3] Such experiences show that not merely the retina, but the trunk and roots of the optic nerve in the brain as well, are capable of giving rise to sensations of light as a result of being stimulated.

Lastly, another powerful agency for stimulating not only the optic nerve but all the other nerves of the body is by a current of electricity. As a rule, the motor nerves do not produce twitching except at the instants when the current traversing them is suddenly increased or diminished; but sensations are excited in the sensory nerves not only by fluctuations in the current but by a steady flow; and the quality of the sensation depends on the direction of the current.

When the optic nerve is stimulated by *fluctuations in the strength of a current of electricity*, bright flashes of light are produced extending

[1] *Phantastische Gesichtserscheinungen.* S. 16.

[2] *Beobachtungen und Versuche, etc.* I. 63, 134. II. 115.

[3] See J. MÜLLER, *Phantastische Gesichtserscheinungen.* S. 30 — A. v. HUMBOLDT, *Gereizte Muskel- und Nervenfaser.* Tl. II. S. 444. — LINCKE, *de fungo medullari.* Lips. 1834.

over the entire visual field. These effects can be obtained by discharges of Leyden jars just as easily as from a galvanic pile, provided a strong enough portion of the current flows through the optic nerve as nearly parallel as possible to the direction of its fibres. A convenient way of doing this is to place one electrode on the forehead or on the closed eyelid and the other on the neck; or the latter may be held in the hand, if the electrical apparatus is so powerful that a great resistance does not matter. The electrodes should be in the form of plates or cylinders; and if they are covered with damp pasteboard and the parts of the body where they are attached thoroughly moistened beforehand, the pain on the skin can be diminished. Not many experiments of this sort have thus far been made by discharges of Leyden jars. On account of the proximity of the brain, it is well to be careful, because FRANKLIN and WILKE[1] noted that discharges through the head may result in unconsciousness. LE ROY[2] passed the discharge through a young man who was blind from cataract. His head and right leg were wound with a brass wire, and a Leyden jar discharged through its ends. At every discharge the patient thought he saw a flame pass rapidly downwards from above, accompanied by a noise as of heavy firing. When the shock was made to pass only through the blind man's head, by attaching metal plates above the eye and at the back of the head, and connecting them with a jar, the patient had sensations of fantastic figures, individual persons, crowds of people in lines, etc.

Experiments with galvanic currents are more numerous. In order to perceive simple flashes of light due to making or breaking the circuit, a few zinc-copper cells are sufficient, or even a single cell in case of excitable eyes. For example, when a piece of zinc is placed on the moistened lid of one eye and a piece of silver on that of the other, and the two pieces of metal brought into contact, a flash appears at the instant of contact, and again at the instant of separation. The experiment is more instructive when one metal is placed on one eye and the other taken in the mouth, because in this way the connection between the brightness of the flash and the direction of the current can be easily made out at the same time. According to PFAFF's observations, the flash is more striking when the circuit is closed, provided the positive metal (zinc) is placed on the eye and the negative electrode (silver) taken in the mouth; because then the positive electricity flows upwards through the optic nerve. The writer has never had any success with these experiments with a simple circuit, probably because his eye is not sensitive enough to such stimulation. But the flashes of light are very

[1] *Mém. de mathém. de l'Acad. de France.* 1755. pp. 86–92.

[2] FRANKLIN, *Briefe über Elektrizität.* Leipzig 1758. S. 312.

brilliant with a small galvanic pile of about a dozen elements. For example, when a battery of DANIELL cells is used that gives a constant current, the flash on closing the circuit is found to be greater when the current flows upwards; whereas the flash on breaking the circuit is greater when the current flows downwards. There are similar differences of effect in the case of the motor nerves depending on the direction of the current; but here these differences are due also to the strength of the current.

In order to perceive *the continuous action of a uniform current*, most eyes require a small galvanic pile, although RITTER perceived it even with a single cell. To avoid blinding the eyes by the flash of light and the unpleasant muscular twitching in opening and closing the circuit, the writer suggests placing two metallic cylinders on the edge of the table near which the patient is seated; the cylinders being wrapped with pasteboard, that has been dipped in salt water, and connected with the two terminals of a DANIELL's battery of from a dozen to two dozen cells. The forehead is pressed firmly against one of the cylinders, and then the hand makes contact with the other. Thus, by gradually touching the electrode, the effects of fluctuations of the current are very slight, and the circuit may be easily made or broken at will. The direction of the current can be reversed by applying the other cylinder to the forehead. In this way pressure is not exerted on the eyes, which is something to be avoided.

When a weak ascending current is conducted through the optic nerves, the dark field of the closed eyes becomes brighter than before and assumes a faint violet colour. During the first moments the optic disc appears in the brightened field as a dark circular area. The brightness quickly diminishes in intensity and disappears completely when the current is interrupted. This effect can be produced without a flash of light by slowly letting go the cylinder in contact with the hand. Then as the field begins to darken, in contrast to the previous blueness, it takes on a reddish yellow tinge due to the intrinsic light of the retina.

On making the circuit in which the current flows in the opposite or descending direction, the striking result is that only that part of the visual field that is illuminated by the intrinsic light of the retina becomes darker than before, and has a somewhat reddish yellow colour. The optic disc is conspicuous on the dark background as a bright blue circular area, although frequently only the half of it towards the middle of the field is visible. When the circuit is broken, the field again becomes brighter and bluish white, and the optic disc appears dark.

The darkening of the field caused by the descending current indicates that in these experiments it is not primarily a question of an electrical stimulation, but that changes of excitability due to the passage of the current are also involved. PFLÜGER's experiments[1] tend to show that the excitability of the nerve is enhanced by a feeble current in the portion where the positive electricity enters it, and reduced where it leaves it. Accordingly, with an ascending current the excitability would be enhanced in the portion of the optic nerve towards the brain and diminished in the portion next the retina; exactly the reverse being the case when the current is a descending one. PFLÜGER's law affords an explanation of the decrease and increase of the intrinsic light of the eye, provided it is assumed that the internal stimuli that produce this effect act on the end of the optic nerve that is towards the brain. This being the case, the ascending current must result in augmenting, and the descending current. in lowering, the intrinsic light. Whether the opposite illumination at the optic nerve is to be regarded as contrast or as internal stimulation near the place where it comes into the retina, is still a moot question. RITTER found that external objects were less clear while the current was descending, and more clear when the current was ascending; which is in conformity with the above explanation; because when the retina itself is stimulated, ascending currents must increase its sensibility. The writer can corroborate this for dimly illuminated objects. Moreover, PURKINJE's explanation of the decrease of clearness in objective vision as being due to the increase of the intrinsic light of the eye, which acts as a kind of mist, is in perfect harmony with the above. At all events this brightening and darkening of the visual field prevents one from being sure whether the light from an isolated object is perceived more strongly or more feebly.

PFLÜGER finds that when the steady current is interrupted there is increased sensibility in those parts of the nerve that had become less sensitive; as is shown in our case by the brightening of the visual field. On the other hand, for a short space (as long as ten seconds) there is at first reduced sensitivity in those parts of the nerve which were previously more sensitive; which is then succeeded by a slight increase of sensitivity again. In our case the darkening of the field when the ascending current is interrupted corresponds to the first state; and the only sign of the latter state is that the darkening seems to be soon succeeded by the normal condition.

With stronger currents obtained by using from 100 to 200 zinc-copper cells, RITTER observed a reversal of colouration, but the increase or decrease of brightness was the same as with weak currents.

---

[1] *Untersuchungen über die Physiologie des Elektrotonus.* Berlin 1859. On this subject, see § 25.

Thus strong ascending currents aroused in him a bright green sensation; which was bright red with still stronger currents. Strong descending currents gave a faint blue sensation. In the former case, when the circuit was broken, the sensation was blue at first, which quickly changed over into the red left behind by the weak current. On the other hand, on interrupting a strong descending current, the sensation was red at the first instant, rapidly changing to the customary blue. The writer's own experience with strong currents[1] is that they produce a wild interplay of colours in which no regularity can be discovered.

Another thing that RITTER reports is that external objects appear not only more indistinct but also smaller when the eye is traversed by an ascending current. This leads us to suspect that his eyes were accommodated for near vision. The current causes so much pain at the place where it enters that it is almost impossible to avoid stretching the adjacent muscles, wrinkling the forehead, and closing the eyelids tightly. Whenever the eye and its adjacent parts are strained, there is a tendency with most people to accommodate for near vision, and this has also a certain influence on the impression one gets as to the size of something seen. Du Bois-REYMOND[2] calls attention to the fact that when an electric current flows through the eye, the pupil contracts; and, doubtless, there is likewise some change in the mechanism of accommodation. Conversely, in the case of descending currents, RITTER reports that objects appeared larger and more distinct.

Finally, PURKINJE describes other special forms of luminous phenomena produced by electrical stimulation, when the current is made to flow from a small pointed conductor either into the middle of the closed eyelids or in the vicinity of the eye. The effect of the current as described above was always most noticeable at the place where the axis of the eye meets the retina. Here there was a diamond-shaped spot surrounded by several alternately dark and bright diamond-shaped bands. On the other hand, the place where the optic nerve enters invariably exhibited the opposite phase of electrical action. For instance, when the current was ascending, the axial point of the eye was like a bright blue diamond immediately surrounded by a dark band, and the optic disc like a dark circle surrounded by a blue sheen. When the current was descending, the axial point appeared as a dark diamond surrounded by red-yellow bands, and the optic nerve

---

[1] The current of 24 DANIELL cells was conducted to forehead and neck by metal plates covered with moist pasteboard. The resistance in this circuit was very much less than in RITTER's arrangement. He used a battery of high resistance and had his arm in the circuit besides. Consequently, the connection between the current-strengths in the two experiments is not easy to be ascertained.

[2] *Untersuchungen über tierische Elektrizität.* Berlin 1848. Bd. I. S. 353.

as a bright luminous disc. As the current became steadier, the figures soon vanished; but when the current was more intermittent (which PURKINJE caused by moving the circuit about), the blue figure persisted, being brighter by far than the red-yellow figure.

These phenomena at the place where the optic nerve enters the eye, as described by PURKINJE, are usually seen by most persons; but instead of the diamond-shaped figures, the writer and others who have tried it at his request can see simply indefinite patches of light. As a result of pressure on the eye, PURKINJE saw entirely similar rhombic figures. So far as the writer is aware, these rhombs have never been seen by any other observer; and it is a question therefore whether their regular form was not due to idiosyncrasies of PURKINJE's eyes.

When the current was introduced near the eye through a small conductor, the appearances of light corresponding to the yellow spot and the optic disc were the same as before. But in addition a dark arc was noticeable on the edge of the field and parallel to it; which kept its apparent place during movements of the eye; whereas the phenomena dependent on the optic nerve and yellow spot seemed to follow the movements of the eye. This dark arc is in the upper part of the field when the electrode is placed below the eye; and on the right when the electrode is on the left, and *vice versa*. Hence it follows that those portions of the retina which are nearest the electrode perceive no light. In order to see this phenomenon distinctly, PURKINJE used chain conductors, so that with every movement of them, the current was interrupted.[1]

In old days, without any positive knowledge of the subject, the theory of the visual sensations was entirely a matter of philosophy. The first thing that had to be comprehended was that the sensations are nothing but the effects of external things on our bodies, and that perception is a result of sensation by means of psychical processes. This is the view of Greek philosophy.[2] It begins

---

[1] G. E. MÜLLER has corroborated the interesting fact that the threshold for galvanic light perception is practically the same for light adaptation and dark adaptation of the eye. This is also true for my eye (writes NAGEL), and is remarkable, because the sensibility for the adequate *light* stimulus increases very much when the eye is dark-adapted. I found too that the threshold of the pressure-phosphene (which, however, cannot be accurately determined) was not appreciably different in the light-adapted eye and the dark-adapted eye. The pressure-phosphene certainly is qualitatively changed at the beginning of dark adaptation. While pressure with a blunt instrument on the temporal side of the eyeball in the light-adapted eye causes a small clear yellowish ring to appear in the dark visual field, the ring is much larger and a brilliant bluish white when the eye has been dark-adapted for a half-hour. This makes the phenomenon more striking; but, as stated, it is impossible to find a threshold difference when the pressure stimuli are nicely regulated.—N.

G. E. MÜLLER, Über die galvanischen Gesichtsempfindungen. *Zft. f. Psych. u. Physiol. d. Sinnesorgane*, XIV. 329.

W. NAGEL, Einige Beobachtungen über die Wirkung des Druckes und des galvanischen Stromes auf das dunkeladaptierte Auge. Ibid. XXXV. 285.

[2] See WUNDT, Zur Geschichte der Theorie des Sehens in HENLE und PFEUFFERS *Zeitschrift für rationelle Medizin*. 1859.

with naïve suppositions as to how images of objects can possibly reach the mind. DEMOCRITUS and EPICURUS believed that the images were let loose from the objects and flew into the eye. EMPEDOCLES made the rays proceed to the object not only from the source, but from the eye also, and argued that the object was thus, so to speak, touched by the eye. PLATO's opinions vacillated. In the *Timaeus* he accepts the views of EMPEDOCLES: the rays issuing from the eye are like rays of light except that they are without heat, and the only way that vision occurs is when the internal light from the eye proceeds to the object and encounters the external light. On the other hand, in the *Theaetetus*, his reflections as to the spiritual basis of the perceptions lead him to entertain views that are not very far apart from the more mature standpoint of ARISTOTLE.

ARISTOTLE[1] made a delicate psychological analysis of the part played by the spiritual reality in the sense-perceptions. Physically and physiologically, sensation is clearly different from what it is psychically; and the perception of external objects does not depend on some kind of delicate tactile feelers emanating from the eye (such as EMPEDOCLES's nerves of vision), but is due to an act of judgment. Physically, indeed, his ideas are very undeveloped, but in the fundamental conceptions the germ of the undulatory theory can be traced. For according to ARISTOTLE, light is nothing corporeal, but an activity (ἐνέργεια) of the intervening transparent medium, which when at rest constitutes darkness. However, he still does not abandon the notion that the effect of light on the eye is not necessarily of the same nature as that of the luminous source by which it is excited. He tries rather to account for this correspondence between cause and effect by the fact that the eye also contains transparent substances, which may be put in the same state of activity as the external transparent medium.

ARISTOTLE's peculiar and striking contributions to the theory of vision passed without notice during the middle ages. FRANCIS BACON and his successors were the first to take up these threads again in their keen discussions of the connection between ideas and sensations: until KANT in his *Critique of Pure Reason* put an end to their theory.

At this same time natural philosophers were interested only on the physical side of the theory of vision, which had developed rapidly from the time of KEPLER. HALLER formulated the general theory of nerve excitability; and described quite clearly and correctly the relation between light and sensation and between sensation and perception.[2] But more exact knowledge concerning excitation of the eye by other stimuli was still lacking; or at least what was known was fragmentary and regarded as simply curious. To GOETHE belongs the credit of having brought the importance of this knowledge to the attention of German scientists; although he did not succeed in winning them over to a revised theory of the physics of light from the standpoint of the direct visual sensations, which was the real purpose of his famous treatise on Colour Theory. Soon after came the important observations of RITTER and other electrical workers concerning excitations of the sensory nerves; and above all, PURKINJE's observations; so that in 1826 J. MÜLLER could state the chief laws of the subject in his Theory of Specific Sense Energy as it was first published in his work on the Comparative Physiology of Vision, to which reference was made at the beginning of this chapter. This work and that of PURKINJE are closely related to GOETHE's Colour Theory, although J. MÜLLER subsequently abandoned its physical concepts. MÜLLER's law of specific energies was a step forward of the greatest importance for the whole

---

[1] *De sensibus, de anima* lib. II. c. 5–8 and *de coloribus*.

[2] *Elem. Physiolog.* Tom. V lib. 16, 17.

theory of sense perceptions, and it has since become the scientific basis of this theory. In a certain sense, it is the empirical fulfilment of KANT's theoretical concept of the nature of human reason.

Even ARISTOTLE was aware of the images produced by pressure on the eye. NEWTON[1] conjectured that mechanical disturbance of the retina produces a motion in it similar to that made by the impact of rays of light. He considered this motion as the cause of the sensation of light. The opinion that in the case of pressure-images, and in other cases also, objective light is developed in the eye has had its adherents until quite recently. An example of this view is the medico-legal case mentioned above in which the capable physician SEILER seemed to think it necessary to admit the possibility of such a contingency. But no one has ever been able to see the light thus developed in another person's eye. To strengthen this view, its adherents have cited the cases of persons like the Emperor TIBERIUS, CARDANUS and KASPAR HAUSER who were able to see in the dark, that is, with very little light. Another argument which they use is the so-called luminosity of animal eyes and of the eyes of albinos and certain other human beings whose eyes are malformed; which is due simply to the reflection of light. Finally, they instance distinct after-images which old people see in the evening after the light is extinguished, and which sometimes persist for a long time; as proving the possibility of development of light in the eye. Quite recently more accurate descriptions of pressure-images have been given by PURKINJE and SERRES D'UZÈS. How THOMAS YOUNG utilized these effects in his theory of accommodation has been mentioned in Vol. I, page 158.

VOLTA was aware of the flash of light when the current flowing through the eye was turned on or off. RITTER perceived the persistent luminous actions even with a simple cell; and subsequently they were minutely described, especially by PURKINJE.

Supplement by HELMHOLTZ in the First Edition

It was expressly stated above that the actions of steady currents of electricity on the visual apparatus were not to be considered as a stimulation (as they used to be regarded), but as changes of excitability due to the electrification. But the author's assumption that the continuous internal excitation of the fibres of the optic nerve, whose sensibility is thereby increased, takes place on the side of the nerve towards the brain, does not agree with the phenomena that occur when an electric current flows through a small electrode right into the eyeball itself. These phenomena as observed by PURKINJE were partly described on page 17. A more probable inference here would be that it is the electrified condition of the radial fibres of the retina that is responsible, and that their steady stimulation takes place on the posterior surface of the retina.

If the negative electrode is placed on the neck, and the positive electrode, consisting of a pointed cone-shaped piece of sponge soaked in salt water and fastened to a handle of metal, is applied to the moistened eyelids near the outer angle of the eye, the visual field

[1] *Optice*, at the end of Quaestio XVI.

appears dark on the nasal side, and bright on the temporal side; and the optic disc which is within the bright portion appears dark. When the eye is turned so that the point of fixation falls on the boundary between the bright and dark areas, a bright tuft of light seems to radiate out from it towards the dark portion and a dark tuft towards the bright portion of the field. These two oval tufts just about cover the area of the yellow spot.

If the direction of the current is reversed, the light and dark areas change places. Breaking the circuit has the same instantaneous effect as reversing the current.

All these phenomena may be simply explained as due to the electrified state of the radial nerve fibres of the retina, on the supposition that there is a permanent weak stimulation at their posterior ends as the result of internal causes; the presence of which seems to be indicated by the intrinsic light of the retina.

When positive electricity enters the eyeball from the outer side of the eye and returns from the inner and posterior side, the excitability of the posterior surface of the retina will be diminished where the current enters and increased where it leaves; and hence the inner half of the visual field, corresponding to the outer half of the retina, must appear dark, and the outer half bright. Probably the optic nerve acts as a poor conductor, so that the current is reduced near the place where this nerve enters the eye; which makes this place stand out through contrast. If the yellow spot is at the border of the portions of the retina through which the current is passing in opposite directions, the current flows through it along the surface of the retina. In the yellow spot, however, there are bundles of fibres which run also along the surface of the membrane. Accordingly, these fibres are traversed by positive electricity from the temporal towards the nasal side, that is, the current flows through the fibres on the temporal side of the fovea in the direction towards their ends that are connected with the cones, and on the nasal side it flows the opposite way. Thus, on the temporal side the excitation will be increased, and on the nasal side diminished; and this is why the bright tuft appears on the nasal side of the point of fixation in the field of view, and the dark tuft on the temporal side.

When the place is changed where the current enters, the entire phenomenon is correspondingly shifted.

———

Note by W. NAGEL.—Neither with ascending nor with descending current has the editor succeeded in showing that there is any variation of the luminous threshold.   N.

Mechanical Stimulation

1706. I. NEWTON, *Optice*, at the end of Quaestio XVI.

1774. EICHEL in *Collectan. soc. med. Havniensis* 1774.

1797. A. v. HUMBOLDT, *Versuche über die gereizte Muskel- und Nervenfaser*. II. 444.

1801. TH. YOUNG, On the mechanism of the eye. *Phil. Trans.* 1801. I. 23.

1819–25.* PURKINJE, *Beobachtungen und Versuche zur Physiologie der Sinne*. I. 78, 126, 136, II. 115.

1825. MAGENDIE, *Journal de Physiologie*. IV. 180. V. 189.

1826. J. MÜLLER, *Über die phantastischen Gesichtserscheinungen*. Koblenz. S. 30.

1832. D. BREWSTER in POGGENDORFFS *Ann.* XXVI. 156.—*Phil. Mag.* I. 56.

1833. SEILER in HENKES *Zeitschr. für gerichtl. Med.* 1833. 4. Quartal. S. 266.

1834. LINCKE, *De fungo medullari*. Lipsiae.

QUETELET, POGGENDORFFS *Ann.* XXXI. 494.

J. MÜLLER in *Archiv für Anat. und Physiol.* 1834. S. 140.

1840. TOURTUAL in J. MÜLLERS *Handbuch der Physiologie* II. 259.

1850. SERRES D'UZÈS, Du Phosphène. *C. R.* XXXI. 375–378.

1854–55.* CZERMAK, *Physiologische Studien*. Abt. I. § 5. S. 42 and Abt. II. S. 32.—*Wiener Sitzungsberichte* XII. 322 and XV. 454.

1856. A. E. LAIBLIN, *Die Wahrnehmung der Choroidealgefässe des eigenen Auges*. *Dissert.* Tübingen.

MEISSNER, Bericht über die Fortschritte der Physiologie im Jahre 1856, S. 568 in HENLES *Zeitschr. für ration. Medizin*.

1858. J. CZERMAK, Über das Akkommodationsphosphen. *Wiener Ber.* XXVII. 78–86.—*Archiv für Ophthalmologie*. VII, 1. pp. 147–154.

Electrical Stimulation

1755. LE ROY, *Mém. de Mathém. de l'Acad. de France*. 1755. pp. 86–92.

1794. PFAFF in GRENS *Journal der Physik* VIII. 252, 253.

1795. PFAFF, *Über tierische Elektrizität*. S. 142.

1798. RITTER, *Beweis, dass ein beständiger Galvanismus den Lebensprozess im Tierreiche begleite*. Weimar 1798. S. 127.

1800. VOLTA, *Colezione dell' Opere*. Tom. II, P. II. p. 124.

*RITTER, *Beiträge zur näheren Kenntnis des Galvanismus*. Bd. II. St. 3, 4. S. 159, 166. § 93.

1801 and 1805 RITTER in GILBERTS *Annalen*. VII. 448. XIX. 6–8.

1819. PURKINJE, *Beobachtungen und Versuche zur Physiologie der Sinne*. Bd. I. Prag 1819. S. 50. Bd. II. Berlin 1825. S. 31. KASTNERS *Archiv für die gesamte Naturlehre* 1825. V. 434.

1823. MOST, *Über die grossen Heilkräfte des in unseren Tagen mit Unrecht vernachlässigten Galvanismus*. Lüneburg 1823. S. 812.

1829. FECHNER, *Lehrbuch des Galvanismus und der Elektrochemie*. Kap. 39. S. 485 ff.

1830. HJORT, *De functione retinae nervosae*. Part. II. Christiania 1830. (Dissert.) p. 34 § 17.

1848. E. DU BOIS-REYMOND, *Untersuchungen über tierische Elektrizität*. I. 283–293; 338–358.

1863. R. SCHELSKE, Über Farbenempfindungen. *Archiv für Ophthalmol.* IX. (3) S. 39–62.

1864. AUBERT, *Physiologie der Netzhaut*. Breslau. S. 333–390.

Note to §17

On the Stimulation of the Visual Apparatus by RÖNTGEN Rays and BECQUEREL Rays. By W. NAGEL

In addition to HELMHOLTZ's account in §17 of the action of adequate and inadequate stimuli of the visual organ, mention should be made of the fact that the sensation of light in the eye can be aroused both by RÖNTGEN *rays* and by the emanations of the so-called *radio-active* substances. The sensation of light produced by the impact of X-rays in the eye was noticed first by BRANDES and DORN[1]. COWL and LEVY-DORN[2] supposed this optical effect could be traced to illusions produced chiefly by electrical action at a distance. But BRANDES and DORN, also RÖNTGEN,[3] HIMSTEDT and NAGEL,[4] and others showed that the luminous sensation was produced when such sources of error were guarded against. The vacuum tube can be enclosed in a light-proof box made of thin sheet aluminum opaque to light; and yet a powerful glow of light will be produced in the eye, provided the eye has been dark-adapted for fifteen minutes or more prior to the test.

On the other hand, if the rays are allowed to fall only on a certain area of the retina, the rest of it being shielded from the action of X-rays by a thick lead screen, the luminous effects are likewise sharply outlined. Thus, for example, when a diaphragm, consisting of a thick plate of lead with a hole in it 3 mm in diameter, is held on one side near the eye, so that the X-rays cross the eyeball from the temporal to the nasal side, the result is that the bundle of rays meets the retina twice; and, consequently, two bright circles are seen, which are projected out in the field exactly in the same way as the pressure-phosphenes.

When the radiation enters the eye from the temporal side, the spot projected on the nasal side is brighter than that on the opposite side. This is easily explained because the nasal glow is the result of stimulation of the temporal half of the retina, and the glow projected on the temporal side is the result of stimulation of the nasal half; but ere the rays reach this part of the retina, they have been absorbed to some appreciable extent in the vitreous humor.

The contrast with the above is very striking when no diaphragm is used at all, and the rays are allowed to fall freely on the eye. The brightest sensation is always on the side from which the rays come; that is, usually on the temporal side, when the radiation is lateral. Radium emanation, as above stated, acts in the same way.

When a screen with a slit in it is moved to and fro between the eye and the RÖNTGEN tube, the phenomena are very instructive. The X-rays traverse the eye without being refracted; and, hence, the lines of intersection of the wedge-shaped bundle of rays with the nearly spherical retina appear projected in the field as curved lines depending

[1] WIEDEMANNS *Ann.* LX. 478, 1897; LXIV, 620, 1897; LXVI, 1171, 1898.

[2] *Arch. f. (Anat. u.) Physiol.* 1897.

[3] *Ber. d. preuss. Akad.* 1897. 576.

[4] *Ann. d. Physik.* IV F. 4, S. 537, 1901.

on the locus of the stimulation. The most conspicuous effects are obtained when the rays come through the diaphragm in the frontal direction from the temporal side of the eye, and when the aperture is in the form of a rectangular cross with vertical and horizontal beams. If the vertical slit is in the equatorial plane of the eye, two crosses are seen composed of approximately straight lines intersecting each other at right angles. If the diaphragm is shifted more towards the back of the eye, the crosses become much distorted and finally blend into their horizontal portions.

HIMSTEDT and NAGEL endeavoured to ascertain whether X-ray stimulation is a direct one, comparable with that of light; or whether fluorescence of the ocular media has a distinct part in it, as is the case in the perception of ultra-violet and BECQUEREL rays (see below). The mere fact that it is possible to stimulate precise parts of the retina by X-rays, indicated that it was extremely unlikely that there was any noteworthy fluorescence of the ocular media. And, as a matter of fact, not a single trace of fluorescence could be detected in these substances. But in the retina itself there was certainly some slight effect of this nature, much less, however, than that produced by ultra-violet rays. But whether the retina in the live eye does not fluoresce still more, is a question that has not been answered.

The eye must be dark-adapted in order to be sensitive to X-rays; and hence it seems likely that the same elements whose sensitivity to *light* rays increases so much in darkness must also be the perceptive agencies for the X-ray stimulation; that is, according to our assumption, the perceptive elements in this case must be the rods. Although the fluorescence of the retina under radiation is feeble, the layer that emits the fluorescent light and the layer that is sensitive to light must be exceedingly close together; in fact, they may partly coincide with each other. From this point of view, it may be that the perceptibility of X-rays has something to do with the fluorescence of the retina. But this explanation still does not account for the fact mentioned above, that the light sensation is greater on that side of the retina where the X-rays come to it through the vitreous humor.

It is often stated that the totally colour-blind are peculiarly able to see X-rays. But the only reason for this that can be suggested is, that these persons are accustomed by experience to shield their eyes as much as possible from bright light, and so when they enter the dark room, they are already more dark-adapted than other subjects with normal vision.

The writer put a bandage over both eyes of a totally colour-blind young girl. It was composed of many layers of black velvet, bound so tight that even after an hour in the lighted room she had not the

slightest sensation of light. When the X-ray tube was started, the
diffused light was visible to her a metre away. With her eyes blindfolded, she was able to tell when a lead plate was placed between her
and the tube, and when it was removed. But the results are similar for
normal individuals after an hour's dark adaptation.

Undoubtedly, the effect of radium emanation or BECQUEREL *rays*
on the visual apparatus is due to the fluorescence of the transparent
parts of the eye, including the retina. HIMSTEDT and NAGEL easily
succeeded in demonstrating this fluorescence in the eyes of various
animals. Since the entire contents of the eye, particularly the lens,
are self-luminous under the influence of radium, there can be no
question of a localization of the stimulus. The glow that is perceived
is therefore likewise a diffused one, except that, just as with X-ray
radiation, the strongest sensation of light is on the side where the
radium is placed.—N.

§18. Stimulation by Light

What we have now to consider is the excitation of the organ of
vision by means of objective light or aether vibrations. The vibrations of the aether are not included among the general agencies
of stimulating nerves such as electricity and mechanical injury, which
can disturb every part of any nerve fibre. It may be demonstrated
that the fibres of the optic nerve within the trunk of this nerve and in
the retina are no more stimulated by light than are the motor and
sensory nerve fibres of other nerves. Some special apparatus in the
retina at the end of the optic nerve fibres must be present, which is
adapted to enable objective light to start a nervous impulse.

First of all, let us show that the nerve fibres in the trunk of the
optic nerve are not stimulated by objective light. The bulk of these
fibres are at the place where the optic nerve comes into the eye through
the sclerotica. This nerve, lying exposed on the side towards the
transparent ocular media, is not overlaid with any black pigment;
and yet it is so translucent that light falling on it may penetrate it to
an appreciable extent. This can be shown with an ophthalmoscope
which often reveals ramifications of the central blood-vessels that are
inside the optic nerve and covered completely by the mass of nerves.
If such ramifications can be recognized in the interior of the nerve-
substance, light must penetrate that far so as to return from there
to the observer's eye. Thus, there is nothing to prevent the light
falling on the eye from penetrating to a certain depth in the substance
of the optic nerve. But *this light that falls on the place where the optic
nerve enters the eye is not perceived.*

Holding the book, with the lines in the usual horizontal position, at a distance of about one foot away, close the left eye, and look at the white cross in Fig. 1 with the other eye. There is a certain adjustment for which the white circle vanishes entirely from the field, and no gap is to be seen in the black background. To succeed with this experiment, one must look steadily at the little cross and not look to one side. When the book is moved closer or farther away, the white disc

Fig. 1.

reappears, and is distinctly seen by indirect vision; and the same thing happens also when the book is slanted so as to throw the white disc a little higher or lower. All other objects, white, black or coloured, that are not larger than the disc, disappear in like manner when they are laid on the disc, and the experiment is conducted in the same way. We learn, therefore, that in the field of each eye there is a certain gap where nothing can be discerned; and that accordingly there is a corresponding place on the surface of the retina that is not conscious of an image when it falls there. This place is called the *blind spot*. As the blind place in the visual field of the right eye is to the right of the point of fixation, and in that of the left eye to the left of the point of fixation, the blind spot of the retina must be on the nasal side of the yellow spot; in the region where the optic nerve comes into the eye.

That the blind spot is actually identical with the place of entrance of the optic nerve had been shown previously by measurement of its apparent size and of its apparent distance from the point of fixation of the eye. A still more direct proof was given by DONDERS[1] with his ophthalmoscope. This instrument was used to reflect the light of a small flame some distance away into the patient's eye; and the latter was made then to turn his eye until the little image of the flame fell on the place where the optic nerve enters the eye. The image here was not sharply outlined, and at the same time the entire optic disc, which was at least twenty times greater than the little image, was rendered

[1] *Onderzoekingen gedaan in-het Physiol. Labor. d. Utrechtsche Hoogeschool.* VI. 134.

quite luminous. This is due to the translucent nature of the nervous substance. On the retina itself, near the disc, he saw scarcely any trace of light that might be due to diffusion in the transparent media of the eye or that was reflected sideways from the brightly illuminated surface of the optic nerve. The patient was not conscious of any sensation of light as long as the little luminous image fell entirely on the disc. Some patients thought they perceived a faint glimmer of light; which possibly might be due to the feeble illumination of the retina mentioned above. By small movements of the mirror, the image could be made to move from one side to the other of the disc, but there was never any consciousness of light until a part of the image was distinctly across the boundary so as to fall on a place where the various layers of the retina were present. This means simply that the blind spot corresponds to the entire area where the optic nerve enters, and certainly is not just at those places where the blood-vessels enter the eye.

Subsequently, Coccius[1] showed how the same experiment could be performed by the observer in his own eye; which is still more instructive. For this purpose, a plane or convex mirror is used, with a hole in it, like the mirror of an ophthalmoscope. The observer holds it close in front of his eye, and allows the light from a lamp to come through the hole to his eye. If the eye is first turned right towards the edge of the hole, the little inverted red image of the flame on the retina of one's own eye can easily be seen. Now trying not to let the image go, turn the eye more and more inwards, until presently the image falls at the place where the optic nerve is; and then make the observations described above. Incidentally, the flame ought to be small or far away; otherwise, too much light will enter the eye. In this way the larger blood-vessels are seen, but the field, of course, is very small. When a larger flame is used, the eye is so blinded by it that it is impossible to see much. If the quantity of light falling on the place where the optic nerve enters the eye is large, a faint glimmer of light will certainly be perceived, but the explanation of it, according to these experiments, is that some of the light spreads out over adjacent parts of the retina. Sometimes too in experiments of this kind there is a red glow of light in the eye, perhaps when a blood-vessel on the surface of the optic nerve is highly illuminated and reflects light. This was seen by A. Fick and P. du Bois-Reymond by using for the object the image of the sun as made by a convex lens.

The form and apparent size of the blind spot in one's own visual field may be easily found as follows. Place the eye 8 or 12 inches above

---

[1] *Über Glaukom, Entzündung und die Autopsie mit dem Augenspiegel.* Leipzig 1859. S. 40, 52.

a sheet of white paper on which a little cross is marked to serve as point of fixation of the eye.

Take a white or at any rate brightly coloured pen, with some ink on its point, and move it over the paper into the projection of the

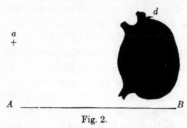

blind spot until the point disappears. Then move it from this place, first in one direction, and then in another, towards the periphery of the spot where it again begins to be visible. Fig. 2 shows the blind spot of the author's right eye, as drawn in this way with respect to *a* as

Fig. 2.

point of fixation. The length of the straight line *AB* is one-third of the distance betwen the eye and the paper for this particular figure. The spot has the form of an irregular ellipse, on which the writer can discern the beginnings of the larger blood-vessels, as seen also by HUECK. If a small black spot is made on the paper, and different points fixated one after another, the continuation of the vessels far in the field of the retina will be found to be blind places. The easiest way to do this is by finding first the direction of the blood-vessels in one's own eye by COCCIUS's method.

Let *f* denote the distance of the eye from the paper; *F* the distance of the second nodal point from the retina (which is about 15 mm on the average); *d* the diameter or any other linear dimension of the blind spot in the drawing; and *D* the corresponding magnitude on the retina; then

$$\frac{f}{F} = \frac{d}{D} ,$$

from which *D* can be calculated. In a measurement of this kind, the magnitude denoted by *F* can never be perfectly accurately determined for the individual eye; and so without using it, a better way is to measure the visual angle, that is, the angle between the direction-lines (see Vol. I, p. 96) corresponding to the different points of the drawing. If the lines of vision drawn to the point *a* in Fig. 2 may be assumed to be perpendicular to the plane of the figure, and if the distance *ad* is denoted by β, and the angle subtended by *ad* is denoted by α, then

$$\frac{\beta}{f} = \tan \alpha .$$

from which the angle a can be calculated. In the same way the visual angle between a and any other point in the drawing may be found. The following are results obtained in this way by different observers:

(1) Apparent distance of the point of fixation from the nearest part of the edge of the blind spot: LISTING[1] 12° 37.5′. HELMHOLTZ 12° 25′. THOS. YOUNG 12° 56′.

(2) Apparent distance of the most distant part of the edge: LISTING 18° 33.4′. HELMHOLTZ 18° 55′. THOMAS YOUNG 16° 1′.

(3) Apparent diameter of the blind spot in the horizontal direction: HANNOVER and THOMSEN[2] for 22 eyes 3° 39′ to 9° 47′; average of all measurements 6° 10′. LISTING 5° 55.9′. GRIFFIN,[3] largest value, 7° 31′. HELMHOLTZ 6° 56′. THOMAS YOUNG, who rather inconveniently used two lights for finding the boundary of the spot, 3° 5′.

(4) Actual diameter of the blind spot, using LISTING's value of 15 mm for F, in LISTING's eye, 1.55 mm. HELMHOLTZ 1.81 mm. HANNOVER and THOMSEN, average, 1.616 mm.

A measurement by E. H. WEBER of the diameter of the place of entrance of the optic nerve in two cadavers gave 2.10 mm and 1.72 mm. The distance from its centre to the centre of the yellow spot was in one eye 3.8 mm; whereas the same distance as calculated for LISTING's eye was 4.05 mm. The greatest and smallest diameters of the vessels in the middle of the nerve were 0.707 and 0.314 mm; the greatest in the other eye 0.633 mm.

Even before DONDERS's experiments it might have been inferred from these measurements that the entire optic disc was insensitive to light.

Another way of forming some idea of the apparent size of the blind spot in the field of view is to try to realize that eleven full moons can be placed side by side along its diameter. In it a human face 6 or 7 feet away will disappear.[4]

That the fibres in the trunk of the optic nerve cannot be stimulated by light, is shown by the phenomena of the blind spot that have been described. That the ramifications of this nerve which spread out from the disc all over the anterior surface of the retina are likewise insensitive to light, may be inferred from the fact that perfectly definite bright places in the field of view are seen also as actually definite places.

---

[1] *Berichte der Königl. sächs. Ges. der Wiss.* 1852. S. 149. E. H. WEBER's observations are also given here.

[2] A. HANNOVER, *Bidrag til Øjets Anatomie.* Kjöbenhavn. Cap. VI. S. 61.

[3] GRIFFIN, Contributions to the physiology of vision. London, *Medical Gazette.* 1838 May. p. 230.

[4] ¶It is related that that "merry monarch," King Charles II, got much amusement by making his courtiers see how they would look when their heads were off their shoulders. (J. P. C. S.)

When light falls on a place A on the retina, it meets here not only those fibres that end in A but also those which pass over A and end in the more peripheral parts of the retina. Now since the place at which a nerve fibre is stimulated is not discriminated in the sensation, so far as sensation is concerned, the result would be the same as if light had fallen on those peripheral parts of the retina. If this were the case, we should see a streak of light extending from every illuminated point to the borders of the visual field, which of course is not the case. In other words, the fibres of the optic nerve spreading out over the retina cannot be stimulated by objective light.

On the other hand, the evidence of the sensitiveness of the posterior layers of the retina to light is afforded by the ability of seeing the shadows of the retinal vessels (Vol. I, 211). The retinal vessels lie in the layer of the optic nerve fibres, some finer ones also in the layer immediately posterior to that of the ganglion cells (No. 6 in Fig. 14 of Vol. I) and in the fine granular layer (No. 5 of same diagram). From the movements of the shadow of these vessels when the source of light is moved, the inference is that the layer by which the shadow is perceived, the layer in which the light on the edge of the shadow gives rise to nerve excitation, must be a very little distance beyond the vessels. According to H. Müller's measurements (Vol. I, p. 220), the distance of the vessels from the surface which perceives their shadow must be between 0.17 and 0.36 mm. The distance of the vessels from the most posterior part of the retina where the rods and cones are, according to the same authority, is between 0.2 and 0.3 mm. Thus in any case the sensitive layer must be one of the most posterior layers of the retina; that is, the layer of rods and cones or the outer granular layer. At the place where vision is most distinct, which, according to Remak and Koelliker is in the central cavity of the yellow spot, there is nothing but ganglion cells and cones; consequently, the latter would seem to be the elements that are peculiarly sensitive.[1] H. Müller and Koelliker express the opinion that the

[1] In the second edition of this treatise, a briefer statement was substituted in place of the rest of this paragraph as given above, which follows the text of the first edition. With respect to the function of the rods, the new statement was different from the original view, and reads as follows (p. 255): "From the perfectly analogous anatomical structure of the rods it is extremely probable that they also have the same sort of capacity; which was the opinion of H. Müller and Koelliker. Nevertheless, they must play an entirely different rôle in the localization of sensations, because, in spite of their being finer and more numerous in the peripheral parts of the retina where they predominate, the power of discrimination between very nearly similar impressions is more imperfect in this region than it is in the fovea.

"Since the investigation of the delicacy of perception of different parts of the retina is essentially bound up with the question as to what elements of the retina are sensitive to light (that is, excite a sensation when light acts on them), and how they are connected with nerve fibres, let us consider this question first.

rods are also sensitive, because, like the cones, they too are connected with similar fibres traversing the retina perpendicularly. But as remarked by E. H. WEBER, this assumption seems to be opposed to the fact that there are nothing but cones at the place of most distinct vision; whereas out towards the periphery of the retina where more and more rods are found between the cones, acuity of vision becomes less and less perfect. If the rods were sensitive elements, it might be expected that the sensitivity and exactness of perception would necessarily be greater where the rods are more numerous, because there are more rods than cones in the same area. The connection with radial fibres is no proof of the nervous nature of the rods, because a large number of the radial fibres are attached to the *membrana limitans*, and it is therefore extremely probable that these are connective tissue, and not nerve fibres at all. In saying that the posterior layer of the retina and particularly the cones are the last elements of the nervous mechanism of vision that are sensitive to light, of course, what is meant is that external light stimulates changes in these structures that result in nervous excitation and, finally, in sensation, if this excitation is transmitted to the brain. In fact, the *light-sensitive* elements of the retina, as they may be called, just as we speak of a sensitive plate in photography, are functionally different from all other parts of the nervous system simply by virtue of their sensitivity to light, just as on the other hand they are in so many respects different in their anatomical structure. Another result also is that the action of light on the peculiar nervous substance of the retina and optic nerve is not an immediate one, as in the case of electricity and of mechanical disturbance, whereby in every nerve fibre at every place in it the molecular changes can be started that constitute the process of stimulation. The action of light is more indirect. It acts directly only on the special light-sensitive apparatus or the cones. We have no idea as to what kind of an effect this is and as to what, if any, similarity there is between it and nerve stimulation; whether a vibration is set up, as NEWTON,[1] MELLONI,[2] SEEBECK[3] and other physicists supposed;

"The part of the retina which is capable of the finest spatial discrimination is a perfectly regular mosaic of individual parts, that is, the cones. Each of these is connected with a nerve fibre, which is then connected with the cells of the retina. Accordingly, the assumption that every single cone has its own independent nerve conduction to the brain, and that, consequently, the sensation excited in it can be distinguished from qualitatively equal sensations in the adjacent cones, does not seem improbable."

For the more modern conceptions of the functional difference between rods and cones, see the Note at end of § 25.—N.

[1] *Optice.* Lib. III. Quaestio XVI.
[2] POGG. *Ann.* LVI. 574.
[3] Ibid. LXII. 571.

whether there is a shift in molecular arrangement, as E. DU BOIS-REYMOND supposes to take place in the electromotor molecules of muscles and nerves; whether there is some heating effect, as DRAPER[1] thinks; or whether this light-sensitive layer of the retina is some part of a photo-chemical apparatus, as MOSER[2] assumed. At any rate, stimulation of those nerve fibres connected with the cones that are acted on by light is merely a secondary result of these changes, whatever they are.

Acuity of visual perception is also connected with the size of the retinal element stimulated by light. The light that falls on a single sensitive element can produce nothing but a single light sensation. In such a sensation there is no way of telling whether some parts of the element are highly illuminated as compared with other parts. A luminous point can be perceived when its image on the retina is very much smaller than a single retinal element, provided the amount of light from it that falls on the eye is sufficient to affect the sensitive element appreciably. Thus, for example, the fixed stars, are perceived as objects of great brilliancy, although their apparent sizes are vanishingly small. Similarly, too, a dark object on a bright background may be perceived even when its image is smaller than a sensitive nerve element, provided the amount of light that falls on the element is perceptibly diminished by the dark image around it. Thus, suppose that with the given degree of illumination, the eye is capable of perceiving differences of two percent in light intensity; then a dark image whose area was two percent of that of a sensitive element might still be perceived. Obviously, on the other hand, two bright points cannot be distinguished as separate unless the distance between their images is greater than the diameter of a retinal element. Were the distance less than this, the two images would have to fall on the same element or on two adjacent elements. In the first case, both would excite simply a single sensation; and in the second case, there would indeed be two sensations, but in adjacent nerve elements, so that it would be impossible to tell whether there were two separate points of light or only one whose image happened to be on the border of both elements. The distance between the two bright images, at least between their centres, must be greater than the width of a single sensitive element if the two images are to fall on two different and non-contiguous elements, with another element in between them that is not stimulated by light at all, or at least is more feebly stimulated than the others.

[1] *Human physiology.* p. 392.
[2] POGG. *Ann.* LVI. 177.

According to HOOKE's dictum,[1] two stars whose apparent distance apart is less than 30″ appear as one; and scarcely one person in a hundred can distinguish two stars when their apparent distance apart is less than 60″. Others, who have made their observations, not on stars, but on illuminated white lines or rectangles, have found the resolving power of the eye rather less than this. The best eye examined by E. H. WEBER was able to distinguish two white marks whose middle lines were 73″ apart. With higher illumination, and under the most favourable conditions, the author has been able to make out lines of this sort that were only 64″ apart. In LISTING's schematic eye a visual angle of 73″ corresponds to a distance on the retina of 0.00526 mm; an angle of 63″ to 0.00464 mm; and an angle of 60″ to 0.00438 mm. KOELLIKER's measurements give for the diameter of the cones in the yellow spot values between 0.0045 and 0.0054 mm. This agrees almost exactly with the above figures, and incidentally also tends to confirm the assumption that the cones are the last sensitive elements of the retina.[2]

At the same time, it is clear that the optical characteristics of a well constructed and correctly accommodated eye are quite sufficient for attaining the resolving power that the eye is actually known to have. As a matter of fact, with a pupil of 4 mm diameter, the blur circle on the retina due to chromatic aberration was found to be 0.0426 mm in diameter (see §13); that is, almost ten times greater than the width of a cone. But it was explained at the time why this blur circle, in spite of its size, did not sensibly disturb good vision. The aberrations due to asymmetry of the eye (see §14) are generally

[1] SMITH's System of Compleat Opticks, Vol. I, Book I, Chap. 3, 97.

[2] ¶See NAGEL's note at end of this section.

From the standpoints of both geometrical and physical optics, it is extremely improbable, even under the most favourable circumstances, that the image on the retina is ever actually so small as not to exceed the diameter of a single cone. It must certainly be larger than this if either diffraction-effects or aberrations are taken into account. It has been found recently that the apparent size of minute objects subtending angles as much as 2 or 3 minutes of arc depends essentially on the intensity of illumination.

The *aligning power* of the eye is essentially different from its *resolving power* in the sense of being able to distinguish the components of a double star. The perception of width, that is, of slight lateral differences of position, is distinctly sharper than that of vertical dimensions. The precision with which the eye can adjust a mark on a vernier scale to coincide with a division on the principal scale is extraordinarily great. Under the best conditions skilled observers succeed in making such settings with an average error of not more than 3″ of arc. In coincidence range-finders the two images can be aligned with an error that usually does not exceed 12″, and in some instances with an error of not more than 2″. —In daylight a dark line on a bright background whose length is not less than a few minutes of arc can be perceived provided its thickness is as much as 1.2 seconds. Under the same circumstances a bright line on a dark background must be at least 3.5 seconds wide to be recognized. (J. P. C. S.)

much smaller and have less bad effect on vision, unless one tries to see horizontal and vertical lines at the same time.

The resolving power is much less in the lateral parts of the retina than in the yellow spot; the decrease near the centre of the retina being less than it is farther away from it. The measurements made by AUBERT and FÖRSTER show that the decrease in different directions from the centre proceeds at different rates, being most rapid up and down, and slowest towards the outer side of the retina. However, individual differences in this respect are fairly large. Another noteworthy result from these measurements is that in accommodation for distance, the falling off of the resolving power towards the periphery of the retina seems to proceed more rapidly than it does in near vision. These observers found that a similar decrease of the power of discrimination of optical images out towards the periphery of the retina certainly does not occur in rabbits' eyes. This proves that the imperfection of vision in the peripheral parts of the retina depends simply on the peculiarity of the retina, and not at all on the quality of the optical images.

TOB. MAYER, and subsequently E. H. WEBER also, used parallel white lines separated by black ones of the same width as test-object for finding the smallest interval that can be discerned. VOLKMANN used spider filaments on a bright background. For convenience of illumination, the author found it better to use a grating of black wires separated by intervals equal to the diameter of the wire; which was set up against the background of the bright sky. TOB. MAYER also used white squares, partly separated by a black grating and partly arranged like a chess board.

In making these tests, the eye should be able to accommodate perfectly. When coarser objects are used, which have, therefore, to be set up farther away, an appropriate concave lens should be placed in front of the eye. The illumination must be strong, but not too dazzling. The author observed a striking change in the form of the bright and dark straight lines. The width of each bright and dark band in his grating was $\frac{1}{2}\frac{3}{4} = 0.4167$ mm. At a distance between 110 and 120 cm the effect began to be apparent; the grating assuming an appearance something like that shown in Fig. 3A. The white lines seemed to be curved partly like waves, and partly like a string of pearls with places alternately thicker and thinner. In Fig. 3B the little hexagons are supposed to be sections of cones in the yellow spot; and a, b, and c represent optical images of three bars of the grating. Above dd these images are shown in their real form; but below dd, all the hexagons, that were predominantly black, are made entirely black, and all that were

predominantly white, are made entirely white; the idea being that the
predominant character is responsible for
the sensation that is perceived. Thus
in the lower portion of Fig. 3*B* a pattern
is obtained that is similar to that in *A*.
PURKINJE[1] saw something of the kind;
and BERGMANN also noticed that sometimes just before the lines of a grating
disappeared completely, the grating
looked like a chess-board, the bands

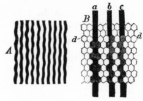

Fig. 3.

sometimes being seen at right angles to their actual direction; all of
which may be explained in the same way as above.[2]

When the widths of two luminous objects used in the test are
vanishingly small as compared with the interval between them, they
cannot be seen as separate unless there is an unstimulated retinal
element between the retinal elements on which their images fall. In
other words, the diameter of such an element must certainly be less
than the interval between the two images. However, if the width of
the object is the same as the dark interval between each pair of
them, it is not absolutely necessary that the retinal elements shall be
smaller than the image of the dark band. A retinal element on
which the image of the dark band falls, and which extends on its
sides partly into the bright bands, is thus in a position to perceive
less light than the adjacent elements; provided the total amount of
light that falls on it is less than that that falls on its neighbours. In
such cases, therefore, the most we can say is that the retinal elements
are smaller than the interval between the middle lines of the bright
bands. As a matter of fact, the results of TOB. MAYER's experiments, as
given below, show that with parallel lines the resolving power remains
the same as before when the width of the black or white bands is
changed, without varying the total width of the two. This is the reason
why the author has always used this sum of the two as the width of the
object, that is, the interval between the middle lines of two adjacent
objects (contrary to the usage of MAYER and WEBER); and this is the
distance used in calculating the smallest visual angle or angle of
distinctness.

The explanation of the greater resolving power of the author's eye
as compared with that of other adults may be due to the brighter
illumination that was possible with his grating. The keenest eye was
that of a ten year old boy examined by BERGMANN. TOB. MAYER
studied the influence of illumination. He found that systems of lines

[1] *Beobachtungen und Versuche.* I. 122.
[2] HENLE and PFEUFFER. *Zeitschrift für ration. Medizin.* (3.) II. 88.

could be seen better when illuminated by quite bright daylight, and that any higher illumination did no good. At night he obtained lesser degrees of illumination by placing a light at different distances from the paper. The farther away the light was, the nearer he had to come. When the distance of the light was gradually increased from 6 inches to 13 feet, the visual angle for white bands with an equally wide interval between them, increased (as above calculated) from 138 to 344″.

Observer	Object	Size of Object in mm	Distance from eye in mm	Distance divided by size of object	Visual angle in seconds
1. HOOKE..........	Fixed stars..........	....	....	....	60
2. TOB. MAYER	(a) Parallel lines with intervals of same width............	1.624	3573	2200	94
	(b) Parallel lines with wider and narrower intervals..........	1.354	3086	2280	90
3. TOB. MAYER.....	White squares separated by black grating..........	1.985	5035	2536	81
4. TOB. MAYER.....	Chess board.........	2.346	3898	1661	124
5. VOLKMANN......	Spider webs.........	0.141	190	1346	153.2
6. N. N. by VOLKMANN.....	Spider webs.........	....	352	2500	80.4
7. TH. WEBER by E. H. WEBER..	Parallel lines with in-intervals of same width............	0.113	249	2210	93.3
8. N. N. by E. H. WEBER..	Parallel lines with intervals of same width............	....	311	2760	73
9. N. N. by E. H. WEBER..	Parallel lines with intervals of same width............	....	249	2210	90.6
10. HELMHOLTZ	Rod grating.........	1.083	3500	3232	63.82
11. O. H. by HELMHOLTZ....	Rod grating.........	....	2400	2215	93
12. BERGMANN......	Parallel lines with intervals of same width............	2	5500 to 8000	2750 4000	75 51.6

He found an empirical formula which corresponds fairly well to his measurements, namely $s = 158'' \sqrt[3]{a}$, where s denotes the visual angle and a denotes the distance of the light. As the brightness $h = \dfrac{1}{a^2}$, it follows that $s = \dfrac{158}{\sqrt[6]{h}}$.

Supplement by HELMHOLTZ (*in the first edition*)

A. VOLKMANN has published an account of some new experiments which lead him to think that the foveal cones are not fine enough to explain the actual visual acuity of the human eye. The principal experiments were made with a pair of fine wires stretched in front of a bright background, which, by means of a micrometer screw, could be brought so close together that the interval between them apparently vanished. VOLKMANN considered this interval as the smallest visible object, and subtracted from its actual value the irradiation fringe by which the width of the wires is apparently increased. Thus he found extraordinarily minute values for the smallest images, apparently very much smaller than the retinal cones. The author, however, is obliged to take exception to VOLKMANN's results, because, as was pointed out above, it is not right to conclude from such experiments that the perceptive elements of the retina are smaller than the image of the space between the wires, but merely that they are smaller than the distance from the middle of one dark band to the middle of the next. These latter distances in VOLKMANN's experiments are not very much smaller than those previously found by other observers.

The experiment with systems of parallel wires, as described above in the text, has been repeated by Dr. HIRSCHMANN, with many variations, in order to find the best conditions. He obtained values of the angle of distinctness in some cases as small as 50 seconds, which means on the retina a width of 0.00365 mm. But the most recent measurements of the diameter of foveal cones are as follows: M. SCHULTZE, 0.0020 to 0.0025 mm; H. MÜLLER, 0.0015 to 0.0020 mm; and WELCKER, 0.0031 to 0.0036 mm. Thus, the cones are minute enough to account for the actual resolving power of the eye.

In other experiments VOLKMANN used letters, figures and other forms of objects, and attempted to establish the fact that the number of cones on which the image of the object fell is not large enough to enable its form to be discerned. But it should be remembered that when the eye is moved, the image of a letter may be formed successively on different groups of cones, in relatively different positions on the single cones; and that differences which perhaps disappear in one position of the image may become clear in another.

The author does not believe, therefore, that we are forced to abandon the view that the retinal cones are the perceptive elements. But it is possible, judging from the most recent observations of M. SCHULTZE, that the rod-like ends of the cones in the yellow spot, turned towards the choroid and separated from each other by black pigment, which measure only 0.00066 mm, may be the only sensory elements, and not the entire cones.

Oculists usually measure visual acuity by means of letters of different size which the patient is made to view from a considerable distance, with spectacle glasses to aid the accommodation. The measure of the visual acuity of the eye is expressed by a fraction, whose numerator is the distance at which those letters are still legible, whereas the denominator is the distance at which they subtend an angle of 5'. These latter distances were used in SNELLEN's test-charts.

. According to VROESOM DE HAAN, the visual acuity at ten years of age is 1.1; at forty years, 1.0; and at 80 years, 0.5; showing a gradual decrease with advancing age. But E. JAVAL finds that when astigmatism is corrected and the illumination is good (equal to 500 candles at a distance of one metre) the visual acuity is from 1/4 to 1/3 higher than that given by DE HAAN.

Note by W. NAGEL

In open daylight or with pretty good artificial illumination, the visual acuity as determined by the SNELLEN test above mentioned is found to be on the average higher than unity. Some letters can be recognized better than others; and therefore at present instead of letters it is common to use hook-shaped figures in the form of E or ⊏, and the test consists in saying which side of the figure is open. Just as in the case of the SNELLEN test-type, the visual acuity is put equal to unity when the hook-figure that can just be distinguished subtends a visual angle of 5'. The figures are constructed so that the width of each separate black line is one-fifth the total width of the figure.

Higher values of the visual acuity are obtained by tests with these hooks than with letters and numerals; for example, with good illumination or sky-light, the visual acuity of the normal eye measured in this way averages between 1.5 and 2.0. And it is not rare to find persons with visual acuity even as high as 4, particularly in the case of savages, some of whom, according to measurements of H. COHN, KOTELMANN and G. FRITSCH, certainly have a visual acuity of 6. COHN finds that the average visual acuity of savages is not strikingly greater than that of civilized people; but the more thorough investigations made by G. FRITSCH indicate a distinct, although no very great, superiority among savages in this respect.[1]

In LISTING's schematic eye, according to the data given above in the text, an angle of 60'' corresponds to a length of 0.00438 mm on the retina.

---

[1] ¶It is well known that the sense perceptions of savages are very extraordinarily developed in some respects, as shown by their astonishing quickness in shooting, hunting, etc. Quality of vision and high visual acuity depend largely on training in youth and practice. HUMBOLDT, describing his adventures in the Andes mountains, relates incidentally how the Indians in his party were able to discern his guide in a white cloak a long way off as a white point moving in front of black basaltic rock walls, before HUMBOLDT himself could make him out through his field glasses; although soon afterwards he also was able to see the guide with his naked eye. The natives were cleverer and quicker in perceiving this faint object, but their actual visual acuity was probably not much higher. Apparently, the visual acuity of mankind has not changed materially in several thousand years. We know from the records of antiquity that the seven stars of the Pleiades appeared the same to former generations as they do today. Stars of the seventh magnitude were invisible to the normal eye then as now. (J. P. C. S.)

With a visual acuity of 5, on the basis of SNELLEN's system of measurement, a letter or hook that could just be discerned would subtend an angle of 60″ or 1′.

Assuming, as HELMHOLTZ did on the basis of KOELLIKER's measurements, that the diameter of the smallest visual element of the retina is 0.0045 mm, the image of the tiniest test-figure that could be discerned by an eye whose visual acuity was equal to 5 would have to be formed on the surface of a single retinal cone. If that were the case, the power of discerning form would be incomprehensible. But, as HELMHOLTZ himself states in his supplement to this section, H. MÜLLER found that the foveal cones are much narrower, their diameters being from 0.0015 to 0.002 mm (which is in accordance with the most recent measurements made by G. FRITSCH). Thus on the assumption of fine cones of this kind, even the high values of the visual acuity recently obtained by COHN and FRITSCH are comprehensible at least for the simple Ⴀ-figures. (N.)

The researches of AUBERT and FÖRSTER as to the precision of vision in the peripheral parts of the retina were carried out by two methods. In the first method, in order to secure the position of the eye and also to protect it from lateral glare, the observer looked through a firmly clamped black tube at an arc (2 feet wide and 5 feet long) on which various characters, letters and numerals, were marked at equal intervals apart. The contrivance could be moved on rollers, so that after each test the portion of it within sight of the observer could be quickly changed. The letters and numerals were in no regular series of any sort, and so the observer could never guess any numbers except those which he had actually seen. A Leyden jar in front of the arc was discharged from time to time, thereby illuminating the characters for an instant. In the intervals it was so dark that, while the observer was barely able to see the place where the letters were, he could not discern their forms. An assistant adjusted the arc with the letters on it in any position he pleased, and after each inspection the observer told what characters he had recognized. Four arcs were used with characters of different size; and the distance between the observer and the objects could be varied.

The angle subtended by the portion of the arc which contained characters that could be recognized, that is, double the angle between the visual axis and the extreme outside visible letter or figure, AUBERT called the *space-angle (Raumwinkel)*; and the angle subtended by the longest dimensions of the visible characters he called the *number-angle (Zahlenwinkel)*. In terms of this nomenclature, the result of the tests was found to be, that *with characters of the same actual size, the ratio between the number-angle and the space-angle was nearly constant*; provided the space-angles were not more than 30° or 40°, in which case the number-angles were rather larger than they should have been in order to obey this rule. On the other hand, *with characters of the same*

*apparent size, small characters nearer the eye were easier to discern than
larger characters farther away.* The following table gives the results
that were obtained in this case for the ratio between the space-angle
and the number-angle:

Actual size of characters in mm	Limiting value of space-angle	Ratio of space-angle to number-angle		
		Minimum	Maximum	Mean
26	25°	7	7.9	7.18
26	40	6	7.3	6.69
13	27	11	12	11.14
7	27	9.7	14.5	12.79

In the second column, under "limiting value of the space-angle,"
the extreme value is given for which the ratio of the two angles was
found to be approximately constant. The last column shows that the
ratio between the two angles increases when the actual size of the
characters is diminished. The reason for this is difficult to explain.
Could it be that the mechanism of accommodation somehow alters the
peripheral parts of the retina? AUBERT supposes that in far vision
the rods are obliquely disposed in the marginal portions of the retina,
and consequently hamper the normal procedure of the rays of light.

In the second method the apparatus represented in Fig. 4 was used
with ordinary daylight. *A* is a strip of white lacquered tin, 30 cm

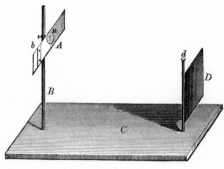

long and 5 cm wide, which
can be turned around the
axle *u* like the wing of a
windmill. It can be raised
and lowered on the up-
right *B* which is fastened
to the baseboard *C*. The
observer's eye is placed
at the other end of the
board, opposite the axle
u; his other eye being
screened by a piece of
black paper *D*, which is

Fig. 4.

fastened to a wooden upright *d* and capable of being turned to the
right and left. The axle of the tin strip is 20 cm away from the middle
of the line connecting the two eyes. The board *C* has a handle underneath.

The observations were made by putting the nose on the wooden rod d, covering one eye with the screen, supporting the chin on the board in front of the screen, and adjusting the axle of the tin strip at the same level with the eyes. Thus stationed, the observer gazes steadily at the middle of the strip (or the tip of the axle). There is a white card b which slides in grooves in the tin strip; and it has two points marked on it. He gradually moves it from one side towards the point of fixation; and as soon as he can distinguish the two points by their images in the periphery of the retina, the card is halted, and the distance between the two points and the point of fixation is read on a scale on the tin strip. The same measurements are repeated with the tin strip inclined to the horizontal at various angles. There were several white cards, each with two round black spots on them, of various sizes and at different distances apart; but the two spots were always symmetrically situated with respect to the axle u.

The results of these measurements for a pair of black spots 2.5 mm in diameter and at a distance of 14.5 mm apart are exhibited in Fig. 5.

The continuous contour line is the diagram for AUBERT's eye, and the dotted line for FÖRSTER's eye. The *radii vectores* all intersect in the point corresponding

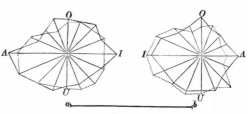

Fig. 5.

to the point of fixation of the eye; and those that are drawn in the figure indicate the directions of the strip of tin for which actual measurements were made. The points designated by O and U are the upper and lower limits of the field in the vertical meridian, and the points designated by A and I are the temporal and nasal limits in the horizontal meridian. The length of the line ab shows the distance of the eye from the tin strip, which was 20 cm; all the linear dimensions in the diagram being one-fifth actual size.[1] Accordingly, these areas are, first of all, those parts of the field of view within which two dots of the given dimensions and interval apart may be distinguished. The corresponding areas on the retina are obtained by inverting these diagrams. The irregular oval form of the contour is quite different even for the two eyes of the same individual.

---

[1] AUBERT states that the dimensions in the diagram are reduced one-fourth; but this does not agree with his numerical data.

The average results of measurements with different pairs of dots are shown in Fig. 6; where a designates the point of fixation. With

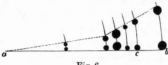

Fig. 6.

each pair of dots the measurements were made on four eyes in eight different meridians. The length of the line ab is the average distance between the eye and the tin strip for one pair of dots; similarly, ac is the average distance for another pair of dots, etc. The pair of dots at c is the pair for which Fig. 5 is drawn. Evidently, the farther away the eye is, the more rapidly the interval increases between the pair of dots. The average results as actually obtained were as follows (distances all given in millimetres):

Interval between dots	Diameter of dot	Average distance from middle of tin strip
3.25	1.25	31
6.5	2.5	50
9.5	3.75	55
12.	1.25	60
14.5	2.5	65
20.5	3.75	77

Moreover, in these tests both AUBERT and FÖRSTER frequently discovered also places in the retina that were insensitive, small blind spots as it were, where one of the dots or both of them suddenly vanished. At some of these places the blindness was apparently only temporary; but there were others where it was more or less permanent and which could always be found again.

The phenomena of the blind spot were discovered by MARIOTTE who was interested in finding out what sort of vision there was at the place of entrance of the optic nerve. The experiment aroused so much interest that he performed it before King CHARLES II of England in 1668. PICARD modified the experiment in such a way that even with both eyes open, the observer could not see anything. The way he did it was to fasten a piece of paper on the wall, and stand off from it at a distance of about ten feet; then holding his finger right in front of his face, he converged both eyes on it so that its image fell on the blind spot of each eye and therefore was not seen at all. Otherwise, under the same circumstances it would have been seen double. MARIOTTE made still another improvement of the experiment by making two objects vanish with both eyes open. Two bits of paper were fastened at the same level on a wall, three feet apart. The observer stands about twelve or thirteen feet from the wall with his thumb held about eight inches from the eye, so that it hides the left-hand piece of paper from the right eye and the other piece from the left eye. Now if he looks at his thumb, both pieces of paper will disappear because their images fall on the blind spot of that eye from which neither of them is screened by his thumb. LE CAT tried also to calculate the size of the blind spot on the retina, but he found it far too small, namely, from 0.20 to 0.25 Paris line. DANIEL BERNOUILLI drew its outline on the floor. The way he did it was to close one eye and hold the cord of a plummet close to the open eye; the plummet itself just missed the floor. Looking vertically down the cord, he tried to find the places on the floor where a coin would have to be put so as just to begin to disappear from view. The figure he got was nearly elliptical. But lacking sufficiently accurate data as to the optical constants of the eye, he got too high a value for the size of the blind spot. According to his calculation its diameter was about one-seventh of that of the eye.

MARIOTTE's discovery led to a lengthy discussion of a question, which, with the meagre knowledge of the nerve-functions at that time, was perhaps bound to arise; namely, as to whether it was really the retina that perceived light, as had been assumed by KEPLER and SCHEINER. MARIOTTE decided that it was the choroid, because this coating was absent in the blind spot, while the fibres of the retina are very numerous there. In fact, a whole line of men notable in optical science, as, for example, MERY, LE CAT, MICHELL and, among more recent ones, BREWSTER, espoused MARIOTTE's view of the matter. Thus, it was argued that, since the retina was transparent, it could not retain the light, and that it was too thick to give a sharp image. LE CAT even tried to show that the choroid was a continuation of the *Pia Mater* of the brain. The sensitivity of the retina to light was defended by PECQUET, DE LA HIRE, HALLER, PORTERFIELD, PERRAULT and ZINN. Curiously enough the chief argument they used to support this view was that the retina was the anatomical development of a very large nerve, whereas the choroid has only a few small nerves. The other arguments that were advanced to support their opinion and to offset the difficulties about MARIOTTE's experiment were not of much value. PORTERFIELD maintained that the optic nerve was still surrounded and permeated by the sinewy sheaths of the nerve at the place where it entered the eye, and was not soft and delicate enough to be sensitive to so nice an agency as light. HALLER also argued that there was no real retina at the entrance of the optic nerve but a white porous membrane which may be unsuitable for vision, without implying that the retina itself is unsuitable. Others, for example, RUDOLPHI, and COCCIUS too at first, believed that the non-sensitive place corresponded merely to the central vessels of the optic nerve; but as soon as the optical constants of the eye were more accurately known, this view was shown to be untenable by authorities like HANNOVER, E. H. WEBER, A. FICK, and P. DU BOIS-REYMOND. J. MÜLLER thought that the matter could be explained on the assumption that the MARIOTTE effect was analogous to the disappearance of the images of coloured objects when they are formed on a white background on the peripheral parts of the retina; which will be discussed later in §23. This is due to fatigue of the retina. But he supposed this occurred very much more rapidly and suddenly at the place of entrance of the optic nerve. The objection to this is that a bright object which emerges suddenly in the invisible gap in the field of view is not perceived at all, and so does not stimulate the visual substance at all; and hence there can be no question of fatigue.

The necessary conclusions from the facts as above set forth were formulated by the writer as long ago as 1851. He took the position then that objective light was incapable of affecting the fibres of the optic nerve as well as the fibres that spread over the anterior surface of the retina. At that time it had not been discovered that there was any anatomical connection between the layer of rods and the nervous elements of the retina; and hence the only assumption that could be made was that the retinal nerve cells or granules were the light-sensitive elements. Soon thereafter H. Müller discovered the radial fibres of the retina connected with the elements by the cones and rods. Koelliker showed that they were in the human eye. Both of them conjectured that the elements of the layer of rods were the light-sensitive elements; and, finally, the physiological proof of it was produced by Müller. It is true the same view had been previously put forth by Treviranus, but without sufficient information as to the microscopical structure. He called the light-sensitive elements *nerve papillae*.

Precision of vision has been an object of research ever since the time when telescopes began to be made. Hooke used the right principle before anybody else, by trying to find out what had to be the angular distance of the components of a double star in order for it to be recognized as such. But nearly all subsequent investigators have tried to ascertain the smallest size of a black dot that can still be made out by the eye; and, naturally, the results obtained have been very various. Among these may be mentioned Hevelius, Smith, Jurin, Tob. Mayer, Courtivon, Muncke, and Treviranus. The influence of illumination in these tests was recognized by Jurin and Mayer. Jurin supposed that the reason why the visual angle has to be greater in order to distinguish two marks as separate from each other than it has to be in order to recognize each mark by itself, was because the eye trembled and hence the images formed on two rods merged together. Volkmann gave the reason why the only way to have a constant measure of visual acuity is by the method of separating two distinct objects. Measurements by this method were made by E. H. Weber, Bergmann and Marié Davy.

Blind Spot and Localization of the Light Sensation

1668. Mariotte, *Oeuvres.* p. 496–516; also in *Mém. de l'Acad. de Paris 1669 et 1682·* *Phil. Transact.* II. 668. *Acta Eruditorum* 1683. p. 68.
1670. Pecquet, *Phil. Transact.* XIII. 171.
    Perrault, ibid. XIII. 265.
1694. De la Hire, *Accidens de la vue.*
1704. Mery, *Hist. de l'Acad. de Paris.* 1704.
1709. De la Hire, ibid. 1709. p. 119. 1711. p. 102.
1728. D. Bernouilli, *Comment. Petropol. vet.* T. 1. p. 314.
1738. Smith, *Optics.* Cambridge 1738. Remarks. p. 6.
1740. Le Cat, *Traité des sens.* Rouen. p. 171. 176–180.
1755. Zinn, *Descriptio oculi humani.* p. 37.
1757. Haller, *Physiologia.* T. V. p. 357, 474.
1759. Porterfield, *On the eye.* II. 252, 254.
1772. Michell in Priestley, *Geschichte der Optik.* 4. Per. 5. Abt. 2. Kap. (German edition, S. 149.)
1819. Purkinje, *Beobachtungen und Versuche.* I. 70 and 83.
1835. D. Brewster, Poggendorffs *Ann.* XXIX. 339.
    G. R. Treviranus, *Beiträge zur Aufklärung der Erscheinungen und Gesetze des organ. Lebens.* Bremen.
1838. Griffin, Contributions to the physiology of vision. *London medical gazette.* 1838, May. p. 230.
1840. J. Müller, *Handbuch der Physiologie.* II. 370.
1844. Valentin, *Lehrbuch der Physiologie.* 1. Ausgabe. II. 444.
1846. Volkmann, Art.: Sehen in Wagners *Handwörterbuch der Physiol.* III. 272.
1850. A. Hannover, *Bidrag til Øjets Anatomie, Physiologie og Pathologie.* Kjöbenhavn. Cap. VI. p. 61.
1851. Helmholtz, *Beschreibung eines Augenspiegels.* Berlin. S. 39.

1852. E. H. WEBER, Über den Raumsinn und die Empfindungskreise in der Haut und im Auge. *Verhandl. der Leipz. Gesellsch.* 1852. S. 138.

    A. KOELLIKER, Zur Anatomie und Physiologie der Retina. *Verhandl. d. phys. med. Ges. zu Würzburg.* 3. July 1852.

    DONDERS, *Onderzoekingen gedaan in het physiol. Labor. d. Utrechtsche Hoogeschool.* VI. 134.

1853. D. BREWSTER, Account of a case of vision without retina. *Report of the British Assoc. at Belfast.* p. 3.

    A. FICK and P. DU BOIS-REYMOND, Über die unempfindliche Stelle der Netzhaut im menschlichen Auge. J. MÜLLERS *Archiv für Anat. und Physiol.* 1853. p. 396.

    COCCIUS, *Die Anwendung des Augenspiegels.* Leipzig. S. 20.

1855. H. MÜLLER, *Verhandl. d. phys.-med. Ges. zu Würzburg.* IV. 100. V. 411–446.

1856. Idem, Anatomisch-physiolog. Untersuchungen über die Retina bei Menschen und Tieren. SIEBOLD und KÖLLIKERS *Zeitschr. für wissensch. Zoologie.* VIII. 1–122.

1857. AUBERT and FÖRSTER, Über den blinden Fleck und die scharfsehende Stelle im Auge. *Berliner allg. med. Zentralzeitung.* 1857. No. 33.. S. 259, 260.

1859. COCCIUS, *Über Glaukom, Entzündung und die Autopsie mit dem Augenspiegel.* Leipzig. S. 40 and 52.

Acuity of Vision

1705. HOOKE, *Posthumous works.* p. 12. 97.

1738. SMITH, *Optics.* I. 31.

    JURIN, ibid. *Essay on distinct and indistinct vision.* p. 149.

1752. COURTIVRON, *Hist. de l'Acad. de Paris.* p. 200.

1754. TOB. MAYER, *Comment. Gotting.* IV. 97 and 135.

1759. PORTERFIELD, *On the eye.* II. 58.

1824. AMICI in: *Ferussac bull. sc. math.* 1824. p. 221.

1829. LEHOT, ibid. XII. 417.

1830. HOLKE, *Disquis. de acie oculi dextri et sinistri.* Lipsiae.

1831. EHRENBERG in POGGENDORFFS *Ann.* XXIV. 36.

1840. HUECK in J. MÜLLERS *Archiv für Anat. und Physiol.* 1840. S. 82.

    J. MÜLLER, *Handbuch der physiologie.* II. 82.

1841. BUROW, *Beiträge zur Physiologie und Physik des menschlichen Auges.* Berlin. S. 38.

1846. VOLKMANN, art.: Sehen in WAGNERS *Handwörterbuch d. Physiol.* III. 331, 335.

1849. MARIÉ DAVY, *Institut.* No. 790. p. 59.

1850. W. PETRIE, *Institut.* No. 886. p. 415.

1852. E. H. WEBER, *Verhandl. der sächs. Ges.* 1852. S. 145.

1854. BERGMANN, Zur Kenntnis des gelben Flecks der Netzhaut. HENLE und PFEUFFER, *Zeitschr.* (2) 245–252.

1855. BUDGE, Beobachtungen über die blinde Stelle der Netzhaut. *Verhandl. des naturhist. Vereins d. Rheinlande.* 1855. S. XLI.

1857. BERGMANN in HENLE und PFEUFFER, *Zeitschr. für rat. Med.* (3) II. 88.

    AUBERT and FÖRSTER in GRAEFE, *Archiv für Ophthalmologie.* III. Abt. 2. S. 1.

1860. G. BRAUN, Notiz zur Anatomie der Stäbchenschicht der Netzhaut. *Wien. Ber.* XLII. S. 15–19.

  — G. M. CAVALLIERI, Sul punto cieco dell' occhio. *Atti dell' Istituto Lombardo.* II. 89–91.

1861. H. MÜLLER, Bemerkungen über die Zapfen am gelben Fleck des Menschen. *Würzburger Zeitschrift für Naturk.* II. 218–221.

1862. H. SNELLEN, *Letterproeven ter bepaling der gezigtsscherpte.* Utrecht.

  — J. VROESOM DE HAAN, *Onderzoek naar den invloed van den leeftijd op de gezigtsscherpte.* Utrecht.

  — A. W. VOLKMANN, *Physiologische Untersuchungen im Gebiete der Optik.* Leipzig. Heft 1, S. 65.

1863. WITTICH, Studien über den blinden Fleck. *Archiv für Ophthalm.* IX. 3. S. 1–38.

  — K. VIERORDT, Über die Messung der Sehschärfe. Ibid. S. 219–223.

1864. AUBERT, *Physiologie der Netzhaut.* Breslau. S. 187–251.
— W. ZEHENDER, Historische Notiz zur Lehre vom blinden Fleck. *Archiv für Ophthalm.*
   X. 1. S. 152–155.
— O. FUNKE, Zur Lehre von den Empfindungskreisen der Netzhaut. *Bericht der natur-*
   forsch. Ges. zu Freiburg i. Br. III. S. 89–116.
— DONDERS, *Anomalies of accommodation and refraction.* London. p. 177–203.

Following references (compiled by H. L.) are to some recent literature concerning Visual Acuity:

1914. H. LAURENS, Über die räumliche Unterscheidungsfähigkeit beim Dämmerungssehen.
   Zeit. f. Sinnesphysiol. **48,** 233–239.
1917. A. GLEICHEN, Beitrag zur Theorie der Sehenscharfe. GRAEFES *Arch. f. Ophth.,* **93,**
   303–356.
1920. J. W. FRENCH, The unaided eye. III. *Trans. of the Optical Soc.* **21,** 127–147.
1920. J. P. C. SOUTHALL, Refraction and visual acuity of the human eye. *Amer. Jour.*
   Physiol. Optics, **1,** 277–316.
1921. C. SHEARD, Some factors affecting visual acuity. *Amer. Jour. Physiol. Optics,* **2,**
   168–184.
1921. C. E. FERREE and G. RAND, An acuity lantern and the use of the illumination scale
   for the detection of small errors in refraction and their correction. *Proc. of the Amer.*
   Psychol. Assoc. Psychol. Bull. **17,** 46, 47. — An apparatus for determining acuity
   at low illuminations, for testing the light and colorsense and for detecting small errors
   in refraction and in their correction. *Journ. Exper. Psychol.,* **3,** 59–71. — Lantern
   and apparatus for testing the light sense and for determining acuity at low illuminations. *Amer. Jour. of Ophthalmol.,* **3,** 335–340. — An apparatus for testing light
   and color sense. *Amer. Jour. of Ophthalmol.,* **3,** 812–814. — Visual acuity at low
   illumination and the use of the illumination scale for the detection of small errors
   in refraction. *Amer. Jour, of Ophthalmol.,* **3,** 408–417.
1922. H. HARTRIDGE, Visual acuity and the resolving power of the eye. *Jour. Physiol.,*
   57, 52–67.
1922. P. W. COBB, Individual variations in retinal sensitivity and their correlation with
   ophthalmologic findings. *Jour. Exper. Psychol.,* **5,** 227–246.
1923. E. E. ANDERSEN and F. W. WEYMOUTH, Visual perception and the retinal mosaic.
   Amer. Jour. Physiol., **64,** 561–594.

A Supplement by W. NAGEL

§18. A.   Changes in the Retina due to Light

There are certain positive effects produced in the retina that are manifestly dependent on the action of light.

1.   *Structural Changes*

When the retina of the eye is subjected to microscopical examina-tion, numerous differences are found between preparations which have been kept in the dark before fixing and staining and those which have been exposed to light.   In the latter case the nuclei in the various layers and the cone-ellipsoids will not take up the stain in the same way as they do when the retina has not been exposed to light.   For example, after exposure to light acid dyes do not produce so marked a stain.[1]

Changes also have been found in the ganglion cells of the retina; particularly by BIRCH-HIRSCHFELD[2] in treatment of preparations by the NISSL method of staining. With exposure to greater illumination these changes may be even great enough to lead to the formation of vacuoles, etc. In such cases it is not certain whether the result is due to direct action of light on the ganglion cells and cone nuclei, or whether this excessive stimulation of light takes place simply in the cones, while the changes in the nerve cells are after-effects of conduction of powerful stimuli. It is more likely, perhaps, direct action of light.

ANGELUCCI[3] found the chemical reaction of the retina was alkaline in the dark and acid in the light; and subsequent researches have confirmed this result.[4]

The phenomena of the phototropic migration of pigment and contraction of the cones under the influence of light have been studied by many investigators. These effects are particularly interesting because the whole microscopical appearance of the retina may be essentially changed as a result of these processes.

F. BOLL[5] found that the retina of a frog's eye that had been kept in the dark for several hours may be easily removed from the eyeball as a translucent membrane; but that when the eye was exposed to light, the retina clung fast to it and usually would not come off except in pieces, which are deep black in appearance. In the latter case, the pigment epithelium remains attached to the layer of rods and cones, whereas in the former case it does not. BOLL,[5] CZERNY,[6] ANGELUCCI,[7]

---

[1] See BIRNBACHER, V. GRAEFES *Arch. f. Ophthalm.* **40,** 1894. Summary of the literature is given by S. GARTEN, GRAEFE-SÄMISCHS *Handbuch der gesamten Augenheilkunde.* I. Teil, III. Band, XII. Kapitel, Anhang.

¶See also brief review of literature on this subject as given by S. R. DETWILER, The effect of light on the retina of the tortoise and the lizard. *Jour. Exper. Zool.,* **20,** 1916, 165–191. (H. L.)

[2] v. GRAEFES *Archiv. f. Ophthalm.* **50,** 1900 and *Arch. f. Anat. u. Physiol.* 1878.

[3] *Encyclopédie française d'opht.* II. S. 108.

[4] ¶See R. DITTLER, Über die Zapfencontraktion an der isolierten Froschnetzhaut. PFLÜGERS *Archiv.,* **117,** 1907, 295–328. Idem, Über die chemische Reaktion der isolierten Froschnetzhaut. Ibid., **120,** 44–50. — S. GARTEN, Die Veränderungen der Netzhaut durch Licht. GRAEFE-SÄMISCH *Handb. d. ges. Augenheilkunde* I. Teil, III. Band, XII. Kap., Anhang. S. 1–130. — G. F. ROCHAT, Über die chemische Reaktion der Netzhaut. *Arch. f. Ophthalm.,* **59,** 1904, 170–188 (in which the position is taken that light does not cause any change in the reaction of the retina). — L. B. AREY, The movements of the visual cells and retinal pigment of the lower vertebrates. *Jour. Comp. Neur.,* **26,** 1916, 121–202. (H.L.)

[5] *Monatsberichte d. K. Akad. d. Wiss. Berlin* 1877, January.

[6] *Sitzungsber. d. K. d. Wiss. Wien* LVI. 1867.

[7] *Arch. f. Anat. u. Physiol.* 1878.

and KÜHNE[1] were all aware that the pigment of the epithelial cells, which consists of fine brown granules and needles, may migrate in between the rods, and that then the individual rods are surrounded by a thick mantle of pigment. What occurs here is not some sort of amoeboid extension and contraction of protoplasmic processes of the pigment-cells, as might be supposed at first thought; for these processes always project between the rods, even when the eye is protected from light. In the dark the pigment simply migrates into the cell-bodies close to the nucleus; but under illumination it migrates away from the light into the processes between the rods. On exposure to light the rods also become somewhat thicker, and consequently the rods and pigment-processes adhere to each other firmly, so that when the retina is removed from the open bulbus, the pigment-layer is torn away with it.

The forward migration of the pigment due to exposure to light takes place more quickly than the return movement in darkness. In sunlight the completed light-position is assumed in about ten minutes, whereas the typical dark-position is not completed for an hour or more. Fifteen minutes is sufficient to complete the migration in an enucleated dark eye in sunlight, while the dark reaction requires a considerably longer time for its completion.[2]

Pigment migration may be observed very distinctly not only in amphibians but in fishes and birds. It is not so distinct in reptiles.[3] Nor can it be said to have been certainly demonstrated in mammals,[4] although likewise in them the retina clings more tenaciously to the choroid when the eye has been illuminated.

The short wave-lengths in the blue part of the spectrum seem to have more effect on pigment migration than the long or red ones. The eye itself being kept dark, it is sometimes sufficient merely to expose the posterior end of the animal in order for the pigment to assume its light-position (ENGELMANN).[5] Various other influences, such as heat, low temperature,[6] irritation of the membrane may also bring about the light-position in the dark, perhaps as a reflex action. But direct action of light on the retina is possible quite independently of the migration

[1] *Untersuchungen aus dem Heidelberger physiol. Institut.*

[2] ¶See L. B. AREY, The function of the efferent fibres of the optic nerve of fishes. *Jour. Comp. Neur.,* **26,** 1916, 213–245. (H. L.)

[3] ¶See S. R. DETWILER, *loc. cit.* Also H. LAURENS and S. R. DETWILER, Studies on the retina. The structure of the retina of Alligator mississippiensis and its photochemical changes. *Jour. Exper. Zool.,* **32,** 1922, 207–234. (H. L.)

[4] ¶See GARTEN, *loc. cit.,* p. 72. (H. L.)

[5] ¶According to L. B. AREY (*loc. cit.,* 1916), this is not the case. See also A. E. FICK, Über die Ursachen der Pigmentwanderung in der Netzhaut. *Viertelj. Naturf. Gesell. in Zürich,* Jahrb. 35, 1890, 83–86. (H. L.)

[6] ¶See L. B. AREY, *loc. cit.*—H. HERZOG, Experimentelle Untersuchungen zur Physiologie der Bewegungsvorgange in der Netzhaut. *Arch. f. Physiol.,* 1905, 413–464. (H. L.)

of pigment in the enucleated eye, as is shown by an experiment described by Kühne. He contrived to illuminate the eye of a frog so that, while some parts of the retina were very bright, the other parts got as little light as possible; and he found that the pigment adhered only to the bright parts and not to the dark places.[1]

A change which occurs in the cones of the retina under the action of light and which is easy to demonstrate was discovered by VAN GENDEREN STORT.[2] This consists in a shortening of the inner segment on exposure to light. The effect is very considerable in the case of a frog, the inner segment being shortened more than 50 percent. It is even greater in many fishes. GARTEN observed a shortening of from 50μ to 5μ in the shiner (Abramis brama).[3] Apparently, this reaction does not take place in the eel. In reptiles and birds the amount of shortening is much less.[4] In mammals it is very slight, but GARTEN seems to have shown that it does certainly occur in monkeys. So far as the human eye is concerned, there is no proof of it.

In amphibians and fishes the displacements produced by shortening of the inner segment are so considerable that the cones, whose outer segment in the dark eye is in the outside zone of the layer of rods, are found in the light eye up against the external limiting membrane. However, many of the cones are stationary, for example, in the frog's eye. These stationary cones are generally near the limiting membrane.

Cone contraction takes place more quickly than pigment migration. For example, when the eye of a frog is exposed to bright daylight, the contraction is complete in two minutes. The sensitivity of the reaction is also much greater; the light-position of the cones being brought about by the light of a candle, although the forward migration of pigment is not affected at all, or very slightly anyhow, by such an illumination.[5]

According to HERZOG,[6] cone contraction is induced not only by direct stimulation of light but by all kinds of irritations of the membrane, in a much greater degree than pigment migration. Ignorance of this fact may be responsible for the erroneous idea that displacements of individual parts of the retina are due to the action of light.

[1] ¶R. DITTLER, *loc. cit.* (H. L.)

[2] *Onderzoek. Physiol. Labor. Utrecht* (3), **9**, 145, 1883.

[3] ¶L. B. AREY, *loc. cit.* (H. L.)

[4] ¶C. HESS, Gesichtsinn in WINTERSTEINS *Handb. d. Vergl. Physiol.*, Bd. 4 (1913), 744, 751. — GARTEN, *loc. cit.* — DETWILER, *loc. cit.* — LAURENS and DETWILER, *loc. cit.* (H. L.)

[5] ¶L. B. AREY, A retinal mechanism of efficient vision. *Jour. Comp. Neur.*, **30**, 343–353. (H. L.)

[6] *Arch. f. (Anat. u.) Physiol.* 1905, 413

It is still a moot question as to whether stimulating one eye by light can bring about a similar light-position of the cones of the other eye, when the latter has not been exposed. ENGELMANN[1] believes that it can, but A: E. FICK[2] denies it. It is not easy to avoid sources of error in carrying out the experiment.

Any theoretical explanation of the photo-mechanical movements of the retinal pigment and cones must be advanced with some hesitation. The first thing to bear in mind is that neither of these processes has been absolutely proved so far as the retina of the human eye is concerned; and that even in the case of mammals, where the tests are more easily carried out, usually there are just faint traces of these phenomena, which are much less in evidence than they are in fishes and amphibians. The fact is, there is not a single positive proof that the changes in the mutual arrangement of the parts of the retina, as they are found to occur in microscopical preparations of light-adapted and dark-adapted eyes, really proceed in the same way during life. With very many other contractile tissues and also with individual contractile cells, such as amoeba, it is impossible or extremely accidental to get fixation in the state either of contraction or of expansion as may be desired. In chemical fixation and in the isolation of elements in maceration preparations violent stimulations of the tissues cannot be avoided; and there is always the possibility that with the microscopical preparation light and darkness have merely a quantitative or qualitative effect on the receptivity of the stimulation by the pigment cells and cones. However, supposing (as is plausible) that the displacements in the normal retina *in situ* take place in the same way as they do in microscopical preparations, we must try to connect these phenomena with the change of excitability of the visual apparatus in the transition from light adaptation to dark adaptation. Many different conjectures of this kind have been made. One question is whether the pigment movement has anything to do with the formation of the visual purple. On the other hand, the isolation of the rods by the insertion of pigment between them has been supposed to be a protection against disturbing diffusion of light in the visual epithelium. Detailed discussion of these·questions had better be postponed until we come to consider the more modern theories concerning the functions of the rods and cones.

[1] *Arch. f. d. ges. Physiol.* **35**, (1885).

[2] *Vierteljahrsschr. naturforsch. Ges. Zürich* **35**, 1890. **40**, 1894—v. GRAEFES *Arch. f. Ophthalm.* **37**, 1891.

2.   The Bleaching of the Visual Purple

The purple or rose-red colouration of the outer segments of the rods, which, under some circumstances, makes the entire isolated retina appear coloured, is evanescent under the action of light, or photolabile. This red colouring matter had already been noticed by H. MÜLLER, LEYDIG and MAX SCHULTZE. Its most interesting property, namely, its high sensitivity to light, was discovered by FR. BOLL.[1] More precise data concerning the "visual purple" or "visual red" were obtained by the researches of KÜHNE,[2] KÖNIG,[3] ABELSDORF,[4] TRENDELENBURG,[5] GARTEN,[6] and other workers.[7]

Visual purple has been found in the rods of man and of all vertebrates that have been investigated. Where there are no rods, there is also no visual purple as in the retina of many birds and reptiles, as well as in the rod-free area (*fovea centralis*) of the human retina.[8] In many animals only parts of the retina contain much purple. In the rabbit there is a horizontal streak—the so-called purple ridge—that is particularly deeply coloured. In the rods of the outer margin of the retina, near the ora serrata, no purple is found.

Besides the red rods, isolated green rods have been seen in the case of the frog.

With a view to seeing the purple colour, the animal should be kept in darkness two hours or longer before it is killed, and the retina then removed from the eye. Owing to the sensitiveness of the colouring matter to green and blue light, the preparation of the retina should be made under illumination by red light or the yellow light of a sodium flame. The entire retina of a frog is easily removed by seizing it with a pointed forceps at the entrance of the optic nerve. The retina of an owl, which is extremely rich in visual purple, can be removed by open-

[1] *Berlin. Monatsber.* 12. Nov. 1876; *Acad. dei Lincei,* 3. Dec. 1876; *Arch. f. Anat. u. Physiol.* 1887.

[2] *Untersuchungen d. physiol. Instituts Heidelberg.* II. III. IV; also summary in HERMANNS *Handbuch der Physiologie.* II. 1879

[3] A. KÖNIG, *Gesammelte Abhandlungen.* XXIV. Über den menschlichen Sehpurpur und seine Bedeutung für das Sehen (Also in: *Sitzungsber. Akad. Wiss. Berlin.* XXX. 1894).

[4] *Sitzungsber. Akad. Wiss. Berlin.* XXXVIII. 1895; *Zeitschr. f. Psychol. und Physiol. d. Sinnesorgane.* 12, 1896.

[5] *Zeitschr. f. Physiol. u. Psychol. d. Sinnesorg.* 37, 1904.

[6] GRÄFE-SÄMISCHS *Handbuch der Augenheilkunde,* 1. Teil, III. Band, XII. Kapitel.

[7] ¶Some recent work in this subject is to be found in the following: V. HENRI, Photochimie de la rétine *Jour. Physiol. et Path. gen.,* 13, 1911, 841–856. — S. HECHT, Photochemistry of visual purple. I. The kinetics of the decomposition of visual purple by light. *Jour. Gen. Physiol.* 3, 1920, 1–13; and by same author, The effect of temperature on the bleaching of visual purple by light. *Jour. Gen. Physiol.,* 3, 1921, 285–290. (H. L.)

[8] ¶EDRIDGE-GREEN and DEVEREUX deny that the visual purple is absent from the fovea of the retina of the monkey's eye (*Trans. Ophth. Soc.,* 22, 1902, 300), but their observations lack confirmation. See PARSONS *Colour Vision,* 12. (J. P. C. S.)

ing the eye under water (or physiological salt solution) and cutting
away the attachment to the optic nerve. The same technique is used
with the eyes of mammals. However, in the latter case, after the eye
has been sectioned equatorially, it is well to let it stay an hour in 4 percent alum solution to harden the retina and prevent it from tearing.
The isolated retina is then laid, rod-side outwards, on a plate of
ground glass or, better still, on a little porcelain dish of the same curvature as the eyeball.

In the eye of an animal that has just been killed or paralyzed by
curari, a strong contrast image can be produced by pointing the eye,
say, at the cross-bar of a window. Under certain circumstances,
KÜHNE got in this way sharply delineated bleaching effects or so-
called *optograms*, which are miniature reproductions of the objects
depicted. The parts that have been exposed to light are bleached,
whereas the shaded portions remain distinctly red.

Good optograms are not so easy to obtain in a frog's eye, because
the illuminated parts of the retina stick so fast to the pigment epithelium that it cannot be taken out entire and laid on a little porcelain
knob. The retina comes away more easily when the frog is first
curarized and then made oedematous by being kept in water for several
hours. According to S. GARTEN, quinine poisoning is similarly effective.

Visual purple cannot be detected by the ophthalmoscope in the
living eye of either man or mammal of any kind, because the transparent retina is seen either on a very darkly pigmented background or
on one that shines with a bright colour (the tapetum of predatory
animals). However, there are some animals that have a white, or
almost white, tapetum; and with these ABELSDORF[1] succeeded in
getting ophthalmoscopic proof not only of the unbleached visual
purple but also of its bleaching in bright light. The shiner (Abramis
brama) among fishes and the crocodile (Alligator lucius) among reptiles
are particularly favourable for this observation.

The visual purple is not soluble in water. Alcohol, ether and
chloroform, as well as most acids and alkalies, quickly destroy its
colour. On the other hand, it is very soluble in solutions of the salts
of the bile acids, which dissolve the substance of the rods almost instantaneously.

If unbleached retinas are placed in the dark in a 2 to 5 percent
solution of sodium glycocolate, and if the liquid is then filtered and
centrifuged, a clear solution will be obtained that shows the purple

[1] *Sitzungsber. Akad. Wiss. Berlin.* XVIII. 1895; *Zeitschr. f. Psychol. u. Physiol. d. Sinnesorg.* 14, 1897; *Arch. f. (Anat. u.) Physiol.* 1898.

colour very distinctly, when it is evaporated in vacuum over sulphuric acid down to a few drops.   This solution is also photo-sensitive. In darkness it keeps its colour; in light it bleaches, in a few minutes in daylight, but more slowly under artificial illumination.

Visual purple both in the fresh retina and in solution has not the same hue in all animals. Thus in the frog and cat it is almost red; in owls and fishes it is a purple containing much violet.   In man also, according to KÜHNE, it is more violet than it is in the frog.

The process of bleaching may run through different gamuts of colour.   Thus under some circumstances the colour gets more and more whitish until finally the retina is almost devoid of colour.   In other instances, the purple changes to red, orange and yellow, in succession, not becoming white for a long time. This second case, when a distinct yellow tint is one of the stages, is characteristic of rapid bleaching under brilliant illumination (sunlight), as GARTEN has shown; whereas simple fading out occurs when the bleaching is pretty gradual.

The visual purple is converted into a very light-stable yellow pigment when it is treated with certain metallic salts, such as zinc chloride or platinum chloride, or with acetic acid.   In some circumstances distinct red colouration is left on the retina by action of formaldehyde.

The quantitative results on the absorption of spectrum light by visual purple, as determined by KÜHNE and by KÖNIG and his pupils, and recently by TRENDELENBURG and GARTEN, are of particular interest. Clear solutions were used in making these measurements, and during the determination of the absorption they must be protected from bleaching as much as possible. If the absorption values are represented by a curve plotted with wave-lengths as abscissae, and the amount of absorption of the separate kinds of light as ordinates, a distinct maximum of absorption is found in the green part of the spectrum.

In the fish retina, which is more of a violet purple, the maximum of absorption is more towards the yellow-green, according to the measurements of KOETTGEN and ABELSDORF.[1]

A comparison of the absorption of unbleached solutions with that of solutions which have been more or less bleached shows first of all a diminution of absorption in the green as a regular effect of the action of light. When the conditions were such that the colour of the retina changed to yellow-red, GARTEN[2] found, along with diminution of absorption in the green, increased absorption in the

[1] *Sitzber. Akad. Wiss. Berlin*, XXXVIII. 1895.
[2] v. GRAEFES *Arch. f. Ophthalm.* LXIII. 1906.

violet. The conclusion was that a yellow decomposition product (KÜHNE's "visual yellow") was the result of the bleaching of the purple. It is not unlikely that some such yellow material may also be produced in slight quantities in the live retina. However, according to the evidence of experiments on the retinas of animals and with solutions of visual purple, an assumption of this kind is not justifiable except in the unusual instance where a retina, which has been kept in the dark for a long period so as to develop a large supply of visual purple, is suddenly exposed to a very strong light.

Proceeding on the assumption that in typical total colour-blindness the formation and bleaching of visual purple takes place normally, the writer has carried out experiments on a totally colour-blind girl which, had they succeeded, might have resulted in proving the development of a "visual yellow" intra vitam. The girl was required to equate green and violet with the HELMHOLTZ spectrophotometer, which she did easily of course. Now if under certain conditions her retina contained a more yellowish pigment than under other circumstances, this might be indicated eventually by the fact that the green-violet adjustment which was right under one set of conditions would be wrong under the other conditions. But the writer could get no uniformity in this respect, although comparisons were made: First, between one eye that had been dark-adapted for one hour and the other eye that in the meantime had been exposed to bright daylight (of course, taking into consideration the very much greater sensitivity of the dark eye, for which both halves of the comparison-field were proportionately dimmed); and, second, between one eye, which was in the average state of light adaptation in daylight, and the other eye which had been kept closed for a long time and was then quickly light-adapted under the action of a bright AUER lamp. The object in view was to compare in this way the slow and rapid bleaching of the visual purple. But one circumstance that operated against the successful performance of this experiment is that an eye of a totally colour-blind person that has been really brilliantly illuminated can generally not see anything at first (for example, after being illuminated by an ophthalmoscope, pupil dilated); and therefore the best that can be done under the circumstances is to use a fairly moderate degree of light adaptation.

The more a certain kind of light is absorbed by the visual purple, the greater is its bleaching effect. KÜHNE found that yellow-green light bleaches visual purple most rapidly, while yellow and red act very slowly. Recently W. TRENDELENBURG has made careful experiments with spectral light. He exposed one of two samples of visual purple to the constant illumination of light corresponding to the sodium line ($\lambda = 589\mu\mu$) and the other sample to some other definite kind of light of the same dispersion spectrum, and then, after a certain interval of time, measured the decrease of the absorption by means of the spectrophotometer. The following table gives TRENDELENBURG's "bleaching values" for rabbit visual purple.[1] The value for sodium light is put equal to unity.

[1] ¶H. LAURENS finds maximum of absorption for wave-lengths of equal energy for visual purple of frog at $510\mu\mu$. The method used is described in a paper by H. LAURENS and H. D. HOOKER, Jr., in *Amer. Journ. Physiol.*, **44**, 1917, 504-516. (H. L.)

Wave-length	589	542	530	519	509	491	474	459
Bleaching value	1	3.40	3.62	3.45	3.09	1.69	0.975	0.299

Both in the live eye and also, under some circumstances, in the enucleated eye, there is a *regeneration of visual purple* after bleaching; and to a certain extent even in isolated retinas and solutions. When both eyes of a live frog have been exposed to sunlight for half an hour, and the animal has then been killed and the eyeballs taken out, the retina of the eye that is opened immediately will be found to be without colour; but if the other eye has been kept an hour in the dark in a damp receptacle, the retina will be a purple-red. In the case of the frog, KÜHNE detected the first trace of red after complete bleaching twenty minutes after shutting off the light; whereas in the case of the rabbit there were signs of this colour in about five minutes. The regeneration is by far the best and most complete when the retina is in contact with the pigment epithelium. A retina taken from an eye that is without pigment never regains the perfect red colour.

According to KÜHNE and GARTEN, the most favourable condition for the regeneration of the purple in the isolated retina was when the bleaching had been permitted to proceed as far as the yellow, the retina then being placed in the dark. Apparently, therefore, the visual purple is most easily produced anew from the products of its own decomposition before they have lost all colour. When the retina has been bleached completely, regeneration does not pass through all the intermediate stages of yellow, orange and red, but the retina becomes bright lilac, and then pink. In this case, therefore, the process of formation of the purple must be different from that when the purple is recovered from the yellowish product.

Both bleaching and regeneration depend on the temperature.[1] Regeneration, in particular, is much retarded by cold; for example, the retina of a frog at 0° C takes nine hours to regain its purple colour. In warm-blooded animals the regenerative ability is lost a few minutes after death or after circulation ceases. Evidently, the damage is greatest in this case to the pigment epithelium which is so important for regeneration. Whatever our knowledge may be as to the physiology of visual purple in solution and in the isolated retina, it is doubtful how far it can be applied in the case of the eye of a warm-blooded animal with circulation intact.

The fluorescence of the retina[2] when radiated by ultra-violet light is another remarkable property. It is much more pronounced in

---

[1] ¶See HECHT, *loc. cit.* (H. L.)

[2] HELMHOLTZ, POGG. *Ann.* XCIV (1855); SETSCHENOW, v. GRAEFES *Arch. f. Ophthalm.* V. 1859.

the bleached retina. This is true, as HIMSTEDT and NAGEL found,[1] also with respect to the retina of the pigeon's eye, which certainly contains very little purple. Solutions of purple in bile acid likewise fluoresce. However, bile acid salt solutions are themselves fluor-.escent, indeed nearly as much so as when they contain unbleached visual purple of a frog's eye. But if a few drops of a solution of sodium glycocolate and of a similar solution containing visual purple are suspended in little platinum dishes and exposed to daylight, what happens is that the solution with the purple in it is subsequently distinctly more fluorescent in the dark than the other solution. Therefore the bleached products of the visual purple are certainly fluorescent, even if there were some doubt as to the visual purple itself.

3. *Electromotive Phenomena in the Eye*

With all vertebrates that have been investigated by electrical methods, there is found to be a difference of potential between the anterior and posterior poles of the eye, both in the living eye as a whole and in the isolated retina as long as it continues to survive; as was observed by E. DU BOIS-REYMOND. If two places in a prepared specimen are placed in contact with suitable electrodes and connected with a sensitive galvanometer, a continuous current will flow through the circuit as long as the preparation stays alive. Most of these experiments have been made on eyes of frogs. This so-called *"Ruhestrom"* ("current of rest") can still be detected for hours after the eye has been taken out of the body of the dead frog. The severed end of the optic nerve is negative with respect to the anterior part of the eye. On the other hand, the optic nerve is positive with respect to the posterior lateral parts of the bulbus.[2]

According to the experiments of KÜHNE[3] and of STEINER,[4] when one electrode is placed on the inner surface of an isolated retina and the other on the outer surface, the rod-layer is found to be electronegative with respect to the layer of nerve fibres.

While a current can be obtained for hours from an enucleated frog's eye, the electromotive force in a fish's eye, and also in the eye of a warm-blooded animal, dies out usually in a few minutes when the blood ceases to circulate.[5]

---

[1] *Festschr. d. Albert-Ludwigs Universität Freiburg f. Grossherzog Friedrich.* 1902.

[2] ¶See J. H. PARSONS, *An introduction to the study of colour vision.* 1915. p. 15. (J. P. C. S.)

[3] *Untersuchungen über tierische Elektrizität.* II. Abteil. 1. Berlin 1849.

[4] *Untersuch. d. physiol. Inst. Heidelberg.* III and IV.

[5] ¶Some recent literature pertaining to this subject may be noted here as follows:

E. C. DAY, Photoelectric currents in the eye of the fish. *Amer. Jour. Physiol.*, **38**, 1915, 369–397. — C. SHEARD and C. McPEEK, On the electrical response of the eye to stimulation

The electromotive force varies considerably in different individuals of the same species. For example, HIMSTEDT and NAGEL[1] found variations between 0.0056 and 0.017 volt in frogs' eyes. The values obtained by other investigators are on the average between 7 and 9 millivolts.

But even with the same specimen the current does not stay constant, nor does it diminish uniformly as a rule. For no apparent reason it increases and decreases again. The fluctuation is slow with frogs, taking several minutes; but in birds, especially in pigeons, it is often quick and apparently without any rule, the galvanometer-needle hardly ever being still for a second. When the experiment is long continued, the direction of the current may be reversed, even in the case of the frog.

The above has reference to the so-called "dark current," the eye being supposed to be kept in the dark. If light falls suddenly on an eye of this sort, the current intensity fluctuates, differently, however, under different conditions. This was discovered first by HOLMGREN,[2] and afterwards independently by DEWAR and McKENDRICK.[3] The following phenomena are most easily demonstrated on the enucleated frog's eye, one electrode being placed on the edge of the cornea and the other on the section of the optic nerve. After an interval of from one to two tenths of a second, the current increases rather quickly until it is between 3 and 10 percent of the strength of the dark current. If the stimulation by light continues longer, in the case of an eye that has been previously made right sensitive by dark adaptation, the current slowly increases still more. With illumination by a bright incandescent lamp, the increase of current can be observed for a minute, and then it begins to fall off, *even if the illumination is continued*. When the illumination is feeble, the current goes on increasing for a longer time. In enucleated eyes taken from light-adapted frogs, the current quickly reaches its maximum strength and then falls off almost just as rapidly again, although as a rule it never quite sinks as low as the dark current.

If the stimulating light is suddenly shut off, a "dark response" occurs after a latent period, as in the light reaction. It is manifested by another quick increase in the flow of current, succeeded by a fairly slow falling off to the strength of the dark current.

---

by light of various wave-lengths. *Amer. Jour. Physiol.*, **48**, 1919, 45–66. — C. SHEARD, Photoelectric currents in the eye. *Physiol. Review*, **1** (1), 1921, 84–111. —SHEARD used freshly excised eyes from young dogs, never starting an experiment later than two hours after enucleation. (H. L.)

[1] *Ber. naturf. Gesellsch. Freiburg i. Br.* 1901; *Ann. d. Physik.* (4) IV, 1901.

[2] *Upsala Läkares Förhandlingar.* 1866 and 1871.

[3] *Phil. Trans. Roy. Soc. Edinburgh* VII. 1871–72.

The reaction takes place differently in other animals. In reptiles and in diurnal birds (birds of prey, hens), on illumination, there is sometimes a latent period lasting from 1/40 to 1/15 second, succeeded by a strong *negative* variation of the current; or else what happens is, at first a short positive "discharge," succeeded then by the negative variation lasting while the illumination continues. If the eye is not illuminated, the current may drop at once to the strength of the "current of rest," or, before doing this, it will show another negative variation. H. PIPER's work[1] has helped a great deal to clarify this subject. With respect to nocturnal birds of prey, he confirmed the observation of HIMSTEDT and NAGEL, namely, that the only result of illumination in this case is a strong positive variation followed by an equally strong negative variation when the light is shut off. In mammals also the reaction consists chiefly of a positive variation.

Every injury of the eyeball changes its electromotive behaviour and tends to promote negative variations. For example, the retina taken from the eye of a frog responds to the light stimulus at first with negative variation succeeded afterwards by a positive one. The positive dark variation occurs also in injured preparations of this kind. In perfectly fresh eyes of various animals GARTEN found that a very brief negative variation preceded the positive variation of the current as a regular result of stimulation.

The sensitivity of these photo-electric reactions is sometimes very considerable, particularly in such animals as have numerous rods in their retinas and much visual purple. For example, in the eye of a frog the threshold value of the energy that is just sufficient to produce variation of current is perhaps very nearly the same as that which will just elicit the sensation of light in the dark-adapted human eye. Under stimulation by X-rays the eyes of frogs and of several species of owls also give a distinct photo-electric reaction, but a hen's eye does not. The light of a cigar, moonlight, phosphorescent paint, each produce distinct photo-electric variations. Ultra-violet light has the same effect, evidently due to production of fluorescence in the ocular media.

By a careful study of the quantitative relation between the retinal current and the intensity of the stimulating light, DE HAAS[2] showed that the reaction does not obey the WEBER-FECHNER law except for a certain range of rather strong stimuli. For weaker stimuli the relation between current and stimulus is more complicated. The surprisingly long duration of the current variation that is observed after a brief "instantaneous" stimulus of sufficient intensity is curious. The

[1] *Arch. f. (Anat. u.) Physiol.* 1905. Supplement.

[2] *Lichtprikkels en retinastroomen in hun quantitatief verband.* Inaug.-Diss. Leiden 1903.

reaction may last a hundred times as long as the duration of the stimulus.[1]

The effects of light of different wave-lengths have been quantitatively compared and the distribution of the stimulus-value ascertained for the animal eye in the different parts of the spectrum. This is done by exposing the eye for a certain length of time to the various colours of the spectrum in succession and measuring the corresponding deflections of the galvanometer. Provided the periods of the single exposures are not too brief, and a sufficient interval occurs between successive exposures, the magnitude of the total deflection for each exposure is a measure of the specific stimulating effect of the kind of light in question. This was the method of finding the relative stimulus-value that was used by HIMSTEDT and NAGEL[2] on the frog; and by PIPER[3] on a number of warm-blooded animals. The results showed that the photo-electric reaction is distinctly different in different animals. Indeed, different stimulus-values are found in the same animal in the states of light adaptation and dark adaptation. In the case of the dark-adapted eye of a frog, the maximum stimulus-value occurs in the yellow-green for $\lambda = 544\mu\mu$; whereas in the same eye, light-adapted, the maximum is in the bright yellow at $590\mu\mu$. Of the various birds examined, the nocturnal birds (different kinds of owls) have a maximum between 535 and $540\mu\mu$; diurnal birds (mousehawk, hen, pigeon) around $600\mu\mu$. The maximum for dogs, cats, and rabbits is somewhere near $535\mu\mu$. This same value was found in the case of the dog, even when the eye had been exposed previously to bright

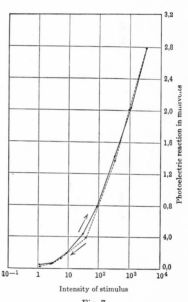

Fig. 7.

Connection between photo-electric response and stimulus (according to DE HAAS).

[1] ¶See paper by E. L. CHAFFEE, W. T. BOVIE and ALICE HAMPSON, The electrical response of the retina under stimulation by light. *Jour. of Opt. Soc. of Amer.*, etc., **7**, 1923, 1–44. — Preliminary report of some of these results in same journal, **6**, 1922, 407 (Paper read at Rochester meeting of Optical Society of America, Oct. 1921)—. (J. P. C. S.)

[2] *Ber. d. Naturf. Ges. Freiburg i. Br.* XI. (1901).

[3] *Arch. f.* (*Anat. u.*) *Physiol.* 1905. Supplement.

illumination and was therefore in the state of light adaptation. On the other hand, according to PIPER, the distribution of stimulus-values in the light-adapted eye of a rabbit is similar to that found by HIMSTEDT and NAGEL for the light-adapted eye of a frog, namely, with a maximum in the yellow ($574\mu\mu$).[1]

The relations of these particular facts to the subjective phenomena of colour vision will be discussed more fully hereafter.

The explanation of the photo-electric response is beset with great difficulties. The time relations of the objectively demonstrable electrical phenomena in the retina are so different from the subjective visual sensations that it is difficult to make a comparison between them.

As a matter of fact, however, the duration of the rise ("*Anklingen*") of the visual sensation, as determined by EXNER,[2] and the latent period of the electromotive reaction in the warm-blooded eye, as found by PIPER, GARTEN and others, do not differ very widely; in both cases it is only a few hundredths of a second. But the other parts of the electrical variations have certain characteristics that are at present difficult to reconcile with the subjective behaviour of the visual sensation, particularly when the stimulus is very brief. It should be noted that it is easier to compare the time process of the photo-electric reaction with the visual sensation, the more nearly the retina on which the measurements are made can be kept under normal conditions. Owls' eyes are particularly suitable for carrying out experiments of this kind without disturbing the function of the eye in any marked degree, and the electrical phenomena are simplest in such eyes; namely, positive variation of current under illumination, and negative discharge soon after shutting off the light. It is natural to think of the negative after-image in this connection. However, such comparisons in the present state of our knowledge are rather fruitless, and we must wait until it has been extended by further experiments on the eyes of warm-blooded animals.—N.

---

[1] ¶In addition to SHEARD's work, previously mentioned, the following are some recent contributions on this subject:

A. BROSSA and A. KOHLRAUSCH, Die Aktionströme der Netzhaut bei Reizung mit homogenen Licht. *Arch. f. Physiol.*, 1913, 449–492. — F. W. FRÖHLICH, Beiträge zur allgemeinen Physiologie der Sinnesorgane. *Zft. f. Sinnesphysiol.*, **48**, 1913, 28–164. — S. GARTEN, Die Produktion von Electrizität. WINTERSTEINS *Handb.* Bd. 3, 2 Hfte; also in GRAEFE-SAEMISCHS *Handb. d. ges. Augenheilk.*, I. Teil, III Bd., XII. Kap., Anhang, p. 213.— A. KOHLRAUSCH and A. BROSSA, Die photoelektrischen Reaktion der Tag- und Nachtvogelnetzhaut auf Licht verschiedener Wellenlänge. *Arch. f. Physiol.*, 1914, 421–431. — A. KOHLRAUSCH, Die Netzhautströme der Wirbeltiere in Abhängigkeit von der Wellenlänge des Lichtes und dem Adaptationszustand des Auges. Ibid., 1918, 195–214. (H. L.)

[2] *Wiener Sitz.-Ber.* **58**, 601.

§19. The Simple Colours

The subject which has now to be considered is the sensations that are excited in the visual mechanism by various kinds of luminous radiation. As has been already stated (§8), there are also other physical distinctions between waves of light of one frequency and those of another frequency, for example, differences of wave-length and refrangibility and differences in the way they are absorbed by coloured media. But the physiological distinction between luminous radiations of different frequencies is manifested generally by the production of sensations of different colours in the eye.[1]

[1] ¶"*Die einfachen Farben*," which is the title of this section in the original, are the colours of the spectrum corresponding to luminous radiations of a definite period of vibration, "single-frequency light" or homogeneous light. They are sometimes called "pure" colours. No refraction can modify the colour that is associated with homogeneous light.

The physical stimulus of light is one thing; the physiological response or sensation of light is a totally different thing. This is so obvious that it scarcely needs to be stated, and yet many persons fail to make the distinction sometimes and are therefore liable to much confusion. The sensation of light can be aroused by other stimuli besides that of objective light, as has been shown in the previous chapters. On the other hand, only those radiations whose frequencies are comprised within a certain rather narrow range can arouse the sensation of light in the visual organ. When so-called luminous radiations are received on the foveal region of the retina of the human eye, the response, in general, is a very complicated one. It may involve elements of both time and space and give rise to a visual "pattern," and at the same time it may consist of "blends" of simpler sensations. Nearly all sensations of colour are mixed sensations which may be produced in a variety of ways. Exactly the same stimulus may produce a totally different sensation in different parts of the visual organ. If it acts on the extreme peripheral parts of the retina, it will produce only a grey sensation ranging anywhere from white to black depending on circumstances. So far as colour is concerned, vision in this region is similar to the vision of the totally colour-blind eye.

The physicist especially is liable to confusion, because he knows that by mixing coloured lights properly he can get white light; and so he concludes that white light is a mixture either of yellow light and blue light or (what is the same thing) of red and green and blue lights; and, hence is a compound light. But that is no reason to infer that the sensation of white is a complex sensation composed of the sensation of yellow and the sensation of blue. On the contrary, there is every reason to think that the sensation of white or grey is the most fundamental and elementary of all the visual sensations. It is the only sensation of the totally colour-blind eye or of the normal eye in the darkness of night when colour vision is entirely in abeyance.

On the other hand, a given visual sensation may be correlated with a vast number of different combinations of specific light-frequencies; a yellow, which is a perfectly unitary sensation, may be due to a homogeneous (unitary) light or it may be due to any one of countless different mixtures of any red light with any green light. In other words, there is absolutely no one-to-one correspondence between the composition of wave-lengths in a given luminous radiation and the light sensation which will be attached to it (provided every link in the nerve chain from retina to cortex is intact).

In the case of the black sensation the question is more difficult still. The physicist is right in thinking of a black object as sending no stimulus to the retina, but he is wrong when he supposes there is no black sensation correlated with this absence of stimulation. It is absurd to say that black is the absence of visual sensation. Black is a positive sensation just like any other visual sensation and just as real and distinct as the sensation of white or of yellow and blue or of red and green.

All known sources of light emit simultaneously radiations of different frequencies. The best way of separating a homogeneous or

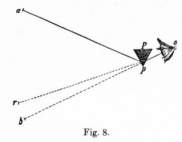

Fig. 8.

pure kind of light from such a mixture is to analyze the light by causing it to go through a transparent prism. Thus, for instance, if homogeneous blue light, proceeding from a distant source *a* (Fig. 8) through a prism *P*, comes to the observer's eye at *O*, the rays will be refracted by the prism into a new direction, and the source

will appear to be shifted to some point *b*, in a direction indicated roughly by the direction in which the refracting angle of the prism is pointed. In this instance the colour of the light will naturally be the same as that of the simple light that is radiated by the source, that is, blue. But if the source emits both red and blue light at the same time, the observer will see simultaneously also a red image at *r* and a blue image at *b*. And, finally, if the source sends out white light containing radiations of all kinds of refrangibility including red light and blue light, each separate colour will have its own special image, all these images being ranged side by side in regular sequence from red to blue according to the degree of refrangibility. Now if the coloured images that are thus inserted between *r* and *b* are very manifold, and if each of them has a certain width, approximately the same as that of the luminous object itself, obviously one image will partly overlap the next. One way of reducing this overlapping and intermingling will be to make the luminous object narrower, and so to diminish the width of each separate image without altering the total width of the spectrum *rb*. While it is not possible to prevent entirely some overlapping between one image and the next when the source of light sends out radiations of all degrees of refrangibility, the luminous object and its images can be made so narrow that the differences of refrangibility between overlapping colours will be vanishingly small.

According to the above explanation, when the source is a very narrow slit illuminated by composite light, each individual point of the slit contributes a line to the spectrum lengthwise. And so the prismatic spectrum appears in the form of a coloured rectangle, the end nearest

---

To sum up, the physicist is in the habit of calling the colours of the spectrum "simple" or "primary" colours when all he means is that their physical stimulus is simple. The simple (unitary) sensations, in the order of their development, are white and black, yellow and blue, and red and green; and they do not need for their production "simple" physical lights. (J. P. C. S.)

the source being red and the opposite end violet. In between there
is a sequence of other colours, each blending imperceptibly into the
next, occurring in the following order, namely, red, orange, yellow,
green, blue and violet. The coloured image of a luminous line obtained in this way by a prism is called a *prismatic spectrum*. In the
illustration here used the spectrum is a *subjective* one, because the
coloured images of the source of light are all virtual images. But a
real image can be projected by adjusting a convex lens on the far side
of the prism where the observer's eye was at first; so as to converge
the rays after they leave the prism into a real image of *rb*, thereby
producing an *objective spectrum* in or beyond the second focal plane of
the lens. In the original illustration the spectrum projected on the
retina of the eye is in a certain sense an objective spectrum. When
the emitted light contains luminous radiations of all possible sorts, the
spectrum is perfectly continuous. But if the source sends out light
of certain definite degrees of refrangibility, the spectrum likewise will
be composed of just so many coloured images, one for each particular
kind of light; and provided the dimensions of the luminous object and
its coloured images are sufficiently small, there will be dark gaps in the
spectrum between some of the coloured images. For example, in the
foregoing illustration (Fig. 8), when it was supposed that the luminous
point *a* sent out simply red and blue light, the red image was formed
at *r*, and the blue image at *b*, with an intervening dark space *br*. Of
course, the same sort of thing occurs, no matter whether there are
two or ten or a hundred or a thousand different kinds of homogeneous
light in the light that comes from *a*.

Now the composition of sunlight is of this nature. When the solar
spectrum is as perfect as we can get it, it is seen to be subdivided by a
great number of dark lines, the so-called FRAUNHOFER lines. Their
presence here implies the absence of light of certain refrangibilities in
sunlight. The purer the solar spectrum is, the more dark lines are
visible in it. FRAUNHOFER and STOKES attached certain letters of
the alphabet to the most conspicuous of these lines, because these lines
proved to be exceedingly sure and convenient guide-posts for finding
the place in the spectrum that corresponded to some perfectly definite
kind of radiation. This notation will be used in this treatise whenever
the species of colour is to be given exactly. The dark lines of the solar
spectrum are exhibited in the figure on Plate I. The relative lengths of
corresponding portions of the prismatic spectrum are different for
prisms of different substances. They are different also from the corresponding intervals in the diffraction spectrum, in which the distribution of colours is simply a function of the wave-length. Consequently,
any representation of the prismatic spectrum is to a certain extent

arbitrary. In the illustration in Plate I the intervals are arranged on the principle of the musical scale, because this seemed to be the best method for physiological reasons. Thus, colours whose wave-lengths are in the same ratio as the interval of a semi-tone between two musical notes are always at equal distances apart in the drawing; or to put it mathematically, equal distances in the drawing correspond to equal differences between the logarithms of the wave-lengths. The numerals on the left-hand side indicate the semi-tone intervals, and the letters on the other side are the designations of the more prominent dark lines, according to FRAUNHOFER and STOKES.

As some uncertainty prevails about the denomination of the different colours,[1] the names used in this book will be employed as follows.

Red is the colour at the less refrangible end of the spectrum, which shows no marked difference of hue from the extreme end of the spectrum to about the line *C*. In pigments it is represented by something like vermilion (cinnabar). *Purple-red* is different from red, and in its lighter tints is *pink-red*. As compared with pure red, it is bluish. This hue which in its most saturated stage is what we shall call *purple*, and in its more reddish forms *carmine red*, is not in the spectrum at all, and can only be produced by mixing the extreme colours in the spectrum, red and violet.

From the line *C* to the line *D* the red passes through *orange*, that is, yellow-red with red predominating, into *golden yellow* or red-yellow with yellow predominating. Among metallic dyes, minium and litharge (oxide of lead) are approximately the same as orange and golden yellow, respectively.

There is a rapid transition of colour from the line *D* to the line *b*. First, there is a narrow strip of pure *yellow* which lies about three times as far from *E* as from *D*. Then comes green-yellow and, finally, pure *green* between *E* and *b*. There are two very good representatives of pure yellow and green among pigments used by artists, namely, finely precipitated bright lead chromate known as chrome yellow and arsenite of copper or SCHEELE's green.

---

[1] ¶"The whole gamut of light-waves is responded to by us subjectively," says CHRISTINE LADD-FRANKLIN (Art. on "Vision" in BALDWIN's *Dictionary of Philosophy and Psychology*), "with only four different sensation qualities—red, yellow, green and blue. These are the sensations which are produced in their purity by about the wave-lengths 576, 505, 470, and a colour a little less yellow than the red end of the spectrum. For all intermediate wave-lengths we have nothing in sensation except combinations of these hues, or *colour-blends*, as reddish-yellow, blue-green, greenish-yellow, etc., but with this very singular peculiarity, that non-adjacent colour-pairs do *not* give colour-blends (red and green reproduce yellow, and blue and yellow give white, or grey); were it not for this latter circumstance, the confusion in the response to ether-radiation distinctions would be far greater than it is now." (J. P. C. S.)

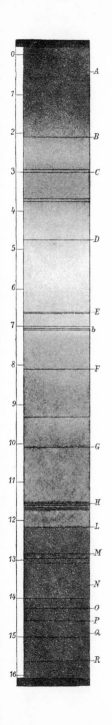

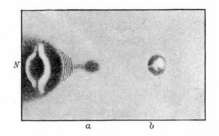

PLATE I

Between the lines E and F the green becomes blue-green and then blue, and from F to G there are different hues of blue. In the prismatic spectrum of sunlight, as NEWTON observed it, the extent of the blue portion is comparatively great, and so he gave different names to different parts of this region distinguishing them as "blue" and "indigo" in English, and as *thalassinum, cyaneum, caeruleum* and *indicum* in Latin, in the order named; violet, *violaceum*, being last of all.[1] The name *indigo-blue* may be retained for the last two-thirds of the interval extending from F to G; but what is commonly known simply as *blue* is the less refrangible blue in the first part of this interval. It is sometimes described also as *sky-blue*, but that is incorrect. The reason why this blue in a spectrum of the proper brightness resembles sky-blue is simply because of the superior luminosity of the sky. The hue of the sky is really an indigo-blue, but this hue as it occurs in the spectrum above mentioned is too dark to match sky-blue. In ordinary language, however, when a thing is said to be blue, it is natural to think of the colour of the blue sky as the principal representative of this hue, and to speak of a less refrangible blue as greenish blue. As it would be unscientific to call this latter hue simply blue as contrasted with indigo-blue, the author proposes to describe the greenish blue part of the spectrum as *cyan-blue*, as suggested by NEWTON's term *cyaneum*. The name *water-blue* might also very well be employed to describe the hue itself, because large masses of very pure water (like the lake of Geneva, glacier ice) do in fact show this colour in their depths. When, for instance, one gazes for a long time into the water of the lake of Geneva on a bright day and then looks up at the sky, the latter appears violet by contrast or even pink-red. But as the colour of a mass of water as it looks ordinarily is very whitish, except possibly in the case of deep crevices of ice, it is preferable to reserve the term water-blue for the lighter shades of *cyan-blue*. The pigments known as Prussian blue (iron ferrocyanide) and ultramarine correspond to cyan-blue and indigo-blue, respectively.

Violet (which is the colour of the flower of that name) is the region in the spectrum from the line G to the line H or L; sometimes called *purple* also. Violet and purple are the hues in the transition from blue

---

[1] ¶See R. A. HOUSTOUN, NEWTON and the colours of the spectrum. *Science Progress*, 1917. Also, volume on *Light and Colour*, 1923. There is much conjecture about what NEWTON meant exactly by "indigo" which is commonly supposed to be "more akin to green than to violet." The question, as HOUSTOUN propounds it (*Light and Colour*, p. 9), is, whether there is "a colour between blue and violet with as much right to a special name in the spectrum as orange has." He tested it with four of his students who all concurred in discriminating a hue, which they preferred to call "dark blue" and which was more blue than violet. The boundary between it and blue was estimated as falling about at wavelength $465\mu\mu$. (J. P. C. S.)

to red. As above stated, the name purple will be used here simply for the more reddish hues of this gradation that are not present at all in the spectrum.

The last region of all, corresponding to the most refrangible side of the spectrum, is *ultra-violet*.[1] This portion, extending from *L* to the end of the solar spectrum at *R*, is invisible unless the brighter parts of the spectrum mentioned above are carefully screened off. The existence of a special kind of radiation here was revealed first by its chemical actions, and consequently these rays were called invisible chemical rays. But, as a matter of fact, they are not invisible, although they certainly do affect the eye comparatively much less than the rays of the luminous middle part of the spectrum between the lines *B* and *H*. When these latter rays are completely excluded by suitable apparatus, the ultra-violet rays are visible without difficulty, clear to the end of the solar spectrum. At low intensity their colour is indigo-blue, and with higher intensity bluish grey. The easiest way to demonstrate the existence of these rays is by the phenomenon of *fluorescence*. For example, when a clear solution of sulphate of quinine is illuminated by ultra-violet light, a pale bluish light emanates in every direction from all the places in it where the ultra-violet rays fall, appearing somewhat like a luminous cloud pervading the liquid. Analyzed by a prism, this pale bluish light turns out not to be ultra-violet light at all, but compound whitish light of medium refrangibility. The simplest description of the phenomenon, therefore, is that as long as the ultra-violet rays fall on the quinine solution, it is self-luminous and emits compound whitish light of medium refrangibility. But the eye, being ever so much more sensitive to this kind of radiation than it is to ultra-violet, is entirely unconscious of the ultra-violet light until it falls on some fluorescent substance, and then the light that was previously invisible becomes visible in this material. Besides quinine, other substances that are highly fluorescent are uranium glass (canary glass), aesculin, platinum cyanide of potassium, etc.[2]

The fluorescent substance itself does not appear to be changed in the least, and it can be made to fluoresce over and over again. And

---

[1] ¶Silver chloride was long known to be sensitive to luminous radiations. J. W. RITTER (1801) found that the greatest effect on this substance was produced beyond the violet end of the visible spectrum. (J. P. C. S.)

[2] ¶Fluorescence is a term derived from fluor spar, which was the first substance that was observed to exhibit this peculiar emission of light. The phenomenon was first investigated by Sir J. HERSCHEL and Sir D. BREWSTER; and subsequently by Sir G. G. STOKES. In every instance the fluorescent light is found to be light of longer wave-length than that of the incident light that excites the effect; all fluorescent phenomena being cases of the so-called degradation of energy. See R. W. WOOD, *Physical Optics*, second edition, 1914, Chapter XX. (J. P. C. S.)

as no heat seems to disappear in the process, the inference from the law of the conservation of energy is that, notwithstanding that the fluorescent light affects the eye more, the actual energy of this radiation is no greater than that of the incident ultra-violet rays. No exact measurements are as yet available as to the ratio between the brightness of the original ultra-violet radiation and that of the same radiation after it has been changed by fluorescence. However, from certain facts to be mentioned later [p. 113] in describing the methods, it may be estimated that the fluorescent light is about 1200 times brighter than the ultra-violet radiation that induces it. Even without making any measurement, it is easy to show that the luminosity of the two kinds of light for the eye is extraordinarily different. This can be done by focusing ultra-violet light that has been completely purified of all more refrangible rays, and letting it fall first on a non-fluorescent screen like white porcelain, and then on quinine. The solar spectrum, at any rate as produced by sunlight that has traversed the atmosphere, does not actually extend beyond the place where the eye, suitably screened from the brighter light, can perceive ultra-violet radiation; because even when an objective spectrum is projected by quartz prisms and lenses on a quinine solution or some other fluorescent substance, there is no fluorescence beyond the limit above mentioned. On the other hand, however, STOKES found that the spectrum of the electric arclight, projected on a fluorescent screen by a quartz optical system, extends much farther than the solar spectrum. Thus, in fact, his method is adapted for detecting also still more refrangible light than is contained in sunlight; and hence, it is to be inferred that the spectrum of sunlight that has been filtered out by the atmosphere really ends at the limit indicated by the eye and fluorescent substances.[1] No experiments have as yet been made on the visibility of the most refrangible rays of the electric arclight. The spark in vacuo that is obtained by an induction coil contains, indeed, a relatively large proportion of ultra-violet as compared with the small amount of less refrangible radiation, but the absolute intensity of the light is too slight to be resolved minutely by a prism.[2]

[1] ¶Owing to absorption by ozone in the higher levels of the atmosphere, the ultra-violet region of the solar spectrum ends at about 290μμ. (J. P. C. S.)

[2] The arclight may be made richer still in ultra-violet by soaking the carbons in solutions of zinc or cadmium salts. Far better still for obtaining this sort of radiation is the spark of a large induction coil which is discharged between cadmium or magnesium electrodes, especially when means are taken to cut out the ordinary luminous rays. Rays of wavelength 257 cause a still perceptible fluorescence in the eye, and hence produce a sensation of light.—N.

¶The beautiful series of researches, beginning with CORNU's work forty years ago, followed by SCHUMANN's investigations (1890), and continued by LYMAN and by MILLIKAN in very recent years, has resulted in the exploration of the ultra-violet region as far as to

At the other end of the spectrum also, when the brighter light that is ordinarily visible is screened off, it is possible to distinguish parts of the spectrum that usually remain invisible. An adequate screen for this purpose is obtained by interposing a piece of red glass in the path of the rays. Red glass coloured by protoxide of copper transmits much orange light, and hence, if necessary, a piece of blue cobalt glass, which absorbs orange but transmits extreme red light, may be used in combination with the red glass. But as compared with the great extent of the ultra-violet spectrum, there is not much that is gained at the red end by this mode of observation. The strip of red light beyond the line A is about as wide as the interval between A and B. The hue of the red does not change up to the extreme end and is not at all purple.

But, as a matter of fact, the solar spectrum extends on the red side farther than the eye can detect. Hitherto the existence of these infra-red rays has not been made manifest except by their thermal effects, and that is why they are called *dark heat rays*.[1] Glass, water and numerous other substances that are transparent to ordinary light are opaque to infra-red, and so rock-salt prisms and lenses must be used to explore this region of the spectrum. The width of the dark heat spectrum as produced by a prism is certainly limited by reason of the fact that, according to the theory of elastic aether vibrations, the refraction approaches a minimum as the wave-length increases. This minimum cannot be surpassed, and the dispersion of colours terminates at it. In Fig. 9 the wave-lengths are plotted as abscissae from an origin that is just as far to the left of the point H as the point b is to the right of this point. The capital letters from B to H correspond to the FRAUNHOFER lines and to their positions in an interference spectrum. The ordinates are the values of the indices of refraction for a flint glass prism used by FRAUNHOFER.

Line	B	C	D	E	F	G	H
Index of refraction	1.6277	1.6297	1.6350	1.6420	1.6483	1.6603	1.6711

The letters $B_{,,}$ $C_{,,}$ etc., on the vertical axis, indicate the positions of the same dark lines in the solar spectrum of this flint glass prism.

---

wave-lengths of only $20\mu\mu$, which "is the limit reached today in the study of radiations by optical means." See C. FABRY, Studies in the field of light radiation. *Jour. of the Franklin Inst.*, **192**, (1921), 277-290. For the most recent work in this farthest region, see R. A. MILLIKAN, *Nat. Acad. Sci. Proc.* **7**, 289-294. Oct. 1921. and R. A. MILLIKAN and I. S. BOWEN, Extreme ultra-violet spectra. *Phys. Rev.*, **23**, 1924. 1-34. (In this paper the exploration extends as far as $13.6\mu\mu$.) (J. P. C. S.)

[1] ¶The thermal action of these dark heat rays was detected by Sir WM. HERSCHEL in 1800; who drew the correct conclusion from his experiment at first, but afterwards changed his opinion. See HOUSTOUN, *Light and colour*, 1923, page 37. (J. P. C. S.)

The base-line Hb corresponds to the index 1.6070 which is the minimum
value for this particular kind of glass. With increasing wave-length
the indices of refraction must approach this minimum value asymptotically.[1] The dotted curve H,d shows, therefore, the refrangibility of the
light as a function of the wave-length, and if it were extended farther,
it would approach the base-line Hb asymptotically. Consequently,
supposing that the refraction spectrum $H,B,$ is extended beyond its
red end at $B,$ so as to include the dark heat rays, its extreme limit must
be on the base-line at $H;$[2] that is, it is about as far from the red end $B,$
visible under ordinary conditions as $B,$ is from the boundary $F,$

between green and
blue; which is a dis-
tance corresponding
roughly to half the
length of the ordinary
visible spectrum. An-
other thing that the
diagram (Fig. 9) shows
clearly is how light at
the blue end $F,G,H,$ of
the refraction spec-
trum $B,H,$ is spread
out, while that at the
red end $B,C,D,$ is con-
densed together, as

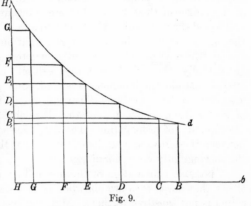

Fig. 9.

compared with the interference spectrum BH. Naturally, this con-
densation of the less refrangible light in the refraction spectrum should
be more and more marked, the nearer we come to the limit of the
infra-red region. Therefore, towards the blue end where the spectrum
is more elongated, the number of visible dark lines becomes greater;
and since the same amount of light or heat is spread out here over a
larger area, brightness and temperature are less. On the other hand,

[1] The value of this minimum has been taken from BADEN POWELL's calculation (POG-
GENDORFF XXXVII); as his interpolation formula agrees closely enough with CAUCHY's
theoretical formula.

[2] According to a remark of FR. EISENLOHR this limit seems actually to have been reached
in MELLONI's experiments. *Kritische Zft. f. Chemie.* Erlangen 1858. S. 229. (In the 2nd
edition the following statement is added here: Theoretically, this was what was to be
expected. However, LANGLEY, *Phil. Mag.*, **21**, 1886, 349, in his observations on infra-red,
which go much farther than any previous work of this kind, has not found any such limit.)

¶The longest waves in the solar spectrum that have been ascertained are about $5000\mu\mu$.
But in the spectra of artificial sources of light, it has been possible to explore the infra-red
region as far as wave-lengths that are almost 400 times as great as those at the red end of
the luminous or visible spectrum, that is, to about $300000\mu\mu$ (or 0.3mm). This is in the neighbourhood of the upper limit of emission spectra. (J. P. C. S.)

towards the red end there are fewer dark lines, and brightness and temperature are greater, than in the interference spectrum. And although the maximum heat effect in the prismatic spectrum is in the infra-red, it does not follow that these particular dark heat rays are present in sunlight in greater numbers than some of the luminous rays. On the contrary, in the interference spectrum the heat maximum falls on yellow.

On account of the characteristics of the refraction spectrum above mentioned, it is extremely difficult to determine the longest wavelengths in the infra-red portion of solar radiation. By a method which appears to be fundamentally sound, FIZEAU has measured the lengths of the longer of these waves that are transmitted through flint glass, and found the maximum to be 0.001940 mm. This is more than double the wave-length of the farthest red light in the ordinarily visible region, which according to the author's determinations is 0.00081 mm. Incidentally, these dark heat rays exhibit the phenomena of interference just like the luminous rays, and, consequently, like them, they are due to aether vibrations. They are subject to exactly the same laws of polarisation, which implies that the vibrations are transverse to the direction of propagation. The only physical difference, therefore, between these rays and luminous rays is that the waves are longer and the refrangibility correspondingly less.

A possible explanation of the invisibility of infra-red radiation is either that these rays are absorbed by the ocular media or that the retina is not sensitive to them. MELLONI has demonstrated that the dark heat rays are absorbed to a great extent by water. BRÜCKE and KNOBLAUCH have made experiments on the transparent media of the eye of an ox. The cornea, vitreous humor and crystalline lens were inserted in a convenient tubular mounting, with the vitreous humor in between the cornea and the lens. Sunlight reflected by a heliostat into the dark room was transmitted through this perfectly transparent system and made to fall on a thermopile. The indicated deflections on the amplifying mechanism amounted to between 26° and 30°. Then both sides of the eye were covered with lamp-black over a turpentine flame, which was accomplished successfully, without producing any other change in the cornea and lens, as was ascertained subsequently. Under such circumstances, it was found that no heat at all was radiated through the eye. But lamp-black is transparent to the dark heat rays and opaque to the luminous rays. If, therefore, a part of the radiation that was transmitted through the ocular media had consisted of dark heat rays, some effect from these would have been manifest through the lamp-black. It would hardly be justifiable to say that this experiment proved that the limits of the visible red coincided with the limits of diathermancy of the ocular media, but it certainly does establish the fact that very little, if any, of the infra-red radiation can get to the retina; and this of itself would seem to be a sufficient explanation of the invisibility of this region of the spectrum.

CIMA[1] has made similar experiments, using a LOCATELLI lamp as source of heat, the radiation being transmitted through the ocular media to a thermopile. He found that about 13 percent of the incident heat was transmitted through the crystalline lens, about 9 percent, through the vitreous humor alone, and also about 9 percent through the eye as a whole.[2]

The mere fact that it is possible to see the ultra-violet spectrum with its dark lines shows that this radiation may traverse the ocular media. DONDERS and REES have demonstrated objectively that these rays go through a glass vessel containing vitreous humor of the eye of an ox, and the cornea and crystalline lens also. The ultra-violet light, after having traversed the ocular media, was made manifest by letting it fall on the surface of a solution of sulphate of quinine where blue fluorescence was excited. Similar experiments had been previously made by BRÜCKE, by testing the action of light on guaiacum solution and on photographic paper after it had been transmitted through the media in the eye.

Guaiacum resin, newly evaporated in the dark from the alcoholic solution, appears blue under the action of blue, violet or ultra-violet radiation, but the blue colour disappears when it is illuminated by less refrangible rays. In ordinary daylight the blue effect is predominant. But the colour of this substance under illumination of daylight that has been filtered through the crystalline lens of an ox is simply yellow-green; and a layer of the resin that has already been coloured blue looks

---

[1] *Sul potere degli umori dell' occhio a trasmettere il calorico raggionante.* Torino 1852.

[2] J. JANSEN (*C. R.*, LI, 128–131; 373–374; *Ann. der Chir.*, (3), XL, 71–93) and R. FRANZ (POGG. *Ann.*, CXV, 26–279) also found that the absorption in the vitreous humor was very similar to that in water and rather more in the cornea and crystalline lens. Similar results were obtained by TH. W. ENGELMANN (*Onderzoek. physiol. Lab. Utrecht.* 3. Reeks, D. VII Bl. 291. 1882).

Concerning absorption of ultra-violet in the eye, it may be added that, according to the researches of SORET and others, there is little absorption of rays between the FRAUN-HOFER lines H and Q, whereas shorter wave-lengths than these are strongly absorbed. See SORET, *C. R.*, **88**, p. 1012; **97**, pp. 314, 572, 642; CHARDONNET, *C. R.*, **96**, p. 509; MASCART, *C. R.*, **96**, p. 571.—N.

¶In connection with this whole subject the following more recent contributions are worth consulting:

W. CROOKES, Preparation of eye-preserving glass for spectacles. *Phil. Trans.*, **213** (1914), 1–25; and VERHOEFF and BELL, The pathological effects of radiant energy on the eye; an experimental investigation. *Proc. Amer. Acad. Arts and Sciences*, Vol. **51**, No. 13, July 1916. (J. P. C. S.)

yellow-green in the same light. This means that the crystalline lens absorbs the bluish rays of daylight more than the others. If ordinary blue and violet light were much absorbed, the lens itself would have to look yellowish; but under normal conditions it is fairly without any colour, and therefore in the light that makes guaiacum look blue it can only be the ultra-violet portion that is absorbed by the lens in any comparatively considerable amount. The results of similar experiments of BRÜCKE's on the cornea and vitreous humor indicate a behaviour of the same kind as that of the lens, only to a much less degree. These conclusions are supported by the fact that the cornea and crystalline lens, as may easily be observed even in the live eye, are themselves fluorescent to a certain extent when violet or ultraviolet light falls on them. Under such circumstances they shine with a pale blue colour like that of the quinine solution. Fluorescent substances, however, always noticeably absorb the rays that make them fluoresce.

Other experiments were made by BRÜCKE with C. KARSTEN's photographic paper. Cornea, vitreous humor, and crystalline lens were mounted for testing in a similar arrangement to that used in the thermo-electric experiments mentioned above. They were traversed by radiations from a spectrum of sunlight produced by a prism, and the sensitive paper was adjusted in the focal plane of the ocular media. After exposure to violet for 90 seconds, a perfectly black point was produced. In the vicinity of the group of lines known as M (according to DRAPER) the effect on the paper ceased entirely, so that even after an exposure of ten minutes no action could be detected. However, it should be remarked that even when the rays do not pass through the ocular media, the photographic action on nearly all sensitive preparations falls off rapidly towards the end of the spectrum. Fluorescence, which was not discovered until after BRÜCKE made the experiments here mentioned, is a much more sensitive means of detecting these effects than photographic action, especially in case of the more refrangible rays; and it has enabled us to explore the spectrum much farther than before. In fact, when the eye is properly screened from the light of the brighter portion of the spectrum, direct observation seems to afford more information of the ultra-violet region than is obtained by photographic methods.[1]

Thus, according to BRÜCKE's researches, ultra-violet rays are absorbed to a considerable extent in passing through the ocular media, especially the crystalline lens, as shown particularly by the effect on guaiacum tincture. On the other hand, DONDERS's experiments tend to show that this absorption is not enough to be noticeable in the ordinary comparisons of brightness by the unaided eye. But it has

---

[1] ¶One difficulty about photographing the ultra-violet spectrum is that glass begins to become very opaque at about wave-length $340\mu\mu$. It can be replaced by quartz, which does very well as far as $185\ \mu\mu$, when it begins to be highly absorbent also. Fluorite enables us to push the limit much farther. Another difficulty is the opacity of the gelatine of the sensitive film which prevents these very short waves from getting to the sensitive salt at all; and, finally, the air itself ceases to be transparent, and it is necessary, therefore, to conduct the experiments in vacuo. (J. P. C. S.)

already been stated that the brightness of ultra-violet light as compared with that of practically the same amount of light emitted by fluorescent quinine solution is about in the ratio of 1:1200. The inference is that absorption in the ocular media cannot be responsible, except to the minutest extent, for the low subjective luminosity of ultra-violet; and that the real explanation of it is probably due to the lack of sensitivity of the retina.

Another thing to be noted is that the colour sensation produced by light of a definite wave-length depends also on its luminosity. Thus, any increase of luminosity tends to make it look more white or pale yellow. This effect is easiest to see with violet; the less blue and the more purple it is, the fainter it gets. On the other hand, with a moderate degree of brightness, such as is obtained by observing the solar spectrum in a telescope, this same colour appears pale grey, with just a faint bluish violet tinge. Another good way to see this, as MOSER suggested, is to look at the sun in a half-clouded sky through a piece of fairly dark violet glass. The sun's disc looks just as white through the glass as the brightly illuminated clouds near by appear to the naked eye. So also for low intensity the blue of the spectrum is more like indigo-blue; with higher intensity, sky-blue; and with still greater intensity (provided the eye can stand it without annoyance), pale blue and finally white. This is the explanation of the wrong use of the name sky-blue as applied to the more refrangible and at the same time more luminous cyan-blue of the spectrum. Green becomes yellow-green and then white; and yellow becomes white directly, but the luminosity is dazzling in its brilliancy. The effect is hardest to see in the case of red; and for the highest degrees of brightness, the most the author has been able to do, either by looking at the spectrum or by looking at the sun through a red glass, is to see it change to bright yellow. These tests can all be made equally well with carefully purified simple light or with mixed light of the given colour as it is obtained with coloured glasses.

There is no part of the spectrum where variation of luminosity produces so much change of hue as it does in the violet and ultra-violet regions. The hues of the most refrangible end cannot be very well compared with each other unless the luminosities are approximately equal. When the brightness is dim, the blue tones in the spectrum are nearer indigo, and the violet is more pink, as has been already mentioned. But from about the line L to the end of the spectrum a reversal occurs in the order of the colours, that is, the hue is no longer more like pink, but from here out is again like indigo. On the other hand, with moderate rise of intensity the ultra-violet looks bluish pale grey, paler than equally luminous indigo-blue, and hence it is called sometimes *lavender grey*.

The reversal in the order of colours exhibited by ultra-violet light at low luminosity probably does not depend on the mode of reaction of the nervous mechanism, but seems to be connected with the fluorescence of the retina itself; which, when illuminated by ultra-violet, emits light of lower refrangibility of a greenish white colour. At least, this was the case with the retina of the eye of a cadaver examined by the author,[1] and with the retinas of perfectly fresh eyes from oxen and rabbits that had just been killed, which were examined by SETS-CHENOW;[2] the fluorescence being, indeed, very slight, and the colour of the light the same as that mentioned above. The degree of fluorescence was less than that of paper, linen or ivory, but still it seemed to be always sufficient to change the colour of the incident ultra-violet light. The author tried to test it by comparing the radiation from the fluorescent places in this retina with ultra-violet light diffusely reflected from a white porcelain plate. In both cases the light was emitted in all directions in space. The retina and porcelain plate were observed through a weak prism that separated the two kinds of radiation, that is, the changed ultra-violet light from that which was unchanged. Under these circumstances, the light produced by fluorescence in the retina appeared about as bright as the unchanged ultra-violet illumination of the porcelain plate. It can hardly be doubted that the retina is sensitive to light produced in its own substance by fluorescence; and on this assumption, the sensation for ultra-violet radiation must be composed pretty evenly of the sensation directly produced by the ultra-violet light and that excited by the fluorescence. As this latter appears paler and more greenish than ultra-violet light, it would seem that the direct sensation of ultra-violet light on a non-fluorescent retina would have to be more like pure violet. For the lavender grey of the ultra-violet rays can be obtained by a proper mixture of violet and greenish white. The fact that the colour of the fluorescent retina is quite different from lavender grey does not warrant us in supposing that the ultra-violet light does not stimulate the retina at all and that the sensation is due simply to the fluorescent light.

A prismatic spectrum, short enough to be viewed in its entirety all at once, appears to consist of only four coloured sections, namely, red, green, blue and violet, the transition-colours disappearing almost entirely by contrast with these main colours. At best yellow may still be discerned in the green next the red. This separation of colours is enhanced by the fact that three of the more prominent dark lines of the solar spectrum, namely D, F and G, happen to lie about on the

[1] POGGENDORFFS *Ann.* XCIV. 205.

[2] GRAEFES *Archiv für Ophthalmologie.* Bd. V. Abt. 2. S. 205.

boundary lines of the four intervals of the spectrum above mentioned. But even without being able to distinguish these lines, the same separation of colours is manifest. The transition-colours are indeed more easily seen in a longer spectrum, but yet the visual impression of them is always considerably modified by the proximity of such brilliant saturated colours as are seen in the spectrum, which prevents the transition-colours from being seen in their own right. To distinguish exactly the series of pure colours in the spectrum, they must be isolated. A way of doing this is to project a fairly pure spectrum on a screen with a small slit in it, which permits the light of some single region of the spectrum to pass through it and be received on another white screen beyond. By gradually moving the slit from one end of the spectrum to the other, the whole series of hues can be inspected separately one after the other. Then it will be found that there is nowhere any abrupt transition in the series, and that the hues merge continuously each into the next. The richness and intense saturation of the succession of colours and the delicate transition of hues makes this experiment at the same time one of the most splendid spectacles that optics has to show.

Owing to the exceedingly gradual blending of the hues, it is naturally impossible also to assign any definite width to the separate coloured regions of the spectrum. In order to indicate as well as possible the positions and distribution of the colours, the hues corresponding to the FRAUNHOFER lines are given in the following table, together with their wave-lengths in millionths of a millimetre:[1]

Line	Wave-length in $\mu\mu$	Colour
A	760.40	Extreme red
B	686.853	Red
C	656.314	Border of red and orange
D	589.625 589.024	Golden yellow
E	526.990	Green
F	486.164	Cyan-blue
G	430.825	Border of indigo and violet
H	396.879	Limit of violet
L	381.96	
M	372.62	
N	358.18	
O	344.10	Ultra-violet
P	336.00	
Q	328.63	
R	317.98	
U	294.77	

[1] ¶The first determinations of the wave-lengths of light of different refrangibilities or colours were made by YOUNG. The values of these magnitudes as found by him for the two ends of the visible spectrum were 266 and 167 ten-millionths of an inch or 676 and 424 millionths of a millimeter. (J. P. C. S.)

The different sensations of colour in the eye depend on the frequency of the waves of light in the same way as sensations of pitch in the ear depend on the frequency of the waves of sound; and so, many attempts have been made to divide the intervals of colour in the spectrum on the same basis as that of the division of the musical scale, that is, into whole tones and semi-tones. NEWTON tried it first. However, at that time the undulatory theory was still undeveloped and not accepted; and not being aware of the connection between the width of the separate colours in the prismatic spectrum and the nature of the refracting substance, he divided the visible spectrum of a glass prism, that is, approximately the part comprised between the lines B and H, directly into seven intervals, of widths proportional to the intervals in the musical scale,[1] namely, $\frac{9}{8}, \frac{16}{15}, \frac{10}{9}, \frac{9}{8}, \frac{10}{9}, \frac{16}{15}, \frac{9}{8}$; and so he distinguished seven corresponding principal colours; *red, orange, yellow, green, blue, indigo* and *violet*. The reason why two kinds of blue are mentioned here, while golden yellow, yellow-green, and sea-green, which appear to the eye at least just as different from the adjacent principal colours as indigo is from cyan-blue and violet, are omitted, is because of the peculiar variation of the index of refraction mentioned on page 68, which causes the more refrangible colours in a prismatic spectrum to be elongated more than the less refrangible ones. The distribution of colours in the interference spectrum has nothing to do with the character of a refracting medium and depends simply on the wavelength; and here the blue-violet region is much narrower, and if the intervals were determined in the same way, this span would not be resolved into three parts, whereas the red-orange portion would be in about three parts.

In the light of subsequent discoveries and measurements, suppose that the spectrum as we now know it is divided on the same principle as the musical scale using the vibration-numbers of the aether waves, as was done in the case of the solar spectrum exhibited in Plate I;

---

[1] ¶A clear description of the actual process that NEWTON used in making the division of the spectrum on the basis of the musical scale is to be found in R. A. HOUSTOUN's *Light and Colour*, 1923, pages 12–14. This writer shows that NEWTON divided the spectrum originally into five colours, and then inserted orange and indigo; and, as to the latter, he concludes that the introduction of indigo was due to an "attempt to find a connection between the spectrum and the musical scale," and that although "the attempt failed completely," as NEWTON himself lived to realize, "indigo remains in the list of colours" "as a witness to it." The same writer points out the mystical influence exerted by PYTHAGORAS's discovery (572–492 B. C.) of the laws of harmony as illustrated by the natural modes of division of a vibrating string, which led to the idea that all the laws of nature were harmonies of some kind, as, for example, the so-called "music of the spheres" which cast its spell over a mind as acute as KEPLER's. An additional reason for dividing the spectrum into seven primary colours is to be traced also to the peculiar significance of the number seven as the "perfect number." (J. P. C. S.)

then if the yellow of the spectrum answers to the tenor C in music and the FRAUNHOFER line A corresponds to the G below it, we obtain for the separate half-tones the following scale of colours analogous to the notes of the piano:

$F^\#$,	end of Red.	$f^\#$,	Violet.
G,	Red.	g,	Ultra-violet.
$G^\#$,	Red.	$g^\#$,	Ultra-violet.
A,	Red.	a,	Ultra-violet.
$A^\#$,	Orange-red.	$a^\#$,	Ultra-violet.
B,	Orange.	b,	Ultra-violet.
c,	Yellow.		
$c^\#$,	Green.		
d,	Greenish blue.		
$d^\#$,	Cyan-blue.		
e,	Indigo blue.		
f,	Violet.		

The hues that comprise octaves are placed side by side. In the figure on Plate I the places corresponding to the tone-intervals are indicated by lines on the left. The end of the infra-red spectrum, according to FIZEAU and FOUCAULT, calculated on the same basis, would be about D, two octaves below cyan-blue; and if CAUCHY's formula for the connection between wave-length and index of refraction can be supposed to be valid so far, the extreme limit of the spectrum of the arclight would be at b', an octave higher than the ultra-violet end of the solar spectrum.

The colour-scale divided in half-tones as above shows that at both ends of the spectrum the colours do not change noticeably for several half-tone intervals, whereas in the middle of the spectrum the numerous transition colours of yellow into green are all comprised in the width of a single half-tone. This implies that in the middle of the spectrum the eye is much keener to distinguish vibration-frequencies than towards the ends of the spectrum; and that the magnitudes of the colour intervals are not at all like the gradations of musical pitch in being dependent on vibration-frequencies.

These physiological studies demand a much more exact differentiation of the homogeneous kinds of light than is usually necessary for purely physical investigations; and hence the theory of refraction by prisms will now be specially considered, to see what are the conditions of obtaining pure spectra by dispersion. Previously, so far as the writer is aware, the theory has been confined to the problem of tracing single rays of light through a system of prisms, without investigating the position and nature of the *images produced by prisms*; and yet in looking through a prism or letting the light that issues from the prism go through lenses and telescopes, the essential thing is to distinguish the prism-images for each kind of homogeneous light. For these images are really to be considered as objects to be imaged by the ocular media and lenses. To supply this lack, we shall proceed to determine the *nature and position of the image in a prism*, although this investigation does not properly belong to physiological optics. However, the results will perhaps be important for everybody who wishes to produce pure prismatic spectra.

In general, a narrow homocentric bundle of incident rays will not be homocentric after emerging from a prism, but will be astigmatic, with two image-points, exactly in the same way as when a homocentric bundle of incident rays is refracted at an ellipsoidal surface or is incident obliquely on a spherical refracting surface.[1] In order to simplify the treatment of the subject, the law of refraction will be used in a form which was given to it by FERMAT soon after its discovery, and which is particularly adapted for investigation of problems in optics where the different portions of the path of a ray are not all in the same plane.

Suppose light traverses a series of refracting media, and consider the path of a single ray. If the length of the path in each medium is multiplied by the index of refraction of that medium, and these products are all added, this sum is what the writer calls the *optical length* of the ray.[2] For example, if r_1, r_2, r_3, etc. denote the lengths of the path of the ray in the first, second, third, etc., medium, respectively, and if n_1, n_2, n_3, etc., are the corresponding indices of refraction, the optical length according to this definition is

$$\Psi = n_1 r_1 + n_2 r_2 + n_3 r_3 + \cdots + n_m r_m .$$

If c_0 denotes the velocity of light in vacuo, and c_1, c_2, c_3, etc. denote the velocities in the different media in succession, then (see §9):

$$n_1 = \frac{c_0}{c_1} , \qquad n_2 = \frac{c_0}{c_2} , \qquad n_3 = \frac{c_0}{c_3} \cdots n_m = \frac{c_0}{c_m} ,$$

and therefore

$$\Psi = c_0 \left[\frac{r_1}{c_1} + \frac{r_2}{c_2} + \frac{r_3}{c_3} + \cdots + \frac{r_m}{c_m} \right] .$$

[1] See end of §14. Vol. I. The theorems that follow are applicable to the monochromatic aberrations of the eye as treated in §14.

[2] ¶It is interesting to note that HELMHOLTZ originated the name for this function that has since been universally adopted. (J. P. C. S.)

Suppose t denotes the time which the light takes to go over the entire path; then

$$t = \frac{r_1}{c_1} + \frac{r_2}{c_2} + \frac{r_3}{c_3} + \cdots + \frac{r_m}{c_m},$$

and therefore

$$\Psi = c_0 t.$$

Accordingly, the optical length is proportional to the time taken by the light to go over the path and is equal to the distance the light would have travelled in vacuo in the same time.

The notion of optical length may be applied also to the case where the ray in the last medium is prolonged backwards beyond the boundary of this medium to a point where a potential image of the luminous point is situated. To find the optical length between the luminous point and its potential image, the same process is employed as before; only the distance from the place where the ray emerges into the last medium to the place where the potential image is must be reckoned as negative. The following theorems will then be perfectly general.

I. *The law of refraction of light is equivalent to the condition that the optical length of the ray from a point on it in the first medium to a corresponding point in the second medium shall have a limiting value, that is, shall be a maximum or minimum.*

The surface of separation of the two media may have any form whatever, provided the curvature is continuous. If the incidence-normal is chosen as the z-axis of a system of rectangular axes, the form of the surface will be given by an equation in which z is a function of x and y; and at the point of incidence

$$x = y = z = 0, \qquad \frac{dz}{dx} = 0, \qquad \frac{dz}{dy} = 0 \ \cdots \qquad (1)$$

Moreover, let a_1, b_1, c_1 denote the coördinates of a point on the incident ray, and a_2, b_2, c_2 those of a point on the refracted ray. If these points are connected with a point (x, y, z) of the refracting surface, the optical length between them along this route is

$$\Psi = n_1 \sqrt{(a_1-x)^2+(b_1-y)^2+(c_1-z)^2} + n_2\sqrt{(a_2-x)^2+(b_2-y)^2+(c_2-z)^2}.$$

In order that this magnitude, which is a function of the independent variables x and y, shall be a maximum or minimum, the first conditions (which here are likewise sufficient) are:

$$\frac{d\Psi}{dx} = 0, \qquad \frac{d\Psi}{dy} = 0,$$

or

$$0 = n_1 \frac{x - a_1 + (z - c_1)\dfrac{dz}{dx}}{\sqrt{(a_1 - x)^2 + (b_1 - y)^2 + (c_1 - z)^2}}$$

$$+ n_2 \frac{x - a_2 + (z - c_2)\dfrac{dz}{dx}}{\sqrt{(a_2 - x)^2 + (b_2 - y)^2 + (c_2 - z)^2}}$$

$$0 = n_1 \frac{y - b_1 + (z - c_1)\dfrac{dz}{dy}}{\sqrt{(a_1 - x)^2 + (b_1 - y)^2 + (c_1 - z)^2}}$$

$$+ n_2 \frac{y - b_2 + (z - c_2)\dfrac{dz}{dy}}{\sqrt{(a_2 - x)^2 + (b_2 - y)^2 + (c_2 - z)^2}}$$

$$(2)$$

Combining these equations with equations (1), we find for the ray that is incident on the surface at the origin of the system of coördinates:

$$0 = n_1 \frac{a_1}{\sqrt{a_1^2 + b_1^2 + c_1^2}} + \varkappa_2 \frac{a_2}{\sqrt{a_2^2 + b_2^2 + c_2^2}}$$

$$0 = n_1 \frac{b_1}{\sqrt{a_1^2 + b_1^2 + c_1^2}} + n_2 \frac{b_2}{\sqrt{a_2^2 + b_2^2 + c_2^2}}$$

$$(2a)$$

If the positions of the points (a_1, b_1, c_1) and (a_2, b_2, c_2) are given in terms of polar coördinates, by the ordinary formulae of transformation, namely:

$$
\begin{aligned}
a_1 &= r_1 \sin a_1 \cos \vartheta_1 & a_2 &= r_2 \sin a_2 \cos \vartheta_2 \\
b_1 &= r_1 \sin a_1 \sin \vartheta_1 & b_2 &= r_2 \sin a_2 \sin \vartheta_2 \\
c_1 &= r_1 \cos a_1 & c_2 &= r_2 \cos a_2
\end{aligned}
\quad \cdots \quad (3)
$$

equations (2a) become:

$$
\begin{aligned}
n_1 \sin a_1 \cos \vartheta_1 &= -n_2 \sin a_2 \cos \vartheta_2 \\
n_1 \sin a_1 \sin \vartheta_1 &= -n_2 \sin a_2 \sin \vartheta_2
\end{aligned}
\quad \cdots \cdots \quad (2b)
$$

Squaring each of these equations, and then adding them, we find:

$$n_1^2 \sin^2 a_1 = n_2^2 \sin^2 a_2 ,$$

that is,

$$n_1 \sin a_1 = \pm n_2 \sin a_2 .$$

The positive sign is the only one that applies here, because the angle a_1 is between $0°$ and $90°$, whereas, according to our convention, the angle a_2 must be between $90°$ and $180°$. Hence $\sin a_1$ and $\sin a_2$ are both positive; and, since n_1, n_2 are always positive, we have therefore:

$$n_1 \sin a_1 = n_2 \sin a_2 \quad \cdots \cdots \cdots \quad (4)$$

Combining this equation with equations (2b) we get:

$$\cos \vartheta_1 = - \cos \vartheta_2 ,$$
$$\sin \vartheta_1 = - \sin \vartheta_2 ,$$

that is,

$$\vartheta_2 = \vartheta_1 + 180° \quad \cdots \cdots \cdots \quad (4a)$$

Equations (4) and (4a), which have been derived from the condition that the optical length of the ray is a limiting value, are, however, identical with the two conditions of the law of refraction. Thus, as follows from equations (3), a_1 is the angle of incidence, ϑ_1 is the angle between the plane of incidence and the xz-plane, and ϑ_2 is the angle between the plane of refraction and the xz-plane. Accordingly, the planes of incidence and refraction are inclined to each other at an angle of $180°$, that is, they are one and the same plane. Exactly the same mode of proof is used when the ray is reflected from the surface instead of being refracted. All we have to do in this case is to put $n_1 = n_2$, because the ray remains in the same medium, and to suppose that both a_1 and a_2 are comprised between $0°$ and $90°$. Then equations (4) and (4a) become:

$$\sin a_1 = \sin a_2 \quad \text{or} \quad a_1 = a_2 ,$$
$$\vartheta_2 = \vartheta_1 + 180°,$$

which are the two conditions of the law of reflection.

Having established the above theorem for a single refracting surface, we can readily extend it to any number of such surfaces. *When a ray of light traverses a series of transparent media, separated by refracting surfaces of continuous curvature, its path can be traced from the fact that the optical length along the ray from a point in the first medium to a point in the last medium is a limiting value, that is, is a maximum or a minimum.*

Let x_1, y_1; x_2, y_2; etc. denote the coördinates of the points where the ray meets the various refracting surfaces in succession; x_m, y_m being the coördinates in the case of the mth or last surface. All these systems of coördinates are chosen so that the z-axis coincides with the normal to the surface and the xy-plane is tangent to the surface. Then the first conditions, that the optical length of the ray, which is denoted by Ψ, shall be a limiting value, are:

$$\frac{d\Psi}{dx_1} = 0 \; , \qquad\qquad \frac{d\Psi}{dy_1} = 0 \; ,$$

$$\frac{d\Psi}{dx_2} = 0 \; , \qquad\qquad \frac{d\Psi}{dy_2} = 0 \; ,$$

$$\text{etc} \; .$$

$$\frac{d\Psi}{dx_m} = 0 \; , \qquad\qquad \frac{d\Psi}{dy_m} = 0 \; .$$

By the theorem just proved, the first pair of these equations is equivalent to the condition that the ray shall be refracted at the first surface according to the known law of refraction; and the second pair of equations is equivalent to the same thing for the second surface; and so on for each pair of equations for each surface in turn. And therefore the path of the ray is given by the above theorem in accordance with the law of refraction.

In this case also the investigation of the first derivatives of the optical length is sufficient. Whether the path of the ray is a maximum for all positions of the point of incidence, or a minimum for all positions, or whether it is a maximum for some positions and a minimum for others, can only be ascertained, of course, by investigating the second derivatives; but this is not the question at present. Hence, in the following discussion, we can speak of all values of the optical length of the ray as limiting values, provided the first derivatives of this function satisfy the maximum and minimum conditions; without stopping to consider the sign and magnitude of the second derivative. The influence of the second derivative on the problem here considered will appear presently.

II. *If a bundle of homocentric incident rays is refracted through a series of optical media, separated by surfaces of continuous curvature, the rays that emerge in the last medium will be normal to a surface which is the locus of all points for which the optical lengths along the different rays have the same value.*

The notation will be the same as that used above. The terminus of the ray is in a curved surface for which

$$\Psi = \text{const} \; . \quad . \quad . \quad . \quad . \quad . \quad . \quad . \quad . \quad (1)$$

The coördinates of the points of this surface will be referred to the systems of axes used for the points of the last refracting surface. Let the coördinates of a point on the surface $\Psi = C$ be denoted by (a, b, c) where c is to be regarded as a function of a and b.

Consider now two adjacent rays of the bundle. The coördinates of the points where the first ray meets each of the surfaces in succession are:

$$x_1 \ , \ y_1 \ ; \ x_2 \ , \ y_2 \ ; \text{etc} \ . \ ; \ x_m \ , \ y_m \ ; a \ , b \ , c \ ;$$

and for the second ray the corresponding coördinates will be:

$$x_1 + \Delta x_1 \ , \quad y_1 + \Delta y_1 \ ; \quad x_2 + \Delta x_2 \ , \ y_2 + \Delta y_2 \ ; \text{etc} \ .$$
$$x_m + \Delta x_m \ , \ y_m + \Delta y_m \ , \quad a + \Delta a \ , \quad b + \Delta b \ , c + \Delta c \ ,$$

The fact that c is a function of a, b is expressed by the equation.

$$\Delta c = \frac{dc}{da} \Delta a + \frac{dc}{db} \Delta b \ .$$

If Ψ, $\Psi + \Delta\Psi$ denote the optical lengths along the two rays, then for infinitesimal values of the differences:

$$\Psi + \Delta\Psi = \Psi + \frac{d\Psi}{dx_1} \Delta x_1 + \frac{d\Psi}{dx_2} \Delta x_2 + \cdot \ \cdot \ \cdot \quad + \frac{d\Psi}{dx_m} \Delta x_m$$
$$+ \left(\frac{d\Psi}{da} + \frac{d\Psi}{dc} \cdot \frac{dc}{da} \right) \Delta a$$
$$+ \frac{d\Psi}{dy_1} \Delta y_1 + \frac{d\Psi}{dy_2} \Delta y_2 + \cdot \ \cdot \ \cdot \quad + \frac{d\Psi}{dy_m} \Delta y_m + \left(\frac{d\Psi}{db} + \frac{d\Psi}{dc} \cdot \frac{dc}{db} \right) \Delta b \ .$$

Now as the value of Ψ is constant over the surface whose points are given by the coördinates a, b, c, we must have

$$\Delta\Psi = 0 \ .$$

Moreover, by the foregoing theorem,

$$0 = \frac{d\Psi}{dx_1} = \frac{d\Psi}{dy_1} = \frac{d\Psi}{dx_2} = \frac{d\Psi}{dy_2} = \text{etc} \ . \ ,$$

hence

$$\left(\frac{d\Psi}{da} + \frac{d\Psi}{dc} \cdot \frac{dc}{da} \right) \Delta a + \left(\frac{d\Psi}{db} + \frac{d\Psi}{dc} \cdot \frac{dc}{db} \right) \Delta b = 0 \ .$$

This equation must be satisfied for all values of $\dfrac{\Delta a}{\Delta b}$; and, consequently, we must have:

$$\left. \begin{array}{l} \dfrac{d\Psi}{da} + \dfrac{d\Psi}{dc} \cdot \dfrac{dc}{da} = 0 \\[3mm] \dfrac{d\Psi}{db} + \dfrac{d\Psi}{dc} \cdot \dfrac{dc}{db} = 0 \end{array} \right\} \quad . \quad . \quad . \quad . \quad . \quad . \quad (2)$$

Let $r_0, r_1, \ldots r_m$ denote the lengths of the portions of the path of the ray in the various media, and let $n_0, n_1, \ldots n_m$ denote the indices of refraction; then

$$\Psi = n_0 r_0 + n_1 r_1 + \cdots + n_m r_m .$$

In this equation r is a function of a, b and c; consequently,

$$\frac{d\Psi}{da} = n_m \frac{dr_m}{da} = n_m \frac{a - x_m}{r_m}$$

$$\frac{d\Psi}{db} = n_m \frac{dr_m}{db} = n_m \frac{b - y_m}{r_m}$$

$$\frac{d\Psi}{dc} = n_m \frac{dr_m}{dc} = n_m \frac{c - z_m}{r_m} ,$$

and hence equations (2) become:

$$\left.\begin{array}{l} (a - x_m) + (c - z_m)\dfrac{dc}{da} = 0 \\[2ex] (b - y_m) + (c - z_m)\dfrac{dc}{db} = 0 \end{array}\right\} \quad \cdots \cdots \quad (2\mathrm{a})$$

The interpretation of these equations is that the straight line drawn from the point (x_m, y_m, z_m) to the point (a, b, c) is the normal to the surface $\Psi = C$ at the latter point.

The easiest way to see this is by recalling that the distance measured along the normal to the surface is itself the longest or shortest distance from a given point to the surface. Now if the distance

$$r_m = \sqrt{(x_m - a)^2 + (y_m - b)^2 + (z_m - c)^2} ;$$

between (x_m, y_m, z_m) and (a, b, c) is to be a maximum or minimum, then we must have:

$$0 = \frac{dr_m}{da} + \frac{dr_m}{dc}\frac{dc}{da} = \frac{a - x_m}{r_m} + \frac{dc}{da} \cdot \frac{c - z_m}{r_m} ,$$

$$0 = \frac{dr_m}{db} + \frac{dr_m}{dc}\frac{dc}{da} = \frac{b - y_m}{r_m} + \frac{dc}{db} \cdot \frac{c - z_m}{r_m} ,$$

These conditions are the same as equations (2a). And so the ray that goes through (a, b, c) is normal to the surface $\Psi = C$ that passes through this same point.

As the light traverses equal optical lengths in equal times, it reaches all points of the surface $\Psi = C$ at the same instant, and hence this surface is a *wave-surface*, that is, it is a surface which contains all those points where the aether-vibrations are precisely in the same phase.[1]

Procedure of an infinitely narrow bundle of rays. Having proved that rays, emanating originally from one point, and undergoing any number of refractions at a system of surfaces of continuous curvature, will all be normal to a certain surface, the so-called *wave-surface*, we have therefore simply to consider a bundle of optical rays as being geometrically the system of normals to a curved surface, and governed therefore by the same laws. Accordingly, if a plane is passed through a certain ray A, it will intersect the wave-surface in a curve whose curvature at the point where the ray meets the surface will generally be different for different azimuths of the plane. According to the theory of curved surfaces, *the sections of greatest and least curvature will be in planes at right angles to each other.* If normals are drawn to the wave-surface that are infinitely near the ray A and that therefore represent adjacent rays, those normals that are in the sections of greatest and least curvatures will intersect the ray A at the centres of the circles of greatest and least curvature, respectively; whereas those normals that do not lie in one or other of these two principal sections will not intersect the ray A at all. Thus, in general, along every ray there are two focal points which are the centres of greatest and least curvature of the wave-surface at the point where the ray crosses it. When the surface has the same curvature at this place in all directions, the two focal points on the ray will coincide; and in this one exceptional case the adjacent rays will all meet the ray A in one point.

In order to formulate these propositions analytically, let us consider a system of rectangular axes whose z-axis coincides with the ray A. The coördinates of any point on the wave-surface will be denoted as follows:

$$x = a , \quad y = b , \quad z = c .$$

The equation of the surface itself will be expressed in such a form that c is given as a function of a and b. For the given set of axes, when

$$a = b = 0 , \text{ then also } \frac{dc}{da} = \frac{dc}{db} = 0 \ . \quad . \quad . \quad . \quad (1)$$

Let x, y, z denote the coördinates of a point on the normal to the wave-surface at the point (a, b, c); then, as in proposition II, equation (2a):

---

[1] ¶This is equivalent to the law of MALUS published in 1808, that *rays of light meet the wave-surface normally;* and, conversely, *The system of surfaces which intersect at right angles rays emanating originally from a point-source is a system of wave-surfaces.* (J. P. C. S.)

$$\left.\begin{array}{l} (a - x) + (c - z)\dfrac{dc}{da} = 0 \\[3mm] (b - y) + (c - z)\dfrac{dc}{db} = 0 \end{array}\right\} \quad \cdot \quad \cdot \quad \cdot \quad \cdot \quad \cdot \quad (1a)$$

The magnitudes $a + \Delta a$, $b + \Delta b$ differ infinitesimally from a, b; and if the former are substituted in the above equations in place of the latter, these equations become:

$$(a + \Delta a - x) + \left(c + \frac{dc}{da}\Delta a + \frac{dc}{db}\Delta b - z\right)\frac{dc}{da}$$

$$+ (c - z)\left(\frac{d^2c}{da^2}\Delta a + \frac{d^2c}{da.db}\Delta b\right) = 0 \,,$$

$$(b + \Delta b - y) + \left(c + \frac{dc}{da}\Delta a + \frac{dc}{db}\Delta b - z\right)\frac{dc}{db}$$

$$+ (c - z)\left(\frac{d^2c}{da.db}\Delta a + \frac{d^2c}{db^2}\Delta b\right) = 0 \,.$$

Putting $a = b = 0$, and also equating to zero the first derivatives of c, according to equations (1), we shall obtain the following equations of a normal to the wave-surface at a point infinitely near that where the ray A meets this surface:

$$\left.\begin{array}{l} \Delta a - x + (c - z)\left(\dfrac{d^2c}{da^2}\Delta a + \dfrac{d^2c}{da \cdot db}\Delta b\right) = 0 \\[4mm] \Delta b - y + (c - z)\left(\dfrac{d^2c}{da \cdot db}\Delta a + \dfrac{d^2c}{db^2}\Delta b\right) = 0 \end{array}\right\} \cdot \;\; \cdot \;\; (2)$$

For all points on the ray A, we have $x = y = 0$. Therefore, if the ray whose equations are given by (2) does intersect the ray A, x and y must vanish on this other ray also for any value of z. Putting $x = y = 0$ in the above equations and eliminating z, we obtain the following equation as the condition of intersection of two adjacent rays:

$$\frac{d^2c}{da \cdot db}\Delta a^2 + \left(\frac{d^2c}{db^2} - \frac{d^2c}{da^2}\right)\Delta a\, \Delta b - \frac{d^2c}{da \cdot db}\Delta b^2 = 0 \quad \cdot \;\; \cdot \;\; (3)$$

If r denotes the distance between the two adjacent points on the surface, and α the angle which it makes with the x-axis (this angle being comprised, therefore, between 0 and π), then

$$\Delta a = r \cos \alpha \,, \qquad \Delta b = r \sin \alpha \,.$$

For abbreviation, let us write

$$2n = \frac{\dfrac{d^2c}{db^2} - \dfrac{d^2c}{da^2}}{\dfrac{d^2c}{da \cdot db}};$$

then supposing $\dfrac{d^2c}{da \cdot db}$ is not equal to zero, equation (3) becomes:

$$\tan^2 a - 2n \tan a = 1 \ \cdot \ \cdot \ \cdot \ \cdot \ \cdot \ \cdot \quad \text{(3a)}$$

and hence

$$\tan a = n \pm \sqrt{1 + n^2} \ \cdot \ \cdot \ \cdot \ \cdot \ \cdot \ \cdot \quad \text{(3b)}$$

The two values of tan a, which are always real, may also be written

$$n + \sqrt{1 + n^2} \quad \text{and} \quad -\frac{1}{n + \sqrt{1 + n^2}}.$$

Accordingly, if a_0 is one of the values of a, the other value is $a_0 + \dfrac{\pi}{2}$ or $a_0 - \dfrac{\pi}{2}$. The two angles differ by a right angle. The magnitude r, which denotes the distance of the normals measured along the wave-surface, vanishes from equation (3a). Hence, the ray A is cut by all adjacent rays that lie in planes that make angles a_0 and $a_0 + \dfrac{\pi}{2}$ with the axis of x.

Thus far the actual positions of the axes of x and y in the plane perpendicular to the ray A have been perfectly arbitrary. Now let us suppose, for simplicity, that the xz-plane and yz plane coincide with the two principal planes of the wave-surface at the origin of coördinates, that is, with the two perpendicular planes in which the adjacent rays lie that intersect the ray A (or z-axis). In this case the two values of tan a will become 0 and ∞, and this means that

$$n = \pm \infty$$

and

$$\frac{d^2c}{da \cdot db} = 0 .$$

The condition of intersection of the ray A by the adjacent rays, as expressed by equation (3), reduces, under these circumstances, to

$$\left(\frac{d^2c}{db^2} - \frac{d^2c}{da^2} \right) \Delta a \, \Delta b = 0 .$$

The Sensations of Vision

Now, as a matter of fact, this latter equation will be always satisfied, provided either $\Delta a = 0$ or $\Delta b = 0$, that is, provided the intersecting normals lie either in the yz-plane or in the xz-plane. And, finally, if at the same time

$$\frac{d^2c}{db^2} - \frac{d^2c}{da^2} = 0 \,,$$

the condition that adjacent rays shall intersect the ray A is satisfied for all arbitrary values of Δa and Δb; that is, all the adjacent rays meet the ray A. Still supposing that $\frac{d^2c}{da\,db} = 0$, and then putting either $\Delta a = 0$ or $\Delta b = 0$, we find, as was mentioned above, the distance z of the point where the adjacent rays meet the ray A by putting $x = y = 0$ in equations (3).

For the rays in the xz-plane, $\Delta b = 0$; hence from equations (2) the distance of the point of intersection from the wave-surface is

$$z - c = \frac{1}{\dfrac{d^2c}{da^2}} \cdot$$

The second of equations (2) becomes $0 = 0$.

For the rays in the yz-plane, $\Delta a = 0$, and

$$z - c = \frac{1}{\dfrac{d^2c}{db^2}} \cdot$$

Finally, if $\dfrac{d^2c}{da^2} = \dfrac{d^2c}{d\,b^2} = \dfrac{1}{\rho}$, then for all adjacent rays without distinction

$$z - c = \rho \,.$$

Moreover, in this case the xz-plane and yz-plane are also the principal sections of the surface for which the curvature has its maximum and minimum values; and the values of the corresponding radii of curvature are:

$$\rho_a = \frac{1}{\dfrac{d^2c}{da^2}}, \qquad \rho_b = \frac{1}{\dfrac{d^2c}{db^2}},$$

and hence the focal points of the bundle of rays are also at the centres of principal curvature of the wave-surface.

Constitution of an infinitely narrow bundle of rays that meets the wave-surface in a circle. In order to get a clearer notion of the way the rays go in an infinitely narrow bundle of rays, let us consider the constitution of a bundle of rays that cuts out a circle on the wave-surface. Therefore, in equations (2), as before, we put

$$\frac{d^2c}{da \cdot db} = 0 \text{ and } \Delta a = r \cos a \, , \Delta b = r \sin a$$

and obtain:

$$r \cos a - x + (c - z) \frac{d^2c}{da^2} r \cos a = 0 \, ,$$

$$r \sin a - y + (c - z) \frac{d^2c}{db^2} r \sin a = 0 \, .$$

In order to find the curve in which the surface of the bundle cuts a plane perpendicular to its axis, we must put $z =$ constant, and eliminate the angle a. By way of abbreviation, let us put

$$p = + r \left[1 + (c - z) \frac{d^2c}{da^2} \right] = + \frac{r}{\rho_a} [\rho_a + c - z] \, ,$$

$$q = + r \left[1 + (c - z) \frac{d^2c}{db^2} \right] = + \frac{r}{\rho_b} [\rho_b + c - z] \, ,$$

so that we may write:

$$\frac{x^2}{p^2} + \frac{y^2}{q^2} = 1 \, .$$

This is the equation of an ellipse, with its axes $2p$, $2q$ parallel to the axes of x and y. The smaller r is, the shorter both axes become; and hence if the bundle of rays meets the first wave-surface not simply in the points in the circumference, but at all the points also in the interior, of a circle, all the rays continue to be comprised inside the space that is formed by the outside rays, so that the form of the bundle is determined by the latter. On the wave-surface itself where the investigation of the bundle begins, we have $c - z = 0$, and therefore the semi-axes $p = q = r$, that is, the cross section at this place is circular. The axis p collapses into a point when

$$z - c = \frac{1}{\dfrac{d^2c}{da^2}} = \rho_a \, ,$$

that is, when the section of the bundle is made at the focal point of the rays lying in the xz-plane. The other semi-axis at this place is

$$q = \pm \frac{r}{\rho_b} (\rho_a + \rho_b) \, .$$

The section of the bundle, therefore, is a straight line parallel to the y-axis, whose length is twice that of the value of q given above.

On the other hand, the section of the bundle will be a straight line parallel to the x-axis, when

$$z - c = \frac{1}{\dfrac{d^2c}{db^2}} = \rho_b ,$$

$$q = 0 , \qquad p = \pm \frac{r}{\rho_a} (\rho_a + \rho_b) .$$

Finally, there is one other place where the section of the bundle is a circle, namely, the place where

$$p = - q ,$$

$$1 + \frac{c - z}{\rho_a} = - 1 - \frac{c - z}{\rho_b} ,$$

$$z - c = \frac{2\rho_a\rho_b}{\rho_a + \rho_b} .$$

and here

$$p = q = \pm r \cdot \frac{\rho_a - \rho_b}{\rho_a + \rho_b} .$$

Between the two circular sections of the bundle one of the linear sections must lie. The longer axes of the elliptical sections that are between the two circular sections are parallel to this linear section; whereas the longer axes of the elliptical sections that are beyond this

Fig. 10.

interval are perpendicular to this linear section. The horizontal line cd in Fig. 10 is intended to represent the central ray of the bundle. A circular diaphragm is supposed to be at c. The focal points are marked at a and b. Below the line are shown the forms of the cross sections of the bundle corresponding to the points in the ray above.

General analytical condition for the positions of the focal points.

Consider a pair of contiguous rays A and B which are supposed to have a common origin. After being refracted at a series of surfaces of continuous curvature, they meet again at a focal point. The optical lengths along these two rays from their starting point to their focal point will be denoted by Ψ and $\Psi + \Delta\Psi$. The different systems of coördinates to which the points on the various refracting surfaces are referred will be chosen again so that the z-axis in each instance is along the incidence-normal belonging to the ray A; the xy-plane being tangent to the refracting surface. The coördinates of the points where the ray B meets the first refracting surface will be denoted by x_1, y_1, z_1; and those of the point where it meets the second refracting surface by x_2, y_2, z_2; and so on, the coördinates for the last surface being x_m, y_m, z_m. However, it will be assumed in this discussion that the optical lengths are expressed as functions of x, y only; that is, that the z's which are themselves functions of x and y have been eliminated. Moreover, as the rays A and B are assumed to be infinitely close to each other, the magnitudes x_1, y_1, etc., to x_m, y_m are regarded as being infinitesimal.

Then by TAYLOR's theorem

$$\Psi + \Delta\Psi = \Psi + \frac{d\Psi}{dx}\, x_1 + \frac{d\Psi}{dx_2}\, x_2 + \cdot \ \cdot \ \cdot \ + \frac{d\Psi}{dx_m}\, x_m$$
$$+ \frac{d\Psi}{dy_1}\, y_1 + \frac{d\Psi}{dy_2}\, y_2 + \cdot \ \cdot \ \cdot \ + \frac{d\Psi}{dy_m}\, y_m \ .$$

Now the optical length along either ray must be a limiting value, according to the first of the theorems proved above, that is, the first derivatives of Ψ and $\Psi + \Delta\Psi$, with respect to each of the coordinates x_1, y_1; x_2, y_2; and so on to x_m, y_m, must be equal to zero. Thus, for the first ray:

$$\frac{d\Psi}{dx_1} = 0 \ , \qquad \frac{d\Psi}{dx_2} = 0 \ , \cdot \ \cdot \ \cdot \ , \frac{d\Psi}{dx_m} = 0 \ ,$$
$$\frac{d\Psi}{dy_1} = 0 \ , \qquad \frac{d\Psi}{dy_2} = 0 \ , \cdot \ \cdot \ \cdot \ , \frac{d\Psi}{dy_m} = 0 \ ;$$

and, taking account of these relations, we have the following system of equations for the second ray:

$$\left.\begin{aligned}
&\frac{d^2\Psi}{dx_1^2}\, x_1 + \frac{d^2\Psi}{dx_1 dy_1}\, y_1 + \cdot \ \cdot \ \cdot \ + \frac{d^2\Psi}{dx_1 dx_m}\, x_m + \frac{d^2\Psi}{dx_1 dy_m}\, y_m = 0 \\[4pt]
&\frac{d^2\Psi}{dy_1 dx_1}\, x_1 + \frac{d^2\Psi}{dy_1^2}\, y_1 + \cdot \ \cdot \ \cdot \ + \frac{d^2\Psi}{dy_1 dx_m}\, x_m + \frac{d^2\Psi}{dy_1 dy_m}\, y_m = 0 \\[4pt]
&\ \cdot \quad \cdot \quad \cdot \quad \cdot \quad \cdot \quad \cdot \quad \cdot \quad \cdot \quad \cdot \quad \cdot \quad \cdot \quad \cdot \quad \cdot \quad \cdot \\[4pt]
&\frac{d^2\Psi}{dx_m dx_1}\, x_1 + \frac{d^2\Psi}{dx_m dy_1}\, y_1 + \cdot \ \cdot \ \cdot \ + \frac{d^2\Psi}{dx^2_m}\, x_m + \frac{d^2\Psi}{dx_m dy_m}\, y_m = 0 \\[4pt]
&\frac{d^2\Psi}{dy_m dx_1}\, x_1 + \frac{d^2\Psi}{dy_m dy_1}\, y_1 + \cdot \ \cdot \ \cdot \ + \frac{d^2\Psi}{dy_m dx_m}\, x_m + \frac{d^2\Psi}{dy^2_m}\, y_m = 0
\end{aligned}\right\} \quad (4)$$

Incidentally, the number of terms in these equations will be considerably reduced by the fact that $\dfrac{d^2\Psi}{dx_f dx_g}$, $\dfrac{d^2\Psi}{dx_f dy_g}$ and $\dfrac{d^2\Psi}{dy_f dy_g}$ will vanish whenever the subscripts f and g differ from each other by more than unity.

There are $2\,m$ equations with $2\,m$ unknowns, namely, the x's and y's from x_1, y_1 to x_m, y_m. However, since all these unknown magnitudes cannot be equal to zero (because the ray B is not the same as the ray A) the equations may all be divided by one of these magnitudes, say, x_1, that is not equal to zero, which will have the effect of reducing the total number of unknown quantities to $(2\,m-1)$ ratios all having the common denominator x_1. Thus, when these $(2\,m-1)$ quantities are eliminated from the $2\,m$ equations, one equation will be left that does not any longer contain x_1, y_1, etc., to x_m, y_m, but simply the second partial derivatives of Ψ. This last equation, obtained by putting the determinant of equations (4) equal to zero, is the required equation for the position of the focal point.

This determinant is easily formed by known methods;[1] it consists of a sum of terms the first of which is the product

$$\frac{d^2\Psi}{dx_1 \cdot dx_1} \cdot \frac{d^2\Psi}{dy_1 dy_1} \cdot \frac{d^2\Psi}{dx_2 \cdot dx_2} \quad \cdot \quad \cdot \quad \frac{d^2\Psi}{dx_m \cdot dx_m} \cdot \frac{d^2\Psi}{dy_m \cdot dy_m}$$

The other terms of the series are easily obtained. The denominator of each of the differential coefficients is a product of two factors. What has to be done is to leave the first factor just as it is, while the other factor is varied in every possible way, merely changing the sign of the term whenever two of these factors are interchanged with each other.

Thus, in the language of the calculus of variations, the position of a ray between its two terminal points is found by putting the first variation of its optical length equal to zero. The terminal points will be conjugate foci, provided the second variation of the optical length vanishes also. In the latter case the optical length is not necessarily a maximum or minimum.

Refraction in a Prism

Let the position of the luminous point be given by the coördinates a, b, c, referred to a system of axes in which the c-axis coincides with the refracting edge of the prism and the bc-plane is the same as that of the first face of the prism, the positive direction of the a-axis being outside the prism. Suppose that the ray is incident on the first face

[1] See Jacobi in Crelles *Journ. für Math.* XXII.

at the point whose coördinates are $a = 0$, $b = y$, $c = z$. Similarly, let a, β, γ denote the rectangular coördinates of a point on the emergent ray, referred to another system of axes whose γ-axis again coincides with the edge of the prism and whose $\beta\gamma$-plane is the same as that of the second face of the prism, the positive direction of the a-axis being likewise outside the prism. The γ's are all measured from the same point in the edge as the c's, that is, the ab-plane of the first system is identical with the $a\beta$-plane of the second system. Let the coördinates of the point where the ray emerges at the second face be denoted by $a = 0$, $\beta = v$, $\gamma = \zeta$. The refracting angle of the prism will be denoted by φ and the relative index of refraction of the two media by n. The lengths of the paths of the three portions of the ray, before entering the prism, inside it, and after leaving it, will be denoted by r_0, r_1 and r_2, respectively; and the total optical length will be denoted by Ψ. Then

$$\left. \begin{aligned} r_0 &= \sqrt{a^2 + (b - y)^2 + (c - z)^2} \\ r_1 &= \sqrt{y^2 - 2yv \cos \varphi + v^2 + (z - \zeta)^2} \\ r_2 &= \sqrt{a^2 + (\beta - v)^2 + (\gamma - \zeta)^2} \\ \Psi &= r_0 + nr_1 + r_2 \end{aligned} \right\} \quad \ldots \quad (5)$$

The coördinates of the second system in terms of those of the first system are given by the formulæ:

$$\left. \begin{aligned} a &= - a \cos \varphi - b \sin \varphi \\ \beta &= - a \sin \varphi + b \cos \varphi \\ \gamma &= c \end{aligned} \right\} \quad \ldots \ldots \quad (5a)$$

If the ray is refracted according to the law of refraction, then, by theorem I above, the following conditions must be satisfied:

$$\left. \begin{aligned} 0 &= \frac{d\Psi}{dy} = \frac{y - b}{r_0} + n \frac{y - v \cos \varphi}{r_1} \\ 0 &= \frac{d\Psi}{dv} = \frac{v - \beta}{r_2} + n \frac{v - y \cos \varphi}{r_1} \\ 0 &= \frac{d\Psi}{dz} = \frac{z - c}{r_0} + n \frac{z - \zeta}{r_1} \\ 0 &= \frac{d\Psi}{d\zeta} = \frac{\zeta - \gamma}{r_2} + n \frac{\zeta - z}{r_1} \end{aligned} \right\} \quad \ldots \quad (6)$$

Here let us introduce the following abbreviations:

$$\left.\begin{array}{l}\dfrac{b-y}{nr_0}=\dfrac{y-v\cos\varphi}{r_1}=\cos m\\[2mm]\dfrac{\beta-v}{nr_2}=\dfrac{v-y\cos\varphi}{-r_1}=\cos\mu\\[2mm]\dfrac{c-z}{nr_0}=\dfrac{\zeta-\gamma}{nr_2}=\dfrac{z-\zeta}{r_1}=\cos\nu\end{array}\right\}\quad\cdot\;\cdot\;\cdot\;\cdot\;(6a)$$

where

$$\sin^2\varphi\sin^2\nu=\cos^2 m+2\cos m\cos\mu\cos\varphi+\cos^2\mu\quad\cdot\;\cdot\;(6b)$$

If the second derivatives of Ψ are developed in terms of this notation, the system of equations (4), which give the positions of the focal points and the relations between the infinitely small differences Δy, Δz, Δv, $\Delta\zeta$ of the coördinates y, z, v and ζ for a pair of adjacent rays intersecting each other at conjugate foci, becomes:

$$\left.\begin{array}{l}\left[\dfrac{1}{r_0}(1-n^2\cos^2 m)+\dfrac{n}{r_1}\sin^2 m\right]\Delta y-\left(\dfrac{n^2}{r_0}+\dfrac{n}{r_1}\right)\cos m\cos\nu\,\Delta z\\[4mm]-\dfrac{n}{r_1}(\cos\varphi+\cos m\cos\mu)\,\Delta v+\dfrac{n}{r_1}\cos m\cos\nu\,\Delta\zeta=0\,;\end{array}\right\}\quad(7a)$$

$$\left.\begin{array}{l}-\left(\dfrac{n^2}{r_0}+\dfrac{n}{r_1}\right)\cos m\cos\nu\,\Delta y+\left[\dfrac{1}{r_0}(1-n^2\cos^2\nu)+\dfrac{n}{r_1}\sin^2\nu\right]\Delta z\\[4mm]-\dfrac{n}{r_1}\cos\mu\cos\nu\,\Delta v-\dfrac{n}{r_1}\sin^2\nu\,\Delta\zeta=0\,;\end{array}\right\}\quad(7b)$$

$$\left.\begin{array}{l}-\dfrac{n}{r_1}(\cos\varphi+\cos m\cos\mu)\,\Delta y-\dfrac{n}{r_1}\cos\mu\cos\nu\,\Delta z\\[4mm]+\left[\dfrac{1}{r_2}(1-n^2\cos^2\mu)+\dfrac{n}{r_1}\sin^2\mu\right]\Delta v+\left(\dfrac{n^2}{r_2}+\dfrac{n}{r_1}\right)\cos\mu\cos\nu\,\Delta\zeta=0\,;\end{array}\right\}\quad(7c)$$

$$\left.\begin{array}{l}\dfrac{n}{r_1}\cos m\cos\nu\,\Delta y-\dfrac{n}{r_1}\sin^2\nu\,\Delta z\\[4mm]+\left(\dfrac{n^2}{r_2}+\dfrac{n}{r_1}\right)\cos\mu\cos\nu\,\Delta v+\left[\dfrac{1}{r_2}(1-n^2\cos^2\nu)+\dfrac{n}{r_1}\sin^2\nu\right]\Delta\zeta=0\,.\end{array}\right\}\quad(7d)$$

Generally, the length of the path of the ray inside the prism (r_1) may be neglected in comparison with the lengths r_0 and r_2 outside the prism. If the four equations above are each multiplied by r_1, and then all terms neglected that contain $\dfrac{r_1}{r_0}$ or $\dfrac{r_1}{r_2}$ as a factor, as being infinitely small, the four equations will reduce to three as follows:

$$\sin^2 m \, \Delta y - (\cos \varphi + \cos m \cos \mu) \, \Delta v - \cos m \cos \nu \, (\Delta z - \Delta \zeta) = 0 \, ,$$
$$- \cos m \cos \nu \, \Delta y - \cos \mu \cos \nu \, \Delta v + \sin^2 \nu \, (\Delta z - \Delta \zeta) \quad\quad = 0 \, , \quad (8)$$
$$- (\cos \varphi + \cos m \cos \mu) \, \Delta y + \sin^2 \mu \, \Delta v - \cos \mu \cos \nu \, (\Delta z - \Delta \zeta) = 0 \, .$$

However, one of these three equations can be deduced from the other two; and hence, after eliminating $(\Delta z - \Delta \zeta)$, we get:

$$(\cos \mu + \cos m \cos \varphi) \, \Delta y = (\cos m + \cos \mu \cos \varphi) \, \Delta v$$

or

$$\frac{\Delta y}{y} = \frac{\Delta v}{v} \quad\quad\quad (8a)$$

or after elimination of Δv:

$$(\Delta z - \Delta \zeta) \, (\cos m + \cos \mu \cos \varphi) = \cos \nu \sin^2 \varphi \; \Delta y$$

or

$$\frac{\Delta z - \Delta \zeta}{z - \zeta} = \frac{\Delta y}{y} = \frac{\Delta v}{v} \, . \quad\quad \cdot \;\; \cdot \;\; (8b)$$

These two equations are simply the conditions that the two rays may be considered as being sensibly parallel during their short routes through the prism; as must obviously be so, provided the point where they meet is infinitely remote as compared with the length of the path inside the prism.

The next step is to express two of the unknown magnitudes Δv and $\Delta \zeta$ in terms of the other two Δy and Δz. This involves obtaining by elimination from equations (7) two new equations which do not contain the small magnitude r_1, and from which the ratios $\frac{\Delta z}{\Delta y}$ and $\frac{r_2}{r_0}$ may be found.

One equation of this kind is obtained by adding (7b) and (7d):

$$- \frac{n^2}{r_0} \cos m \cos \nu \, \Delta y + \frac{1}{r_0} (1 - n^2 \cos^2 \nu) \, \Delta z + \frac{n^2}{r_2} \cos \mu \cos \nu \, \Delta v$$
$$+ \frac{1}{r_0} (1 - n^2 \cos^2 \nu) \, \Delta \zeta = 0. \quad\quad \cdot \;\; \cdot \;\; (8c)$$

In order to obtain the second equation, multiply equation (7a) by

$$y = \frac{r_1}{\sin^2 \varphi} (\cos m + \cos \mu \cos \varphi) \, ,$$

equation (7c) by

$$v = \frac{r_1}{\sin^2 \varphi} (\cos \mu + \cos m \cos \varphi) \, ,$$

and equation (7b) by

$$z - \zeta = r_1 \cos \nu \; ;$$

and add the three equations thus obtained. All the terms that are multiplied by $\frac{1}{r_1}$ will vanish, and we shall get:

$$
\left.
\begin{aligned}
&\frac{y}{r_0} \left\{ (1 - n^2 \cos^2 m) \, \Delta y - n^2 \cos m \, \cos \nu \, \Delta z \right\} \\
&\quad + \frac{z - \zeta}{r_0} \left\{ - n^2 \cos m \cos \nu \, \Delta y + (1 - n^2 \cos^2 \nu) \, \Delta z \right\} \\
&\quad + \frac{v}{r_2} \left\{ (1 - n^2 \cos^2 \mu) \, \Delta v + n^2 \cos \mu \cos \nu \, \Delta \zeta \right\} = 0
\end{aligned}
\right\} \quad \cdot \; \cdot \; (8d)
$$

If the values of Δv and $\Delta \zeta$ in terms of Δy and Δz as obtained from equations (8a) and (8b) are substituted in equations (8c) and (8d), two equations will be obtained containing the unknown quantities $\frac{\Delta z}{\Delta y}$ and $\frac{r_2}{r_0}$. When one of them is eliminated, the other is given by a quadratic equation which has two roots. Thus, for any arbitrary combination of values of the angles m, μ, ν, we get at least one definite numerical value of the ratio $\frac{r_2}{r_0}$. Consequently, for a given direction of the bundle of rays r_2 is proportional to r_0, supposing that the latter varies. If r_0 is infinite, so also is r_2. It is not worth while actually to give the elimination equations here. We shall merely investigate certain special cases that are of interest to us.

First, let us inquire in what cases *a homocentric bundle of incident rays will issue from the prism as a homocentric bundle of emergent rays.*[1] If all the rays emanating from the luminous point are to intersect each other, the conditions (8c) and (8d) must be satisfied, no matter what values we take for Δy and Δz. Each of these magnitudes, therefore, may be put equal to zero, and thus the following conditions are obtained.

1. If we put $\Delta y = 0$ in equations (8c), which, according to equations (8a) and (8b), means also that $\Delta v = 0$ and $\Delta \zeta = \Delta z$, then

$$\left(\frac{1}{r_0} + \frac{1}{r_2} \right) (1 - n^2 \cos^2 \nu) = 0 \quad \cdot \; \cdot \; \cdot \; \cdot \; \cdot \; \cdot \; (9a)$$

---

[1] ¶This whole subject has been beautifully treated synthetically by L. BURMESTER, *Homocentrische Brechung des Lichtes durch das Prisma. Zft. f. Math. u. Phys.*, XL (1895), 65–90. See also: J. P. C. SOUTHALL, *The principles and methods of geometrical optics*, 1910, pp. 97–105. (J. P. C. S.)

Since by equation (6a) $n \cos \nu = \dfrac{c - z}{r_0}$, the second factor of the above equation cannot be equal to zero unless $r_0 = c - z$, that is, unless the ray of light grazes the first face of the prism and therefore does not enter it. Consequently, the first factor of equation (9a) must be zero, that is,

$$r_2 = - r_0.$$

2. If we put $\Delta z = 0$ in equation (8d) and $r_2 = -r_0$, then

$$0 = (1 + n^2 \sin^2 \nu + n^2 \cos^2 \nu) \, (\cos^2 m - \cos^2 \mu) \,.$$

The first factor is equal to $(1+n^2)$, which is never zero; consequently,

$$\cos m = \pm \cos \mu \quad \ldots \ldots \ldots \quad (9\mathrm{b})$$

3. If we put $\Delta z = 0$ in equation (8c) or $\Delta y = 0$ in equation (8d), and $r_2 = -r_0$, then, taking account of equation (6b), we get:

$$(1 - n^2) \cos \nu \sin^2\varphi = 0 \,.$$

Since φ is the refracting angle of the prism, $\sin \varphi$ cannot be zero; and hence

$$\left. \begin{array}{l} \cos \nu = 0 \,, \\ c = z = \zeta = \gamma \,. \end{array} \right\} \quad \ldots \ldots \ldots \quad (9\mathrm{c})$$

Accordingly, the ray lies wholly in a principal section of the prism, that is, in a plane perpendicular to its refracting edge. Under these circumstances, let us write equation (9b) in conformity with (6a) in the form:

$$y - v \cos \varphi = \pm \, (v - y \cos \varphi) \,,$$
$$y(1 \pm \cos \varphi) = \pm \, v(1 \pm \cos \varphi) \,,$$

that is,

$$y = v \quad \ldots \ldots \ldots \ldots \quad (9\mathrm{d})$$

Let ϵ, ϵ_1 denote the angles of incidence and refraction at the first face of the prism, and η_1, η the angles of incidence and refraction at the second face (the symbols with the subscript referring to the two angles inside the prism); then

$$\cos \epsilon_1 = \frac{v \sin \varphi}{r_1} \,, \qquad \cos \eta_1 = \frac{y \sin \varphi}{r_1} \,,$$

and hence under the given conditions:

$$\cos \epsilon_1 = \cos \eta_1 \,,$$

and therefore also

$$\sin \epsilon = n \sin \epsilon_1 = n \sin \eta_1 = \sin \eta \,.$$

In other words, the angle of emergence at the second face is equal to the angle of incidence at the first face.

If the bundle of emergent rays is to be homocentric, the path of the chief ray through the prism must be in the direction of minimum deviation.

When the coördinates a, b, c, x and y as referred to the first system of axes are transformed by equations (5a) into those of the second system, the cosines of the angles which the incident ray makes with the axes of α, β and γ in the second system are found to be as follows:

$$- \frac{a \cos \varphi + (b - y) \sin \varphi}{r_0} , \quad \frac{(b - y) \cos \varphi - a \sin \varphi}{r_0} , \quad \frac{c - z}{r_0} ;$$

and the cosines of the angles made with these same axes by the emergent ray are:

$$\frac{a}{r_2} , \qquad \frac{\beta - v}{r_2} , \qquad \frac{\gamma - \zeta}{r_2} .$$

Let ω denote the angle between the directions of the incident and emergent rays; then

$$\cos \omega = - \frac{[a \cos \varphi + (b - y) \sin \varphi]}{r_0} \frac{a}{r_2} + \frac{[(b - y) \cos \varphi - a \sin \varphi]}{r_0} \frac{(\beta - v)}{r_2} + \frac{(c - z)}{r_0} \frac{(\gamma - \zeta)}{r_2} \tag{10}$$

The variables a, b, c, α, β and γ may be eliminated from formula (10) by means of equations (5) and (6). In the first place

$$\frac{a}{r_0} = \sqrt{1 - n^2 \frac{(y - v \cos \varphi)^2 + (z - \zeta)^2}{r_1^2}} = \sqrt{\frac{n^2 v^2 \sin^2 \varphi}{r_1^2} - (n^2 - 1)}$$

$$\frac{a}{r_2} = \sqrt{1 - n^2 \frac{(v - y \cos \varphi)^2 + (z - \zeta)^2}{r_1^2}} = \sqrt{\frac{n^2 y^2 \sin^2 \varphi}{r_1^2} - (n^2 - 1)} \tag{10a}$$

If one of the two radicals here should be imaginary, the ray will be totally reflected at the corresponding face of the prism. Equations (6) give at once convenient expressions for the quotients $\dfrac{b - y}{r_0}$, $\dfrac{c - z}{r_0}$, $\dfrac{\beta - v}{r_2}$, $\dfrac{\gamma - \zeta}{r_2}$. When these values are substituted in formula (10), the cosine of the angle of deviation will be given in terms of y, v, z and ζ. Indeed, it can easily be contrived so that the last two of these magnitudes do not occur at all except as they are involved in r_1. Thus, the following expression is found:

$$\left.\begin{aligned}
\cos \omega = \; & -\, n^2 + n^2 \frac{\sin^2 \varphi}{r_1{}^2}\, (y^2 - y\, v\, \cos \varphi + v^2) \\[2mm]
& - n\frac{\sin \varphi}{r_1{}^2}(y - v \cos \varphi)\, \sqrt{n^2 y^2 \sin^2\varphi - (n^2-1)r_1{}^2} \\[2mm]
& - n\frac{\sin \varphi}{r_1{}^2}(v - y \cos \varphi)\, \sqrt{n^2 v^2 \sin^2\varphi - (n^2-1)r_1{}^2} \\[2mm]
& - \frac{\cos\varphi}{r_1{}^2}\, \sqrt{n^2 y^2 \sin^2\varphi - (n^2-1)r_1{}^2}\, \sqrt{n^2 v^2 \sin^2\varphi - (n^2-1)r_1{}^2}
\end{aligned}\right\} \quad \text{(10b)}$$

Supposing that x and y are constant, let us try to find the values of v and ζ for which the angle ω is a maximum; in which case

$$\frac{d\omega}{dv} = 0 \quad \text{and} \quad \frac{d\omega}{d\zeta} = 0 \;.$$

As ζ does not occur in the expression for $\cos \omega$ except as it is involved in r_1, the second equation above may also be written:

$$\frac{d\omega}{d\zeta} = -\, \frac{1}{\sin \omega}\, \frac{d(\cos \omega)}{d(r_1{}^2)} \cdot (\zeta - z) = 0 \;.$$

This equation is satisfied for all values of v, provided

$$\zeta - z = 0 \;.$$

But this condition would not be sufficient, either if $\sin \omega = 0$, that is, if the ray were not deviated at all (as would be the case if the prism were a plate with its two faces parallel to each other), or if the derivative of $\cos \omega$ should become infinite due to the fact that one of the denominators in the expression for this function happened to vanish. It is evident from (10b) that r_1 and the two radicals are the only functions that could occur as denominators in the expression for the derivative. But as long as y and v are positive, even if their values are infinitely small, as they must be if the ray is to go through the prism, r_1 cannot vanish. Moreover, on account of equations (6a), the expressions under the radicals cannot vanish if the ray is to extend on either side of the prism itself. Accordingly, the condition

$$\frac{d\omega}{d\zeta} = 0$$

will be satisfied by putting

$$z = \zeta \;.$$

Consequently, we have also by equations (6)

$$z = c \quad \text{and} \quad \zeta = \gamma \;,$$

which means, as above stated, that the ray lies wholly in the plane of a principal section of the prism.

The other condition which has to be satisfied in order that the angle of deviation shall be a maximum is that

$$\frac{d\omega}{dv} = 0 \, ,$$

and, with this in mind, let us first simplify the expression for cos ω by imposing the condition $z = \zeta$, that is,

$$r_1{}^2 = y^2 + v^2 - 2 y v \cos \varphi \, .$$

Introducing here a new variable q in place of v by writing

$$v = q y \, ,$$

we contrive to make both y and v disappear together from the expression for cos ω as given by equation (10b), so that cos ω becomes then simply a function of q, which may be written therefore

$$\cos \omega = f \, (q) \, .$$

But as the expression for cos ω is not altered by interchanging the letters y and v whenever they occur, it follows that for any value of q we may write:

$$\cos \omega = f(q) = f\left(\frac{1}{q}\right)$$

Moreover, if $f' \, (q)$ denotes the derivative of $f \, (q)$ with respect to q then

$$\frac{d \cos \omega}{dv} = \frac{1}{y} f'(q) = - \frac{1}{y} f'\left(\frac{1}{q}\right) \frac{1}{q^2} \, .$$

Now for $v = y$, that is, for $q = 1$,

$$f'(q) = - f'(q) \, , \qquad \text{or} \qquad f'(q) = 0 \, ;$$

that is,

$$\frac{d \cos \omega}{dv} = 0 \, ..$$

Accordingly, unless sin $\omega = 0$ at the same time,

$$\frac{d\omega}{dv} = - \frac{d \cos \omega}{dv} \cdot \frac{1}{\sin \omega} = 0 \, .$$

Hence, if

$$z = \zeta \quad \text{and} \quad y = v \, ,$$

we have both

$$\frac{d\omega}{d\zeta} = 0 \quad \text{and} \quad \frac{d\omega}{dv} = 0 \; ;$$

and the angle ω is a limiting value. Investigation of the second derivative shows that in this case ω is a maximum. Accordingly, the angle between the prolongation of the incident ray and the refracted ray (which is the real measure of the deviation) is a minimum.

The maximum value of the angle ω is found by putting $y = v$ and $z = \zeta$ in formula (10b); which gives

$$\omega = \varphi + 2\arccos\left[n \sin\frac{\varphi}{2} \right] \quad \cdots \cdots \quad (10c)$$

The condition that a narrow homocentric bundle of incident rays shall emerge from a prism as a homocentric bundle is that the chief ray shall go through the prism with minimum deviation, that is, shall lie in a principal section of the prism and shall make equal angles with the two faces of the prism.

Under such circumstances, therefore, the prism produces a potential image of a luminous point, lying on the same side of the prism as the luminous point and at an equal distance from the prism. The image, however, is not where the source is, but is displaced towards the refracting edge of the prism through an angle equal to $(\pi/2 - \omega)$

Image of a Luminous Line in a Prism

The requirement for a distinct image of a luminous point is that the bundle of emergent rays that enter the eye shall be homocentric. However, when the source of light is a luminous line, deviations (or aberrations) of the rays in the direction of the image of this line do not tend to impair the exactness of the image. Now this is the case that ordinarily occurs in the spectrum. If the luminous line is parallel to the refracting edge of the prism (z-axis), deviations in the direction of z are not objectionable at all, whereas deviations in a plane passed through the ray at right angles to the z-axis do affect the definition of the image. If there are to be no deviations from homocentricity except in the direction parallel to the z-axis, then in equations (8) we must put $\Delta y = 0$, and therefore also $\Delta v = 0$, $\Delta z = \Delta\zeta$; and thus from equations (8c) and (8d) we obtain:

$$\left(\frac{1}{r_0} + \frac{1}{r_2}\right)(1 - n^2\cos^2 v) = 0 \; ,$$

that is,

$$r_2 = -r_0 \; ; \quad \cdots \cdots \cdots \cdots \quad (11a)$$

and, secondly:

$$(1 - n^2) \cos \nu \sin^2 \varphi = 0 ,$$

whence we derive as above:

$$\cos \nu = 0$$
$$c - z = z - \zeta = \gamma - \zeta = 0 .$$

If the last condition is satisfied the deviations Δy will be in a plane passed through the ray at right angles to the deviations Δz. Accordingly, the second plane of convergence which has to be regarded as perpendicular to the other is the one in which these deviations occur. The place where the rays intersect that lie in the plane at right angles to the edge of the prism is found by putting $\Delta z = 0$ and $\cos \nu = 0$ in formula (8d); consequently $\Delta \zeta = 0$ also, and

$$\frac{1}{r_0} (1 - n^2 \cos^2 m)y^2 + \frac{1}{r_2} (1 - n^2 \cos^2 \mu)v^2 = 0 .$$

If, as formerly, the angles of incidence and emergence are denoted by ϵ and η and the angles inside the glass by ϵ_1 and η_1, that is, if

$$\cos \epsilon_1 = \frac{v \sin \varphi}{r_1} \qquad \cos \eta_1 = \frac{y \sin \varphi}{r_1}$$

$$\sin \epsilon = n \sin \epsilon_1 = n \frac{y - v \cos \varphi}{r_1} = n \cos m$$

$$\sin \eta = n \cos \mu ,$$

then

$$\frac{r_2}{r_0} = - \frac{\cos^2 \epsilon_1 \cos^2 \eta}{\cos^2 \epsilon \cos^2 \eta_1} \cdot \quad . \quad . \quad . \quad . \quad . \quad . \quad (11b)$$

or

$$r_2 \frac{\cos^2 \eta_1}{\cos^2 \eta} = - r_0 \frac{\cos^2 \epsilon_1}{\cos^2 \epsilon} ,$$

$$r_2 \left[1 + \frac{n^2 - 1}{\cos^2 \eta} \right] = - r_0 \left[1 + \frac{n^2 - 1}{\cos^2 \epsilon} \right] .$$

In this latter form, it is easy to see that when η decreases and ϵ increases, r_2 increases and r_0 decreases. The point of intersection of the rays is therefore more remote from that face of the prism that corresponds to the smaller of these two angles.

For minimum deviation ($\epsilon = \eta$), $r_2 = -r_0$, so that the point of intersection of the rays in the plane perpendicular to the edge of the prism is at the same distance as the point of intersection of the rays in the plane parallel to the edge.

The image of a luminous line parallel to the edge of the prism is formed at the place where, according to equation (11b), the rays meet that lie in the plane of a principal section of the prism. Hence, *the distance between the prism and the image of a luminous line parallel to the edge of the prism is greater than the distance of the object, provided the angle of incidence at the first face of the prism is greater than it is for minimum deviation; and, conversely, the image is nearer the prism than the object, when the said angle of incidence is less than it is for minimum deviation.*

If, therefore, a luminous line adjusted in this way is viewed through a prism either by the naked eye or with the aid of a telescope, the focusing for minimum deviation is for the same distance as that of the object itself. But if the prism is rotated out of this position around an axis parallel to its edge, the focusing of eye or telescope will have to be changed accordingly. The image will not be at infinity unless the object is infinitely distant also; and then the focusing is the same for all positions of the prism.

If the luminous object is a bright vertical line, emitting a definite kind of homogeneous light, say, red light, its image in a vertical prism (that is, a prism with its edge vertical) will be a vertical line. But if the source emits violet light as well as red, there will be a violet image also consisting of a vertical line, but farther from the object than the red image because the violet rays are more refrangible than the red rays. And, if, finally, the luminous line-source emits light of all kinds of refrangibility, there will be a special image of it for each special kind of light, all these linear images being ranged in order side by side between the red image at one end and the violet at the other, and constituting a spectrum in the form of a rectangle. On the supposition that the luminous source sends out light of every possible degree of refrangibility between certain limits, the spectrum will be continuous. On the other hand if light corresponding to some particular wave-lengths is missing, the corresponding images in the spectrum will be missing also, and there will be dark vertical lines at these places, the so-called FRAUNHOFER lines.

Apparent Width of Image in Prism

It is impossible to have a luminous object corresponding to a geometrical line. A luminous object as actually employed in optical experiments necessarily has some superficial extent. Therefore, the image of a so-called luminous line will likewise have a certain width, which we proceed now to determine.

If ϵ, ϵ_1 denote the angles of incidence and refraction at the first face of the prism, and η_1, η the corresponding angles for the second face of the prism, then

$$\left.\begin{aligned}
\sin \epsilon &= n \sin \epsilon_1 \\
\sin \eta &= n \sin \eta_1 \\
\eta_1 + \epsilon_1 &= \varphi
\end{aligned}\right\} \qquad \cdots \cdots \cdots (12)$$

where φ denotes the refracting angle of the prism. Suppose the slit is very far away and that the angle it subtends at the prism is denoted by $d\epsilon$; then the angles of incidence of light coming from opposite sides of the slit will be ϵ and $\epsilon + d\epsilon$. The angles ϵ_1, η_1 and η for one side of the slit will become, therefore, $\epsilon_1 + d\epsilon_1$, $\eta_1 + d\eta_1$ and $\eta + d\eta$ for the other side. Differentiating equations (12), we obtain:

$$\begin{aligned}
\cos \epsilon \, d \epsilon &= n \cos \epsilon_1 \, d\epsilon_1 \,, \\
\cos \eta \, d \eta &= n \cos \eta_1 \, d\eta_1 \,, \\
d\eta_1 + d\epsilon_1 &= 0 \,.
\end{aligned}$$

Eliminating $d\epsilon_1$ and $d\eta_1$, we have:

$$- \frac{\cos \epsilon \cdot \cos \eta_1}{\cos \eta \cdot \cos \epsilon_1} d\epsilon = d\eta \qquad \cdots \cdots \cdots (12a)$$

Now $d\eta$, as given by this formula, is the angle subtended by the image of the slit in the prism. Suppose the prism is adjusted in the position of minimum deviation; then

$$\epsilon = \eta \,, \qquad \epsilon_1 = \eta_1 \,,$$

and, consequently,

$$- d\epsilon = d\eta \,.$$

The greatest value of ϵ is a right angle, which happens when the ray grazes the first face of the prism. In this case the other angles continue to be acute angles, so that their cosines do not vanish, and hence

$$d\eta = 0 \,.$$

For this focusing, therefore, the image of the slit is infinitely narrow; but although it may be possible in actual experiments to approximate this limiting position, of course, it cannot be perfectly accomplished. The opposite state of affairs occurs when the prism is adjusted so that the light issues from the second face very nearly at grazing emergence, and therefore $\cos \eta$ is nearly zero. In this case

$$\frac{d\eta}{d\epsilon} = - \infty \,.$$

If the distance of the slit from the prism is r_0, and if the apparent distance of its image from the prism for horizontal rays is r_2, then from (11b)

$$\sqrt{r_0} : \sqrt{r_2} = d\eta : d\epsilon \quad . \quad . \quad . \quad . \quad . \quad . \quad (12b)$$

Purity of the spectrum. The smaller the difference of refrangibility dn for colours in the same part of the spectrum, the purer the spectrum will be; and therefore the magnitude of dn may be taken as a measure of the impurity.

Suppose we consider the refracted ray that comes from the given place in the spectrum to the nodal point of the eye; so that both its position and the angle η are definite and fixed. On the other hand, the angle ϵ varies for rays coming from different parts of the slit, and the index of refraction varies for different colours. In the equations

$$\sin \epsilon = n \sin \epsilon_1 \, ,$$
$$\sin \eta = n \sin \eta_1 \, ,$$
$$\eta_1 + \epsilon_1 = \varphi$$

let us treat φ and η as constant and ϵ, ϵ_1, η_1 and n as variable. By differentiation we get:

$$\cos \epsilon \, d\epsilon = \sin \epsilon_1 \, dn + n \cos \epsilon_1 \, d\epsilon_1 \, ,$$
$$0 = \sin \eta_1 \, dn + n \cos \eta_1 \, d\eta_1 \, ,$$
$$d\eta_1 + d\epsilon_1 = 0 \, .$$

Eliminating $d\epsilon_1$ and $d\eta_1$, we have:

$$\cos \epsilon \cdot \cos \eta_1 \cdot d\epsilon = (\sin \epsilon_1 \cos \eta_1 + \cos \epsilon_1 \sin \eta_1) \, dn$$
$$= \sin \varphi \cdot dn \, .$$

Now if $d\epsilon$ is the angle subtended by the width of the slit at the prism, the measure of the impurity of the spectrum is

$$dn = \frac{\cos \epsilon \cdot \cos \eta_1}{\sin \varphi} \, d\epsilon \quad . \quad . \quad . \quad . \quad . \quad . \quad (13)$$

As the light tends to graze the first face of the prism, the angle ϵ is more and more nearly a right angle, and therefore $\cos \epsilon$ tends to vanish, so that ultimately $dn = 0$. In this case, therefore, for a slit of given size the spectrum is purest, but at the same time the aperture of the prism also becomes very small for such oblique incidence, and the loss of light by reflection is very large. On the whole, therefore, it is better to try to get a pure spectrum by narrowing the slit (that is, by diminishing $d\epsilon$) which can generally be done without special difficulties.[1]

---

[1] ¶Concerning purity of spectrum and resolving power of prism or a prism-system, see Lord RAYLEIGH, Investigations in Optics. *Phil. Mag.* (5) VIII, 1879, pp. 261–274, 403–411, 477–486, and (5) IX, 1880, pp. 40–55. See also J. P. C. SOUTHALL, *Principles and methods of geometrical optics*, 1910, pp. 492, foll.; and R. W. WOOD, *Physical Optics*, 2nd ed., 1914, pp. 108, foll. (J. P. C. S.)

So far as the *luminiosity* of the spectrum is concerned, the brightness of the slit for any special colour is to that of its image in the inverse ratio of their widths $d\epsilon$ and $d\eta$, provided we leave out of account losses of light by reflections at the sides of the prism, and provided the aperture of the prism is greater than that of the pupil of the eye or than the object-glass of the telescope, if the spectrum is observed through that instrument. Thus, if the brightnesses of slit and image are denoted by h and h_1, then

$$h\, d\epsilon = h_1 d\eta$$

and hence by equation (12a):

$$h_1 = h\, \frac{\cos \eta \cos \epsilon_1}{\cos \epsilon \cos \eta_1} \ .$$

Let H denote the luminosity at some place in the spectrum; being equal to the sum of the luminosities h_1 of all the separate homogeneous kinds of light that contribute to the illumination at this place. As a rule, it may be assumed that the brightness of simple colours of nearly the same wave-length λ is the same. If, therefore, $d\lambda$ denotes the difference of wave-length and dn the difference of refrangibility for colours that overlap at a certain place in the spectrum, we may write

$$H = h_1\, d\lambda = h_1 \frac{d\lambda}{dn}\, dn\ ,$$

and hence, when the value of dn as given by equation (13) is substituted in this expression, the following formula is obtained:

$$H = h\, \frac{\cos \eta \cos \epsilon_1}{\sin \varphi}\, d\epsilon \cdot \frac{d\lambda}{dn},$$

where $d\epsilon$ denotes the apparent width of the slit. To get a clear idea of the meaning of this expression for H, suppose that we had an actual geometrical line of light instead of an illuminated slit, and that the problem was to find the angular width $d\eta$ of the interval in an absolutely pure spectrum corresponding to the positions of two coloured images whose difference of refrangibility was dn. The ratio $\frac{d\eta}{d\lambda}$, which will be denoted by l, is found by differentiation in the same way as above; thus

$$\frac{d\eta}{dn} = \frac{d\eta}{d\lambda}\frac{d\lambda}{dn} = l\frac{d\lambda}{dn} = \frac{\sin \varphi}{\cos \eta \cos \epsilon_1}\ .$$

In this case, therefore,

$$H = \frac{h \cdot d\epsilon}{l} \, .$$

Accordingly, apart from losses of light by reflection and absorption, *the luminosity of the spectrum*, regarded as something that is independent of the dispersion of the prism and the geometrical conditions, *is directly proportional to the luminosity of the given colours in the spectrum and to the apparent width of the slit, and inversely proportional to the apparent length of the portion of the spectrum under consideration.*

When the prism is adjusted for minimum deviation, the apparent widths of the slit and image are equal, and $l/d\epsilon$ may be regarded as the measure of the purity of the spectrum. Under these circumstances therefore, *the luminosity of the spectrum, for constant luminosity of the slit, is simply inversely proportional to the purity of the spectrum.* This means, therefore, that to get the greatest purity, the light should be as brilliant as possible.

On the other hand, it would be theoretically possible to obtain rather greater luminosity for the same degree of purity in the spectrum, by increasing the angle of incidence at the first face of the prism and making the slit broader; but in order not to vary the length of the spectrum, the refracting angle of the prism would have to be increased also. However, no practical advantage is gained in this way, because there is always more light lost by reflection, and, besides, if the faces of the prism are not truly plane, slight errors of this kind become more manifest in the image at large angles of incidence.

It has been assumed above that the prism was used without the aid of any other optical system. But the prismatic spectrum like any other optical image may be made the object for inspection through a telescope and may be magnified at pleasure. Of course, this will not affect the purity of the spectrum; and if the aperture of the telescope is large enough to show the object in its natural brightness, and if the aperture of the prism is as great as that of the telescope, the luminosity of the magnified image will also remain unchanged. The above rules also concerning luminosity and purity of the spectrum are not altered, provided $d\epsilon$ is understood to mean the apparent size of the slit, $d\eta$ that of its image, and l the length of the portion of the spectrum under consideration, as these magnitudes appear through the telescope. Incidentally, the condition formulated for the luminosity of the spectrum shows why quite small prisms are sufficient in observations where no telescope is employed, whereas the size of the prism increases with the magnifying power of the instrument, when the apparatus is designed to be used with a telescope.

In focusing a telescope on a spectrum, another point to be noticed is that the coloured bands and dark lines appear distinct when the rays that diverge horizontally are brought to a focus (supposing that slit and prism-edge are vertical, which is always to be understood); whereas the upper and lower boundary lines of the spectrum and any other horizontal lines, which may easily be produced in the spectrum by some irregularities in the edges of the slit or by particles of dust on them, will show up distinct if the vertically diverging rays are the ones that are converged to a focus. It is only when the prism is in the position of minimum deviation that the telescope can be focused for vertical and horizontal lines at the same time. And, in fact, provided the faces of the prism are perfectly plane, the focusing is the same as it would be to see the slit distinctly when the prism was out of the way. But if, starting with the prism in the position of minimum deviation, the edge is rotated more towards the object-glass of the telescope, the latter will have to be focused for a greater distance in order to see the coloured bands and dark lines; whereas when the prism is turned the other way, the telescope must be focused for a nearer object. For horizontal lines the focusing is the same, no matter which way the prism is turned.

––––––––––

A spectrum is obtained by letting the light from an illuminated slit go through a prism. The transmitted light may enter the eye directly, or it may be sent through a telescope into the eye, or it may be focused by a lens to project an objective image of the spectrum.

Any luminous body may be the source of light. The luminosity of the various colours, as is well known, is different for light of different sources, terrestrial as well as celestial; and the spectra are different both in the bright portions and in the dark portions. If it is desired to use the spectrum of sunlight for experimental work, and it is not necessary to see any but the more conspicuous dark lines and merely such colours as are ordinarily visible, skylight reflected from a mirror or a sheet of paper illuminated by sunlight will be sufficient; except that in the former case the yellow and orange will be a little faint. One advantage of this kind of illumination is that it remains the same for a long time. The more prominent dark lines D, F, and G can be seen simply by looking with the naked eye through a flint glass prism of 50° angle at a slit 1 mm wide and 40 cm away. If the observer is twice as far from the prism as the slit is, he will be able to discern most of the lines which FRAUNHOFER designated by capital letters. He must find out, however, precisely the adjustment of the prism for which the eye can be accommodated for the lines.

If a spectrum of greater purity is necessary, so as to see also the finer dark lines, or if the extreme limits of the spectrum are to be made visible, a mirror must be adjusted to reflect light from the parts of the sky close to the sun or from the sun itself through the slit on to the prism; and, as the sun moves in the sky, the mirror will have to be adjusted again about every three minutes unless it is attached to a heliostat and moved by clock-work so as to keep pace with the sun.

The *slit* itself, which is to be illuminated and which is the peculiar object for the prismatic image, may be easily cut out of a piece of opaque paper, if it is to be used for experiments in which the finer dark lines do not matter, or provided it is placed far enough away from the prism. But if a very fine slit has to be used, the GRAVESANDE slit is the best. Two straight bars *ab*, *ab* (Fig. 11) are screwed in a rectangular plate of brass. Between the ends *aa* a plate *aacc* is fastened with its edge *cc* beveled. Opposite it is the beveled edge *dd* of another plate *ddee* which can slide between the two parallel bars. It is adjusted by a screw *f* with a very fine thread, which goes

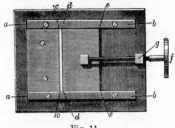

Fig. 11.

through the nut *g* fastened to the base. Thus the two knife-edges *cc* and *dd* can be nicely adjusted at a very slight distance apart, always being parallel to each other, if the contrivance is properly constructed. The part of the base-plate where the slit is formed by the knife-edges is cut away to let the light pass.

The GRAVESANDE slit has to be fastened in the centre of a sufficiently large dark screen and the side towards the observer must be blackened. The screen must be big enough not to allow any luminous object to be visible anywhere in the vicinity of the slit, whose spectrum might extend as far as that of the slit. Unless there is not to be any trace of white light at all, the main thing usually is that the screen where the slit is shall be *uniformly* dark rather than *absolutely* dark. Wherever there is any difference of illumination, even if it be no more than the contrast between velvet black and grey black, the prism shows colours; but when the surface is the same everywhere and evenly illuminated all over, there will be no colours. Many such tests can be carried out perfectly well in a bright room, provided the slit is inserted in a large enough screen that is painted uniformly black.

On the other hand, when it is necessary to get rid of every vestige of white light, as, for example, in the case of experiments that are intended to show that homogeneous light cannot be resolved any further or changed at all, and also in investigations of the limits of the spectrum, the screen where the slit is must be absolutely dark. The easiest way of accomplishing this is to do the work in a dark room specially designed for optical experiments and provided with suitable window-shades that do not allow any light to come through. The brass plate with the slit in it may then be inserted in an opening in the shutter itself. Incidentally, it is often possible to produce the same conditions even in an ordinary living-room by closing the shutters and window-hangings and leaving just a small slit for the light to come through. The slit should be placed in the back of a box painted black on the inside, the open front side of the box being towards the spectator. The sides of the box will keep the lateral light from falling on the back, so that the latter will be very dark. Two strips of black velvet should be glued on the back of the box on either side of the slit, of such dimensions that when the spectrum is supposed to be projected backwards on the velvet it will be wholly on it. In this way the spectrum will be actually seen on a black or non-luminous background. Another useful precaution consists in adjusting dark screens to prevent any possible illumination in different parts of the room from falling on the prism and telescope or on the observer's eye.

But an absolutely dark screen in a dark room is not enough by itself to prevent any visible traces of white light from disturbing the spectrum, if very intense light of several colours is being transmitted through the optical apparatus into the eye. In the theory of the formation of prismatic images, as developed above, it was tacitly assumed that all the light was refracted regularly. But it must not be forgotten that some of the light is also *reflected*; and a small amount of light is always diffused in all directions when light passes through any transparent medium, solid or liquid.

Reflections occur, in the first place, at the base of the prism unless it is painted black with some suitable varnish to prevent this very thing. If it is a ground glass surface, it will usually be illuminated whenever light traverses the prism. In Fig. 12, suppose that *dcba* is the path of a ray through a prism, and that the eye of an observer is at *a*. He will see a reflected image of the base of the prism *fe* in the apparent position *fε* and if the base is illuminated, the image will appear bright, and thus diffused white light will be scattered throughout the field of view. But if the base of the prism is also polished, the light will be regularly reflected from it. In a prism whose section is an equilateral triangle, the observer will not only get light along *dcba* but also along the path *dcbgcba* after the light has been reflected three times at *b*, *g* and *c* in succession. This light is not dispersed in colours, but is white. It forms a faint white image of the slit in the field of view, which may be utilized for adjusting the prism in the position of minimum deviation. In a prism of this particular form, the white image of the slit coincides exactly with the colour in the spectrum for which the deviation is minimum. But this faint white image of the slit is usually not a serious matter at all so far as spectrum observations are concerned, because it takes up a comparatively small space in the field and is not so harmful in its effects as the reflected image of the base of the prism when the latter is a ground glass surface. On the other hand, it is possible also for light from surrounding objects to get to the eye through the base of the prism, and this must be carefully avoided. In any case, it is best to paint the whole prism black except the two refracting faces.

Fig. 12.

When the spectrum is observed with a telescope, the reflections at the two surfaces of each of the lenses have to be taken into account. The effect of these reflections is to produce tiny little regular images of objects in front of the telescope, but most of them are so situated that the observer cannot accommodate for them; so that what they do is to make a faint white illumination in the field. This illumination can be easily noticed by pointing a telescope at a dark black object surrounded by very bright ones. The field will then appear feebly illuminated as contrasted with the black diaphragm of the ocular.

A similar defect, which is much more difficult to obviate, is the diffusion of the light in the body of the glass itself. On close observation any piece of clear glass held against a black background will appear whitish throughout when the sun shines on it, especially if the line of sight is in very nearly the same direction as the transmitted light. The same phenomenon is observed in the cornea and crystalline lens of the human eye (see Vol. I, pages 18, 193). Accordingly, we must take into account that any mass of glass traversed by light scatters some of it, even if it be only a small portion, and that the field of view contains everywhere some diffused illumination of this kind. Similarly, there is always a very small amount of each kind of light that comes into the eye spread over the entire retina. The intensity of this irregularly diffused light is certainly exceedingly low, as compared with that which is regularly refracted or reflected. And yet it may be appreciable when faint portions of the spectrum are under observation. For example, this is the reason why, under ordinary circumstances, the extreme red corresponding to the line *A* and the ultra-violet region of the spectrum are not perceptible. It is very noticeable when the luminosity of individual parts of the spectrum is considerably lowered by coloured glasses, for then the hues at these places are decidedly altered by the faint light scattered by diffusion throughout the field of view.

In experiments on the faintly luminous parts of the spectrum the only way to surmount these difficulties completely is not to let any light come through the slit and fall on the prism and telescope except light of high intensity of precisely the kind that is to be investigated. All other kinds of light must be excluded as far as possible. In certain special cases this can be done simply by interposing coloured filters between the source and the slit; for example, a piece of red glass in order to see the farthest red in the spectrum. A better and more general method consists in using two slits and two prisms. The image of the second slit is the spectrum. The only kind of light that is allowed to pass through this slit is the particular light that is to be investigated. A diagram of the arrangement is shown in Fig. 13. The incident ray *ab*

Fig. 13.

falls on the mirror of the heliostat at *b* and is reflected through a slit in the screen *c*, which as a rule does not have to be very narrow. The light passes then through the lens *d* and the prism *e*, and arrives at the screen *f*. This screen is adjusted so that the rays that diverge from the slit *c* are focused on it and form there an image of the slit expanded into a spectrum. This first spectrum does not generally have to be pure. Indeed, if a somewhat extended region of the spectrum is to be studied, say, the ultra-violet portion, this original spectrum should be so impure that all the ultra-violet light falls at one place in it. To regulate this according to circumstances, instead of putting the prism *e* beyond the lens, it is even better to insert it in the system ahead of the lens. The effect of bringing the screen nearer the prism and moving the lens correspondingly farther from it, will be to make the spectrum shorter and more impure. If the screen and prism are farther apart, the spectrum will be longer and purer. The screen *f* has a fine slit in it between two GRAVESANDE knife-edges, which is adjusted so that the precise colour of the spectrum that is to be studied is projected on it. Thus, suppose the ultra-violet light is under investigation; then the slit is moved so as to be close to the extreme edge of the visible violet, and then regularly refracted ultra-violet light, as intense as it occurs in sunlight, will pass through the slit, along with it also some little white light diffusely scattered from the glass prism and lens or reflected several times from their surfaces. This latter light is certainly far more feeble than the other, but yet it is intense enough to cover completely the ultra-violet on the screen *f*. Having passed through the second slit, the light falls now on a second prism *g*, and then enters the eye directly or after traversing a telescope; unless one prefers to substitute a lens for the telescope and project an objective image of the spectrum on a screen placed in the focal plane of the lens. As some white light after all has come through the slit *f*, a complete spectrum is produced here also, but it is very faint everywhere except in the ultra-violet region or whatever portion of the spectrum was focused on the second slit. Some light will be irregularly scattered in the second prism *g*, in the lenses that compose the telescope *h*, and in the ocular media of the observer's eye *o*; but all the other light except the ultra-violet is by this time too faint for its small scattered portions to be still perceptible. As a matter of fact, with this arrangement, it is possible to see the spectrum even in a telescope projected on a completely dark black background, so black that it cannot be distinguished from the blackness of the ocular stop, the edge of the latter not being visible except where it crosses the spectrum. Not until this deep blackness of the background has been obtained, can one be certain that it is pure monochromatic light that is seen. Under these circumstances, the ultra-violet light of sunlight also becomes directly visible to the eye; and it is only by such precautions that the unchangeableness of the colour of homogeneous light can be successfully demonstrated when it is filtered through a coloured glass. As long as there is still a small amount of diffused white light mixed in the spectrum, coloured filters, that absorb largely the particular kind of light in question, apparently also change their hue. Blue cobalt glass, for example, absorbs spectrum yellow almost entirely, but allows the blue rays of the diffused white light to pass unaffected, and this latter light, getting mixed with the faint yellow that is not absorbed, produces a white or bluish white compound colour in place of the yellow. However, this compound colour is not due, as BREWSTER supposed, to light of a single degree of refrangibility, because it can be resolved again by another prism into light of different colours and different refrangibilities. On the other hand, if the experiment is performed again with a spectrum that is completely purified of diffused light, the homogeneous yellow is found to remain pure yellow after passing through the blue glass, no matter how faint it is. From these experiments and similar ones we are not justified, therefore, in inferring, as BREWSTER has done, that light of definite refrangibility and wave-length may be still further decomposed into three different kinds of light whose colours are merely mixed in different proportions in different parts of the spectrum, and might be separated from each other by absorption by coloured media. The experiments on which he bases this conclusion depend partly on the circumstance above mentioned, partly too on contrast actions, and lastly on the fact that the hue is a function of the intensity of the light, as has been previously stated.[1]

By the method just described, as represented in the diagram (Fig. 13), the ultra-violet spectrum in its entire length can be made directly visible to the eye, without having to use any fluorescent substance; but for the farthest ultra-violet the prisms and lenses should all be made of rock crystal (quartz), and not of glass, because the latter absorbs to a considerable extent the more extreme ultra-violet radiations of the solar spectrum. But with quartz apparatus, the unusually large number of dark lines that occur in this part of the spectrum can be very distinctly seen. The author supposed the luminosity of the ultra-violet spectrum as seen in the telescope could be increased by inserting in the ocular stop a thin layer of quinine solution between two quartz plates. The spectrum in this case is projected right on the quinine surface causing it to fluoresce. The image as viewed through the ocular is similar to that which is seen without the quinine preparation, except that it does not consist of ultra-violet light but of pale blue light of medium refrangibility. But, contrary to expectation, the luminosity of this image in the actual experiment was no greater than that of the directly viewed ultra-

[1] HELMHOLTZ über D. BREWSTERS neue Analyse des Sonnenspektrums. POGG. *Ann.*, LXXXVI, 501. — BERNARD, *Ann. de Chim.* XXXV, 385–438.

violet image, but almost the same and rather less, and, owing to the thickness of the film of quinine, the dark lines were more indistinct. The reason of this is because, although the cone of light that enters the instrument through the object-glass is a small one, practically all this light comes to the eye and illuminates the retina, provided the film of quinine is not present. But when the ultra-violet light falls on the quinine solution, it is scattered there in all directions in space, and only a very small part of the light that comes from the quinine gets to the observer's eye; and hence, in spite of the greater luminosity of the fluorescent light, the retina itself is not so highly illuminated. This experience is the basis of the estimate given above as to the ratio between the luminosity of the original ultra-violet light and that of the fluorescent light produced when it falls on quinine.

Let a denote the aperture of the object-glass or of the prism in front of it, if it is the latter that determines the cone of rays; and let r denote the distance of the image. With the position of the image as centre, describe a sphere of radius r. Supposing that the ultra-violet light is propagated without any interference, the portion of this spherical surface that is illuminated will be an area not greater than a. But if the image were projected on quinine, the entire spherical surface of area $4\pi r^2$ would be uniformly illuminated. Thus, the light in the first case is more concentrated than in the latter case in the ratio of $\dfrac{4\pi r^2}{a}$; and if an eye, whose pupil is completely inside the region of radiation for both kinds of light, sees both equally bright, then, for the same manner of distribution, the fluorescent light must be brighter in the ratio above mentioned. In the author's experiment, the value of this fraction, after making the necessary corrections, was 1200. Hence, ultra-violet light received on a quinine screen must appear about 1200 times brighter than it does when it falls on a smooth white surface of porcelain that does not fluoresce.

Fluorescence of highly fluorescing substances may be easily observed and detected in any spectrum. However, when it is a question of perceiving the weakest sort of fluorescence, for example, that of the retina, the apparatus represented in Fig. 12 may be employed with the following modifications. The first spectrum is made very impure by removing the first slit at c altogether and moving the prism e near the screen f. The slit in this screen is opened wide; and adjusted on the edge of the violet. The object-glass is the only part of the telescope that is used here. The substances to be tested are placed at the focus of this lens where the ultra-violet light is most concentrated, and where there is no white light. There is scarcely any material that will not show signs of fluorescence under these circumstances. As the unchanged ultra-violet light may also still be visible in these experiments, the substance under investigation should be examined through a yellow or green glass (uranium glass is best), that absorbs ultra-violet, or through a thin prism that separates ultra-violet from the colours of medium refrangibility. The fluorescence of the cornea and crystalline lens of the eye is easy to demonstrate by focusing ultra-violet light on the eye of a living person. The crystalline lens is so illuminated in this way that its position right behind the iris and its form can be much better distinguished than by illumination with ordinary light (Vol. I, p. 18). Of course, a large amount of bluish white light is uniformly scattered by the fluorescent lens over the entire background of the eye. When, on the other hand, an ultra-violet spectrum is viewed by the eye, it shows up very fine and distinct. It must not be inferred from this that the fluorescence of the lens is what makes ultra-violet light visible to the eye. Fluorescent light would never produce a well defined image on the retina.

The infra-red region is studied in the same way as the ultra-violet.

The methods of measuring wave-lengths of light are described in treatises on physical optics and do not belong here.

Previous to the time of NEWTON, the theory of colour consisted chiefly of vague hypotheses. The intensity of the coloured light that was derived from the total white light being always necessarily less than that of the whole, the old-fashioned idea was that this decrease of intensity was an essential thing about colour, and ARISTOTLE's opinion that colour is a mixture of white and black had many adherents. He himself was undecided whether this mingling of white and black was to be considered as a real blending or more as an atomic superposition or juxtaposition. He supposed that darkness must be due to reflection from bodies, because every time light is reflected, it gets fainter. This was the prevalent view until the beginning of more modern times, as can be seen, for instance, in the doctrines of MAUROLYCUS, JOH. FLEISCHER, DE DOMINIS, FUNK, NUGUET (see GOETHE's history of the theory of colour). And in very recent times GOETHE has tried to uphold it again in his *Farbenlehre*. This theory of colour does not pretend to give an explanation of colour phenomena in the physical sense—considered in that way, GOETHE's propositions would be void of any meaning; but all that he tries to do is to formulate in a general way the conditions of the production of colours. Colours must be manifested distinctly in some original phenomenon (*"Urphänomen"*). He considers the colours of cloudy media as being this original phenomenon. Many media of this sort give a red colour to light that passes through them, whereas the incident light as seen against a dark background looks blue. Thus, although GOETHE follows ARISTOTLE's view in general, and supposes that light is darkened or has to be mixed with darkness to produce colours, he imagines that in the phenomena of cloudy media he has discovered the special kind of darkening that produces, not what we call grey, but colours as usually understood. What change occurs in the light itself under these circumstances, he never does explain. He does, perhaps, say that the cloudy medium gives the light something corporeal, shadowy, which is necessary for the production of colour. But what he means by it, he does not explain more precisely. He cannot possibly suppose that something corporeal escapes from bodies along with the light they emit; and yet as a physical explanation scarcely any other meaning can be attached to it.

Moreover, in GOETHE's way of looking at the matter, all transparent bodies are a little cloudy; and this is true of a prism too. Thus, he assumes that the prism communicates something of its cloudiness to the image which the spectator beholds. Apparently, what he means by this is that the image in a prism is never quite sharp, but is confused and indistinct; for in his theory of colour he classifies such images with the secondary images produced by plane parallel glass plates and crystals of Iceland spar. The image made by a prism certainly is confused in heterogeneous light, but it is perfectly sharp in homogeneous light; but this is something that apparently GOETHE never did see, as he disdained to consider at all the array of arguments that prove this fact. When a bright surface on a dark background is viewed through a prism, his idea is that the image is shifted and clouded by the prism. The anterior edge of the bright area is shifted over the dark background, and being a bright cloud over darkness, looks blue. But the other edge of the bright area, being overlapped by the cloudy image of the black background that succeeds it, is a bright thing behind a dark cloud, and is therefore yellow-red. Why the anterior edge appears in front of the background and the other edge behind it, and not the other way, he does not explain. This presentation of the matter is likewise absolutely meaningless if it is intended to be a physical explanation. For the prism image, as thus seen, is a potential one and is therefore simply the geometrical place where the rays of light that come to the spectator would intersect if they were prolonged backwards; and hence this image cannot have the physical effects of an image seen through a cloudy medium. These representations of GOETHE's are therefore not to be regarded as physical explanations at all, but merely as figurative illustrations of the process. In his scientific work he does not attempt anyhow to go beyond the domain of sensory perception. But every physical explanation must be in terms of the forces that come into play, and these forces, of course, can never be the object of sensory perception, but are simply concepts of the mind.

The experiments which GOETHE uses to support his theory of colour are accurately observed and vividly described. There is no dispute as to their validity. The crucial experiments with as homogeneous light as possible, which are the basis of NEWTON's theory, he seems never to have repeated or to have seen. The reason of his exceedingly violent diatribe against NEW-TON[1] was more because the fundamental hypotheses in NEWTON's theory seemed absurd to him, than because he had anything cogent to urge against his experiments or conclusions. But NEWTON's assumption that white light was composed of light of many colours seemed so absurd to GOETHE, because he looked at it from his artistic standpoint which compelled him to seek all beauty and truth in direct terms of sensory perception. The physiology of the sense-perceptions was at that time still undeveloped. The complexity of white light, which NEWTON maintained, was the first decisive empirical step in the direction of recognizing the merely subjective significance of the sense-perceptions. GOETHE's presentiment was, therefore, correct when he violently opposed this first advance that threatened to ruin the "fair glory" (*schönen Schein*") of the sense-perceptions.

The great sensation produced in Germany by GOETHE's *Farbenlehre* was partly due to the fact that most people, not being accustomed to the accuracy of scientific investigations, are naturally more disposed to follow a clear, artistic presentation of the subject than mathematical and physical abstractions. Moreover, HEGEL's natural philosophy used GOETHE's theory of colour for its purposes. Like GOETHE, HEGEL wanted to see in natural phenomena the direct expression of certain ideas or of certain steps of logical thought. This is the explanation of his affinity with GOETHE and of his chief opposition to theoretical physics.

In developing the theory of the rainbow, DESCARTES advanced a new hypothesis, by assuming that the particles of which light is composed not only had a rectilinear motion but also rotated about their axes, and that the resultant colour was due to the velocity of rotation. Moreover, the action of transparent bodies may change the rotation and along with it the colour also. Similar mechanical conceptions were formulated by HOOKE and DE LA HIRE. The latter assumed that the colours were dependent on the force of the impact of the light on the optic nerve.

Finally, NEWTON[2] proved the heterogeneous nature of white light. He isolated homogeneous light from it, and showed that this latter light was coloured. This colour was characteristic homogeneous light, and could not be altered any more by absorption and refraction. He found that light of different colours had different refrangibilities; and that the colours of natural bodies were due to peculiarities of absorption and reflection. Incidentally, he explained the colour of the rays of light as being entirely the result of their

[1] ¶In GOETHE's work not only were NEWTON's theories misstated and derided, but NEWTON himself was heaped with abuse, and accused of being no better than a mere charlatan—"this Cossack Hetman," as GOETHE calls him. At the same time GOETHE, in spite of his absurdities, performed a real service, as HELMHOLTZ says. (J. P. C. S.)

[2] ¶NEWTON's original prism experiments on the decomposition of sunlight were carried out at Trinity College in Cambridge in 1666. (J. P. C. S.)

action on the retina. The rays themselves were not red, but they produced the sensation of red. He leaned towards the emission (corpuscular) theory of light; but he advanced no hypotheses as to the physical differences between homogeneous kinds of light of different colours.

About the same time, in 1690, HUYGENS proposed the hypothesis that light consisted in undulations of a delicate elastic medium. EULER showed how NEWTON's discoveries could be explained on this basis, and deduced the result that the simple colours in the spectrum were the effects of light of different frequencies of vibration. As a matter of fact, however, his first assumption was that the red vibrations were the faster ones, but subsequently he discovered the mistake. HARTLEY correctly supported this view in explaining the colours of thin plates. But a crucial test could not be made until the principle of interference had been discovered by YOUNG and FRESNEL; and it was this discovery also that led first to a general acceptance of the undulatory theory.

NEWTON's inference that the colours of the rays depended on the refrangibility, and that light of given refrangibility was homogeneous in all other ways and invariable in colour, was opposed by BREWSTER. He thought he had found that homogeneous light could change colour in traversing a coloured medium, and that in this way it might be possible to get white light from homogeneous light. He was led thus to infer that there were three different kinds of light, corresponding to the three so-called fundamental colours, red, yellow and blue, and that each of these kinds of light gave rays of every degree of refrangibility within the range of the spectrum, in such fashion, however, that red light predominates at the red end, yellow light in the middle, and blue light at the blue end. His idea was that light of given refrangibility would be absorbed by media of various colours to different extents, and that the colours would be separated in this way. BREWSTER's views were opposed by AIRY, DRAPER, MELLONI, HELMHOLTZ and F. BERNARD. Outside of some cases in which, owing to contrast effects with adjacent vivid colours, the hue appeared to be different after the light had been greatly reduced in intensity by being filtered through coloured glasses, and some other cases in which the above mentioned variation of colour was connected with the intensity of light, most of BREWSTER's observations were probably due to the circumstance, to which attention has already been called, that small quantities of white light were diffused over the field of view as a result of repeated reflections at the various surfaces or of scattered reflection inside the prism substance and in the ocular media.

The comparison between the spectrum colours and musical notes was suggested first by NEWTON. But the comparison he made was between the widths of the coloured areas in the spectrum of glass prisms and the musical intervals of the Pythagorean scale. LAMBERT pointed out long ago that this division was largely arbitrary, because there were no fixed limits to the spectrum; and that it does happen to be similar to the musical scale in one respect, inasmuch as the quantitative relations in the distribution of the colours in the spectrum are concerned not so much with the sum of the widths of the coloured bands themselves as with the sum of the ratios of these intervals. DE MAIRAN was of the same opinion. Meantime, however, Father CASTEL tried to make this analogy the basis of a colour-piano, intended to produce pleasing effects by a certain play of colours similar to the effects of music. HARTLEY endeavoured to show that differences of colour were due to vibrations of different amplitudes which enabled him to make a more direct comparison with the vibration-numbers of musical notes. This was what YOUNG had in mind when he said that the entire range of the spectrum as then known was equal to a major sixth, and that red, green and blue correspond about in the ratios of 8 : 7 : 6. More recently, thanks especially to FRAUNHOFER's measurements, the values of the wave-lengths of light of different colours have been ascertained, and, with the aid of these data, DROBISCH has tried again to find a connection between the colour scale and the musical scale. Like NEWTON, he compared the width of the colours with the intervals of the so-called Pythagorean scale: $1 : \frac{9}{8} : \frac{6}{5} : \frac{4}{3} : \frac{3}{2} : \frac{5}{3} : \frac{16}{9} : 2$. But since the width of the ordinary visible spectrum, as measured by FRAUNHOFER, is less than an octave, he raised each of those ratios to a certain power, which had the value $\frac{2}{3}$ at first, afterwards $\frac{6}{7}$. In this way he got the following table, in which the wave-lengths are given in millionths of a millimetre:

Red	$\begin{cases} 688.1 \end{cases}$	Line $B = 687.8$
Orange	$\begin{cases} 622.0 \end{cases}$	$C = 655.6$ $D = 588.8$
Yellow	$\begin{cases} 588.6 \end{cases}$	
Green	$\begin{cases} 537.7 \end{cases}$	$E = 526.5$
Blue	$\begin{cases} 486.1 \end{cases}$	$F = 485.6$
Indigo	$\begin{cases} 446.2 \end{cases}$	$G = 429.6$
Violet	$\begin{cases} 420.1 \\ 379.8 \end{cases}$	$H = 396.3$

In this scheme the boundaries between the colours themselves agree fairly well with the natural ones. Possibly, it might be better to use the major third instead of the minor third, that is, to make the whole comparison on the basis of the major scale, as DROBISCH himself suggested. Then the border between orange and yellow instead of being at D in the golden yellow, as in the above arrangement, would fall nearer the pure yellow. Even so, it must not be forgotten that any comparison between sound waves and light waves ceases to have any sense at all as soon as the numerical values of the musical intervals are modified entirely by the process of raising them all to a certain fractional power. Moreover, the spectrum is broken off arbitrarily at both ends, because, as a matter of fact, the faint terminal colours of the spectrum extend much farther on both sides. And, finally NEWTON's division into seven principal colours was perfectly arbitrary from the beginning and deliberately founded on the musical analogies. Golden yellow has just as much right to a place between yellow and orange as indigo has between blue and violet; and the same is true with respect to yellow-green and blue-green. Indeed, there are no real boundaries between the colours of the spectrum. These divisions are more or less capricious and largely the result of a mere love of calling things by names. In the author's opinion, therefore, this comparison between music and colour must be abandoned.

Lastly, quite recently UNGER has endeavoured to establish a theory of aesthetic colour harmony by an analogy between the wave-length ratios and the musical intervals. In his actual statements about harmony of colours there seems to be a good deal of truth, in large measure borrowed correctly from works of art; but the theory itself, the analogy with the musical ratios, is rather far-fetched. On his chromo-harmonic disc he has assembled a lot of hues intended to correspond to the 12 semi-tones of the octave, but for this purpose he has inserted purple reds between violet and red, although the purples do not exist as simple colours. He makes the FRAUNHOFER lines G, H, A fall in these purple hues, whereas G and H are the borders of the violet, and A belongs to pure red. The simple colours that lie beyond violet are, as a matter of fact, blue and not purple-red. The most perfect harmony should correspond to the major chord. This will give on his disc, for example, the composition of red, green and violet that is so common in the work of Italian painters. But if green is taken as major third, the correct major chord would be red, green, and indigo blue. The ancient painters did not have any good red pigment. They used minium (red lead), which is an orange colour, for red, and made the chord consisting of orange, green blue and reddish violet. The effect of the minor chords is milder and sadder, and that of the diminished and augmented triads is piquant and not so pure artistically. The writer's belief is that some other basis must be sought for the correct explanation of the colour effects described by UNGER, instead of forced musical analogies. In fact, the saturated colours do constitute a recurrent series, provided the gap between the ends of the spectrum is filled in by the purple hues; and it seems to be agreeable to the eye when three colours are presented to it that are about equally far apart in the series. The celebrated composition of the Italian painters alluded to above, namely, red, green and violet, which does not correspond to any correct major chord, does indeed correspond to YOUNG's three fundamental colours, and it may be that this is the explanation of the aesthetic effect in this case. Other colours, chosen at correct distances apart, produce a similarly satisfying impression. If two of them come too near together, the impression is less pure. This is probably the significance of UNGER's observations. At any rate, it is clear that in the so-called colour harmony no such absolutely definite relations are to be expected as are characteristic of the musical intervals.

384–322 B. C. ARISTOTELES, *De coloribus.*

1571. JOH. FLEISCHER, *De iridibus doctrina Aristotelis et Vitellionis.* Vitembergae 1571, p.86.

1583. JO. BAPT. PORTA, *De refractione libri novem.* Neapoli 1583. lib. IX.

1590. BERNARDINI TELESII, *Opera.* Venetiis 1590. De Iride et coloribus.

1611. M. ANTONI DE DOMINIS, *De radiis visus et lucis in vitris perspectivis et Iride.* Venetiis 1611.

1613. MAUROLYCUS, *De lumine et umbra.* Lugd. 1613. p. 57.

1637. CARTESIUS, *De meteoris.* Kap. VIII.

1648. JO. MARCUS MARCI, *Thaumantias, liber de arcu coelesti, deque colorum apparentium natura, ortu et causis.* Pragae 1648.

1665. R. HOOKE, *Micrographia.* London 1665. p. 64.

1675. *I. NEWTON in *Phil. Trans.* 1675. (First accounts of his views).—*Optics.* London 1704. (Complete development of his optical discoveries).—*Lectiones opticae.*

1711. DE LA HIRE, *Mém. de l'Acad. des Sc.* 1711. p. 100.

1746. EULER. Nova theoria lucis colorum in den *Opusculis varii argumenti.* Berol. 1746. pp. 169–244.

1752. EULER in *Mem. de l'Acad. de Prusse* 1752. p. 271. Essai d'une explication des couleurs.

Opposed to NEWTON

1727. RIZETTI, *Specimen physico math. de luminis affectionibus.* Ven. 1727.

1737. LEBLOND, *Harmony of colouring.* London.

1740. CASTEL, *L'optique des couleurs.* Paris.

1750. GAUTHIER, *Chroagenesie ou génération des couleurs contre le système de Newton.* Paris. 2 vol. 8.

1752. GAUTIER, *Observations sur l'histoire naturelle, sur la physique et la peinture.* Paris.

1754. COMINALE, *Anti-Newtonianismus.* 4. Napoli.

1780. MARAT, *Découvertes sur la lumière.* Paris. 8.

1784. MARAT, *Notions élémentaires d'optique.* Paris. 8.

1791–92. GOETHE, *Beiträge zur Optik.* Weimar.

1794. WÜNSCH, *Kosmologische Unterhaltungen.*

1810. GOETHE, *Zur Farbenlehre. Entoptische Farben, zur Naturwissenschaft.* 126-190.

Concerning NEWTON and GOETHE

1811. SEEBECK, Von den Farben und dem Verhalten derselben gegeneinander. SCHWEIG-
GERS *Journal* 1811. p. 1.
MOLLWEIDE, *Demonstratio propositionis quae theoriae colorum Newtoni fundamenti
loco est.* Lipsiae 1811.
PFAFF, Über die farbigen Säume der Nebenbilder des Doppelspats mit besonderer Be-
rücksichtigung von GOETHES Erklärung der Farbenentstehung durch Nebenbilder.
SCHWEIGGERS *Jahrbücher* VI. 177.
POSELGER in GILBERTS *Annalen* XXXVII. 135.
1817. WERNEBURG, *Merkwürdige Phänomene durch verschiedene Prismen zur richtigen
Würdigung* NEWTONscher *und* GOETHEscher *Farbenlehre.* Nürnberg 1817. 4.
1827. BRANDES, Art. Farbe in GEHLERS *neuem physik. Wörterbuch.*
1833. REUTHER, *Über Licht und Farbe.* Kassel 1833.
STEFFENS, *Über die Bedeutung der Farben in der Natur. Schriften alt und neu.*
1835. HELWAG, NEWTONS *Farbenlehre aus ihren richtigen Prinzipien berichtigt.* Lübeck
1835.
MOSER, Über GOETHES Farbenlehre. *Abh. der Königsberger deutschen Gesellsch.*
1853. HELMHOLTZ, Über GOETHES naturwissenschaftliche Arbeiten; in *Kieler Monatsschrift
für Wissenschaft und Lit.* 1853. May, S. 383.
1857. GRÄVELL, GOETHE *im Recht gegen* NEWTON. Berlin 1857. — Reviewed by Q. ICILIUS
in KEKULES *kritischer Zeitschr. für Chemie, Physik und Math.* Erlangen 1858. 2.
und 3. Heft.
1859. GRÄVELL, *Über Licht und Farben.* Berlin. (Rejoinder.)

Individual Theories

1816. READE, *Experimental outlines for a new theory of colours, light and vision.* London 8.
1824. HOPPE, *Versuch einer ganzneuen Theorie der Entstehung sämtlicher Farben.* Breslau. 8.
1828. RÖTTGER, *Erklärung des Lichts und der Dunkelheit.* Halle.
1830. SCHÄFFER, *Versuch einer Beantwortung der von der Akad. zu Petersburg aufgegebenen
Preisfrage über das Licht.* Bremen. 8.
WALTER CRUMM, *An experimental inquiry into the number and properties of the
primary colours, and the source of colours in the prism.* London, 1830.
1831. D. BREWSTER, Description of a monochromatic lamp with remarks on the absorption of the Prismatic Rays. *Edinb. Trans.* IX. P. II. p. 433.
Idem, On a new analysis of solar light.   *Edinb. Trans.* XXII. P. I. 123.—POGG.
Ann. XXIII. 435.
1834. EXLEY, *Physical optics or the phenomena of optics.* London.

As to BREWSTER's Theory

1847. AIRY in *Phil. Mag.* (3.) XXX. 73.—POGG. *Ann.* LXXI. 393.
BREWSTER, *Reply.* Ibid., XXX. 153.
DRAPER in SILLIMAN *Journ.* IV. 388.—*Phil. Mag.* XXX. 345.
BREWSTER, *Phil. Mag.* XXX. 461.
MELLONI, *Bibl. univ. de Genève.* Aug. 1847.—*Phil. Mag.* XXXII. 262.—POGG.
Ann. LXXV. 62.
BREWSTER, *Phil. Mag.* XXII. 489.
1852. HELMHOLTZ, Über Herr D. BREWSTERS neue Analyse des Sonnenlichts. POGG.
Ann. LXXXVI. 501. — *Phil. Mag.* (4) IV.
F. BERNARD, Thèse sur l'absorption de la lumière par les milieux non crystallisés.
Ann. de Chim. (3.) XXXV. 385–438.
1855. D. BREWSTER, On the triple spectrum, *Athen.* 1855, p. 1156.—*Inst.* 1855, p. 381.—
Report of Brit. Assoc. 1855. 2. pp. 7–9.

Limits of Sensitivity

1845-46. BRÜCKE in MÜLLERS *Archiv für Anat. und Physiol.* 1845. S. 262. 1846. S. 379.—
　　　　POGG. *Ann.* LXV. 593. LXIX. 549.
1852. CIMA, *Sul potere degli umori dell' occhio a trasmettere il calorico raggiante.* Torino.
1853. DONDERS, In Onderzoekingen gedaan in het physiol. Laborat. van de Utrechtsche.
　　　　Hoogeschool. Jaar VI. p. I MÜLLERS *Archiv* 1853. S. 459.
1854. G. KESSLER in GRAEFE *Archiv für Ophthalmologie* I. Abt. 1. S. 466.
1855. HELMHOLTZ, Über die Empfindlichkeit der menschlichen Netzhaut für die brech-
　　　　barsten Strahlen des Sonnenlichts. POGG. *Ann.* XCIV. 205.—*Ann. de Chim.*
　　　　(3.) XLIV. 74.—*Arch. de sc. phys.* XXIX. 243.

Comparison with Musical Scale

1704. I. NEWTON, *Optics.* Lib. I. Pars 2. Prop. 3.
1725-35. L. B. CASTEL, Clavecin oculaire in *Journ. de Trevoux.*
1737. DE MAIRAN in *Mém. de l'Acad. des Sc.* 1737. p. 61.
1772. LAMBERT, *Farbenpyramide.* Augsburg 1772. §19.
　　　　HARTLEY in PRIESTLEY *Geschichte der Optik.* S. 549.
1801. TH. YOUNG in *Phil. Trans.* 1802. p. 38.
1852. DROBISCH, *Abhandl. d. sächsischen Gesellsch. der Wiss.* Bd. II. *Sitzungsberichte,*
　　　　Nov. 1852.—POGG. *Ann.* LXXXVIII. 519-526.
　　　　UNGER in POGG. *Ann.* LXXXVII. 121-128.—*C. R.* XL. 239.
1854. Idem, *Disque chromharmonique.* Göttingen.
1855. HELMHOLTZ in *Sitzber. d. Akad. d. Wiss. zu Berlin* 1855. S. 760.—*Inst.* 1856. p. 222.
　　　　J. J. OPPEL, Über das optische Analogon der musikalischen Tonarten. *Jahresber.*
　　　　der Frankfurter Vers. 1854–55. pp. 47–55.
　　　　E. CHEVREUL, Remarques sur les harmonies des couleurs. *C. R.* XL. 239-242.—
　　　　Edinb. Journ. (2.) I. 166–168.

§20. The Compound Colours

We have seen that homogeneous light of different refrangibilities and frequencies produces sensations of different colours in the organ of vision. Now when one and the same place on the retina is stimulated at the same time by light of two or more different vibration-frequencies, new kinds of colour sensations are produced which, generally speaking, are different from those of the simple colours of the spectrum. A peculiarity of these sensations is that it is not possible to recognize the simple colours that are contained in the mixture. The fact is that generally the sensation of any given compound colour may be produced by several different combinations of spectral colours, without its being possible for the most practised eye to tell by itself what simple colours are concealed in the compound light. In this respect, there is a funda-mental difference between the eye in its reaction to the aether vibra-tions and the ear, which responds to sound-waves of different pitch by combining the separate notes, it is true, in a compound sensation of a chord, and yet is able to detect separately each single note in it. Thus, two chords consisting of different musical notes never do appear identical to the ear, as different aggregates of compound colours may be for the eye.

All this applies to the immediate sensory perception, and is not invalidated at all by the fact that an act of judgment sometimes enables us to recognize the composition correctly, at least as to its main features. Anybody who has had some experience with the effect of mixing coloured light may occasionally fancy that he really does see the simple colours that are contained in a compound colour, and may judge whether there is more of one colour in it than of another. But in this case an act of judgment based on experience is confused with an act of sensation. For instance, looking at purple, one may know that it is predominantly red and violet and about in what proportion the two are mixed. But nobody can tell whether there are also subordinate quantities of orange and blue in it. Were it a matter of sensation, and not simply a question of judgment based on experience, the latter could be detected just as well as the former. The sensation of white can be produced by the greatest variety of combinations; but nobody can make out what simple colours are in it, whether two or three or four, and which ones in particular. Green shows how easy it is to be deceived here. Even persons like GOETHE and BREWSTER, misled by the mixture of pigments, have insisted that they could see both yellow and blue in green, although, as a matter of fact, we know now that green cannot be produced at all from these colours, unless modifications of them are employed that already have some green in them.

The most curious illusion is when two simple colours are seen in the same place at the same time, the surface being illuminated simultaneously by two different colours, one of which predominates at certain places and the other at other places; especially if one of them covers the whole background while the other is in the form of a regular figure upon it. When the figures or spots can be made to change their position, the illusion is even more perfect. In a case of this kind we often imagine we see the two colours simultaneously at the same place, one through the other, as it were. The effect is very much as if objects were seen through a coloured veil or mirrored in a coloured surface. We have learned by experience, even under such circumstances, to form a correct judgment of the true colour of the object, and this distinction between the colour of the background and that of the light that is irregularly distributed over it is taken into consideration in all similar cases. To get the sensation of the mixture of colours without any disturbing element, the light must be evenly mixed over the entire field where it is displayed.

Under special circumstances, for example, when two colours that are far apart in the spectrum have sharply defined positions in the field of view, the marginal colours may be recognized as separate by virtue of the chromatic aberration of the eye (see Vol. I, p. 174). This does not amount to any real contradiction of the fact above stated, because in this case the eye itself acts like a prism and causes light of different colours to fall at different parts of the retina.

The following are the methods of mixing light of different colours and of testing the action of compound light in the eye:

1. Two different spectra may be superposed, or different parts of the same spectrum; whereby combinations of pairs of simple colours are obtained.

2. Two coloured surfaces may be adjusted symmetrically with respect to a transparent plate of glass. Rays from one of them traverse the glass obliquely and enter the eye, while rays from the other are reflected into the eye from the side of the plate next the eye. Thus the observer gets light of both colours simultaneously at the same part of the retina of his eye. This method is particularly convenient for mixing the colours of natural bodies.

3. Discs with sectors of different colours can be rotated rapidly on the colour-top. When the rotation is fast enough, the impressions made on the retina by the different colours blend into the sensation of a single compound or mixed colour.

All three methods are equivalent, so far as mixing the colours is concerned. However, the actual process will be described more in detail below. The method of mixing powdered or liquid pigments must not be employed for this purpose, although NEWTON and many other physicists have supposed that it was equivalent to the first method, that is, the method of mixing the colours of the spectrum. For the mixed pigment does not give at all a colour that would be the resultant of mixing the two kinds of lights that are reflected separately from each of the ingredients.[1]

To make this clear, consider first the mixture of coloured liquids. When light passes through them, some of the coloured rays of the white light become so spent after they have gone a short way in the liquid that they vanish entirely, while others can traverse longer paths in the liquid without being appreciably enfeebled. These latter rays predominate in the emergent light, which has therefore the colour of the rays that are least absorbed by the liquid. The absorption of certain colours of the spectrum can be easily demonstrated by sending the light through a prism after it has traversed a coloured liquid or glass. In the spectrum thus obtained a series of colours will be missing; or

---

[1] ¶"The failure to recognize the fact, first made plain by HELMHOLTZ, that mixtures of pigments are not the same thing as mixture of colour (the former are a phenomenon of subtraction and not of addition) was the cause of much confusion and error"— CHRISTINE LADD-FRANKLIN in article on "Vision" in BALDWIN's *Dictionary of Philosophy and Psychology*. (J. P. C. S.)

these colours will be faint, while the parts of the spectrum corresponding to the colour of the liquid will be bright as usual.

Now suppose two coloured liquids are mixed together without any chemical action taking place, so that each of them has the same power of absorption for light as before. Then no rays will go through the mixture except those which are not absorbed by either of the two ingredients. Ordinarily, the rays which pass will be those that correspond to the portion of the spectrum that is midway between the colours of the two liquids before they were mixed. Most blue substances, like the cupric salts, for example, let the blue rays through unimpaired, and the green and violet also to a less extent, but they absorb most of the red and yellow. Yellow liquids, on the other hand, let almost all the yellow light through without loss, and some red and green also, but intercept most of the blue and violet. When, therefore, a yellow liquid and a blue liquid, like those mentioned, are mixed, on the whole it is green light that is transmitted, because the blue liquid absorbs red and yellow, and the yellow liquid absorbs blue and violet. The effect is similar to that obtained by sending the light in succession through two plates of glass of different colours. In such a case the emergent light is always weaker than it would be if it had passed through two plates of the same colour. But it is obvious that what takes place here is not a summation of the light which is allowed to go through each liquid separately, but, on the contrary, a kind of subtraction, since the yellow liquid takes away from the rays that have traversed the blue liquid those rays which it absorbs itself. As a rule, therefore, mixtures of coloured liquids are much darker, than either one of the liquids by itself.

The behaviour of powdered pigments is quite similar. Each individual particle of the coloured powder must be regarded as a tiny little transparent body which colours the light by absorbing some of it. It is true that the powdered pigment as a whole is exceedingly opaque. But whenever we examine pigments in coherent masses of uniformly thick structure, we find that at any rate in the form of thin sheets they are transparent. Crystallized vermilion, verdigris, lead chromate, blue cobalt glass, etc., which are used as pigments in form of fine powders, are some examples.

Now when light falls on a powder of this kind made up of transparent parts, a certain portion of it will be reflected from the outer layer, but most of it will not be reflected until it has penetrated into the interior to some extent. A single plate of white glass reflects four percent of the light incident normally on it, while two such plates reflects nearly twice as much; and a large pile of plates reflects almost all the light. Consequently, when the glass is pulverized, we must suppose that only four percent of the light that falls perpendicularly on it is reflected from the first layer, and that all the rest is reflected from the interior layers. The same thing must happen when blue light falls on blue glass. Accordingly, only a very small fraction of the light that comes from a coloured powder is reflected from the top layers; by far the greatest part of it being reflected from the deeper layers. In non-metallic reflection, the light that is reflected from the outside surface is white, but that which comes from the interior begins to be coloured by absorption; the farther the light penetrates, the deeper being the colour. This is why a coarser powder is darker in colour than a finer one of the same substance. So far as reflection is concerned, it is simply a question of the number of facets involved, and not a question of the thickness of the particles. The larger the latter, the farther the light has to go inside the material, before meeting the same number of facets as when the particles are smaller. Therefore, in a coarse powder the absorption of light is higher than it is in a fine powder of the same material. The colour of the coarse powder is darker and more saturated. When the powder contains some liquid to make it cohere, the index of refraction of the liquid being nearer that of the particles than that of air, the internal reflection of light is thereby diminished. And so dry pigment powders are usually paler than when they are mixed with water or with oil, which has a still higher index of refraction.

Now if a uniform mixture of two coloured powders merely reflected light from its outer surface, this light would really be the sum of the two kinds of light obtained from each powder separately. But, as a matter of fact, most of the light is reflected back from the interior, and the behaviour is just like that of a mixture of coloured liquids or of a series of coloured glasses. This light has had to pass on its way particles of both sorts, and so it contains merely such rays as were able to get through both elements. Thus, most of the light reflected from a mixture of coloured powders is due, not to an addition of both colours, but to a subtraction in the sense explained above. This is the reason too why mixtures of pigments are much darker

Fig. 14.

than the separate ingredients, especially if the colours of the latter are far apart. Vermilion and ultramarine, for instance, make a dark grey with scarcely a trace of violet, although that is the compound colour of red and blue light. The reason is that one pigment almost completely absorbs the rays that the other lets pass. A convenient way of exhibiting the distinction here is to paint the sectors a and b (Fig. 14) on the edge of a colour-disc in two different colours, while the central portion c is painted with a mixture of the two pigments. Thus, if the sectors are cobalt-blue and chrome-yellow, the appearance is pale grey when the disc is rotated so as to get the impression of both colours at once; but the mixture of the two pigments in the centre is a much darker green.

Evidently, therefore, the result of mixing pigments cannot be used to deduce conclusions as to the effect of combining different kinds of light. The statement that yellow and blue make green is perfectly correct in speaking of the mixture of pigments; but it is not true at all as applied to the mixture of these lights.

"Colour mixture" and "mixed colour" are terms that are employed with reference to mixing pigments; but we shall continue to use them here in speaking of the composition of coloured light, although it is not really correct. However, let us say here once for all, that these terms are not used in this book to mean the mixture of pigments and the result of such a mixture; unless the contrary is expressly stated.[1]

The simultaneous action of different simple colours at the same place on the retina produces a new series of colour sensations that are not excited by the simple colours of the spectrum by themselves. These new sensations are those of *purple* and *white*, together with the transitions of white into the spectrum colours on the one hand and into purple on the other hand.[2]

Purple-red results from mixing the simple colours at the two ends of the spectrum. It is most saturated when violet and red are mixed; and is paler or *pink-red* when blue and orange are used instead of violet and red. Purple-red passes through carmine-red into the red of the spectrum, and is distinctly different from red and violet at the extreme ends of what is ordinarily meant by the visible spectrum. For the eye, however, it is a transition between the two with continuous intermediate gradations. It forms the link that closes the chain of *saturated colours*, that is, the colours that are least like white.

White can be produced by combining different pairs of simple colours. Colours which combined in a definite ratio make white are

---

[1] ¶Mrs. FRANKLIN insists that the term *mixture* should be used for the physical procedure only. The various different psychological effects of light-ray mixtures may then be referred to as: (1) *colour-blends* when the elements of the mixture are still perceptible in the result, as blue and green in the blue-greens or peacocks; (2) *colour-fusions* (or *colour-extinctions*) when the elements of the colour have disappeared in the process of mixing, as red and green in making yellow, and yellow and blue in making white." — Art. on "Vision" in BALDWIN's *Dictionary of Philosophy and Psychology.* (J. P. C. S.)

[2] ¶"We have in the purples an example of a sensation which *must* be a blend of several sensations, for there is no physical cause for their production except the combination of the causes of blue and red; we therefore know the character of a colour-blend, and we know that white and yellow are sensations wholly destitute of this character."— CHRISTINE LADD-FRANKLIN in article on "Vision" in BALDWIN's *Dictionary of Philosophy and Psychology.* (J. P. C. S.)

said to be *complementary*. The complementary colours of the spectrum are:

> Red and greenish blue;
> Orange and cyan-blue;
> Yellow and indigo-blue;
> Greenish yellow and violet.

There is no simple colour that is complementary to the green of the spectrum. The complementary colour to green is a compound colour, namely, purple.

In order to discover whether there are any regular connections between the wave-lengths of the simple complementary colours, the writer has measured these magnitudes for various pairs of complementary colours, the values (in millionths of a millimetre[1]) being exhibited in the following table.

Colour	Wave-Length	Complementary Colour	Wave-Length	Ratio of the Wave-Lengths
Red....................	656.2	Green-blue.......	492.1	1.334
Orange................	607.7	Blue............	489.7	1.240
Golden yellow..........	585.3	Blue............	485.4	1.206
Golden yellow..........	573.9	Blue............	482.1	1.190
Yellow.................	567.1	Indigo-blue......	464.5	1.221
Yellow.................	564.4	Indigo-blue......	461.8	1.222
Green-yellow...........	563.6	Violet...........	from 433 on	1.301

On account of the low luminosity in the violet, the extreme rays from wave-length 433 must all be included together.

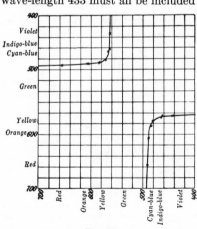

Fig. 15.

The results are plotted in Fig. 15, with reference to a pair of rectangular axes, which indicate the wave-lengths of the colours in the spectrum from 400 to 700. The curve, therefore, shows the wave-length of the complementary colour as a function of that of each of the simple colours. The names of the colours are inserted along the two axes at the proper places. The values actually measured are indicated by the points marked on the curve. This curve, com-

[1] In the first edition the unit used was the Paris inch. In the second edition the numbers were given in terms of the millimetre, and the adjoining figure changed accordingly.—N.

posed of two branches, shows a striking irregularity in the distribution of the complementary colours in the spectrum. Proceeding along the horizontal axis from the violet to the red, we see that the wave-length of the complementary colour changes at first very gradually, as shown by the almost horizontal procedure of the curve. But when we reach the greenish blue colours, the curve suddenly turns downwards almost vertically, and the wave-lengths of the complementary colours change very rapidly. The same thing happens in the yellow; and then in the red the change is again very gradual. This is connected with the fact, mentioned in the preceding chapter, that at the ends of the spectrum the hue changes exceedingly slowly as compared with the wave-length, whereas it changes very fast in the middle of the spectrum. The result is that there is no simple or constant connection between the wave-lengths of the pairs of complementary colours. To use the musical notation, it varies between that of the fourth (1.33) and that of the minor third (1.20).

Incidentally it may be added that the intensities of the light of two complementary simple colours, that are together just equivalent to white, do not by any means appear always equally bright to the eye. The only case where we have to take quantities of the two colours that appear to the eye to be about equal is when we mix cyan-blue and orange. But violet, indigo-blue and red all appear to be darker than the complementary amounts of greenish yellow, yellow and greenish blue, respectively. It will be shown in the next chapter that when proportional amounts of light of two different colours appear to the eye to have the same luminosity, the absolute luminosity is in fact very different; and, consequently, no definite figures are available for the relative luminosity of complementary amounts of two different colours.

The colours of the spectrum, therefore, have different colour-values in mixtures, and are, so to speak, colours of different degrees of saturation. The most saturated is violet, and the order of the others is about as follows:

> Violet
> Indigo-blue
> Red   Cyan-blue
> Orange Green
> Yellow
> ―――――――――

Note by W. NAGEL.

We have now some more recent determinations of pairs of complementary colours by other observers. Their discrepancies with each other and with HELMHOLTZ's data are perhaps not to be attributed to errors of observation so much as to individual peculiarities of the colour system. Some of these measurements were noted by HELMHOLTZ in the second edition. The subjoined table exhibits side by side the data of HELMHOLTZ, V. FREY and V. KRIES (*Arch. f. Anat. u. Physiol.* 1881. 336. The numbers were converted into wave-lengths by A. KÖNIG.), KÖNIG and DIETERICI (WIED. *Ann.* XXXIII. 1887), and ANGIER and TRENDELENBERG (*Zft. f. Psychol. u. Physiol. d. Sinnesorg.* XXXIX. 284. 1905).[1]

Table of the Pairs of Complementary Colours according to several observers

HELMHOLTZ		v. KRIES		v. FREY		KÖNIG		DIETE-RICI		ANGIER		TRENDE-LENBURG	
656.2	492.1	656.2	492.4	656.2	485.2	675	496.5	670	494.3	669.3	490.9	669.4	491.2
607.7	489.7	626	492.2	626	484.6	663	495.7	660	494	654.6	489.0	654.9	490.5
585.3	485.4	612.3	489.6	612.3	483.6	650	496.7	650	494.3	641.2	490.2	641.3	490.4
573.9	482.1	599.5	487.8	599.5	481.8	638	495.9	635	494	628.1	487.9	628.4	489.2
567.1	464.5	587.6	484.7	587.6	478.9	615.3	496	626	493.1	616.2	487.4	616.2	487.9
564.4	461.8	579.7	478.7	586.7	478.7	582.6	483.6	610	492.2	604.8	487.0	604.8	487.3
563.6	from 433 on	577	473.9	577.7	473.9	578	476.6	588	485.9	593.8	484.7	593.9	485.7
		575.5	469.3	572.8	469.3	576	467	585.7	485.7	583.3	480.6	583.5	482.8
		572.9	464.8	570.7	464.8	574.5	455	578	476.6	572.9	473.3	572.4	469.1
		571.1	460.4	569	460.4	573	450	575.6	470				
		571	452.1	568.1	452.1			571.5	455				
		570.4	440.4	566.3	440.4			571.3	448				
		570.1	429.5	566.4	429.5			571.4	442				

Lastly, there is still to be considered the effect of mixing colours that are not complementary. Concerning this matter, the following rule may be given: When two simple colours are mixed that are not so far apart in the spectrum as complementary colours, the mixture matches one of the intermediate colours in hue; being more nearly white in proportion as the two components are farther apart, and more saturated the nearer they are together. On the other hand, the mixture of two colours that are farther apart than complementary colours, gives a purple hue or a match with some colour comprised between one of the given colours and that end of the spectrum. In this case the resultant hue is more saturated when the two components are farther apart in the spectrum, and paler when they are nearer together; provided, of course, that the interval between them always exceeds that of a pair of complementary colours.

For instance, when red, whose complementary colour is greenish blue, is mixed with green, the result is a pale yellow, which for different proportions of the two components may pass either through orange into red or through greenish yellow into green. A mixture of orange

[1] ¶The curve shown in Fig. 15 suggests the form of a rectangular hyperbola. From the results found by various observers, as given in the table above, GRÜNBERG has derived the following empirical formula connecting the wave-lengths of the pairs of complementary colours in the spectrum:

$$(\lambda - 559)(498 - \lambda') = 424; (\lambda > \lambda').$$ (J. P. C. S.)

and greenish yellow may also match pure yellow, but it is more saturated than that produced by red and green. On the other hand, by mixing red and cyan-blue, we get pink (pale purple-red); and by changing the proportions of the mixture, we can make this pink pass into red or through violet and indigo-blue into cyan-blue. But red mixed with indigo-blue or, better still, with violet gives a saturated purple-red.

These results are exhibited in the subjoined table. The pure simple colours are at the tops of the vertical columns and at the left-hand ends of the horizontal rows. The place where a column and row intersect contains the resultant mixed colour; but this latter can be changed through the intermediate colours in the spectrum series into either of the two simple component colours by varying the proportions of the mixture.

	Violet	Indigo-blue	Cyan-blue	Blue-green	Green	Green-yellow	Yellow
Red	Purple	Dark pink	Pale pink	White	Pale yellow	Golden yellow	Orange
Orange	Dark pink	Pale pink	White	Pale yellow	Yellow	Yellow	
Yellow	Pale pink	White	Pale green	Pale green	Green-yellow		
Green-yellow	White	Pale green	Pale green	Green			
Green	Pale blue	Water-blue	Blue-green				
Blue-green	Water-blue	Water-blue					
Cyan-blue	Indigo-blue						

Incidentally, too, it appears that in these mixtures the degree of saturation of the colours of the spectrum is different. Thus red mixed with green of equal brightness gives a reddish orange; and violet mixed with green of equal brightness gives an indigo-blue close to the violet. On the other hand, when equally saturated colours of the same luminosity are mixed, the resultant compound colour is about midway between the two components.

No new colours are obtained by mixing more than two simple or homogeneous colours. The number of different colours is exhausted by mixing pairs of simple colours. Indeed, in these latter mixtures we have seen already that most compound colours can be produced in this way. In general, the result of mixing compound colours is the same as that of mixing spectrum colours that are similar to them; except that the mixture is paler than the spectrum colours to the same degree that the mixed colours themselves are already paler.

Accordingly, with all possible combinations of systems of aether-waves of different frequencies of vibration, there is after all a comparatively small number of different states of stimulation of the organ of vision which can be recognized as different colour sensations. First of these are the series of *saturated* colours, composed of the colours in the spectrum, along with purple which links the ends of the series. Each of these hues again may occur more or less pale in different gradations. The paler it is, the less saturated it appears. The palest degrees of these hues pass at last into pure white. Thus, we have here two kinds of differences between colours, namely, first, differences of *hue*, and, second, differences of *saturation*. Differences of hue are such as are exhibited by the differences of colour in the spectrum.[1] When these colours are supposed to be mixed with more or less white light, we obtain the different degrees of saturation of each one of the hues. Thus, the degree of saturation may be denoted by the proportion between the amounts of the saturated colour and white that go to make up the mixture. Ordinarily, we do not have special names for these pale colours, as, for example, pink in speaking of pale purple, flesh-colour when we mean pale red, sky-blue to denote pale blue; but we describe them by adding some word like bright, pale or white. For instance, "bright blue" is about the same as sky-blue, "pale blue" is a whiter blue still, and "white blue" is a blue that is hardly to be distinguished from white. The use of the word "bright" in connection with these paler tones deserves special comment, because, strictly speaking, it means high luminosity, whereas this mode of speech here does not differentiate between luminosity and paleness (or whitishness). It was mentioned in the preceding chapter that even the saturated colours in the spectrum appear to be whitish when the luminosity is high.

Lastly, in ordinary speech we are wont to describe differences of luminosity as differences of colour; however, only in case colour is considered as a characteristic of bodies. Absence of light is called *darkness*. But when a body does not reflect any light that falls on it, we say it is *black*. On the other hand, a body that scatters all incident light is said to be *white*. A body that reflects an equal share of all the incident light without reflecting all of it is called *grey*; and one which reflects light of one colour more than that of another is said to be a coloured body. Accordingly, in this sense *white*, *grey* and *black* are colours also. Saturated colours of low luminosity are said to be "dark," as, for example, dark green, dark blue. But when the luminosity is extremely low, the same names are used as for pale colours of low luminosity. Thus, red, yellow and green of low luminosity are called *red-brown*, *brown* and *olive-green*, respectively; whereas exceedingly pale colours of low luminosity have names such as *reddish grey, yellow-grey, blue-grey*, etc.

[1] ¶Thus change of hue may be said to involve primarily change of wave-length. (J. P. C. S.)

Black is a real sensation, even if it is produced by entire absence of light. The sensation of black is distinctly different from the lack of all sensation. A spot in the field of view which sends no light to the eye looks black; but no light comes to the eye from objects that are behind it, whether they are dark or bright, and yet these objects do not look black,—there is simply no sensation so far as they are concerned. With eyes shut, one is perfectly conscious that the black field of view is limited, and it never occurs to anybody that it extends behind him. It is simply those parts of the field whose light we can perceive when there is any light there, that appear black when they do not emit any light.

The easiest way of recognizing that grey and brown and red-brown are the same as white and yellow and red of low luminosity, respectively, is to analyze the light by a prism. It is more difficult to do this by projecting light of the given colour intensity on a screen, because there is a continual tendency to distinguish between the part of the colour and appearance of the body that depends on the illumination and the part that is characteristic of the surface of the body itself. Therefore, the experiment should be arranged so that the observer is prevented from knowing that there is any special illumination. A grey sheet of paper exposed to sunlight may look brighter than a white sheet in the shade; and yet the former looks grey and the latter white, simply because we know very well that if the white paper were in the sunlight, it would be much brighter than the grey paper which happens to be there at the time. But if a round grey spot is on a sheet of white paper, and if light is concentrated on it with a lens, so that it is highly illuminated while the surrounding white paper is not, the grey spot can be made to look whiter than the white paper. In a case of this kind, where the unconscious influence of experience is excluded, the quality of the sensation appears to be dependent on the luminosity alone.

Similarly, the writer has succeeded in making the homogeneous golden yellow of the spectrum look brown. The method, which will be described presently, consisted in illuminating a little rectangular area with this yellow light on an unilluminated white screen; while at the same time a larger neighbouring portion of the screen was illuminated by brighter white light. Red used in the same way gave red-brown, and green olive-green.

Accordingly, taking the intensity of the light into account also, we find that the quality of every colour impression depends on three variable factors, namely, *luminosity*, *hue* and *saturation*.[1] There are no other differences of quality in the impression made by light. This result may be expressed as follows:

The colour impression produced by a certain quantity of mixed light x *can always be reproduced by mixing a certain amount of white light* a *with a certain other amount of some saturated colour* b *(spectrum colour or purple) of definite shade.*

This statement limits the number of different kinds of colour impressions; for while they may still be infinite in variety, they must be fewer than they would be if every possible combination of different simple colours were responsible for a separate colour impression. The complete determination of the objective nature of a mixture of different kinds of light involves telling how much light it contains for every different value of the wave-length. But the number of different wave-lengths is infinite; and therefore the physical quality of such

Fig. 16.

Fig. 17.

an admixture of light must be represented as a function of an endless number of unknowns. But *the impression that any admixture of light makes on the eye may always be represented as simply a function of three variables*, capable of being given numerically, namely: 1. The quantity of saturated coloured light; 2. The quantity of white light which mixed with it gives the same colour sensation; and 3. The wave-length of the coloured light. This enables us also to obtain finally a basis for arranging all the colours systematically in order. Thus, suppose at first we leave out of account differences of luminosity; then there will still be two variables left on which the quality of the colour depends, namely, the hue and the proportion between coloured light and white light. All the various colours may be represented, therefore, according to their two dimensions, by points lying in a plane, just like the values of any other function of two variables. The saturated colours constitute a closed series, and hence they must

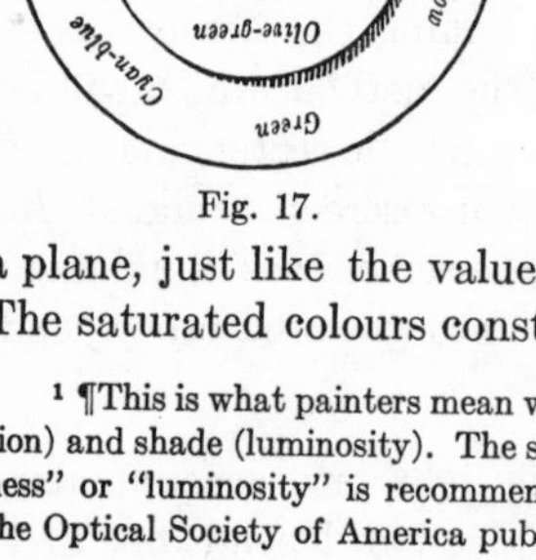

---

[1] ¶This is what painters mean when they say that colour may vary in hue, tint (saturation) and shade (luminosity). The substitution of the word "brilliance" in place of "brightness" or "luminosity" is recommended in the report of the committee on colorimetry of the Optical Society of America published in the *Journal*, VI, 1922, 527–596. (J. P. C. S.)

lie on a closed curve, which NEWTON chose to be a circle with white placed in the centre (Fig. 16). The transitions from white to any saturated colour at a point on the circumference of the circle lie along the radius drawn to this point, so that the paler shades of this hue are nearer the centre, and the more saturated ones nearer the circumference. Thus we get a *colour chart* containing all possible kinds of colours of the same luminosity arranged according to their continuous transitions. When the different degrees of luminosity are also to be taken into account, the third dimension of space has to be utilized, as was done by LAMBERT. The darkest colours for which the number of discriminable shades continually gets less and less may be made to culminate in a point corresponding to black. In this way we get a *colour pyramid* or a colour cone. Three sections of a cone of this sort are shown, one on top of the other, in Fig. 17. The largest, corresponding to the base, ought to show the same distribution of colours as the colour circle in Fig. 16. The middle one, taken from the middle of the cone, contains red-brown, brown, olive-green, grey-blue on the outer edge, with grey in the centre. And, lastly, the smallest, from near the apex of the cone, is black, as shown in the figure.

NEWTON also used the arrangement of the colours in one plane to express the law of colour mixture. He conceived the intensities of the mixed colours as being expressed by weights, which were attached at the places in the chart occupied by the colours concerned. Then the centre of gravity of these weights was to be the place of the compound colour in the chart, and the sum of the weights its intensity. GRASSMANN has developed and formulated the principles that are really implied in NEWTON's method. In addition to the proposition mentioned above, namely:

1. *Any mixed colour, no matter how it is composed, must have the same appearance as the mixture of a certain saturated colour with white;* the following laws are also necessary:

2. *When one of two kinds of light that are to be mixed together changes continuously, the appearance of the mixture changes continuously also;* and

3. *Colours that look alike produce a mixture that looks like them.*

On the basis of these three assumptions, an arrangement of the colours in one plane may be made that enables us to find the mixed colour by a centre-of-gravity method. A colour chart on which the mixed colours are found by the principle of centre-of-gravity constructions, will be called a *geometrical colour chart*. Now as there is no general unobjectionable method of making quantitative comparisons by the eye of the intensities of light of different colours, in constructing a chart of this kind it must be stipulated in advance, that the unit quantity of light for each colour is to be determined by NEWTON's rule of colour mixture itself. Suppose three colours are taken at random, except that no two of them can be combined to make the third. If three arbitrary places are assigned to them on the chart, not all on one straight line, and if the unit intensity for each of these colours is determined in any convenient way, then the position and unit of intensity for every other colour on the chart will be uniquely determined.[1]

Construction of the Colour Chart. Suppose A, B, C are the three colours with which we start; and suppose the units of their intensities

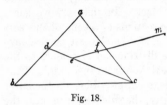

Fig. 18.

have been defined and also their positions a, b, c (Fig. 18) in the colour chart. Let us take the amounts a and β of the colours A and B, and put the mixed colour at the centre of gravity of the weights a and β, that is, at a point d in the straight line ab such that

$$a . ad = \beta . bd .$$

Thus, all mixtures of the colours A and B will lie on the line ab.[2] Suppose now that a quantity γ of some third colour C is to be mixed with the quantities a and β of the colours A and B; all we have to do is to consider that we have a quantity $(a + \beta)$ of the mixed colour corresponding to the point d, and to find the position of the centre of gravity e of the weights $(a + \beta)$ at d and γ at c. This is the place where the compound colour lies, its quantity being

$$\epsilon = a + \beta + \gamma .$$

At the same time the unit luminosity of this mixed colour is also determined from the fact that

$$1 = \frac{\epsilon}{a + \beta + \gamma} .$$

Evidently, by this method every mixture of the three colours A, B and C must lie *within* the triangle abc; for both its position and its unit luminosity are found as above described.[3]

[1] ¶Thus any colour that differs from one of the colours in the chart in luminosity only is referred to this colour as a unit, and in this way its quantity is estimated. (J. P. C. S.)

[2] ¶Thus the rule for finding the result of mixing two colours in the diagram is to divide the line joining them inversely in the ratio of the quantities of the two components. (J.P.C.S.)

[3] ¶The result obtained in this way would be a triangular portion of NEWTON's diagram. (J. P. C. S.)

On the assumption that the positions and units of measurement have been found for all the results that can be obtained by mixing together the three colours A, B and C, we may then proceed to determine the same functions for all the colours that cannot be produced by combinations of these three. Suppose M is such a colour. It is always possible to choose the amount μ of this colour so small that the result of mixing it with one of the colours of the triangle will be also a colour lying inside the triangle. For example, it may be mixed with an amount ϵ of the colour defined by the point e, where ϵ is measured in terms of the unit found above. If the amount of M is supposed to be infinitesimal at first and then to be increased gradually up to the value μ, the mixture will begin by having the same colour as E itself and will continually change into the adjacent colours, according to the fundamental axioms assumed above. When the amount of M finally gets to be equal to μ, let us suppose that the result is a certain colour defined by a point f that is still inside the triangle. In the first place, the amount of this colour F, according to the rule, must be

$$\varphi = \epsilon + \mu \ .$$

The quantity μ is dependent therefore on the units of measurement that have been previously determined. Moreover, the position of the point f must be the same as that of the centre of gravity of μ at m and ϵ at e; which means that the point m must lie in the prolongation of the line ef, so that

$$\frac{mf}{ef} = \frac{\epsilon}{\mu} \ .$$

This proportion, therefore, settles also the place and amount of the colour M; and the same method is pursued for finding all the other colours that cannot be produced by mixing A, B and C.

Proof of the above construction. What has to be demonstrated now is that in a chart thus constructed, for which also the metrical units of the amounts of the different colours are determined in the manner above described, the colour obtained by mixing any two colours is at the centre of gravity of the component colours, and its luminous intensity, as measured by the stipulated units, is equal to the sum of the amounts of the parts of the mixture.

Let m_1, m_2, etc. denote the masses of a set of particles whose positions are given by the coördinates x_1, y_1; x_2, y_2; etc., respectively. The coördinates X, Y of the centre of gravity are given by the equations:

$$X(m_1 + m_2 + m_3 + \text{etc} .) = m_1 x_1 + m_2 x_2 + m_3 x_3 + \text{etc} . \ ;$$
$$Y(m_1 + m_2 + m_3 + \text{etc} .) = m_1 y_1 + m_2 y_2 + m_3 y_3 + \text{etc} .$$

The coördinates of a point designated by a letter n will be denoted by x_n, y_n.

A. Two colours E_0 and E_1 are to be mixed, each of which can be obtained by a mixture of three originally chosen colours A, B and C. Let ϵ_0 and ϵ_1 be the amounts of the colours E_0 and E_1 obtained by mixing the amounts a_0, β_0, γ_0 and a_1, β_1, γ_1 of the colours A, B and C, respectively. Then, if x_0, y_0 denote the coördinates of the point where E_0 is in the colour chart, and x_1, y_1 those of the point where E_1 is, according to the above rule:

$$x_0(a_0+\beta_0+\gamma_0) = a_0 x_a + \beta_0 x_b + \gamma_0 x_c$$
$$x_1(a_1+\beta_1+\gamma_1) = a_1 x_a + \beta_1 x_b + \gamma_1 x_c$$
$$y_0(a_0+\beta_0+\gamma_0) = a_0 y_a + \beta_0 y_b + \gamma_0 y_c$$
$$y_1(a_1+\beta_1+\gamma_1) = a_1 y_a + \beta_1 y_b + \gamma_1 y_c$$
$$\epsilon_0 = a_0 + \beta_0 + \gamma_0$$
$$\epsilon_1 = a_1 + \beta_1 + \gamma_1 \ .$$

Now by the axiom that two colours that look alike give a mixture of the same colour, the mixture of ϵ_0 and ϵ_1 is the same as that of $a_0\beta_0\gamma_0$ and $a_1\beta_1\gamma_1$; and in the construction of the colour chart, the coördinates X, Y of the point that belongs to this latter mixture are given by the equations:

$$X(a_0+\beta_0+\gamma_0+a_1+\beta_1+\gamma_1) = (a_0+a_1)x_a + (\beta_0+\beta_1)x_b + (\gamma_0+\gamma_1)x_c \ ,$$
$$Y(a_0+\beta_0+\gamma_0+a_1+\beta_1+\gamma_1) = (a_0+a_1)y_a + (\beta_0+\beta_1)y_b + (\gamma_0+\gamma_1)y_c \ .$$

If the six equations above are used to eliminate x_a, x_b, x_c and y_a, y_b, y_c from these two last equations, then

$$X(\epsilon_0+\epsilon_1) = \epsilon_0 x_0 + \epsilon_1 x_1 \ ,$$
$$Y(\epsilon_0+\epsilon_1) = \epsilon_0 y_0 + \epsilon_1 y_1 \ .$$

Thus, the coördinates X, Y of the colour obtained by mixing E_0, E_1 are the same as those of the centre of gravity of ϵ_0 and ϵ_1.

The total amount of light (q) obtained by mixing E_0, E_1 in the quantities ϵ_0, ϵ_1, respectively, must also be equal to that obtained by mixing the amount $a_0+\beta_0+\gamma_0$ and the amount $a_1+\beta_1+\gamma_1$; that is,

$$q = a_0+\beta_0+\gamma_0+a_1+\beta_1+\gamma_1 = \epsilon_0 + \epsilon_1 \ .$$

Thus the rule given for constructing all colours obtained by mixing A, B and C in the same way as they are located on the colour chart is proved to be correct.

B. *Two colours M_0 and M_1 are to be mixed, neither of which can be obtained by a mixture of A, B and C.* Let x_0, y_0 denote the coördinates of the position of the colour M_0, and let μ_0 denote the amount of this colour; similarly, let x_1, y_1 denote the coördinates of the position of the colour M_1, and let μ_1 denote the amount of it. Suppose the position of M_0 in the colour chart has been found from the fact that when the quantity μ_0 is mixed with the quantity ϵ_0 of a colour E corresponding to the point e, the result is a quantity φ of a colour F corresponding to the point f; then

$$\epsilon_0 + \mu_0 = \varphi$$
$$\varphi x_f = \epsilon_0 x_e + \mu_0 x_0$$
$$\varphi y_f = \epsilon_0 y_e + \mu_0 y_0 .$$

Likewise, suppose the position of M_1 has been found from the fact that when the quantity μ_1 of this colour is mixed with the quantity ϵ_1 of the same colour E as above, the result is a quantity ψ of a colour G corresponding to the point g; then

$$\epsilon_1 + \mu_1 = \psi$$
$$\psi x_g = \epsilon_1 x_e + \mu_1 x_1$$
$$\psi y_g = \epsilon_1 y_e + \mu_1 y_1 .$$

To get the place of the result of mixing μ_0 and μ_1 in the same way, they must be mixed with the quantity $\epsilon_0 + \epsilon_1$ of the colour E. But this is equivalent to mixing the quantities φ and ψ of the colours F and G. Let the coördinates of the position of this mixed colour be denoted by ξ, v, as given by the equations

$$(\varphi + \psi)\xi = \varphi x_f + \psi x_g$$
$$(\varphi + \psi)v = \varphi y_f + \psi y_g .$$

The coördinates X, Y of the position of the colour obtained by mixing μ_0 and μ_1 will be given then by the following equations, in which η denotes the as yet undetermined amount of this colour:

$$(\varphi + \psi)\xi = (\epsilon_0 + \epsilon_1)x_e + \eta X$$
$$(\varphi + \psi)v = (\epsilon_0 + \epsilon_1)y_e + \eta Y$$
$$\varphi + \psi = \epsilon_0 + \epsilon_1 + \eta .$$

Eliminating φ, ψ, x_e, and y_e by the aid of the previous equations, we obtain:

$$\mu_0 x_0 + \mu_1 x_1 = \eta X$$
$$\mu_0 y_0 + \mu_1 y_1 = \eta Y$$
$$\mu_0 + \mu_1 = \eta ,$$

Consequently, the resultant colour obtained by mixing μ_0 and μ_1 is found to be actually, as desired, at the centre of gravity of these two masses, and its amount is equal to the sum of those of the two components.

C. *Two colours are to be mixed, one of which can be obtained by mixing A, B, and C, while the other cannot be so obtained.* The procedure is similar to that in the preceding case. Let μ_0 denote the amount of the colour that cannot be obtained by mixing A, B and C; and suppose that the coördinates x_0, y_0 of the position of this colour have been found from the fact that when it is mixed with an amount ϵ_0 of a colour E

corresponding to the point e, the result is a quantity φ of a colour F corresponding to the point f; then

$$\mu_0 x_0 + \epsilon_0 x_e = \varphi x_f$$
$$\mu_0 y_0 + \epsilon_0 y_e = \varphi y_f$$
$$\mu_0 + \epsilon_0 = \varphi .$$

In order to find the point corresponding to the colour obtained by mixing μ_0 with an amount η of the colour that can be produced by mixing A, B and C, we mix η with ϵ_0, and then proceed by the rule given above. But since η is composed of μ_0 and μ_1, another way would be to mix μ_0 and ϵ_0 first, which, according to the assumption, will give the amount φ of the colour F, and then mix φ with μ_1. The centre of gravity of the two is the position of the colour resulting from the mixture of η and ϵ_0, its coördinates ξ and v being given by the following equations:

$$(\varphi + \mu_1)\xi = \varphi x_f + \mu x_g$$
$$(\varphi + \mu_1)v = \varphi y_f + \mu y_g .$$

The coördinates X, Y of η, according to the above rule, are to be found by the equations:

$$(\varphi + \mu_1)\xi = \eta X + \epsilon_0 x_e$$
$$(\varphi + \mu_1)v = \eta Y + \epsilon_0 y_e$$
$$\varphi + \mu_1 = \eta + \epsilon_0 .$$

Thus we derive finally:

$$\eta X = \mu_0 x_0 + \mu_1 x_g$$
$$\eta Y = \mu_0 y_0 + \mu_1 y_g$$
$$\eta = \mu_0 + \mu_1 ,$$

which was to be proved.

Hitherto, the places of colours that cannot be obtained by mixing A, B and C have been always found by mixing them with a single colour E; but the last proposition shows that if any other colour G is used, the place found for a given colour of the kind mentioned will turn out to be the same as before.

It is not possible to tell in advance the form of the curve on which the simple colours will lie in a construction of this kind. Indeed, these curves can be very manifold, depending on the choice of the three colours to begin with and on the arbitrary units by which they are measured. One unit has to be arbitrary always, and likewise the positions of the points where two of the chosen colours are placed. When two points on the curve are specified, the form of the curve will depend simply on the other four selections. Accordingly there are four more conditions which may in general be satisfied by a corresponding choice of the four arbitrary factors that are still left. Thus, for instance, it might be desirable that the distances of five certain simple colours from white should all be equal on the chart. Then the curve containing the simple colours would hardly be appreciably different from NEW-TON's colour circle as shown in Fig. 16; except that the chord which is drawn in that diagram between the extreme red and violet would have to be the continuation of the curve instead of the arc, because purple, which can be obtained only by mixing red and violet, would have to lie on the straight line joining those two colours. Besides, from the methods of the construction, each pair of complementary colours must be at opposite ends of a diameter of the circle, because the mixed colour white must always be on the lines connecting the two colours that produce it. This condition is also satisfied in Fig. 16.

As to the units of luminosity of light of different colours, in those cases where the boundary of the colour chart has been designed in the form of a circle, complementary amounts of the complementary colours, that is, amounts which produce white when they are mixed, must be considered as being equal, because by hypothesis their mixed colour, white, is midway between them. Moreover, such amounts of other non-complementary colours would be considered as being equal which when combined with a sufficient quantity of their complementary colour in each case will produce equal quantities of white. From what has been stated about the different saturation of the colours of the spectrum, it follows that the quantities which are here considered as equal do not by any means look equally bright to the eye. However, in the next chapter it will be seen that very different results are obtained in estimating brightness by the eye at different absolute intensities of illumination; and that, on the contrary, a deter-mination of the unit of measurement of different colours by the results of mixtures continues to be valid in a certain sense at least for all degrees of luminosity.

On the other hand, supposing quantities of light of different colours are to be considered as being equal, when for a certain absolute intensity of light they look equally bright to the eye, we shall get an entirely different form for the curve on which the simple colours lie, like that shown in Fig. 19. Saturated violet and red must be farther from white than their less saturated complementary colours, because, as the eye estimates it, it takes less violet than yellow-green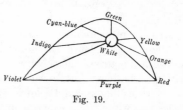

Fig. 19.

when we mix these two complementary colours together to get white. Hence, if white is to be in the position of their centre of gravity, the smaller amount of violet must have a longer lever-arm than the larger amount of yellow-green. Incidentally, here also, as before, the spectrum-colours themselves would be ranged along a curve and the purples on a chord; complementary colours lying at the opposite ends of chords that all pass through the point on the chart that corresponds to white. In these respects the chart is similar to the colour circle in Fig 16.

NEWTON's device of exhibiting the laws of colour mixture by the method used for constructing centres of gravity was intended originally simply as a kind of mathematical picture for expressing graphically a large mass of facts; the justification for it consisting in the fact that the results as found by this process were qualitively in accordance with experimental realities, even if they had not been tested quantitatively. However, quite recently the method has been still further supported by careful quantitative measurements made by MAXWELL. He used a colour top, for which two sets of circular sectors were made, the radii of one set being longer than those of the other set. These sectors were cut out of highly coloured papers (vermilion, bright chrome yellow, Paris green or ·emerald-green, ultramarine, white, and black). They were placed on the surface of the colour top in such a way that the angles of the sectors at the centre of the circle could be adjusted at pleasure; and also so that one combination of colours could be produced out towards the edge of the disc and at the same time another combination in towards the centre. The experiment generally consisted in varying the angular widths of the sectors until the outer and inner colours appeared exactly alike when the colour top was spinning rapidly; and then the angles of the exposed portions of the sectors were measured. Endless varieties of combinations of colour can be made in this way, and the laws of colour mixture may be tested by them. In accordance with the ideas developed above, the plan of this method may be easily explained as follows. Suppose a colour chart is constructed with three fundamental colours, say, red, green and blue, the same colours as used on the colour top; the brightness or luminosity of each of them being put equal to unity according to some arbitrary system of measurement. Hence, in any experimental combination of these three colours, the luminosities must be equal to the ratios between the arcs of the coloured sectors and the circumference of the circle. The first thing we can do is to make a grey by a combination of the three fundamental colours, and to match it by a combination of black and white. This experiment will enable us to locate the position of white in the colour chart and to find also unit luminosity for white.

The next experiment might be to make two grey-yellow matches, by using red and green for one mixture and yellow, white and black for the other. By the aid of the rules given above, this determination will enable us to locate where yellow belongs on the chart and to find its unit luminosity. This preliminary work being out of the way, we can proceed then, either by construction with the chart or by calculation, to show how any mixture of three of the five colours, red, yellow, green, blue and white, can be matched by mixing any other three of them; and these predictions can then be verified experimentally, every such test tending to confirm the correctness of the centre-of-gravity method of finding the result of mixing colours. Incidentally, the colour top is nicely adapted also for numerical evaluations of the colours of natural bodies.

Every difference of impression made by light, as we have seen, may be regarded as a function of three independent variables; and the three variables which have been chosen thus far were (1) the luminosity, (2) the hue, and (3) the saturation, or (1) the quantity of white, (2) the quantity of some colour of the spectrum, and (3) the wave-length of this colour. However, instead of these variables, three others may also be employed; and in fact this is what it amounts to, when all colours are regarded as being mixtures of variable amounts of *three so-called fundamental colours*, which are generally taken to be *red, yellow* and *blue*. To conceive this theory objectively, and to assert that there are simple colours in the spectrum which can be combined to produce a visual impression that will be the same as that produced by any other simple or compound light, would not be correct. There are no such three simple colours that can be combined to match the other colours of the spectrum even fairly well, because the colours of the spectrum invariably appear to be more saturated than the composite colours. Least suited for this purpose are red, yellow and blue; for if we take for blue a colour like the hue of the sky, and not a more greenish blue, it will be impossible to get green at all by mixing these colours. By taking a greenish yellow and a greenish blue, the best we can get is a very pale green. These three colours would not have been selected, had it not been that most persons, relying on the mixture of pigments, made the mistake of thinking that a mixture of yellow and blue light gives green It would be rather better to take *violet, green* and *red* for fundamental colours. Blue can be obtained by mixing violet and green, but it is not the saturated blue of the spectrum; and a dead yellow can be made with green and red, which is not at all like the brilliant yellow in the spectrum.

If we think of the colours as plotted on a colour-chart by the method sketched above, it is evident from the rules given for the construction that all colours that are to be made by mixing three colours must be contained within the triangle whose vertices are the places in the chart where the three fundamental colours are. Thus, in the adjoining colour circle (Fig. 20), where the positions of the colours are indicated by the initial letters of their names (I =indigo-blue, C =cyan-blue, Y =yellow, G =green, etc.), all the colours that can be made by mixing red, cyan-blue and yellow

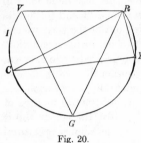

Fig. 20.

are comprised within the triangle RCY. Thus, as we see, two large pieces of the circle are missing, and all that could be obtained would be a very pale violet and a very pale green. But if, instead of cyan-blue, the colour of the blue sky, indigo-blue, were taken, green would be missing entirely. The triangle VRG comprises the colours obtained by mixing violet, red and green, and a larger number of the existing colours would indeed be represented. But, as the diagram shows, large portions of the circle are still missing, as must always be the case according to the results of experiments on the mixture of the colours of the spectrum. The conclusion is that the boundary of the colour chart must be a curved line which differs considerably from the perimeter of the triangle.

BREWSTER, endeavouring to defend the objective nature of three fundamental colours, maintained that for every wave-length there were three different kinds of light, red, yellow and blue, mixed merely in different proportions so as to give the different colours of the spectrum. Thus, the colours of the spectrum were considered as being compound colours consisting of three kinds of light of different quality; although the degree of refrangibility of the rays was the same for each individual simple colour. BREWSTER's idea was that light of all three fundamental colours could be proved to exist in the different simple colours by the absorption of light by coloured media. His entire theory is based on this conception, which was shown in the preceding chapter to be erroneous.

Apart from BREWSTER's hypothesis, the notion of three fundamental colours as having any objective significance has no meaning anyhow. For as long as it is simply a question of physical relations, and the human eye is left out of the game, the properties of the compound light are dependent only on the relative amounts of light of all the separate wave-lengths it contains. When we speak of reducing the

colours to three fundamental colours, this must be understood in a
subjective sense and as being an attempt to trace the *colour sensations*
to three *fundamental sensations*. This was the way that YOUNG
regarded the problem;[1] and, in fact, his theory affords an exceedingly
simple and clear explanation of all the phenomena of the physiological
colour theory. He supposes that:

1. The eye is provided with three distinct sets of nervous fibres.
Stimulation of the first excites the sensation of red, stimulation of the
second the sensation of green, and stimulation of the third the sensation of violet.

2. Objective homogeneous light excites these three kinds of fibres
in various degrees, depending on its wave-length. The red-sensitive
fibres are stimulated most by light of longest wave-length, and the
violet-sensitive fibres by
light of shortest wave-
length. But this does not
mean that each colour of
the spectrum does not
stimulate all three kinds
of fibres, some feebly and
others strongly; on the
contrary, in order to ex-
plain a series of phe-
nomena, it is necessary to

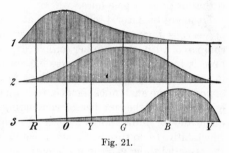

Fig. 21.

assume that that is exactly what does happen. Suppose that the colours
of the spectrum are plotted horizontally in Fig. 21 in their natural
sequence, from red to violet, the three curves may be taken to indicate
something like the degree of excitation of the three kinds of fibres,
No. 1 for the red-sensitive fibres, No. 2 for the green-sensitive fibres,
and No. 3 for the violet-sensitive fibres.

---

[1] ¶MAXWELL in his lecture "On colour vision" at the Royal Institution (see *Scientific
Papers of* JAMES CLERK MAXWELL, II. pp. 266–279), speaking of YOUNG's theory, says:

"We may state it thus:—We are capable of feeling three different colour-sensations.
Light of different kinds excites these sensations in different proportions, and it is by the different combinations of these three primary sensations that all the varieties of visible colour
are produced. In this statement there is one word on which we must fix our attention.
That word is, Sensation. It seems almost a truism to say that colour is a sensation; and
yet YOUNG, by honestly recognizing this elementary Truth established the first consistent
theory of colour. So far as I know, THOMAS YOUNG was the first who, starting from the
well-known fact that there are three primary colours, sought for the explanation of this
fact, not in the nature of light, but in the constitution of man. Even of those who have
written on colour since the time of YOUNG, some have supposed that they ought to study
the properties of pigments, and others that they ought to analyse the rays of light. They
have sought for a knowledge of colour by examining something in external nature—something out of themselves." (J.P.C.S.)

Pure *red* light stimulates the red-sensitive fibres strongly and the two other kinds of fibres feebly; giving the sensation red.

Pure *yellow* light stimulates the red-sensitive and green-sensitive fibres moderately and the violet-sensitive fibres feebly; giving the sensation yellow.

Pure *green* light stimulates the green-sensitive fibres strongly, and the two other kinds much more feebly; giving the sensation green.

Pure *blue* light stimulates the green-sensitive and violet-sensitive fibres moderately, and the red-sensitive fibres feebly; giving the sensation blue.

Pure *violet* light stimulates the violet-sensitive fibres strongly, and the other fibres feebly; giving the sensation violet.

When all the fibres are stimulated about equally, the sensation is that of *white* or pale hues.

It might be natural to suppose that on this hypothesis the number of nervous fibres and nerve-endings would have to be trebled, as compared with the number ordinarily assumed when each single fibre is made to conduct all possible colour stimulations. However, in the writer's opinion there is nothing in YOUNG's hypothesis that is opposed to the anatomical facts in this respect; because we are entirely ignorant as to the number of conducting fibres, and there are also quantities of other microscopical elements (cells, nuclei, rods) to which hitherto no specific functions could be ascribed. But this is not the essential thing in YOUNG's hypothesis. That appears to the writer to consist rather in the idea of the colour sensations being composed of three processes in the nervous substance that are perfectly independent of one another. This independence is manifested not merely in the phenomena which are being considered at present but also in those of fatigue of the nervous mechanism of vision. It would not be absolutely necessary to assume different nervous fibres for these different sensations. So far as mere explanation is concerned, the same advantages that are afforded by YOUNG's hypothesis could be gained by supposing that within each individual fibre there might occur three activities all different from and independent of one another. But the form of this hypothesis as originally proposed by YOUNG is clearer in both conception and expression than it would be if it were modified as suggested, and hence it will be retained in its original concrete form, for the sake of exposition if for nothing else. Nowhere in the physical (electrical) phenomena of nervous stimulation either in the sensory or motor nerves can there be detected any such differentiation of activity as must exist if each fibre of the optic nerve has to transmit all the colour sensations. By YOUNG's hypothesis it is possible even in this connection to transfer directly to the optic nerve the simple conceptions as to the mechanism of the stimulation and its conduction which we were led to form at first by studying the phenomena in the motor nerves. This would not be the case on the assumption that each fibre of the optic nerve has to sustain three different kinds of states of stimulation which do not mutually interfere with one another. YOUNG's hypothesis is only a more special application of the law of specific sense energies. Just as tactile sensation and visual sensation in the eye are demonstrably affairs of different nervous fibres, the same thing is assumed here too with respect to the various sensations of the fundamental colours.

The choice of the three fundamental colours is somewhat arbitrary. Any three colours which can be mixed to get white might be chosen. YOUNG may have been guided by the consideration that the terminal colours of the spectrum seem to have special claims by virtue of their positions. If they were not chosen, one of the fundamental colours would have to have a purplish hue, and the curve corresponding to it in Fig. 21 would have two maxima, one in the red and one in the violet. This would be a more complicated assumption, but not an impossible one. So far as the writer can see, the only other way of determining one of the fundamental colours would be by investigating the colour-blind. To what extent such investigation confirms YOUNG's hypothesis for red at least, will be shown later.

That each of the three chosen fundamental colours of the spectrum stimulates not only the nervous fibres that are designated by the same name as the colour in question but the other fibres also in a less degree, has been already proved by the results of colour mixture, certainly in the case of green. For if we think of all the colour sensations that are composed of the three fundamental colours as being plotted on a plane chart according to NEW-TON's system, it follows from what has been stated above that the colour area must be enclosed in a triangle. This triangle must include within it the colour area shown in Fig. 22 which comprises all colours that are miscible from the colours of the spectrum. It would be possible to do this by shifting the sensation of pure green towards A, as is done in Fig. 22, on the assumption that spectrum red and violet, R and V,

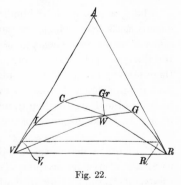

Fig. 22.

are pure fundamental colours. In this case the colour triangle that contains within it all possible colour sensations would be AVR. This assumption, as stated, would satisfy the actual facts of colour mixture. On the other hand, however, certain other facts to be mentioned presently, in connection with colour blindness and the change of hue due to increase of intensity of the light and the phenomena of after-images, render it necessary to assume that neither spectrum red nor violet corresponds to a simple sensation of one fundamental colour, but to a slightly mixed sensation. Accordingly, the positions of spectrum red and violet in the colour triangle Fig. 22 would have to be displaced about to $R_{,}$ and $V_{,}$ and the closed curve $ICYR_{,}V_{,}$ would then embrace all possible colours of objective light.

Thence it follows that there must be a series of colour sensations still more saturated than those which are evoked under ordinary circumstances by objective light, even by that of the spectrum. In Fig. 22 the colours aroused in the normal eye by external light are comprised within the area bounded by the curve and the straight line $V_{,}R_{,}$. The rest of the triangle corresponds to colour sensations that cannot be excited directly by external light. Since these latter sensations are all farther separated from white than the colours of the spectrum, they must be even more saturated than those colours themselves, which are the most saturated objective colours of which we have any knowledge. And, as a matter of fact, when we come to the theory of after-images, produced by fatiguing the eye by the complementary colours, we shall see how to produce colour sensations beside which the colours of the spectrum look pale.

The fact above mentioned, that the different colours of the spectrum do not appear to be all saturated to the same degree, is easily explained by this theory.

The eyes of some individuals are not able to distinguish as many colours as those of ordinary persons. The visual perceptions in cases of *colour blindness* (*achromatopia, achrupsia*) are of particular interest for the theory of colour sensations. A. SEEBECK has demonstrated that there are two classes of colour-blind people. Individuals belonging to each group confuse the same set of colours, and differ from each other merely in the degree of their difficulty. On the other hand, individuals in one class recognize most of the mistakes made by those of the other class.

The most numerous cases, especially in England, appear to belong to SEEBECK's second division. Their trouble is often called *Daltonism* (or *anerythropsia*, by GOETHE), after the celebrated chemist J. DALTON, who himself belonged to this group and was the first to investigate this condition carefully.[1] As some English scientists have protested against this mode of perpetuating the name of their renowned countryman by one of his defects, let us call this condition *red blindness*.[2] Individuals in whom it is completely developed see only two colours in the spectrum, which they usually describe as blue and yellow. They include in the latter all of the red, orange, yellow and green. They call the green-blue hues grey, and the remainder blue. They do not see the extreme red at all when it is faint, but they may do so when it is intense. Thus, they usually put the red end of the spectrum at a place where normal eyes still see distinctly a faint red. In pigments they confuse *red* (that is, vermilion and reddish orange) with *brown* and *green*; whereas to the normal eye in general the confused red hues are much brighter than the brown and green. They cannot distinguish between *golden yellow* and *yellow* or between *pink-red* and *blue*. On the other hand, all mixtures of different colours that appear alike to the normal eye appear alike also to the red-blind. With regard to DALTON's case, Sir J. HERSCHEL[3] has already advanced the opinion, that all colours discriminated by him might be considered as being composed of two fundamental colours instead of three.[4] This view has been recently confirmed by MAXWELL by his method of measuring colours with the mixtures on the colour top. In the case of a healthy eye, as has been shown, a colour match may be formed between any given colour and three suitably chosen fundamental colours, plus white and black. In case of red-blind persons, as the writer himself has verified, only two colours are needed besides white and black (for instance, yellow and blue) to make a colour match on the colour top with any other colour.

In the author's experiments with Mr. M., who was a student in the polytechnic institute, accustomed to physical investigations and fairly sensitive to such differences of colour as he could still recognize at all, chrome yellow and ultramarine were used as principal colours. A mixture on the colour top of 35° of yellow and 325° of black, which was olive-green to an average person, seemed to him identical with a *red* about like that of sealing wax. The experiments indicated that a

[1] According to more modern determinations, SEEBECK's second form of colour blindness, called "green blindness" by HELMHOLTZ, is more frequent, and the only reason why it is more often unnoticed than "red blindness" is because its symptoms are rather less striking. As to new suggestions for designating the forms of colour blindness, see the section on this subject in the appendices at the end of this volume.—N.

[2] ¶Red-blind individuals, as HELMHOLTZ calls them, are termed *protanopes* by v. KRIES, and green-blind *deuteranopes*. (J. P. C. S.)

[3] In a letter quoted in G. WILSON, *On colour Blindness*. Edinburgh 1855. p. 60.

[4] ¶These types of colour blindness have colour systems that are functions of two variables, whereas normal colour vision, as has been stated, is a function of three variables. Thus normal individuals are said to be *trichomats* as distinguished from these abnormal *dichromats*. (J. P. C. S.)

mixture of 327° of yellow and 33° of blue, which looks grey-yellow to the normal eye, was to him the same as *green* of hue about corresponding to the line E in the spectrum. And 165° of yellow mixed with 195° of blue, which ordinarily gives a faint reddish grey, was the same to him as *grey*. As all other hues could be mixed from red, yellow, green, and blue, the result was that, so far as Mr. M. was concerned, they could all be obtained by mixing yellow and blue.

From GRASSMANN's laws of colour mixture, as applied to an eye that confuses red with green, it follows directly that the hues which it does differentiate can all be obtained by mixing two other colours, say, yellow and blue. For if red and green appear to be the same, necessarily all mixtures of these two colours will appear to be the same. Moreover, since colours that look alike produce a mixture that looks like them, every mixture of a given amount of yellow with a given amount of any one of the colours made by mixing red and green, which has the same appearance to a colour-blind person, will give a resultant colour that looks the same to him. But for the healthy eye one of the colours obtained by mixing red and green can be made also by mixing yellow and blue; and hence for the colour-blind eye this colour can be substituted for all combinations of red and green. Consequently, all mixtures of yellow, red and green may be produced also by mixing yellow and blue, so far as the colour-blind eye is concerned; and the same thing may be proved likewise for all mixtures of blue, red and green. And, lastly, since all hues for the healthy eye can be obtained by mixing red, yellow, green and blue, all hues for the colour-blind eye can be obtained by mixing yellow and blue.

If the colours are plotted on a plane chart by the method of constructing the centres of gravity, all such colours as appear to a colour-blind person to be the same at suitable luminosity will be ranged along a straight line, since a mixture of two colours must be on the straight line joining these two points, and the mixture must appear to have the same hue as its components, if the latter look alike. Moreover, it may be proved that all these straight lines intersect in one point (which may be at infinity, in which case they will all be parallel), and that the colour corresponding to this point must be invisible to the colour-blind eye.

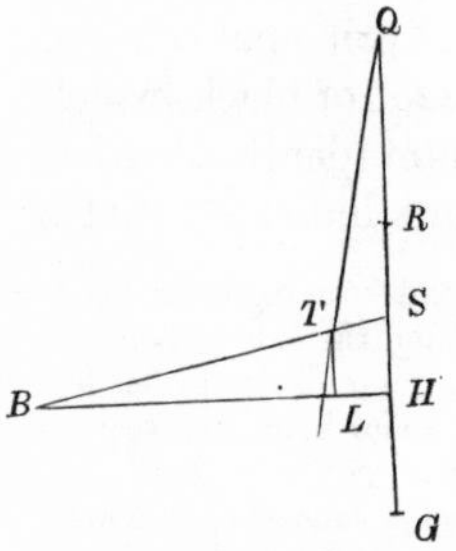

Fig. 23.

To the colour-blind person the quantity r of the colour at R in Fig. 23 appears the same as the quantity g of the colour at G. Now

$$r = nr + (1-n)r.$$

The quantity ng of the colour G looks just like the quantity nr of the colour R. Thus, supposing that n is a proper fraction, the quantity r of the colour R appears the same as the mixture of the quantity $(1-n)r$ of the colour R with the quantity ng of the colour G. In the colour chart this mixed colour will be at the point S in the line RG such that

$$RS : SG = ng : (1-n)r \quad . \quad . \quad . \quad . \quad . \quad . \quad (1)$$

and the quantity of this mixed colour will be

$$s = ng + (1-n)r.$$

So far as the colour-blind eye is concerned, the appearance of this colour will not depend on the value of n.

Suppose now that the quantity b of the colour B is mixed with the quantity s of the colour S; the result will be a mixed colour whose appearance to the colour-blind eye is independent of the variable magnitude n. Let T be the place of this mixed colour in the chart and t its quantity; then

$$t = b + s = b + ng + (1-n)r$$
$$TS : BT = b : s = b : [ng + (1-n)r] \quad . \quad . \quad . \quad . \quad (1a)$$

From B let fall the perpendicular BH on RG and from T the perpendicular TL on BH; and put

$$LH = x \qquad\qquad BH = h$$
$$TL = y \qquad\qquad HG = a$$
$$RG = c$$

Then by (1a):

$$\frac{x}{h} = \frac{LH}{BH} = \frac{TS}{BS} = \frac{b}{b + ng + (1-n)r} \quad . \quad . \quad . \quad . \quad (1b)$$

$$\frac{y}{h-x} = \frac{TL}{BL} = \frac{SH}{BH} = \frac{SG-a}{h} .$$

Since from equation (1)

$$SG = c \cdot \frac{(1-n)r}{ng + (1-n)r},$$

therefore

$$\frac{y}{h-x} = \frac{(c-a)\ (1-n)r - ang}{h[ng + (1-n)r]} \quad . \quad . \quad . \quad . \quad (1c)$$

Eliminating the variable n from (1b) and (1c), we obtain an equation connecting the rectangular coördinates of the point T, as follows:

$$0 = ybh(g-r) - x[crg + br(c-a) + abg] + bh[(c-a)r + ag] \quad . \quad . \quad . \quad (1d)$$

As this is a linear equation between x and y, the locus of the point T is a straight line, and all the mixed colours that lie on this line appear to be the same to the colour-blind eye. Suppose TQ is this straight line meeting the straight line RG in the point designated by Q; then the value of y for $x = 0$ will be $QH = y_0$ as given by the equation

$$y_0 = \frac{(c-a)r + ag}{r-g}. \quad \ldots \quad \ldots \quad \text{(1e)}$$

This value of y_0 is independent of the amount b of the colour that is to be mixed with S; and every straight line that is the locus of points corresponding to colours that all look alike, obtained by mixing the colours R, G and B, will pass through this point $\dot{Q}$; and in case $r = g$, that is, when y_0 becomes infinite, the point Q will be the infinitely distant point of the straight line RG, and the system of lines TQ will be a pencil of parallel lines.

The distance of Q from the point R is

$$y_0 - c + a = \frac{cg}{r-g} = QR. \quad \ldots \quad \ldots \quad \text{(1f)}$$

When an amount q of the colour Q is mixed with the amount g of the colour G so as to make the colour R, then we must have

$$\frac{QR}{RG} = \frac{g}{q}$$

and therefore by equation (1f), since $RG = c$:

$$\frac{g}{r-g} = \frac{g}{q}$$

$$q = r - g .$$

The amount of the mixed colour R in this case is:

$$r = g + q .$$

But by hypothesis r looks the same to the colour-blind eye as g; and since, in general, the amount $q = r - g$ is different from zero, the conclusion is that *the colour-blind eye cannot be sensitive to the colour Q at all.*

The point of intersection of the straight lines that are the loci of points corresponding to colour-mixtures that look alike falls therefore at the place of the colour which is missing in the colour sensations of the colour-blind eye.

On YOUNG's hypothesis this colour that is not visible to the colour-blind person is necessarily one of the fundamental colours; for if there were sensation for all the fundamental colours, no other colour sensation composed simply of these fundamental ones could be lacking.

Now when we try to discover those colours that look like white (or grey), they will be found to be those which for the normal eye are colours of the hue of the missing fundamental colour or of its complementary colour, mixed with white in different proportions. For all these colours that look like white must lie on a straight line. But every straight line drawn through the point on the chart that corresponds to white contains on its two opposite sides colours of the same hue in different degrees of saturation. But the colours on one half of the line are complementary to those on the other half. Every line of this sort containing colours that all look alike must, however, as just proved, pass through the point where the missing fundamental colour is, and, consequently, must contain on one of its two halves colours of the same hue as the fundamental colour. In the experiments which the writer conducted with Mr. M. it was found that the same appearance as pure grey was produced by a red which corresponded very nearly to the extreme red of the spectrum in hue (38° of ultramarine and 322° of vermilion), perhaps leaning a little to the purple side, and by a corresponding complementary blue-green (59° ultramarine and 301° emerald-green). MAXWELL has obtained similar results, namely, 6 percent ultramarine and 94 percent vermilion for the red, and 40 percent ultramarine and 60 percent emerald-green for the green. And, besides, as for normal eyes the red appeared much darker than the grey and green, with equal luminosity, there can be no more doubt that it is red, and not green, that is the missing colour. On YOUNG's hypothesis, therefore, red blindness would be explained as a paralysis of the red-sensitive nerves.

If a red not far from the extreme red of the spectrum is really one of the fundamental colours, the two others cannot be very far anyhow from the green and violet as chosen by YOUNG.

The result of this would be that people who are red-blind are not sensitive except to green and violet and blue, which is a mixture of the first two. The *red* of the spectrum which seems to stimulate the green-sensitive nerves just a little and the violet-sensitive nerves almost not at all, according to this, would have to appear to red-blind persons as a *saturated green of low luminosity*, containing appreciable amounts of the other colours mixed with it. Red of low luminosity which is still adequate to excite the red-sensitive nerves of the normal eye is, on the contrary, no longer adequate to excite the green-sensitive nerves, and therefore this sort of light appears black to red-blind individuals.

The *yellow* of the spectrum will appear as *brilliant saturated green*, and doubtless it is just because it does give the saturated and more luminous shade of this colour that the red-blind select the name of this colour and describe all these peculiar hues of green as being yellow.

Green as compared with yellow begins to show an admixture of the other fundamental colours, being therefore indeed a more luminous but yet a pale shade of green, like that produced by red and yellow. According to SEEBECK's observations, the most luminous part of the spectrum for red-blind individuals is, not in the yellow as for normal vision, but in the green-blue.[1] As a matter of fact, on the assumption that green stimulates the green-sensitive nerves most, as must be the case, the maximum of the total stimulation for red-blind persons will be rather towards the side of the blue, because here the stimulation of the violet-sensitive nerves increases. What a red-blind individual means by white is naturally a mixture of his two fundamental colours in some definite proportion, which looks green-blue to us; and therefore he regards the transitional shades in the spectrum from green to blue as being grey.

Farther on in the spectrum the second fundamental colour, which a red-blind person calls blue, begins to predominate, because although indigo-blue is still rather pale to him, yet by its luminosity it appears to his eye to be a more striking representative of this colour than violet. Such an one can distinguish the difference of appearance between blue and violet. The subject H. who was examined by SEEBECK knew where the boundary came, but explained that he preferred to call violet *dark blue*. Incidentally, the blue hues must look to the red-blind pretty much as they do to normal persons, because with the latter also there is not much admixture here with red.

All these colours of the spectrum must appear to the red-blind to have certain differences, even if they are less marked. Evidently therefore by paying more attention to them and by practice, they may even learn to call very saturated colours by their right names. But for paler colours the distinctions above mentioned must be too much for them, as they cannot get rid of the confusion.

With respect now to the other group of colour-blind persons comprised in SEEBECK's first division, there are not yet sufficient observations to enable us to define their condition perfectly. According to SEEBECK's data, the difference between them and the red-blind is that they have no difficulty in detecting the transition between violet and red, which to all red-blind persons appears blue. On the other hand, they are confused between green, yellow, blue and red. Both classes confound the same hue with green, but individuals of SEEBECK's first class choose a more yellow-green than red-blind persons do. They

[1] In the yellow-green is more correct.—N.

are not insensitive to the farthest red, and the brightest part of the spectrum for them is in the yellow.[1] They also discriminate only two hues in the spectrum, which they call, probably quite correctly, blue and red. Accordingly, it may be conjectured that their difficulty is due to insensitivity of the green-sensitive nerves, but further investigations on this point are desirable.

Besides total insensitivity, of course, also there may occur all kinds of degrees of lowered sensitivity of the nerves of one sort or the other, with a resultant inability of discriminating colours to a greater or less extent. Cases have also been reported by WILSON and TYNDALL where the trouble was not congenital, but appeared suddenly as a result of serious injuries to the head or eye-strain.

So far as examination of colour-blind persons is concerned, naturally extremely little information can be obtained by asking them how they call this or that colour; for these persons are obliged to use the system of names to describe their sensations which has been devised for the sensations of the normal eye, and which therefore is not adapted for their case. It is not only not adapted because it contains the names of too many hues, but because in the series of colours in the spectrum the differences we speak of are differences of hue, but to colour-blind persons these are merely differences of saturation or of luminosity. Whether what they call yellow and blue corresponds to our yellow and blue, is more than doubtful. Hence, their replies to questions about colours are usually hesitating and perplexed, and seem to us muddled and contradictory.

SEEBECK's method of giving colour-blind persons a selection of coloured papers or worsteds with instructions to arrange them according to their similarity is much better, though still far from satisfactory. But the number of colour tests would have to be enormous in order to include the hues that are characteristic of the difficulty, in their precise admixture with white and of the right luminosity, so that it would be possible to formulate the complete equation for the colour-blind eye. But as long as it is merely a question of similarity, it will be hard to tell whether the difference is one of hue, saturation or luminosity. It is simply by accident, therefore, that a few definite results can be obtained.

On the other hand, the colour top as designed by MAXWELL enables us to obtain quickly the requisite data with great accuracy, because it is easy to make a set of colours by mixture that to the colour-blind eye appear to be *absolutely alike*. Here the chief thing denoting the fundamental character of the trouble is to ascertain

[1] A little towards the orange, about at wave-length $600\mu\mu$.—N.

what two colours are confused with pure grey as obtained on the colour top by mixing white and black. One of them, which in this case appears comparatively much darker to the colour-blind eye than it does to the normal eye, is the missing fundamental colour. At the same time it will be easy too to discover whether there is still some trace of sensitivity for the missing fundamental colour, or not.

To test the theories here propounded, it will be necessary besides to determine whether every given colour, and especially the principal colours of the spectrum, can be compounded for the colour-blind by mixing two suitably selected colours.

G. WILSON has directed particular attention to the danger for navigation and railways that might be caused by not being able to detect coloured signals on account of colour blindness. He found on the average one colour-blind person in every 17.7 individuals.

Lastly, one other thing must be mentioned: colours cannot be distinguished by the eye unless they occupy a certain extent of field, and unless a certain amount of coloured light comes to the eye. The farther the coloured field lies towards the borders of the visual field and of the retina, the larger it has to be for its colour to be recognized. If the coloured field is too small, it will look grey or black on a brighter background, and grey or white on a darker background. Yet it is possible also to recognize the colours of infinitely small fields, in case the amount of light emitted is finite. For example, the colours of the fixed stars may be distinguished. According to AUBERT's experiments,[1] a blue square and a red square, each one millimetre along the side, looked black on a white background at distances of 10 and 20 feet, respectively. A yellow and a green square fused completely into the white background at a distance of 12 feet. On the other hand, when the background was black, the green and yellow squares looked like grey points 16 feet away, and the red square looked the same way 12 feet away. Blue looked blue when it was seen at all.

According to the same observer, the colour of coloured squares disappears at a distance of 200 mm on the average, for the following angular distances from the visual axis:

	Red				Blue			
Side of square..........	1.	2.	4.	8.	1.	2.	4.	8.
White ground..........	16°	19°	26°	37°	15°	22°	36°	49°
Black ground..........	30	32	42	53	36	48	54	72
Average..............	23	26	34	45	26	35	45	61

[1] *Archiv für Ophthalmologie.* Bd. III. Abt. II. S. 60.

	Yellow				Green			
	1.	2.	4.	8.	1.	2.	4.	8.
Side of square..........	21°	31°	44°		20°	36°	44°	50°
White ground..........	30	32	49	47°	24	27	35	45
Black ground..........	26	32	42		22	32	40	47
Average...............								

Before the colours quite disappear, they undergo a change of hue similar to that produced by increasing their intensity. Thus, red and green become distinctly yellow, blue seems to pass directly into grey-white, and in the purple mixtures of blue and red, blue predominates on the edges of the field of view. PURKINJE had found that purple looked blue on the farthest edges of the field, and became violet as it was moved more into the field until it finally took its own colour. To the author pink likewise looks bluish or violet-white on the borders of the field. The last mentioned effect is most noticeable with mixtures of pairs of colours. For instance, if by the method to be described farther on a small coloured field is illuminated by simple red and green-blue so that it looks white in direct (foveal) vision, seen indirectly even a slight distance from the point of fixation, it looks green-blue. From these experiments it appears that the peripheral parts of the retina are more sensitive to blue and green than to red. To a certain extent, it approaches there the state of red blindness.

Here also may be mentioned OPPEL's experiment,[1] in which he found that an orange-yellow spot on a blue ground viewed from a distance looks brighter than the background, whereas viewed close by, where the blue extended more towards the borders of the visual field, it looks darker.

Besides YOUNG's colour theory, reference should be made to certain theories of colour mixture based directly on the undulatory theory of light. Attempts in this direction have been made by CHALLIS and GRAILICH. The latter in particular has tried to develop this in a very laborious work. He investigates the compound vibratory movements of the aether particles resulting from two trains of waves of different wave-lengths, and computes the intervals of time during which the particles are on one side or the other of their positions of equilibrium. These intervals are, in general, different in the case of a compound vibration, whereas for a simple colour they are equal. Now GRAILICH assumes that every displacement of the aether particles on one side of their positions of equilibrium produces the same colour impression as would be produced by that simple colour for which the displacement

[1] *Jahresbericht des Frankfurter Vereins.* 1823–1854. S. 44–49.

from the position of equilibrium lasts just as long. Thus, on his assumption, the compound wave motion stimulates different colour impressions in the eye in rapid succession which are combined into a single sensation; and, as a rule, this sensation is paler in colour in proportion as the number of different successive sensations is greater. The impression of white itself should be composed of the rapidly alternating impressions of the middle hues of the spectrum from yellowish green to orange. In the case of the compound waves there are vibration-frequencies also that are outside the range of the visible spectrum; and so GRAILICH assumes that they produce the impression of purple.

GRAILICH's calculations are based on the intensity-ratios of the colours of the spectrum of the flint glass prism as measured by FRAUN-HOGER; and if GRAILICH's last two assumptions are admitted, his results are in agreement with the writer's experiments with the v-shaped slit on mixing the colours of the spectrum. However, it should be added that in these experiments the luminosity of the colours of the spectrum was by no means maintained unchanged, but that in most cases what was attempted was to produce those mixed colours that are equally far apart from their two primaries.

Now in those cases where the amplitudes of the two colours are different, the result cannot be determined in advance by a general theory; and all that can be done is to calculate it for certain numerical examples, as GRAILICH did. In each special case then the calculation gives a series of different colour impressions which have to succeed one another; and by following GRAILICH's principles, the nature of the total impression may be estimated by them, but only in a pretty vague way. Bad for this theory, however, in the writer's opinion, is the fact, that when the two trains of waves are supposed to have equal amplitudes, in which case the mathematical theory may be actually worked out, the agreement with experiences is very far wrong, as GRAILICH himself admitted. Let $\lambda_{,}$ denote the wave-length of one train of waves and $\lambda_{,,}$ that of the other; and let x denote the distance of any point measured along the ray; then the displacement s of the aether particle from its position of equilibrium at any given instant will be:

$$s = A\sin\left(\frac{2\pi}{\lambda_{,}}x + c_{,}\right) + A\sin\left(\frac{2\pi}{\lambda_{,,}}x + c_{,,}\right)$$

$$= 2A\cos\left[\pi x\left(\frac{1}{\lambda_{,}} - \frac{1}{\lambda_{,,}}\right) + \frac{c_{,} - c_{,,}}{2}\right]\sin\left[\pi x\left(\frac{1}{\lambda_{,}} + \frac{1}{\lambda_{,,}}\right) + \frac{c_{,} - c_{,,}}{2}\right]$$

This expression may be abbreviated by making the following substitutions:

$$\frac{2}{l_{,}} = \frac{1}{\lambda_{,}} - \frac{1}{\lambda_{,,}} \qquad\qquad 2\gamma_{,} = \varsigma_{,} - c_{,,}$$

$$\frac{2}{l_{,,}} = \frac{1}{\lambda_{,}} + \frac{1}{\lambda_{,,}} \qquad\qquad 2\gamma_{,,} = c_{,} + c_{,,}$$

Thus we obtain:

$$s = 2A \cos\left(\frac{2\pi x}{l_{,}} + \gamma_{,}\right) \sin\left(\frac{2\pi x}{l_{,,}} + \gamma_{,,}\right).$$

The distances of the points for which $s = 0$ are easy to find in this case. Thus the points for which the factor $\sin\left(\dfrac{2\pi x}{l_{,,}} + \gamma_{,,}\right)$ vanishes are at intervals apart equal to $\frac{1}{2}l_{,,}$; and those for which the cosine function vanishes are at much greater intervals apart, namely, $l_{,}$. These latter points may be in between the others or they may coincide with them. In the latter instance, particularly, we should get by GRAILICH's theory genuinely equal wave-lengths in the compound motion which would all produce the same colour impression; and even if the zero-points of the two factors did not fall together, the less frequent ones of the cosine factor could not essentially disturb the impression due to the shorter waves of the sine factor. But by GRAILICH's own calculation the result of this is that violet and red would have to give green, although as a matter of fact they make purple-red. And on the whole the results for small differences of wave-length are in accordance with experience, but for large differences the discrepancies are considerable, since the value of $l_{,}$ must always come between $\lambda_{,}$ and $\lambda_{,,}$ and must correspond to one of the middle hues of the spectrum. In the writer's opinion, therefore, the assumptions in GRAILICH's theory will have to be considerably modified yet before it can be made to agree with the facts of experience, supposing the attempt is made to explain things in this fashion.

The easiest way to mix simple colours of the prismatic spectrum, and at the same time to get all combinations of pairs of these colours, is to use a v-shaped slit like that shown in Fig. 24, which is inserted in a dark screen with its two arms *ab* and *bc* inclined at 45° on both sides of the vertical. This slit placed in front of a bright background is viewed through a prism with its refracting edge vertical. Thus, two spectra will be obtained, partly superposed, as represented in Fig. 25 where $a\beta\beta_{,}a_{,}$ is the spectrum from the slit *ab* and $\gamma\beta\beta_{,}\gamma_{,}$ is that from *bc*. The bands of colour in the first are parallel to *ab* and *aβ*, and in the second parallel to *bc* and *βγ*, as shown by the dotted lines. In the central triangular field $\beta\delta\beta_{,}$, common to both spectra, all the coloured bands of one spectrum intersect all the coloured bands of the other spectrum, and thus at these places all mixtures are produced of all the pairs of simple

colours. If the widths of the slits cannot be altered, the relative amounts of
the mixture can be varied by inclining the prism and thereby causing the

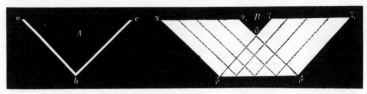

Fig. 24.   Fig. 25.

spectra to have the forms shown in Fig. 26. The spectrum $\beta\gamma\beta,\gamma,$ in which
the same amount of light is distributed over a smaller area becomes brighter,
while the other spectrum whose area is increased gets dimmer.

Most of the results mentioned above can be found by this method. But
it is difficult to form accurate judgments of the mixtures, particularly the
paler ones, first, because
the single colours take
up too much room, even
when a telescope is used,
and, second, because a
number of other bril-
liant colours are near by
in the field of view, and
the contrast effects al-
ter the appearance of
the less saturated col-
ours.

These disadvantages

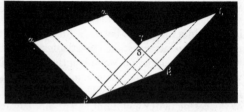

Fig. 26.

are avoided by another method, which requires a more complicated apparatus,
as shown in plan in Fig. 27. Sunlight is reflected by a heliostat through a
vertical slit into a dark room. The beam of light is made to pass through a
prism P and an achromatic lens $L_{,}$. In the focal plane of this lens there is a
screen $S_{,}$, on the front side of which an objective spectrum is projected.
Between lens and screen there is a rectangular diaphragm D. There are two
vertical slits in the screen $\gamma,$ and $\gamma_{,,}$ which let through two coloured bands of

Fig. 27.

the light that is converged here in the spectrum; while all the other coloured
light is retained on the screen. Beyond the screen there is another achromatic
lens $L_{,,}$ of shorter focus, which projects on a second screen $S_{,,}$ an image $\delta,\delta_{,,}$
of the diaphragm D. The width of the incident beam of white light is $a,a_{,,}$.
Beyond the lens $L_{,}$ the outside rays of the two bundles of coloured rays whose
focal points are at the two slits $\gamma,$ and $\gamma_{,,}$ are shown by dashed lines for the
more refrangible light, and by dotted lines for the less refrangible. The opening
in the diaphragm D must be made so narrow that it is completely filled by
rays of both bundles, so that from every point in the aperture rays of the
given colour go to every point in the slits $\gamma,$ and $\gamma_{,,}$. If the anterior side of the

diaphragm is painted white, the beam of light will be projected on it as a white spot with coloured edges (blue at $\epsilon_{,}$ and red at $\epsilon_{,,}$.) To fulfil the required condition, the opening in the diaphragm must be wholly in the white centre of the illuminated place. Under these circumstances, the opening is, so to speak, the luminous object which sends two kinds of light through the slits in the screen $S_{,}$ to the lens $L_{,,}$. Light of both kinds will thus be uniformly distributed over the image $\delta_{,}\delta_{,,}$ of the diaphragm projected by the lens on the farther screen; and hence this area will be coloured by a mixture of the two kinds of light. By screening off one of the slits, the image can be made to show up in one of the two simple colours that are to be mixed.

To enable the investigator to vary the hue and intensity of the mixture very gradually, just as he chooses, a special construction of the screen $S_{,}$ will be needed, as depicted in detail in Fig. 28. The screen itself is a rectangular brass plate $AABB$ supported at C by a cylindrical rod, which is fitted in an upright split tube D. This tube is mounted on a baseboard or tripod with three leveling screws. The screen can be raised or lowered by its holder C and clamped at any conven-

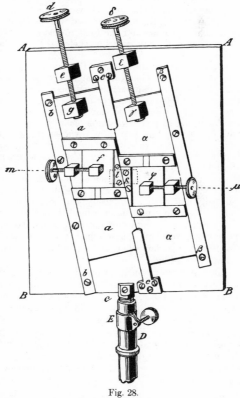

Fig. 28.

ient height by means of the collar and thumb-screw at E. The brass plate $AABB$ carries two bed-plates aa and $\alpha\alpha$ that can be displaced on it in a diagonal direction between the guides bb, $\beta\beta$, c and c, by means of the thumb-screws d and δ, which work in nuts e and ϵ that are fastened to the plate $AABB$. The ends of these screws turn in the blocks g and γ which are attached to the sliders aa and $\alpha\alpha$. The slider $\alpha\alpha$ in its turn carries another slider f that can be adjusted between a pair of parallel guides by means of the screw m; and likewise the slider aa carries another slider φ which is adjusted in the same fashion by means of the screw μ. Between the parallel edges of the plates f and φ that are nearest to each other there are also the two small triangular pieces l and λ, the former being fastened to $\alpha\alpha$ and the latter to aa. The adjacent parallel knife-edges of f and l and of φ and λ form two pairs of Gravesande slits (cf. Fig. 11).

A corresponding portion of the large plate $AABB$ behind the slits is removed in order to let the light pass through them and go on its way. The front sides of f, l, φ and λ are tarnished with a rough surface of silver to receive the projection of the spectrum. The position of the spectrum is indicated by the little dotted rectangle.

By shifting the plates aa and $\alpha\alpha$ by means of the screws d and δ, the slits can be transferred to other places in the spectrum to let light of other hues go through them. The widths of the slits themselves can be adjusted by the screws m and μ so as to regulate the amounts of the transmitted portions of light.

The main thing is that the focus of rays of a given colour, after they have traversed the lens $L_{,}$, shall be exactly in the plane of the screen $S_{,}$; otherwise, the colour-field on the screen $S_{,,}$ will show different hues from right to left. The slits must be parallel to the dark lines in the spectrum, which can be accomplished by means of the leveling screws in the base-board of the screen. Moreover, both lens and prism must be carefully cleansed of any spots that might make patches in the colour-field. NEWTON's rings may easily be formed between the two parts of the achromatic double lens $L_{,}$ and be projected on the colour-field; but this can be prevented by using Canada balsam between the two components of the lens. However, the farther the diaphragm D is away from the lens $L_{,,}$, the more confused will be the image of spots and imperfections in the glasses, and the less troublesome they will be. Therefore, the disposition of the apparatus as sketched here is better than that which the writer has described elsewhere.

In this method the extent of the field is larger than it was in the first one, and all the other colours that might give trouble by contrast effects are removed. However, in numerous instances there are still a number of handicaps that make it hard to form a calm, sure judgment of the mixed colour. In the first place, the colour dispersion of the eye itself is much more noticeable for combinations of just two simple colours that are far apart than it is with white light (see Vol. I, p. 175). And so the margin of the colour-field may easily show one of the two simple colours while the other one predominates in the centre. Then with some white mixtures, particularly in the case of white made from red and green-blue, the eye is extraordinarily sensitive to the smallest admixtures of one of the original colours; so that the slightest irregularities in the apparatus, or possibly after-images that may be in the eye, especially with higher luminosity, can be very disconcerting. In this connection, also, differences of impression between the central and peripheral parts of the retina are very pronounced. Comparatively speaking, it is easiest to make white with yellow and indigo, harder to make it with yellow-green and violet or with golden yellow and water-blue, and hardest of all to make it with red and green-blue.

The way the writer determined the wave-lengths of the pairs of complementary simple colours was by removing the lens $L_{,,}$ and the screen $S_{,,}$ and using a telescope to see the slit in the screen $S_{,}$ at some distance away. A glass plate with fine, equidistant vertical lines ruled on it was inserted in front of the object-glass. Then diffraction-spectra of the slits will be seen; their apparent distances from the corresponding slits being proportional to the wave-lengths. Therefore, all that is necessary is to measure in the same way the distances of the diffraction-spectra for one of the dark lines in the spectrum, for which the wave-length has been found by FRAUNHOFER, in order to calculate immediately the wave-lengths of the two mixed colours concerned.

The simplest way of mixing the coloured light of pigments and other natural bodies is as follows. At some distance (1 foot) above a black table-top, adjust a small plane-parallel plate of glass a in a vertical plane

which meets the top of the table in a point designated by d in Fig. 29. An observer looking obliquely downwards through the glass plate will see a portion of the table on the far side of d by means of light that is transmitted through the plate to his eye; and
at the same time he will see another
portion of the table on the other side of
d by means of light that is reflected from
the plate into his eye. The two fields
are thus apparently coincident. Suppose
now that two coloured wafers are placed
at b and c at equal distances on opposite
sides of d; then the reflected image of c
will coincide with b. The coloured light
from c is reflected from the anterior side
of the glass plate along exactly the same
path to the eye that is pursued by the

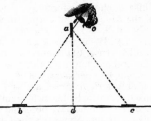

Fig. 29.

coloured light from b, so that the two kinds of light are mixed in the eye at o; and therefore the common image of b and c which the eye gets must be seen in the mixed colour. The relative intensity can be regulated by shifting the two wafers; the closer they are to d, the more intense will be the reflected light that comes from c and the less intense will be the transmitted light that comes from b.

In this way too light may be used for mixing that has been filtered through coloured glasses or liquids. Apertures can be made in the table-top bc to let the light pass for this purpose. Thus, also, the light of the blue sky reflected by a mirror can be mixed with that of chrome-yellow and proved to give a reddish white like that obtained by mixing ultramarine and chrome-yellow; showing that sky-blue, therefore, is a pale indigo-blue and is not the same as the less refrangible so-called cyan-blue in the spectrum.

This last method is preferable in one respect to the method of mixing colours on the colour top, because the pale mixtures we get in this way are not grey but white. The colour top will be described more in detail in §22. Among other methods of mixing coloured light, an experiment of VOLKMANN'S, in which he looked at coloured surfaces through coloured fabrics held close to his eye, deserves to be mentioned. However, it is hard to get a very uniform mixture of the two colours in this way, and the transparency of the fibres themselves is a difficulty, because to some extent it is like looking at a coloured surface through a coloured glass. CZERMAK adapted SCHEINER'S experiment by looking through two stenopaic openings in a screen which were covered by glasses of different colours. As long as the objects were seen single, they appeared also in the mixed colour. HOLTZMANN caused light that was diffusely reflected from two pieces of coloured paper to fall on a sheet of white paper. CHALLIS mentions some experiments, which incidentally had already been tried by MILE; in which papers with bands of different colours painted on them were observed from such a distance that the bands could no longer be separately recognized. Lastly, DOVE has described methods of mixing colours produced by interference and absorption. He used silvered mirrors made of coloured glasses. The anterior surface of a mirror of this kind gives polarised white light, while the posterior surface gives unpolarised light coloured by absorption. When the light thus mixed is passed through a mica plate and a NICOL prism, the latter kind remains unchanged. But the polarised white light is so coloured by interference in the crystal between the ordinary ray and the extraordinary ray that it corresponds to one of the shades of colour in NEWTON'S coloured rings. The two kinds of light are mixed when they enter the observer's eye.

The theory of colour-mixture originated from the experience of painters in mixing pigments. PLINY tells us that the ancient Greek painters knew how to prepare all colours with four pigments, although in his day, when there were many more materials available, it was not possible to get as many different effects as formerly. And even in the celebrated fresco, The marriage of the Aldobrandini, dating from Roman times, the profusion of pigments is very small, as DAVY's chemical investigations showed. (See GILBERT's *Ann.* LII. 1.) Besides black and white, which, however, are not colours in the peculiar sense, LEONARDO DA VINCI names four simple colours, yellow, green, blue and red; but in another place he speaks also of orange (*lionato*) and violet (*morello, cioè pavonazzo*) as being needed in painting. It is curious that he invariably reckons green as being a simple colour, knowing that it could be mixed; because by his own definition simple colours were such as could not be mixed. Could he have observed that unmixed green is much more vivid than mixed? Before NEWTON's time the three fundamental colours were commonly assumed to be red, yellow and blue. This is mentioned by WALLER, in an attempt at classifying colours and pigments, as being at that time a generally accepted scientific fact. The fact that three fundamental colours were found to be sufficient implies already the discernment of the truth that the character of a colour is a function of only three variables. Experiences with mixed pigments exercised the most decisive influence on the choice of the fundamental colours, which not until long afterwards WÜNSCH and YOUNG tried to change. It was supposed that green could be made from yellow and blue. This is true with respect to pigments, but not for coloured light.

NEWTON was the first to mix the light of different colours in the prismatic spectrum; but in conjunction with this method he used mixtures of coloured powders to get the law of colour-mixture, and did not attach much importance to the differences between the two processes, although he seems to have perceived them to some extent. He did not have the experimental facilities for tracing the facts more accurately. He states that only a pale green can be obtained from *subflavum* and *cyaneum* (that is, from greenish yellow and cyan-blue). NEWTON was the first too to formulate a more exact expression of the law of colour mixture, as it was he who traced it back to the graphical method and centroid-constructions that have been explained above. His law tallied with the available experimental data, and he did not try any more exact test. His colour circle was a development of the system of three objective fundamental colours; but as to the insufficiency of the latter system he has not anywhere expressed any opinion.

On the other hand, most of the later physicists, in their efforts to arrange the system of colours, returned to the notion of three fundamental colours; for example, LE BLOND (1735), DU FAY (1737), TOBIAS MAYER (1758), J. H. LAMBERT (1772), D. R. HAY and J. D. FORBES. Usually, their colour-systems were carried out practically by mixing given pigments in given proportions by weight. MAYER used vermilion, royal yellow (lead chromate) and mountain-blue (cobalt glass); and LAMBERT used carmine, gamboge, and Prussian blue (iron ferri-ferrocyanide). The latter also determined the saturation-ratios of these pigments, by finding the weights in which they had to be mixed in pairs to produce a mixed colour which was equally far from the colours of its two constituents. He found it was necessary to take 1 part of carmine, 3 parts of Prussian blue and 10 parts of gamboge. He chose these weights then as units for making the mixtures. Incidentally, mixtures of pigments so far apart from one another always turn out to be rather unattractive and grey.

Later observations, which, in circumstances where mixing of coloured light was to be expected, gave results that differed from the previous rule, were made by PLATEAU in 1829 with the colour top and by VOLKMANN in

1838 on blurred images; without leading, however, to a closer investigation of the discrepancy. The author's own experiments on mixing the colours of the spectrum resulted in his finding out that a mixture of light and a mixture of pigments were two different things; and he tried to find the reason for it. In these experiments the colours of the spectrum were mixed by means of the v-shaped slit, and white was not obtained from any other pair of colours except yellow and indigo-blue. This contradicted NEWTON's law of mixtures and led GRASSMANN to make a more minute examination of the principles of this law. The writer's improved method of investigating the mixtures 'of the colours of the spectrum removed the apparent contradiction of NEWTON's rule so far as it related to the centre-of-gravity construction; but on the other hand, in spite of GRASSMANN's arguments, the circular form of the colour-field was left as a question that was still debatable. Finally, the principles of NEWTON's law of mixture were experimentally confirmed by MAXWELL in 1857.

YOUNG's theory of the colour sensations, like so much else that this marvellous investigator achieved in advance of his time, remained unnoticed, until the author himself and MAXWELL again directed attention to it. It is sufficient to assume that the optic nerve is capable of sensations of different kinds, without trying to find out why the system of these visual sensations is just what it is.

1519. LEONARDO DA VINCI, *Trattato della pittura.* Paris 1651.

1686. R. WALLER, A catalogue of simple and mixte colours. *Phil. Trans.* 1686.

1704 *NEWTON,,*Optice.* Lib. 1. P. II. Prop. IV–VI. '

1735. LE BLOND. *Il Coloritto.* London.

1737. DU FAY, *Mém. de l'Acad. roy. de Paris* 1737.

1758. T. MAYER in *Göttinger gelehrte Anz.* 1758. St. 147.

1772. J. H. LAMBERT, *Beschreibung einer Farbenpyramide.* Berlin.

1792. WÜNSCH, Versuche und Beobachtungen über die Farben des Lichts. GILBERTS *Ann.* XXXIV. 10.

1807. TH. YOUNG, *Lectures on natural philosophy.* London.

1829. PLATEAU, *Dissert. sur quelques propriétés des impressions produites par la lumière sur l'organe de la vue.* Lüttich.

1836. CHALLIS in POGGENDORFFs *Ann.* XXXVII. 528.

1838. VOLKMANN in J. MÜLLERS *Archiv für Anat. und Physiol.* 1838. S. 373.

1839. MILE, Ibid., 1839. S. 64.

D. R. HAY, *Nomenclature of colours.*

1843. J. MÜLLER, Zusammensetzung des weissen Lichts aus den verschiedenen Farben. POGGENDORFFS *Ann.* LVIII. 358, 518.

1847. DOVE, Über die Methoden aus Komplementärfarben Weiss darzustellen, und über die Erscheinungen, welche polarisiertes Licht zeigt, dessen Polarisationsebene gedreht wird. *Berliner Monatsber.* 1846. S. 70; POGGENDORFFs *Ann.* LXXI. 97; *Phil. Mag.* XXX. 465; *Inst.* Nr. 712. p. 176; *Arch. d. sc. ph. et nat.* V. 276.

CHEVREUL, Exposé d'un moyen de définir et nommer les couleurs d'après une méthode rationelle et expérimentale. *Quesneville revue scient.* XXIX. 382.—*C. R.* XXXII. 693.—*Inst.* No. 906. p. 155.—*Dingl. polyt. J.* CXXI. 367.—*Athen.* 1851. p. 272.

1848. BRÜCKE, Über das Wesen der braunen Farbe. POGGENDORFFS *Ann.* LXXIV. 461.— *Phil. Mag.* XXXIII. 281.—*Inst.* No. 785. p. 21.

HARLESS, *Physiologische Beobachtung und Experiment.* Nürnberg 1848. S. 45. (One colour seen through the other.)

CHR. DOPPLER. *Versuch einer systematischen Klassifikation der Farben.* Prag 1848, from *Abhandl. der böhm. Ges.* V. 401.

1849. J. D. FORBES, Hints towards a classification of colours. *Phil. Mag.* XXXIV. 161.

1852. *H. HELMHOLTZ, Über die Theorie der zusammengesetzten Farben. MÜLLERS *Archiv für Anat. und Physiol.* 1852. S. 461–482.—POGGENDORFFS *Ann.* LXXXVII. 45-66.— *Phil. Mag.* (4) IV. 519–534.—*Cosmos.* II.112–120.—*Ann. de chim.* (3) XXXVI. 500– 508.—FECHNER, *Zentralblatt* 1853. pp. 3–9.

1853. L. FOUCAULT, Sur la récomposition des couleurs du spectre en teintes plates. *Cosmos.* II.232.—POGGENDORFFS *Ann.* LXXXVIII. 385–387.

*H. GRASSMANN, Zur Theorie der Farbenmischung. POGGENDORFFS *Ann.* LXXXIX. 69–84.—*Phil. Mag.* (4) VII. 254–264.

HOLTZMANN, Apparat zur Darstellung von Farbenmischungen. *Tagblatt der deutschen Naturforscherversammlung* 1853.

J. PLATEAU, Reklamation. POGGENDORFFS *Ann.* LXXXVIII. 172–173—*Cosmos.* II. 241.

FECHNER, *Zentralblatt.* 1853. p. 365.

H. HELMHOLTZ, On the mixture of homogeneous colours. *Athen.* 1853. pp. 1197,1198— *Cosmos.* III.573–575.—*Rep. of Brit. Assoc.* 1853.2.p.5.—POGGENDORFFS *Ann.* XCIV. 1–28.—*Ann. de chim.* (3) XLIV. 70–74.—*Arch. d. sc. phys.* XXIX. 242.

1854. J. GRAILICH, Beitrag zur Theorie der gemischten Farben. *Wiener Ber.* XII. 783–847. —XIII. 201–284.

J. CZERMAK, Physiologische Studien. *Wien. Ber.* XII. 322. §6 and XVII. 565.

1855. *J. C. MAXWELL, Experiments on colour, perceived by the eye, with remarks on colour blindness. *Edinb. Trans.* XXI. 275–297.—*Edinb. Journ.* (2) I. 359–260.—*Proc. of Edinb. Soc.* III. 299–301.—*Phil. Mag.* (4) XIV. 40.

G. WILSON, Observations on Mr. MAXWELL's paper. *Edinb. J.* (2) I. 361.

J. D. FORBES, Observations on Mr. MAXWELL's paper. *Edinb. J.* (2) I. 362.

1856. J. C. MAXWELL, On the theory of compound colours with reference to mixtures of blue and yellow light. *Athen.* 1856. p. 1093.—*Edinb. J.* (2) IV. 335–337.—*Inst.* 1856. p. 444.—*Rep. of British Assoc.* 1856. 2. p. 12–13.

CHALLIS, On theory of the composition of colours on the hypothesis of undulations. *Phil. Mag.* (4) XII. 329–638 and 521.

G. G. STOKES, Remarks on CHALLIS's paper. *Phil. Mag.* (4) XII. 421.

1857. DOVE, Eine Methode Interferenz- und Absorptionsfarben zu mischen. *Berl. Monatsber.* March 11, 1857.—POGGENDORFFS *Ann.* CII.

Colour Blindness

HUDDART, *Phil. Trans.* LXVII. I. 14.

COLLARDO, *Journ. de Physique.* XII. 86.

WHISSON, *Phil. Trans.* LXVIII. II. 611. *Journ. de Phys.* XII.

GIROS V. GENTILLY, Theorie der Farben (published in English and French under the pseudonym G. PALMER). LICHTENBERG *Mag.* I. 2. 57.

HARVEY, *Edinb. Phil. Trans.* X. 253. *Edinb. J. of Sc.* VII. 85.

J. BUTTERS, *Edinb. Phil. Journ.* XI. 135.—*Archiv für Physiol.* v. MECKEL. V. 260. NICHOLL, *Medico chir. Trans.* VII. 477. IX. 359.—*Ann. of Phil.* N. S. III. 128. v. GOETHE, *Zur Naturwiss. und Morphologie.* 1. Heft. 297. *Zur Farbenlehre.* 1. §103. MECKEL, *Archiv für Physiol.* I. 188.—*Ann. of philos.* 1822. Feb. p. 128.

WARDROP, *Essays on the morbid anatomy of the human eye.* London 1818. II. 196. MECKEL, *Archiv für Physiol.* V.

BREWSTER, *Edinb. Journ. of Sc.* VII. 86.XIX. 153.—*Edinb. phil. J.* VI.—POGGENDORFFS *Ann.* XXIII. 441.

J. HERSCHEL, Art. Light in *Encyclop. metrop.* p. 434. §507.

COLQUHOUN from *Glasgow Med. Journ.* in FRORIEPS *Notizen.* XXIV. 305.

J. DALTON, *Memoirs of Lit. and Phil. Soc. of Manchester.* V.—*Edinb. Journ. of Sc.* IX. 97.

SOMMER in GRAEFE und WALTHER *Journal für Chirurgie.* V.

Salzburger mediz. chirurg. Zeitung. IV.

GALL, *Anat. et Physiologie du système nerveux.* IV. 98.

REZIER, *Observ. sur la physique.* XIII.

BREWSTER, *Briefe über natürl. Magie.* German translation, S. 44.

HELLING, *Prakt. Handbuch der Augenkrankheiten.* I. S. 1.

1837. *A. SEEBECK, Über den bei manchen Personen vorkommenden Mangel an Farbensinn. POGGENDORFFS *Ann.* XLII. 177–233.

1849. WARTMANN, *Bull. de Brux.* XVI. 1. 137—*Inst.* XVII. No. 799. p. 131.

   D'HOMBRE FIRMAS. *C. R.* XXIX. 175.XXX. 60, 376.—*Inst.* No. 815. p. 259

1852. SCHNETZLER, *Arch. d. sciences phys.* XXI. 251–252.

   BURCKHARDT, *Verh. der naturf. Gesellsch. in Basel.* X. 90–93.

1854. WILSON, *Proc. of Edinb. Soc.* III. 226–227.

   EICHMANN in FECHNER *Zentralblatt* 1854. pp. 294–295.—*Med. Z. S. des Ver. f. Heilkunde in Preussen.* 1853. 224.

1853–55. G. WILSON in *Monthly J. of med. science.* Nov. 1853 to Dec. 1854. *Edinb. Journ.* (2) IV. 322–327.

   Idem, *Researches on Colour-Blindness.* Edinb. 1855. Here also MAXWELL, *On the Theory of Colours in relation to Colour-Blindness.* p. 153.

1856. W. POLE, *Proc. of Roy. Soc.* VIII. 172–177.—*Phil. Mag.* (4) XIII. 282–286.

   J. TYNDALL, *Phil. Mag.* (4) XI. 329–333.—SILLIMAN *J.*(2) XXII. 143–146.—*Arch. d. sc. phys.* XXXIII. 221–225.

Supplement by HELMHOLTZ, *from the first edition*

J. C. MAXWELL carried out an important series of experiments on mixture of spectral colours, for the purpose of determining the hues of the three fundamental colours and the form of the three intensity-curves, Fig. 21, which in YOUNG's theory express the intensity of the separate fundamental colours for each place in the spectrum. In his method white light was admitted in a dark box through three slits whose width and position could be altered. The light then traversed a couple of prisms and was focused on a screen by a lens, where consequently three partially overlapping spectra were produced. A slit in this screen permitted a mixed colour to proceed through it to the observer's eye. Looking through the slit, the observer saw the surface of the lens uniformly covered by the given mixed colour. The same white light was admitted through another section of the box, but in this case it did not pass through a prism. A mirror of black glass was adjusted so as to reflect this white light also to the observer's eye, so that he would see it as a white field right by the lens. His problem was to vary the adjustments and widths of the three slits which were responsible for the light resolved by the prisms until the mixture of the three prismatic colours gave a perfect match with the white light reflected by the mirror.

Subsequently, MAXWELL gave the apparatus a more convenient form by causing the light after it had passed through the prisms to be reflected back through them by a concave mirror. Thus the whole contrivance can be made shorter, and the observer can sit so close to the slit that he can adjust it himself, which is a great advantage.

The fundamental colours selected by MAXWELL were: (1) a *red* between the FRAUNHOFER lines *C* and *D*, twice as far from *D* as from *C*; according to our previous colour notations, this would be a scarlet-red tending to orange; (2) a *green* near the line *E*; and (3) a *blue* between *F* and *G*, twice as far from *G* as *F*, about where cyan-blue changes to indigo-blue.

In one set of observations, from time to time white was made again with these three colours, the required widths of the slits being noted, so as to verify in this way the unchanged mixture of the normal white light. The amounts of light necessary for this were measured by the widths of the slits. Between these tests white was made by mixing each pair of fundamental colours with some arbitrary third colour, the place of this third colour in the spectrum, along with the widths of the three slits, being noted on a scale placed near them.

If the white remained sufficiently constant, a set of colour-equations was obtained in this way, by which, the positions of the chosen three fundamental colours on a colour-chart being arbitrarily taken, the corresponding places of the observed colours of the spectrum could be found. Thus, by actual experiments, the form of the curve in Fig. 22 was obtained, which, as there represented, is simply a rough estimate. The curves traced by MAXWELL and his assistant enclose the perimeter of the triangle *ARV* very much more nearly than is the case in Fig. 22, two portions of the curve being almost straight. Its most marked bendings appear, therefore, to be nearest the vertices of the complete colour-triangle about corresponding with the aforesaid three fundamental colours. But the results obtained by one of the observers made the blue fall more towards the end of the spectrum, whereas those of the other observer made the red fall more towards the end. But it was precisely in case of the faint extreme colours of the spectrum that observation was difficult. Another difference between MAXWELL's projections and Fig. 22 is that the colour curve with its two ends in the red and violet appears to lie along the third side of the triangle.

On page 129 the writer stated as the result of actual experiments that the mixture of two colours of the spectrum is invariably rather paler than the simple colour in the spectrum that comes nearest to it in hue; but MAXWELL's result does not entirely agree with this. If the above were correct, it would mean that the colour curve cannot have straight portions anywhere; for colours lying on a straight line can be obtained by mutual mixtures with one another. The explanation of the contradiction between MAXWELL's results and those of the writer may be that the relative change of hue is necessarily greatest right at the borders of the colour triangle; hence, although the convexity of the sides of the triangle (which is not definitely shown to exist in MAXWELL's more indirect method of investigation) may be very slight, so that there is very little difference between the chord and the arc, still the colours that lie along the chord may be appreciably different in appearance from those on the arc.

Moreover, from the results of his experiments MAXWELL calculated the amounts of the three fundamental colours chosen by him that were present in the individual colours of the spectrum; and by these data he constructed curves corresponding to the schematic curves shown in Fig. 21. His curves have rather sharper peaks than those, and the red curve ascends again at the violet end of the spectrum, and the blue curve ascends a little at the red end.

Experiments like MAXWELL's should be made to see whether it is possible actually to make perfectly pure spectrum yellow from yellowish green and golden yellow, perfectly pure spectrum violet from the extreme red and indigo-blue, etc.; so as to determine still more directly from these results the contour of the spectrum colour chart. Incidentally, the mixtures of the spectrum colours that gave white were not precisely the same as found by MAXWELL and his assistant. Each insisted that what was white for the other was not exactly white for him. Also, the curve of brightness, as obtained by MAXWELL himself, showed more of a drop in the region of the F line than the other observer found. MAXWELL thinks it probable that this was due to different degrees of pigmentation of the yellow spot, as the yellow pigment (see §25) seems to absorb especially the light of the line F. Hence, white mixtures that contain this particular kind of blue, do not look white any longer even in indirect vision; as the writer himself had likewise previously noticed. (See p. 160.)

Thus, for different individuals the spectral lights have to traverse layers of yellow substance of different degrees of intensity in order to get to the central parts of the retina, and hence the effect must be different in different cases. This explains why the colour triangles for two different persons show variations in the distribution of colours such as would occur when the units of luminosity of the three fundamental colours were varied. These units, by the way, are determined arbitrarily. Thus in MAXWELL's eye the red effect was comparatively greater and the blue comparatively weaker than in the other observer's eye.

SCHELSKE finds also that the colour sensations produced by steady *currents of electricity* may be compounded with objective colours, and that the results are similar. The ascending current admixes a bluish violet light with the externally visible colours, whereas the descending current removes some of this colour from them. In fact, colour matches can be made with two colour discs, whose images are formed on two halves of the retina that are traversed by a current in opposite directions.

The *red blindness* in the periphery of the visual field, mentioned on page 154, has been studied more closely by SCHELSKE. He made colour matches for the peripheral parts of the retina between a yellow-blue mixture and red or grey or green. The colours of the spectrum in indirect vision were such that the region of the F line looked almost white, and the violet dark blue, while the intermediate portion appeared blue. On the other side of the F line, the appearance was green, until for the farthest red it was very faint and colourless or greyish.

Numerous observers have confirmed the fact that all colours that can be discriminated by a colour-blind eye may be compounded out of two fundamental colours. However, these experiments have not as yet established more definitely which one of the fundamental colours is missing, because experiments with coloured discs at different times and with different individuals give quite variable results. Sometimes change of the external illumination or light reflected from coloured objects or from the walls of the room may have much to do with the matter, as not only MAXWELL but E. ROSE also has noted. The pigmentation of the yellow spot caused too just the same sorts of differences in colour-blind persons as were found by MAXWELL in healthy eyes. This absorption in the yellow pigment does not alter simply the luminosity of the colours on the painted colour disc, but it alters their combinations also. Thus, assuming that the positions of the two real fundamental colours and of black are fixed in the colour triangle, the colours on the disc will have different positions depending on the intensity of the pigmentation of the eye. But if definite positions in the triangle are assigned to three of the pigment colours considered as being fundamental colours, then, conversely, the real fundamental colours and black will be found to have different positions for different individuals. Variations of this kind in the position of black have been observed by E. ROSE in colour-blind persons even when the tests were all made at the same time and under the same external conditions in every respect. He inferred therefore that YOUNG's theory could not be correct. But the supposed contradictions admit of simple explanation on the basis of the given conditions. ROSE himself states that constant matches could not be obtained unless the colour-blind persons always fixed the same place on the colour disc; the colour match being different for many of them every time the fixation-point was changed. This shows the difference in the colour sensation produced by the pigmentation of different parts of the same retina.

Cases of incomplete colour blindness also occur, as described by Mr. GLADSTONE and as found also by Mr. HIRSCHMANN in the author's laboratory in the case of a student. In this instance the admixture of quite large amounts of red in a colour was not noticed; although beyond a certain limit it was perceived. Leaving this out of account and considering such an eye as being totally red-blind, we cannot expect that its colour matches will agree exactly with the theoretical requirements.

E. Rose's experiments made by daylight located the black point near that of scarlet-red more towards its bluer side; which agrees with Maxwell's result and that of the writer's. But in most of Rose's observations with artificial illumination he used a kerosene oil lamp, which is rather unfortunate perhaps, because this light is comparatively poor in blue rays, especially when the flame varies owing to variations of the supply of air. Now as colour-blind folks lack the red sensation, and as the amount of blue in the flame itself is very slight and variable, this being true also with respect to the more refrangible blue which is particularly liable to absorption in the pigment of the yellow spot, the result is that with this illumination green must be by far the most predominant colour for red-blind persons; and hence it is not surprising that under these circumstances the colour matches made by different colour-blind observers even in the same evening were not very concordant. In every case the position of black in the colour triangle was located between blue and red, but, being dependent on the feebleness of the blue, it was nearer the position of blue than it was with daylight illumination.

E. Rose's experiments, therefore, are quite inadequate to shake the validity of Young's theory.

Some of the methods which this same observer used for investigating colour blindness deserve to be mentioned. In the first place, interference spectra were produced by ruling fine parallel lines on a plate of glass through which the patient looked at an illuminated slit. The series of spectra on each side of the slit that are obtained in this way are quite familiar. But the first of these spectra is the only one that is entirely isolated from the others, and the red of the second begins to overlap the violet of the third. The red end of the spectrum is shortened for colour-blind persons, and so they see the second spectrum too as separate from the third. However, naturally much will depend here on the intensity of illumination of the slit. But for a preliminary idea of the peculiarity of an eye under examination this procedure appears to be quite useful.

In the second place, instead of using the colour top, which takes much time and patience to adjust properly, E. Rose hit on the happy idea of employing the colours of quartz plates with polarised light. The instrument, called a colorimeter, consists of the following parts arranged in order in a tube: A Nicol prism A, a rectangular slit B, a double refracting prism C, a quartz plate D 5 mm thick, and a second Nicol's prism E; then the eye of the observer. The latter sees two images of the slit B, projected close together by the double refracting prism C. In consequence of the rotation of the plane of polarisation by the quartz plate, the two images are exactly complementary in colour, and their colours may be altered by turning the Nicol prism A. Without changing the composition of the colours, their luminosity may be varied by turning the other Nicol prism E. This prism is needed to make both images equally bright. With a quartz plate of the given thickness, a normal eye cannot get any colour match, but a red-blind eye may do so. The colours that are found to match in this case are red and blue-green; but even here different red-blind persons make somewhat different matches. By using thicker plates of quartz or a set of several plates all rotating the plane of polarisation the same way, and adding also a plate of variable thickness composed of two prisms, as employed in Soleil's saccharimeter, the apparatus can be used also for making colour matches with the normal eye, as one white can be made from red, green and violet and another white from yellow and blue. But even with this arrangement, as was to be expected from Maxwell's experiments, a difference was found to exist between Dr. Hirschmann's eye and the writer's eye, neither of which was colour-blind.

Incidentally, by using santonin a healthy eye may be made temporarily blind to violet. From 10 to 20 grains[1] of *sodium santoninate* is about right to get quick action that does not persist too long. The change begins in 10 or 15 minutes and lasts several hours. It is accompanied by nausea, great lassitude and visual hallucinations, so that there are attendant hardships in this experiment. Animals are killed by larger doses. Persons under the influence of santonin see bright objects as green-yellow, whereas dark surfaces appear to be covered with violet. The violet end of the spectrum disappears. Their colour system is dichromatic or at least approximately so. Experiments made with the quartz plate indicated that for moderate intensity of illumination colour matches could be made by such persons with only two fundamental colours, but not when the intensity of illumination was higher. But the matches that were obtained did not last long, and the condition varied continuously in a quite noticeable manner. Yellow and violet compound colours were declared to be alike. The disc of the optic nerve, as viewed by the ophthalmoscope, was not

[1] A grain = 0.06 g.—N.

coloured yellow, and hence there was at least no appreciable yellow stain present in the ocular media. On the other hand, the blood-vessels of the retina were much gorged.

Interpreting these phenomena on the assumptions of YOUNG's colour theory, we should infer that the inherent sensibility of the violet-sensitive nerve-fibres has not been lost, but that the terminal organs (cones of the retina) have become insensitive to the action of violet light. Thus violet and blue light ceased to affect the eye, notwithstanding all darker objects appeared to be violet; which was evidently due to internal causes of stimulation. It reminds one of the green appearance of all dark surfaces when a red glass is held close up to the eyes. It is hard to tell whether there is just the ordinary degree of internal retinal stimulation in the santonin poisoning or a higher degree of it. Indeed, it is a question whether it is not simply here a matter of stimulation of the violet-sensitive fibres by the santonin, which lowers the sensitivity of the eye to objective violet light by fatiguing it, and thus produces an incomplete violet blindness.

The change in the objective colours may be considered on the whole as violet blindness. Whether the fluctuations of judgment as observed by E. ROSE both with colour discs and with polarisation-colours of quartz are due to the variable injection of blood in the retinal vessels, which might act to some extent like a coloured absorbing medium, cannot yet be decided from the experiments.

Here also, just as in the case of persons who are naturally colourblind, it is possible to suppose that the power of the nerve-fibres to function has not been abolished, but that the form of the intensity curves (Fig. 21) for the three kinds of light-sensitive elements has been changed; in which case there might be then a much greater variability in the appearance of objective colours to the eye. In favour of this idea, it may be mentioned that in santonin poisoning, as was noticed several times by E. ROSE, red and yellow light were seen, but taken for violet, as if the cones of the violet-sensitive fibres had become similar to those of the red-sensitive fibres in their reaction to light. On the other hand, according to HIRSCHMANN's observations, it appears sufficient to explain this phenomenon by the diffusion of subjective violet light over the whole field of view, which is one of the effects of santonin.

1858. DE MARTINI, Effets produits sur la vision par la santonine. *C. R.* XLVII, 259–260.

—   A. V. BAUMGARTNER, Ein Fall ungleichzeitiger Wiederkehr für verschiedene Farben. *Wiener Ber.* XXIX. 257–258.

—   G. WILSON, A note on the statistics of colour blindness. *Year book of facts.* 1858. pp. 138–139.

1859. J. F. HERSCHEL, Remarks on colour blindness. *Proc. of R. Soc.* X. 72–84.—*Phil. Mag.* (4) XIX. 148–158.

— W. POLE, On colour blindness. *Phil. Trans.* CXLIX. 323–339.—*Ann. de chimie.* (3) LXIII. 243–256.

— T. L. PHIPSON, Action de la santonine sur la vue. *C. R.* XLVIII. 593–594.

— LeFÈVRE, Action de la santonine. Ibid. 448.

— E. ROSE, Über die Wirkung der wesentlichen Bestandteile der Wurmblüten. VIRCHOWS *Arch.* XVI. 233–253.

1860. J. J. OPPEL, Einige Beobachtungen und Versuche über partielle Farbenblindheit. *Jahresber. d. Frankfurter Vereins.* 1859–1860. S. 70–114.

— GLADSTONE, On his own perception of colour. *Athen.* 1860. II. 24.—*Rep. of Brit. Assoc.* 1860. (2) pp. 12–13.

— E. ROSE, Über die Farbenblindheit durch Genuss der Santonsäure. VIRCHOWS *Archiv.* XIX. 522–536. XX. 245–290.

— A. DE MARTINI, Sur la coloration de la vue et de l'urine produite par la santonine. *C. R.* L. 544–545.—*Inst.* 1860. pp. 108–109.

— GUÉPIN, Note sur l'action de la santonine sur la vue et son action thérapeutique. *C. R.* LI. 794–795.

— J. C. MAXWELL, On the theory of compound colours and the relations of the colours in the spectrum. *Proc. Roy. Soc.* X. 404–409; 484–486.—*Phil. Trans* CL. 57–84.—*Phil. Mag.* (4) XXI. 141–146.—*Cimento* XII. 33–37.—*Rep. of Brit. Assoc.* 1860. (2) p. 16.

1861. J. J. OPPEL, Nachträgliche Bemerkungen zu dem vorjährigen Aufsatze über Farbenblindheit. *Jahresber. d. Frankf. Vereins.* 1860-1861. S. 42-47.

— J. Z. LAURENCE, Some observations on the sensibility of the eye to colour. *Phil. Mag.* (4) XXII 220–226.

— E. ROSE, Über stehende Farbentäuschungen. *Archiv. für Ophthalm.* VII. (2) 72–108.

1862. J. J. OPPEL, Zur Veranschaulichung der Achromatopsie für nicht damit Behaftete. *Jahresber. d. Frankf. Vereins.* 1861–1862. S. 48–55.

1863. R. SCHELSKE, Über Farbenempfindungen. *Archiv für Ophthalm.* IX. 3. S. 39–62.

— E. ROSE, Über die Halluzinationen im Santonrausch. VIRCHOWS *Archiv.* XXVIII.

1864. AUBERT, *Physiologie der Netzhaut.* Breslau. S. 154–186.

1865. SCHELSKE, Über Rotblindheit infolge pathologischen Prozesses. *Archiv. für Ophthalm.* XI (1) 171–178.

— C. BOHN, Über das Farbensehen und die Theorie der Mischfarben. POGGENDORFFS *Ann.* CXXV. 87–118. (Attempt at a theory similar to that of GRAILICH.)

1866. E. BRÜCKE, *Die Physiologie der Farben für die Zwecke der Kunstgewerbe.* Leipzig.

§21. On the Intensity of the Light Sensation

The intensity of the objective light itself is measured by the kinetic energy of the aether vibrations; which for monochromatic simple polarised light is proportional to the square of the maximum velocity of the particles. When the light comes from different sources or is polarised in different planes, the total intensity is equal to the sum of the separate intensities.

We shall inquire, first, how the intensity of the light sensation is affected by changes in intensity of the objective light, without any change of colour. These relations may be studied with white light. The behaviour of pure coloured light in this respect is in no wise different.

The first thing is to show that the smallest perceptible gradations of the light sense do not correspond to equal changes of objective

luminosity. Let the luminosity of a white surface illuminated by a dim
light be denoted by h. Now interpose an opaque body that casts a
shadow on the surface so that the parts of it in the shadow do not get
any light from the source. Then add a second light which by itself
would produce the luminosity H; which may be varied by varying the
distance between the surface and the second light. Then the objective
luminosity in the shadow is H, and outside the shadow it is $(H+h)$.

Now if the luminosity H is very low, the eye will detect the shadow,
that is, it will distinguish between the luminosity H and the luminosity
$(H+h)$. But no matter how great h may be, it appears that there is
always a higher luminosity H for which the shadow is invisible; for
which, therefore, the difference h in the objective luminosity no longer
produces any perceptible increase of sensation.

A light equivalent to moonlight makes a perceptible shadow on
white paper; but if a good lamp is brought near the paper, the shadow
disappears. Again, the shadow made by the lamplight disappears in
sunlight. Indeed, the luminosity of the surface of the flame of a bright
oil-burner with a circular wick can hardly be distinguished by the
eye from double the luminosity. A flame of this sort is transparent
enough to show this, as may be easily seen by looking at its faint image
reflected in a plate of glass, and then shoving a second flame behind the
first. The outlines of the latter can be quite distinctly recognized.
But if both flames are viewed by the naked eye, the farther one will not
be seen through the other, at least not through its brightest part;
unless, perhaps, the intensity of the sensation gets blunted by looking
at the lights too long. It is just as hard to tell by the naked eye that
the edge of the flame as seen lengthwise through the glowing film of
gas is very much brighter than the middle where the film is least deep;
but it is easy to see this by looking at the image of the flame reflected
in a plate of glass. The same explanation applies also to the disappearance of the stars in the daytime, and to the disappearance of images in
a glass plate when it reflects other light, etc.

So far the difference of luminosity has been kept constant while the
absolute value of the total luminosity has been varied; but we may
also let the difference increase in the same proportion as the luminosity.
Suppose a drawing is made on a transparent plate of glass in very dilute
black india ink; or suppose the plate is covered with a thin film of
lampblack and lines drawn on it; or, best of all, suppose we have a
photograph made on transparent glass, with soft shadows in some
places and deep ones in others. If a diagram of this sort is held against
a bright background of steadily increasing luminosity, the soft shadows
will be found to be invisible when the luminosity is low; and then as
the luminosity gradually increases, they will begin to be seen and con-

tinue at about the same degree of distinctness for quite a time, until finally they begin to disappear again. The deeper the shadow in the picture, the less is the luminosity that is needed to make it show up, and the higher it must be to make it disappear. Now the difference between the luminosity of the bright portions and that of the shaded portions is a definite fraction of the total luminosity. If the luminosity of the bright portions is denoted by H, the luminosity of the shaded portions may be put equal to $(1-a)H$, where for a given place on the drawing a denotes a constant proper fraction. Thus the difference of luminosity between the part of the drawing under consideration and the bright background, which is equal to aH, increases or decreases along with the luminosity H. Therefore, notwithstanding that with increasing luminosity the differences of absolute luminosity between the various shaded parts of the drawing become greater, there are no longer perceptible differences of sensation corresponding to the variations of the light itself. Hence there must be certain medium degrees of intensity of illumination for which the eye is most sensitive to a small percentage variation of the total luminosity. These are the degrees of illumination ordinarily used in reading, writing and working that are convenient and agreeable to the eye; ranging, therefore, from about that luminosity at which reading is feasible without difficulty to that of a white surface illuminated by direct sunlight. Within these limits of luminosity where the sensitivity for fractional differences reaches its maximum, the degree of sensitivity is also nearly constant; as is characteristic in general of the gradual mode of variation of a continuous function in the neighbourhood of its maximum value. This is apparent even in ordinary observation of such objects as paintings and drawings, where there are numerous gradations of shadows. They are about as easy to discern by candlelight as in broad daylight; so that usually nothing new in the way of objects and nuances is revealed in the picture by bright illumination that was not visible before when the illumination was dim. Thus, FECHNER remarked that when bright objects like the sky and sunlit clouds are viewed through dark grey glasses, none of the gradations of shadow disappear that were visible before, nor do new ones make their appearance. More accurate photometrical measurements confirm these observations. In general, such measurements indicate that for very different degrees of luminosity the difference of luminosity that can just be made out is nearly the same fraction of the total luminosity. The way that BOUGUER and FECHNER tried to find out the amount of this difference was by illuminating a white screen by two equal candles, so that when a rod was placed between the screen and the candles there were two shadows of it on the screen. Then one of the lights was moved away from the screen until the shadow it made ceased to be visible. Suppose the distance of the nearer candle from the screen is denoted by a, and that of the farther candle by b; then the intensities of illumination of the screen due to the candles are about in the ratio $a^2 : b^2$. BOUGUER found that one of the lights had to be about 8 times farther than the other for the shadow to vanish. FECHNER, aided by VOLKMANN and other observers, found that the distance of one of the candles was about 10 times farther than that of the other. Thus, BOUGUER could just discern a difference amounting to 1/64 of the total luminosity, whereas FECHNER's associates discerned a difference of 1/100. ARAGO noticed that when movement was also involved even finer differences could be recognized; and under the most favourable conditions he obtained the value 1/131 for this fraction. MASSON's experiments were made with rotating white discs with small black sectors; and he found that when the vision was poor, sometimes a difference of not more than 1/50 was the best that could be recognized, but that when the vision was good, the fraction might occasionally be even less than 1/120. Another thing he discovered was that the limit of sensitivity for instantaneous illumination by electric sparks was fairly independent of the luminosity. Indeed, with this illumination, if it were sufficient, the black and white sectors were visible for an instant. Suppose the rotating disc is steadily illuminated by a lamp of brightness L, and then also by an electric spark of brightness l; then for an instant on the white sectors the luminosity is $(L+l)$, whereas on the black sectors it is only L; so that the sectors can just be recognized provided $(L+l)$ can be distinguished from L. When the distances of the two sources of light from the disc were altered, L and l had to be altered in the same proportion in order to keep at the limit of the sensitivity of the eye. Consequently, the same law holds for the ability of perceiving instantaneous difference of light as in the case of constant light.

The fact that within a wide range of luminosity the smallest perceptible differences of the light sensation correspond to (nearly) constant fractions of the luminosity, was used by FECHNER in formulating a more general, so-called *psycho-physical* law, which is found to be true also in other regions of the sensations. Thus, for example, differences of pitch seem to us to be equal when the difference between the vibration-numbers is a certain fraction of the vibration-number itself. According to E. H. WEBER's investigations, the case is similar also with our ability to recognize differences between weights and linear magnitudes.[1] Now as pitch is measured by the logarithm of the

---

[1] ¶"The next great step in the advance of our knowledge of the relationships subsisting between physical stimuli and sensations was made by E. H. WEBER, the founder of modern psycho-physical methods. In general terms it may be stated that a stimulus must attain

vibration-number, it is natural to measure the intensity of sensation in the same way; since here also, just as in the other case, differences dE of intensity of sensation E that can be perceived equally distinctly may be considered as being equal in amount. Accordingly, therefore, within a wide range of luminosity H, we have approximately

$$dE = A\frac{dH}{H} ,$$

where A denotes a constant. By integration, we obtain:

$$E = A \log H + C ,$$

where C is the constant of integration.[1] If e denotes the intensity of the sensation corresponding to a certain luminosity h, then

$$E - e = A \log \frac{H}{h} .$$

This mode of estimating brightness by the eye has been shown by FECHNER to have had a definite influence in the determination of the magnitudes of the stars. The orders of magnitude of the stars were determined at first by the impressions they made on the human eye, without photometrical measurements of the objective quantities of light emitted by them. Such measurements were not made until recent times, but now we are in a position to compare the actual brightness of a star with its supposed order of magnitude. With the aid of the photometrical determinations of J. HERSCHEL and STEINHEIL, FECH-NER made a comparison of this sort; the result being that the order of magnitude (G) for HERSCHEL's measurements is given by the formula

$$G = 1 - 2.8540 \log H ,$$

a certain intensity in order to excite a sensation and that stimuli of greater intensity excite stronger sensations. There is therefore a quantitative relation between the stimulus and the sensation. The minimum effectual intensity of stimulus is called the *general threshold* or *the general liminal value*. A higher value may arouse a sensation differing in quantity from the other; this value is called the *specific threshold* or the *specific liminal* value. Thus a coloured light of low intensity may excite a colourless sensation; when of higher intensity it may excite a sensation of colour." J. H. PARSONS, *An introduction to the study of colour vision.* 1915. page 19. (J. P. C. S.)

[1] ¶"FECHNER's law states that the *sensation varies as the logarithm of the stimulus*; i. e. the sensation changes in arithmetical proportion as the stimulus increases in geometrical proportion." It is a "questionable assumption that it is permissible to integrate small *finite* quantities," such as are involved here. PARSONS (*loc. cit.*, p. 20), commenting on this law, says: "The bases are insecure on mathematical as well as on physiological grounds. So far as the latter are concerned we have no unit of sensation, and the variations, though quantitative, are only relative. The chief difficulty, however, is to be found in the ever-changing condition of the sensory apparatus. The deductions are not without value, for *some* quantitative relationship certainly exists, even if it be not so simple as FECHNER's law implies." (J. P. C. S.)

and for STEINHEIL's measurements by the formula

$$G = 2.3114 - 2.3168 \log H .$$

Both formulae are in agreement with those given above, since the orders of stellar magnitudes are higher for the fainter stars. The formulae also agree well enough with the results of observation. FECHNER found too that STRUVE's measurements harmonized sufficiently well with his law. Incidentally, the same law was found by BABINET,[1] who, according to observations of JOHNSON and POGSON, gives 2.5 for the value of the coefficient of $\log H$ in FECHNER's formula.

FECHNER thinks that the effect of disturbing circumstances accounts for the fact that the law proposed here for the intensity of the sensation is not obeyed either at very low or at very high luminosities. For example, at very low luminosities the influence of the intrinsic light of the eye must make itself felt. Together with the stimulation due to external light, there is always besides a stimulation due to internal causes, the amount of which may be considered as being equivalent to the stimulation by a light of luminosity H_0. It would be more accurate, therefore, to write the formula for the least perceptible degrees of the intensity of the sensation as follows:

$$dE = A \frac{dH}{H + H_0}$$

or

$$dH = \frac{1}{A}(H + H_0)dE .$$

This implies that the increment of luminosity must be rather more in order for it to be perceptible than it would be if H_0 were neglected; and particularly when the values of H are small, the difference will become considerable. FECHNER devised a method of comparing the intensity of the intrinsic light H_0 with that of the objective light, which is based on this formula; but this method unquestionably takes for granted that at the so-called threshold of the light sensation there is nothing else to invalidate the law above mentioned but this intrinsic light of the eye. Suppose an eye that is able to detect a change of luminosity of one percent views a surface, part of which gets no external light at all, while another part is illuminated, and has a luminosity denoted by h; then, taking into account the intrinsic light, the apparent luminosity of the unilluminated portion is H_0, and that of the illuminated portion is (H_0+h). Now if h is the least perceptible luminosity, then, by FECHNER's method of reasoning, we must have $h = \frac{1}{100}H_0$; and thus the brightness

[1] *Comptes rendus.* 1857. p. 358.

H_0 of the intrinsic light would be measured ⌐in terms of an objective light. VOLKMANN made some experiments and found that the intensity of the intrinsic light H_0 was equal to the luminosity of a black velvet surface illuminated by a tallow candle at a distance of 9 feet.

The discrepancy between the law and the facts for the upper limits of luminosity may be attributed to the fact that the visual organ begins to be impaired, as FECHNER supposes. The internal changes in the nerves that have to communicate the impression of the stimulus to the brain cannot exceed a certain definite limit without destroying the organ; and hence every action of the stimulus has an upper limit set for it, to which must necessarily correspond also a maximum intensity of sensation.

But, moreover, whatever may be the circumstances that tend to upset the validity of FECHNER'S law at the upper and lower limits of luminosity, the same conditions make their influence felt in accurate measurements even with medium degrees of luminosity; although, of course, that is no reason why the law should not still be regarded as being a first approximation to the truth. Unquestionably, most paintings, drawings and photographs of ordinary objects can be seen equally well under very different degrees of illumination. And yet in some photographs the writer has discovered gradations of shade which do not come out perfectly clear except for a very definite intensity of light. This is particularly noticeable in pictures of landscapes in which far distant chains of mountains are represented as half floating in cloud. But, so far as the writer is concerned, the most striking instance of this peculiarity was in the case of some stereoscopic views of Alpine scenery photographed on glass, which showed parts of glaciers or peaks covered with snow. By lamplight or moderately bright daylight such

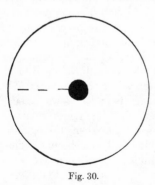

Fig. 30.

surfaces of snow look like uniformly white areas; but when they are turned towards the bright sky delicate shades appear, indicating a sort of moulding of the white fields of snow; and then they disappear again with still brighter light. Of course, delicate shades of this kind are found in photographs simply by accident; and in paintings and drawings they are unexpected. But the rotating disc affords an easy way of producing very delicate shades, of any desired luminosity as compared with the white background. MASSON also has already made use of them for photometrical experiments. These shades are easy to get by making a

pattern on the disc like that shown in Fig. 30.   A broken line is made
with a pen along one or two radii, the parts being all of the same
thickness.   When the disc is set spinning, these black marks make
grey circles on the disc.   Suppose d denotes the width of the mark, and
r denotes the distance of a point on it from the centre; then if the
luminosity of the disc itself is taken as unity, the luminosity h of the
grey ring produced by rotating the disc will be

$$h = 1 - \frac{d}{2r\pi} . \qquad \cdot$$

Thus the greater r is, the less the grey rings will differ in luminosity
from that of the disc.   The inner rings are darker and the outer ones
brighter, and so we get a series of very delicate gradations.   In the
experiment all that has to be done is to see how far the edges of the
grey rings can still be discerned.   They can be seen better by looking
here and there at different places on a circle than by looking steadily
at one place.   When the gaze is fixed on one spot, the fainter circles
disappear quickly, even if they have been seen before.   Usually,
however, the differences are not all equally apparent at first sight,
and it is necessary, to gaze at the disc a long time at first.   Incidentally,
the disc must be made to turn fast enough for the grey rings to be
continuous in appearance, and not to flicker.   In the latter case even the
fainter rings can be discerned, because, every time a black mark goes
by, the impression it makes lasts too short a time for the darkening to
be appreciated.   On bright summer days near a window, it was possible
for the writer by shifting his gaze still to see one edge sharply where
the difference of luminosity was $\frac{1}{133}$.   Another edge could be vaguely
seen where the difference was $\frac{1}{150}$, and for a single instant one for
which the difference was $\frac{1}{167}$.   Up to $\frac{1}{150}$ with the disc illuminated by
direct sunlight, the perceptions were rather more troublesome and
fatiguing.   In the interior of the room at the same time, the writer could
not detect edges for which the difference was less than $\frac{1}{117}$, although
occasionally and uncertainly he could go as far as $\frac{1}{133}$.

Thus here, too, a certain narrowly limited range of luminosity is
indicated as being required in order to get the greatest sensitiveness of
perception.   Accordingly, in the equation

$$dE = A\frac{dH}{H}$$

the coefficient A should not be considered as absolutely invariable, not
even within the ordinary range of illumination; but it must rather be
regarded as dependent on H, although for medium degrees of illumina-

tion it is nearly constant. Likewise the formula derived from it by integration

$$E = A \log H + C$$

will be only approximately correct for medium values of the luminosity. In comparing the intensity of sensation for different colours, it will be still more apparent that a formula of this kind cannot be sufficient.

Even when the intrinsic light of the eye is taken into account and the equations are written as follows:

$$dE = A\frac{dH}{H + H_0}$$

$$E = A \log(H + H_0) + C ,$$

the formula does not quite fit the facts, because it implies that the sensitivity would have to increase as long as the luminosity increased; whereas the facts stated above indicate that the intensity of the sensation gets to be a maximum value which is not exceeded even when H continues still to increase. Therefore for this value, $\frac{dE}{dH}$ must vanish. Hence, also in the last differential equation we should have to consider A as still being a function of H, which for moderate values of H is approximately constant, but which vanishes when H gets to be infinite. The simplest function of this sort would be

$$A = \frac{a}{b + H} ,$$

where b must be supposed to be very great. If, therefore, we put

$$dE = \frac{a\,dH}{(b + H)\,(H_0 + H)} ,$$

then

$$E = \frac{a}{b - H_0} \log \frac{H_0 + H}{b + H} + C .$$

The phenomena might, perhaps, be completely expressed by some such formula as this. The magnitude denoted here by C would be the maximum intensity of sensation corresponding to an infinitely great value of H, and the maximum of sensitivity would occur for $H = \sqrt{b\,H_0}$.

The connection between the intensity of the sensation and the luminosity which has thus been shown to exist explains a fact which the writer has often noticed, namely, that on dark nights bright objects are much brighter as compared with their environment than they are in daytime, so that sometimes it is hard not to believe they are self-luminous. When the luminosity is very low, the intensity of the sensation is considered as being proportional to the luminosity; whereas with greater illumination the sensation for brighter objects is relatively weaker. Now since we are accustomed to compare the brightness of familiar objects when they are highly illuminated, under feeble illumination bright objects are relatively too bright, and dark ones relatively too dark. Painters also make use of this circumstance in moonlight scenes, to produce the impression of faint illumination. They bring out the light places much more brilliantly than when they are representing daylight.

Let us turn now to the comparison of the intensities of light of different colours. If the intensity of objective monochromatic light of different kinds is supposed to be measured by the kinetic energy of the aether-vibrations, then, according to the general law of the conservation of energy, it must be proportional to the amount of heat developed by absorption of the light in question. Hitherto this has been the only available physical method of comparing the intensities of aether-waves of different frequency. When the luminous power of aether-waves of different frequency is estimated by the eye, the result, as has been explained in §19, is that the intensity of the light sensation is by no means proportional to the kinetic energy of these aether-vibrations as measured by the development of heat. When a spectrum is projected by a prism of rock salt, which of all substances is most uniformly transparent to different kinds of rays, the maximum thermal effect, as found by MELLONI, was in the infra-red where the eye is no longer sensitive to light at all; and the thermal effect in the spectrum rises steadily from the violet to the red, whereas the maximum luminous effect is in the yellow. Likewise, attention has already been called to the fact that the luminous power of ultra-violet light is extraordinarily augmented by transforming it by fluorescence into light of medium refrangibility; although it is not to be supposed that the kinetic energy is increased by this process. Thus, *the intensity of the light sensation depends not only on the kinetic energy of the aether-vibrations, but also on their vibration-frequency.* The consequence is that all comparisons of the intensities of compound light of different kinds that are made entirely by the eye have no objective value apart from the nature of the eye.

We have seen that for a given kind of light the sensation does not increase in the same ratio as the objective intensity of the light, but that the intensity of the sensation is a more complicated function of the intensity of the light. But on comparing light of different colours, it appears that *the intensity of the sensation for different kinds of light is a different function of the intensity of the light.* PURKINJE[1] has already noticed that blue was visible for the weakest light and red only at higher illumination. Subsequently, DOVE called attention to the fact that in comparing the luminosities of surfaces painted in various colours for different degrees of illumination, sometimes one was brighter and sometimes another. As a rule, the less refrangible red and yellow colours predominate when the illumination is high, and the more refrangible blue and violet colours when it is low. If pieces of red and blue paper appear equally bright by day, then with the approach of night the blue gets bright while the red often looks perfectly black. So also in picture galleries towards evening (supposing the sky is cloudy and twilight disappearing) the red colours are the first to fade away, and the blue ones continue visible longest. And on the darkest nights, when all other colours are gone, the blue of the sky can still be seen.[2] If the apparatus described in the preceding section, as sketched in Fig. 27, is used for mixing the colours of the spectrum, and if a vertical rod is held in front of the field illuminated by the two colours, it casts two differently coloured shadows. Since the two coloured lights fall on the illuminated field from different directions, proceeding from the two slits in the last screen (S_ι, Fig. 27), they cast their shadows at different places. Thus, if, say, violet and yellow were mixed, there would be one shadow which would not be illuminated by violet but would be illuminated by yellow, so that it would look yellow; and there would be another shadow which would not be illuminated by yellow but would be illuminated by blue, so that it would look blue; whereas the rest of the field would be white or whitish. Now if the slit in the screen which lets the violet through is made wider, the violet becomes stronger, and the violet shadow therefore is more luminous. By regulating the two slits properly, the violet shadow can be made to look just as bright as the yellow one. Now if the single slit in the first screen, through which the light reflected from the heliostat passes to the prism, is opened more or closed more, the total amount of light that goes through the apparatus will be increased or diminished, all the different colours in the same proportion; and hence the amounts of light in the yellow and violet

---

[1] *Zur Physiologie der Sinne.* II. 109. With respect to this, see the notes in the Appendix I. I. B., 1–5.—N.

[2] ¶The explanation of these phenomena is to be found in the difference between "cone vision" and "rod vision." In darkness the colour sensation disappears entirely and all that remains is a pure luminosity sensation. As evening descends all colours begin to fade and disappear and in moonlight even bright red tile-roofs cannot be distinguished as to colour. (J.P.C.S.)

shadows will be changed in equal fashion also. The result is that even a slight increase of light will make the yellow come out brighter, and a slight decrease will make the violet look fainter. The difference here will be much less when the two colours are both in the less refrangible half of the spectrum, and much more when both colours are from the more refrangible half; it will be greatest of all when they are taken from the two ends of the spectrum.

In Fig. 31 the abscissae measured along the line *ad* are supposed to be proportional to the objective intensity of the light, whereas the ordinates represent the intensity of the light sensation. Let the curve *aebg* indicate the intensity of the sensation for yellow light; and suppose that the units for yellow and violet light are so chosen that for the quantity of light *ac* the intensity of the sensation is the same for both kinds of light.

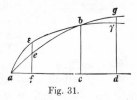

Fig. 31.

Then from the facts given above the curve representing the intensity of sensation for the violet light must have the position *aεbγ* as compared with the other curve. If the two quantities of light are diminished in the ratio *af*: *ac*, the intensity of sensation for yellow light as given by the ordinate *fe* will be less than that for violet light as represented by the ordinate *fε*. Conversely, if the quantities of the two kinds of light are increased to the amount *ad*, the intensity of the sensation for yellow as given by the ordinate *dg* will be greater than that for violet as given by the ordinate *dγ*.

Consequently, it is not possible to devise units for measuring light of different colours, such that, for equal amounts of two kinds of light as measured in terms of them, the intensities of the sensations produced in the eye will be also always equal. The fact is that the mathematical functions that exhibit the connection between the intensity of the sensation and the objective intensity of the light are of different degrees for light of different colours.

Suppose white has been obtained by combining two complementary colours. If then the intensities of the two coloured lights are increased or decreased in the same proportion so that the ratio of the mixture remains the same, the mixed colour remains, too, unchanged white; in spite of the fact that under such circumstances the intensities of the sensation for the two simple colours may be materially altered. For example, if, with the apparatus described above, violet and green-yellow are mixed to give white, the amount of green-yellow light may be reduced by narrowing the slit until it appears of the same luminosity as the violet. Since the amount of transmitted light is proportional to the width of the slit, by measuring the latter the ratio by which the quantity of light has been diminished can also be obtained. Thus, the writer has found that violet, which mixed with a certain amount of green-yellow gives white, looks as bright as one-tenth of the green-yellow when the intensity of illumination is increased; whereas it looks as bright as one-fifth of the green-yellow when the intensity of illumination is diminished; although in both cases the ratio of the objective amounts of light is the same. When indigo-blue and yellow were mixed, the blue appeared to be one-fourth as bright as the yellow for higher intensity of illumination, and one-third as bright for lower intensity. The differences were too small to be measured for the less refrangible complementary colours. Thus, when whites of different luminosity are obtained by mixture, the amounts of the complementary colours are in a constant ratio to each other in objective intensity, but in a very variable ratio to each other in subjective luminosity. Consequently, when units of measurement for light of different colours are obtained by mixing the colours, as was explained in the preceding chapter, these units will have little or no connection with the intensity of the light.

Apparently, the reason why mixed colours look about the same for different intensities of light, whereas the comparative intensity of the action on the organ of vision is entirely different, is because sunlight, which is regarded as normal white by day, must itself change its colour for different intensities of light in the same manner as other white or pale mixtures of colours with which it is compared. A colour mixture, which looks just like sunlight toned down to the same degree of luminosity, is white to us. Thus in case of the colour mixture in question, although the impression of blue is stronger in dim light than it is in bright light, still it does not appear to be a bluish white, because when sunlight is toned down to just the same extent, the impression of blue must preponderate about as much. However, the fact that the impression of blue really does prevail in dim sunlight, and the impression of yellow in bright sunlight, may be easily verified with a little pains. In paintings the effect of brilliant sunshine is always conveyed by predominating yellow hues, and the effect of moonlight or starlight by blue hues. The painter tries to imitate nature, but he does not have at his command all the gradations of intensity of light; and so by copying the variegated hues he endeavours to supplement the impression of intensity of light. A similar effect is the impression of brilliant sunshine illumination produced by looking at a landscape on a cloudy day through a piece of yellow glass; whereas a sunlit scene viewed through a piece of blue glass seems to have what is sometimes called a cold illumination.

It has already been stated that the impression made by the pure colours varies also in the same way, so that with increasing intensity of light they look as if they were mixed with yellow. Red and green pass right over into yellow, but blue becomes pale just as it would do if it were mixed with yellow.

The consequence is that with very great intensity of light the discrimination of hues is more imperfect than it is with moderate brightness. But likewise this discrimination is also imperfect with very low intensity of light; which agrees with the fact that it is more imperfect also in the case of colours that occupy a very small portion of the visual field than it is when the colour fields are more extensive. Thus, if the retinal image of a coloured field is smaller than the sensitive elements of the retina, the element in question is no longer stimulated to full intensity; the stimulation being less in proportion as the part of the element which is occupied by the image of the coloured area is smaller.

These variations of the colour sensation with the intensity of the light are accounted for in Young's theory by the assumption that there are three kinds of nerves in the retina, red-sensitive, green-sensitive and violet-sensitive; provided we suppose, as we have done, that each kind of nerve is stimulated by light of any kind, even by homogeneous light, but in very different degrees, and that in each of the three sets of nerves the intensity of sensation is a different function of the intensity of the light. Thus, in the violet-sensitive nerves with rising intensity of the light it increases more rapidly at first, and then more slowly, than it does in the green-sensitive nerves; and the same way in the latter as compared with the red-sensitive nerves.

If the violet light of the spectrum stimulates the violet-sensitive nerves highly, the green-sensitive nerves feebly, and the red-sensitive nerves more feebly still, the sensation of violet will predominate in dim light; but in bright light where the violet sensation approaches its maximum, the green sensation may succeed in becoming more appreciable by comparison with the other, and subsequently even the red sensation. Thus, initially the sensation of violet light must pass through mixed green into blue, and ultimately through mixed green and red into white.

Suppose, moreover, that the green light of the spectrum stimulates the green-sensitive nerves highly and the red-sensitive and violet-sensitive nerves moderately. Then the sensation of green must pass first into yellow, because the sensation of red grows more rapidly with the intensity of light than that of violet; and ultimately when all three sensations approach their maxima, the green sensation becomes white. Moreover, as to the red rays, we have supposed that they stimulate the red-sensitive nerves highly, the green-sensitive feebly, and the violet-sensitive more feebly still or not at all. This would explain how the sensation of bright red light passes into that of yellow.

Thus, discrimination of hue would depend on the fact that the relative amount of light that stimulates each of these sets of nerves is perceived by comparing the intensities of their sensations. Now we have seen that the relative intensity of two quantities of light can be judged best in a certain medium illumination. Hence, also, the discrimination of hues must be most accurate with medium illumination. The application of this consideration to very luminous colours will be obvious already from what has been stated. If with mixed colours all three sets of nerves are near the maximum degrees of stimulation, necessarily, each colour will have to become more and more nearly white. On the contrary, supposing that the violet-sensitive nerves were stimulated to the faintest perceptible extent, we could not possibly tell whether it was accompanied by a somewhat slighter degree of stimulation of the other two sets of nerves, that is, whether the colour of the light was pure violet or indigo-blue or purple or bluish white. Thus here, too, when the light is quite dim, discrimination of hues will be imperfect.

Another series of facts, heretofore classified as phenomena of *irradiation*, can be explained by the fact that the intensity of the light sensation is not proportional to the objective intensity of the light. What is common to them all is that highly illuminated areas appear to be larger than they really are, whereas the adjoining dark areas appear to be correspondingly smaller.

The phenomena themselves are very varied depending on the form of the patterns observed. Generally, they are easiest to see and most pronounced, when the eye is not exactly accommodated for the observed object. It makes no difference whether the accommodation is too much or too little, or whether the eye is provided with a glass lens, convex or concave, which is not suited for the particular distance of the object. But even when the eye is accommodated exactly, irradiation will be manifest to some extent. In fact, it can be distinctly noticed even then, provided the objects are very bright and particularly small. Evidently, the reason why the effect is more marked in the case of small objects is because the size of a small object is relatively more enlarged by the small blur circles than that of a bigger object. The diameters of such tiny blur circles as are present when the eye is well accommodated are practically negligible in comparison with the dimensions of large objects.

1. *Bright areas appear magnified.* The dimensions of narrow apertures and slits illuminated by light from behind are never estimated correctly. They invariably look wider than they really are, even with the most perfect accommodation. Similarly, too, the fixed stars seem to be small bright surfaces, even when we look at them through a concave glass in order to be able to accommodate exactly. In a grating of fine dark bars with intervals exactly as wide as the bars themselves (ordinary wire grating for interference experiments), held in front of a bright background, the intervals appear to be wider than the bars. When, in addition, the accommodation is not perfect, the phenomena are much more striking and are visible even with larger objects. Fig. 32 shows a black square on a white background alongside of a white square on a black background. With good illumination and insufficient accommodation, the white square appears larger, although they are both equal.

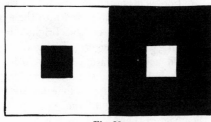

Fig. 32.   Fig. 33.

2. *Adjacent bright areas tend to flow over into each other.* A fine wire held between the eye and the sun or a bright flame disappears, because the two bright surfaces adjacent to it in the field of view encroach on it from both sides and fuse together. With patterns composed of white and black squares like a chess-board, as shown in Fig. 33, the white squares fuse by irradiation at adjacent corners and separate the black ones. PLATEAU used squares of this sort also to measure the spread of irradiation. The white fields were cut out of a dark screen and illuminated from behind. One of the two black squares could be shifted horizontally by a screw, and was adjusted so that the two middle vertical lines appeared to the spectator to coincide in one line. For measurements at longer distances the black fields were made of little boards, but for shorter distances they were made of little steel plates. The error made in adjusting the square was called the spread of the irradiation.

3. *Straight lines become broken.* If the edge of a ruler is held between the eye and a bright flame or the sun, it seems to have a break in it where the bright object protrudes above it, as represented in

Fig. 34. With reference to this particular effect, it may be noted here at the same time, that when the bright body is a lamp flame with cylindrical wick, the indentation at the edge of the flame, where, as above stated, the absolute brightness is higher, appears to be deeper than in

Fig. 34.

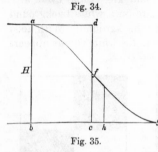

Fig. 35.

the middle of the flame, in spite of the fact that the eye is not consciously aware of the difference of brightness in the two parts of the flame.

The fundamental thing about all these appearances is that the edges of bright areas in the field of view are, as it were, shifted and tend to encroach on the adjacent darker areas. This encroachment is more and more noticeable in proportion as the accommodation is more inexact, in which case the blur circles projected into the eye from each point of the bright area get bigger and bigger. However, even when accommodation is most exact, blur-circles are not entirely lacking,

because we know they must be present on account of colour dispersion and the so-called monochromatic aberrations of the eye, which were discussed in § 14. Now the effect of these blur-circles is to make the light spread beyond the geometrical edge of the retinal image of a bright area; but the darkness also infringes over the edge in the sense that the light begins to fade within the contour where it should still have its full strength. In Fig. 35 suppose that c is a point on the edge of a bright area, and that bg is a straight line drawn perpendicular to the edge. At right angles to this line let ordinates be erected that are proportional to the objective brightness at the corresponding places along bg. If the image of the area were perfectly exact, the broken line $adcg$ would represent the magnitude of the luminosity. Thus from b to the edge of the surface at c it would be uniform and equal to H, and from c to g the luminosity would be zero. But if, through lack of accommodation, the image were blurred, then, as was explained in connection with Fig. 71 in Vol. I, the luminosity falls off as shown by the curve afg. Thus, from c to g bright encroaches on dark, and from b to c dark encroaches on bright; naturally, whatever light spreads beyond the edge being borrowed from the bright portion inside. Accordingly, as long as it is simply a question of objective brightness, the bright areas cannot appear magnified by the blur circles. On the contrary, the area of full brightness has been reduced by the blurring, although the total area that gets light in some fashion has been augmented. But now taking into consideration the fact that the light sensation is practically, if not actually, the same for the higher degrees of objective luminosity, the effect is that the falling off of the illumination inside the surface is less noticeable than the illumination of places beyond the edge that were previously dark. Thus, so far as sensation is concerned, the spread of brightness, and not that of darkness, must be the result. The phenomenon will be most striking when the surface is bright enough for the light sensation inside the blur-circle to reach its maximum there. For instance, if this were the case for the point *h* in Fig. 35, the apparent brightness at *h* would no longer be distinguished from the full brightness in the interior of the area; and hence the full brightness of the area would appear to extend to *h*; and even beyond *h* it would fall off very gradually until it vanished entirely at *g*. This makes it plain too why the effect of irradiation is easier to get when the brightness is great, and when, therefore, the place where the maximum light sensation is reached lies nearer to *g*. This is the explanation also of why the irradiation continues to increase when the brightness of the background is enhanced, even if the sensation of this brightness cannot keep pace with it. With increase of objective luminosity all the ordinates of the curve *ag* will be elevated in the same proportion as *H* is, which means that the ordinate corresponding to the maximum of the sensation of sufficient brightness will lie farther out nearer to *g*. Quantitative experiments on the influence of brightness were carried out by PLATEAU; the result being that the amount of irradiation was found not to increase in proportion to the brightness, but less than this. As the brightness is increased, the irradiation approaches a maximum asymptotically, as follows likewise from the explanation given here.

Another result of this theory is the explanation of the fact that the irradiation spreads more when the blur-circles are larger.

With most persons the blur-circles of points that are too far away are wider vertically than they are horizontally. Hence, a bright square on a dark background which is a little too far for the accommodation seems to be higher than it is broad; and a black square on a bright background just the reverse. Even with exact accommodation, most people see the vertical elongation of a white square, because it seems that in this case they accommodate for the vertical lines. On the other hand, white rectangles, whose horizontal dimension is somewhat longer than the vertical, look like squares. A. FICK[1] found in his

---

[1] HENLE und PFEUFFER, *Zeitschrift für rationelle Medizin.* Neue Folge. II. S. 83.

experiments that, for a practised eye that was not near-sighted, a rectangle, 450 cm away, whose horizontal side was 22 mm and vertical side 20 mm, appeared to be a square; and that another one with a horizontal side of 21 mm and a vertical side of 20 mm was taken for a vertically elongated rectangle. With other eyes that see a distant point of light as a star with three rays, there are also manifested in the other cases of irradiation three main directions in which the effect is greatest; as described by JOSLIN.[1]

In the preceding discussion, the term irradiation has been used merely with respect to those cases where there is no consciousness of blurring as such, but where the area of full illumination is apparently enlarged. However, very recently this term has come to be applied to the formation of blur-circles generally, even where they are recognized as being fainter parts of the image. Perhaps, however, a special new name is not needed for these cases. Incidentally, new boundary-lines may also be produced by the blur-circles, causing the object to appear changed in size, otherwise the intensity of the light itself having no special influence. As a case in point, VOLKMANN[2] found that very fine black threads on a white background, and also white threads on a black background, were regarded as being thicker than they really were; whereas with the kind of irradiation considered thus far it is only the brighter area that is magnified. VOLKMANN's threads were 0.0445 mm thick, and the eye was one-third of a metre away. Consequently, they should have appeared to the eye much smaller than the smallest perceptible width. By means of a micrometer-screw, the threads could gradually be brought closer together, and the problem consisted in adjusting them until the interval was just the same as the width of the threads. But every individual made the interval too wide, even when it was bright and the threads were dark. Hence, VOLKMANN also used these measurements to determine the width of the little blur-images with good accommodation. He himself found the interval to be on the average equal to 0.207 mm, whereas the thickness of the thread, which should have been the same as the width of the interval, actually was only 0.0445 mm. From this he calculated the width of the blur-image on the retina as being 0.0035 mm. For other persons, in case of a bright background, this latter quantity varied between 0.0006 and 0.0025. These dimensions are smaller than the least perceptible width (0.0044 mm) and than the diameters of the cones in the yellow spot (0.0045 to 0.0054). Possibly, therefore, the latter persons may have determined the width of the black image. Doubt-

[1] POGGENDORFFS *Ann.* LI. Ergänzbd. S. 107.
[2] *Berichte der sächsischen Ges. d. Wiss.* 1857. S. 129–148.

less, in the case of such a subtle exercise it is not surprising that such
wide discrepancies should occur in the results.

But even black stripes of discernible width, viewed with such insufficient accommodation that the blur-circles are much wider than
the stripes, will look wider than they are.
The writer is disposed to think that this
is due to the distribution of the light in
the blur-circle. In Fig. 36 let *ab* represent the section of a sheet of paper on
which a black line is drawn as indicated
in the diagram by the point *c*. Owing to
faulty accommodation, suppose there
are blur-circles of radius *fc*. Then

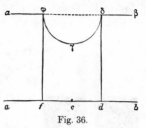

Fig. 36.

according to the principles developed in § 13, leaving out of account
disturbances due to the asymmetry of the crystalline lens, the curve
representing the light-intensity at the various points on the line *ab* as
it is reproduced in the retinal image will be shown by the line $a\varphi\gamma\delta\beta$.
The light-intensity at φ and δ undergoes here a sudden drop, and hence
these places appear as border-lines. If the line *c* where a white line on a
black background, $a\beta$ would have to be taken as abscissa-axis, and the
negative ordinates of the curve $\varphi\gamma\delta$ would show the light-intensity.
Then too there will be a sudden falling off of light-intensity at *f* and *d*.
Incidentally, the rotating disc will prove that the lines that appear as
border-lines are those for which the derivative of the light-intensity
becomes infinite. When a white disc with a round circular spot on it
like that represented in Fig. 37 is made to rotate, the black spot looks
like a grey circle whose light-intensity would be expressed by a curve
quite similar to $a\varphi\gamma\delta\beta$ in Fig. 36; as follows from the laws to be developed in the next chapter.   The grey
ring in this case appears to be perfectly
sharply defined on both sides.   The unequal degrees of brightness in its interior
are scarcely noticed, and it appears
rather to be coloured almost uniformly
grey.   Incidentally, in the blurred images of small black lines usually there
is an admixture of double images due
to the asymmetry of the crystalline
lens (see Vol. I, Fig. 73), whereby the
distribution of light in the blurred image
is indeed changed, but yet in every case

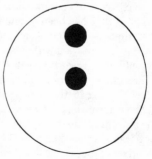

Fig. 37.

the width of the image continues to be greater.

As soon as the black line ceases to be very small as compared with the width of the blurred image, the brightness also falls off gradually at its edge, as in Fig. 35, and then the edges appear a vague grey, and the middle black. Then the existence of blur-circles is recognized and the illusion vanishes. The distinction is strikingly manifest in one of VOLKMANN's experiments. When the diagram in Fig. 38 is viewed at a distance for which the accommodation is considerably out, it will

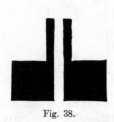

Fig. 38.

be found that the middle white stripe, which is the same width everywhere, seems to have the shape of a club, broadening out at the lower end between the wide black areas, and on the other hand closing in at the upper end between the narrow black strips, thus making, so to speak, the handle of the club. The white portion between the wide black surfaces spreads out in the ordinary way of irradiation. The narrow black pieces, on the other hand,

change into wider grey ones and thus encroach on the extent of the white in between them. Similar phenomena have been described by PLATEAU, but he argued that the irradiation of two adjacent white edges was mutually restrictive.

These last mentioned phenomena of the spreading out of dark lines are therefore simple cases of blurred images, not dependent on the degree of illumination and on the laws of the intensity of the light sensation. The writer would prefer, therefore, not to include them under irradiation and to reserve this term for those cases where the effect is dependent on the degree of illumination.

Very many physicists and physiologists have adopted another explanation of the phenomena of irradiation, which was specially advocated and elaborated by PLATEAU. The idea is that in the retina a fibre that has been stimulated is in the position to induce the state of stimulation in adjacent fibres also, so that these latter likewise arouse the light sensation without being acted on by any objective light. This would be a case of so-called *synaesthesia*. Sympathetic sensations of the same sort occur in other sensory nerves. For instance, many people feel tickling in the nose when vivid light falls on the eye, or a cold shiver down the back on hearing shrill or squeaky tones. In these and other cases the transference of the stimulation from the primarily excited nervous fibres to the others cannot happen except within the central organ, because the optic nerve has no anatomical communication with the sensory nerves of the nose (*nervus trigeminus*) nor the auditory nerve with the cutaneous nerves of the trunk except through the central organ. Incidentally, cases of synaesthesia of this kind invariably occur in fairly isolated instances only, and the explanation of it as given above cannot be considered as firmly established, because possibly also reflex discharges in the secretory glands of the nose or the vascular muscles of the blood-vessels in the skin might evoke similar sensations directly. In the great majority of cases it is evident from common experience that the stimulation of a sensory fibre is not transferred to other fibres, because individual impressions that are communicated to the organs of sense can be recognized as isolated sensations. If a place on the skin is pricked and the corresponding nervous fibre thereby stimulated, diffused sensations of pain would be aroused at many places in the skin, on the supposition that there was a regular and constant transference to other nervous fibres; and we would not know how to distinguish the first place that was stimulated from the secondary stimulations. But as a rule the sensation due to stimulation of a single place on the skin is felt just simply at the place where the stimulation acted, and nowhere else; and so there is no synaesthesia. But if the local pain is very acute and lasts a long time, undoubtedly there may be pains also in the adjacent parts which are commonly supposed to be sympathetic; but they may indeed be due also to the spread of the mischief that causes the pain or to inflammation. PLATEAU also recalls the fact that when the image of a black spot on a sheet of white paper falls on the place where the optic nerve comes into the eye, the only sensation in the corresponding place in the visual field is that of white; and he assumes that here also the stimulation spreads over the optic disc. But we shall see later that this phenomenon is of quite a different kind. Thus, if irradiation in the eye is explained as being synaesthesia, this view will have to be supported merely by analogies in other parts of the nervous system that are themselves still doubtful. On the other hand, the phenomena of irradiation in the eye are all such that objective light also falls or may fall on the parts of the retina where the synaesthesia is presumed to take place. The amount of irradiation is proportional throughout to the size of the blur-circle, and the whole effect in all its details can be deduced from other well established principles of explanation. In a case like this the author believes it is unjustifiable to employ new modes of explanation that are not themselves securely established.

Here some account must be given of the methods of photometry[1], in so far as the physiological properties of the eye enter into the question. In this survey all methods in which comparisons of brightness are made, not by the eye, but by means of photochemical effects or absorption of heat, will be omitted. It is worth saying that the eye can be employed very well to make

[1] With regard to this subject, see Appendix II at the end of this volume.—N.

a comparison between two quantities of light of the same quality, for example two quantities of white light or two quantities of light of the same simple colour. For when two quantities of light of the same quality under the same circumstances produce equal effects in the eye, the inference may be drawn that the objective intensities are likewise equal. In such cases the eye may be used as a convenient and sensitive reagent, with the special characteristics of which we do not need to be concerned, and hence the results obtained are objectively valid. Strictly speaking, therefore, this part of photometry is not in the domain of physiological optics according to the limitations of this science as prescribed in Vol. I, p. 47. The subject will be treated here merely in so far as the physiological idiosyncrasies of the eye have any influence on the sensitivity of the photometrical measurements.

On the other hand, as has been clearly enough brought out by the facts cited above, we must keep steadily in mind that any comparison of light of different colours as made by the eye has merely a physiological value, and tells us nothing about the objective strengths of the lights that are compared; so that all photometrical measurements of this kind remain entirely within the field of physiological optics.

Generally speaking, the procedure in photometry is as follows. Suppose it is required to determine the ratio of two luminosities A and B, where B, say, is greater than A. The intensity of B is then lowered, by any process that enables us to determine in what ratio it is diminished, until B looks just as bright as A. Suppose the reduced luminosity of B is nB, where n must be a proper fraction of known size; then

$$A = nB,$$

and thus the ratio between A and B is found. The various methods of photometry differ from one another, in the first place, by employing different means for reducing the brighter light in a known ratio. So far as this point is concerned, the method to be selected will necessarily always depend chiefly on the nature of the problem. However, they also differ in the ways and means of presenting the two luminosities to the observer's eye for comparison. With respect to this matter, it should be stated that the eye discriminates best between the luminosities of the two surfaces when they are directly juxtaposed, so that there is nothing to indicate the border between them save the difference of brightness. Moreover, the sensitiveness seems to be more increased still by not having a simple straight line to separate the two luminous areas, but when one of them forms a complicated design in the other (rings, letters, etc.), with manifold alternations of bright and dark. Lastly, the two areas to be compared must have also a certain spatial extent, not too small. Of course, those methods are very much more disadvantageous in which the intensity of a light is measured by reducing its effect on the eye by some means until it vanishes. For, evidently, the limits of sensitivity of the eye are not so definite and so constant that measurements can be made to depend on it. In different circumstances (intensity of illumination, motion, etc.) the same eye will perceive a difference of light-intensity of $1/60$, and then again of $1/120$. If, therefore, the sensitiveness of the eye was used as a gauge, quantities of light might be put equal to each other when one of them was twice as great as the other or perhaps more still.

BOUGUER[1] had two white surfaces illuminated by the lights to be compared, and placed himself so that he saw them both in perspective near each other. Then he altered the distance of one of the surfaces from the light until

[1] *Essai d'Optique* 1729 in 12 mo. — *Traité d'Optique sur la gradation de la lumière.* Paris 1760. Latin translation, Wien 1762.

the illumination was the same. In LAMBERT's famous *Photometria*[1] the first complete system of theoretical photometry was expounded with marvelous acumen and resourcefulness. Along with various other methods adapted to special purposes, the particular process he used was to illuminate a white surface by two lights which cast two shadows of an opaque rod on it. Then the distance of one of the lights was varied until the two shadows were equally bright. RUMFORD[2] also used the same method, and the necessary apparatus for the purpose is known as RUMFORD's photometer. To enable the observer to have a more convenient position, POTTER[3] used two transparent surfaces instead of the two opaque white ones; and RITCHIE[4] added besides two mirrors inclined at 45°, which threw the light on the white surfaces and allowed the sources of light to be placed opposite each other. Sir. J. HERSCHEL[5] insisted on fulfilling the condition of close contact between the two surfaces that have to be compared in RITCHIE's photometer, which meant increased accuracy. Incidentally, in these cases there are two disturbing factors in the use of the law of the inverse square of the distance for measuring the illumination. In the first place, when this rule is employed, the extent of the source of light is supposed to be infinitely small as compared with its distance from the illuminated surface; and this is not the case when the intensities of light are great, and the light must be very close. In the second place, especially when the light is far away, there must not be in the back of the room any appreciably luminous objects, and this condition will always be hard to satisfy when the experiments are conducted in a room. PERNOT[6] modified POTTER's method by illuminating the two transparent illuminated surfaces from the opposite side by still a third light, which was gradually brought closer. If the two areas are equal, they must disappear at the same time. In BUNSEN's photometer a piece of paper which is partly soaked in kerosene is exposed to light on both sides. When the light on one side is faint, the transparent spot appears dark, and when the light is too strong, the spot appears bright.

Absorption of light was used by DE MAISTRE[7] for reducing the intensity. He combined two equal prisms, one of blue glass and the other of white glass, in such a way that the two external surfaces were parallel. The light traversed them without being deviated but it was absorbed differently in different parts of the double prism. Similarly, QUETELET[8] used two blue glass prisms which could be shifted with respect to each other so as to make a plane parallel plate of variable thickness. But the colour of the transmitted light is changed by the blue glass plate employed in this arrangement, and it has already been stated that it is not possible to make an accurate measurement when lights of different colours are compared. More questionable still are two other instruments in which the measurement does not consist in a comparison between two different lights, but absolute intensities of light are to be determined from the fact that they disappear entirely with definite amount of absorption. This method was proposed by LAMPADIUS.[9] He looked at the bright object through a number of thin horn-plates and added to them until

[1] *Photometria sive de mensura et gradibus luminis, colorum et umbrae.* Augustae Vindelicorum 1760.

[2] *Philos. Transact.* LXXXIV. p. 67.

[3] *Edinb. Journal of Science*, New Ser. III, 284.

[4] *Annals of Philosophy.* Ser. III. Vol. I. 174.

[5] *On light.* p. 29.

[6] DINGLERS *polyt. Journ.* CXIX. 155.—*Moniteur industr.* 1850. No. 1509.

[7] *Bibl. univ. de Genève.* LI. 323.—POGGENDORFFS *Ann.* XXIX. 187.

[8] *Bibl. univ. de Genève.* LII. 212.—*POGGENDORFFS Ann.* XXIX. 187–189.

[9] GEHLERS *Wörterbuch.* 2. Auflage. VII. 482.

the object just vanished. Instead of horn-plates, DE LIMENCY and SECRETAN[1] used paper discs. The other instrument is the *lamprotometer*, proposed by an unknown person[2], for measuring the brightness of daylight. The method consisted in finding the strength of a litmus solution required to cause a platinum wire illuminated by daylight to disappear when it was viewed through a glass cell filled with this substance. The limit of sensitivity of the eye is, however, too indefinite for measurements of this kind, and the errors might be three or more times as great as the magnitudes concerned. A photometer designed by ALBERT[3] and another one by PITTER[4] depend on the same principle.

On the other hand, there were two other ways along which the more perfected methods now in use were gradually developed. One of these ways was intended for measuring the brightness of stars. By inserting a diaphragm in front of the telescope, Sir. J. HERSCHEL reduced the aperture of the instrument and thus diminished the amount of light coming from the brighter star at which the telescope was pointed. A. v. HUMBOLDT's astrometer is based on the same principle. This is an ordinary mirror sextant. The telescope in the instrument is pointed towards a mirror, one half of which is silvered and the other not, one star being seen directly through the unsilvered portion and the other star by means of the silvered portion and another mirror. By shifting the telescope at right angles to the dividing line between the two halves of the mirror, more rays will be received from one star and fewer from the other, and thus the images of two stars or the two images of one star can be made equal or unequal at will, and the intensities of the light compared in the two cases. The advantage of HUMBOLDT's method is that the two stars to be compared are seen close together in the field of the same telescope. But the comparison of such small intense point-sources of light is more difficult than the comparison of bright surfaces. This fault is remedied in STEINHEIL's objective photometer.[5] This is a telescope with its objective divided in half. In front of each half there is a reflecting right-angle glass prism. The instrument is so adjusted that the observer sees one of the stars to be measured through one half of the objective, and the other star through the other half. Then the two halves of the objective are each shifted a little so that the images of the two stars are blurred and no longer distinct; the intensity of illumination being diminished in proportion as the areas covered by the images are increased by shifting the two halves of the objective. Each half is provided with a rectangular diaphragm which may be exchanged for another one of a different size. When the adjustment is right, the two images of the stars appear juxtaposed as two large rectangles of nearly the same size and of equal brightness, so that the conditions are the most favourable for detecting any small differences of brightness. This was the first instrument that enabled us to make accurate measurements of the light of the fixed stars and planets. SCHWERD[6], on the other hand, used diffraction effects of small circular diaphragms to produce bright surfaces.

But for researches in physics, where we are concerned with ascertaining how much of the light has been lost on the way by refractions, reflections and other adventures, a good way of reducing the more intense light is by re-

[1] *Cosmos.* VIII. 174.—*Polyt. Zentralblatt* 1856. 570—DINGLERS *polyt. Journ.* CXLI. 73.

[2] POGGENDORFFS *Ann.* XXIX. 490.

[3] DINGLERS *polyt. Journ.* C. 20 and CI. 342.

[4] *Mechanics Magazine.* XLVI. 291.

[5] POGGENDORFFS *Ann.* XXXIV. 646. — *Denkschriften der Münchener Akad. Math.-phys. Klasse.* Bd. II. 1836. — JOHNSON's method in *Cosmos.* III. 301–305 is similar.

[6] *Bericht über die Naturforscherversammlung* 1858.

fraction and reflection with unsilvered plates of glass. BREWSTER[1] and
QUETELET[2] employed multiple, nearly perpendicular reflections, in order to
compare a strong light with a weak one. Thus, for example, sunlight is extinguished by 28 or 29 such reflections. DUWE[3] employed in the same way
reflections from plates of black glass such as are used in polarisation apparatus.
POTTER[4] utilized the different degrees of reflection for different angles of
incidence. His source of light was a white screen in the form of a semi-cylinder.
It must be supposed to be uniformly illuminated, but this is difficult to contrive. The cleverest application of this principle was made by ARAGO in his
photometer; which has been used for making very accurate measurements
of light-intensity.[5] The source of light in this instrument is a plane, vertical,
transparent paper screen, placed at a window, and necessarily uniformly
illuminated all over; although, incidentally; this can be regulated by the
instrument itself. A plane parallel plate of glass is mounted vertically at
right angles to the screen. Underneath the middle of this plate there is a rod,
and around this rod as axis a tube can be turned in a horizontal plane. The
tube is pointed horizontally at the centre of the plate, and the observer
looking through it sees partly through the plate a portion of the paper screen,
and partly reflected from the plate another portion of the screen. To right and
left of the glass plate, and between it and the screen, horizontal black bars
are mounted at somewhat different levels. These are seen close together,
partly through the plate and partly by reflection in it. Where the reflected
image of a black bar is, the observer gets simply light from the screen that is
transmitted to him through the plate; but where he sees a black bar through
the plate, the light he gets from the screen is light that has been reflected from
the plate. The tube is now adjusted so that the two black bands appear
equally bright, and the angle between the axis of the tube and the plate is
measured by a suitable scale on the instrument. The incident or reflected
light may now be subjected to all sorts of other actions, the result being that
generally another angle will be found for which the two images appear to be
of equal brightness. In order to calculate from this angle how much the intensity of the light has been reduced, the instrument has to be calibrated by
preliminary experiments, and the ratio between the amounts of reflected and
transmitted light determined empirically for different angles of incidence.
For this purpose, ARAGO proposed a special method depending on the fact
that the two beams of light in a double refracting crystal are equal in intensity,
each being half as strong as that of the undivided beam. Thus, by halving or
quartering one of the two beams of light by double refraction, the positions
were found for which the transmitted light was one-fourth and one-half that
of the reflected light, and twice as much and four times as much. Then by
interpolation the required values of the ratio can be found also for all the
intermediate angles.

ARAGO had also suggested another method for reducing the intensity of
light depending on polarisation in double refracting crystals. If completely
polarised light of intensity I falls on a crystal of this sort, and if ϕ denotes
the angle between the plane of polarisation and the corresponding principal
section of the crystal, the intensities of the two emergent beams will be
$I\cos^2\phi$ and $I\sin^2\phi$. If this angle can be measured, the relative intensity of the

---

[1] *Edinburgh Transactions.* 1815.

[2] *Bibl. univ. de Genève.* LII. 212.—POGGENDORFFS *Ann.* XXIX. 187–189.

[3] POGGENDORFFS *Ann.* XXIX. 190 Anm.

[4] *Edinburgh Journal of Science.* New Ser. IV. 50 and 320. — POGGENDORFFS *Ann.*
XXIX. 487.

[5] *Oeuvres* de FR. ARAGO. X. pp. 184–221.

beam of refracted light can be directly determined by it. One of the two refracted beams is eliminated entirely by a NICOL prism, the other one being all that is left. This is the principle of F. BERNARD's photometer.[1] The two beams to be compared with each other are parallel. Each of them passes through a separate pair of NICOL prisms that can be rotated. Then they are totally reflected by a right-angle glass prism so as to enter the observer's eye as two parallel beams close together. By properly adjusting the angle between the principal sections of the pair of NICOL prisms traversed by the more intense beam, the observer endeavours to make the intensities the same. When the beams to be compared originate from the same source of light, one pair of NICOL prisms can be dispensed with, and instead of them a double refracting prism can be employed, which splits the light from the source into two equal halves polarised in different planes. BEER's photometer[2] is very similar in principle. The two beams arrive at the instrument horizontally from the right and left; and each of them traverses a NICOL's prism. A double mirror, made of steel, with two reflecting surfaces inclined at 45° to the horizon, makes the beams vertical; and now they both traverse a third NICOL prism and enter the observer's eye. What he sees is a circular field, the right and left halves of which correspond to the two reflecting surfaces of the double mirror. By turning the NICOL prism the brightness of the two fields can be matched. ZÖLLNER's photometer[3] is similar to this also.

BABINET[4] employed a means of comparing the intensities of two beams of polarised light which greatly facilitated the operation. His photometer was primarily intended for comparing the brightness of gas flames. A tube branches out in two arms, one being the prolongation of the tube itself and the other making an angle of 70° with it. They are both closed by ground glass plates. At the junction of the two arms a set of glass plates is placed in the tube along the bisector of the angle. If sources of light are adjusted in front of the ends of the two branches, the light from one source enters the common tube after having traversed the pile of plates; and is polarised by refraction in a plane at right angles to the plane of incidence. The light from the other source, being reflected at the pile of plates, is polarised in the plane of incidence when it enters the common tube. At the end of this tube there is a SOLEIL polariscope. As long as the intensities of the two amounts of light polarised at right angles to each other are unequal, four complementary semi-circles will be visible. The colours disappear when the two quantities of light are equalised by varying the distance of the flames. In this instrument, therefore, the comparison of the light-intensities for the eye is reduced to comparing the colours of adjacent surfaces.

WILD's photometer[5], based on an idea of NEUMANN's, is similar in principle; but, by changing the physiological part of the apparatus, the highest degree of sensitivity appears to have been attained in this instrument. The two beams of light to be measured are parallel to each other when they come to the instrument. They are finally united, one of them being reflected at the polarising angle, first from a glass plate A, and then from a pile of glass plates B parallel to A, being thus completely polarised; and the other traversing the pile of glass plates. But before this second beam arrives at the pile B at the polarising angle, it has already traversed a similar pile C. This latter pile

[1] *Annales de Chemie.* (3) XXXV. 385–438.—*Cosmos.* II. 496–497 and 636–639—*C. R.* XXXVI. 728–731.

[2] POGGENDORFFS *Ann.* LXXXVI. 78–88.

[3] *Photometrische Untersuchungen.* Dissertat. Basel 1859.

[4] *C. R.* XXXVII. 774.

[5] POGGENDORFFS *Ann.* XCIX. 235.

can be turned around an axis so that the light can traverse it at various angles, which can be measured accurately; the result being that the quantity of transmitted light and its polarisation ratio can be altered. Incidentally, the pile of plates C is so adjusted that the polarisation which it produces in the beam of light is opposite to that which would be produced by the pile B. If the second beam is allowed to traverse C perpendicularly, it falls on B without being polarised, and here it is oppositely polarised to the first or reflected beam. The two beams are here united and proceed on their way together. By inclining C more and more, the quantity of polarised light in the second beam will be more and more diminished, in a ratio that can be calculated from the measurement of the angle of incidence. Thus, the light in the first beam is completely polarised, and mixed with it is the light of the second beam composed of variable quantities of oppositely polarised light and natural light. Finally, this mixture of light traverses a plate of Iceland spar cut perpendicular to the axis and a tourmalin plate. If the amounts of polarised light in the two beams are equal, the familiar cross with rings characteristic of Iceland spar will not be seen at all; but if the amounts of polarised light are not equal, this cross will be visible. The sensitivity of the eye was found to be extraordinarily high, so far as recognizing the polarisation pattern of the crystal was concerned, and the difference of intensities for repeated settings did not amount to more than half of one per cent. A higher accuracy still has been attained by WILD[1] in his new photometer. In this instrument the piles of glass plates are replaced by double refracting crystals, and the polariscope consists of two crossed plates of rock crystal cut at an angle of 45° to the axis. The rays that are transmitted are made parallel by means of lenses. Plates of this sort show a system of rectilinear fringes. When the instrument is properly adjusted, it is simply a diagonal portion of this system that is extinguished, the colours on the two sides being complementary. It is possible to focus the cross-wires very sharply on the middle of the extinguished fringes. The error for a single setting, according to WILD's data, does not amount to more than between one and two thousandths of the total intensity of the light.

TALBOT[2] used a rotating disc with opaque and transparent sectors for reducing the intensity of the light. This same means was also utilized by BABINET and SECCHI[3] for measuring stellar brightnesses.

In order to relieve the physiological part of the photometrical process, POUILLET[4] suggested using daguerreotypes made on polished silver plates. In order to get a positive view of such an image, it must be illuminated from the side, but the observer must be placed so as to see some dark body reflected in the plate, but none of the incident light. If, on the contrary, he sees a very bright body reflected in the plate, the image looks like a negative, the parts that should be bright being dark, and *vice versa*. In between, however, there is a certain brightness of the surface for which the image disappears entirely, and with the slightest change of brightness one way or the other, the image comes out positive or negative as the case may be.

SCHAFHÄUTL[5] has employed a physiological principle of photometry entirely different from any used before; but as yet he has not proved that the

[1] *Mitt. der bernischen naturf. Ges.* 1859. No. 427–429.

[2] POGGENDORFFs *Ann.* XXXV.¹457, 464.—*Phil. Mag.* Nov. 1834. p. 327. With reference to this: PLATEAU in *Bullet. de l'Acad. de Bruxelles*, 1835. p. 52.

[3] *Arch. d. sc. phys. de Genève.* XX. 121–122.—Memorie dell' osservatorio di roma. *Cosmos.* I. 43.

[4] *C. R.* XXXV. 373–379.—POGGENDORFFs *Ann.* LXXXVII. 490–498.—*Inst.* 1852. p. 301.—*Cosmos.* I. 546–549.

[5] Abbildung und Beschreibung des Universal-Vibrations-Photometer. *Münchner Abhandl.* VII. 465–497.

principle is correct. He states that the time that can elapse between two similar light-impressions without the eye noticing the interruption is proportional to the square-root of the intensity of the light. His apparatus consists of a strip of steel clamped at its lower end so that it stands vertically when in equilibrium. On its upper end it carries a rectangular screen made of thin blackened copper-foil with a rectangular hole in the centre of it. Through a horizontal tube with peepholes at both ends the observer sights the screen on the top of the strip of steel. Beyond it the source of light is adjusted so that its light can only get to the observer's eye when the aperture in the screen is directly in line with the axis of the tube. The strip is set to vibrating and shortened until there is no flicker in the light, and it seems to shine steadily. The intensity of the light is supposed to be (inversely?) proportional to the square of the vibration time of the spring, that is, to the fourth power of its length. Even admitting that the intensity does vary in this manner, the latter part of the above statement would not apply to the case of a vibrating spring loaded at the top.

Lastly, it remains to mention the method used by FRAUNHOFER[1] for comparing with each other the intensities of the light of different colours of the

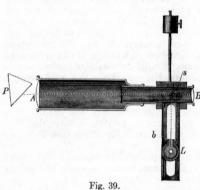

Fig. 39.

spectrum made by a glass prism. The spectrum was observed as usual by a telescope, a prism P being placed in front of the objective A (Fig. 39). The ocular is at B. A small steel mirror s, inclined at 45° to the axis of the telescope, is mounted in the ocular tube. A sharp edge of this mirror lies in the focal plane of the ocular lens and intersects the axis of the telescope. In the half of the ocular opening that is not screened by the mirror a part of the prismatic spectrum may be seen. The mirror, however, reflects the light that comes from a small lamp flame L, which is in a tube inserted in the ocular tube at right angles to it. This lateral tube is open above and below, and the flame L can be shifted in position. A little diaphragm b in front of the flame limits the portion of it that can be seen. The observer sees this light merely as a large blurred circle whose intensity of illumination is inversely proportional to the square of the distance sb. The lamp is now moved until the illuminations of the two semi-circular fields as seen through the ocular appear to be equal, that is, until the border between them is most indistinct. The numerical results of FRAUNHOFER's measurements of the brightness of the different portions of the spectrum agreed very poorly, mainly, no doubt, because he was ignorant of the effect of the absolute intensity on the relative luminosity of the colours.

The first measurements on the sensitivity of the eye to differences of light were made by BOUGUER; the result being, according to him, that the least perceptible difference is a nearly constant fraction of the total intensity. Subsequently, the same result was obtained by STEINHEIL, MASSON, ARAGO and VOLKMANN by photometrical measurements; and the law was thoroughly investigated by FECHNER.

[1] GILBERTS *Ann.* 1817. Bd. 56. S. 297.

Observations concerning the different relative luminosities of colours were made to a certain extent by PURKINJE, and afterwards more thoroughly by DOVE, and by HELMHOLTZ with respect to the colours of the spectrum.

None of the matters treated in this section has been the subject of so much investigation and controversy as the phenomenon of irradiation. Naturally, the fact that bright objects appear to be magnified under certain circumstances, was bound to attract attention very soon. PLATEAU quotes a letter from EPICURUS to PYTHOCLES in which it is mentioned that a far away light looks smaller by day than it does by night, and that therefore perhaps the stars might look too large also; and then he quotes the beginning of the third satire of PERSIUS:

> *Iam clarum mane fenestras*
> *Intrat et angustas extendit lumine rimas.*

Later it was the astronomers especially who investigated the phenomena of irradiation, because it was a serious difficulty in observations of the sizes of the celestial bodies. KEPLER[1] attributed it mainly to faulty accommodation, and unquestionably he put his finger on the essential thing in most of the phenomena of this kind. GALLIEO[2] likewise studied it more in detail. He stated that the effect was more pronounced when there was more contrast between the bright object and the dark background; that, while bright objects were invariably magnified, dark objects on a bright background (for example, Mercury and Venus in front of the Sun) were diminished in size; and that the magnification of very small objects was the greatest of all. At first, like GASSENDI[3], he believed that it was necessary to suppose that luminous objects illuminated the surrounding air, but afterwards he endeavoured, more correctly, to find the explanation in irregular refractions in the eye. GASSENDI subsequently changed his opinion also and supposed that the reason why the stars look larger at night is because the pupil is dilated. In his own case, the apparent diameter of the moon varied between 33′ and 38′, depending on the brightness of the background. The reduction in the size of small objects on a bright background was discussed especially by SHICKARD,[4] who suggested at the same time that at the edge of dark objects light spread over into the region where the shadow was. This explanation was like that offered later by LE GENTIL,[5] who tried to show that irradiation was due to diffraction. On the other hand, HORROCKES[6] tried to show that the origin of the phenomenon of irradiation was in the eye in the same sense as GALILEO maintained. DESCARTES argued that the pupil was contracted in looking at a bright object, the eye becoming like a near-sighted eye, and that, therefore, the judgment of the distance and size of such objects was altered; but that, besides this, the disturbances of the retinal elements, especially if they were very considerable, could be transmitted to adjacent elements, and that consequently the image perceived would look bigger. Thus, DESCARTES was the originator of the theory of irradiation based on the transference of the nervous stimulation. Later on, when astronomers began to use high-power telescopes of good construction, it was discovered that irradiation was hardly noticeable any more in the case of the bigger stars; and its existence, while

---

[1] *Paralipomena.* p. 217, 220, 285.

[2] *Opere di Galilei.* T. II. p. 18; 255–257, 396, 467–469. *Systema cosmicum.* Lyon 1641. Dial. III, p. 248.

[3] *Opera omnia.* Florenz 1727. T. III. p. 385, 567, 583–585. T. I. p. 499–508.

[4] *Pars responsi ad epistolas* P. GASSENDI *de Mercurio sub sole viso.* Tubingae 1623.

[5] *Mem. de l'Acad. d. Sc. de Paris.* 1784. p. 469. (Communicated in 1743).

[6] *Venus in sole visa.* Cap. XVI. Inserted after HEVELIUS *Mercurius in sole visus.*

recognized by some astronomers,[1] began to be doubted and denied.[2] In the case of astronomical observations, the effects of the chromatic and spherical aberrations in the telescope were generally involved with those of the imperfections of the eye; and, necessarily, opinions on this subject were apt to be different, depending on the quality of the telescope in each case. In particular, in the observation of the transit of Mercury across the Sun in 1832, BESSEL showed that, with the best telescopes, irradiation is no longer appreciable in the measurements.

While astronomers were engaged chiefly in discussing whether there was any such thing as irradiation, without inquiring into the causes of it, other natural philosophers began to take up the latter question. At first J. MÜLLER[3] considered irradiation, as we have done above, as due to a spreading out of objective light. Later on, like most other physiologists of that time, when the theory of synaesthesia was being developed, he also was influenced by PLATEAU's very complete work on irradiation,[4] and attributed this effect to a transference of the stimulation from one element of the retina to the other. The phenomena that PLATEAU described as irradiation are such as an eye that is a little near-sighted ought to see in looking at more distant objects, that is, they are generally phenomena of imperfect accommodation. But PLATEAU rejected this explanation, because he had also observed the slight irradiation exhibited by very bright objects at the distance of distinct vision, and because he was ignorant then of the other reasons for the spreading out of light in the eye, which in this case are the effective ones. Moreover, he relied on the fact that, according to his experiments, the apparent spread of the irradiation was always the same for objects at different distances; but in his measurements the distances did not exceed more than 60 cm, that is, they were distances within which the errors of accommodation are not appreciable any longer. It is curious that his experiments with lenses, that produced the correct distance of distinct vision and thus abolished irradiation, did not lead him to the correct explanation. Likewise, his statement, that two adjacent irradiations mutually enfeeble each other, is hard to reconcile with any theory of synaesthesia. For if the parts of the retina lying along the image of the black band are stimulated from both sides, they must be stimulated more than if a bright field invaded them from one side only. PLATEAU must have made the above statement in order to explain why a fine black line in a bright field cannot usually be seen when the line is narrower than the irradiation-fringe. But on the supposition that irradiation is due to blurred images, the explanation is simple.

PLATEAU's work was reviewed and criticized by FECHNER; and, subsequently, a more thorough criticism was made by H. WELCKER.[5] The latter went back to KEPLER's explanation, which, as a matter of fact, does include by far the greatest number of cases of irradiation. The only thing to be added to WELCKER's work is that even at the distance of most distinct

---

[1] HASSENFRATZ, *Cours de physique céleste.* 1810. p. 23 — J. HERSCHEL, *On light.* T. I. §697. — QUETELET, *Positions de Physique.* 1829. T. III. p. 81. — BRANDES in GEHLERS *physikal. Wörterbuch.* Revised ed. V. 796.—ROBISON, *Mem. of the Roy. Astron. Soc. of London.* V. p. 1.

[2] BIOT, *Traité élémentaire d'astronomie physique.* edit. 2me. p. 534, 536. — DELAMBRE. *Astronomie théorique et pratique.* T. II. chap. 29. §12. — BESSEL, *Astronom. Nachrichten,* 1832. No. 228.

[3] *Zur vergleichenden Physiologie des Gesichtssinnes.* 1826. S. 400.

[4] *Mém. de l'Acad. de Bruxelles.* T. VI.—POGGENDORFFS *Ann.* Ergänzungsband. I. S. 79, 193, 405.

[5] *Über die Irradiation und einige andere Erscheinungen des Sehens.* Giessen 1852.

vision irradiation is exhibited by very minute bright objects, due to the other kinds of aberration of light in the eye. Other investigators agreed with WELCKER's conclusions and explained irradiation by means of various kinds of scattering of light in the eye. FLIEDNER,[1] H. MEYER (of Leipzig),[2] and CRAMER, in particular, directed attention to the monochromatic aberrations, and FICK to the chromatic aberrations in the eye. But all the previous objective explanations of irradiation failed to show why the spread of brightness is perceived on a dark background without perceiving at the same time a reduction of brightness at the edge of the bright surface. The author ventures to think the reason for this has been demonstrated in the treatment given above.

Measurement of the sensitivity

1760. BOUGUER, *Traité d'Optique sur la gradation de la lumière*, publ. par Lacaille. Paris 81.

1837. STEINHEIL, *Abhandl. der math.-phys. Klasse der bayr. Akademie*. 1837. S. 14.

1845. MASSON, *Ann. de chim. et de phys.* XIV. 150.

1858. ARAGO, *Oeuvres complètes*. X. 255.

1858. *G. TH. FECHNER, Über ein wichtiges psychophysisches Gesetz. Leipzig. From the *Abhandl. der sächs. Gesellschaft der Wissenschaft. Math.-phys. Klasse*. IV. 457.—Supplemented in *Berichte des sächsischen Gesellschaft* 1859. S. 58.

Comparison of Luminosities of Different Colours

1814. J. FRAUNHOFER in *Denkschr. der bayr. Akad.* V. 211.

1825. PURKINJE, *Zur physiologie der Sinne*. II. 109.

1852. *DOVE, Über den Einfluss der Heiligkeit einer weissen Beleuchtung auf die relative Intensität verschiedener Farben. *Berl. Monatsber.* 1852. S. 69–78.—POGGENDORFFS *Ann.* LXXXV. 397–408.—*Inst.* 1852. p. 193.—*Phil. Mag.* (4) IV. 246–249.—*Arch. d. sc. phys.* XXI. 215–219.—*Cosmos.* I. 208–211.

POUILLET, *C. R.* XXXV. 373–379.—POGGENDORFFS *Ann.* LXXXVII. 490–498.—*Inst.* 1852. p. 301.—*Cosmos.* I. 546–549.

1855. H. HELMHOLTZ in POGGENDORFFS *Ann.* XCIV. 18–21.

Irradiation

1604. KEPLER *ad Vitellionem Paralipomena*. Frankfurt 1604. p. 217.

1619. GALILÆI, Discorso delle comete di Mario Guiducci. *Opere.* II. 256, also *Op.* II. 18, 396, 467–469. *Systema cosmicum*. Lyon 1641. *Dial.* III. p. 248.

1632. SCHICKARD, *Pars responsi ad epistolas* P. GASSENDI *de Mercurio sub sole viso*. Tubingae 1632. (The planet is reduced in size by irradiation.)

1637. DESCARTES, *Dioptrique*. Leyde 1637.—*Discours.* VI. pp. 67 and 68.

1642. GASSENDI, Epistola III de proportione, qua gravia decidentia accelerantur. *Opera omnia*. III. 585.

1738. JURIN. *On distinct and indistinct vision*. §53, in SMITH's *Optics*.

1743. LE GENTIL, *Mém. de l'Acad. des sc. Paris*. 1784. p. 469.

1810. HASSENFRATZ, *Cours de physique céleste*. 1810. p. 23.

1811. BIOT, *Traité élémentaire d'astronomie physique*. édit. 2me. pp. 534, 536.

1814. DELAMBRE, *Astronomie théorique et pratique*. T. II. Chap. 26. §197. T. III. Chap. 29. §12.

1826. J. MÜLLER, *Zur vergleichenden Physiologie des Gesichtssinns*. S. 400.

---

[1] POGGENDORFFS *Ann.* LXXXV. 348.

[2] POGGENDORFFS *Ann.* LXXXIX. 540.

1828. BRANDES in GEHLERS *Neuem physik. Wörterbuch.* V. 796.
J. HERSCHEL, *On light.* I. §697.
1829. QUETELET, *Position de physique.* III. 81.
1832. BESSEL in *Astronom. Nachrichten.* 1832. No. 228.
1838. *PLATEAU, Mémoire sur l'irradiation. *Nouv. mém. de l'Acad. de Bruxelles.* T. XI.—POGGENDORFFS *Ann.* Ergänzungsbd. I. S. 79, 193, 405.
1840. FECHNER, Von den sogenannten Irradiation. POGGENDORFFS *Ann.* L. 195.
1849. BADEN POWELL, Sur l'irradiation. *Inst.* 1849. No. 818. p. 288.—*Memoirs of the London astron. Society.* XVIII. p. 69.—*Inst.* No. 840. p. 47.—*Report of British Assoc.* 1849. 2. p. 21.
1850. HAIDINGER, Das Interferenzschachbrettmuster. *Wiener Ber.* VII. 389.—POGGENDORFFS *Ann.* LXXXV. 350.—*Cosmos* I. 252, 454. (Case of irradiation, mixed with monochromatic aberrations.)
1851. DOVE, Über die Ursache des Glanzes und der Irradiation. POGGENDORFFS *Ann.* LXXXVIII. 169.—*Berl. Monatsber.* 1851. p. 252.—*Phil. Mag.* (4) IV. 241.—*Arch. d. sc. phys. et nat.* XXI. 209.—*Inst.* No. 991. p. 421.
1852. *H. WELCKER, *Über Irradiation und einige andere Erscheinungen des Sehens.* Giessen 1852.
FLIEDNER, Beobachtungen über Zerstreuungsbilder im Auge, sowie über die Theorie des Sehens. POGGENDORFFS *Ann.* LXXXV. 348.
TROUESSART, Note concernant ses recherches sur la théorie de la vision. *C. R.* XXXV. 134–136.—*Arch. d. sc. phys.* XX. 305–306.
L. L. VALLÉE, Mémoire XIII. De la vision considérée dans les influences en quelque sorte moléculaires, exercées dans les réfractions, et du phénoméne de l'irradiation. *C. R.* XXXV. 679–681.
1853. H. MEYER, Über die sphärische Abweichung des menschlichen Auges. POGGENDORFFS *Ann.* LXXXIX. 540–568.—FECHNER, *Zentralblatt.* 1853. p. 864.
1854. F. BURCKHARDT, Zur Irradiation. *Verh. der naturforsch. Gesellschaft zu Basel.* I. 154–157.
1854. J. J. OPPEL, Über den Einfluss der Beleuchtung auf die relative Lichtstärke verschiedener Farben. *Jahresber. des Frankf. Vereins.* 1853–54. S. 44–49.
1855. A. CRAMER, Beitrag zur Erklärung der sogenannten Irradiationserscheinungen. *Prager Vierteljahrsschrift* 1855. IV. 50–70.
1856. A. FICK, Einige Versuche über die chromatische Aberration des menschlichen Auges. *Archiv für Ophthalmol.* II. 2. p. 70–76.
1857. A. W. VOLKMANN, Über Irradiation. *Bericht der sächs. Gesellschaft* 1857. p. 129.
1858. A. C. TWINING, *The relation of illumination to magnifying power, when visibility is maintained.*
1861. H. AUBERT, Beiträge zur Physiologie der Netzhaut. *Abhand. der schlesischen Gesellsch.* 1861. S. 49–103.
VOLKMANN, Über den Einfluss der Extension eines Lichtreizes auf dessen Erkennbarkeit. *Göttinger Nachrichten.* 1861. S. 170–176.
Idem, Über die Irradiation, welche auch bei vollständiger Akkommodation des Auges statt hat. *Münchener Ber.* 1861. (2) 75–78.
1862. AUBERT, Über subjektive Lichterscheinungen. POGGENDORFFS *Ann.* CXVII. 638–641
1863. V. WITTICH, Über die geringsten Ausdehnungen, welche man farbigen Objekten geben kann, um sie noch in ihrer spezifischen Farbe wahrzunehmen. *Königsberger Mediz. Jahrbücher.* IV. S. 23–25.
VOLKMANN, *Physiologische Untersuchungen im Gebiete der Optik.* Heft 1. Leipzig 1863.
1864. G. TH. FECHNER, *Über die Frage des psychophysischen Grundgesetzes mit Rücksicht auf* AUBERTS *Versuche.* Leipziger Ber. 1864.
AUBERT, *Physiologie der Netzhaut.* Breslau. S. 23–153.

§22. Duration of the Sensation of Light[1]

When a motor nerve is excited by a brief electric shock, a short time (about a sixtieth of a second) elapses before the effect of the stimulus on the muscle disappears again. The change produced in the organic structures as a result of the stimulation lasts much longer, therefore, than the electric discharge which causes the reaction. The same thing takes place in the eye. We cannot as yet demonstrate, it is true, that the sensation arises after the light has begun to act, but we can easily show that it continues after the light has quite ceased to act.[2]

The more intense the light, and the less fatigued the eye, the longer the after-effect will persist. After glancing towards the sun or at a bright flame for an instant, and then suddenly closing the eyes and covering them with the hand, or looking at an absolutely dark background, one will continue to see for a short time a bright appearance in the dark field, of the same form as the object itself was, which gradually fades away, changing its colour at the same time. The after-images of very bright objects are easiest to see because they last longest. Incidentally, even with less brilliant objects after-images such as those described can be obtained, provided the eye has been rested sufficiently beforehand in the dark, and the object is then observed for a moment. The after-image of a bright body on a dark ground has the colour of the object at first, and often shows very accurately still the details of the object in correct form and shading. For example, when a person takes a last look at a lamp just in the act of extinguishing it and before being left completely in the dark, he

[1] See Appendix B. 7 by W. NAGEL at the end of this volume.—N.

¶See also Appendix II. 4 by v. KRIES. (M. D.)

[2] ¶That there is a demonstrable latent period following the instant of stimulation, before the visual sensation develops, is brought out by HELMHOLTZ a little later in the discussion of rotating discs. Moreover, that the instant of stimulation of the retina is followed by a measurable latent period has been known since the work of DEWAR and McKENDRICK (*Trans. Roy. Soc. Edinb.* 1873. XXVII. 141). They made the first approximate measurements using eyes of birds, mammals, fishes, frogs, lobsters. EINTHOVEN and JOLLY (*Quart. Jour. Exp. Physiol.* 1908. I. 373) state that for the frog's eye the latent period, as indicated by the electrical variation following stimulation, varies from 0.01 to 2.0 sec, depending on the intensity of the stimulus. They say, also, that these values agree well with the latent period of the perception of light by the human eye. Temperature is also a factor, as shown by HECHT (*Journ. Gen. Physiol.* 1919. I. 657–667.) What the latent period of the cerebral centres involved may be, we have no way of knowing exactly.

For recent work on the latent period of the organ of vision consult EINTHOVEN and JOLLY (loc. cit.); BRÜCKE (*Arch. f. d. ges. Physiol.* 1906. CXIV. 569); FRÖHLICH (*Zft. f. Sinnesphysiol.* 1913. XLVIII. 28); HECHT (*loc. cit.*); CHAFFEE, BOVIE and HAMPSON (*Journ. Op. Soc. Amer.*, 1923, VII. 1); BILLS (*Psy. Monog.* 1920. XXVIII, No. 127, 101) (a lengthy paper on the 'lag' or inertia, in the rise of a visual sensation to its maximum intensity). (M. D.)

continues to see the bright image of the flame afterwards in the dark, surrounded by the rather fainter glow of the globe and the other portions. When the eye moves, the after-image moves in the same way, always occupying the place in the field of view that corresponds to the part of the retina on which the light fell originally. In order for the after-image to be sharply delineated, a single point on the object should be steadily focused. If the eye has wavered, the image will be faded, or perhaps there may be two or three images of the object partly overlapping. If the after-image is quite sharply delineated, details in it can be noticed under proper conditions that had not attracted attention in gazing at the object itself and had therefore been overlooked.

After-images of bright objects, in which the light portions appear light and the dark parts dark, are called *positive* after-images. As they gradually begin to vanish, they are usually mingled with other images, in which the light parts of the object look dark, and the dark light, so-called *negative* after-images. Apparently, these latter effects are due mainly to the fact that the sensitivity of the retina for light has been altered also by its previous stimulation. The two kinds of phenomena cannot be kept strictly separate from each other in a description of them. Accordingly, the more detailed description of both positive and negative after-images will be reserved for the next chapter; while this chapter will be devoted to describing the effects of quickly recurrent light stimuli, in which the persistence of the light impression appears pure and simple, without being affected essentially by changed sensitivity of the retina.

The leading fact here is that *intermittent light stimuli of a uniform kind, occurring with sufficient rapidity, produce the same effect on the eye as continuous illumination.* For this purpose, all that is necessary is that the repetition of the impression shall be fast enough for the after-effect of one impression not to have died down perceptibly before the next one comes.

The easiest way to show this is with revolving discs. When a black disc with a bright white spot on it is rotated fast enough, a grey ring appears instead of the revolving spot. This ring looks everywhere perfectly uniform, and there is no longer any movement to be seen. As the eye looks steadily at some one place of the apparently stationary ring, the places of the retina on which the image of the ring is formed receive in swift repetition the image of the white spot that traverses the circle. They get, therefore, a light impression which appears continuous on account of the rapidity with which it is repeated. Of course, it is not as strong as it would be if continuous white light fell on the retina; and so the ring looks grey instead of white. On the other hand, if the eye itself is moved, carrying the point of fixation around with the white spot, the latter may become visible, and thus the apparent continuity of the grey ring will be destroyed. Obviously, if the point of fixation of the eye moved so as to keep pace with the white spot and remained fastened on it, the image of the spot would stay right on the fovea, and on all the other parts of the retina there would be simply the image of the black disc. Under these circumstances the eye realizes the existence of a white spot instead of the grey ring. This is the case even when the motions of the fixation point and the white spot are not absolutely concordant, provided, however, the relative motion with respect to each other is comparatively slight.[1]

If there is another white spot at the same distance from the centre of the disc as the first, it likewise will be drawn out in a bright ring, which will coincide with that of the first spot. The impressions of the two points on the retina are summated. It is the same way when there are a number of white spots all on the same ring. Suppose, therefore, that on a disc of this sort concentric rings are drawn around the centre of the disc where the axis of rotation is. Then when the disc is rotated, all the places of one circular ring taken separately produce the impression of a uniformly illuminated ring, and all these circular images of the separate points fall on the same part of the retina and unite there into a total image. The following law can now be stated in regard to this phenomenon: *The appearance of each circle whose centre is in the axis of the rotating disc is the same as if the entire light due to all the points in it by themselves were uniformly distributed over the whole circumference.* This law appears to be just as valid for monochromatic light as for polychromatic. With reference to the activity of the retina itself, it may be stated as follows: *When a certain place on the retina is stimulated always in the same way by regular periodic impulses of light, then, provided each recurrent stimulus is sufficiently short-lived, the result is a continuous impression, equivalent to what would be produced if the light acting during each period were uniformly distributed over the entire time.*

Fig. 40.

The truth of this law can be tested by making discs like that represented in Fig. 40. One half of the central ring is white and the other half black; two opposite quadrants (that is, again half) of the middle ring are white; and in the outside ring four octants of white alternate with four octants of black. When the disc is set in rotation, it

[1] See Dove in Poggendorffs *Ann.* LXXI. 112. — Stevelly in Silliman's *J.* (2) X 401. — Montigny, *Bull. de Bruxelles.* XVIII. 2. p. 4. *Institut.* 1847. No. 928. p. 332.

looks a uniform grey all over. All that is necessary is to turn it fast enough for the inside ring to make a continuous impression. As far as that goes, the white can be distributed over the circumference in any way we like, provided that in each ring the sum of the lengths of the white arcs is equal to the sum of the lengths of the black portions. The same grey colour will always be obtained. Different colours can be used instead of black and white; and then the same mixed colour will be obtained in all the rings, provided the sum of the arcs of one colour in each ring is equal to the sum of the arcs of the other colour.

By such devices the law can easily be tested in a great variety of ways. Of course, the comparison must always be made between one intermittent light and another; and obviously the conditions must be such that the quality of the two alternating impressions is the same in the various comparisons.

In order to test the validity of the law also for comparisons between intermittent and continuous light, the author has used the disc illustrated in Fig. 40, on which the white and black arcs are equal. When it is in rotation, the grey has half the luminosity of the white. On the other hand, a grey of this sort can be obtained by laying a white strip of paper on a black ground and looking at it through a double refracting prism. In this case there will be two images of the strip, each half as bright as the strip itself. A larger grey surface of this sort is produced by placing alternate stripes of white and black of equal width side by side, and then holding the prism at such a distance that the double images of the white stripes come exactly over the black ones. Then the whole surface looks grey and half as bright as the white stripes. Now this grey is exactly the same as that produced by rotating the disc in Fig. 40. Of course, for this comparison the same black and white must be used on the disc as that with which the parallel stripes were made, and the two surfaces must be illuminated exactly alike. The rotating disc must also be viewed through the double refracting prism, but without separating its two images, in order that the light from the disc shall also be subjected to just the same reflection and absorption in the prism as that of the white stripes. The way PLATEAU demonstrated this law was as follows. He adjusted two rotating discs, one with white and black sectors and the other pure white all over, at different distances from a light until they looked equally bright. If n denotes the number of white sectors, and if w denotes the angular width of each of them, the width of all taken together will be nw. Let H denote the luminosity of the white at unit distance from the illuminating light, and suppose that the light which it gives out is distributed uniformly over the whole disc; then the luminosity will be diminished in the ratio of the area of the white sectors to that of the whole disc; and hence it will be $\frac{nw}{360}$ H. Let r and R denote the distances of the sectored and pure white discs, respectively, from the source of light, when they both look equally bright; then

$$\frac{nw}{360} \frac{H}{r^2} = \frac{H}{R^2} \quad \text{or} \quad \frac{r^2}{R^2} = \frac{nw}{360}.$$

PLATEAU's measurements agree very well also with this law.

The author has used another method too as follows. In the case of a disc covered with narrow black and white sectors, an apparently uniform distribution of the light from the white sectors can be produced over the entire disc by viewing it through a convex lens that prevents accommodation. If the pupil of the eye is at the second focal point of the lens, so that the image of the disc in the lens falls on the surface of the pupil and more than covers it, the light from the bright sectors will appear to be spread out uniformly over the whole field seen through the lens. On the other hand, when the lens is nearer the disc, the separate white and black sectors will be seen more or less distinctly as long as the disc is stationary. If it is in motion, the luminosity is just as great, whether the lens is nearer the eye or nearer the disc; and hence it is evident that the eye is affected by the intermittent light just as much as it would be by an equal amount of steady light.

The truth of the above proposition as far as coloured light is concerned is shown by DOVE's experiments on the phenomena of rotatory polarisation. When double refracting crystals are inserted between two NICOL prisms, well-known colour effects are obtained in many instances for certain positions of the latter. To some extent the colours are distributed uniformly over the entire field, but they may also form coloured patterns. In all these phenomena, however, the colour of each point of the pattern, as can be demonstrated by the theory of the polarisation of light, will become precisely complementary to what it was at first, if one of the NICOL prisms is turned through a right angle. This is experimentally confirmed by turning one of the prisms quickly, in which case what the eye sees is white. If a coloured glass is also inserted, then for two positions of the prism 90° apart the colours are such that together they must give the colour of the glass; as is actually found to be the case when the prism is turned quickly.

Incidentally, the law is verified for intermittent coloured light also by the agreement between the results of colour mixing on colour tops with those obtained by direct composition of coloured light, as by the agreement between the results of colour mixing with colour tops and those obtained by direct composition of coloured light, as was stated in §20 in the theory of colour mixing. Usually, in order to see the whole disc uniformly covered with the mixed colour, it is divided into sectors of different colours, each of which however must be of the same colour all over. Then the entire disc will appear in the mixed colour when it is rotated. But in this case the luminosity of the mixed colour, according to the above law, is always the average luminosity of the colours separately. Now with the same illumination all pigments look more dark than white, because they reflect only certain colours that constitute a part of the total white light. Hence also the mixed colour is invariably less bright than white; and so, if it is not much saturated, it looks grey.

If a coloured star on a ground of another colour (Fig. 41) is mounted on a colour top and rotated, the colour of the star will be seen in the

centre and that of the background out on the edge, while in between there will be all continuous transitions from one colour through the series of mixed colours into the other. In fact, by proper choice of the contours of the sectors of the colour top, the luminosity or the colour mixture can be made to vary in any way we please from the centre out to the edge. This was done, for example, in Fig. 37, so as to get a certain distribution of the half-tone.

Fig. 41.

The individual points of a rotating disc describe circles. Of course, the same continuity of effect is obtained by making a bright spot traverse any other closed curve. Consider for example, a taut metal wire painted black, except at one point which shines out by contrast when it is properly illuminated. When the wire is set to vibrating, the path of this point will show up as a continuous line of light, often very complicated in form. When the luminous point describes thus a path that does not exactly close in on itself but in each successive revolution comes very near to its previous course, the eye sees a line of light which gradually changes its form and position. This illustration enables us to study the motion of a stretched string; and there are many other useful applications of the same principle in physics.

If while the luminosity of the moving point is the same at every place in its path, its speed varies, the brightest places in the line of light will be at the points where the motion is slowest. The bright point loiters at these places, as it were, comparatively longer, and hence its light has a longer time to act on the corresponding places of the retina than on the places where the motion is faster. An illuminated vibrating string, for instance, looks brightest farthest from the position of equilibrium, where for a moment its speed is zero.

Here also belong the characteristic effects of intermittent illumination, which are produced best by the regular periodic sparks of an electro-magnetic induction coil with a rotating armature or with NEEF's vibratory interrupter. Every single spark of this apparatus lasts for a very short interval and seems instantaneous as compared with the movements of material things; and yet the light from these sparks is strong enough during this extraordinarily brief moment to make a perceptible impression on the retina. Illuminated by a single electric spark, all moving objects appear instantaneously at rest. Of course, the eye can perceive them only as they were at the moment when they were illuminated. As to their position before and after this moment, it has nothing to go by. Hence, if the duration of the illumination is so short that during this time no perceptible displacement of the body could occur, its outlines will look just as sharply defined as if it were absolutely at rest.

If a series of electric sparks succeed each other at very short intervals, stationary objects illuminated in this way look just as they do by steady illumination in continuous light, whereas moving objects appear manifold. That is, each single spark reveals the moving object in the position in which it is at the given moment; and as all these impressions last a little time, they are all present simultaneously and cause the moving object to appear multiple. The quicker the movement, the farther apart the images of the body will be, because the distance it goes during each interruption of the light gets greater.

Multiple images are obtained in the same way by moving the eye instead of the object. If there is a steady luminous point in the field of view, and the eye is moved, the image of the point glides over to another part of the retina. During the movement it traverses in succession all continuously adjacent points of a line connecting its first position with its last. All these points are stimulated, and thus for an instant the same sensation must be produced on the retina as would be aroused in the immobile eye by a line of light. Ordinarily, we are not cognizant of this sensation. It must accompany every movement of the eye when there are bright objects in the field. But we notice it when the continuity of the line is interrupted in some unusual way by intermittent light. If we employ as a bright object the region of the induction apparatus where the sparks occur, the bright point will appear multiple when the eye is moved. If we think of the line described by the image of the place of the spark as being traced on the retina, then only single places on this line will be stimulated by the intermittent sparks. Corresponding images will be projected in the field of view.

When a moving object illuminated by intermittent light describes a closed path and happens to be at exactly the same place at each flash, it appears single and stationary. For example, the vibrating spring or the rotating armature of the familiar induction coil appears to be standing still in the light of its own sparks. The same thing happens when any other body of periodically changing form is illuminated by intermittent light, provided the flashes always occur during the same phases of the change; as, for example, when a jet of water in the act of breaking up in drops is illuminated so that at the instant of the flash a new drop arrives regularly at exactly the same place; and hence the spectator sees the jet resolved into motionless drops. This happens when the period of the flash coincides exactly with that of the formation of the drop, or is a multiple of it. If these periods do not correspond exactly, or if one is not a multiple of the other, for example, if the period of the flash is a little longer, there appears to be a slow movement of the drops, similar to the actual movement except that it is very much retarded. In this case the phases of the drop formation revealed by successive flashes will not be exactly the same, but each phase of the phenomenon will be a little later one than the preceding. On the other hand, if the frequency of the flashes is greater than that of the formation of the drops, the phenomenon is reversed, and the spectator seems to see the drops ascending and vanishing in the jet. By such means periodic phenomena of this sort that are too rapid to be discerned directly can be exhibited in their single stages and analyzed. Various artificial contrivances of the same kind will be considered presently when we come to describe the apparatus.

The duration of the impression on the eye can be most easily determined with colour tops, whose periods of revolution can be varied and measured. In this method all that can be measured accurately is the rate of revolution needed to make the appearance of the top perfectly uniform all over. Thus it is found that the speed of revolution has to be increased for higher luminosity. Under these circumstances there seem to be differences also between different colours. PLATEAU made a disc with twelve white or coloured sectors and twelve black ones of equal width; and rotated it in ordinary daylight. Thus the time required for a black sector to pass was one twenty-fourth of the period of revolution. When the impression was uniform in appearance, this period was:

	PLATEAU	EMSMANN[1]
For white.........	0.191 sec.	0.25 sec.
For yellow........	0.199 sec.	0.27 sec.
For red...........	0.232 sec.	0.24 sec.
For blue..........	0.295 sec.	0.22 to 0.29 sec.

Not much value can be attached to the comparison of the different colours here, because there was no way of giving them all exactly the same luminosity; and this latter factor has a very great influence on the duration of the after-effect. This is easily realized by rotating a colour top a few feet away from a lamp, at a rate that just gives a continuous impression, and then bringing the lamp nearer; at once the revolving surface begins to flicker again. In direct sunlight still greater rates of revolution are required. Incidentally, PLATEAU's numerical results are strikingly large. Using a disc with black and white sectors all of the same width and illuminated by the strongest lamplight, the author finds that the transit of black does not take more than about one forty-eighth of a second for all flicker to cease; and only one-twentieth of a second by the dim light of the full moon. PLATEAU noticed, by the way, that when the ratio between the widths of the white and black s ectors is changed with-out altering the number of sectors, the period of revolution needed to get a uniform impression is the same. This can be shown very easily by a disc like that in Fig. 42, where the black sectors are wider in towards the centre and the white out towards the edge. With increasing speed of revolution the flicker ceases all over almost at the same time. The sensation is stronger when the white sectors are wider, and hence it diminishes more rapidly when the stimu-

Fig. 42.

lus ceases; and so the interruption, that is, the width of the black sector, must be less than it is when the white sectors are narrower. And so perhaps it is better to make the measurements by investigating the duration of an entire period of the change of illumination, that is, the

[1] POGGENDORFFS *Ann*. XCI. 611. (As to importance of state of adaptation, see NAGEL's Appendix I. B. 6, at end of volume.—N.)

sum of the times of transit of a white and black sector. Thus in the author's experiments this time was a twenty-fourth of a second with strongest lamplight, and a tenth of a second in dim light. LISSAJOUS observed the path of a very bright luminous point attached to the prong of a vibrating tuning fork and found an even shorter time for the higher degree of illumination, namely, that it took a thirtieth of a second for the entire curve to look continuous.

Accordingly, if a rotating disc is to give an entirely uniform impression, it must make from 24 to 30 revolutions a second. But the same result can be obtained with slower speeds by repeating the pattern regularly at equal angular intervals. Thus, for instance, in case of the disc in Fig. 42, it takes only six revolutions per second to fuse the black and white of the eight sectors of the outside ring into a uniform grey; while the middle ring takes twelve, and the inside ring takes twenty-four revolutions per second. The more the luminosity is diminished, the harder it is to determine how long the impression persists before it completely disappears. Obviously, from what has been stated, this time depends also on the luminosity. The after-image of the sun may last even several minutes. Thus, while the effect of bright light decreases most rapidly at first, yet on the whole it persists longest; just as a hot body cools off more rapidly in cold surroundings, the hotter it is, although it takes a longer time to cool down to the temperature of the surroundings. With his colour tops PLATEAU also made measurements of this effect by finding the time of transit of a black sector when the colour of the bright sectors was so distributed over the black that the black no longer appeared pure anywhere. The results were as follows:

For white.....0.35 sec;   for yellow....0.35 sec
For red.......0.34 sec;   for blue......0.32 sec

The duration of the after-effect is found to be different also for the different colours with respect to the changes of colour that occur in the after-image of a white light on a dark ground before it disappears entirely. However, these phenomena are related in many ways to those that will be described in the next chapter, and therefore it will be better to postpone their description until then.

From the facts described here it follows that light that has fallen on the retina leaves behind it a primary effect on the nervous mechanism of vision, which is not transformed into sensation until some moments later. The magnitude of the primary change which is left behind by an instantaneous impression of light depends simply on the amount of light which has impinged on the part of the retina in question; and hence it is just the same whether very intense light has acted for a short time or weaker light for a longer time, provided that in any case the time the light acts is not less than the fifteenth of a second. Thus the instantaneous primary action of very intense light does not prove to be relatively weaker than that of moderate light, as seems to be the case with prolonged sensation of light of different intensities.

There is no conflict here, as might be supposed at first. For the lack of proportionality was found to be between the objective intensity of the light and the resultant sensation. But here we have simply to do with the instantaneous primary action that is not transformed into sensation until afterwards; and there is nothing to prevent us from supposing that the magnitude of the instantaneous primary action in the nervous substance follows another law from that of the secondary effect or the sensation. Probably the best way to explain the connection is by comparison with the magnetic needle of a galvanometer which is deflected by a current that is frequently interrupted. In this case also the deflection depends simply on the total quantity of electricity that traverses the coil in the unit of time, but it is not proportional to it. But here too there is an effect proportional to the quantity of each single impulse of electricity; and that is the slowness with which the magnet turns and is forced by the earth's magnetism to wait until the next impulse arrives if the deflection is to be kept constant. The magnet seems to be deflected to a stationary position, when its fluctuations due to the single impulses are too small to be perceived. And an intermittent light produces a continuous sensation when the fluctuations in the intensity of the sensation are less than the smallest perceptible degrees of sensation.

The simplest contrivance of rotating disc, mentioned first by MUSSCHENBROEK,[1] is the top. In most of his experiments the author uses a simple top turned out of brass; shown in elevation in Fig. 43 in one third actual size. It is set spinning by hand; and so it can be easily started at any time without preparation, and its velocity can be regulated at will, although the greatest velocity that can be imparted by hand is not more than about six revolutions per second; which is enough to keep it going three or four minutes. Owing to the slow speed, the disc has to be divided in four or six sectors, with the same distribution of colour, light and shade in each of them, to get a perfectly uniform impression of light. If the number of identical repetitions of the patterns is less than this, the result is, with strong light at least, an

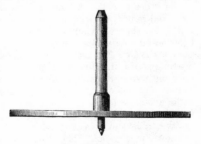

Fig. 43.

[1] *Introductio.* §1820.

effect of more or less play of colours. The patterns can easily be mounted on the top while it is spinning, and they can also be readily altered by mounting a disc with sectors cut out of it on top of a complete disc. The upper one can be adjusted on the lower one by touching it with the finger or by blowing on it with the lips. Thus a great many variations can be made while the top is in action. Suppose, for instance, the disc has blue and red sectors of equal width; and another one is placed on top of it with black sectors alternating with gaps all of the same width. When the top is set spinning, it will all look blue, provided the black sectors of the upper disc coincide with the red ones of the lower disc; but it will look red, if the black sectors of the upper disc cover the blue ones of the lower disc. In intermediate positions different mixtures of red and blue will be obtained, and so during the motion one colour can be made to change gradually into the other by varying the position of the upper disc by touching it with the finger or blowing on it. If the borders of the various sectors are not straight lines but curved or broken, very manifold and variegated systems of rings can be easily produced.

Fig. 44.

In order to make the top spin faster, a cord can be wound around the stem and pulled; the simplest contrivance for this purpose being that shown in Fig. 44; where c is a hollow wooden cylinder held by a handle d. It has two holes b and c on opposite sides of its surface, and half way between them a piece is cut out. The stem of the top goes through the two holes. The end of a strong cord is inserted in a hole in the stem, and the top is turned by hand until the cord is wound up, which makes the stem so thick at this place that it cannot slip out of the cylinder c. Now hold the top by the cylinder a little above a table, and pull the cord quickly, which sets the top to spinning fast; and as soon as the cord is unwound, the top drops down on the table and spins for a long time. The construction of the top is shown in Fig. 45. The discs can be clamped on it by means of the handle, as has to be done in MAXWELL's experiments for verifying NEW-TON's law of colour mixing. For this purpose what is needed is a set of round discs of different sizes made of stiff paper, each of which contains a central opening and a radial slit, as shown in Fig. 46. Each disc is made in one uniform colour. By using two or more of them together and adjusting them with respect to each other, sectors of the separate discs will be exposed on each side, whose width can be varied at pleasure, and thus the proportions in which the colours are mixed can be altered as desired.

BUSOLT'S colour top (Fig. 47) is the most perfect construction, when it is necessary to have it spin very fast. The disc, made of an alloy of zinc and lead, is a decimetre in diameter and

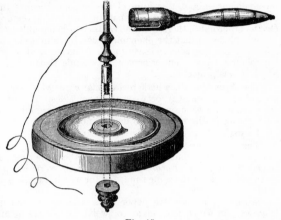

Fig. 45.

weighs five pounds. The brass axle ends beneath in a nicely rounded point of unhardened steel. The cylindrical part of the axle is made rough so that the cord will not slip on it. To set the top in motion, the cord is wound round the axle, and the latter is inserted in the notches in the iron arms *dd*, and a plate placed underneath it. The operator seizes the cord with his right hand and pulls it hard, at the same time holding the lever *e* with the

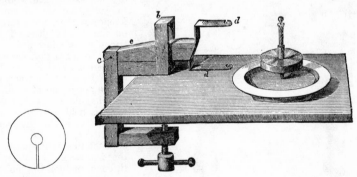

Fig. 46. Fig. 47.

other hand. Before starting, the top must be as near the edge of the plate as possible; and the length of the cord should be half a foot shorter than the length of the operator's arm, and it should have a handle at its end. The plate with the top spinning in it is pulled out from under the arms of the lever *e*, whereupon the latter rises, being pivoted at *c*. By pulling the cord quickly, the top can be made to execute as many as 60 revolutions a second, and it will continue in motion for 45 minutes.

Various other kinds of revolving discs have been used also, with their axles in cone bearings, which are operated by clock-work or by an endless chain or by a draw-cord like that used with a top. Generally, there is an inconvenience about this kind of mechanism, because the discs cannot be changed without stopping the apparatus and taking them from their support. On the other hand, there is the advantage of being able to rotate the disc in a vertical plane, so that the phenomena can be exhibited in a large auditorium; and with tops this is not so easy to do. MONTIGNY also used a rotating prism for colour mixing. The spectrum was made to traverse a white screen on which it was projected.

The *thaumatrope* is a little rectangular card, which can be made to revolve around an axis midway between it longer sides. A bird, say, is painted on one side, and a cage on the other. When it is rapidly revolved, the bird is seen sitting in the cage. The device, now used as a toy, was invented by Dr. PARIS.[1] (But see p. 5 of HOPWOOD and FOSTER's *Living Pictures* (1915)).

There are various more complicated devices for observing a rotating disc through slits which are in rotation at the same time. Here may be mentioned STAMPFER's *stroboscopic discs*, which were independently invented by PLATEAU about the same time, and for which the name *phenakistoscope* was used.[2]

Stroboscopic discs are paper discs from six to ten inches in diameter (Fig. 48), on which from eight to twelve figures are arranged in a circle at

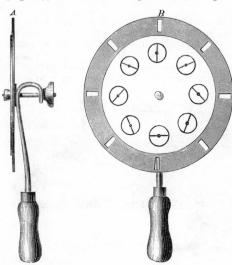

Fig. 48.

equal distances apart, representing successive instants of some periodic motion. One such disc is laid concentrically on another disc that is dark and a little bigger. This second disc has as many apertures ranged along the circumference as there are figures on the smaller disc. The two discs are fastened together by a nut that screws on the front end of a small iron axle, which is attached to the upper end of a suitable handle. The instrument is held in front of a mirror with the figures towards it, and the eye is adjusted to see the image of the figures in the mirror through one of the holes on the edge of the larger disc. The discs are then set in rotation, and the

---

[1] *Edinb. Journal of Science.* VII. 87.—POGGENDORFFs *Ann.* X. 480.

[2] As early as November 1830, PLATEAU sent a model of it to FARADAY by QUETELET. STAMPFER completed his first one in December 1832. PLATEAU described his invention in a communication dated January 20, 1833, in the *Correspondance math. et physique de l'observat. de Bruxelles.* VII, 365; STAMPFER in a special paper, *Die stroboskopischen Scheiben oder optischen Zauberscheiben, deren Theorie und wissenschaftliche Anwendung,* the preface of which is dated July 1833.

figures seen in the mirror appear to execute the movement, which they are intended to represent, although each of them stays at the same place on the disc.

If the apertures are designated by numbers, so that the eye looks first through number one, then, as the disc turns, through number two, etc.; and if also the diagrams along the radii drawn to these apertures are designated by the same numbers; then when the spectator looks through aperture No. 1, he will see in the mirror the image of diagram No. 1 opposite the image of his eye. As the disc turns, aperture No. 1 goes past his eye, and for the time being the image in the mirror is completely hidden by the dark disc, until aperture No. 2 arrives in front of his eye, and then he sees an image again. But now diagram No. 2 is there instead of diagram No. 1, that is, on the radius drawn to the eye. Then there is darkness again until aperture No. 3 comes in front of the eye, and diagram No. 3 appears at the same place where the other two diagrams were just before. If all the diagrams were exactly alike, the spectator would get a series of separate but equal visual impressions; and if they were repeated fast enough, they would fuse into a prolonged sensation of an object at rest. But if each diagram is a little different from the preceding one, the separate impressions will be fused also in the image of an object; which, however, seems to be continually changing in the way that the images succeed one another.

When the number of diagrams is not the same as the number of apertures, the diagrams appear to be moving forwards or backwards. Suppose there are n apertures and m diagrams, the numbers n and m, however, not being very different; and that at first one of the diagrams is located on the radius directed towards the observer's eye opposite one of the apertures. When the disc is turned through the arc $\dfrac{2\pi}{n}$, the next aperture arrives in front of the eye. But the distance of the second diagram from the radius above mentioned is equal to an arc $\left(\dfrac{2\pi}{n} - \dfrac{2\pi}{m}\right)$. Now if this arc is small enough so that the second diagram is nearer the place, where the first diagram was first seen, than any other diagram now visible, this second digram now in sight will be identified with the first one that was seen before; and the impression is that the first diagram has been seen to traverse the corresponding arc. Usually, m is taken equal to $(n+1)$ or $(n-1)$. In the former case, the diagrams advance with the motion of the disc, and in the latter case the movement is in the opposite direction.

The narrower the apertures in the larger disc, the less of the images will be seen; but the fainter they will be too. UCHATIUS[1] constructed an apparatus for projecting the images on a screen. A useful application of the stroboscopic disc was made by J. MÜLLER[2] for exhibiting the phenomena of wave motion.

The *daedalion* of W. G. HORNER is a similar affair, except that the holes are on the surface of a hollow cylinder, and the figures partly on the inner surface (preferably transparent), and partly on the base.

In the devices described so far the figures and apertures revolve with the same angular velocity. We obtain another set of phenomena when the angular velocities are different.

One of the simplest contrivances of this kind is the top (Fig. 44) made by J. B. DANCER of Manchester, when a second disc is attached to the upper part of the axle, as in Fig. 49. This disc has holes in it of different shapes; and a piece of string is tied to the edge, as shown in the cut. Owing to the friction

[1] *Sitzungsberichte der k. k. Akad. zu Wien.* X. 482.
[2] POGGENDORFFS *Ann.* LXVII. 271.

on the axle, the upper disc turns with the top, but not so fast on account of the considerable resistance of the air to the thread flying around. If the lower disc contains several sectors of different colours, the patterns cut out of the upper disc appear multiplied and executed in the different colours of the lower disc; a much variegated picture, which appears to move sometimes continuously, sometimes in a jerky fashion.

Consider a single aperture of the upper disc, and reckon its angular distance from the position it has at the beginning of the time of observation.

Fig. 49.

An eye placed in the prolongation of the vertical axis of the top will see one of the colours of the lower disc through the aperture, and this place is the index-point for the measurement of the angle. Suppose the upper and lower discs make m and n revolutions per second, respectively, both in the same direction; then the angular displacement of any point of the upper disc in the time t will be $2\pi mt$, and the corresponding angle for a point on the lower disc will be $2\pi nt$. Accordingly, at the end of this time t a point on

the lower disc will be in advance of a point on the upper disc, which was vertically above it at the beginning of this time, by an angle equal to $2\pi(n-m)t$. Hence, the angular distance of the portion of the lower disc that is visible through the given aperture in the upper disc at the time t will be $2\pi(m-n)t$ from the place that was seen at first; the angles being reckoned positive in the sense of the rotation, and negative in the opposite sense. Therefore, at the end of the time $t = \dfrac{1}{n-m}$ all the colours of the lower disc will have appeared once in the hole in the upper disc, and then the same series will begin again and be repeated. However, during this time the hole itself has turned through the angle $2\pi mt = 2\pi\dfrac{m}{n-m}$, and the series of colours that succeeded one another in the aperture must appear distributed over this angle, and in fact in the reverse order from what they are on the disc, if $n > m$, as is here supposed. The same series of colours occurs again during each successive interval of time in which the aperture turns through an angle equal to $2\pi\dfrac{m}{n-m}$. Now if

$$\frac{m}{n-m} = \frac{1}{p}, \quad \text{that is, if} \quad n = (p+1)m,$$

and if p is a whole number, then in one complete revolution of the upper disc the series of colours in the aperture will have been repeated exactly p times, and with each successive revolution will appear again at exactly the same place as during the first one. What we see on the upper disc in this case is a stationary coloured ring with p repetitions of the colours of the lower disc. If p is not a whole number exactly, the positions of the colours in the second revolution will not be precisely the same as those in the first revolution, and the coloured ring will appear to be gradually turning. If

$$\frac{m}{n-m} = \frac{2}{2p+1}, \quad \text{that is, if} \quad n = \left(p + \frac{3}{2}\right)m,$$

and if p is a whole number, the colours will have new positions during the second revolution, but during the third the same positions as in the first, and in the fourth the same as in the second. Thus a stationary colour effect may be obtained, provided the top spins fast enough for the impression on the eye to outlast the time it takes the hole to make two revolutions. In this case there are $(2p+1)$ repetitions of the same sequence of colours; but this sequence is not now the same as the sequence of colours on the lower disc, but consists of mixtures of pairs of colours that are opposite each other on the lower disc. For instance, if $p=1$, that is, if $\dfrac{m}{n-m}=\dfrac{2}{3}$, the initial colour will appear again for the following angles:

0°, 240°, 480° (or 120°), 720° (or 0°), 960° (or 240°), etc.,

that is, always for 0°, 120° and 240°. On the other hand, the colour on the lower disc on the other half of this same diameter will appear as being midway between the above angles, that is, at 120°, 360° (or 0°), 600° (or 240°), etc.; and hence at the same three places as the other colour so as to be mixed with it.

And, in general, when the fraction $\dfrac{m}{n-m}$ reduced to its lowest terms is equal to $\dfrac{q}{p}$, and the impression on the eye outlasts q revolutions of the lower disc, there will be p repetitions of a sequence of colours caused by mixing pairs of colours on the lower disc that are at the distance q apart. But if the impression on the eye does not persist so long, the colours appear to dance to and fro.

By varying the number, shape and size of the holes in the upper disc, of course very variegated kaleidoscopic patterns may be obtained in this way. In the case of this particular contrivance, these pictures are more variegated still, and the patterns are sometimes very delicate, on account of peculiar oscillations that take place in the upper disc. As soon as the upper disc is dropped in its place, the top begins to hum loudly; and if the lower disc is pure white, the pattern on the upper disc does not change into a system of concentric rings, as it would have to do if the upper disc revolved uniformly, but what is seen is a great number of repetitions of the form of the hole. From this it may be inferred that the rate of revolution of the upper disc is retarded and accelerated in regular alternation. These oscillations must be due to the friction of the upper disc against the axle. Moreover, there is another system of oscillations in which the centre of the upper disc moves to and fro horizontally; as is shown by certain peculiarities of the pattern as it appears against a white background.

These phenomena are exhibited in a more orderly way by PLATEAU's *anorthoscope*. Two small pulleys of different diameters, whose axles lie one directly behind the other in the same straight line, are driven by two endless cords, both of which run around the periphery of a larger disc. The latter is turned by a crank. A transparent disc with a distorted diagram on it is fastened to one pulley, and on the other there is a black disc with one or more slits. When the discs are revolved, the drawing appears in its correct form.

Letting m and n denote the number of revolutions per second made by the screen and the pattern, respectively, we saw that all points of the pattern that are at the same distance from the centre will appear in turn on an arc traversed by a point in the slit in the screen whose angular measure is $2\pi\dfrac{m}{n-m}$. But in the distorted drawing on the transparent disc these points are made to take in the entire periphery. Suppose, therefore, that the points of the original object and its distorted drawing are given by polar coördinates, and that ρ denotes the radius vector drawn from the centre as pole, and ω denotes the angle between it and a fixed radius; and let ρ_0 and ω_0 be the coördinates for the correct figure and ρ_1 and ω_1 for the distorted figure; then

$$\rho_0 = \rho_1$$
$$\omega_0 : \omega_1 = m : (m-n).$$

By means of these equations the distorted figure can be constructed by varying the angles ω in the given ratio. In order that the same figures shall be visible again with every revolution of the disc, the arc $2\pi\dfrac{m}{m-n}$ must be an aliquot part of the circumference, as before; that is, $\dfrac{m}{m-n}$ must be a positive or negative whole number.

If both discs turn the same way, that is, if m and n are positive and $n>m$, then ω_0 and ω_1 have opposite signs, and so they must be taken in opposite directions. Now $\dfrac{m-n}{m} = 1 - \dfrac{n}{m}$ will be a negative whole number, provided $\dfrac{n}{m} = p$ is a whole number; that is, if the transparent disc makes p complete revolutions, while the dark disc makes one. The image is repeated $(p-1)$ times on the circumference of the disc. In this case the dark disc can have p equidistant radial slits.

When the two discs turn in opposite directions, that is, $m = -\mu$, then

$$\omega_0 : \omega_1 = \mu : (n+\mu).$$

The two angles, therefore, are to be taken on the same side. If $\dfrac{n}{\mu} = p$, and if p is a whole number, the number of images will be $(p+1)$, and the dark disc may again have p slits.

Finally, if the discs turn the same way, that is, if m and n are positive, but $m>n$, then ω_0 and ω_1 again have the same sign, but whereas before ω_1 was equal to or greater than ω_0, now it is less. In the other cases the distorted figure could occupy the whole circumference, and then each separate correct figure took up an aliquot part of the circumference. But in this case evidently the greatest value of ω_0 is 2π, and consequently the greatest value of the other angle is $\omega_1 = \left(1 - \dfrac{n}{m}\right)2\pi$. Hence, the distorted figure may be reproduced on the transparent disc several times, and indeed it will be an advantage, because more light will be obtained. In order therefore for this same appearance to recur always, the maximum value of ω_1 must be, as above given, an aliquot part of the circumference, that is, $\dfrac{m}{m-n}$ must be a whole number, p; and hence

$$\frac{n}{m} = \frac{p-1}{p}.$$

In this case the number of possible repetitions of the distorted figure will be p, and the correct figure will be single. The number of slits may be made equal to $(p-1)$.

However, in this case also a single slit can be used, and by slight variations in the repetitions of the distorted figure to make it represent successive stages of a movement, a correct image can be obtained that appears to execute this motion.

If the required relations between the frequencies m and n are to be exactly maintained, the axles must be driven by gear wheels. With pulleys the ratio between the diameters and the special peculiarities of the cord can never be so nicely adjusted together as to prevent the gradual occurrence of small deviations from the required relations, and then the restored images on the disc will gradually revolve around their central point. PLATEAU, by the way, utilized this unavoidable inaccuracy in the procedure of the cord to produce a very gradual change of colour. He made two pulleys as nearly alike as possible; a transparent disc with coloured sectors of equal width was fastened to one of them, and a black disc with one or two equal sectors cut out of it was fastened to the other. If in the beginning the opening stands right in front of one of the coloured sectors of the rear disc, then on rotation the entire field will appear in this colour. However, little by little the discs will be displaced relatively to each other; at first a little bit of another sector of the coloured disc will be exposed, and by and by more and more, the colour of this sector continually being added to the mixture, while that of the first disappears to the same extent. Thus the colour can be made to change by imperceptible degrees.

Here also should be mentioned certain curves that are seen when two sets of straight and curved rods are moved one behind the other. The first case of this kind to attract attention consisted of certain figures that appear on a carriage wheel when it goes past a row of palings.[1] The simplest illustration is the phenomenon observed by FARADAY. He made two equal toothed wheels revolve rapidly in opposite directions one behind the other, their axes being in the same straight line. Owing to the rapidity of the motion, it was not possible to see the separate teeth of either wheel, but when he observed them so that one row of teeth could be seen through the other, he beheld a stationary wheel with double as many teeth. If we think of the teeth as being bright on a dark ground, then a certain amount of light will be distributed apparently uniformly over the dark ground by the rapidly moving bright teeth of each wheel, and the amount of light due to the two rows of teeth will be doubled at those places where first a tooth of one wheel and then a tooth of the other wheel goes by. But where a tooth of the front wheel hides one in the other wheel, the light from the latter will be removed for a moment, because it cannot reach the observer's eye, and a place like this appears, therefore, only half as highly illuminated as the adjacent places where the two sets of teeth send their light to the eye unmolested. Thus, in the bright effect produced by the two sets of teeth those places look darker where a pair of teeth are superposed during the motion of the wheels. If ω is the angular interval between one tooth and the next, then, supposing the two sets of teeth are superposed to begin with, another superposition will occur when one wheel has moved through an angle $\frac{\omega}{2}$ in one direction, and the other has moved through an equal angle in the opposite direction. Hence, the angular distance apart of the dark bands will be only $\frac{\omega}{2}$, and there will be twice as many of them as there are teeth. One of the wheels can be dispensed with, as was pointed out by BILLET SÉLIS, provided a concave mirror is adjusted behind the other wheel so as to form an inverted image of it that coincides with it. The same method can be used very nicely also for showing how a jet of water decomposes into drops.

EMSMANN observed a similar phenomenon with the familiar model used for explaining the earth's oblateness, which consists of two elastic brass rings, corresponding to two perpendicular meridians of the earth. On being revolved rapidly around an axis that represents the earth's axis, they are bent by the centrifugal forces into an elliptical form. The curved surface which they

[1] ROGET in *Phil. Transact.* 1825. I. 131. POGGENDORFFS *Ann.* V. 93.—PLATEAU, Ibid. XX. 319.—FARADAY, Ibid. XXII. 601.—EMSMANN, Ibid. LXIX. 326.

describe during their rapid motion shines out brightly owing to the light that is reflected by them, and dark lines are seen on this surface at the places where a front piece of the ring hides one behind it. The general principle of these phenomena has been enunciated by PLATEAU. When two illuminated curves traverse the field of view so rapidly as to leave behind them an apparently continuous illumination of the surface, there will be a dark line in this field of light connecting the points where the curves intersect each other if the light from one curve cannot pass through the other.

NEWTON[1] estimated the duration of the light impression as being equal to one second. Subsequently it was measured by various individuals by finding how long the impression lasted when a red-hot coal was revolved in a circle. SENGER[2] found the time to be a half of a second; D'ARCY,[3] eight sixtieths of a second; and CAVALLO,[4] one-tenth of a second. PARROT[5] found that the impression lasted for a shorter time in a bright room than in a dark one. Then followed PLATEAU's subsequent measurements[6] on the different durations of the impressions of different colours; and those of EMSMANN.[7]

MUSSCHENBROEK[8] mentions colour tops without naming any older observer. Special forms of such devices were described by E. G. FISCHER,[9] LÜDICKE,[10] and BUSOLT.[11]

The almost simultaneous invention of the stroboscopic discs by PLATEAU and STAMPFER at the end of the year 1832 has already been mentioned. The construction of the anorthoscope by PLATEAU[12] came in January 1836. The latter also developed the theory of the phenomena in much detail.

1704. I. NEWTON, *Optice.* Quaestio XVI.

1740. SEGNER, *De raritate luminis.* Gottingae 1740.

1760. MUSSCHENBROEK, *Introductio ad philos. natur.* §1820.

1765. D'ARCY, Sur la durée de la sensation de la vue. *Mém. de l'Acad. des Sc.* 1765. p. 450.

1795. T. CAVALLO, *Naturlehre,* translated by TROMMSDORF. III. 132.

1800. A. F. LÜDICKE, Beschreibung eines Schwungrades, die Verwandlung der Regenbogenfarben darzustellen. GILBERTS *Ann.* V. 272.

1810. Idem, Versuche über die Mischung prismatischer Farben. Ibid. XXXIV. 4. Beschreibung eines Chromoskops. Ibid. XXXVI. and LII.

1819. PARROT, *Entretiens sur la Physique.* Dorpat 1819–24. III. 235.

1825. ROGET in *Philosophical Transact.* 1825. I. 131; POGGENDORFFS *Ann.* V. 93. (Curves of wheel-spokes).

1827. E. G. FISCHER, *Lehrbuch der mechanischen Naturlehre.* Berlin II. 267. (Colour tops.) PARIS, Thaumatrop. POGGENDORFFS *Ann.* X. 480; *Edinb. Journ. of Sc.* VII. 87. TH. YOUNG, Optische Erscheinung bei einer schwingenden Saite. POGGENDORFFS *Ann.* X. 470–480.

---

[1] *Optice.* Quaestio XVI.

[2] *De raritate luminis.* Gott. 1740.

[3] *Mém. de Paris.* 1765. p. 450.

[4] *Naturlehre* translation of TROMMSDORF. III. 132.

[5] *Entretiens sur la Physique.* Dorpat 1819–24. III. 235.

[6] POGGENDORFFS *Ann.* XX. 304–324.

[7] POGGENDORFFS *Ann.* XCI. 611.

[8] *Introd. ad philos. natur.* §1820.

[9] *Lehrbuch der mechanischen Naturl.* Berlin 1827. II. 267.

[10] GILBERTS *Ann.* V. 272 and XXXIV. 4.

[11] POGGENDORRFS *Ann.* XXXII. 656.

[12] *Bull. de Brux.* 1836. III. 7. Idem in POGGENDORFFS *Ann.* XX. 319–543. XXXII. 646. XXXVII. 464. LXXVIII. 563. LXXIX. 269. LXXX. 150, 287.

1829. PLATEAU in POGGENDORFFS *Ann.* XX. 304–324, 543. (Different duration of colour impression; curves of wheel-spokes.) *Dissert. sur quelques propriétés des impressions produites par la lumière sur l'organe de vue.* Liège 1829.

1831. FARADAY, On a peculiar class of optical deceptions. *Journ. of the Roy. Inst.* I.— POGGENDORFFS *Ann.* XXII. 601. (One toothed wheel seen through another; screw motion.)

1833. PLATEAU, *Correspond. math. et phys. de l'observat. de Bruxelles.* VII. 365.—POGGEN- DORFFS *Ann.* XXII. 647.—*Ann. de chim. et de phys.* LIII. 304.

STAMPFER, *Die stroboskopischen Scheiben oder optische Zauberscheiben, deren Theorie und wissensch. Anwendung.* Vienna. POGGENDORFFS *Ann.* XXIX. 189. XXXII. *Jahrbuch d. polytechn. Inst. zu Wien.* Bd. XVIII.

BUSOLT, Farbenkreisel. POGGENDORFFS *Ann.* XXXII. 566.

1834. HORNER, Dädaleum. POGGENDORFFS *Ann.* XXXII. 650.—*Phil. Mag.* (3) IV. 36.

TALBOT, *Phil. Mag.* Nov. 1834. p. 327, and IV. 113. (Rotating discs used for photo- metry.)

1835. PLATEAU in *Bull. de l'Acad. de Bruxelles.* 1835. p. 52.—POGGENDORFFS *Ann.* XXXV. 457–464. (Measurements of luminosity of intermittent light.)

DOVE, *Über Diskontinuität des Leuchtens der Blitze.*

ADDAMS, Optische Täuschung bei Betrachtung eines in Bewegung begriffenen Körpers. POGGENDORFFS *Ann.* XXXIV. 384; *Phil. Mag.* V. 373.

1836. PLATEAU, Anorthoskop. *Bull. de l'acad. de Bruxelles.* III. 7 and 364.—POGGENDORFFS *Ann.* XXXVII. 464.

1845. EMSMANN, Optische Täuschung, welche sich an dem Abplattungsmodelle zeigt. POGGENDORFFS *Ann.* LXIV. 326.

DOPPLER in *Abhandl. der böhmischen Ges. d. Wiss.* V. Folge. Bd. 3.

1846. DOVE, Über die Methoden aus Komplementärfarben Weiss darzustellen, und über die Erscheinungen, welche polarisiertes Licht zeigt, dessen Polarisationsebene ge- dreht wird. *Berl. Monatsber.* 1846. p. 70.—POGGENDORFFS *Ann.* LXXI. 97.—*Phil. Mag.* XXX. 465.—*Inst.* No. 712. p. 176.—*Arch. d. sc. ph. et nat.* V. 276.

Idem, Über ein optisches Verfahren die Umdrehungsgeschwindigkeit einer rotie- renden Scheibe zu messen. *Berl. Monatsber.* 1847. p. 77.—POGGENDORFFS *Ann.* LXXI. 112.—*Inst.* No. 712, p. 177.

MÜLLER, Anwendung der strobosk. Scheiben zur Versinnlichung der Wellenlehre. POGGENDORFFS *Ann.* LXVII. 271.

1849. PLATEAU, Sur de nouvelles applications curieuses de la persistance des impressions de la rétine. *Bull. de Brux.* XVI. I. 424, 588. II. 30, 254.—*Inst.* XVII. No. 818. p. 277. No. 830. p. 378. XVIII. No. 835 p. 5.—*Phil. Mag.* XXXVI. p. 434, 436.— POGGENDORFFS *Ann.* LXXVIII. 563. LXXIX. 269. LXXX. 150. 287.—FRORIEPS *Notizen.* X. 221. 325.

1850. J. TYNDALL, Phenomena of water jet. (Illumination by electric sparks.) *Phil. Mag.* (4) I. 105.—POGGENDORFFS *Ann.* LXXXII. 294.—*Edinb. Journ.* L. 370.— *Inst.* No. 924. p. 303.

H. BUFF, Einige Bemerkungen über die Erscheinung der Auflösung des flüssigen Strahls in Tropfen. LIEBIG *und* WÖHLER LXXVIII. 162. (Illumination by inter- mittent light.)

BILLET SÉLIS, Sur les moyens d'observer la constitution des veines liquides. *Ann. d. chim. et de phys.* (3) XXXI. 326.—POGGENDORFFS *Ann.* LXXXIII. 597.

1850. W. SWAN, On the gradual production of luminous impressions on the eye and other phenomena of vision. SILLIMAN *J.* (2) IX. 443.—*Proc. Edinb. Roy. Soc.* 1849. p. 230.

STEVELLY, Attempt to explain the occasional distinct vision of rapidly revolving coloured sectors. SILLIMAN *J.* (2) X. 401.—*Rep. of British Assoc.* 1850. 2. p. 21.

SINSTEDEN, Eine optische Stelle aus den Alten. POGGENDORFFS *Ann.* LXXXIV. 448.—*Cosmos.* I. 116.

1852. MONTIGNY, Procédé pour rendre perceptibles et pour compter les vibrations d'une tige élastique. *Bull. de Brux.* XIX. 1. p. 227–250.—*Inst.* 1852. p. 216–220, 268.— POGGENDORFFS *Ann.* LXXXIX. 102–121.

1853. A. Poppe, Das verbesserte Interferenzoskop. Poggendorffs *Ann.* LXXXVIII. 223–230.

F. Uchatius, Apparat zur Darstellung beweglicher Bilder an der Wand. *Wiener Ber.* X. 482–485.

W. Rollmann, Über eine neue Anwendung der stroboskopischen Scheiben. Poggendorffs *Ann.* LXXXIX. 246–250.

J. Plateau, Sur le passage de Lucrèce où l'on a vu une description du fantascope. *Arch. d. sc. phys.* XX. 300–302.—*Cosmos.* I. 307–309. (Answer to Sinsteden.)

1854. Emsmann, Über die Dauer des Lichteindrucks. Poggendorffs *Ann.*XCI.611–618.—*Inst.* 1854. p. 276.

1855. Lissajous, Note sur une moyen nouveau de mettre en évidence le mouvement vibratoire des corps. *C. R.* XLI. 93–94.—*Inst.* 1855. p. 245.—*Cosmos.* VII. 81–83.—*Arch. d. sc. phys.* XXX. 159–161.

Idem, Note sur une méthode nouvelle applicable à l'étude des mouvements vibratoires. *C. R.* XLI. 814–817.—*Cosmos.* VII. 608–609.—*Inst.* 1855. p. 402–403.

1856. Idem, Mémoire sur l'étude optique des mouvements vibratoires. *C. R.* XLIII. 973–976; XLIV. 727. XLV. 48–52.—*Inst.* 1856. p. 411. 1857. p. 237.—*Cosmos.* IX. 626–629. XI. 80–83, 110–112, 431–432.—*Ann. d. chim. et de phys.* (3) LI. 147–231.

Supplement by Helmholtz in the first edition.

E. Brücke has called attention to the fact that when discs like that represented in Fig. 40 are revolved at a certain rate, the intermediate rings look brighter than the inside and outside ones; and hence that for a certain frequency of alternation of white and black the total impression of light is not only greater than it is with less frequency when each colour comes into view by itself without being disturbed by the other, but is also greater than it is with greater frequency when white and black are fused into a uniform grey. He found that the effect was greatest for 17.5 stimuli per second, and that about twice as many were required to see a perfectly uniform grey.

When he looked at a disc, in which the white sectors were cut out, and which was covered with a red glass disc, the red got lighter for the same frequency that gave the maximum action of light effect. Brücke thought this had something to do with the blending of the positive complementary after-image of red, mentioned in the next chapter (p. 251). Under the same conditions, spectral green becomes yellower, and spectral blue is not altered.

Evidently, we are concerned here with a complex antagonistic action between stimulation and fatigue of the retina. As often as the impression of white begins, at first the stimulation rises for a short time to a maximum, and thereafter dies down again, owing to the gradually increasing fatigue. Using white-black discs, the author has succeeded in developing after-images of the flicker, both with and without the interposition of the red glass. His experience is that the final persistent condition of fatigue is exactly the same for all parts of the disc, and that no trace of any difference can be detected in the after-image between the rings that flicker and those that do not;

notwithstanding the fact that the after-image was so distinct that the edge of the disc could be plainly recognized and the small knob that formed the end of the axle.

On the assumption that after each transit of a black sector this average state of fatigue recurs, as it finally persists in the after-image, it must be the first moments of the impact of white that make the deepest impression. If the effect is then interrupted, when it has reached its maximum, all the sectors of this set produce just this maximum impression. But with a smaller number of more persistent impressions the number of these maxima is smaller, and the duration of the gradually failing impression cannot make up for the diminution of their number. So far as the author is concerned, the flicker impression with a disc of this kind is not such that there is a greater brightness all over the flickering ring, for there are always dark places in the ring as a whole. But the white, where it is visible, appears to be relatively brightest and purest in the flickering rings, and for this reason it makes a comparatively strong impression on the eye. Anyhow the impression of a bright light does not cease all at once, to be succeeded abruptly by darkness.

When a revolving disc is viewed through a red glass, the complementary blue-green of the intrinsic light of the retina (see p. 242) is seen very distinctly on the black sectors, just as it looks in the final after-image. On the flickering sectors, where the red appears in its maximum brightness and purity, it is certainly striking to see how in contrast with it the complementary blue-green is likewise more strongly forced on the attention, so that, especially in indirect vision, these rings appear downright bluish on the red ground of the disc. But the author must differ from BRÜCKE's description about one matter; because he finds that the red is precisely more saturated and more brilliant in the ring between this flickering blue-green than in the other rings, when attention is directed to it. In this case it is as if two colours of opposite kind were seen superposed at the same place; and in the author's judgment it is the colour that is the most altered, even if it is less luminous, that is, the blue-green, that attracts attention most. Still it must be admitted that this whole theory of the fading of coloured light is complicated by too many unexplained phenomena for anyone at present to be able to elucidate the details.

PLATEAU's experiment mentioned on p. 208 has been repeated by A. FICK; who thinks that he has found small variations from the law there advanced, namely, that the impression of a rotating disc is the same as if the light from each ring were distributed uniformly over the whole ring.

1858. D. BREWSTER, On the duration of luminous impressions of certain points of the retina. *Athen*. 1858. II. 521.

1860. H. W. DOVE, Über einen besonderen Farbenkreisel des Herrn LOHMEIER in Hamburg. *Berl. Monatsber*. 1860. S. 491.

GOODCHILD, Trocheidoskop. DINGLER J. CLVII. 181–184.—*Pract. mechan. J*. 1860. April 4. (Colour discs used for contrast phenomena).

1862. F. ZÖLLNER, Über eine neue Art anorthoskopischer Zerrbilder. POGGENDORFFS *Ann*. CXVII. 477–484.

J. J. OPPEL, Vorläufige Notiz über eine eigentümliche Augentäuschung in Bezug auf Rotationsrichtungen. *Jahresber. d. Frankf. Vereins*. 1861–1862. S. 56–57.

D. BREWSTER, On the compensation of impressions moving over the retina. *Rep. of Brit. Assoc*. 1861 (2) p. 29.

1863. A. FICK, Über den zeitlichen Verlauf der Erregung in der Netzhaut. REICHERT und DU BOIS *Archiv*. 1863. S. 739–764.

1864. E. BRÜCKE, Über den Nutzeffekt intermittierender Netzhautreizungen. *Wiener Ber*. XLIX. 21. Jan. 1864.

AUBERT, *Physiologie der Netzhaut*. Breslau. S. 96–103.

§23. Variations of Sensitivity[1]

We have seen that after light acts on the retina, the nervous mechanism of vision continues in the state of excitation for a long time still. The best way to realize this persistence of the impression is to turn the eye to a perfectly dark field after it has been gazing at bright objects. But there is another very noticeable effect after bright light has been acting on any part of the retina. To new light falling on it from outside, this place now responds differently from those other parts of the retina that were not affected previously. In other words, the sensitivity of the visual organ to external stimuli has been altered here by the action of light.

The main thing, therefore, in this chapter will be to find out what sensations arise when a part of the retina that has been previously stimulated by bright light is acted on by other external light. However, it should be stated at once that some of the phenomena that are visible in an apparently dark field will have to be considered here also, because, as a matter of fact, there is no such thing as an absolutely dark visual field. Even when all external light is completely excluded, there still remains a certain feeble stimulation due to endogenous causes as manifested by the *light chaos* or *intrinsic light of the dark visual field* (§17). Now the sensitivity of the retina to these internal stimuli seems to be altered in the same way as its sensitivity to objective light; and hence part of our present subject is concerned with phenomena that occur in the dark visual field after the retina has entirely ceased to be stimulated. In this connection it may be added that in bright surroundings mere closing of the eyelids is not sufficient to

---

[1] Concerning the long-continued variations of sensitivity produced by adaptation to different intensities of light, see NAGEL's Appendix I, at end of this volume.—N.

exclude all objective light from the visual field, because it is easy to notice the added darkness that comes from squeezing the eyes tighter or from putting the hand in front of them. Indeed, in direct sunlight it is not even sufficient to put the hand in front of the eye, because a perceptible amount of red light comes through it still. Accordingly, what is to be understood here by a completely dark field is that of an absolutely dark room from which all traces of external light are excluded, or the field that exists in a lighted room when the eyes are closed and each of them covered tightly, but without pressure, by the palm of the hand or a dark bandage.

Moreover, the light that acts first on the retina and changes its sensitivity will be called hereafter the *primary light*, as distinguished from that which acts afterwards on the place in the retina that has been changed, and which may be called the *reacting light*;[1] because it is for us, so to speak, a reagent by which we test the sensitivity of the retina.

The diversity of the phenomena of this kind is indeed very great, and although quite a number of notable observers have investigated this field, many parts of it are still uncertain and incomplete. The difficulty about it is that at first every observer has to gain a certain practice in apprehending and judging accurately the phenomena encountered here; and in doing this generally these experiments soon prove to be so trying to the eyes that severe and dangerous ocular and nervous trouble may ensue if they are pursued too long. Hence most observers thus far have been able to establish themselves only a comparatively few facts and to make a few new discoveries. And every future observer who wishes to make experiments of this sort is advised not to do too many on any one day, and to take a long rest from such work the moment he notices slight pains in his eyes or head after making the experiments, or in general in looking at a bright light or vivid colours, or whenever the after-images begin to become more prominent and persistent than they are in the healthy eye.

There is the same distinction between *positive* and *negative after-images* as between positives and negatives in photography. *Positive* images are those in which the bright parts of the object are likewise bright and the dark portions dark. *Negative* images, on the contrary, are those in which the bright parts of the object appear dark and the dark bright.

The phenomena will be described at first simply with respect to luminosity, and without reference to the change of colour that in most instances accompanies change of brightness, being due probably to the

---

[1] ¶Or the "secondary stimulus." The primary stimulus is "the tuning light" (*das umstimmende Licht*) by which the retina is "tuned" for the "reacting light" (*das reagirende Licht*). (J. P. C. S.)

fact that the duration of the single stages of the phenomenon is different for different colours. In order to watch the normal course of after-images without being disturbed, the retina must first get rid of the after-images of previous luminous impressions; and for this purpose it is usually necessary and sufficient to sit a few minutes with the eyes tightly bandaged, until nothing is any longer to be seen in the dark visual field except the light chaos, whose characteristic patterns (bright clots, so to speak, separated by dark bands scattered like branches and network) we soon learn to recognize. When no traces of the outlines of external objects can be discerned any longer, and when they are not revealed by such exceedingly feeble illumination as may penetrate even through the closed lids, the eye is in condition to receive the impression.

Now if the eyes are directed for a short time towards a bright object, preferably a window, without having to be turned thither for the purpose, and then simply opened and closed, directly afterwards there will be left behind a positive image of the primary bright object, as was stated in the preceding chapter. The less the eyes have turned, the sharper and more distinct this image will be; and, according to the author's experience, it will be brightest provided the illumination of the retina by the primary light has not lasted more than about a third of a second. The experiments described in the previous chapter showed that the intensity of stimulation by light increases during the first moments of its action, but soon reaches its maximum. If the illumination continues for more than a third of a second, the intensity of the after-image, corresponding to the intensity of the residual stimulation of the nervous substance, diminishes rapidly. The probable reason for this will be shown later. Moreover, the greater the intensity of the primary light, the brighter is the positive after-image, and the longer it lasts. It should be noted here that degrees of brightness can often be discerned in the positive after-image that were not noticed in the direct observation, because the brightness was too intense. For instance, when a lamp with a round wick is quickly extinguished, by watching the flame vanish, we can see by the after-image that the flame was brighter at the edges than in the middle; although (see §21) it is hard to see this by looking directly at the flame itself. AUBERT noticed the same thing in the after-image of the electric spark. Viewed directly, the spark appeared to be a faded streak of light, but in the after-image it was sharply delineated. Incidentally, even with very moderately illuminated objects, for example, white paper bright enough for writing or reading, positive after-images can be obtained by the above method that can be recognized for about two seconds; whereas, on the other hand, the bright after-image of the sun often lasts several minutes.

For obtaining really beautiful positive after-images, the following additional rules should be observed. Both before and after they are developed, any movement of the eye or any sudden movement of the body must be carefully avoided, because under such circumstances they invariably vanish for a while. After having been tightly blind-folded for a long enough time, the observer, keeping his hands over them, should direct his eyes towards the object, being careful not to let them move; then he should quickly remove his hands and just as quickly replace them again. But this movement of the hands must be executed gently and lightly, without any strong exertion or shaking of the body. If this procedure has been well practised, the positive after-image can sometimes be seen so sharp and bright, that it gives the impression as if the hands over the eyes were transparent, and the actual objects were visible. There is time enough to notice in these after-images a number of individual circumstances besides, which there was not time to see during the actual observation. The dim surfaces disappear most rapidly, without altering their colour perceptibly. The brighter surfaces persist a longer time, during which their colours pass through bluish hues into a violet-pink, afterwards yellow-red. At the time when the brighter regions pass from blue into violet the design of the after-image often becomes quite indistinct, apparently because by that time the relative loss of light in the bright portions exceeds that in the fainter places, so that the brightness is more evenly distributed all over; and because, anyhow, as we shall see presently in the next chapter, nice discriminations cannot be made except when the state of stimulation of the retina is being changed; and the power of doing so is soon lost when the stimulation has reached a steady stage. Subsequently, the less brilliant objects in the positive after-images become quite dark, and the more brilliant ones, now coloured pink, alone survive for a longer time. The author was much impressed by the after-image of a bright carpet lighted by a sunbeam that came through the window and fell on it. A time came when the design on the carpet was perfectly distinct and everywhere equally bright, and when the spot of sunlight no longer attracted attention. Presently the design disappeared, and then the figure of the brighter spot came out again in pink-red light and remained to the last. Thus, perhaps also for certain degrees of illumination, the features of the image may become very indistinct in whole or in part, and afterwards more distinct; that is, apparently the image can almost disappear and then clear up again.

But by being keenly alert, it will be noticed that the ground of the image is distinctly brighter at the time when the character of it becomes confused than it is afterwards when the brightest places again appear outlined on a wholly black ground. In such cases, therefore, it is not that the luminous impression has vanished and returned, but simply that the contrasts of brightness are temporarily more subdued, and the power of perceiving them has to be restored by new changes of colouring and brightness of the after-image. Moreover, with images that comprised a variety of objects of different degrees of brightness, the author's invariable experience has been that the brighter a particular object was, the longer it took to disappear entirely from the positive image. The after-images which AUBERT got by illuminating the object by electric sparks were probably faint; and yet his experience was that the positive after-images persisted longer when the sparks were feeble than when they were strong.

On the other hand, if there has been any violent movement or pressure or shaking of the eye in uncovering and covering it, the result at first will be a confused light chaos, out of which then the after-image may gradually evolve. Similarly, an after-image already developed will be temporarily or entirely obliterated by pressure, movement, or trembling of the eye, or by external light.

Supposing that the external light had acted only a very short time, and was not excessively brilliant, and that the field of view has been kept entirely free from all traces of external light, usually the positive image will disappear without passing into a negative one.[1] But if while the positive after-image is still there, or just after it has disappeared, the eye is turned towards uniformly illuminated surfaces, or even with closed eyelids is directed to bright surroundings, a negative after-image appears. The stronger the positive after-image, the stronger also must be the reacting light to transform it into a negative one. There is always a certain intensity of the reacting light for which the positive image simply disappears without becoming negative. If the reacting light is more intense than this, a negative image comes out; if it is less intense, the image remains positive and simply becomes less distinct. Incidentally, as the intensity of the reacting light is increased, the distinctness of the after-image also becomes greater; until the intensity exceeds the degree that is best suited for discerning small fractional differences of luminosity, and then the image begins to get less distinct. In this way too after-images of fainter primary light can be obtained by using more intense reacting light, but they have

[1] Concerning the so-called PURKINJE after-image following brief stimulation by light, see pages 383, 444 at end of this volume.—N.

to be carefully watched, because they disappear very quickly. Moreover, after the positive after-image has disappeared, the negative one remains visible on bright backgrounds a short time still; but it likewise gradually fades and disappears. In fact, when the field is perfectly dark, the effect may consist in a perceptible decrease of brightness of the intrinsic light of the retina. Usually then this intrinsic light itself in the immediate vicinity of the dark after-image looks a little brighter by contrast with it.

More intensity of the primary light imparts more clearness and longer duration to the negative after-image. Also, when the primary source of light is a brilliant object, those parts of it of different objective intensities, but without any difference of luminosity so far as the sensation is concerned, can be differentiated in the after-image. After looking at the setting sun, the author has often noticed that objects which covered a part of the sun's disc could be distinctly recognized in the negative after-image, although on account of irradiation there was no trace of them to be seen in gazing directly at the sun. Even little things like branches and leaves 'of trees may subsequently become visible in this way. The sensitivity of those parts of the retina where the image of the sun itself was formed is, therefore subsequently more altered than that of the places affected by the blur circles and the diffused light; although there was no distinction between them in the original sensation. This is likewise the reason why after-images of the sun are usually bigger at first than the sun's disc, and become smaller afterwards; because at first there is joined with it an after-image of the blur circles on the outer edge of the sun, but it becomes negative more rapidly and then disappears before that of the centre of the sun, where the sun's full brightness has acted.

The influence of the duration of the primary illumination is not the same for the negative after-image as it is for the positive. That is to say, the intensity of the negative after-image increases with the duration of the illumination and appears only with longer duration to approach asymptotically a certain maximum. By long exposure to powerful illumination a permanent change in fact can be produced in the corresponding place of the retina, as happened to RITTER[1] after gazing steadily at the sun from ten to twenty minutes. To obtain distinct negative after-images, the primary illumination should be allowed, therefore, to continue a considerable time (about 5 or 10 seconds with moderate light). Then the positive after-image will be faint and will disappear quickly; but the negative will be clearer and will last longer. For example, after observing bright clouds through

---

[1] *Beiträge zur näheren Kenntnis des Galvanismus.* 1805. Bd. II. S. 175–181.

the window for a third of a second, the positive after-image fades away in about 12 seconds, and the negative image on a brighter ground in about 24 seconds. But on looking at the same object between 4 and 8 seconds, it was 8 minutes before the negative after-image disappeared. In this case the field of view was kept entirely dark, except that from time to time a little faint light was admitted through the closed lids, to test whether the after-image was still there. To keep the negative after-image quite sharply outlined, a definite point of the bright object ought to be sharply focused during the illumination. It is still easier in the negative after-image than in the more transitory positive one to recognize details afterwards that had escaped observation in direct vision. If two different points of the object have been fixated one after the other, two partly overlapping images will be noticed afterwards also. Thus, when the sun is in the field of view, and the eye is made to traverse the field rapidly, the entire path traced on the retina by the sun's image may be depicted also in the after-image. When the gaze has been fastened for a moment on single places in the field, there will be more intense round after-images of the sun at these points, and they will remain positive longer; and, when they have become negative, they will be darker and last longer. They are connected with each other by narrower faded bands, which are indeed at first bright also; but they soon become negatively darker, being more faintly outlined where the movement of the eye was more rapid. These bands are narrower than the sun's disc and faded along the edge, because only a chord of the round image of the sun has passed over the part of the retina corresponding to their edge, whereas the middle portion has been traversed by a diameter, and therefore the sunlight has acted longer on the latter.

After-images, whether positive or negative, follow the movements of the eye. Their apparent position in the field of view always corresponds to the place where an object would have to be whose image would fall on the part of the retina acted on by the primary light. Thus, if the yellow spot has been stimulated by bright light, no matter where the eye turns, the after-image will always be at the fixation point; and, when it is very active, it keeps finer objects from being seen. If there is a very vividly outlined after-image right by the fixation point, the spectator is easily tempted to try to fixate it. He turns his eye towards it, but apparently, like the *mouches volantes*, it always flees from the point of fixation toward the edge of the field. But if the spectator fixates a stationary point more to the outside, the after-images also stand still. Their movements depend always simply on that of the eye.

From the phenomena thus far described certain things can be inferred as to the state of the part of the retina and the corresponding part of the nervous mechanism of vision which have been stimulated by the primary light. In the first place we find that the state of stimulation persists there for a long time still after extinction of the primary light, as is indicated by the positive after-images; and, secondly, that the nervous substance in question is less sensitive to new reacting light falling on it than the rest of the retina that was not previously stimulated. Thus, *after light has acted on the eye*, (1) *stimulation keeps right on*, and (2) *the sensitivity to new stimuli is lowered*. That stimulation leaves behind a condition of lowered sensitivity for stimuli, is something that takes place also in the motor nerves and in other sensory nerves. Such a condition is called *fatigue*.[1]

With increased intensity of the reacting light the negative after-images go on getting more distinct, until the intensity reaches the point where small percentage reductions of it can be perceived best; and hence we infer that fatigue of the nervous substance affects the sensation of new light about in the same way as if the objective intensity of this light were reduced by a definite fraction of its amount. There is a lack of sufficient metrical data here, and hence in what follows all that will be attempted will be to indicate the general process of the intensity of the sensation of a fatigued portion of the retina considered as a function of the intensity of the reacting light. As long as the positive image still exists along with the negative, the stimulation of the retina is compounded of the stimulation due to the primary light which still continues and the stimulation due to the reacting light which has been diminished by fatigue. In this sense we can regard the brightness of the after-image as the sum of the brightness of the positive image and the brightness of the reacting light reduced by fatigue. Now if the diminution of the brightness of the reacting light is greater than the brightness of the positive image, the entire brightness of the after-image will be less than the brightness of the reacting light, as it looks to the unfatigued portions of the retina. And so the after-image will become negative. This is what happens when the reacting light is brighter. But when it is less bright, the brightness of the positive image is more than sufficient to make up for the loss by fatigue; and the image is positive.

Let H denote the apparent brightness of the reacting light in the unfatigued parts of the retina, and aH in the part that has been fatigued, where $a < 1$; and let I denote the apparent brightness of the

---

[1] Concerning more modern investigations as to the sensitivity of the retina resulting from "adaptation" to darkness or to brightness. See NAGEL's Appendix I. A.—N.

positive image; then, according to the above, a must stay fairly constant when H varies. Supposing this to be the case, the brightness of the after-image will be $aH + I$, and that of the background on which it appears will be H. When

$$H = \frac{I}{1 - a}$$

then

$$I + aH = H,$$

and the after-image, having the same brightness as the background, becomes invisible. When

$$H > \frac{I}{1 - a}$$

then

$$I + aH < H;$$

that is, the after-image is negative. Finally, when

$$H < \frac{I}{1 - a}$$

the after-image is positive. If I is very small, the apparent brightness of the intrinsic light of the retina may be more than $\frac{I}{1 - a}$; then the negative image will appear even in the darkest field. If, finally, the positive image has completely vanished, then H is the brightness of the ground, and aH that of the after-image. If with disappearing fatigue $1 - a$ has become very small, a certain medium intensity of the reacting light will be necessary to make the difference appreciable. In the dark field it will not be seen then. At last when $1 - a = 0$, the after-image vanishes completely.

As to the negative images in the absolutely dark field, the evidence is that they arise by diminution of the intrinsic light of the retina. This intrinsic light, therefore, which we must attribute to the action of internal stimuli on the visual organ, is subject to the effects of fatigue, just as the impressions of external light are. That fatigue of the eye by stimulation affects its sensitivity to other stimuli, may also be shown, by the way, for electrical and mechanical stimulation of the retina. When a negative after-image has been developed, and then an ascending electric current is sent through the eye and optic nerve, the result being the bright bluish illumination of the field, the negative after-image will be reinforced by it; and when an image is in the act of changing from positive to negative, an ascending current will make it negative; and a descending current will make it positive. Thus when the eye is fatigued for light, it reacts more feebly to the electrical stimulus also. If colour sensations in the eye have been aroused by steadily maintained pressure, on releasing the pressure the images that persist still in the dark field can be made negative by letting light penetrate through the closed lids, or by looking at a lighted surface. Thus, fatigue due to stimulus by pressure also makes the eye less sensitive to light stimulus.

In cases of this sort where a fading after-image has been rendered visible for a moment by reacting light, occasionally directly afterwards a faint positive after-image again makes its appearance in the dark field. The inference here is that, while the stimulation in the fatigued area of the retina due to the reacting light is indeed weaker than in the unfatigued parts, it lasts longer. There is an analogy to this, by the way, in motor nerves; the contraction of a fatigued muscle being less powerful indeed but of longer duration than that of one that is not fatigued. This alternation between positive and negative images, which may sometimes occur, with hardly noticeable changes of illumination, from pinching the lids or moving the eyeball under the closed lids, perhaps too in consequence of subjective luminous phenomena produced by sudden pressure on the eyeball, has led some observers, PLATEAU in particular, to assume a spontaneous change in the condition of the nervous mechanism during the continuance of the after-effect. So far as this is concerned, the author shares FECHNER's opinion, that in most cases variation of illumination, movements of the eye or body, etc. are responsible for this change. But, of course, where two antagonistic influences are exactly evenly balanced, the least accessory circumstance may turn the scale one way or the other. It may be recalled that even the respiratory movements affect the intrinsic light of the retina. Sometimes too the images simply disappear, without changing into the opposite kind; indeed, as AUBERT aptly describes it, just like a moist spot drying up on a hot griddle. Incidentally, faint objective images sometimes vanish also in similar fashion when the gaze is riveted on an object, for example, in looking at a landscape by night. The impression the author gets is that it is impossible to compare the intensity of stimulation of different portions of the retina unless the stimulation changes from time to time. In case of objective images this can be accomplished every time by changing the point of fixation; but this cannot be done with subjective images. Reference will be made to the matter again in the theory of contrast. Incidentally, it appears that in trying to rivet the attention on images of this sort and to keep the eye from being distracted at all, there is the greatest feeling of exertion when the images are just fading out. After a while the strain ceases, and then the images come back. As to what internal change is involved here, the author has nothing to suggest.

The following phenomena, which are explained by the above principles, belong here also.

When a bright object, like a piece of white paper, is observed on a grey ground, and then the object is suddenly removed without changing the direction of the eye, a darker after-image of the white paper appears, as in the cases previously described. But if a little piece of black paper is observed on the grey ground, and this is pulled away, then a bright after-image appears. The place on the retina affected by the image of the white paper is more fatigued, that affected by the black image is less fatigued, than the rest of the retina on which the grey ground was imaged. Subsequently, the entire retina is acted on uniformly by the light from the grey ground, and therefore this light acts most strongly on the part of the retina where the black image was first, less strongly on that where the grey was before, and least strongly on that where the white image was. Now the experiment with the piece of black paper is important, because it shows that by prolonged observation of the grey ground the retina is fatigued where this light falls, and hence it becomes continually less and less sensitive to this light. Accordingly, when the black paper is removed, the light of the grey ground falls on an unfatigued part of the retina and produces there just the same impression which was made by the background at first. In the meantime, however, the portions of the retina on which the grey acts become fatigued, and so it looks much darker as compared with the fresh impression made on the unfatigued places of the retina. The difference between this experiment and the previous ones is that here the primary stimulus and the secondary stimulus are identical, both being the light of the grey ground. It shows that *external light of constant intensity acting uninterruptedly on the retina for a longer time arouses a sensation in it that continually gets weaker and weaker.* In fact, particuarly when the light is very weak, the intensity of the stimulation may fall off to such an extent as to be actually imperceptible. When night is approaching, suppose that a person gazes steadfastly at some dimly perceptible object without altering the direction of his eye; it soon vanishes completely, and it is not until he moves his eye away that the object will usually come in sight again as a negative after-image. This phenomenon is very striking at twilight on the sea especially when one tries to scan the horizon, because here the after-images of each part of the horizon are congruent with every other part; and, no matter where the look is specially directed, the after-image of the darker sea falls on sea and that of the brighter one on sky. If the eye is then elevated a little, a brighter streak appears on the lower part of the sky, bordered below by the edge of the sea, again becoming visible, and above by a line running parallel to this which goes through the new point of fixation. This streak is the negative after-image of the sea projected on the sky. If the eye is lowered instead of being elevated, a black streak appears, the negative after-image of the sky on the sea, bordered above by the horizon, and below by a line parallel to it. Thus, the horizon can be made visible by indirect vision, but it invariably vanishes on trying to look right at it.

Similar phenomena occur also in looking at a white or black square on a grey ground and then varying the point of fixation a little. Then the after-image of the paper does not completely cover the paper itself, and the brightness of the edges is changed. The portions of the after-image of the white paper that fall on the grey ground seem to be darker; and the portions of the after-image of the grey ground that overlap the white paper seem to be brighter. With black paper it is just the reverse. If the gaze has been riveted a long time on a certain point of the paper, and then if it is suddenly turned towards another point near by, the edges of the after-image will also come out distinctly, and the real nature of the object may be easily recognized. But if the point of fixation has been continually shifted, the after-images will be badly defined, and the bright ground in the region of the white paper seems merely to be a faint dark shade, the edge of the white paper being likewise a bright shade. A similar thing happens in looking a long time at a white square on a dark ground, and then, without changing the point of fixation, suddenly coming nearer the object, so as to increase its apparent size. In this case the edge of the square, except where it is still covered by the after-image of the previously observed pattern, appears to flare up brilliantly. On the other hand, by suddenly moving farther off, after having gazed steadily at the square for some time, it will appear on the dark ground surrounded by a darker border.

As to the peripheral portions of the retina, both PURKINJE and AUBERT noticed that the impression of bright objects disappears more quickly there than it does in the centre. Accordingly, this part of the retina seems to be fatigued much more rapidly. AUBERT found that the negative after-images on the periphery are not so intense as the central ones, but that otherwise they behave similarly. The author's experience shows that they are much more easily overlooked than central after-images, even on bright backgrounds; and that they cannot be readily noticed unless there is a change of the intensity of illumination.

Let us proceed now to the colour phenomena of after-images. After looking at coloured objects and observing the after-images on a wholly dark or white ground of different brightness, the image will be positive or negative depending on circumstances. In the beginning when the positive image is brightest, the colour is the same as that of the object; and the colour of the negative image, by the time it is fully and strongly developed, is complementary to that of the object.[1] The positive image is generally changed into the negative image by the interposition of pale or grey hues of another sort; and in fact, as a rule, the sequence of these colours is the same, no matter whether the transition takes place by gradual decline of the stimulation or by increase of the brightness of the ground.

The best way to develop positive images is by instantaneous action of the primary light. When a series of objects of various colours are seen by instantaneous exposure, the resultant positive after-image reveals the objects at first exactly in their natural colours. In most instances it disappears, a pink-red tinge spreading over it in which the colours that were there originally almost wholly fade out and are succeeded by faint yellowish-grey tones in which the positive image vanishes or is transformed into a dimly outlined negative after-image.

Negative after-images are obtained better by longer fixation at first. The way to see them is to place a bit of coloured paper on a grey ground, and fasten the attention on a special point of the coloured paper, and then suddenly pull the paper aside. A sharply defined negative after-image of the complementary colour will be seen then on the grey ground. Thus the after-image of red is blue-green; that of yellow is blue; that of green is pink-red, and *vice versa*. In general, what has been stated in connection with the after-images of white objects is true also of these after-images so far as duration and intensity are concerned.

Thus an eye which has been acted on by yellow light, say, is thereafter in a condition in which the blue components of white light affect it more than yellow does. Accordingly, the effect of fatiguing the retina is not uniformly extended to every kind of stimulation, but chiefly to stimulation similar to the primary stimulation. This fact is explained very simply by Young's assumption of three different kinds of sensory nerves for the different colours. For since coloured light does not stimulate these three kinds of nerves all to the same

---

[1] ¶Consequently, we speak of the negative after-image as the "'complementary after-image" and the positive after-image as the "homochromatic after-image." (J. P. C. S.)

extent, different degrees of fatigue must also be the result of different degrees of stimulation. When the eye has been exposed to red, then the red-sensitive nerves are strongly stimulated and much fatigued; whereas the green-sensitive and violet-sensitive nerves are feebly stimulated and not much fatigued. If afterwards white light falls on the eye, the green-sensitive and violet-sensitive nerves will be relatively more affected by it than the red-sensitive nerves; and hence the impression of blue-green, which is complementary to red, will predominate in the sensation.

Corresponding results are obtained in observing negative after-images of coloured objects on coloured background. Invariably it is principally those constituents which were predominant in the colour of the primary object that disappear from the colour of the ground. Thus, a green object on yellow ground gives a red-yellow after-image; and on blue ground, a violet after-image. Considering yellow as composed of red and green and blue as composed of green and violet, and supposing then that the green is diminished in both of them owing to the effect of fatigue, we should expect that the after-image in the yellow will be nearer the red, and in the blue nearer the violet. Generally, the colour of the after-image is always between that of the ground and the colour complementary to that of the object; and in hue, but not in luminosity, may be regarded as being a mixture of the two.

The cases where the colour of the object is the same as that of the ground, or complementary to it, are of special interest. The best way of making observations in the first case is to place a black object on a coloured ground, and after gazing steadily for a while at a point on the edge of it, to remove it suddenly. Under these circumstances the portion of the ground that is seen near the black is to be regarded as the primary coloured object, and the entire coloured ground, after the black object has been removed, as the reacting light (or secondary stimulus). In this case a bright after-image of the black object will be obtained, in which the colour of the ground is not merely more intense but is also more saturated than in the region outside, so that as compared with the latter it seems to be mixed with a great deal of grey. With careful scrutiny, the development of dark and grey on the coloured ground can be noticed even before the black object is taken away. The effect is very striking at the latter instant, because then the colour at this place is seen in the way it affects the unfatigued eye at the first moment of beholding it. This development of grey in the ground does not occur simply with colours which are mixed with white, and in which it may be so noticeable that the hue of the ground disappears entirely, but even with homogeneous spectral colours and certain kinds of coloured glass, from which all foreign white light has been most carefully excluded. For instance, suppose a piece of red glass coloured with copper oxide, which transmits only red rays, is placed in front of the eyes, the head and the edge of the glass being enveloped in a dark cloth, so that nothing but red light can get to the eyes. Now if the observer looks through the glass at a white surface, and places a black object in front of the surface, and then suddenly removes it, the contrast between the red-grey ground and the saturated red of the after-image will be very distinctly manifested. The explanation of this phenomenon evidently is that the retina was fatigued for red by looking at the red ground, and hence this part of the retina is less sensitive than the unfatigued parts where the image of the black object was. If the red is also mixed with white, the sensitivity for red is lowered to a relatively greater extent than for the other colours in the white admixture, and hence the colour must become relatively whiter from fatigue of the retina; but as it also becomes less intense at the same time, it looks grey. However, this is not only the case with pale red, but also with perfectly pure red, and here the explanation becomes more doubtful. It might be natural to suppose that it was connected in some way with the "light-mist" of the dark visual field. If the eye is closed and completely darkened while the after-image is being developed, there is visible in the "light-mist" a clearly defined after-image of the ground in complementary colour, that is, blue-green in this particular case. The internal stimuli which arouse the sensation of the "light-mist" elicit simply the sensation of blue-green in the part of the retina that is fatigued for red, just as objective white light would do. Now if this sensation is compounded with that of objective red, then a pale (or grey) red must be the result of it, as is observed in the experiment.

Nevertheless, the author is not satisfied with this explanation; for the apparent intensity of the "light-mist" in front of the closed eye is certainly very slight. It is hard indeed to say exactly what its value is. However, the way the red turns grey can be observed even in very bright pure red light, for example, when white clouds illuminated by sunlight are viewed through red glass. YOUNG's hypothesis would afford the explanation in this case. As was explained above, we should have to suppose then that although the spectral colours highly stimulated only one or two kinds of nerves, at the same time they excited the others a little. This modification of the hypothesis was necessary to account for the change of hue in pure spectral colours with light of high intensity and for the results of mixing spectral colours. The same assumption is evidently adapted to explain the present phenomenon. If while pure red light stimulates the red-sensitive nerves excessively, it also excites the others a little; and if, owing to the strong stimulation, the sensitivity of the former fibres is more rapidly lowered than that of the latter, the colour impression must approach pale or grey red.

When the primary colour is complementary to the reacting colour of the ground, the latter colour comes out more saturated in the extension of the after-image than it does on the parts of the retina that have not been fatigued or on the parts that have been fatigued by the colour of the ground. If a blue-green object is placed on a red ground, and then removed after having been steadily fixated, a saturated red after-image appears, just as if a black object had been removed. But it is easy to realize that the colour in the after-image of a complementary object is even more saturated than in the after-image of a black object. The simplest way of doing it is to prepare an object which is part black and part coloured, for example, blue-green. Now place it on a complementary (red) ground and look at a point on the ground close to the border between black and blue-green; and then take the object away, and all over the after-image the colour of the ground will come out clearer than it was previously in the part of the ground that was uncovered. The after-image of the blue-green is somewhat darker than that of the black, but it is not as if the red were less luminous there; it is more as if the red in the after-image of the black were overspread by a pale mist, which does not interfere with the red in the after-image of the blue-green. Thus the after-image of red on red looks grey-red; of black on red white-red; and of blue-green on red, saturated red. These distinctions come out very plainly when the experiment is performed with all three shades side by side.

On the supposition that there is some white in the red of the ground, the result is easily explained. The eye is not at all fatigued by black. Its sensitiveness to the whitish red in the after-image of the ground is unaltered. The eye is fatigued for red by red. Its sensitiveness to red in the after-image is lowered, but its sensitiveness to the other constituents of white is practically undiminished, the sensation being that of faint whitish red (grey-red). On the other hand, blue-green renders the eye less sensitive to the non-red constituents of the ground light, and therefore leaves the red to stand out in the after-image with less foreign admixtures.

Similar experiments are just as successful with pure spectral colours. In the field of a telescope the author has projected separate portions of the spectrum, taking every possible precaution to get rid of the last traces of white light. The ground was so densely black that the outline of the diaphragm of the telescope could not even be distinguished on it, and all that could be seen were the cloudy patterns of the "light mist" of the eye itself. The eye was not exposed to any other light except that of a small portion of the spectrum. Upon this coloured field after-images of complementary spectral colours were projected. This was accomplished as follows. A little adjustable steel mirror was placed in front of the ocular at an angle of 45°. In it was reflected part of another very bright spectrum, suitably limited by a circular diaphragm. For this second spectrum such a high degree of purity is not necessary. The arrangements were such that the entire circle was all of one colour. When the little mirror in front of the ocular was drawn aside, the observer no longer saw the circle previously seen by reflection, but he looked through the telescope at the pure spectrum. On it appeared the after-image of the coloured circle. Exactly the same results were obtained here as in similar experiments with pigments. That is to say, the after-image of the complementary colours appeared to be more saturated as compared with the colour of the ground. The latter again seemed to be covered with a whitish "light-mist", which was drawn aside, as it were, where the after-image was, thus letting the colour of the ground come out in its greatest purity. The important conclusion from these experiments was that *the pure spectral colours, which are the most saturated objective colours in existence, still do not elicit in the unfatigued eye the most saturated colour sensation that it is possible to have.* This highest degree of saturation is obtained by making the eye insensitive to the complementary colours.

Here also it might be conjectured that the white sheen that spreads over the ground is the internal "light-mist," its disturbing factors having disappeared in the after-image. As a matter of fact, when the eye is directed on the dark ground beside the spectrum, a complementary after-image is seen. This explanation likewise seems unsatisfactory to the author because the phenomenon can be seen on very bright spectral colours as compared with which the apparent brightness of the "light-mist" is presumably utterly negligible. On YOUNG's theory, on the other hand, we would have here the pure colour sensations of the separate kinds of nerves, in contrast with which the spectral colours must always look somewhat paler, because, by the necessary modifications of that theory, each single kind of homogeneous light must stimulate more than just one single kind of nerve fibre by itself.

All these experiments on after-images of coloured objects on coloured ground may also be modified in various ways exactly as was done in the case of white objects; for instance, the point of fixation can be changed, or the object can be brought nearer the eye or moved farther away. Thus, suppose we have a blue disc on a yellow ground, and that after gazing steadfastly at a point of the disc, the point of

fixation is altered; then the after-image of the blue disc will fall partly
on the ground and partly on the disc; and the same way with the after-
image of the ground. Where the after-image of the disc falls on the
ground, the yellow looks more saturated; and likewise where the
after-image of the ground falls on the disc, the blue looks more saturated. But where the after-image of the disc falls on the disc, and the
after-image of the ground falls on the ground, the blue and yellow
seem to be mixed with grey. The result of the other variations of
these experiments can be understood without special explanation.
Contrast phenomena are sometimes involved also. If a little bit of
white paper on a red ground is fixated, and if the after-image is then
projected on white, the after-image of the red ground will be blue-
green, and that of the small white field will be red by contrast with the
green, as will be shown in the next chapter. The best way to perform
the experiment is to lay the coloured paper on a white sheet, and
then holding the bit of white paper on the coloured paper with a forceps, to pull the coloured paper away. There is also a faint contrast
colouring of this sort around the after-image of a coloured square on a
white ground.

However, coloured after-images, usually with very diverse variations of colours, may be obtained also from white objects, not simply
from coloured ones. These phenomena are commonly known as the
chromatic fading of after-images. The sequence of the colours is
different here, according to the duration and the intensity of the
primary impression. The colour sequence after instantaneous observation the author finds is like that described by FECHNER[1] and SÉGUIN.[2]
The original white passes quickly through greenish blue (green,
SÉGUIN) into a beautiful indigo-blue, later into violet or pink-red.
These colours are bright and clear. Then follows a dingy or grey
orange, during which the positive after-image nearly always changes
into a negative one, and in the negative image this orange often
becomes a dingy yellow-green. After very brief action of the primary
stimulus orange is usually the last colour, and the image fades out
before it becomes negative. AUBERT also found the same colour
sequence after looking at the rather bluish spark of a Leyden jar,
except that the orange was not easy to make out on a dark ground;
although both it and the subsequent green were very distinct on white.
The image is surrounded by a yellow halo, perhaps the negative
after-image of bluish light diffused in the eye by irregular refraction.

[1] POGG. *Ann.* L. 220.
[2] *Annales de chimie.* 3. Ser. XLI. 415–416.

The phenomena described so far have to do with the behaviour of the after-image in the perfectly dark field. As to the formation of negative after-images in this case, they seem to be merely nebulously sketched-in in the intrinsic light of the dark field. If, during the existence of an after-image of this sort, reacting light is gradually admitted by slowly withdrawing the hands or a dark cloth that has been over the eyes, it is generally noticed that the after-image in this case passes into the later stages of its colour development, and retreats again when the reacting light becomes fainter once more. For instance, if light is allowed to enter when the image is blue amid perfect darkness, it fades through pink-red into a negative yellow image. On again covering the eye quickly enough the blue reappears. If the image is pink-red amid perfect darkness, dim light makes it yellow-red, etc. After the positive after-image in the dark field has finally gone completely, a grey or green-grey negative after-image on a faintly illuminated ground may still be seen for a while longer; the brighter ground surrounding it, which corresponds to the unfatigued portions of the eye, now being pink-red.

In explanation of these phenomena PLATEAU supposed that the duration of the separate stages of the after-images may be different for different colours; and he tried to demonstrate this also directly by the experiments described in the previous chapter. A complete explanation would involve knowing perfectly not only the deportment of the residual stimulation but also that of the fatigue. Still some conclusions can be drawn from these experiments. Thus, in the perfectly dark visual field the first brightest stages of the phenomenon are fairly independent of the degree of fatigue, because this does not come into consideration until the brightness of the positive after-image can no longer be clearly distinguished from that of the intrinsic light. It is probable, therefore, that the green-blue, blue and pink-red phases are simply due to the residual stimulation, and that in the yellow and green phases, when the negative after-image develops, fatigue is

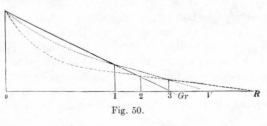

Fig. 50.

a factor also. Accordingly, it is to be inferred that the residual stimulation for the three colours, red, green and violet, declines in some such way as that indicated in Fig. 50. The abscissae denote time, and the ordinates of the curves represent the intensity of stimulation. The unbroken line corresponds to green, the dotted line to violet, and the broken line to red. The positive after-effect for all colours falls off continuously, the drop being greatest for red at first and afterwards least; the case being just the other way for green. For the intensities of colour sensation here represented, blue-green will predominate during the time from 0 to 1; blue at 1; violet at 2; purple at 3, which gradually changes more into red. However, owing to fatigue a greenish after-image is developed in the pale internal "light mist," and so this factor has to be considered as a matter of fact; and thus the fatigue for green, whose residual stimulation has disappeared most rapidly, appears finally to be the least. This green negative image, mixed with positive red, will give a yellow, which may appear brighter or darker than the ground according to the greater intensity of one colour or the other, and at last will change over to green, when the red also is extinguished. In PLATEAU's experiments on the duration of colour impressions, the same law of decline was obtained; those impressions which fall off most rapidly at first persisting longest ultimately in faint traces. The series of colour phenomena is quite different when fatigue has become more pronounced, as it is after prolonged action of white light or after the action of very intense light. FECHNER's observations indicate that with prolonged exposure to the stimulus of white the influence of fatigue is manifested by the white's becoming coloured even while it is still visible. Having kept his eyes shut a long time so as to get rid of the effects of previous impressions, he directed them at a white field on black paper illuminated by sunlight. During the first moments there was a sort of blinding, and he could not be certain about the presence or absence of colour. In fact, it seems that colour does not develop until after some time. But soon the paper was coloured distinctly *yellow*, then *blue-grey* or *blue* (without going through any transition stage of *green*, so far as could be detected in numerous experiments), the *red-violet* or *red*. The yellow phase was the shortest. The blue often lasted quite long before it changed to the next. No other colours succeeded red or red-violet, although the experiment was continued until the eye was under much strain. Even in diffused daylight he often perceived the given series of col-

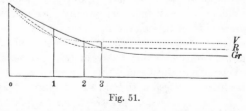

Fig. 51.

ours, but sometimes more distinctly than at others. The last two colourations could generally be recognized here better than the yellow. The phenomena were represented by FECHNER by three curves, but with different fundamental colours; as shown in Fig. 51, where again the abscissae are proportional to the time, and the ordinates indicate the intensity of stimulation of the retina in continuing to look at a white surface. The continuous curve represents green, the dotted curve red, and the broken curve violet. In the time from 0 to 1 the colour would be yellow-green; at time 1, pale green; at time 2, pale blue; at time 3, violet, and afterwards pink-red.

After longer and more intense action of primary white light the after-image on a wholly dark field shows the following colour series: *White, blue, green, red, blue*; and on white ground, ultimately *blue-green* and *yellow* besides. In the red the image becomes negative. SÉGUIN includes some intermediate stages in his description. The colours of the first series are for him *white, green, blue*; those of the second (negative) series being *yellow, red, violet, blue, green*. If the action of the white light has exceeded a certain time, this colour series is constant and is not changed any more by longer action. On briefer, but still not just instantaneous, exposure to a primary stimulus of white light that was distinctly tinged with yellow, the colour series was *yellow, blue, red-yellow*; then it became negative green. BRÜCKE gives: *Green, blue, violet, red*; after which the image is negative without distinct colour. Thus the blue phase seems to be always the first variation of the primary light impression; then follows a pink-red, red-yellow to green positive phase, depending on the duration of the primary impression.[1]

In these coloured after-images also, as was the rule with the others, the later phases of the after-image are produced by making the background whiter; whereas when the reacting light is reduced in intensity, the after-image may return through its earlier phases. Whenever the author has observed after-images of uniformly lighted surfaces, with the eye properly accommodated to see them, the alterations of colour were either simultaneously visible over the whole area of the after-image or they could be seen advancing from one side or the other, perhaps not very regularly. But after looking at the sun or some brilliant object of that sort, usually the changes of colour of the image proceed from the edge towards the centre. Irregularities of refraction, which, in the case of very bright objects, always scatter a great deal of light in the vicinity of the image, have something to do with these phenomena. But besides this, the eye is so blinded by the light that it is almost impossible to hold the accommodation steady and keep the

---

[1] For me and other deuteranopes (says NAGEL here) a deep blue after-image appears on looking at a dark ground after the action of bright white light. While this after-image lasts, all red, yellow and yellow-green colours (homogeneous lights as well as pigments) shade off to white or grey.—N.

eye fixed. The result is that the place on the retina where the image is
formed of the central part of the sun is subjected more constantly and
more intensely to the action of light than the part near the edge of the
image. The sun itself is surrounded by the afterglow of the light
diffusely scattered in the atmosphere and in the eye itself. When the
eye has been in the dark and is then suddenly exposed to the sun for a
moment, the contour of the sun's body can hardly be discerned in the
dazzlingly luminous surface. Thus in these cases there is always a
gradually diminishing action of light from the centre towards the
edge, and the result is a correspondingly different deportment of the
separate phases of the after-image. The more intense the action, the
more slowly do the individual phases proceed on the whole; and hence
at the edge of the after-image generally the earlier stages are seen
gradually advancing towards the centre. Besides, owing to the slighter
degree of fatigue, the sequence of colours out towards the edge is
usually somewhat different from that in the centre. In keeping with
this explanation, the after-image in its first stages has a greater extent
than the apparent size of the sun, and it is natural to mistake the
entire after-image for the image of the sun's disc alone, and to suppose
that the different coloured rings developed there belong to it, when
in fact they correspond to its halo. The best way of getting a well
developed after-image of the sun is to take a very dark coloured glass
(or a smoked glass or a pile of several glasses of complementary
colours) and look at the sun through it. Then it will appear simply as
a dimly visible disc of light. Now remove the glass for a moment, and
close the eyes immediately. The action on them has been comparatively slight, and they have not had much time to change their adjustment. Meanwhile, however, the after-image develops very brilliantly.
And in this case the author can also see a nucleus in the after-image
which is uniformly coloured all over and is about the size of the apparent disc of the sun. Therefore, the deviations on the border may
be attributed to errors of refraction in the eye.

Under these circumstances, in the environs of the sun's image the
phases of the after-image due to white objects that have been seen
for an instant pass rapidly in review: positive blue, pink-red passing
through yellow into negative dark green; while the image of the sun
itself in this *first phase* appears as a faded, more or less round *white
spot*, which, at about the time when the ground has become pink-red,
enters the *second phase* and is colored *bright blue*. The second phase
usually passes rapidly into the *third*, by the blue becoming green
first at the edge, then at the centre also, while a red-yellow border
arises at the edge which is darker than the surrounding field, and on

the outer edge of which, still in this same phase, a still darker blue-grey border is traced. If during this phase the eyes are directed to a white field, the positive green passes through violet into the negative blue-red of the following phase.

The *fourth phase* arises by the red of the border spreading itself over the centre of the image. The blue-grey border thereupon becomes broader and darker. The entire after-image now is darker than the surroundings. In contrast with it the latter appears whitish or greenish. This is the last negative green of the image of the sky. The after-images of any window-bars that happen to be in the field appear bright on it. If in this phase the eye is directed towards a white ground, the red passes into green-blue.

Finally, in the *fifth phase* the entire after-image takes on the blue colour of the previous border and disappears in the dark field generally in this stage of the blue, whereas on a white field it appears green-blue.

These are the phases as given by FECHNER. The author would like to add a *sixth phase*, in which there is nothing of the after-image any longer perceptible in the dark field, but perhaps still a yellow or brownish appearance on a white field. Finally, after quite a little time this disappears also. If during this time, and even still later, when the yellow appearance has gone, the eyes are exposed to white and then suddenly closed, a faint positive bluish after-image reappears, but it quickly fades out again. Then if the eyes are opened and exposed to white, the yellow after-image instantly reappears. In the writer's opinion the explanation of this effect is due to the fact already mentioned, that in a fatigued nerve the new stimulation dies out more slowly than in the surrounding unfatigued parts of the retina.

Incidentally, the way these after-images of intense light act does not seem to be essentially different for different persons when they are developed under the same conditions. At any rate the writer's observations in this connection are in accordance with those of FECHNER and SÉGUIN, as far as they go.

In this complicated colour sequence it may be conjectured that both the time needed for the impressions of the individual colours on the retina to disappear and for the perception of the intrinsic light may be altered by the ensuing fatigue; and since we have no exact knowledge of these relations and do not know how the various degrees of the fatigue itself die out in the separate colour sensations, it is impossible to give a complete explanation of the individual stages of this colour fading. The progress of fatigue and its effect on the progress of the stimulation for the separate purer colour impressions would first have to be determined and compared.

The phenomenon is certainly very much simpler in case of the fading of the after-image produced by the impression of saturated colours, but even then it is not entirely without colour changes. The main features of the phenomenon have already been described. First, there is a positive image in the same colour as the primary light, and afterwards a negative complementary image. But when the luminous impressions have been quite vivid, usually the transition from positive to negative does not occur by one image simply fading out and the other then becoming visible; but in this transition stage the colour changes by passing through whitish tones. In case there were no other colour in the field of vision but that of the primary light, the colours of the fading image always still seem to be tolerably saturated; and they have been so described by several observers, because there is nothing to compare them with in the dark visual field. But if at the moment of exposure the primary object displayed various colours of about the same luminosity, the after-images in the transition stage from positive to negative will exhibit much slighter differences of colour than the original colours; being all strongly mixed with the pink-red or yellowish white that appears also in the after-images of instantaneously exposed white objects. The after-image obtained by looking at a prismatic spectrum for a moment is particularly interesting in this connection. After the primary colours in the after-image have been visible for some seconds, and the faint colours at the ends of the spectrum have become entirely dark, the whole after-image changes into a whitish-red streak of the same form as the spectrum, in which colour differences are scarcely any longer indicated; except that the former yellow and orange tend towards blue somewhat, and here at the place where red was formerly its green-blue after-image is formed, being negative by this time. In order to tell where the previous colours had been, the writer made a black mark on the white screen where the spectrum was projected, parallel to the bands of colour which continued visible in the after-image. And thus he realized that the reddish-white after-image corresponds to the whole extent of the spectrum from orange to indigo. The same result is obtained by exposing coloured papers of nearly the same luminosity in sunlight, and then developing an after-image by taking a quick look at them.

The conclusion is that when coloured objects have been exposed to the eye for a moment, first, the predominating colour disappears in the after-image, and so the image becomes like that of a white object, usually the pink-red phase being specially prominent in this case. Then the complementary colour of the negative after-image develops gradually; but it may be visible even before the positive image has changed to negative, and thus it may look brighter than the

dark ground. The author believes that the emergence of the complementary colour is due to the fact that by this time the positive image,
having become faint and white, coincides with the negative and
complementary image arising in the intrinsic light due to the fatigue
of the eye. Obviously, such a coincidence between positive white and
negative blue-green, as might be obtained by looking at red, may give
a greenish-white positive image. These positive complementary images
are mentioned by several observers.[1] When they are by themselves
in the visual field or together with the primary colours only, the complementary colour appears to be tolerably saturated. But when they
can be compared with after-images of other colours, the author's
invariable experience has been that the complementary colour seemed
to be strongly mixed with white or grey, as long as it was still brighter
than the ground. It is in the negative after-image that it first becomes
more saturated.

The way these phenomena would be explained by YOUNG's colour
theory is thus: Each objective colour, even the most saturated, is
subjectively mixed with white. The strong stimulation corresponding
to the prevailing colour declines relatively faster than the weak stimulations due to the other colours contained in the white, and hence the
resultant colour impression becomes weaker and at the same time
approaches white. Then during the dimmer stages of the positive
image, the negative image induced by fatigue finally gets the upper
hand and exerts an appreciable influence by its colouration.

The fading that occurs after momentary exposure of the eye to
single colours proceeds in a somewhat different manner, depending on
their connection with the hues of the waning white. It is usually
simplest with *green*, because its complementary pink-red is the same
as the pink-red of the waning white. This hue is developed therefore
in special intensity and beauty. *Greenish* blue passes through blue
and violet, and *blue* through violet, into pink-red. In the latter case
the succeeding phase of yellow comes out purer and more vivid, because
it coincides with the complementary blue. In the case of the colours
mentioned first, the green-blue and blue phase of the fading white
preceding the pink-red phase may perhaps not be noticeable on
account of their similarity to these colours themselves; but it seems
to be the case with *yellow*, which passes through greenish white into
violet, and with *red*. In the case of red there is more of a violet, subsequently grey-green colour, instead of pink-red. Incidentally, it
disappears comparatively soonest of all. It has been mentioned that

[1] PURKINJE, *Zur Physiologie der Sinne.* II. 110. — FECHNER in POGGENDORFFS *Ann.*
L. 213. — BRÜCKE, Untersuchungen über subjektive Farben, in the *Denkschr. der Akad.
zu Wien.* Bd. III. S. 12. (See also NAGEL's Appendix I. B.—N.)

when there are no other colours in the visual field for comparison, the green stage frequently looks like a saturated green. AUBERT's experiments are also in essential agreement with these observations. He examined the electric spark through coloured glass. The only difference he got was that much adulterated yellow gave him still the yellow stage of the waning white after the violet, before it reached the negative blue. Usually too a corona of light formed, and ran through the stages more rapidly.

After longer or more intense action of primary coloured light, during the transition from the positive homochromatic image to the negative complementary one, some of the phases exhibited by white light are likewise noticeable at this time. In particular, the red border surrounded by the blue-grey one often appears. FECHNER has made experiments of the same sort by looking at the sun through combinations of various coloured media which transmitted only one or two colours of the spectrum. The author can supplement them by some observations of his own on prismatic colours, made by viewing a circular diaphragm illuminated by sunlight which had been transmitted through a prism. When the coloured light is so intense that it looks white or yellow, this effect remains also in the after-image at first, but gradually the characteristic colour is then developed clearly.

FECHNER obtained homogeneous *red* light by looking at the sun partly through a red glass and partly through a thick layer of litmus tincture. By direct observation it appeared yellow on account of its high intensity. The after-image too was yellow at first, the edge being red; and afterwards as the intensity diminished, it got red all over, and at the same time a dark blue-green border came into view. In this experiment when the field is dark, usually no distinct negative image develops. But on white ground the green-blue colour of the border becomes central. The author has noticed the same thing with prismatic red. In these experiments the transition from red to green-blue was made through violet. But after looking at a flame through a red glass for quite a while, the transition usually is made through a positive yellow-green followed by green-blue.

FECHNER obtained homogeneous *yellow* by combining two pale yellow glasses with a green glass and a pale red glass; so that except for a little green nothing but yellow was transmitted. The after-image looked yellow with red edge, the latter being surrounded by a dark blue-green ring. With a simple yellow glass, which transmitted red, yellow, green, and a trace of blue, there followed yellow, green, then blue-grey, with red-black encircling ring. With pure prismatic yellow, the author likewise observed the transition into green and the red-black ring. The green and red occur under the same conditions in the after-image of white. On the other hand, after having exposed his eye to a candle flame between 12 and 60 seconds, PURKINJE[1] saw the following colour series: brilliant white, yellow, red, blue, faint white, black.

FECHNER got a tolerably pure *green* mixed with yellow, by using a green glass with a bright blue glass and two bright yellow glasses. Through this combination the sun looked greenish-white; and so did the after-image, surrounded by a black-red ring. He got green, mixed with very little blue and yellow, with three green glasses and a yellow one. The sun looked almost white, the after-image being a little greenish with bluish-white border, and afterwards bluish-white with black-red ring around it, encircled for a while by a faint lilac sheen. With prismatic green the author got a green after-image bordered by blue; and on a white ground, dark purple bordered by yellow.

With a copper sulphate solution FECHNER got *blue* mixed with green. The sun looked white through it. At first the after-image was also white, and then blue. Then a positive green developed, surrounded by a negative red edge. With prismatic blue the author also got the purple border, but the surrounding area was complementary golden yellow.

With a thick layer of copper sulphate solution and ammonia and a piece of violet glass FECHNER got homogeneous *violet*. The sun appeared bluish-white. And so did the after-image at first; then it got dark violet, with a black-red ring around it, the ground beyond being greenish. The phenomenon disappeared before the dark red became central.

In all these cases where the border of the after-image begins to become negative, there is the same red border that occurs also with the after-images of white, as if the homogeneous colour were mixed with white; the fading phases of which become noticeable at the time when the positive after-effect of the principal colour is evenly balanced with the complementary negative one.

When the intensity of the primary stimulus of white or coloured light is low, or when it is moderate but very short-lived, positive images are left behind that fade out through very pale coloured whitish tones of indefinable hue, which may be changed in the most striking way by contrast; and this change is responsible for some very curious apparent conflicts in the results. When there are many different coloured objects in the visual field, the colour differences fade out in the after-image. The after-images obtained by AUBERT by illuminating coloured objects by the electric spark were apparently also of this sort. Thus, red squares on white were red to him in the after-image. On the

[1] *Beobachtungen und Versuche.* I. 100.

other hand, a broader red strip, cut from the same paper, with white squares on a white ground, gave green. The after-image of blue and yellow strips with black squares on a black ground was always yellow to him. On a white ground both strips gave blue after-images. What these differences are due to, is yet to be ascertained.

Other phenomena of the fading out of colour may be observed with colour tops with black and white sectors, by not letting them revolve so fast as to make a perfectly steady impression on the eye. If the top is made to spin slowly at first, and then gradually faster, while the eye watches it steadily without trying to follow the movement, it will be noticed that the white is coloured; being reddish on the front advancing edge, and bluish on the edge coming on behind. With fainter light the reddish hue tends more to red-yellow and the bluish to violet; but when the light is stronger, the first hue is more pink and the latter more green. With slower rotation the bluish hue at first is spread over a wider part of the white than the reddish. But when the speed is faster, red spreads out all over the white as pink-red, and green-blue extends over into the black sectors; and on the whole, violet appears then to predominate on the disc. With still greater speed, the different sectors can no longer be distinguished apart, and seem then to be sprinkled over with some fine particles, and little sparks flicker back and forth between violet-pink and green-grey. At last, when the speed is still further increased, the sparkling becomes fainter, and the grey mixture of white and black comes out more and more; being sometimes overspread by spots of violet-pink of variable size which are formed like the spots and streaks in watered silk.[1]

These various stages of the phenom-enon may be seen side by side very nice-ly by using a disc with three concentric rings, like that in Fig. 52; in which the inside ring is composed of two, the mid-dle ring of four, and the outside ring of eight equal sections, alternately white and black. When the disc is revolved at a certain speed, the inside field will look white with a greenish colouring, the middle field will be pink-red, and the outside field will exhibit the finely mot-tled flicker. With higher speed, the in-

Fig. 52.

side field shows the pink-red colouring and the middle field the finely mottled flicker, while the outside field gives a grey with violet tinge.

---

[1] See also BIDWELL, *Proc. Roy. Soc.* London LXI, 268–272, and v. KRIES, "Farbeninduktion durch weisses Light" in NAGELS *Handbuch d. Physiol. d. Menschen* Bd. III, S. 245.—N

It may be added that the ring where the pink-red is developed most purely always looks darker than an adjacent ring where the alternation is proceeding more slowly or more rapidly. The order of the colours, as they show up at first on the white areas of a disc of this kind cannot be

Fig. 53.

recognized without some practice. It is easier to do it with a disc composed of two spirals of equal width, one black and the other white, as shown in Fig. 53. What this means is, that when a point on the retina is exposed to rapid alternations of whiteness and blackness, so that the stimulation is increased and lowered in quick succession, *the maximum stimulation does not occur at the same instant for all colours*, but the stimulation for red and violet begins sooner than that for green.[2]

These colour phenomena generally do not begin until some time after the observation has been in progress; and then they become gradually always more brilliant. Apparently, therefore, the eye has to be fatigued by the flicker to a certain degree before this result can be obtained. Moreover, other phenomena besides are connected with it which seem to proceed from an unequal sensitivity of different parts of the retina to this sort of stimulation. Thus, in the flickering light certain patterns become visible which are partly connected with definite places on the retina, that is, what is known as PURKINJE's *"shadow figure."*[1] When the revolution of the disc is so rapid that the single sectors can no longer be distinguished apart, the number of sectors appears to be greater, and they form, as it were, a lattice work of faintly outlined curved bars, whose meshes are longest in the direction of the radius of the disc. With increased speed of revolution the design becomes more delicate, like that of a piece of embroidery; and in that part of the flickering field corresponding to the yellow spot there is a peculiar round or oval pattern delineated by sharper contrasts of light and shade, which might possibly be compared with a rose of many petals, that are, however, more hexagonal in form. In its centre there is a dark point surrounded by a bright circle. The same figures can also be produced by turning with closed eyelids towards a bright light and moving the wide-spread fingers to and fro in front of the eye, thereby

---

[1] ¶On this point see also BIDWELL, *Proc. Roy. Soc.* London, 1896–7. LX, 368. (M.D.)

[2] *Beobachtungen und Versuche zur Physiologie der Sinne.* Bd. I. Prag 1823. S. 10.

exposing and shading it in rapid alternation. The whole point is to produce in some way this rapid change of light and shadow. In these figures PURKINJE makes a distinction between primary and secondary forms. The primary forms in his right eye are larger and smaller squares, changing from dark to bright like a checkerboard, which spread over the greater part of the visual field. It is only downwards from the centre that he sees a row of larger hexagons. Apparently, he observed only isolated features of the rosettes of the yellow spot, which are quite regular so far as the author is concerned. On the other hand, in the author's case the spots outside the centre are neither regular squares nor hexagons, but irregular, and increasing in size towards the periphery. PURKINJE got practically the same effect in his other (weak, left) eye also. The secondary forms were obtained especially when he turned his closed eyelids towards the sun. PURKINJE describes them as being eight-rayed stars and peculiar sharply broken spiral lines, which develop out of the primary patterns by displacement of the bright and dark squares; being, by the way, very changeable. He saw these secondary forms with either eye, merely symmetrically transposed in one eye as compared with the other.

On rotating discs these phenomena tend to disappear more and more as the speed of revolution is increased, the only traces that finally remain being the iridescent spots mentioned above. When the flicker is most vivid, sometimes the entire figure vanishes as you watch it steadily, and a dark red ground comes up behind it, which seems to be intersected by a lot of currents. This is the phenomenon in which VIERORDT[1] thought he recognized circulation. In the author's own case the image of this movement corresponds more to currents where there are no banks, continually changing their bed and shifting back and forth. Of course, it might be supposed that intermittent illumination makes the movement of the blood corpuscles visible, exactly as the movement and forms of drops can be exhibited in a jet of water. However, the author would not venture to give this explanation of the observations he himself has made.

When coloured light is made to alternate with black on the flickering discs, either by using coloured sectors or by looking at the black and white sectors through coloured glass, homogeneous colours show signs of colour fading even under these conditions. For instance, through a red glass that is opaque to everything but red, the advancing edge of the bright fields is orange, and the following edge is pink-red, corresponding to yellow and blue in white light. At the same time the black ground becomes covered with complementary green. The com-

---

[1] *Archiv für physiol. Heilkunde.* 1856. Heft II.

plementary colour[1] becomes even more distinct when one of the spiral bands on the disc is coloured and the other grey, and the top is stopped suddenly after it has been spinning some little time. This effect is obtained also under similar conditions when the disc consists of alternate white (or grey) and coloured sectors. SINSTEDEN[2] used for the same purpose an orange-red disc, with sectors cut out of it, which rotated over a white shaded one. When he stopped the upper disc, the lower one appeared vivid blue.

E. BRÜCKE also obtained similar results by setting a small black disc in vibration in front of a coloured glass plate. In this case the appearance in front of a green disc was especially curious, because the places, in front of which light and dark alternated, appeared pink-red; whereas the parts that were completely covered or uncovered were green.

The so-called *fluttering heart* is a characteristic phenomenon that probably belongs here.[3] On coloured sheets of stiff paper figures are made in some other vivid colour. Red and blue seem to work best. The colours must be very vivid and saturated. When one of these cards is moved laterally to and fro at a certain rate in front of the eye, the figures themselves seem to shift their positions with respect to the paper and dance about on it. Apparently, the explanation is that the luminous impression in the eye does not come and go with equal rapidity for the different colours, and so the blue apparently lags a little behind the red in the path traversed by the card. Something like it occurs also when the eye moves instead of the object. Thus, WHEATSTONE[4], BRÜCKE and E. DU BOIS-REYMOND,[5] looking over red and green carpet in gaslight, saw the pattern apparently move. BREWSTER states that the phenomenon occurs also when bright daylight enters an otherwise dark room through a small hole.

In this discussion so far the view has been adopted which is espoused especially by FECHNER; that is, that all phenomena of after-images depend partly on a persistent stimulation of the retina and partly on a lowered sensitivity to stimulus. As a matter of fact, if we adhere to our previous conception of stimulation and sensitivity, we must speak of stimulation as continuing to exist when we see a positive after-image in absolute darkness, and we must regard the sensitivity to stimulus as being lowered when the place in the eye

---

[1] DOVE in POGGENDORFFS *Ann.* LXXV. 526.
[2] Ibid. LXXXIV. 45.
[3] See page 446.
[4] *Inst.* No. 582. S. 75.
[5] *Die Fortschritte in der Physik im Jahre 1845*, reviewed by KARSTEN. I. 223.

where the negative after-image is developed is less sensitive to external light than the unfatigued retina. Thus the persistence of stimulation and the lowering of sensitivity is not an hypothesis but a direct consequence of facts. Moreover, these two circumstances suffice to explain by far the greatest number of the more obvious and constant phenomena in this region, especially the phenomena of the altered intensity of light and of positive homochromatic and negative complementary after-images. To bring the very intricate phenomena of colour waning of intense or persistent luminous impressions entirely within a simple scheme, would probably be a very difficult task indeed at present and would involve all sorts of arbitrary assumptions. However, we can inquire why these phenomena must be so variable. We really know neither the law by which a more or less advanced fatigue of the eye for a single colour disappears, nor how far the after-effect of light depends on fatigue. In FECHNER's opinion negative complementary images in the dark field are to be regarded as new modes of response to the internal stimuli of the retina. On the other hand, many physicists have looked on these images as effects of a new antagonistic activity of the retina. PLATEAU[1] in particular, has elaborated this view into a consistent theory. He demonstrated that the same complementary coloured images may be seen even without any external light at all; and as he was not then cognizant of the intrinsic light of the eye, he knew no other way of explaining the phenomenon except as a new antagonistic activity of the retina. Moreover, having noticed also subsequent variations of the positive and negative images, he advanced the proposition that whenever the retina was strongly stimulated by light, it experienced a series of oscillations, before it came to rest, which involved its passing successsively and alternately through opposite stages. These antagonistic conditions would correspond to the sensation of complementary colours. He connected this with certain contrast phenomena, which will be considered more directly in the next section; and assumed for the spatial extension of the impression a series of such oscillations. On the other hand, it must be remembered that negative complementary after-images do not consist in a lively activity of the retina, but, on the contrary, are rendered visible by being diminutions of the already existing sensation of intrinsic light; and that, moreover, as is almost always discovered on closer attention, those alternations between positive and negative images are dependent on external conditions, especially on slight changes in the illumination of the fundus of the eye. In the author's opinion it is very hazardous to develop a theory on the basis of such delicate and extremely un-

---

[1] *Ann de Chim et de Phys.* LIII. 386.—POGGENDORFS *Ann.* XXXII. 543.

steady phenomena as after-images are at the time of their conflict between positive and negative in the dark visual field, when the organ from which the light has long been excluded is in a state of greatly increased sensitivity, and when external influences that can be shown to be hardly perceptible are responsible for the transformation of the image. However, it is not surprising that under these circumstances we still do not know always what is the reason for the changes that take place. Incidentally, FECHNER has pointed out another difficulty in PLATEAU's theory. The latter has to assume that in the after-images complementary colours, being antagonistic activities of the retina, offset each other and induce darkness. For example, when there is a complementary after-image, the perception of the primary colour is affected. If the eye has been fatigued by green and red in succession, the after-image will be black. But how can this assertion be reconciled with the fact that sensations evoked simultaneously by objective complementary lights fuse into that of white, which is brighter than either of the two colours by itself?

BRÜCKE regards positive complementary after-images as incompatible with FECHNER's theory. In this connection the author pointed out above that the colouration of these images is in fact very pale; and that it is simply by contrast with the previously seen primary colour, and from not having other colours for comparison, that the complementary colour comes out so vividly. All one has to do is to look at two primary colours in quick succession, in order to see that in the last stages of the positive condition of their after-images there is just a faint suggestion of the complementary colours. And hence the author believes he may venture to consider these images as being a mixture of a positive pale after-image and a negative complementary one, and thus succeed in including these phenomena also in FECHNER's explanation. There is yet to be mentioned a puzzling phenomenon described by AUBERT in the case of after-images of objects which were illuminated by electric sparks. In this instance he saw, with black and red squares on a white ground, negative images apparently produced at the same time with the sparks. But with white squares on a black ground they failed to show up. Sometimes they seemed to be displaced with respect to the original object. They were succeeded by the homochromatic positive images. The after-images of coloured stripes on a white or black ground were always complementary and always brighter than the ground.

In this extremely perplexing region of the most manifold phenomena, the author believes it is best to be guided strictly by a theoretical opinion such as that of FECHNER's which easily explains the great mass of relevant phenomena, and which gives a good explanation especially of all those effects that are characterized by their energy, distinctness and constancy; even if we also find isolated and more transitory phenomena for which at present there is no perfectly satisfactory explanation. This is the case with the colour transformations that occur at the moment when the image changes from positive to negative, and when the antagonistic influences of the persistent stimulation and fatigue are found in a very unstable equilibrium. At present, the author does not know any phenomenon that is positively irreconcilable with FECHNER's principles of explanation.

Positive and negative after-images of windows were described by PEIRESC[1] in 1634. Afterwards the experiment became a kind of magician's trick. BONACURSIUS made a wager with the Jesuit, ATHAN. KIRCHER,[2] that he could make a person see just as well in the dark as in the light; and he won his bet by making KIRCHER look steadily at a drawing fastened in an opening of the window in a dark room. Then the room was made perfectly dark, and KIRCHER plainly saw the drawing again by looking at a piece of white paper held in his hand (which was not necessary). KIRCHER's explanation of it was that the eye sent the light out again that had been absorbed, and so illuminated the paper in front of him. MARIOTTE[3] repeated similar experiments. NEWTON was acquainted with images produced by intensely brilliant light and is said to have regarded them as being of a psychical nature,[4] because by fastening his attention on them, he could continue to elicit the after-images of the sun for quite a while. What led him to try these experiments was an inquiry from LOCKE, who had run across something about them in BOYLE's book *de coloribus* (published in English in 1663). A more complete theory of the phenomena was proposed by JURIN[5] in 1738, which was based on the assumption that as soon as a strong sensation ceased, another one was automatically aroused, which was in some measure a continuation of the original sensation and also something opposite to it. BUFFON[6] published minute descriptions of the phenomena which were afterwards used by Father SCHERFER[7] as the material for the basis of his theory. As opposed to JURIN, he maintained that after-images (those that he had in mind were almost all negative) were due to lowered sensitivity of the fatigued retina. He made use of the same conception for explaining complementary colours, supporting his notion by NEWTON's rule for colour mixing. Another theory, which is rather artificial in some ways, and which suggests at once PLATEAU's oscillations, was proposed by GODART.[8] A great store of new observations especially with respect to coloured after-images was accumulated by different observers, among whom may be mentioned chiefly: DARWIN,[9] AEPINUS,[10] DE LA HIRE[11]

---

[1] *Vita.* pp. 175, 296.

[2] *Ars magna.* p. 162.

[3] MARIOTTE, *Oeuvres.* p. 318.

[4] D. BREWSTER, NEWTONS *Leben* (GOLDBERG's German edition) Leipzig 1833. S. 263.

[5] Essay on distinct and ind. vis. p. 170 in SMITH's *Optics.* Cambridge 1738.

[6] *Mém. de Paris.* 1743. p. 215.

[7] *Abhandlung von den zufälligen Farben.* Vienna 1765. — Latin edition, 1761; also in *Journal de Physique de* ROZIER. XXVI. 175 and 273. (1785).*

[8] *Journal de Physique.* 1776. VIII. 1 and 269.

[9] *Philos. Transact.* 1786. LXXVI. 313. — *Zoonomie* translated in German by BRANDIS. Hannover 1795. II. 387.

[10] *Journ. de Phys.* XXVI. 291. — *Novi Comment. Petrop.* X. 286.

[11] In PORTERFIELD *On the eye.* I. 343.

(on the coloured fading out of the sun's image), GERGONNE,[1] BROCKEDON[2] (who also tried to make use of them in a theory of esthetic colour harmony), LEHOT[3] (who directed special attention to the phenomena produced by suddenly varying the distance of the coloured field), GOETHE,[4] BEER[5] (on the way colours vanish when persons who have been operated on for cataract look far off), HIMLY and TROXLER,[6] PURKINJE,[7] OSANN,[8] SPLITTGERBER,[9] KNOCKENHAUER,[10] DOVE[11] (on subjective colours in case of objects in motion), SINSTEDEN,[12] SCORESBY,[13] GROVE[14] (on the reviving of after-images by alternate brightening and darkening of the field), SÉGUIN,[15] BRÜCKE[16] (who made numerous accurate observations on the fading of colours), and AUBERT[17] (on after-images produced by electric sparks).

Among the various efforts to coördinate this mass of material and give a consistent theory of the phenomena may be mentioned the attempt of PRIEUR DE LA CÔTE D'OR[18] to interpret them on the principle of contrast; and likewise BREWSTER's theory[19] that the complementary colour develops at the same time with the colour that the eye actually sees and tends to dim it. All these conflicting views were at last clearly brought out in the two comprehensive works published by PLATEAU[20] and FECHNER.[21] The arguments in favour of opponent activities of the retina were presented by PLATEAU in logical form. With extraordinary self-sacrifice FECHNER carried out an immense series of experiments in this field involving subjective measurements on himself. He gave the first satisfactory explanation of negative images on the principle of fatigue. The present state of the science is still essentially as indicated by these two works. Possibly, the conception of fatigue of the eye for a single colour would require to be more carefully defined. And this is done in YOUNG's colour theory. The author has tested it by experiments on the after-images of spectral colours,[22] the result being that he was particularly impressed by the great distinctness of positive after-images due to instantaneous action of light.

---

[1] *Journ. de Mathemat.* XXI. 291.

[2] *Quart. Journal of Sc.* No. XIV. 399; *Wiener Zeitschr.* VIII. 471.

[3] FECHNER, *Repertorium.* 1832. p. 229.

[4] *Farbenlehre.* I. 13, 20.

[5] *Das Auge oder Versuch das edelste Geschenk des Schöpfers zu erhalten.* S. 1–8.

[6] HIMLY, *Ophthalm. Bibl.* Bd. I. Stück 2. S. 1–20. Bd. II. St. 2. S. 40.

[7] *Beiträge.* I. 72, 96.

[8] POGG. *Ann.* XXXVII. 288.

[9] Ibid. LI. 587.

[10] Ibid. LIII. 346.

[11] Ibid. LXXI. 112. LXXV. 524, 526.

[12] Ibid. LXXXIV. 45.

[13] *Phil. Mag.* (4) VIII. 544. (1854.)

[14] *Phil. Mag.* (4) III. 435–436.

[15] *Ann. de Chimie et de Phys.* Ser. 3. XLI. 413–431.—*C. R.* XXXIII. 642. XXXIV. 767. XXXV. 476.

[16] *Denkschr. der k. k. Akad. zu Wien* III.—POGG. *Ann.* LXXXIV. 418.

[17] MOLESCHOTT, *Untersuchungen zur Naturl.* Bd. V. 279.

[18] *Ann. de Chimie.* LIV. p. 1.

[19] *Phil. Mag.* II. 89. IV. 354. — POGG. *Ann.* XXIX. LXI. 138.

[20] *Ann. de Chimie et de Phys.* 1833. LIII. 386; 1835. LVIII. 337.—POGG. *Ann.* XXXII. 543. Most complete in *Essai d'une Théorie génér. comprenant l'Ensemble des apparences visuelles, qui succèdent à la contemplation des objets colorés.* Bruxelles 1834.

[21] POGG. *Ann.* XLIV. 221, 513; XLV. 227; L. 193, 427.

[22] Presented before the *Niederrheinischen Gesellschaft für Natur und Heilkunde,* in Bonn, July 3, 1858, and in the *Naturforscherversammlung zu Karlsruhe.* Sep. 1858.

1634. PEIRESCII *Vita.* p. 175, 296.

1646. ATHAN. KIRCHER, *Ars magna.* p. 162.

1668. MARIOTTE, *Oeuvres.* p. 318.

1689. DE LA HIRE in PORTERFIELD, *On the eye.* I. 343.

  I. NEWTON, Experiments on ocular spectra produced by the action of the sun's light on the retina. *Edinb. Journ. of Sc.* IV. 75; NEWTONS *Leben* by BREWSTER, German trans. of GOLDBERG. Leipzig 1833. S. 263.

1738. JURIN, *Essay on distinct and indistinct vision.* p. 176. In SMITH's *Optics.* Cambridge 1738.

1743. BUFFON, Dissertation sur les couleurs accidentelles. *Mém. de Paris.* 1743. p. 147.

1765. SCHERFFER, *Abhandlung von den zufälligen Farben.* Wien 1765; Latin ed. 1761.— *Journ. de Physique de* ROZIER. XXVI. 175 and 273.

  AEPINUS de coloribus accidentalibus. *Nov. Com. Acad. Petr.* X. 282.—*Journal de Physique.* 1776. XXVI. 291.

1776. GODART, *Journ. de Physique.* VIII. 1 and 269.

1786. DARWIN, On the ocular spectra of light and colours. *Phil. Trans.* 1786. p. 313.— *Zoonomie,* German trans. by BRANDIS. Hannover 1795. II. 387.

1798. COMPARETTI, *Observationes dioptricae et anatomicae de coloribus apparentibus.* Patav. 1798.

1804. PRIEUR DE LA CÔTE D'OR, Bemerkungen über die Farben und einige besondere Erscheinungen derselben. *Ann. de Chim.* LIV. p. 1.—GILB. *Ann.* XXXI. 315.

1810. v. GOETHE, *Zur Farbenlehre.* I. 13, 20.

1817. SCHULZ, Über physiologische Farbenerscheinungen, insbesondere das phosphorische Augenlicht als Quelle derselben betrachtet. In GOETHE *für Naturwiss.* II. 20, 38.

1819. PURKINJE, *Beiträge zur Physiologie der Sinne.* I. 92.

1826. J. MÜLLER, *Zur vergl. Physiol. des Gesichtsinnes.* Coblenz. p. 401.

1830. LEHOT, *Annales des sciences d'observ. par* SAIGEY *et* RASPAIL. 1830. III, 3.—FRORIEPS *Notizen.* XXVIII. 177.—FECHNER *Repertorium.* 1832. p. 229.

  GERGONNE in his *Journ. de Mathem.* XXI. 291.

1833. BREWSTER in *Philos. Mag.* II. 89; IV. 354.—POGG. *Ann.* XXIX.

  PLATEAU. *Ann. de chim. et de phys.* LIII. 386; LVIII. 337; POGG. *Ann.* XXXII. 543.—Most complete in *Essai d'une Théorie génér. comprenant l'ensemble des apparences visuelles, qui succèdent à la contemplation des objets colorés et de celles, qui accompagnent celle contemplation, c'est à dire la persistance des impressions de la rétine, les couleurs accidentelles, l'irradiation, les effets de la juxtaposition des couleurs, les ombres colorées.* Bruxelles 1834.

1836. OSANN, Über Ergänzungsfarben. POGG. *Ann.* XXXVII. 287.

1838. *G. TH. FECHNER, Über die subjektiven Komplementärfarben. POGG. *Ann.* XLIV. 221–245; 513–530.

  Idem, Scheibe zur Ergänzung subjektiver Komplementärfarben. POGG. *Ann.* XLV. 227.

1840. *Idem, Über die subjektiven Nachbilder und Nebenbilder. POGG. *Ann.* L. 193–221, 427–465.

  SPLITTGERBER in POGG. *Ann.* XL. 587.

  D. BREWSTER in *Phil. Mag.* XXIII. 354.—POGG. *Ann.* LXI. 138.

1841. KNOCHENHAUER, Über Blendungsbilder. Ibid. LIII. 346.

1845. WHEATSTONE, Sur un effet singulier de juxtaposition de certaines couleurs dans des circonstances particulières. *Inst.* 1845. No. 582. p. 75.

1848. H. W. DOVE, Über Scheiben zur Darstellung subjektiver Farben. POGG. *Ann.* LXXV. 526.

  GRÜEL, Über einen Apparat für subjektive Farbenerscheinungen. POGG. *Ann.* LXXV. 524.

  H. TAYLOR, On the apparent motion of the figures in certain patterns of blue and red worsted. *Phil. Mag.* XXXIII. 345.—FRORIEPS *Notizen.* IX. 33.—*Arch. d. sc. ph. et nat.* X. 304.

1850. J. M. Séguin, Sur les couleurs accidentelles. *C. R.* XXXIII. 642. XXXIV. 767–768. XXXV. 476.—*Ann. de chim. et de phys.* (3) XLI. 413–431.—*Phil. Mag.* (4) III. 77.—Silliman J. (2) XIII. 441.

Sinsteden, Über einen neuen Kreisel zur Darstellung subjektiver Komplementärfarben und eine eigentümliche Erscheinung, welche die Orangefarbe dabei zeigt. Pogg. *Ann.* LXXXIV. 45.

E. Brücke, Untersuchungen über subjektive Farben. Pogg. *Ann.* LXXXIV. 418.—*Wiener Denkschr.* III. 95—*Arch. d. sc. phys. et nat.* XIX. 122.

1852. W. R. Grove, On a mode of reviving dormant impressions on the retina. *Phil. Mag.* (4) III. 435–436.—*Inst.* 1852. p. 251–252.—*Arch. d. sc. phys. et nat.* XX. 227–228.—*Cosmos.* I. 237–238.

Dove in Pogg. *Ann.* LXXXV. 402. Explanation of "fluttering hearts."

1854. J. J. Oppel, Über das Phänomen der flatternden Herzen. *Jahresber. des Frankfurter Vereins* 1853–1854. S. 50-54.—*Hallesche Zeitschr. für Naturwissenschaft.* V. 319.

W. Scoresby, An inquiry into some of the circumstances and principles which regulate the production of pictures on the retina of the human eye with their measure and endurance, their colours and changes. *Phil. Mag.* (4) VII. 218–221; VIII. 544.—*Inst.* 1854. S. 154–156.—*Proc. of Roy. Soc.* VI. 380–383. VII. 117–122.—*Athen.* 1854. 1272.

1855. S. Marianini, Sur une manière de voir facilement les couleurs accidentelles. *Arch. d. sc. phys.* XXX. 235—*Cimento.* I. 165.

1856. Séguin, Couleurs accidentelles. *Cosmos.* IX. 39.

Vierordt, *Archiv für physiol. Heilk.* 1856. Heft 2.

1857. Melsens, Recherches sur la persistance des impressions de la retine. *Bull. de Bruxelles.* (2) III. 214–252. *Cl. d. sc.* 1857. pp. 735–777.

1858. H. Aubert, Über das Verhalten der Nachbilder auf den peripherischen Teilen der Netzhaut. Moleschotts *Untersuchungen zur Naturlehre.* IV. 215–239.

J. M. Séguin, Notes sur les couleurs accidentelles. *C. R.* XLVII. 198–200.

Helmholtz, Über Nachbilder. 34. *Vers. deutscher Naturf. in Karlsruhe.* S. 225.

H. Aubert, Über das Verhalten der Nachbilder auf den peripherischen Teilen der Netzhaut, in Moleschotts *Unters. zur Naturlehre,* IV. 215.

1859. Idem, Über die durch den elektrischen Funken erzeugten Nachbilder. Ibid. V. 279.

H. Aubert, Über die durch den elektrischen Funken erzeugten Nachbilder. Moleschotts *Untersuchungen.* V. 296–314.

1861. J. Smith, On the chromoscope. *Rep. of Brit. Assoc.* 1860 (2), p. 65–66. Ibid. 1861. (2) 33.

1862. Aubert, Untersuchungen über die Sinnestätigkeiten der Netzhaut. Pogg. *Ann.* CXV. 87–116. CXVI. 249–278.

Rose, Presentations of colour produced under novel conditions. *Rep. of Brit. Assoc.* 1861 (2) p. 33.

1864. Aubert, *Physiologie der Netzhaut.* Breslau. S. 347-386.

1865. E. Brücke, Über Ergänzungsfarben und Kontrastfarben. *Wiener Sitzungsber.* LI.

§24. Contrast[1]

In the previous chapter the question was, What effect is produced by seeing colours one *after* the other? But what we have to do now is to investigate the mutual influence of different luminosities and colours appearing together in the visual field *side by side* with each other.

The result of such a juxtaposition usually is that each portion of the visual field next a brighter one looks darker, and *vice versa*; and a

[1] Concerning the special relations of colour contrast in case of the so-called anomalous trichromats and certain dichromats, see v. Kries's Appendix I. — N.

colour alongside another colour resembles more or less the complementary colour of the latter. The opposition thus manifested is implied in the term *contrast*. CHEVREUL draws a distinction between *simultaneous contrast*, as applied to the phenomena belonging here, and *successive contrast*, where two colours appear in succession upon the same retinal area.

However, cases also occur in which the colour of a part of the visual field is so altered by being adjacent to another colour that it becomes similar to the latter itself, and not to its complementary colour; and in these instances the term "contrast" might not seem to apply so directly, although, perhaps, as a matter of fact the alteration of one colour here is by a contrast with the complementary to another colour. So as to include these cases also, BRÜCKE calls the colour that is evoked by the action of one existing adjacent to it in the visual field, the *induced colour*; and the one that is responsible for the appearance of the other, the *inducing colour*. And so when the field, whose colour is altered, is itself coloured, we shall speak of this colour as the *reacting* colour, as formerly. The alteration of the reacting colour by the induced one leads to what may be called the *resulting* colour. In general, therefore, the idea of contrast is not directly appropriate except in the ordinary cases where the induced and inducing colours are complementary. But there are instances where the induced colour is identical with the inducing one.

The phenomena of successive contrast, which will be considered first, are easily comprehended from what has been stated in the previous chapter. After looking at a field of colour A and medium brightness, suppose the eye turns to look at another field of colour B. Then as a rule, the residual stimulation of the impression A will not be strong enough for a positive after-image to be projected on a second field of medium brightness; and so there will be a negative after-image of A upon the field B. Thus those parts of the colour B that are like A will be diluted. If B is of the same hue as A, it becomes whiter by contrast; if it is complementary, it becomes more saturated. If it lies on one side or the other of the colour circle between A and its complementary colour, it changes into an adjacent hue farther from A and nearer the complementary colour. Incidentally, the brighter A was, the darker B looks. Accordingly, this would be the general law of successive contrast, on the supposition that the luminosities of the two fields were such that only negative after-images could occur.

Even in comparing coloured areas with each other that lie side by side in the visual field, successive contrast, that is, contrast caused by after-images, is a very important factor, as any one can easily verify.

It has generally been supposed that in these cases it was simply a matter of simultaneous contrast, because hitherto in the theory of contrast little account has been taken of a certain characteristic of human vision. Under ordinary circumstances, we are accustomed to let our eyes roam slowly about over the visual field continuously, so that the point of fixation glides from one part of the observed object to another. This wandering of the eye occurs involuntarily, and we are so used to it that it requires extraordinary effort and attention to focus the gaze perfectly sharply on a definite point of the visual field even for 10 or 20 seconds. The moment we do it, unusual phenomena immediately take place. Sharply defined negative after-images of the objects develop, which coincide with the objects as long as the gaze is held steady, and hence cause the objects soon to get indistinct. The result is a feeling of not seeing and of having to strain the eyes, if we persist in trying to look at the fixed place; and the impulse to move the eye becomes more and more irresistible. The little deviations of its position are scarcely noticeable in the strain, but they are revealed by parts of the negative after-images flashing up on the edges of the objects, first on one side and then on the other. This wandering of the gaze serves to keep up on all parts of the retina a continual alternation between stronger and weaker stimulation, and between different colours, and is evidently of great significance for the normality and efficiency of the visual mechanism. For nothing affects the eye so much as frequent development of negative after-images caused by staring a long time at surfaces even only moderately illuminated. Strong negative after-images are, indeed, always an indication of a high degree of retinal fatigue.

Now let us consider what happens when the eye wanders in this way over a field where there are different colours or areas of different luminosity. If we observe a limited coloured field with the eye accurately focused on some point of it, a sharply defined after-image will be developed, which is therefore easily recognized. If two different points of the object in the same line of sight have been observed for a long time, two well defined after-images will be formed partly overlapping each other; but without special attention they are not now easily recognized as being copies of the object. But if the gaze has moved slowly over the object, without being held on any point, naturally the after-image will be simply a faded spot, and it is no longer so easy to recognize, although it is actually there for the attentive observer. Now if the look is transferred to an adjacent field of another colour, this colour of course will be altered by the influence of the after-image, exactly as if we had had these different colours one after the other in the field of vision. Accordingly, in a case like this, we do not have simultaneous contrast, at least not by itself; but we have here also successive contrast, and the phenomena are entirely, or in large part, identical with those described in the preceding chapter. In order to have simultaneous contrast alone, special pains must be taken to keep the fixation of the eye absolutely steady during the experiment.

Later we shall examine more carefully the phenomena of pure simultaneous contrast which continue during steady fixation of the eye. Now the phenomena will be described that belong partly to simultaneous, but mainly to successive contrast, as they are manifested under ordinary natural conditions of vision. The colour changes that occur in these circumstances are exactly the same as those already described for pure successive contrast. In general they are much more distinct and striking than those of pure simultaneous contrast; and when the two might cause different results, those of successive contrast invariably predominate in the natural use of the eye; and when both evoke the same effects, the alterations of colour always become much more considerable when the gaze ceases to be steady and begins to wander.

In general, contrast effects are promoted when the inducing colour is more intense than the reacting one, because then the after-images of the former are more vivid and more lasting. For example, if a small wafer of white paper is laid on a coloured sheet, this white will have the complementary colour. The colouring is more impressive, however, when grey is used instead of white; or even black, since in these subjective experiments all black is to be considered as a dark grey. However, as a rule, a medium grey is more satisfactory for the experiment than black. In such cases the contrast action may go so far that a tolerably vivid colour is reversed into the complementary. For example, if a small piece of orange-red paper (coloured with red lead) is laid on a red glass disc and held up against the bright sky, the reddish paper looks a vivid green-blue, that is, complementary to the colour of the red glass, being almost its own complementary colour too.

Moreover, it is conducive to have the inducing colour occupy a large part of the visual field, because then the various regions of the retina will be frequently and continuously stimulated by this colour and fatigued by it. The result is that the contrast colours are particularly vivid when the reacting colour occupies a small field surrounded by an extensive ground filled with the inducing colour. In this case, it is chiefly simply the colour of the small field that is altered, not that of the large field. But the contrast effects are not absent even when the two fields are of the same size; the influence then being a mutual one, and the colour of each being changed by that of the other.

Finally, the nearer together the inducing and reacting areas are in the visual field, the greater will be the contrast effect; because when the eye glides from one space over to the other, the after-image will be more strongly developed the sooner the gaze encounters the other field. This is shown very strikingly in the arrangement which CHEVREUL has selected for his experiments. From each of two colours, say, yellow and red, he cuts out two similar bands and places them side by side close to each other. Let us call them Y_1 and R_1. Then next the yellow band Y_1 he lays a second yellow band Y_2 at a little interval, and in the same way next the red band R_1 another one R_2. In this case the contrast action is not manifested anywhere except at the two middle bands Y_1 and R_1. The yellow of Y_1 becomes greenish by approaching blue-green that is complementary to R_1, and R_1 looks purple by being admixed with some indigo-blue that is complementary to Y_1. On the other hand, the two outside bands Y_2 and R_2 are not altered in appearance, so that there is a good opportunity of recognizing the contrast action. When the fields in contact are somewhat wider, this is also precisely why the contrast colouring is manifested particularly at the margins. Every time the eye sweeps from one field over A into the other field B, those parts of the retina that have just left the field A will be most fatigued by the colour A; and these are the places where the image of the edge of B falls now. Those parts of the retina which left A a little sooner and have already moved farther into the field B will be less fatigued; and hence for them the induced colour is not so strong. Consequently, every time the eye passes over to the field B, the marginal parts of B are most altered by contrast, and the parts farther from the edge less and less in proportion to their distance away. Thus, for instance, when a green and a blue field are in contact, the edge of the green looks a little more yellowish than the middle, and the edge of the blue a little more violet than its middle; because in the first case there is an admixture of yellow that is complementary to blue, and in the latter case an admixture of purple-red that is complementary to green. The play of after-images at the border of such surfaces can be watched very nicely by marking several points of fixation, and jerking the eye from one to the next, after holding it at each place for a brief time. It is easy to see then the well-defined after-images moving over on the other field. The earlier images, being shifted on ahead, will be paler, while the latest, lingering next the border, will be more intense.

If the question involves not difference of colour, but difference of luminosity, the reacting field will appear to be less bright when it is adjacent to an inducing field that is brighter than it; whereas next to a darker field, the luminosity of the reacting field will seem to be increased.

Incidentally, as compared with the methods of seeing negative images which were described in the preceding chapter, there are also other factors in these experiments that are conducive to eliciting the complementary colour. In general, a coloured object has to be deliberately focused for several seconds in order to obtain afterwards a distinct after-image that will persist for some time on a uniformly coloured ground. But in the experiments on contrast it appears that a tolerably cursory observation of one colour is sufficient to induce the complementary colour on the other field, and that this complementary colour is afterwards much more lasting than an after-image would be which was obtained under the same circumstances. In order to recognize an after-image on a uniformly coloured ground, it must be well developed and clearly outlined. It moves about as the eye moves, and so has to be perceived as any other subjective phenomenon. Ordinarily, we pay attention only to objective visual phenomena. But if a faded after-image covers a smaller coloured field, which has its own objective limitation and always appears under the influence of the after-image, this influence cannot be immediately separated in the perception from the other objective phenomena of the visual field, and hence it becomes much more easily an object of our attention. In Part III (Volume III) we shall have to study more closely this peculiarity of the way the attention is attracted.

In addition, the fatigue of the retina in these contrast phenomena is being always renewed, and so the effect is persistent; whereas in most methods of producing after-images it dies out pretty rapidly.

Let us turn now to the *phenomena of pure simultaneous contrast*. In order to recognize them positively as such, care must be taken in the arrangement of the experiments that no after-images can arise, and that the portion of the retina which is to perceive the induced colour has not been previously affected *en passant* by the image of the inducing field. As a rule, this can only be perfectly achieved by not letting the inducing colour be visible until after the eye has been focused on a definite point of the induced field. During the whole time of the experiment this point must be fixed steadily. If the inducing colour is not too intense or too saturated, all that is necessary then is for the eyes, which have been wandering about over dark, slightly coloured objects, or else have been closed, to be turned quickly towards the induced field and focused on a point there, without letting them previously linger in the inducing field. In most cases this last method is sufficient, especially because the contrast phenomena of this group are most clearly exhibited precisely when the differences of colour between the inducing and induced fields are slight; whereas, conversely, the phenomena of successive contrast are promoted by strong antagonisms of colours and illumination.

In the author's opinion the phenomena belonging here are of an entirely different kind from those heretofore considered. In general, they may be characterized as cases in which it is not possible to make an exact estimate of the reacting colour by comparing it with other or inducing colours. Under such circumstances we are disposed to regard those differences which are distinctly and positively perceived in the observation as being greater than those which either stand out indistinctly or must be estimated by the aid of the memory. Doubtless, this is a general law in all our perceptions. By the side of a big fellow a man of medium size looks small, because at the moment we see clearly that there are larger men, but not that there are also smaller ones. The same man of medium size placed by the side of a small one will look large.

Now two colours or two luminosities can be compared most accurately when they are side by side in the visual field, with nothing but the difference between them to indicate their boundary. The farther they are apart, the harder it is to compare them. It is harder still when one of the colours has to be supplied by memory. Consequently, when a coloured field (the reacting field) is surrounded by another (the inducing field), the difference between the colour of the reacting field and that of the inducing field will be more distinctly perceived than the difference between that of the reacting field and other colours that are far away. The latter comparison becomes most difficult when the inducing field takes in the entire field of vision or at least most of it; and hence other colours will be perceived only by the peripheral parts of the retina, where colour discrimination is imperfect, or simply by the memory. In general, therefore, in accordance with the rule given above, the difference between the reacting field and the inducing field will appear to be too large as compared with the difference between the reacting field and other colours; and, in fact, the effect will be more decided in proportion as the inducing colour excludes all others from the visual field.

Moreover, we are more liable to err in estimating small differences than big ones; and, consequently, contrast phenomena are also relatively more distinct when the differences of illumination are slight than when they are considerable.

Finally, a difference appears bigger when it is the only thing that differentiates two adjacent surfaces than when it is merely one among several differences; and hence in general simultaneous contrast is more vivid when there is nothing between the induced field and the inducing field except the difference of colour.

Incidentally, there is one other point: the object must not continue to be focused too long. When fixation is long maintained, a series of phenomena occur resulting from fatigue of the eye that partly entail the opposite result from that of the original contrast.

Let us proceed now to the description of individual cases. The so-called *coloured shadows* are most conducive of all to vividness of contrast, because here the three mentioned conditions are generally fulfilled simultaneously.   Among all contrast phenomena, therefore, coloured shadows have attracted most attention.

The easiest way to observe them is to illuminate a sheet of paper by weak daylight on one surface and by candle light on the other. Daylight or white light (reflected from a clouded sky or from any white surface lighted by the sun) or even moonlight is admitted through an aperture sufficiently small for the shadows cast by it to be distinct. Then an opaque object of any sort (a finger or a lead pencil) is placed on the paper. Two shadows will be perceived. The one that would be there if the candle were absent may be called the *daylight shadow*; and the one which depends on the presence of the candle, the *candle shadow*. The daylight shadow is illuminated by red-yellow candle light, but not by daylight. It appears in its objective colouration, namely, red-yellow.   The candle shadow is illuminated by white daylight, but not by the red-yellow candle light. And thus while it is objectively white, it appears blue or complementary to the colour of the ground, which is a pale red-yellow, since the unshaded portions of the paper are simultaneously lighted by the white daylight and the red-yellow candle light. The colourations are most distinct when the intensities of the two sources are so equalized that both shadows are equally dark.

The blue in the candle shadow becomes more vivid when the eye is allowed to wander frequently over the red-yellow ground, but it also arises wholly without the assistance of after-images. Suppose a point *a* lying in the blue shadow is noted and marked; and an opaque screen is placed in front of the candle, so that for a while nothing but daylight falls on the paper, until the after-effect of the red-yellow light is completely gone, and the daylight again appears quite white. Now look at the point *a*, and take the screen from in front of the candle. Immediately the candle shadow becomes blue and stays blue, provided there has not been the slightest deviation in the gaze of the eye. Moreover, the contrast colour immediately appears in the shadow when the eyes are closed and covered for a while and then suddenly opened and turned towards the shadow.

Take a tube painted black inside, and adjust it so that on looking through it the eye sees only places on the paper that lie in the shadow of the candle light. If at first nothing but daylight falls on it, and then while the eye is looking through the tube the candle light is allowed to fall on it too, the observer will see nothing of the places illuminated by the candle light; he does not notice their presence at all, and the appearance of the regions of the paper which he sees through the tube remains unaltered. Incidentally, the objective colour of the paper in the shadow of the candle light is not changed. The reason for noting this fact here is because it was doubted by OSANN.

On the other hand, if the tube is held to the eye and directed so that a part of the field surveyed is illuminated by the red-yellow light of the candle, the shadow from the candle light becomes blue. When the blue has become real intense, let the tube again be pointed so that nothing but this subjective blue is in the visual field. The blue now persists, no matter whether the candle light is allowed to shine on the rest of the paper, or whether the candle is screened, which, of course, so far as the observer is concerned, amounts to the same thing; because under these conditions he is not aware of it at all. The blue colour in such case is so constant that OSANN has concluded from similar experiments that it is objective. This opinion is easily refuted at once by the fact that the blue colour persists even when the candle is extinguished. But at the moment when the black tube is removed from the eye, the subjective blue disappears also, because it is then recognized to be identical with the white that occupies the rest of the visual field. No experiment shows more impressively or more clearly the influence of judgment on our determination of colour. As the result of contrast, whether it be successive or simultaneous, once the judgment has been formed that the colour in the shadow of the candle light is blue, the colour continues to appear blue, although the circumstances that led to the decision may have ceased to exist; until the black tube is removed so as to enable us to make a new comparison with other colours and to form a different judgment in the light of new facts.

Instead of the red-yellow colour natural to candle light, other colours may be used too. The candle light may be coloured by interposing a piece of coloured glass in front of the candle, thus combining coloured candle light either with daylight or with uncoloured candle light. However, the phenomena are most brilliant when the experiment is conducted in a dark room, where coloured sunlight is admitted through an opening in the shutter covered with coloured glass, and white daylight through another small opening. In all these cases, whether the eye is held steady or not, the white light shows up in the colour complementary to the coloured light.

When the eye wanders, the complementary colour appears indeed even on absolutely black surfaces and on surfaces that are dimly illuminated by the prevalent colour. When the eye is kept steady, a dark area sometimes appears in the complementary colour and sometimes in the same colour. It is generally the first way by dim light, and the latter way by bright light. However, after somewhat prolonged fixation, it is always the same colour as that of the prevalent light, the complementary colour flashing up simply at the edges, owing to the unavoidable tiny fluctuations of the visual axis to and fro. As soon as the eye is allowed to wander, the complementary colour invariably comes out, or gets more brilliant in case it were dimly there before.

In fact, the complementary colour comes out when the light is made to go through two pieces of glass of the same colour, one of which, however, is not so highly coloured as the other; or when two pieces of the same kind of glass are used, provided some white light also is incident on one of them. In such cases, therefore, the hue of the paler shadow is thus converted into the opposite hue exactly.

The same contrast phenomena obtained with the coloured shadows invariably occur whenever most of the visual field is occupied by a predominating colour, or when a great part of the field is unilluminated, and there is in the illuminated portion a colour which is predominant in its extent and intensity.

Hold a little piece of white or grey paper in a short pair of nippers, or attach it to a wire and hold it directly in front of one eye; and close the other eye and look at it. Then insert behind it a large sheet of coloured paper or a large plate of coloured glass, so that most of the visual field is occupied by this coloured surface. As soon as this happens, the complementary colour appears on the little piece of paper. As a rule, the reacting white must not be too bright. If the experiment is performed in a room where the light comes from a lamp or from not too large an aperture in a window, the brightness of the white paper may easily be altered by letting the light fall on it more or less perpendicularly until the proper brightness is found. It is best to get a medium brightness of the white, which is about like that of the coloured ground. If the white is too bright or, on the other hand, too darkly shaded so that it begins to look black, the contrast colours will be less distinct or will not appear at all. The more of the visual field that is occupied by the coloured surface, the brighter the white can be made. By increasing the distance between the eye and the objects and thereby diminishing their apparent sizes, the induced colour will be found to get fainter or to disappear entirely. It likewise disappears with sustained fixation and becomes just like the inducing colour; all the more readily, the smaller the apparent size of the inducing field is, the more intensely it is illuminated, and the darker the induced field is. If the latter consists of a small black disc which is placed in front of a plate of coloured glass fastened in an opening of the shutter where the sky can be seen through it, the colour of the glass from the very start will frequently spread over the black disc, provided after-images are avoided. In this case the author's experience is that there is no difference in the various colours except that usually the commercial red glasses are darker than the yellow, green and blue glasses; and therefore more intensity of light, for instance, the light from sunlit clouds, is required for red glass to elicit the same colour at the start. In the case of the blue glasses, which also exhibit the phenomenon with tolerably dark colouring, it might be that the fluorescence of the crystalline lens and cornea also had something to do with the distribution of blue light over the dark disc. After brief fixation, the colour is always the same as that of the glass, and it is only at the edge of the black field that the complementary border appears, being due to the wavering of the visual axis of the eye.

Leaving out at first cases where the induced colour and the inducing colour are the same, we may express the main result of the preceding experiments thus. When a particular colour is made dominant in the visual field, a paler shade of the same hue will look white to us, and real white will seem to be the complementary colour. Thus the idea of what we mean by white is altered in this case. Now the sensation of white is not a simple sensation, but consists of the sensations of three fundamental colours compounded in a definite proportion. In a particular case, in order to recognize a given colour as being white, when it is impossible to compare it with something that is known to be white, we must again be able to recognize whether the relative intensities of the three fundamental colours of which it is composed have been altered or not. But, as we saw in §21, the comparison of the intensity of different sensations of colour is extremely uncertain and inaccurate. And, therefore, any determination of white based on such a comparison must be inaccurate too; and pretty considerable variations will be possible in our estimates of white on different occasions, as is actually found to be the case.

At the same time this explanation shows also why these caprices as to what is white do not ever go to the extent of making us take for white a colour that is saturated like the red in glasses that are stained with copper oxide, which transmit only light from the red end of the spectrum; even when we happen to be a long time in a place that gets all its light through a glass of this sort. As a matter of fact, in comparing a very bright red with a faint blue, there is no doubt about which is brighter. We decide positively about big differences, but not about little ones. If, therefore, homogeneous light is presented to the eye, and in it the sensation of the red fundamental colour is very intense as compared with the sensation of the other two fundamental constituents, the colour is pronounced to be red without deliberation. We do this even when the sensation of red has already been very much enfeebled by fatigue of the eye. It is true that a somewhat pale but still tolerably saturated red may be taken for white under such circumstances, as in the experiment described above, where a piece of paper coloured with red lead looked green in front of a highly illuminated red glass.

There is one other circumstance that keeps us from making too big an error in a case like this. This is the intrinsic light of the retina, which, when the eye has wandered about for some time, appears complementary to the prevailing colour and becomes noticeable in all perfectly dark places in the visual field. When we look steadily through a red glass, soon all perfectly dark objects appear to be a vivid green. Thus, alongside the red its complementary colour becomes visible, and we are thereby compelled to recognize red as red; we cannot confuse it with white. With dominant white illumination the mist looks white in the dark places, and for just this reason it requires careful attention to see it. Even in dim coloured light, for instance, the light of a lamp or candle, the intrinsic light of the retina becomes noticeable in this manner. All that is necessary is to hold a small black object, entirely unilluminated, in front of a white paper surface lighted by the candle, and let the eye wander over it and the paper surface; the indigo-blue sheen on the black, which is complementary to the red-yellow of the candle light, will then soon be perceived. White paper appears white just as well by candle light as by daylight. But if the paper is viewed through a tube blackened on the inside, which has only a small opening, and the appearance of the small part of the paper surface that is still seen is compared with the dark field, it is soon perceived that the former is red-yellow and the latter looks bluish; whereas by daylight there is no such difference. This is a means of recognizing the colour of the prevailing illumination even when there is no daylight for comparison. Consequently, too, the colour of the intrinsic light of the eye matches the white of daylight, and hence this white is of special significance for the eye still and is entitled to the name of white before all other whitish colours.

Of course, the intrinsic light of the eye is too feeble to be used in diffused coloured illumination for making comparisons in order to determine white exactly.

Hence, if there are a limited number of coloured objects in the field of vision, we are in a much better position for determining the relative differences between the various colours present and between each colour and their mean colour than the difference between this mean colour and white. Now, by the normal illumination of daylight, when a large variety of objects can be freely compared, the white of sunlight is the mean colour, from which the deviations of the other colours in the various directions of the colour chart are estimated. But if another colour A is predominant, so that the average of all colours seen at the same time resembles the colour A, we are inclined to use this average as the starting point of our temporary colour discriminations and to identify it with white.

In the author's opinion the characteristic thing about this interpretation of the phenomena is that, when after-images are avoided, a very weak colouration of the dominant light elicits quite as distinct contrast colourations as the most saturated. The weak red-yellow of candle light gives the coloured shadows a very intense blue. The author's experience is that there is no tendency for this blue to become more vivid and more distinct when the eye looks at it steadily, supposing an exceedingly red-yellow paper or red glass is used as background. But as soon as the eye is allowed to wander, the latter saturated colours certainly do give also much more saturated after-images than candle light.

The effect of slight differences is manifested in exceedingly striking fashion in a method devised by H. MEYER.[1] A sheet of nice white letter paper and one of coloured paper, green, say, are cut exactly the same size, and superposed so that one covers the other perfectly. A little piece of grey paper, just as dark as, or darker than, the green is inserted between them. Black or white paper is not so good. The green and grey underneath just manage to show through the outside white paper, and where the grey is now appears a very distinct and decided pink-red. With a different colour of the background the little piece of grey invariably shows through the white in the complementary colour. Frequently conditions are obtained that succeed in bringing out the complementary contrast colour more distinctly than the weak colour of the ground. The author's experience is not simply that in these cases the contrast colour is just as easily seen as if the background were a saturated colour; but that it seems to be easier to see it; for it took much practice and perseverance to succeed with the experiments on contrast colours in which the eye has to stare at a little piece of paper while a coloured sheet is shoved under it.

The two phenomena may be directly compared in the following manner. The sheet of red paper is covered with the translucent white paper, and a little piece of opaque white paper held by a forceps is laid

[1] POGGENDORFFS *Ann.* XCV. 170.

on the latter. The observer then looks steadily at the little piece of paper until it distinctly takes on the complementary colour; but not too long, otherwise the difference of colour is quickly obliterated by the after-images. Then he suddenly pulls the white letter paper away, and now he sees the little piece on the uncovered red paper. The complementary colouring is scarcely stronger than before, unless there was too much delay.

As a matter of fact, according to the above explanation of the vacillations as to what is meant by white, there is a certain limit always to the change which this conception can undergo. This limit has already been reached when the coloured ground is not very much saturated, and then, unless after-images are involved, it does not seem able to extend much farther. On the other hand, the nature of a colour can be determined much more positively by comparing it with a colour that is very much like it than by comparing it with a much more saturated colour. Moreover, two colours are easier to compare when they have the same luminosity than when their luminosities are very different. In the author's opinion this is the reason why contrast colouring is most positive where inducing and reacting colours are equally bright, and their difference is not one of luminosity but simply of colour.

This seems also to be the explanation of the following phenomenon. Holding a little piece of white paper with a forceps over an equally bright white ground, insert a coloured paper in between the two. If the new coloured ground is large enough, the little piece of paper shows up now on it in the complementary colour. Leave the coloured paper where it is for from two to four seconds, and then pull it away again, always taking care to look steadily at a point of the little piece of white paper. At this instant the latter will take on the same colour as that of the first inducing field just as distinctly and definitely as when it assumed the complementary colour before. Indeed, in all such cases, where the coloured ground was not very extensive, the way the same colour as that of the ground comes out will be even more distinct than the way the complementary colour came out before. In fact, when the coloured paper is removed, the white ground has a faint tinge of the complementary colour, and is nearly as bright as the little piece of white paper; and the effect of this is to promote the development of the contrast colour more than it was promoted by the more intense colouring of the coloured paper that was inserted under it at first. It is the same way when the ground and the little piece of paper are both black. In this case also the similar colouration that occurs when the coloured ground is removed is plainer than when it was inserted.

Of course, it is exactly the same way when the little piece of paper is removed along with the coloured ground, and then the after-images of both are projected on a white or black field. In the previous chapter the colour of the after-image of white in this case was explained as being a contrast colour; and now we see the justification for it.

Before leaving the cases of contrast where the induced colour constitutes the greatest part of the visual field, we must still consider the reason why the reacting field occasionally has the same colour as that of the inducing field. There are two conditions when this occurs: first, when the inducing field has a very great luminosity, and second, when the same point is fixated a long time.

When the inducing field has a very great luminosity, the author does not consider the appearance of the homonymous colouration in the reacting field as being a subjective phenomenon but as being caused by a scattering of objective light. Every transparent solid or liquid diffuses everywhere small quantities of light passing through it, and hence when much light traverses it, it appears to be dimly illuminated itself. The fact that this is also the case with the cornea and crystalline lens of the eye has already been stated (Vol. I, p. 193). Moreover, the entoptical objects in the vitreous humor will be recalled in this connection, because undoubtedly they must partially deflect the light in its passage through this medium. Light is reflected from the illuminated places of the retina to the other parts of the fundus. The effect of all this is that when a large amount of light penetrates the eye, invariably considerable quantities of it will be diffused over more or less of the fundus of the eye. This illumination by diffused light is manifested most distinctly in the second method of showing the vessels of the retina, by moving a candle flame to and fro below the eye, as described in §15, Vol. I. The shadows of the retinal vessels appear in the light mist, which in this case completely fills the fundus of the eye. Certainly, therefore, the illumination is an objective one and not simply a distribution of the sensitivity for light in the retina. It is easy to show by objective experiments with ordinary glass lenses that diffusely scattered light is always most in evidence in the vicinity of the regularly refracted beam of light, and that it gets less and less farther away from this beam. If sunlight passes through an opening in a black screen and falls on a distant lens, so that the image of the bright aperture is projected on a white screen, the little bright image will be surrounded by a white cloudy effect; which can also be seen when the image of the bright opening itself is allowed to pass close by the edge of the screen. That white cloudy effect, therefore, is no irradiation originating in the eye, but an objective phenomenon. It

can be seen still better by making a small opening in the screen near
the image of the bright aperture, but without letting it coincide with
it. On looking at the lens through the opening in the screen, it will
appear to be more brightly illuminated, the nearer the eye comes to
the optical image of the source of light. A perfectly analogous phenomenon occurs in the eye. Look at a flame in front of a very dark field, for
instance, in front of the open door of an absolutely dark room; it seems
to be surrounded by a whitish cloud which is brightest in its immediate
vicinity. This lustre can be noticed best by interposing a small opaque
object between the eye and the flame, so that the latter is no longer
visible. Instantly, the cloud of light in front of the background vanishes also, and the latter is seen in its characteristic black. If the light
is coloured, then, of course, the diffused cloud of light is also of the
same colour. In this case too the author believes that undoubtedly
this light cloud comes from the diffusion of objective light, because
the distribution of light is exactly the same as would be produced by a
system of glass lenses under the same circumstances. But here, it is
true, there is no proof by means of the shadows of the retinal vessels,
like that which could be given in the case first mentioned. In the case
of blue light we have to take into account also the white-bluish light
diffused by the fluorescence of the lens, which likewise is scattered
over the whole fundus of the eye. And so when a large amount of
coloured light penetrates the eye, those parts of the retina where images
of dark objects fall will invariably be feebly illuminated also by the
dominant light, and this illumination will be greater in proportion as
those places are nearer the images of bright surfaces. Besides, in the
region of the dark image there is the internal stimulation of the nervous
substance, which is responsible for the whitish intrinsic light of the
retina. By itself this latter would appear by contrast complementary
to the prevailing colour. But if much of the inducing light of the same
colour is mixed with it, this colour will predominate from the start in
the impression that is produced. And hence, as was noted above, a
small black disc in front of coloured glass will show the complementary
colour when the luminosity is low, and the same colour when the
luminosity is high.

The second case, where the induced colour is the same as that of
the inducing light, as is the case with long fixation, is explained by the
gradual fading out of the images when the eye is held steady for a long
time, as was described in the previous chapter. It was noticed there
that if a place on the retina has been receiving the same impression of
light continuously, the luminosity sensation gets weaker and weaker,
and the colour becomes less and less saturated. However, this change

of the impression is only noticed when comparisons are made with the impression produced by the same light on unfatigued areas of the retina. In this case, therefore, we cling to the judgment of the colour and luminosity that we formed at first glance.

If the surface on which the eye is focused contains portions of different relative luminosities, these differences gradually disappear as the impression gets weaker. Select some point on the surface for the point of fixation; but when the borders between bright and dark parts are faded, be careful about not obtaining too distinct after-images in consequence of slight movements of the eye. When the fixation is sharp and steady, differences of light that are often quite marked will fade out in from 10 to 20 seconds. The way this happens is at first by the brighter parts getting darker, and at the same time the darker parts getting brighter. It is striking too to watch here how sometimes a large mass changes into a faded dark spot, or a bright mass into a pale bright spot, as if the objects were painted with diluted colours and these ran together. Incidentally, the experiment is hard to perform in this way on account of the long steady fixation involving much strain. Every time the eye winks or moves ever so little, the image returns. It is much more convenient and satisfactory to use objects that have fixed positions on the retina itself, such as the retinal vessels. The methods of making the retinal vessels visible have been described in §15, Vol. I. What is common to all these methods consists in letting the shadows of the vessels fall in some unusual direction or in trying to prolong the umbrae of the shadows. But in this case it is also necessary to change continuously the direction of the light that casts the shadow, and only those vessels are visible whose shadows are shifted. As soon as the source of light is kept steady, the ramifications of the vessels disappear in a few seconds by becoming as bright as the rest of the visual field. They vanish more rapidly and more completely than the images of external objects that are hard to focus; and the weaker the illumination, the more quickly they disappear. The way to keep them longest is by concentrating sunlight with a lens on the external side of the sclerotica, because here the field is brightest.

Simple considerations easily show, by the way, that the disappearance of the retinal vessels is due to the same causes as the disappearance of all steadily fixated images, and that no special peculiarity of the parts of the retina behind the vessels is involved at all in this case. There is no ground for supposing that these places are endowed, say, with a higher sensitivity than the rest of the retina, and that, therefore, even if they are screened, the sensation there would be just as intense as elsewhere. For when the shadows are projected in an unusual direction, by illuminating a part of the sclerotica through the pupil or

from outside so that it becomes a source of light for the fundus of the
eye, the new parts of the retina where the shadows fall behave exactly
in the same way as the places that are accustomed to them. The image
disappears quickly on them too unless its location is varied, and the
parts where the shadows usually fall cannot be distinguished at all by
any continuously greater luminosity. Of course, bright gleams flash
out spasmodically along with the shadow after it has stayed still a long
time, and then begins to move again. But this happens just as well
with lateral as with frontal illumination. In this case, therefore, it may
be that the shaded parts of the retina recuperate, and when light falls
on them again, they are more sensitive to it. But the after-effect of
repose, as shown by the bright negative after-image of the shadow,
does not last any longer than the after-image of dark outside objects.
Undoubtedly, in the author's opinion, the rapid disappearance of the
shadows of the vessels is exactly the same sort of thing as the disappearance of any objective image with moderate differences of luminosity which is steadily focused by the eye, except that in the former
case the difficulties of fixation are absent.

Suppose now that a place A on the retina is continuously illuminated more highly than another place B; then, of course, since A is more
fatigued than B, the initial difference of stimulation will be diminished
to a certain extent, and so it gradually gets to be imperceptible and
disappears wholly and entirely; possibly because it becomes really too
weak to be perceived, or, as the writer is inclined to think, because our
powers of discrimination for continuous nervous stimulations are much
more imperfect than for varying stimulation. But since in these cases
we stick to our judgment of the colour as we saw it first, and fail to
notice the gradual change in it, the surfaces A and B in this experiment
seem to us to get more alike, their average luminosity appearing to be
about constant. As a general thing the brighter one A, in this case,
becomes darker, and the darker B gets brighter. Thus, for example,
when the writer stares a long time at a wall covered with silver-grey
paper with dark grey leaves on it and some copper engravings, it looks
as if it had a film of milk over it.

If there are different colours in the visual field, it is likewise only
at the first moment that the impression of them is perfectly vivid. As
we continue to look at them, all colours invariably grow darker and
greyer, and therefore similar to one another. We notice that they do
become similar, but we do not notice the change of the dominant colour;
not accurately anyhow when there are no fresh impressions for comparisons; and so generally we consider it as not having changed.

Accordingly, after looking at a white field on red ground until the two colours become more and more alike, our judgment is that the white becomes red. The result is that every time the eye wanders to the border between the two fields, a green after-image flashes up on the white and a saturated red one on the red, the effect being augmented by contrast.

The tendency of the two colours to become like each other is very plainly manifested by looking at a small red field on broad white ground. FECHNER noticed that in this case too the white becomes reddish after a time, and uniformly so all over. Another small coloured field far off to one side has no influence on the progress of the phenomenon. But if the point of fixation is located on the border of two small fields of different colour, both lying on a white ground, according to FECHNER, the ground becomes coated over with the mixture of the two colours. And so this experiment shows that the colour perceived by the yellow spot is given a special preference, perhaps because this colour is judged most sharply and accurately, the colour sensation on the peripheral parts of the retina being much more imperfect.

In the cases heretofore considered where the inducing colour was supposed to occupy most of the visual field, or at least to dominate the others by its intensity and vividness, the contrast phenomena are very constant and distinct, and seem moreover to depend on no minor considerations. It is different when the field of the inducing colour is not so large and there may be a sufficient number of white and other objects besides near it on the border of the field of view. In this case the contrast effects throughout are not so constant any more, and will depend on many accessory conditions; which in the author's opinion are very important for the theory of these phenomena. If the field of vision outside the inducing and induced fields is dark, this does not matter much. But when the dark region comprises a very large part of the visual field, as is the case, for instance, in looking through a black tube, the intrinsic light of the retina seems to supply the lack of a white illumination, and the contrast phenomena become uncertain.

When a little piece of white, grey or black paper is laid on a coloured quarto or octavo leaf, and inspected from a distance of about a foot, as a rule, supposing the fixation is exact, no contrast colour is perceived except maybe some doubtful traces of it. However, if, as in MEYER's experiment above, the coloured octavo leaf is covered with a sheet of thin letter paper, it is remarkable how perfectly clear and constant the contrast colour comes out, in spite of the fact that the colour antagonisms are very greatly reduced by this method. Here also it is best for the little piece of paper to be grey and of about the same luminosity as the coloured paper.

The coloured paper covered by the letter paper makes a very faintly coloured whitish ground. Where the piece of grey paper is underneath, the objective colour of the upper paper is pure white. Now it might be supposed that by covering the objective white place with a white or bright grey bit of paper laid on top of the letter paper, it too would appear complementary to the ground. But, strange to say, that is not what happens. The little piece of paper exhibits its own objective colour, without contrast. Indeed, if a piece of paper is selected of exactly the same colour and brightness as the letter paper over the place where the grey is, and if this is inserted at the corresponding place of the letter paper, and now if the colours of the two places are accurately compared with each other, the contrast effect disappears even on the white place of the letter paper, where it was originally; and this place now looks white as long as the other little piece of paper is there beside it for comparison. Moreover, the contrast colour disappears also when the contour of the piece of grey paper underneath is traced on the letter paper in black lines. Thus the contrast colour continues only so long as there is no difference between the two fields except their difference of colour. The moment one field is outlined as a distinct body or by a definite contour, the effect disappears, or at least becomes very much more doubtful.

Secondly, the experiments with coloured shadows succeed even when a comparatively small part of the visual field is illuminated by coloured light; for instance, when a coloured plate is mounted vertically on a white sheet of paper, so that only part of the paper gets coloured light.

In the third place, contrast colours are brought out very beautifully also with a coloured field of moderate extent in the following method devised by RAGONA SCINA. In Fig. 54 *ab* and *ac* are two white paper surfaces, one horizontal, the other vertical; and *ad* is a coloured plate of glass inclined to the two paper surfaces at 45°; *e* and *f* are two black spots. An observer at *B*, looking down on the apparatus from above, sees the surface *ab* through the coloured glass, and the surface *ac* reflected in it. The image of *ac* coincides apparently with *ab*, and the image of the black spot *f* is at

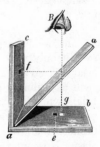

Fig. 54.

g, say, not far from the spot *e*. The light transmitted through the coloured glass is coloured; but the reflected light consists partly of pure white light that comes from the first surface, and partly of coloured light in comparatively small amounts that is reflected at the rear surface, or has been reflected several times inside the plate. Thus when the colour of the plate is dark, the reflected light is almost white; anyhow it is much less coloured than the transmitted light. Consequently, the light the observer gets from the image of *f* at *g* is all transmitted or coloured light coming from *ab*; and the light from the bright ground is partly transmitted coloured light and partly reflected white light; whereas the light from the black spot *e* is all reflected white light. Now although this latter light is not altogether white, but always contains some of the coloured light of the glass itself, still by contrast with the colour of the ground it appears in the complementary colour. On the other hand, the spot *g*, of course, shows up in the saturated colour of the glass. For example, if the glass is green, then *e* appears pink-red, and *g* appears green.

Here too care must be taken not to have too much difference between the luminosity of *e* and that of the ground; and so with a coloured glass that transmits a lot of light the surface *ab* ought to be shaded by a white paper. Incidentally, the contrast colour of *e* is more distinct, when the spot *f* shows up there in the same colour as the ground than when it does not. Both spots are seen here under apparently the same conditions, and the contrast is heightened by comparing the way they look. Now if the observer will find a grey paper of exactly the same colour as that in which the spot *e* would appear to him without contrast, and hold a small piece of it over the coloured plate so as to hide half of the spot *e*, this little piece of paper will not appear in the complementary colour at all or even show any suspicion of it; and the moment the colour of the spot *e* is compared with it, and seen to be the same, the complementary colour of *e* disappears also and changes into a simple grey. This is exactly the same phenomenon as shown by the first method.

The following are some similar phenomena, which, it is true, exhibit only very small fields coloured by contrast, yet the effect is clear and vivid. Take a rather thick plate without much colour in it, such as ordinary greenish window glass, and notice the image of a bright white surface reflected in it. In this case the front surface of the plate reflects pure white light, and the rear surface greenish light, because the latter has been exposed to the absorption action of the glass. Now interpose a narrow black rod between the plate and the bright surface. There will be two images of it in the glass, one due to reflection at the front face of the plate, and the other due to reflection at the rear surface. Where the image in the front surface is seen, the eye still gets greenish light from the rear surface; and where the image in the rear surface lies, the eye still gets white light from the front surface. Hence the ground looks white and hardly at all greenish. The first image looks green; and the second image by contrast is very distinctly pink-red. The phenomenon is even more distinct when the rear surface of a coloured plate of glass of this sort is covered with tinfoil, and the after-images are observed at such oblique incidence that both of them seem to be equally intense.

The following experiment is similar. Place a coloured paper, green, say, on a white one (a grey one of the same luminosity is better). Near the edge where the green and white fields meet, make a small black spot on each of them, and place a crystal of Iceland spar over this place. Through the crystal all points of the base will be seen doubled. In the middle there will be a green-white strip, where the ordinary image of the white is covered by the extraordinary image of the green. It must be so arranged that one of the images of each of the two black spots will be seen in this strip. In the ordinary image of the black spot situated on the white, white is absent, but green is present; so the spot is green. In the extraordinary image of the black spot situated on the green, green is absent, but white is present; by contrast it appears a vivid pink-red.

In these last experiments the contrast action no longer depends simply on a definite distribution of colours in the field of vision. We have seen that this effect can be exactly the same with two different simple modifications of the experiment, and yet in the one case the contrast effect appears, in the other it does not. The moment the contrasting field was recognized as an independent body laid over the coloured ground, or was even divided off enough by something to indicate that it was a separate field, the contrast was absent. Accordingly, since the *judgment* of the position in space, i. e., of the corporeal independence of the object in question, is the decisive factor in the determination of the colour, the consequence is that the contrast colour here is not due to an act of sensation but to an act of judgment. The nature of this act of judgment by which we reach the perception of objects with definite characteristics will be more accurately described in Part III (Vol. III). As the acts of judgment here spoken of are always executed unconsciously and involuntarily, naturally it is often hard to determine what chain of impressions is responsible for the final result, and in the nature of the case very different circumstances may affect it. The author will endeavour to indicate here some of these conditions, as well as he has been able to ascertain them considering how new the subject is.

The experiments which have been described above have something in common which seems very much to support the occurrence of contrast action, although contrast can also occur without this condition. That is to say, in all of these cases a coloured illumination, or a transparent coloured veil, seems to be spread over the field. The immediate impression is not that this colouration is absent where there is white, that is, it is not just a mere substitution of the complementary colour of the ground in place of the white; but the idea seems to be that two new colours are substituted in the place of the white, namely, the colour of the ground and the complementary colour. The connection is clearest in the arrangement shown in Fig. 54, where the observer looks through the green glass inclined at an angle of 45°. He decides that the black spot on the horizontal surface is pink-red, but he also decides that this spot, as well as the entire surface with its pink-red colour is seen through the green glass, and that the green colour given by the glass extends uninterruptedly over the entire lower surface, and even over the dark spot. Thus he believes that he sees two colours together at this place, that is, green, which he attributes to the glass plate, and pink-red, which he attributes to the paper behind it; and the two of them together do, in fact, give the true colour of this place, that is, white. As a matter of fact, an object which, seen through a green glass, sends white light to the eye, as this spot does, would have to be pink-red. But when a white object of exactly the same appearance is placed above the plate of glass, every reason for resolving the colour of the object into two disappears; it looks white to us.

It is the same way when coloured surfaces are covered with translucent paper. If the ground is green, the paper itself seems to be greenish. Now if the substance of the paper extends without a perceptible break over grey underneath, the observer thinks he sees an object shining through the greenish paper; and an object of this kind must, on the other hand, be pink-red in order to give white light. But if the white place is outlined as an independent object, and there is lack of continuity between it and the greenish part of the surface, it is regarded as being a white object lying on this surface. In §20 above, it was stated that this sort of separation of two colours that are present in the same part of the visual field is a matter of judgment. We were confronted with this condition there as something that was an obstacle to the free realization of the sensation of a compound colour. A separation of this sort is a very frequent occurrence whenever the two colours are unevenly distributed. These phenomena were noticed first by VOLKMANN,[1] and he describes the effect by saying that we seem to see one colour *through* the other. In the author's opinion the faculty of making such a separation depends on the following circumstance. Colours have their greatest significance for us in so far as they are properties of bodies and can be used as marks of identification of bodies.

[1] MÜLLERS *Archiv für Anat. und Physiol.* 1838. S. 373.

Hence in our observations with the sense of vision we always start out
by forming a judgment about the colours of bodies, eliminating the
differences of illumination by which a body is revealed to us. In §20 it
was noticed that in this sense we make a plain distinction between a
dimly illuminated white surface and a highly illuminated grey one.
Therefore, we have a certain difficulty about realizing that brightly
lighted grey is the same as dimly lighted white. By some device the
intense light must be confined strictly to the grey field, so that we
cannot infer from the sense impression that the grey is more highly
illuminated than the rest of the field of vision. It is then only that we
recognize its identity with white. Just as we are accustomed and
trained to form a judgment of colours of bodies by eliminating the
different brightness of illumination by which we see them, we eliminate
the colour of the illumination also. There is plenty of opportunity of
investigating these same corporeal colours in sunshine outdoors, in the
blue light of the clear sky, in the weak white light of the overcast sky,
in the red-yellow light of the setting sun, and by red-yellow candle
light. And besides all this there are the coloured reflections of surrounding bodies. In a shady forest the illumination is predominantly
green. In rooms with coloured walls it is the same colour as the walls.
We are never distinctly conscious of these latter variations of illumination, and yet they can be demonstrated often enough by the coloured
shadows. By seeing objects of the same colour under these various
illuminations, in spite of the difference of illumination, we learn to
form a correct idea of the colours of bodies, that is, to judge how such
a body would look in white light; and since we are interested only in
the colour that the body retains permanently, we are not conscious at
all of the separate sensations which contribute to form our judgment.

Thus too when we view an object through a coloured mantle, we
are not embarrassed in deciding what colour belongs to the mantle
and what to the object. We do the same thing in the experiments
described above, even when the mantle over the object is not coloured
at all; and it is this that causes, or at any rate promotes, the illusion
into which we fall, and as a result of which we attribute a wrong colour
to the body, complementary to that of the coloured part of the mantle.

But although we are trained to recognize correctly the colours of
bodies in monochromatic light, our experience does not enable us to do
so when two illuminations in different colours come from two different
directions and from limited sources of light that cast sharp shadows.
For in most of the cases of coloured illumination mentioned above, the
coloured surfaces are very broad, and hence the coloured light is
tolerably uniformly distributed over all sides of the observed object.
Hence, with all coloured surfaces without distinction, wherever they

are in the sphere of the coloured illumination, we get accustomed to subtracting the illuminating colour from them in order to find the colour of the object. We do the same thing with the coloured shadows where two coloured illuminations coalesce. Where candle light and daylight come together, the illumination of the ground is whitish red-yellow. This red-yellow of the illumination we subtract too from the colour of the shadow that gets no candle light at all, and consider it as blue, although it is white. How the idea is actually obtained that the coloured illumination is removed in these coloured shadows and also in the translucent paper cover over the objective white spot, can be seen especially when little irregularities of the paper make the illumination spotted; then the observer thinks he sees these little spots in the coloured light, although they are not there at all.

Some other illustrations of our faculty of distinguishing the colours apart of two objects placed one behind the other will also be added here. The first one is connected with VOLKMANN's experiment alluded to above. He held two small strips of coloured paper in front of his eye, one quite close and the other at the distance of distinct vision; and noticed that, instead of seeing the mixed colour, he saw one colour through the other. Hold a green veil close in front of the eyes, which is so highly illuminated that the entire field of view has a green tinge, whereas the pattern and creases in the veil are seen merely as a very faint blurred image. Then there will be no difficulty in recognizing correctly the colours of objects seen through the veil, although on the retina some of the green light of the veil is mixed in with all colours. It is even more striking still when presently the retina becomes fatigued for the green light; and then the objects seen through the veil will even be pink-red, although green light is mixed in their retinal images. The best way to see this is to close the left eye and look through the green veil with the other eye. Presently a white paper seen through the veil will look not simply *white* but even *reddish-white*. Then if the right eye is closed and the uncovered left eye opened, the paper will look *green* to this eye by contrast. When the eyes are opened alternately, the paper looks reddish with the right eye where the retinal image of the paper is greenish white; and, conversely, it looks greenish with the left eye where the retinal image is white.

The same result is obtained in the experiment described by SMITH of Fochabers (Scotland),[1] which was afterwards modified and theoretically explained by BRÜCKE.[2] When a bright flame is placed close by the side of the right eye, or when the eye is illuminated from the right

---

[1] *Edinb. Journ. of Science*, V. 52.—POGG. *Ann.* XXVII. 494.
[2] *Denkschr. der k. k. Akad. zu Wien.* III. Bd.—POGG. *Ann.* LXXXIV. 418.

side by the sun, so that no light goes directly into the pupil, the other eye meantime being shaded, white objects will look greenish to the right eye and reddish to the left eye. This is seen distinctly by opening the two eyes in succession, sometimes the right eye and sometimes the left eye; or by looking steadily with both eyes at a white sheet of paper and holding a little black rod vertically midway between the paper and the eyes. Then two images of the rod will be seen projected on the paper, one for each eye. The image on the left, where the surface of the paper is seen by the left eye, but not by the right eye, will look red, and the other image will look green. On the other hand, when a person looks steadily at a black plate and holds a white object in front of it some distance away, so that there are two images of it, the right image, which now is the one seen by the left eye, will be red, and the left image will be green. Thus, white looks greener to the eye that is illuminated from one side than it does to the eye that is not illuminated. Now under these circumstances, light penetrates through the sclerotica and eyelids into the illuminated eye, and this light is red, as we already know from previous experiments (Vol. I, p. 213). If sunlight is allowed to shine on the eye from one side, the red colour will be recognized on dark objects too. For example, on looking at a printed page, the black letters appear a beautiful red and the white paper green. This red light coming in from the side is diffused over most of the fundus of the eye, and the places on the retina of the illuminated eye where the image of a white object is formed are therefore simultaneously illuminated by white and red light, but the sensation is greenish white. The greenish colouring gets more and more distinct as the experiment goes on, because it depends on the eye's being fatigued for red. But with excessive red illumination of the retina the only way this can happen is by the illumination already diffused over the ground getting separated from the additional light coming from the objects; and thus this latter light looks greenish because the eye is fatigued for red. In contrast therewith pure white looks reddish in the eye that has not been affected.

Consider, moreover, the image of the wall-paper and of the ceiling of a room which is reflected in the highly polished surface of the top of a mahogany table. When the eye is accommodated for these images, the colours either look natural or, it may be, a little bluish, complementary to the colour of the table. On the other hand, when the eye is accommodated for the top of the table, the total light coming from it is overwhelmingly red-yellow. The author's experience in this case is that the complementary colouring of the images occurs especially when the reflected light of the object is feeble as compared with the illumination of the table. But if the light falls very obliquely so as to increase very much the intensity of the reflected light, and at the same time cause the grain of the wood to disappear, the images, on the contrary, will often look reddish, because then there is no inducement any more to complete the separation.

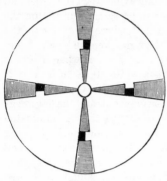

Fig. 55.

Although these circumstances that prompt us to effect a separation of white light into two portions are very conducive to the appearance of contrast, still they are not necessary. Similar contrast phenomena occur also in other cases, where a faint difference of colour is all that separates the induced from the inducing field. The effects are shown very beautifully on the colour top by inserting small coloured sectors on a white ground, so that the disc is like that shown in Fig. 55. Halfway from the centre the coloured sectors are interrupted by a piece composed of white and black. Thus when the disc revolves, naturally there should be a grey ring on a slightly tinted whitish ground. But as a matter of fact, this ring does not look grey. The colour is complementary to that of the sectors, and is most intense when its luminosity is the same as that of the ground or a little less. If the coloured sectors are wide, and consequently the colour of the ground too intense, the complementary colour of the ring will be fainter, or anyhow more doubtful, than when the ground is not so highly coloured. It is the same way when the grey ring is enclosed by two narrow black circles that sharply divide it from the ground. In the latter cases the contrast colouring is probably not entirely lacking, but it is connected with a considerable uncertainty of judgment as to the colour of the induced field; and by comparing it with a white field situated near the colour top, it is easy to reach the conclusion that the induced field is really white; whereas when the circles are absent, there is no doubt about the complementary contrast colour asserting itself in the perception. On the other hand, when a little bit of white paper is taken in a forceps and held over the greenish disc, absolutely no contrast colour whatever is seen on it, even when it is contrasted with the greenish field by no deep shadows. And when it is so turned towards the light that its luminosity is exactly the same as that of the grey zone, even the latter suddenly appears white in the vicinity of the little bit of paper, and like it; whereas the more distant parts of the ring generally continue to be coloured. If the grey zone is outlined by black lines, its colour in this experiment is recognized as pure grey all over. In this case it cannot be said that one colour was seen through the other. But in deciding as to the colour of the ring we start with the colour of the ground, and consider the colour of the ring as being a departure from the colour of the ground. When the two colours belong to two different bodies, there is no reason for connecting them together. We try rather to decide about the colour of each object independently of any accidental juxtaposition. But if a continuous flat surface, of the same structure and material all over, shows different colours in different places, the individual differences of these places being therefore in the colouring, necessarily in our judgment of them these different colours as such have to be connected and compared with one another. The result of this comparison, as experiment shows, is that the difference between the colours appears to be too great; whether it is because this difference, if it is the only one present and alone attracts the attention, makes a stronger impression than when it is one among several, and, therefore, is involuntarily considered as larger in the first case than in the second; or whether it is because in this case also the different colours of the surface are considered as being variations of the single fundamental colour of the surface, such as might be produced by shadows falling on it, by coloured reflections, or by being moistened by coloured fluids or sprinkled with coloured powders, etc. As a matter of fact, in order to produce an objectively white-grey spot on a greenish surface, a reddish pigment would have to be used.

Incidentally, it comes out plainly in the capricious results of these experiments, how hard it is for us to make accurate comparisons of luminosity and colour of two surfaces that are not directly in contact with each other and have no border between them. In the case of photometric methods we saw that the only certain and exact way of making the comparison was when there was nothing to distinguish the border between the two fields except difference of colour or illumination. The farther they are apart, the more inexact the comparison becomes; so that in such a case there is distinctly a wider latitude for the influence of accessory circumstances on our judgment of luminosity or colour. In the experiments which have been described the difference between the induced and inducing surfaces is brought out under the most favourable conditions; but the induced surface has to be compared with other surfaces lying off to the side in the visual field, so that this comparison can only be very imperfect.

This is shown still more plainly in the experiments now to be described, where the induced surface is in contact with two different colours on opposite sides. Then it will have the complementary colour on the corresponding edges. Or when the induced surface touches a darker surface on one edge and a brighter one on the other, the first edge will look brighter and the second edge darker. However, these contrast phenomena are likewise not distinct unless the only distinction between the inducing and induced fields is simply the difference of colour or luminosity, with no other border of any kind.

The experiments can readily be performed with transparent paper covers. Pieces of green and pink-red paper are fastened together so as to make a single sheet, half one colour and half the other. On the border line between the two colours a little strip of grey paper is attached; and over it all is laid a sheet of thin letter paper just large enough to cover it. The grey strip, where it touches the green, will now look pink-red, and where it touches pink-red it will look green. In the middle of it the two colours fuse into each other through an indefinite hue which perhaps is really grey, although it cannot be definitely recognized by us as such. The phenomenon is much more vivid when the length of the grey strip is oblique to the line of separation of the colours. Then the part of the grey that projects into the green may look just as vividly pink-red as the pink-red ground of the other side. The contrast colour is fainter, yet distinctly perceptible, when the middle longitudinal line of the grey strip is directly over the line of separation of the colours. Then the lateral edges of the grey appear coloured with a narrow border of complementary colour faded out towards the middle.

Similar effects are obtained by laying thin sheets of paper on top of each other step-fashion, so that the edge of each sheet is exposed in turn. If light is allowed to shine through a layer of paper whose thickness varies in this way, the objective brightness in each step will be constant of course, and yet each step will look darker at the edge where it touches the next brighter one, and brighter on the other edge where it touches the next darker one.

However, all these phenomena can be much more beautifully produced and delicately regulated on the colour top. The disc is made in black and white with sectors formed as shown in the accompanying Fig. 56. When it is set in· revolution several concentric rings will be seen, the outer ones being always brighter than the next interior ones. Within every ring of this sort the angular

Fig. 56.

width of the black segments is constant; and hence, with rapid rotation the luminosity is constant too. The luminosity varies simply from
one ring to the other. And yet each ring looks brighter on the inside
where it connects with the next darker ring; and darker on the outside
where it joins the next brighter ring. If the differences of luminosity
of the rings are very slight, it can scarcely be noticed sometimes that
the inner rings are darker than the outer; and what the eye sees rather
is simply the regular alternation of bright and dark at the edges.

If different colours are used instead of white and black, the colour
of each ring will look different at the edges, although objectively the
colour of each single ring is the same all over. Each element of the
compound colour comes out more intensely on that edge of a ring
where it joins another ring containing less of this colour. For instance,
suppose that blue and yellow are mixed, and that blue predominates
in the outer rings and yellow in the inner rings; then each ring will look
yellow on the outside and blue on the inside. And if the differences
of colour between the separate rings are on the whole very slight, here
again we may get the illusion of the disappearance in the various rings
of the differences of colour that are really there, and the alternating
blue and yellow contrast colouring of the edges will seem to be applied
on a uniformly coloured ground. It is very characteristic too that
usually in these cases the compound colour does not make an impression, but what we seem rather to see are the two colours separately
side by side and all in disorder.

These very striking contrast effects disappear, however, when the
boundary between each pair of rings is outlined by fine black circles.
Then each ring looks, as it really is, of the same luminosity and colour
all over. Here too perfect continuity and uniformity of the parts of the
different fields except as to colouring is again a decisive factor; and
so here too we have to do with variations, not of sensation but of
judgment. The differences of illumination of the various parts of the
surface assume special importance again as individual perceptible
differences; and since the differences between two elements of surface
are plainer and more certainly detected when they are directly in
contact than when they are farther apart, the differences of illumination along the edges of each pair of fields will be particularly forced on
the attention; and because the perception of them is surest and most
distinct, these differences look bigger than those between a pair of
middle portions of two fields as to which the mind is more in doubt.
In the experiments here described there was no sudden change of
illumination in the middle of each field that could be perceived; and
therefore the appearance was as if the colour of one edge had passed
gradually through the middle of the field into that of the other. How-

ever, if a black mark is made in the middle of the induced field, or if a grey field, the two halves of which are unequally bright and separated by a clear line of division, is interposed between two coloured ones, the complementary colourings will extend from each side up to this boundary line and be separated by it. If the colour-differences between the induced and inducing fields are so marked that there is no doubt about detecting the difference everywhere, the contrast action disappears, or at any rate is much more uncertain: If there is some other delimitation of the induced field besides, the difference between its colouring and that of the inducing field is detected with far less certainty, and the contrast likewise disappears or is less pronounced.

Note (added by HELMHOLTZ to the first edition).—BURCKHARDT has devised a series of experiments on contrast colours in after-images which on the whole are extraordinarily vivid, because the conditions are especially conducive here to the production of contrast. The same cases are mentioned above on pages 244 and 278. The after-image of white surrounded by a monochromatic ground shows the same colour as this ground. If two different colours of equal extent come in contact with the white field, the after-image of the white will be a mixture of the two colours of the ground. If the after-image is projected on a coloured ground, the colour of this ground contributes in addition the colour that the after-image would show on white ground. The following experiment is very beautiful. Look steadily at a disc with two coloured sectors while it is standing still. Then suddenly begin to rotate it without moving the eyes. The after-image will be seen on the disc with the colouring of the sectors reversed.

In the theoretical explanation of contrast phenomena the earlier observers invariably assumed that the mode of reaction of the nerves, that is, the sensation, is altered at the induced places on the retina, and therefore that contrast phenomena belonged in some sense in the domain of sympathetic sensations (or synaesthesia). Many investigators have been inclined to explain irradiation in this way also. Undoubtedly, in a certain sense there is some justification for speaking of altered sensation, in the case of observations where no precise distinction is made between successive contrast and simultaneous contrast, and where, therefore, there might certainly be a modification of sensation due to after-images. Here, as far as possible, the author has endeavoured, methodically in every case, to make a distinction between successive contrast and simultaneous contrast; the result being that, wherever the inducing colour did not overshadow all others by its extent and luminosity, the occurrence of the contrast colour has been shown to be due to conditions which were established simply by the psychic activities by which it reaches visual perception. If the inducing field is supposed to be an independent body, usually the contrast colour does not come out so as to be perceived. The nature of the illusion of judgment that occurs in this case has already been indicated. Invariably we have to do with cases where a certain modicum of doubt exists as to the nature of the induced colour, because an exact comparison of it with white is not feasible; and where, therefore, our faculty of perception is influenced by subsidiary circumstances so as to misplace the colour in question first at one and then at the other limit of the interval in which the uncertainty exists. To those readers who as yet know little about the influence of psychic activities on our sense-perceptions it may perhaps seem incredible that through psychic activity a colour can appear in the visual field where there is none. The author must beg them to suspend judgment until they have become acquainted with the facts in Part III of this work, which will deal with the sense-perceptions. There they will find many examples of a similar kind. The present chapter has brought us already to the theory of the perceptions of vision; and it has been allowed to remain here in the theory of sensations, because heretofore contrast has always been considered as belonging here, and because the most ordinary phenomena in this region are of mixed nature.

Since most contrast phenomena are dependent on the extent of the uncertainty in the judgment of the intensity and quality of our visual sensations, practice in judging colours is bound to have a considerable influence on the appearance of contrast. An eye that is trained in estimating size, distance, etc., will be on its guard against many illusions into which an untrained eye will be betrayed, and it is the same way with determinations of colour; and hence the author's belief is that practised eyes generally see contrast less vividly than unpractised eyes. His experiments were easily verified for him by persons who were skilled in optical observations. On the other hand, in many books contrast phenomena are described in such fashion that he is compelled to suppose that many observers can see them much more easily and more frequently than he can do.

Whereas, owing to the dependence of the colouring on other circumstances which are simply matters of judgment, there can be no doubt as to the interpretation of contrast phenomena when the inducing field is circumscribed, the contrasts are much more constant when the inducing field is not circumscribed, and might therefore seem to imply rather that they are aroused by changes of the sensation itself. However, the conditions for reaching positive decisions as to the colour of the inducing field are evidently far more unfavourable still in these latter cases than they are in the former, simply because there is no other white with which to compare the colour of this field, or at any rate the comparison is much more restricted. Besides, although contrasts occur more constantly in an inducing field that is not circumscribed, at the same time so far as their intensity relations are concerned, they are perfectly analogous with those of the circumscribed field. In all these cases the contrast colour is evoked in full intensity even by a very low intensity of the inducing colour, and is but little augmented by increase of the latter. On the other hand, it may be distinctly augmented the moment the sensation is actually altered by after-images. It will finally be maintained in full intensity by the judgment when all other colours are removed from the visual field. And so the author does not doubt that when the inducing field is large, just as when it is small, the explanation of the phenomena must be that the contrast colour is determined simply by an exercise of judgment, although in the former cases he cannot yet give as satisfactory proof of this explanation.

LEONARDO DA VINCI was quite familiar with contrast phenomena. He says that of all colours of equal purity those are the most beautiful that are placed side by side with their opposites; that is, white with black, blue with yellow, red with green.[1] Later the contrast phenomena that especially attracted attention more than all others were coloured shadows. OTTO v. GUERICKE[2] knew about them and tried to utilize them to prove ARISTOTLE's statement, that blue could be obtained by mixing white and black. But more general attention was first directed to them by BUFFON.[3] However, his observations were merely occasional and always made at sunrise or sunset, when they were sometimes blue, sometimes green. Abbé MAZEAS[4] produced them by the light of the moon and of a candle. Moreover, he thought he was able to explain them as being due to diminution of the light. On the other hand, MELVILLE[5] and BOUGUER[6] tried to explain the phenomena on NEWTON's colour theory. The colours were supposed to be objective, because, in point of fact, blue shadows illuminated by the light of the blue sky are objectively blue in colour. BEGUELIN,[7] in particular, showed that the blue sky light is really the cause of blue shadows in many cases. The subjective nature of the colour of one of the shadows seems to have been discovered first by RUMFORD,[8] by observing it through a narrow tube. GOETHE,[9]

---

[1] *Trattato della pittura.* Kap. CC. — .Coloured shadows in Chapters CLVI and CCCXXVIII.

[2] *Exper. Magdeb.* S. 142.

[3] *Mém. de l'Acad. de Paris.* 1743. p. 217.

[4] *Abh. der Akad. zu Berlin.* 1752.

[5] *Edinb. Essays.* Vol. II. p. 75.

[6] *Traité d'Optique.* p. 368.

[7] *Mém. de l'Acad. de Berlin.* 1767. p. 27.

[8] *Philos. Transact.* LXXXIV. 107; GRENS *Neues Journal der Physik.* II. 58.

[9] *Farbenlehre.* S. 27.

GROTHUSS,[1] BRANDES,[2] and TOURTUAL[3] adopted the same view. On the other hand, other observers still contended for a long time for the objective nature of both shadow colours; for example, v. PAULA SCHRANK[4] (who attributed the colour of the blue shadow to diffraction), ZSCHOKKE,[5] OSANN,[6] and POHLMANN[7] (who adopted the view of BEGUELIN). But it was FECHNER[8] chiefly that proved the subjective nature of these phenomena. Among other things he demonstrated also how the contrast colour once aroused might be maintained by an exercise of judgment; and, although he made a great many new observations, he did not venture to propose any theory of these phenomena. PLATEAU[9] included contrast phenomena in his theory of afterimages; just as the change of the retina to the opposite state was a function of the time, it should likewise be a function of the (exciting) surface, the result being that right around the region of excitation the same phase occurs that is manifested in irradiation phenomena, and a little farther away the opposite phase that arouses contrast.

The explanation of contrast phenomena as being due to after-images had been proposed by JURIN,[10] and afterwards by BRANDES. It was true for some of the phenomena, but not for all; and FECHNER, in particular, showed that even without preceding fatigue of the retinal areas concerned, contrast colours could arise.

The modifications of individual colours by their juxtaposition to others were accurately described by CHEVREUL.[11] The complementary reflex images in plates of coloured glass were described by BRANDES[12] and OSANN. The best method of making this experiment was devised by DOVE.[13] It was further modified by RAGONA SCINA.[14] The cases in which the induced field has the same colour as the inducing field were discovered by FECHNER and BRÜCKE.[15] H. MEYER[16] showed that a faint difference between the colours is more conducive than a big one. Incidentally, almost all the later observers adopted PLATEAU's view, that contrast is due to a change in sensation. The author himself has endeavoured in this article to separate the various concurrent causes more fully than has been done heretofore; and has taken pains to show that pure simultaneous contrast is due to a change, not of sensation, but of judgment.[17]

---

[1] SCHWEIGGERS *Beiträge zur Chemie und Physik.* III. 14.

[2] GEHLERS *Neues Wörterbuch.* Art. Farbe.

[3] *Die Erscheinungen des Schattens.* Berlin 1830.

[4] *Münchener Denkschr.* 1811 and 1812, S. 293, and 1813, S. 5.

[5] *Unterhaltungsblätter für Natur- und Menschenkunde.* 1826. S. 49.

[6] POGG. *Ann.* XXVII. 694; XXXVII. 287; XLII. 72.

[7] Ibid. XXXVII. 319–341.

[8] Ibid. XLIV. 221. L. 433.

[9] *Ann. de chim. et de phys.* LVIII. 339.—POGG. *Ann.* XXXII. 543; XXXVIII. 626.

[10] *Essay on distinct and indistinct vision.* p. 170.

[11] *Mém. de l'Acad.* XI. 447–520.

[12] GEHLERS *Neues Wörterbuch.* Art. Farbe. IV. 124.

[13] POGGENDORFFS *Ann.* XLV. 158.

[14] *Racc. fisico-chimici.* II. 207.

[15] *Denkschr. d. Wiener Akademie.* III. October 3, 1850.

[16] POGGENDORFFS *Ann.* XCV. 170.

[17] ¶HELMHOLTZ's contention that errors of judgment are at the basis of our ideas of contrast (especially of simultaneous contrast and also of successive contrast in some cases) has been vigorously opposed by E. HERING and others. HERING (*Arch. f. d. ges. Zeit. f. Psychol. u. Physiol. d. Sinnesorg.* 1890. I. 18) has furnished striking evidence that the excitation of one region of the retina may modify the physiological state of contiguous

1651. Leonardo da Vinci (*1519),*Trattato della pittura.* Chapters CLVI,CC,CCCXXVIII.

1672. Otto v. Guericke, *Experimenta nova, ut vocantur, Magdeburgica de vacuo spatio.* Amstelod. 1672. p. 142.

1738. Jurin, *Essay on distinct and indistinct vision.* p. 170.

1743. G. de Buffon, Sur les couleurs accidentelles. *Mém. de Paris.* 1743. p. 217.

1752. Mazeas, *Mém. de l'Acad. de Berlin.* 1752.

1760. Bouguer, *Traité d'optique sur la gradation de la lumière.* Paris 1760. p. 368.

Melville, Observations on light and colours. Essays and observations. *Phys. and Litt.* Edinburgh II. 12 and 75.

1767. Beguelin, Mémoire sur les ombres colorées. *Mém. de l'Acad. de Berlin.* 1767. p. 27. 1783. p. 52.

1778. v. Gleichen alias Russworm. Von den Farben des Schattens. *Act. Acad. Mogunt.* 1778. 308.

1782. H. F. T., *Observations sur les ombres colorées.* Paris 1782.

1783. Flauguergues, Sur les ombres colorées. *Mém. de Berlin.* 1783. p. 52.

Opoix, *Journal de Physique.* 1783. Dec.

Petrini, *Mem. di Mat. e di Fisica della Soc. Ital.* XIII. p. 11.

1787. Carvalho e Sampago, *Tratado das Colores.* Malta 1787.

1805. Prieur, Bemerkungen über die Farben und einige besondere Erscheinungen derselben. Gilb. *Ann.* XXI. S. 315.—*Ann. de Chim.* LIV. p. 1.

Hassenfratz, Sur les ombres colorées. *Journ. de l'école polytech.* Cah. XI.

1810. v. Goethe, *Zur Farbenlehre.* S. 27.

1811. Grothuss, Über die zufälligen Farben des Schattens. Schweiggers *Journal.* III. 14.

v. Paula Schrank, Über die blauen Schatten. *Abh. d. Münchener Akad.* 1811. p. 293 and 1813. p. 57.

---

areas (theory of retinal induction). He holds this reciprocal relation of retinal areas to be of fundamental importance in contrast and does not accept the explanation of the phenomenon given by Helmholtz. More recent experimental work in favour of Hering's theory may be found in the publications of Sherrington (*Journ. Physiol.* 1897. XXI. 33), Bidwell (*Proc. Roy. Soc.* London 1901, LXVIII, 262) and Burch (*Physiological Optics,* Oxford 1912); see also Starling (*Human Physiology,* 1920, p. 573). The most recent paper (supporting Hering) is by C. v. Hess (*Arch. f. d. ges. Physiol.* 1920. 179. p. 50).

Although the experiments of these writers have been pretty generally accepted as furnishing convincing evidence that the view of Helmholtz was wrong, the problem is not so simple as it seems. Helmholtz certainly recognized this fact, and so did Bidwell, who distinctly agrees (*loc. cit.*) with Helmholtz that mental judgment is sometimes the sole cause of contrast phenomena. Greenwood (*Physiology of the Special Senses.* London 1910) has proposed an explanation of simultaneous contrast which helps to harmonize the two conflicting theories, and Allen's recent paper (Reflex Visual Sensations and Color Contrast, *Journ. Op. Soc. Amer.* etc. 1923. VII. 913) is important. v. Kries (*Allgemeine Sinnesphysiologie.* Leipzig 1923) in his recent critical analysis of the problem, has clearly set forth the complexity of contrast phenomena and pointed out the basis of the controversy. See also v. Kries's Note at end of this chapter.

For extensive discussions of contrast and related phenomena the reader is referred to articles by Tschermak (*Ergeb. d. Physiol.* 1903. II. (2) 726), who gives a full bibliography to 1902; Rivers (in Schafer's *Textbook of Physiology.* 1900. II. p. 1060), and v. Kries (*loc. cit.*). For literature since 1902 the *Zeitschrift für Psychologie und Physiologie des Sinnesorgane* (separated in 1906 into the *Zft. f. Sinnesphysiologie* and *Zft. f. Sinnespsychologie*) and the *Psychological Index* are indispensable. For reviews of literature see the *Psychological Review* up to Vol. X, the *Psychological Bulletin* and *The American Journal of Physiological Optics.* 1921. II. pp. 232, 316 (Reviews of progress of visual science, by Troland; see also his important monograph on "The present status of visual science." *Bull. Nat. Res. Counc.* 1922. Vol. 5. part 2. No. 27). — (M.D.)

1820. Muncke, Über subjektive Farben und gefärbte Schatten.—Schweiggers *Journ.* XXX. 47.

1826. Zschokke, *Die farbigen Schatten, ihr Entstehen und ihr Gesetz.* Aarau 1826.—*Unterhaltungsblätter für Natur- und Menschenkunde* 1826. S. 49.

1827. Brandes, Art.: Farbe in Gehlers *Neuem physik. Wörterbuch.* IV. 124. Treschel, *Biblioth. univers.* XXXII. 3.

1830. Tourtual, *Über die Erscheinungen des Schattens und deren physiologische Bedingungen, nebst Bemerkungen über die wechselseitigen Verhältnisse der Farben.* Berlin 1830.
Lehot in: *Annales des sciences d'observation par* Saigey *et* Raspail. 1830. III. 3.—Frorieps *Notizen.* XXVIII. p. 177.

1832. Osann, Vorrichtung zur Hervorbringung komplementärer Farben und Nachweis ihrer objektiven Natur. Poggendorffs *Ann.* XXVII. 694; XXXVII. 287; XLII. 72.
Smith (of Fochabers) in *Edinb. Journ. of Science.* V. 52.
Brewster, Über den Versuch von Smith in Poggendorffs *Ann.* XXVII. 494.
Chevreul, Sur l'influence, que deux couleurs peuvent avoir l'une sur l'autre, quand on les voit simultanément. *Mém. de l'Acad. de Paris.* XI. 1832. — *De la loi du contraste simultané des couleurs.* Strasbourg 1839.

1834. J. Müller, in his *Archiv für Anat. und Physiol.* 1834. S. 144.—*Lehrbuch d. Physiol.* 2. Aufl. II. 372.
Plateau in: *Ann. de chim. et de phys.* LVIII. 339.—Poggendorffs *Ann.* XXXII. 543. XXXVIII. 626.

1836. Pohlmann, Theorie der farbigen Schatten. Poggendorffs *Ann.* XXXVII. 319–341.

1838. *Fechner, Über die Frage, ob die sogenannten Farben durch den Kontrast objektiver Natur seien. Poggendorffs *Ann.* XLIV. 221–245.
Dove, Über subjektive Komplementärfarben. Poggendorffs *Ann.* XLV. 158.

1840. *Fechner, Tatsachen, welche bei einer Theorie der Farben durch den Kontrast zu berücksichtigen sind. Poggendorffs *Ann.* L. 433.

1847. D. Ragona Scina, Su taluni fenomeni che presentano i cristalli colorati. *Racc. fis. chim.* II. 207.

1851. E. Brücke, Untersuchungen über subjektive Farben. *Wiener Denkschr.* III. 95.—Poggendorffs *Ann.* LXXXIV. 418.—*Arch. d. sc. phys. et natur.* XIX. 122.

1852. A. Beer, Über das überzählige Rot im Farbenbogen der totalen Reflexion (Kontrastfarbe). Poggendorffs *Ann.* LXXXVII. 113–115. *Cosmos.* II. 95.

1855. H. Meyer, Über Kontrast- und Komplementärfarben. Poggendorffs *Ann.* XCV. 170–171.—*Ann. de chim.* (3) XLV. 507.—*Phil. Mag.* (4) IX. 547.

1858. Chevreul, Note sur quelques experiences de contraste simultané des couleurs. *C. R.* XLVII. 196–198.—Dingler *J.* CXLIX. 435–436.

1859. Nardo, Nota sulle ombre colorate ottenute col solo concorso di luce bianche. *Cimento.* IX. 352-356.—*Atti dell' Istit. Veneto.* V.—*Zeitschr. für Chemie.* 1860. pp. 18–20.
Ragona, Su taluni fenomeni di colorazione soggetiva. *Atti dell' Acad. Palermit.* III.—*Zeitschr. für Chemie.* 1859. pp. 20–24.

1860. G. Th. Fechner, Über die Konstrastempfindung. *Leipzig. Ber.* 1860. S. 71–145.
Osann, Über Ergänzungsfarben. *Würzb. Zeitschr.* I. 61–77.
Fechner, Einige Bemerkungen gegen die Abhandlung Prof. Osanns über Ergänzungsfarben. *Leipz. Ber.* 1860. 146–165.
J. J. Oppel, Über farbige Schatten bewirkt durch weisses Licht. *Jahresber. des Frankf. Vereins.* 1859—1860. S. 65—69.

1861. Rossolini, Sulle ombre colorate. *Atti dell' Istit. Lombardo.* II, 318—321.

1862. H. Aubert, Beiträge zur Physiologie der Netzhaut. *Abhandl. der schlesischen sellsch.* 1861 (1). S. 49–103. S. 344.
G. Th. Fechner, Über den seitlichen Fenster- und Kerzenversuch. *Leipz. Ber.* 1862. S. 27–56.

1865. Fr. Burckhardt, Die Kontrastfarben im Nachbilde. *Basler Verhandl.* 1865.

Note by v. Kries (prepared especially for the present English edition).[1]

It is well known that the theoretical explanation of simultaneous contrast, with respect to both luminosity and colour, has been a subject of particular controversy. As opposed to HELMHOLTZ's opinion of our having to do here invariably with what he calls "mental illusions", another view, due mainly to HERING, which has been prevalent for a long time, is that, by virtue of a reciprocal physiological action of adjacent portions of the visual organ, which follows simple laws, a change takes place in the sensation itself in the strict sense of the word. Thus, for example, the sensation at one place in the visual field might be darkened by high illumination at an adjacent place, or it might be shifted towards green by red illumination at an adjacent place, and so on. It is not possible to go into this subject here in detail, and the reader is referred therefore to other works where the writer has discussed it (NAGEL's *Handbuch der Physiologie*, III, pp. 232 foll.; also v. KRIES's *Allgemeine Sinnesphysiologie*, Leipzig, 1923, p. 261 and especially pp. 275 foll.). Perhaps here it will suffice simply to say a few words as to the present status of the question. To begin with, it may be regarded as certain that there actually is a reciprocal physiological action as HERING supposed, especially with respect to luminosity-contrast. However, it is another question as to whether this is the sole cause of contrast phenomena or whether conditions of another sort are likewise involved, especially conditions that are identical with, or at any rate not very far removed from, those which HELMHOLTZ inferred. At present the latter must be considered as being probably the case. All the facts that led HELMHOLTZ at the time to attribute these phenomena to mental illusions and that were adduced by him in support of this hypothesis are in its favour. Moreover, some very searching experiments on this point have been made very recently by JAENSCH and his pupils; the conclusion being that many, in fact most, contrast phenomena are *not* to be accounted for by a reciprocal physiological action such as HERING assumed. Consequently, instead of speaking of a simple change of sensations, JAENSCH employs the term "transformation" of luminosity or colour.[2] However, the idea that is meant to be

[1] ¶Concerning the above note on "Contrast," Professor v. KRIES writes (from Freiburg, January 6, 1924) that it had been originally intended to add an extensive article on this subject in the third edition, but that owing to the fatal illness of Professor NAGEL, who had been entrusted with this task, the plan had ultimately to be abandoned. Professor v. KRIES expressed the hope that some effort would be made to supply this deficiency in the English edition, and kindly offered to place the brief note above at the disposal of the editor to be utilized for that purpose in any way he deemed best. However, it was finally decided to insert here Professor v. KRIES's note just as it stands. (J. P. C. S.)

[2] R. E. JAENSCH and A. E. MÜLLER, Über die Wahrnehmung farbloser Helligkeiten und den Helligkeitskontrast. *Zft. f. Psychol.*, LXXXIII. p. 266. — O. KROH, Über Farbenkonstanz und Farben-Transformation. *Zft. f. Sinnesphysiologie* LII. p. 113.

conveyed here by the use of the term transformation amounts to saying that the connection between the sensation strictly so-called and the conceptions that are retained in the memory can be shifted; and so in any case it is not far removed from HELMHOLTZ's hypothesis of mental illusions.[1] —K.

§25. Various Subjective Phenomena

Some subjective phenomena of vision still remain to be described, the explanation of which is as yet unknown or at any rate is very doubtful, and which therefore could not be included in the preceding chapters.

1. *Phenomena of the yellow spot.* The yellow spot is a place on the retina which is distinguished in many respects. The peculiarities of its anatomical structure have been described in Vol. I, §4. Moreover, physiologically, it is characterized by the keenness of its perception of tiny images, wherein the fovea centralis far surpasses all other places of the retina. Its importance as point of fixation is a consequence of this extraordinary sensitivity. In Vol. I, §15, pp. 213-217, it was shown how the yellow spot could be made visible in the entoptical image. In this mode of observation it is characterized by the absence of vessels at its centre, and also by the shadows cast by the lateral slopes of the fovea in oblique illumination. With respect to the sensations of this place on the retina, we have already mentioned that when a current of electricity goes through the eye, the yellow spot is outlined sometimes as dark on a bright ground, sometimes as bright on a dark ground, depending on the direction of the current. Moreover, in intermittent light of moderate frequency the yellow spot appears as a peculiar star-shaped design in the iridescent patterns of the retina.

Another fact has now to be mentioned. In uniformly diffused illumination, especially in blue light, the yellow spot is characteristically outlined. Then different parts of the yellow spot, not always all at the same time, appear with different distinctness under different conditions. The centre of the yellow spot is the fovea centralis, and there the retina is very thin, transparent and without colour. According to KOELLIKER, its diameter is between 0.18 and 0.225 mm. Its distance from the posterior nodal point of the eye is 15 mm, and therefore on the average 75 times as great as its diameter. Hence, its apparent size in the field of view is that of a circle whose angular diameter is from 40 to 50 minutes of arc. Ordinarily, when visible, it looks like a regular well outlined circle. Surrounding the fovea centralis a dark halo is frequently observed, whose size about

[1] Concerning this, see v. KRIES, *Allgemeine Sinnesphysiologie* p. 139 and pp. 281-284.

corresponds to the place of the yellow spot where there are no vessels, as it looks when the vessels are made entoptically visible. The external boundary of this so-called *non-vascular* halo is indistinct. Its diameter, being about three times that of the fovea centralis, amounts therefore to something over two degrees. Sometimes its border is fairly circular in appearance, especially in dim light, and then again it is like a rhomb with its longer diagonal horizontal. It appears the latter way to the author, especially in good light. Anatomically, this place corresponds to the central, intensely yellow, part of the yellow spot. Its horizontal diameter as measured by H. Müller in two eyes was 0.88 and 1.5 mm; and its vertical diameter 0.53 and 0.8 mm. Incidentally, the yellow colouring extends much farther yet, but it is weak and faded.

Finally, in good light the dark non-vascular halo is seen surrounded also by a bright halo, whose outer border is very indefinitely indicated, and which likewise looks to the author more rhomboidal than circular. Its two diameters are some three times as large as that of the dark non-vascular halo. An anatomically well-defined substratum of this place cannot be designated. The yellowish faded colouring of the outer parts of the yellow spot coincides to some extent with this bright halo. Still nothing can be said about the congruence of their areas, because the extent of the faint yellow colouring is too different in different eyes. Perhaps this outermost bright halo owes its origin simply to a contrast action also. It may be called Loewe's ring after its discoverer, to whom it appeared to be circular in form.

Loewe[1] discovered this ring by looking at a bright surface through a clear sea-green solution of chromium chloride. The ring appeared violet in comparison with the greenish ground surrounding the central darker halo, and so Haidinger compared it with an image of the iris surrounding the dark pupil. Haidinger showed that dichromatic means are not necessary for the production of the rings, and that they appear in the homogeneous blue of the prismatic spectrum, and also in mixed light with enough blue in it. In the latter case the differences of colour are different from the rest of the ground, depending on the quality of the colours admixed with the blue. This ring seems to appear with more distinctness to some eyes than to others; and in fact many eyes cannot see it at all. It is only with a certain medium brightness, about like that which is satisfactory for reading and writing, that the author can see it. By holding a blue glass in front of his eyes, and resting them a while by closing the lids, and then looking through the glass at a white paper surface, he can see distinctly the non-vascular corona as a rhombic shadowy spot surrounded by a rhombic bright blue strip, which is Loewe's ring. With slightly more or less luminosity than this

---

[1] Haidinger in Pogg. *Ann.* LXX. 403. LXXXVIII. 451.—*Wiener Sitzungsber.* IX. 240.

the ring looks smaller; and for any greater changes of luminosity all that the writer can see then is the dark non-vascular halo without a bright encircling border.

The dark non-vascular halo is the most constant feature of the phenomenon. Its behaviour was first accurately investigated by MAXWELL.[1] According to him, it always appears in blue, and not in other colours, when homogeneous light is used. Incidentally, it appears in mixed colours also, when they contain a great deal of blue; especially too in white, but faint. When the eye, after being rested, is turned towards a blue surface, it comes out, but soon vanishes again, more quickly in bright than in dim illumination. MAXWELL recommends placing blue and yellow glass or blue and yellow paper in front of the eye alternately. The spot appears in blue, and disappears in yellow. The author observes it most beautifully on the evening sky when the first stars begin to appear, and after having been outdoors for some time, so that the eyes are sufficiently rested. Closing them for a moment and then opening them towards the sky, the observer will see the non-vascular halo very distinctly for some time, often too the fovea centralis in its interior as a little brighter spot of pure blue, pretty sharply outlined. It is a singular thing here, as was noticed also by MAXWELL, that the luminous impression in the central places of the retina develops into sensation a moment later than it does in the peripheral parts. To show this, MAXWELL caused a series of dark bands to pass in front of a blue field at a certain rate. However, it may be plainly seen by simply opening the eyes. The darkness of the closed eyes plainly vanishes from the periphery of the visual field towards the centre, and the last remnant of it lingers as the MAXWELL spot. With certain degrees of brightness, particularly with that of the sky mentioned above when the first stars become visible, the phenomenon when the eyes are opened is more complex still. Thus while the darkness disappears from the periphery towards the centre in the manner described, we also see either the fovea centralis by itself or the entire MAXWELL spot flare up bright. Perhaps the bright flash precedes the dark phenomenon a little, but the time is so brief that they are apparently simultaneous, similar to what AUBERT noticed in after-images with illumination by electric sparks.

Sometimes, when the fovea centralis appears very distinct, the writer can detect in the non-vascular halo faint patterns of lines like the contours of a flower with many petals (for example, a georgina or dahlia). Perhaps they are indications of the same pattern that comes out more plainly in intermittent light.

[1] *Athenäum.* 1856. p. 1093.—*Edinb. Journ.* (2) IV. 337.—*Inst.* 1856. p. 424.—*Rep. of British Association.* 1856. II. 12.

Finally, the writer must mention also that often on getting up in the morning he has accidentally seen the MAXWELL spot, bright on a dark ground, in case the eye was first directed to a bright window with a broad luminous surface. So far he has not succeeded in eliciting the phenomenon deliberately. In this case it appears as a brilliantly bright circle of the size of the non-vascular halo, shaded off towards the edges and with indications of stellar design. This latter appearance suggests that when the eye is thoroughly rested and sensitive, the impression of light in the yellow spot persists longer than in the other parts of the retina; while, on the other hand, the action at the same place appears to begin later, as indicated by the phenomena obtained on opening the eye, which were described above. The reason why the highly pigmented part of the yellow spot looks dark on a blue field, is apparently on account of the absorption of blue light by the yellow pigment. Precisely those parts are yellow here that are directly in front of the elements or cones which are peculiarly sensitive to light. Incidentally, the explanation of why the spot is but faintly outlined subjectively, and is very transient, is the same as that of the fugitive appearance of the vascular figures. But the occasional bright flaring up of the yellow spot on opening the eye cannot yet be explained.[1]

The phenomena as described thus far relate to unpolarised light. But if the eye is directed to a field emitting polarised light, HAIDINGER's *polarisation brushes* appear at the point of fixation. For instance, they will be seen on looking through a NICOL prism at a well lighted sheet of white paper or at the surface of a bright cloud. The brushes are reproduced in Fig. 1, Plate III,[*] as they appear when the plane of polarisation is vertical. The brighter spots bounded by the two branches of a hyperbola look bluish on a white field. On the other hand, the dark brush separating them, which is narrowest in the centre and broader towards its ends, is yellowish in colour. When the NICOL is turned, the polarisation pattern turns through the same angles. BREWSTER noticed that the dark brush is much narrower at its centre when it is horizontal (that is, parallel to the line between the two eyes) than when it is vertical, as shown in the illustration; and the writer has verified this observation. Both MAXWELL and the writer find that the surface covered by the polarisation pattern seems to be the same

---

[1] The condition under which MAXWELL's spot is produced and in general the entoptical perceptions in the macular zone have recently been very thoroughly investigated and described by GULLSTRAND (GRÄFES *Arch. f. Ophthalmol.* LXII. 1905, 1; LXVI. 1907, 141) and by DIMMER (ibid. LXV. 1907, 486). A more detailed consideration of these investigations would lead us too far here. It may be simply stated that GULLSTRAND considers the yellow colouring of the macula to be a post mortem appearance.—N.

[*] Plate III faces page 384.

size as the non-vascular halo of the yellow spot. The edge of the fovea centralis about passes through the brightest part of the blue surfaces. BREWSTER estimates the diameter of the polarisation brushes as somewhat larger, namely 4°; and SILBERMANN gives 5°, the difference being perhaps due to the fact that they seem to be very much more distinct for some eyes than for others, and hence some persons perceive the faintest parts of the pattern to the farthest edge, while others do not. Thus, twelve years ago, immediately after HAIDINGER's discovery, the author took the greatest pains to perceive these brushes and could not do it at all. Recently, when he tried it again, he saw them the moment he looked through the NICOL prism. The centre of the dark brush is much darker in his left eye than in the other eye. It may be that the variable colouring of the yellow spot is responsible for it. Incidentally, when they are visible, they always quickly disappear again, as is the case with every subjective phenomenon connected with a structure of the retina. Then they reappear again when the polariser is turned through a right angle.

Individuals who perceive the brushes quite distinctly see them also in light that is only partially polarised, on brilliant surfaces, on the sky, etc.; and it enables them to tell equally well under any circumstances the direction of the plane of polarisation. However, STOKES showed that blue was the only one of the homogeneous colours that exhibited the polarisation brushes. In the less refrangible parts of the spectrum they do not show. In a blue field the bluish hyperbolic surfaces look bright, and the yellow brushes between them look dark, as, for example, in looking at a white surface through a strongly coloured blue glass in conjunction with the polariser. The writer fails to see the brushes, not merely in homogeneous green, yellow and red, but even in the mixed, tolerably saturated shades of these hues obtained with coloured glass. Consequently, even in white light the phenomenon depends on variations of the blue. At the place where the yellow brushes are there is no blue, and just for that reason they look yellow and darker.

When light is polarised by refraction, reflection or double refraction, all the colours are always almost equally affected by the polarisation. It is only when coloured light is absorbed in double refraction that light of certain colours may be polarised, while light of other colours is not. The most familiar example of this sort is the absorption by tourmalin, which is so often used for polarising light. This property, by the way, is very common among coloured crystals that are double refracting. It may be produced by colouring them artificially, and it depends on the fact that sometimes the ordinary ray is more absorbed (as in tourmalin), and sometimes the extraordinary ray (as in titanium dioxide and tin oxide). But most organic fibres and membranes are double refracting to a slight extent, both of them usually behaving like uniaxial crystals, with the axis in the fibres longitudinal, and in the membranes perpendicular to their surfaces. The phenomenon of the polarisation brushes may be explained by supposing that the yellow elements in the yellow spot are double refracting to a slight degree, and that the extraordinary ray of blue is more absorbed by them than the ordinary ray.

If blue light polarised in any way passes through a mass of fibres of this sort along the direction of their axes, it will be much absorbed. But if it traverses them at right angles, it will not be strongly absorbed unless it is polarised parallel to the fibres; being only feebly absorbed when the plane of polarisation is perpendicular to the direction of the fibres. Now in the yellow spot the so-called radial fibres of H. MÜLLER, which at other places of the retina are perpendicular to its surface, run diagonally, their posterior ends being nearer the fovea centralis.[1] In the fovea centralis the nuclear layers and the intermediate nuclear layer are either absent entirely or are anyhow very thin. On the other hand, in the region around the fovea centralis the inner nuclear layer and the intermediate nuclear layer are thicker than elsewhere. Something of the same sort is true with respect to the layer of ganglion cells, although even in the fovea centralis it is still three cells deep. Thus it seems as if the other elements belonging to the cones of the fovea centralis were heaped up in the region around this little pit and therefore the connecting fibres of nerves and tissue must run diagonally. At the edge of the fovea centralis, where the direction of the fibres is mainly diagonal towards its centre, according to the above supposition, light would be more strongly absorbed where the fibres were parallel to the plane of polarisation. Thus if the latter is vertical, darker places will be formed above and below the fovea centralis, and brighter places to the right and left. Likewise, the places where the fibres are not oblique to the surface of the retina, that is, in the fovea centralis itself, and out towards the outer border of the yellow spot, would have to be darker. Now the phenomenon of the polarisation brushes actually does agree with these consequences.

There are other opinions as to the origin of the polarisation brushes. One of these in particular, which was suggested by ERLACH and specially developed by JAMIN, has met with much favour. Their idea was that the brushes might be produced by multiple refractions at the boundaries of the ocular media. As a matter of fact, light polarised vertically and entering the eye from above or below would be more

[1] BERGMANN in HENLE und PFEUFFER *Zeitschr. für rat. Med.* (2) V. 245, (3) II. 83. — MAX SCHULTZE, *Observationes de Retinae structura penitiori.* Bonn 1859. p. 15.

strongly reflected, and less of it would get through, than in the case of the same kind of light entering the eye from one side; and hence the upper and lower quadrants of the visual field would have to be a little darker than the right and left. But if polarisation by refraction were responsible for the effect, in the first place the brushes would have to appear almost equally distinct in all homogeneous colours, whereas they appear distinct only in blue. In the second place, they would have to increase in intensity continuously out towards the edges of the visual field. On the contrary, they are restricted to a very small central part. In the third place, their centre would have to be where the optical axis meets the retina, and not at the point of fixation, these two places being different always. STOKES, BREWSTER and MAXWELL have all pointed out the insufficiency of this explanation, and the two latter have noted that the extent of the brushes agrees with that of the yellow spot. Various other explanations, not clearly worked out however, have been given by HAIDINGER and SILBERMANN.

According to HAIDINGER's description, there are also bright X-shaped lines in the blue field where LOEWE's ring is seen, but as yet they have not been observed by anybody else. The writer cannot see them.

1844. W. HAIDINGER, Über das direkte Erkennen des polarisierten Lichts. POGGENDORFFS *Ann.* LXIII. 29.
1846. Idem, Über komplementäre Farbeneindrücke bei Beobachtung der Lichtpolarisationsbüschel. POGGENDORFFS *Ann.* LXVII. 435.
    Idem, Beobachtung der Lichtpolarisationsbüschel in geradlinig polarisiertem Lichte. POGGENDORFFS *Ann.* LXVIII. 73.
    Idem, Beobachtung der Lichtpolarisationsbüschel auf Flächen, welche das Licht in zwei senkrecht aufeinander stehenden Richtungen polarisieren. POGGENDORFFS *Ann.* LXVIII. 305.
    SILBERMANN, Essai d'explication des houppes ou aigrettes visibles a l'œil nu dans la lumière polarisée. *C. R.* XXIII. 624.—*Inst.* No. 665. p. 327.
1847. v. ERLACH, Mikroskopische Beobachtungen über organische Elementarteile bei polarisiertem Licht, in MÜLLERS *Archiv für Anat. und Physiol.* 1847. p. 313.
    HAIDINGER, Helle Andreaskreuzlinien in der Sehachse. *Ber. d. Freunde der Naturwiss. in Wien.* II. 178.—POGGENDORFFS *Ann.* LXX. 403.
    BOTZENHART, Polarisationsbüschel am Quartz. *Ber. d. Fr. d. N. W. in Wien* I. 82.
    Idem, Sur une modification des houppes colorées de HAIDINGER. *C. R.* XXIV. 44.—*Inst.* No. 680. p. 11.—POGGENDORFFS *Ann.* LXX. 399.
1848. JAMIN, Sur les houppes colorées de HAIDINGER. *C. R.* XXVI. 197.—POGGENDORFFS *Ann.* LXXIV. 145.—*Inst.* No. 737. p. 53.
1850. D. BREWSTER, On the polarizing structure of the eye. SILLIMAN's *J.* (2) X. 394. *Rep. of British Assoc.* 1850. II. 5.—*Wiener Ber.* V. 442.
    G. G. STOKES on HAIDINGER's brushes. SILLIMAN's *J.* (2) X. 394.—*Rep. of British Assoc.* 1850. II. 20.
    W. HAIDINGER, Das Interferenzschachbrettmuster und die Farbe der Polarisationsbüschel. *Wien. Ber.* VII. 389.—POGGENDORFFS *Ann.* LXXXV. 350.—*Cosmos. I.* 252, 454.
1852. Idem, Die LOEWESCHEN Ringe eine Beugungserscheinung. *Wien. Ber.* IX. 240–249. —POGGENDORFFS *Ann.* LXXXVIII. 451–461.

1854. W. HAIDINGER, Dauer des Eindrucks der Polarisationsbüschel auf der Netzhaut. *Wien. Ber.* XII. 678–680.—POGGENDORFFS *Ann.* XCIII. 318–320.

Idem, Beitrag zur Erklärung der Farben der Polarisationsbüschel durch Beugung. *Wien. Ber.* XII. 3–9.—POGGENDORFFS *Ann.* XCI. 291–601.

Idem, Einige neuere Ansichten über die Natur der Polarisationsbüschel. *Wien. Ber.* XII. 758–765.—POGGENDORFFS *Ann.* XCVI. 314–322.

STOKES, Über das optische Schachbrettmuster. *Wien. Ber.* XII. 670–677.—POGGENDORFFS *Ann.* XLVI. 305–313.

1856. J. C. MAXWELL, On the unequal sensibility of the foramen centrale to light of different colours. *Athen.* 1856. p. 1093.—*Edinb. Journ.* (2) IV. 337.—*Inst.* 1856. p. 444.—*Rep. of Brit. Assoc.* 1856. II. 12.

1858. POWER in *Phil. Mag.* (4) XVI. 69.

1859. BREWSTER in *C. R.* XLVIII. 614.

---

2. *Bright mobile points* appear in the field of view in looking steadily at a large uniformly illuminated surface like the sky or snow, especially during walking or other bodily exercise. At different places in the visual field little points leap up and run away quite rapidly in very different paths, which are generally not entirely straight. Then after little intervals new ones appear along the route one of them has blazed, and pursue the same path. PURKINJE noticed that in gazing at a luminous area of limited dimensions, a window say, every point on the side away from the centre of the visual field draws a little shadow after it. As they seem to keep to fixed paths, many observers (J. MÜLLER) have been disposed to regard them as having something to do with the circulation of the blood. But in the author's opinion these phenomena are much too sporadic to be taken for blood corpuscles. Their paths also are too far apart from each other, and their movements are too rapid, to correspond to a capillary network. If their appearance really has anything to do with the circulation of the blood, the most we could say about it would be that single lymph corpuscles, perhaps containing much fat, floating through larger vascular stems, may be manifested in this way. This phenomenon, by the way, seems to be readily seen by most people.[1]

[1] It is easy to recognize a connection between this phenomenon and the circulation of the blood, because in many persons the movement of the luminous corpuscles invariably shows a pulsating acceleration, and with all persons the movement can be easily retarded by a slight pressure on the temporal side of the eyeball and changed into a very distinct pulsating one. The little points are shoved forwards rhythmically with the pulse; with stronger pressure they move just a little with each beat of the pulse, and between times remain almost still. When the pressure is increased still more, the motion ceases, and at the very instant the images of the objects that are seen dissolve away.

ROOD (SILLIMAN'S *Journ.* (2)XXX. 264 and 385)noticed long ago that the movement of the little points can be seen particularly plainly by looking through a blue glass. If the phenomenon is investigated when the field of view is illuminated by monochromatic light of various colours, it will be found that no trace of the corpuscles can be seen in red, yellow or green light and also in cyan-blue light; but that they are very plainly visible in indigo and violet light, and can be seen to a remarkable extent even in yellow-green light (between

Incidentally, the blood corpuscles are just large enough, if they were on the retina and did make an impression on it, to be recognized. On the average their diameter amounts to 0.0072 mm, and the size of the smallest perceptible distance is 0.005 mm (see §18). Various observers have also seen rows of advancing little globules and vaguer undulations and currents. The peculiar appearance of meandering currents, which occurs with intermittent light, and which is connected by VIERORDT with the circulation of blood in the choroid, has been alluded to above. Incidentally, something similar to this may be seen sometimes without intermittent light, by gazing at a bright surface, especially after the blood has been driven to the head by bending over. As soon as the retina is so far fatigued by the action of the light that the surface becomes dark, there appears, as it were, behind the vanishing bright surface a spotted reddish surface, with its spots sometimes in motion and sometimes still. STEINBACH and PURKINJE[1] have seen rows of little flowing globules, especially when mild pressure is exerted on the eye. The latter saw them first by observing the dark accommodation pattern, which in his case consisted of a central white circle surrounded by a brownish halo without any definite border. Alongside the white circle on the right and left, he saw two vertical lines of light, with rows of tiny balls moving along them, down on the right and up on the left. So far the author has not seen anything like this. During congestion in the cranial region, or when he bent over and then suddenly rose up, JOHANNES MÜLLER[2] saw something that looked like black bodies with tails to them, jumping and flying about in the most manifold directions. He compared it with the creepy sensations in the tactile nerves.

Sometimes, too, the writer has noticed a flicker on a wall roughly plastered with lime and very obliquely lighted by a small window, as of tiny objects in motion. The wall appears to be studded with a quan-

---

570 and $560\mu\mu$). These are precisely the kinds of light that are most strongly absorbed by hemaglobin, and in view of this fact there can hardly be any doubt about its being a question here of images of the *red* corpuscles. The comparatively small number of corpuscles visible at one time might be due to the fact that, in the first place, only those corpuscles in a perfectly definite plane of the retina (very close to the *membrana limitans interna*) are under favourable conditions for being seen, and, in the second place, even these are perhaps not easy to see unless they are oriented in a certain way in which they are particularly absorbent of light. Since the little points that move look *bright*, it might be supposed that this is due to spaces in the row of blood corpuscles that occupy a capillary.

Generally, the foveal region always remains free from this circulation effect. On this subject, see G. ABELSDORFF and W. NAGEL, Über die Wahrnehmung der Blutzirkulation in den Netzhautkapillaren. *Zft. f. Psychol. u. Physiol. der Sinnesorgane*, XXXIV. 291. 1904.—N.

[1] *Beobachtungen und Versuche*. I. 127.

[2] *Physiologie*. II. 390.

tity of small black irregular points. But these might perhaps have been after-images of the small points flaring up from unavoidable little perturbations of the eye.

Some other phenomena are described by PURKINJE that are produced by agitating the vascular system or by straining the eyes. His description reads[1]: "On a bright day when I have been out walking briskly for fifteen minutes or half an hour and then suddenly enter a dim room, or at least one very much darkened, a dull light waves and flickers in the field of vision, like the expiring flame of alcohol spilled on a horizontal surface, or like a place rubbed with phosphorus faintly flickering in the dark. On looking more closely, I notice that the flickering haze consists of innumerable extremely tiny luminous points moving amongst each other along various lines, piling up now here, now there, and forming vaguely bounded spots which are again torn asunder to be reassembled elsewhere. Each point leaves a trail of light behind it as it moves, and these trails form manifold intersecting nets and little stars. A large tract in the interior of the visual field teems with this sort of thing and interferes with distinct vision. The appearance is more like the swarming of the motes of sunbeams than anything else."

When he covered his right eye and looked at a bright surface with his weak farsighted eye, he got the same effect; and likewise when the pressure on his left eye was gradually increased more and more. The points appear more vivid with the eye open than with it closed, especially when it is turned towards a distant place that is not entirely dark. Thus, external light is requisite for the effect.[2]

If he had been running or if he pressed on his eye or coughed violently, he would see pulsating spheres on the surface of the bright sky. There would be a pair of them on the right side of the visual field, a row of them below, and three on the left side. The point of fixation pulsated too; and there were grey bands also, partly circular vascular bands surrounding the point of fixation and partly radial bands.[3]

3. *Figures, which become visible when the retina is uniformly illuminated.* PURKINJE[4] noticed that when he gazed steadily at a large rather brilliant surface (for instance, at a uniformly clouded sky or at a candle flame close by), in a few seconds luminous points kept on leaping up in the middle of the visual field; which without having changed their position quickly disappeared again, leaving black points behind, which likewise quickly vanished. If, while the luminous

[1] *Beobachtungen und Versuche* I. 63.
[2] See footnote on page 8 of this volume.—N.
[3] *Beobachtungen und Versuche.* I. 134.
[4] Ibid. I. 67.

points were leaping out, he turned his eye towards a very dark place, or closed it, the phenomenon proceeded in the same manner, only in a diminished light; as if the points had been simply kindled by the preliminary gazing and then glowed by themselves alone. The writer likewise has frequently seen luminous points of this sort by accident, which could not be after-images, because there were no corresponding small bright objects in the field of vision, and which left dark after-images behind them. Usually, however, there was only one at a time, and rarely a repetition of it.

Here too we must mention PURKINJE's figure of the spider web,[1] consisting of luminous reddish lines on a red ground, imitating the web of the garden spider, sometimes more simply, sometimes in a more complex way. In order to make the figure come out well, PURKINJE laid down in such a position that the rays of the rising sun were bound to fall on his eyelids. On waking, he saw the figure behind the closed lids.

PURKINJE's work generally is exceedingly full of subjective observations of a similar kind, and will be for a long time still a rich mine for work in this region. But many of the phenomena which he describes have not been verified by other observers; and concerning them there is for the time being a question as to whether they were not due to individual peculiarities of his organ of vision.[2]

Note by W. Nagel

The appearance of flicker or flare, which occurs particularly in the dark visual field, and the causes of which are unknown, also deserves to be mentioned. The flicker observed in pathological conditions, which lasts from a quarter to a half hour and which is accompanied or followed by headaches of the nature of migraine, is best known. The flicker is an alternation between bright and dark sensation, and spreads during the attack over constantly increasing areas of the visual field. At the same time these areas become wholly or partially insensitive to external light stimuli (so-called flicker scotoma). Closely related qualitatively to this flicker phenomenon is a physiological one, which can occur in perfectly normal conditions, and which in the case of many observers, including the writer, occurs very frequently without any special conditions to account for it. The writer notices it only in the dark, generally when there is, or has been, some slight pressure on the eye, but also without such pressure. The frequency of the intermission

[1] Ibid. II. 87.
[2] See also the phenomena in No. XXII of the first volume, and in Nos. IV, V, XV of the second volume of his observations and experiments.

appears to be very regular, probably just as in pathological flicker scotoma, about 10 to 15 oscillations per second, according to the writer's estimate. However, though the pathological flicker phenomenon usually continues a long time in a uniform way, the physiological type invariably occurs periodically in the writer's experience; being perceptible for one or two seconds, rising in intensity during this time and then falling off again. This is succeeded by a pause from three to five times as long without any flicker, after which the process is repeated.

As to the causes of this phenomenon, as also of the flicker in migraine, positive opinions can hardly be ventured at present.—N.

Appendix by W. Nagel.

Adaptation, Twilight Vision, and the Duplicity Theory.[1]

A. The Adaptation of the Eye for Different Intensities of Light.

1. Dark Adaptation

What is meant by the *adaptation of the eye*[2] is an adjustment of the degree of sensitivity of the retina for different intensities of illumination. By virtue of this capacity, the eye is enabled to go on seeing in very dim light, and, on the other hand, to bear the brightness of the sunshine on a summer day without being blinded by it or harmed. When little or no light falls on the retina, thanks to the process of adaptation, its sensitivity becomes far and away higher, as compared with the stimulus, than that of an eye that has been gazing for a long time at a bright surface, like the daylight sky for instance. This change which takes place with complete, or almost complete, exclusion of light is called the *dark adaptation* of the eye. The reverse process of becoming accustomed to bright light is called *light adaptation*. However, these terms are employed also to describe the states of the eye resulting from long-continued darkness in one case and from long-continued exposure to bright light in the other case. Experiment shows, as might have been inferred in advance, that the change is a limited one, and reaches a fairly stationary stage after a certain time.[3] When outside light is shut out entirely, the sensitivity of the eye increases for several hours; whereas the reverse process of light adaptation by exposure to bright light is completely accomplished in a few minutes. These changes and the limitations of the capacity of adaptation will be treated more in detail presently.

[1] ¶In connection with the subjects treated in this Appendix, the following comparatively recent works may be consulted: W. DE W. ABNEY, *Researches in colour vision.* 1913; and J. H. PARSONS, *An introduction to the study of colour vision.* 1915. See also: L. T. TROLAND, The progress of visual science in 1920. *Amer. Journ. Physiol. Optics* II. 1921, 316–391. Idem, Brilliance and chroma in relation to zone theories of vision. *Jour. Opt. Soc. Amer.* VI. 1922, 3–26. — Idem, The present status of visual science, *Bull. Nat. Research Counc.* V. (part 2), 1922, 1–120. — Report of committee on colorimetry for 1920-21. *Jour. Opt. Soc. Amer.* etc. VI. 1922, 527–596. (H.L.)

[2] For literature prior to 1902, consult A. TSCHERMAK, Die Hell-Dunkeladaptation des Auges, usw.; *Ergebnisse der Physiologie.* I. 2, S. 695. 1902.

[3] ¶The terms *photopia* and *scotopia* are also convenient for describing the states of light adaptation and dark adaptation, respectively. Thus also we may speak of the photopic eye or the scotopic eye. (J. P. C. S.)

Undoubtedly, it would be taking a rather one-sided view to estimate the state of adaptation of an eye merely by the threshold stimulus at the moment, that is, by the minimum effectual intensity of stimulus; because it is by no means certain in advance that the sensitivity to stimuli that are appreciably above threshold value must always proceed parallel to "threshold sensitivity." In other words, it is doubtful, for example, whether we have the right to suppose that in the case of an eye A, whose threshold stimulus is a hundred times lower than that of another eye B, a definite "super-liminal" intensity of light must be reduced to a hundredth of its value in order that A and B shall have equal sensations of subjective brightness. Such comparisons are of course only possible between the two eyes of the same observer, and for this very reason cannot be made very precisely. Moreover, the moment a stimulus appreciably above threshold value acts on the retina, its state of adaptation is changed extraordinarily quickly; and therefore, such comparisons between the sensitivity of two eyes can be made only at one instant. Under such circumstances, the agreement may be considered sufficiently accurate when the sensitivity measured for threshold values and the susceptibility to stimulation as determined binocularly for greater than threshold values turn out to be of the same order of magnitude. Now according to the writer's observations, this is always the case; and his impression is that the values of the sensitivity as determined by the two methods will be found to be more and more nearly in agreement, the more pains are taken to avoid the sources of error above mentioned; and that consequently also the determination of the state of adaptation by the threshold values is justifiable.

The first systematic investigations of dark-adaptation were made by H. Aubert,[1] who likewise proposed the word "adaptation". He took the trouble of determining the threshold stimulus of the organ of vision after it had been kept in darkness for various lengths of time. After coming into the dark room, where the experiments were conducted, the threshold was found to be lower. The reciprocals of the threshold values afforded a measure of the degree of sensitivity of the eye for the time being, which could be exhibited in the form of a curve, where the abscissae denoted the number of minutes spent in darkness and the ordinates the corresponding values of the sensitivity. Many such curves showing the process of dark adaptation have been published since the time of Aubert. His method of making the measurements was to send a current of electricity from a constant cell through a platinum wire until its glow was just visible in the dark room. The length of wire traversed by the current could be varied, and the longer it was, the fainter it shone. In a few minutes after entering the dark room, Aubert found a rapid rise of sensitivity to light, and that the sensitivity continued to increase more slowly thereafter on remaining longer in the dark. After two hours in darkness the sensitivity had increased to about 35 times its original value according to Aubert's calculation.

[1] *Physiologie der Netzhaut.* Breslau 1865. Among older works on adaptation the following are important still: Charpentier, Expériences sur la marche de l'adaptation rétinienne. *Archives d'ophtal.* VI. 1887. Treitel, Über das Verhalten der normalen Adaptation. v. Graefe's *Arch. f. Ophthalm.* 1887.

More recent investigations indicate a much greater increase of the sensitivity. In these determinations of relative values of sensitivity, naturally, much depends on the conditions under which the observations are made, and above all on the starting point of the series of determinations, that is, on the state of adaptation of the observer's eye when the dark room is entered. Apparently, AUBERT began his experiments with his eye in a medium state of adaptation, but we do not know definitely what it was. But for other reasons, which will be apparent later, the results obtained by his method of measuring sensitivity could not be of general value.

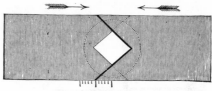

Fig. 57.

Oculists usually determine the capacity of an eye for adaptation by means of an instrument designed by FOERSTER,[1] called a *photometer* or *photoptometer*. It consists of a wooden box blackened on the inside, with two apertures on one side where the patient puts his eyes. On the opposite interior wall there is a white sheet of paper with broad black bands or other

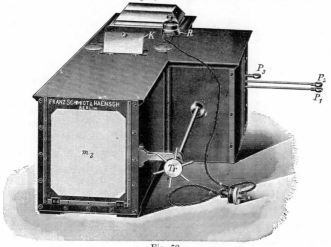

Fig. 58.

figures on it. This is the object to be observed. It is illuminated by a little window 5 cm square, in the same side of the box where the eye-holes are. The window is closed with translucent white paper or milk-glass; and on the outside there is a little lantern with a candle in

[1] R. FOERSTER, *Über Hemeralopie und die Anwendung eines Photometers in der Ophthalmologie.* Breslau 1875.

it which shines on the window. The amount of light from the window that falls on the object is regulated by a square diaphragm, as represented in Fig. 57. The size of the opening in square millimetres can be read off on a scale.

A normal eye, which has been previously dark-adapted from 15 to 20 minutes, with an aperture of 2 square millimetres, can distinguish the bright from the dark parts of the object on the back of the box.

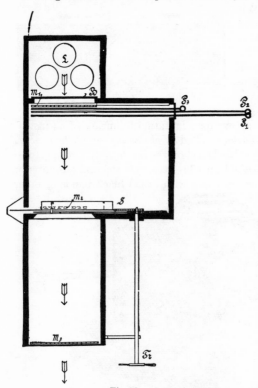

However, in this case the assumption is that the eye was not completely light-adapted before the dark adaptation was begun, but that it was in the medium state of adaptation such as exists in a moderately bright room.

In FOERSTER's instrument, the amount of variation in the size of the diaphragm is far too little for measuring the threshold value of the eye for each state of adaptation. Thus, while the apparatus is well suited for ophthalmological practice and for finding gross irregularities in the power of adaptation, it is not designed for more accurate measurements.

Fig. 59.

For such purposes the writer devised an apparatus called an *adaptometer*.[1] Its construction is shown in Figs. 58 and 59.

On the front side of a wooden box 80 cm long there is a milk-glass plate m_3 which acts as object. The source of light is situated on the opposite side. It consists of three incandescent lamps each equivalent to 25 candles. A bright blue glass plate is interposed in the path of the light to make the lamp light as pure white

[1] W. NAGEL, Zwei Apparate für die augenärztliche Funktionsprüfung usw. *Zeitschr. f. Augenheilk.* XVII. 1907.

as possible. There are two contrivances for reducing the intensity of the light. Just in front of the lamps three plates are inserted, made of metal and provided with holes of such size that each of the discs reduces the amount of light falling on it by one twentieth. Thus with two screens the intensity is diminished to 1/400; and with all three to 1/8000. Moreover, in the middle of the box there is a square diaphragm as in FOERSTER's instrument (see Fig. 57), which is intended for finer adjustments of the degree of intensity of light. It has a milk-glass plate behind it, and its size can be varied from 1 square millimetre to 10000. Thus the intensity of light falling on the front side of the milk-glass plate can be diminished from its maximum to $\dfrac{1}{8000} \cdot \dfrac{1}{10000} =$ $\dfrac{1}{80000000}$ and the interval from 1 to $\dfrac{1}{8000000}$ can be evaluated with sufficient accuracy.

A similar apparatus has been described by H. PIPER[1]. By means of contrivances of this kind the complete course of dark adaptation can be followed. If comparisons are to be made of the powers of adaptation of different individuals with healthy eyes, and eventually with diseased eyes also, so as to study the process of adaptation under different conditions, it is a good plan to use a definite and constant size of field, because, as will be seen, the threshold stimulus is dependent on the size of the retinal area stimulated. The writer has chosen for this purpose a circular field of 10°. The way this is obtained is by putting a circular diaphragm 10 cm in diameter in front of the milk-glass plate of the adaptometer, and placing the eye 57 cm away from the apparatus. This is a convenient distance because the observer can then reach the handle of the instrument and adjust the intensity of the light for himself. If the problem is simply to determine the threshold for a particular degree of adaptation, the gaze ought not to be fixed, but the eye should be allowed to roam about in the field, so that the image of the disc of the adaptometer falls on various portions of the retina in succession. On the other hand, if the object of the experiment is to test the sensitivity of a particular part of the retina, a fixation mark is provided for the eye in the form of a little dark red point. If this mark emits a pure red light, it is more easily seen in the fovea centralis than in the peripheral parts of the retina, and hence the gaze is attracted by it. A contrivance designed for this purpose has been described by the writer elsewhere.

To reach the threshold of the light sense when the eye is in a good state of light adaptation, it is necessary to get fairly close to the

[1] H. PIPER, Zur messenden Untersuchung und zur Theorie der Hell-Dunkeladaptation. *Klin. Monatsbl. f. Augenheilk.* XLV. 357. 1907.

highest intensity of light that this apparatus will afford. All three of the screen plates must be removed.

To bring about such a state of "good light adaptation", all that is necessary is to stay outdoors 20 or 30 minutes on a bright sunny day, looking mainly at bright objects that are, however, not particularly dazzling. After such preparation the threshold stimulus for the majority of eyes is practically the same. It amounts approximately to an intensity of illumination on the adaptometer disc equal to one metre-candle; in other words, a white surface subtending an angle of 10° will just be visible when it is illuminated by a standard candle at a distance of one metre.

In order to compare the sensitivity in the state of dark adaptation with this, the observer retires to a perfectly dark room and stays there for an hour, or his eyes are tightly blindfolded for that length of time. For eyes thus dark-adapted an illumination of one metre-candle is dazzlingly bright. To find the threshold value, the illumination must be diminished to between fifty and one hundred and fifty thousandths. In other words the sensitivity to light has been increased anywhere from fifty to a hundred and fifty thousand times. The increase of sensitivity after dark adaptation for one hour in the case of an eye that was previously in a state of "good light adaptation" may be called the *"amplitude of adaptation"* of the eye in question. Its numerical value is the difference between the threshold of the light-adapted eye and that of the dark-adapted eye. As a matter of fact, dark adaptation takes longer than an hour to be complete, as was shown by AUBERT; and as has been confirmed many times by tests made by PIPER and the writer. After dark adaptation of both eyes for eight hours, PIPER[1] obtained twice as high a value of the sensitivity to light as he got after dark adaptation for one hour. The writer has kept one eye closed for sixteen hours, without being able to decide whether the limit of the process of dark adaptation was reached. Still by the end of the second hour further increase of sensitivity is very slight. In the experiment just mentioned, the monocular amplitude of adaptation amounted to 270,000.

When the weather is not very bright, the degree of light adaptation is not generally reached for which the threshold is one metre-candle. Moreover, it takes a good deal of preparation and practice to make very quickly the first measurement of sensitivity after going from the bright region to the dark. When the day is a little cloudy, even after being outdoors, the sensitivity is found to be from ten to twenty times higher than it is with complete light adaptation. If the state of light

[1] H. PIPER, Über Dunkeladaptation. *Zeitschr. f. Psychol. u. Physiol. der Sinnesorgane.* XXXI. 1903. 161–214.

adaptation attained in cloudy daylight is compared with the value of the sensitivity after dark adaptation for one hour, the latter is found to be only between three and eight thousand times more. If the experiment is started with the state of adaptation that is reached after being in a room a long time in daylight, the sensitivity is found to be one thousandth of that in case of dark adaptation for one hour. Even on sunshiny days, complete light adaptation is not developed indoors at longest, but the sensitivity is about one or two hundred times more than that of an eye adapted to the brightness outdoors.

In pathological cases, in what is known as *night blindness* or *hemeralopia*, which is a symptom of many eye diseases, the amplitude of adaptation is very considerably diminished. MESSMER,[1] who investigated a number of patients afflicted with night blindness, measured amplitudes of adaptation with the adaptometer which were as low as 125, 25, and even 14. In slight cases he found values of 1250 and 1666;

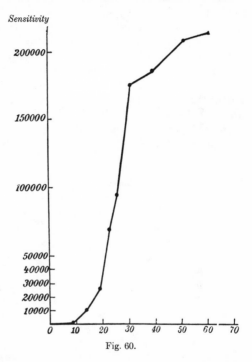

Fig. 60.

whereas for normal observers the amplitudes were between 3332 and 10415. Similar results were obtained by HEINRICHSDORFF and others.[2]

It should be particularly noted that these measurements of sensitivity to light are for eyes showing normal pupil reaction. In order to compare the values of light adaptation with those obtained after long dark adaptation, to be really accurate, the diameter of the pupil in each measurement must be known; otherwise, the actual retinal sensitivity under the different conditions cannot be compared. However, since all the measurements, including those

[1] MESSMER, Über die Dunkeladaptation bei Hemeralopie. *Zeitschr. f. Sinnesphysiol.* XLII. 83. 1907.

[2] ¶F. BEST, Über Nachblindheit. *Arch. f. Ophthalm.* XCVII. 1916, 168–197. — W. DE W. ABNEY, Two cases of congenital night blindness. *Proc. Roy. Soc.*, 90 B. 1917. 69–74. (H.L.)

made after light adaptation, are carried out in a dark room, the size of the pupil is of less influence than it would be under different conditions. The pupil always takes a certain time after being in the dark to reach the equilibrium condition corresponding to the lack of light, but this had practically been reached already before the measurements here described were made.

With the aid of the adaptometer or some similar instrument, the progress of dark adaptation through its various phases may be more accurately followed, by determining the threshold value at regular intervals, say, every five minutes, after entering the dark room. The results obtained by plotting the reciprocals of these values as ordinates and the numbers of minutes spent in darkness as abscissae, will be "adaptation curves" similar to those constructed by AUBERT and other investigators. An example of the typical progress of dark adaptation in a normal eye is given in Table I; and the results are exhibited graphically in Fig. 60. As a matter of fact, on account of the wide range of variation of the sensitivity, the ordinates have to be represented on an enormous scale, in order to get a true picture.

Table I

Increase of Sensitivity in the Dark

Minutes in Darkness	Values of the Sensitivity (1 unit sensitivity being that for which the intensity of 1 metre-candle is the threshold)
0.5	20
4	75
9	1850
14	10400
19	26000
23	69500
26	94700
31	174000
39	195000
51	208000
61	215000

The steepest part of the curve is comprised between the 19th and 31st minutes, the ascent being more gradual thereafter. This is typical of the normal curve of adaptation, the ordinates indicating the absolute degree of sensitivity at the time.

It is not without interest to consider the same process in another way, by exhibiting the *relative* increase of sensitivity. The table shows that between the 4th and 9th minutes the sensitivity is increased about 25-fold; whereas in the same length of time, between the 9th and 14th

minutes, the increase is not more than 5.6-fold, and in the twelve
minutes between the 19th and 31st minutes the increase is 6.7-fold.
By plotting the logarithms of the values of the sensitivity as
ordinates the *rela-*
tive increase in this
sense will be ex-
hibited. A defi-
nite increase in
the height of the
ordinate of the
curve will mean a
rise of sensitivity
in a definite ratio
(that is, its multi-
plication by a
certain coeffi-
cient), and the
steepest parts of
the curve will be at
those times when
the relative in-
crease of sensitivity
to light was most
rapid. In this way

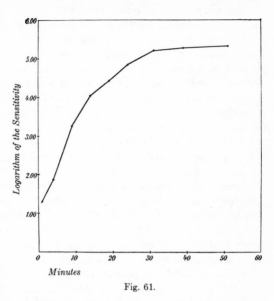

Fig. 61.

curves like that shown in Fig. 61 will be obtained. It is steeper at the
beginning of the hour of dark adaptation than it is in the middle. It
is usually steepest between the second and eighth minutes, just where
the curve in Fig. 60 is almost horizontal.

Comparing the adaptation of a large number of persons with normal
eyes, we shall find that it proceeds very much the same way in all of
them, the only variation being in the final limit attained. But in those
diseases of the eye, where night blindness occurs (see p. 319), the
sensitivity at the end of an hour is not only apt to be much less than in
the case of the normal eye, but the form of the curve of adaptation may
be abnormal also. It is very common to find an unusually flat stretch of
curve for the first quarter of an hour, that is, a retarded increase;
although at the end of the hour the final sensitivity may be similar to
the normal. Such persons are much annoyed by not being able to get
accustomed to the change from a bright to a dimly lighted chamber as
quickly as normal individuals can do. At first they see practically
nothing. In the more severe cases the sensitivity increases but little
in the course of hours, and naturally such individuals are still more
helpless in twilight.

For further information concerning adaptation in pathological cases, the reader may consult the works of HEINRICHSDORFF[1], MESSMER[2], LOHMAN[3], and HORN.[4]

According to the investigations of PIPER (*loc. cit.*) and WÖLFFLIN[5], there is no particular connection between the amplitude of adaptation or the course of adaptation and the time of life. Moreover, TSCHERMAK's statement[6], that special characteristics of dark adaptation are peculiar to different types of colour vision, has not been confirmed. The fact is rather that the capacity for adaptation has nothing to do with the type of colour system; and in this respect both normal and anomalous trichromats do not differ from the partially colour-blind (dichromats). Even the so-called achromats, or totally colour-blind, are not abnormal in this matter. In the case of a totally colour-blind girl, MAY[7] and the writer found the amplitude of adaptation below the average, but still within normal limits (around 5000).

Among other agencies that may modify the course of dark adaptation, the action of the nerve poisons, strychnin and brucin, should be mentioned. Injected under the skin, both of these poisons, according to the experiments of DRESER[8] and WÖLFFLIN[9], produce a distinct increase of one-fifth or one-fourth in the amplitude of adaptation. The rate of adaptation appeared to be increased also. WÖLFFLIN used doses of between two and five thousandths of a gramme of strychnin, and two hundredths of a gramme of brucin. FILEHNE[10] claims that santonin tends to retard adaptation; but this is a mistake, as has been shown by KNIES[11] and WÖLFFLIN (*loc. cit.*). In conjunction with VAUGHAN[12], the

[1] HEINRICHSDORFF, Die Störungen der Adaptation und des Gesichtsfeldes bei Hemeralopie. GRAEFES *Arch. f. Ophthalm.* CX. 405. 1905.

[2] MESSMER, Über die Dunkeladaptation bei Hemeralopie. *Zeitschr. f. Sinnephysiol.* XLII. 83. 1907.

[3] LOHMANN, Untersuchungen über die Adaptation usw. *Habilitationsschrift*. MÜNCHEN und GRAEFES *Archiv f. Ophthalm.* 65, 1907.

[4] HORN, Über Dunkeladaptation bei Augenhintergrundserkrankungen. *Dissertation*, Tübingen 1907.

[5] WÖLFFLIN, Der Einfluss des Lebensalters auf den Lichtsinn bei dunkeladaptiertem Auge. GRAEFES *Arch. f. Ophthalm.* 61, 524. 1905.

[6] TSCHERMAK, *Über physiologische und pathologische Anpassung des Auges.* Leipzig (VEIT u. Co. 1900); also: *Ergebnisse der Physiologie.* I. 2. S. 700. 1902.

[7] MAY, Ein Fall totaler Farbenblindheit. *Zeitschr. f. Sinnesphysiol.* XLII. 69. 1907.

[8] DRESER, Über die Beeinflussung des Lichtsinns durch Strychnin. *Arch. f. exp. Pathol. u. Pharm.* XXXIII.

[9] WÖLFFLIN, Über die Beeinflussung der Dunkeladaptation durch künstliche Mittel; GRAEFES *Arch. für Ophthalm.* 65.302.1907. See also SINGER, Brucin und seine Einwirkung auf das normale Auge. Ibid., 50.

[10] FILEHNE, Über die Wirkung des Santonins usw. PFLÜGERS *Arch. f. d. ges. Physiol.* LXXX. 96. 1900.

[11] M. KNIES, Über die Farbenstörung durch Santonin. *Arch. f. Augenheilk.* XXXVII.

[12] C. L. VAUGHAN, Einige Bemerkungen über die Wirkung des Santonins auf die Farbenempfindungen. *Zeitschr. f. Sinnesphysiol.* XLI. 399. 1906.

writer has made a large number of experiments with santonin poisoning, large doses and small doses, without discovering any effect whatever so far as adaptation is concerned.

In an indirect way the mydriatics have an effect. For example, when the pupil is dilated by atropin, abnormally large amounts of light can enter the eye and produce a state of blindness or glare. The writer has occasionally exposed one of his eyes, with the pupil dilated, for about a half hour to the glare of the sun in the street, and then found that adaptation was much retarded. The first qr flat part of the sensitivity curve, as seen in PIPER's curves (also in the curve shown in Fig. 60), extends over 20 minutes, instead of from 8 to 10 minutes. Thereafter the sensitivity increased rapidly and reached its normal value in from 70 to 80 minutes.

AUBERT noticed that the progress of dark adaptation was not only not impeded by flashes of light considerably above the threshold intensity, but that, in fact, it was aided in some measure. This observation has since been confirmed many times in the writer's laboratory. That the instantaneous light of a match reflected from dark walls into the observer's eye lowers the threshold of the light sense considerably, as much perhaps as one-third, can easily be verified. This effect does not wear off for several minutes. It is particularly distinct when the observer has reached a practically stationary condition of adaptation after having been in the dark for an hour.

In peculiar contrast to this, is the fact that after being in the dark for a very long time, a sensitivity is attained which is diminished by stimuli that are close to threshold value. For example, the above mentioned maximum sensitivity attained by the eye after 16 hours of darkness, in which an illumination of 1/270,000 metre-candle on the adaptometer field was found to be the threshold value, is merely transitory. A few observations in which the eye was exposed to stimuli not more than three times as strong as the liminal value sufficed to lower the sensitivity to about one-half. The writer, having repeatedly made similar observations, can state that the increase of sensitivity which takes place after an hour in darkness is of a much more transient nature than that which occurs during the first hour.

It has never been certainly demonstrated that the state of adaptation of one eye has any influence on that of the other. The dark adaptation in each eye seems to be independent. It may be that occasionally with just one eye dark-adapted one gets the impression of not attaining the same degree of sensitivity in monocular observation as when both eyes are dark-adapted; but this is partly due to subjective luminous appearances that are apt to occur when the state of adaptation is not the same in both eyes. It may be partly due also to the fact that it is

more difficult than one might suppose to bandage an eye so tightly
that not a glimmer of light can be detected after long adaptation. In
investigations of this nature, it must be remembered that in the dark-
adapted state, the threshold stimulus for monocular vision is found to
be higher than for binocular vision (see below, page 339).

So far as the final degree of sensitivity is concerned, it is of no
importance whether the eyes are free during dark adaptation or
whether they are under more or less pressure from being bandaged.[1]
Even the passage of an electric current through the eye was found by
the writer and his assistants to have no effect on the threshold stimulus
for light. Accordingly, it has not been shown that there is any change of
excitability of an electrotonic nature.[2]

2. Light Adaptation

The decrease of sensitivity to light connected with the process of
light adaptation cannot be so conveniently followed over a long interval
as the reverse process, because precise sensitivity determinations can
only be made by threshold methods and in a dark room. A quantitative
investigation of the decrease of sensitivity in light adaptation can
therefore only be carried out, by first finding the threshold value after
being in the dark for a long time, then exposing the eye to a brighter
light for a definite time, then suddenly cutting off this light adaptation,
darkening the room again, and quickly making another threshold
measurement, before the dark adaptation has had time to be appreciable. In this manner it has been possible to determine how much the
sensitivity to light is lowered by a definite intensity of illumination of
known duration. W. LOHMANN[3] has taken no little trouble to make a
large number of measurements of this sort. He varied systematically
the intensity of the light that was used in the light adaptation, and also
the duration of the exposure of the eye. LOHMANN performed the
experiment above described, first, with a light adaptation lasting for
one minute; then, after re-inducing the state of dark adaptation, he
used light adaptations of 2 minutes, 3 minutes, 6 minutes, etc. In this
way he got an idea of the behaviour of the process of light adaptation
with a given intensity of illumination. The starting point of his
experiments was invariably a state of dark adaptation produced by

---

[1] NAGEL, Einige Beobachtungen über die Wirkung des Druckes und des galvanischen
Stromes auf das dunkeladaptierte Auge. *Zeitschr. f. Psychol. und Physiol. d. Sinnesorgane.*
XXXIV. 285. 1904.

[2] ¶See S. HECHT. The dark adaptation of the human eye. *Jour. Gen. Physiol.* II. 1920.
499. 517; also, The Nature of foveal dark adaptation. Ibid. IV. 1921. 113-141. (H. L.)

[3] W. LOHMANN, Über Helladaptation. *Zeitschr. f. Sinnesphysiol.* XLI. 290 1906.

being in the dark for 45 minutes. Adaptation in broad daylight proceeds with extraordinary rapidity, as has been stated, and probably may be completed at the end of a minute under some circumstances. And so LOHMANN generally used moderate intensities, by which the process could be followed more closely. In observations of this kind it must be kept in mind that after extinguishing the light used for light adaptation, the sensitivity begins to rise again immediately, faster, indeed, in proportion as the light adaptation was more moderate. Consequently, the threshold determination must be made as quickly as possible after extinguishing the light. But it must not be done too quickly, because during the first few seconds in the dark observation is extremely difficult on account of successive after-images.

For these reasons those measurements of LOHMANN's are mentioned first in which the threshold determination was made 10 seconds after extinguishing the light. As a matter of fact, the sensitivity will have increased a little in this time, to a different extent also for different periods of light adaptation. But this is an error that can hardly be avoided. Incidentally, it does not diminish the value of LOHMANN's results. The difficulty of the task compels us here to put up with approximate determinations.

Table II

Decrease of Sensitivity to Light during Light Adaptation under different degrees of Illumination and for different durations of Light Adaptation.

Intensity of illumination of the white surface at which the subject gazes for being light-adapted	Duration of Light Adaptation						
	⅓ min.	⅔ min.	1 min.	2 min.	3 min.	6 min.	10 min.
	Sensitivity Value						
5 metre-candles.....	23000	17500	10400	8130	5200	3470	3000
25 metre-candles.....	9950	7440	5200	3360	2740	2040	1450
50 metre-candles.....	5800	3700	3250	2600	2038	1600	1130
moderate daylight...	435	230	200	115	87	48	40

Table II is based on LOHMANN's results. Instead of using his threshold value, the sensitivity values here have been reduced to unit sensitivity (threshold at one metre-candle). The results are exhibited in Fig. 62 in the form of a curve. We see how the sensitivity falls off abruptly during the first minute. When the adaptation is for diffusely reflected daylight, the sensitivity is enormously reduced in 20 seconds. The ordinate which would indicate the degree of sensitivity before beginning the light adaptation would have to be about five times as high as the tallest ordinate of the curves shown in the diagram.

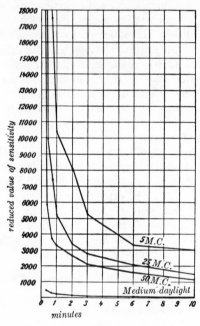

minutes

Fig. 62.

After the first precipitous drop, the descent of the curve becomes much more gradual. Light adaptation therefore continues beyond the first two minutes, but very slowly. But for all that, even in adaptation to daylight, the lowering of sensitivity can be traced for at least ten minutes. From the experiences of daily life it would be natural to suppose that, especially under the action of light of low intensity, the sensitivity would quickly reach a definite level, as would be indicated by horizontal procedure of the curve. But, as LOHMANN's tests show, this is not so. For illuminations of 25 and 50 metre-candles, LOHMANN continued the experiments farther still. The results are given in Table III, the sensitivities being referred to unit sensitivity, as in the preceding table.

Table III

Decrease of Sensitivity for long-continued Light Adaptation

Duration of Light Adaptation in minutes	10	15	29	34	39	49	60	70	79	80	99	109	110
25 metre-candles	1450	1000		250		125	95	62		54			54
50 metre-candles	1130	312	104		46		36		28		25	24	

We see from the table and from Fig. 63 that the sensitivity continues to fall off after the first ten minutes, and it is more than a half hour before adaptation reaches a kind of level. This level, by the way, is curiously different in height according to the intensity of the light used for adaptation. For obvious reasons the scale

of coördinates is not the same in Figs. 62 and 63, but since in both cases the ordinates denote the values of the sensitivity based on the same unit, the
curves may readily be compared with each other and likewise with the curve of dark adaptation shown in Fig. 60.

The fact that moderate intensities of light are slow in nullifying the effect of dark adaptation, may easily be verified. If one eye is tightly bandaged for half an hour and the other ex-

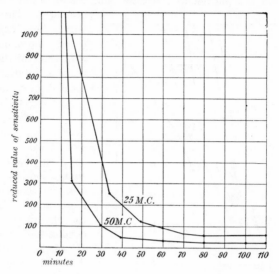

Fig. 63.

posed to diffused daylight for the same length of time, on removing the bandage, the sensitivity of the eye that was closed sinks rapidly down to a certain point; but in a dimly lighted room continues then for a half hour or an hour distinctly higher than that of the other eye which has not been closed. The difference can be perceived by alternately opening and closing the eyes.

The basis of all the quantitative results on light adaptation which have been given above is the measurement of the liminal value made ten seconds after extinguishing the light used for light adaptation. Another set of LOHMANN's experiments affords a picture of the rise of sensitivity during the first minutes in darkness, that is, of the after-effects of light adaptation during the early period of dark adaptation. Without going into the method of these experiments, the way the dark adaptation proceeds, after previous light adaptation with an intensity of illumination of 75 metre-candles, is exhibited in Fig. 64. Having been previously thoroughly dark-adapted, the observer gazed at a white surface illuminated by 75 metre-candles, for one, two, three, six or ten minutes. The gradual renewal of sensitivity during the first four minutes in darkness is then determined. The first measurement is made after ten seconds. In the diagram the numbers of seconds reckoned from the completion of light adaptation are plotted as abscissae, and the values of the sensitivity as ordinates.

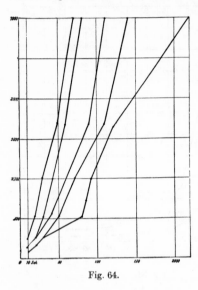

Fig. 64.

These values are relative, but they may be compared, approximately at least, with those of the foregoing curves of adaptation, by noting that the highest ordinate in the figure corresponds to a sensitivity value of about 16000 on the basis of the unit of sensitivity in the previous diagrams. Fig. 64 brings out clearly how, after brief light adaptation lasting only one minute, the sensitivity rises again more quickly than it does after the illumination of 75 metrecandles has acted a longer time. If the light adaptation is produced with lower intensities, the curves get steeper still and start off with higher ordinates.

When we consider the rapidity with which the sensitivity of a retina adapted to moderately strong light starts to rise as soon as the light is extinguished and also on suddenly changing into a dimly lighted room, it is easy to explain the following observation, which may be regarded as a special kind of after-image. When one comes from the street into a comparatively dark vestibule and looks steadily for some seconds at an object with strong contrasts of brightness (for example, a bright wall with an inscription in large letters), a very vivid after-image is obtained, which is always negative. This is because the adaptative increase of sensitivity has taken place more quickly in the parts of the retina where the dark letters are imaged than in the more highly illuminated portions. Thus a stage of adaptation at which the sensitivity is rapidly rising is a prerequisite. Subjectively, the intensity of illumination may seem to be just as bright as it was in the experiment in the dark vestibule, and yet if the observer is in a more or less stationary state of adaptation, he will try in vain to produce negative after-images of considerable intensity, because in such a case much stronger stimuli will be needed for that.

At the suggestion of the writer, Mr. H. J. WATT[1] carried out an investigation on the production and behaviour of negative after-images, comparing the results in the case of a light-adapted eye and the case of a thoroughly dark-adapted eye, the subjective brightness being the same for both eyes. No marked difference could be detected in the two cases. It is rather just at that particular stage when the sensitivity is rapidly rising, at the beginning of dark adaptation, that the conditions are peculiarly favourable to the production of those characteristic negative after-images.

[1] H. J. WATT, Über die Nachbilder subjektiv gleich heller aber objektiv verschieden stark beleuchteter Flächen. *Zeitschr. f. Sinnesphysiol.* XLI. 312. 1906.

3. Local Variations in Retinal Sensitivity

When a person in a state of medium adaptation enters a dark room where there is a very faintly luminous object, it can be perceived better with the peripheral parts of the retina than with the central parts, as may be easily verified. If the luminous object is small, subtending a visual angle of from 1° to 2°, this difference between peripheral and central vision persists even after long dark adaptation; in fact, it becomes more pronounced. But with objects whose apparent size is 10° or more (for instance, the disc of the adaptometer), the difference between the centre of the retina and the periphery disappears more and more with protracted stay in the dark, and after an hour's adaptation can scarcely be detected. More exact investigations enable us to explain this phenomenon as follows.

The centre of the retina, the so-called fovea centralis, behaves quite differently from the rest of the retina so far as the process of adaptation is concerned. Indeed, it shares with the rest of the retina the very rapid rise of sensitivity that occurs in the first two or three minutes of darkness, but after that it remains stationary[1]; whereas in the other parts of the retina it is then that the sensitivity to light has its biggest increase. Thus the foveal region behaves quite analogously to the total retina of an eye afflicted with a bad case of hemeralopia, so that we can use v. KRIES's expression and speak of a "physiological hemeralopia" of the fovea.

This explains why in dark adaptation *small* objects are more easily seen by the peripheral retina than by the fovea. The reason why, on going into a dark room, the periphery is better suited for seeing faint objects (even those that are too big for the fovea) than the central part, is different. Even in a bright room the light that reaches the extreme peripheral parts of the retina in the equatorial region is, as a rule, essentially less than that that goes to the centre of the fundus of the eye. The periphery therefore is in a condition more nearly like that of dark adaptation, and hence in dim light it is from the very start better adapted for perceiving feeble light stimuli.

Systematic investigations of the distribution of the sensitivity to light in the dark-adapted retina have been carried out under the direction of v. KRIES.[2] The eye of the observer fixated a tiny luminous point. At the same time a small white object, whose illumination can

---

[1] ¶See S. HECHT, *loc. cit.* (H. L.)

[2] J. v. KRIES, Über die absolute Empfindlichkeit der verschiedenen Netzhautteile im dunkeladaptierten Auge. *Zft. f. Psychol. u. Physiol. d. Sinnesorgane.* XV.327. 1897. Among earlier investigations should be mentioned especially those of GUILLERY, in *Zft. f. Psychol. usw.* XII. 261, 1896; XIII. 187. 1897; PFLÜGERS *Arch. f. d. ges. Physiol.* 66. 401. 1897.

be gradually regulated at will, was presented to the eye at various lateral distances from the point of fixation. In this way the sensitivity of the separate parts of the retina could be compared. The results of these measurements for a small region of the central part of the retina, extending 4° to right and left of the point of fixation, are exhibited in Table IV; and graphically in Fig. 65. In these experiments the angular diameter of the object was 0.35°, and it was illuminated by bluish white light.

Table IV

Sensitivity (relative value)	Temporal distance in degrees	Nasal distance in degrees	Width of blind area in degrees
1	1.07	0.85	1.92
1.78	1.22	1.06	2.28
7.12	1.70	1.36	3.08
16.02	2.3	1.92	4.22
28.48	3.0	2.50	5.58
44.50	3.75	3.33	7.08
64.08	4.04	4.04	8.08

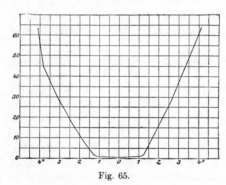

Fig. 65.

It is evident how the sensitivity begins to rise rapidly a little more than 1° away from the point of fixation; and how the lowest sensitivity is in the foveal field over an angular diameter of about 2°. Still farther towards the periphery the sensitivity to light in the uniformly dark-adapted eye goes on increasing, and, according to the investigations made by v. KRIES and his students, reaches a maximum at an angular distance from the fovea of from 10° to 20°. In some experiments made by BREUER and the writer together, taking the sensitivity at 6° from the centre as unity, the sensitivity at 12° on the temporal side was found to be 1.38, and at 18° 1.64; on the nasal side at 12° it was 1.54, but at 18° it fell to 1.37. Numerical comparisons of the sensitivities in the foveal and extra-foveal regions, as will be explained presently, are of no value except for a particular quality of light. For an eccentricity of 10°, in case of good dark adaptation, PERTZ (see v. KRIES, *loc cit.*) found the sensitivity for a blue light (subtending an angle of 8.6′) to be about 1400 times more than the foveal sensitivity. Using mixed white light, subtending an angle of half a degree, after an hour's adaptation, the writer found the sensitivity in the most sensitive part of the periphery to be in round numbers a thousand times greater than it was in the fovea under the same conditions. In this connection, it should be noted that the distribution of sensitivity in the light-adapted eye is entirely different, the maximum sensitivity to light in this case being in the fovea centralis. This is easy to prove by having a small point-source of light of intensity just a little above the foveal threshold somewhere in a dark room. If the eye is thoroughly light-adapted, it is very difficult to enter the room and find this spot of light right away. It is almost by accident that it is seen, and then it is surprisingly distinct, although it may be quite easily lost again. On the other hand, a dark-adapted eye will have no difficulty in discovering the luminous spot immediately, because the peripheral sensitivity is greater than that in the fovea.

Accurate measurements of the decrease of sensitivity from the fovea to the periphery of the light-adapted eye, with due consideration for the state of adaptation, cannot be made except with coloured lights. However, in the observations on the distribution of sensitivity to coloured lights in the light-adapted eye, as carried out at the writer's suggestion by C. L. VAUGHAN and A. BOLTUNOW[1], the decrease of sensitivity out towards the periphery was found to be exactly of the same nature for red, green, and blue lights; and, perhaps, therefore, the quantitative results of these observers may be applied without hesitation to all light of any kind at all. What they found was that the sensitivity 10° to one side of the centre of the fovea was not more than one-fourth of its value in the fovea; at 20° away it was one-tenth; and at 35° away one-fortieth.

The relative central scotoma of the dark-adapted eye. As has been already stated, light stimuli, whose intensities are below the threshold value of the fovea cannot be seen in a central region of about two degrees, but are visible immediately as soon as they fall on the retina outside this area after it has been made more sensitive by being dark-adapted. The region within which stimuli of still lower intensity cannot be perceived is correspondingly wider. The dimensions of this "blind region" are given in the fourth column in Table IV for the intensity of light employed in that case.

[1] VAUGHAN u. BOLTUNOW, Über die Verteilung der Empfindlichkeit für farbige Lichter im helladaptierten Auge. *Zeitschr. f. Sinnesphysiol.* XLII. 1. 1907. See also GUILLERY, *Zeitschr. f. Psychol. u. Physiol. d. Sinnesorg.* XII. 261. 1896; XIII. 189. 1897.

In ophthalmology those parts of the visual field from which no sensation of light can be aroused in the eye are called *scotomata*. The scotoma is said to be *absolute* when no light at this place, however brilliant, can arouse a sensation in the eye; and it is said to be *relative* when the part of the retina concerned requires a much stronger stimulus for excitation than the surrounding parts. In this sense there is a relative scotoma in the visual field of the dark-adapted eye at the place corresponding to the fovea centralis.

The existence of this scotoma can be very easily verified as soon as dark adaptation has proceeded far enough. Astronomers all know that a faint star can be seen better by not looking straight at it, but a little to one side of it, in other words, by letting the image fall near the fovea.[1] The best way to see this is to consider a cluster of stars, like the Pleiades, in which there are some bright stars and some fainter ones side by side. Looking directly at this constellation, four stars, or five at most, will be visible; but looking a little to one side, straightway a whole lot of fainter stars come into view. Gazing at the sky with its myriad stars on a clear night, one will be surprised how many of them become invisible when he stares straight at them. It is not so easy for some persons to be convinced of the existence of this relative central scotoma, because there is some difficulty in looking straight at an object which disappears as soon as it is fixated. R. SIMON[2] investigated the relations of fixation in the dark-adapted eye. The subject was told to look at a luminous point whose light-intensity was below the foveal threshold; and by locating exactly where the blind place was, the point on the retina was found which was focused under these conditions by a dark-adapted eye. CHRISTINE LADD-FRANKLIN[3] had found that, in fixating a point of light so dim as to be below the foveal threshold in intensity, individual observers looked in different directions. SIMON corroborated this. In his own case this spot was above the fovea on the temporal side in his right eye, and right above the fovea in his left eye.

It is an interesting fact that this fixation place varies under certain circumstances even in the same individual. Thus, from the tendency to fixation, a luminous point whose intensity is near the foveal threshold is focused on the retina at a place very close to the fovea. The dimmer the light, the farther away is the part of the retina that is used in looking at it. The change in the subjective brightness of the

---

[1] ¶ARAGO said: "Pour apercevoir un objet très peu lumineux, il faut ne pas le regarder." (J. P. C. S.)

[2] R. SIMON, Über Fixation im Dämmerungssehen. *Zeitschr. f. Psychol. u. Physiol. d. Sinnesorg.* XXXVI. 186.

[3] See A. KÖNIG, *Ges. Abhand.* S. 353.

point, induced by progressive dark adaptation, proceeds in the same direction as the change in the objective intensity of the light stimulus. Thus, with a luminous point having a certain intensity below the foveal threshold, Simon found that, after 10 minutes dark adaptation, his point of fixation was about 2° on one side of the fovea; after 10 minutes more about 1.5°; and at the end of an hour only about 1°. Thus, perhaps, for every eye there is a fixed *direction* in which it turns in the tendency to fixate when the light-stimulus is below the foveal threshold, although the distance from the fovea of the point used for fixation may be variable. What is the direction from the fovea of the point on the retina that is selected for the fixation of dim lights, probably depends essentially on muscular and dioptric conditions, and to a less extent on the fact that certain parts of the retina immediately surrounding the fovea are prominent as being sensitive and are preferred, therefore, for fixation.

In general, we have no notion of the focusing of a point that is outside the fovea, that is, of an unusual point for fixation. For this reason many observers are sceptical at first when the attempt is made to demonstrate foveal hemeralopia to them. They are persuaded that a dim object has to be fixated in the same way as a bright one; although as a matter of fact they do not look straight at the dim object, and that is how they see it. With many persons the experiment succeeds better when they look first in any other direction, and then suddenly direct the gaze on the faint spot that is to be descried. Then immediately it vanishes for a time, until by slight involuntary ocular movements the image is again shifted to a more sensitive part of the retina near the fovea. The following experiment is exceedingly instructive. A small round white paper disc between 5 and 6 cm in diameter is fastened on the black outside wall of a box, which has a tiny electric light inside. A little hole is made in the centre of the disc, and a piece of red paper inserted behind it, so that the light from the lamp shines through it. The white paper disc is illuminated from the front, on the side where the observer stands, by a small lamp whose intensity can be regulated. This may be a little gas jet or an electric lamp in a milk-glass lantern with an iris diaphragm. The observer, having been previously dark-adapted, stands about 3m away and looks at the little red spot, at the same time regulating the illumination of the white disc, until it ceases to be visible to him. Then if he turns his eye the least bit so as to make the image of the disc fall outside the fovea, it straightway reappears, dark grey at first, becoming bright white when the eccentricity is increased.

Anyone who has had some practice in this experiment with this fixation-point, can usually perform it afterwards with the same result when the red point is extinguished. Thus all that is needed is practice in learning how to direct the eye in a dark room towards a dim object that disappears when it is fixated. The reason why it seemed worth while to describe this experiment in detail is because competent observers have been heard to say, either that there is no such thing as a central scotoma, or that it is merely a trivial difference of sensitivity between the fovea and the rest of the retina. The experiment which has just been described has invariably converted such sceptics.

4. Increase of Sensitivity to Light in the Fovea Centralis in Darkness

Although the fovea is hemeralopic in comparison with the retinal periphery, it is not entirely devoid of the power of adaptation.[1] Undoubtedly, it is very much less than it is in the other parts of the retina. A measurement of the amplitude of adaptation is beset with difficulties, at least in the later stages, where the sensitivity of the periphery increases faster than that of the fovea; the result being, therefore, that it requires much practice to succeed with the foveal fixation of the stimulus-light used for the measurement. The determinations are easier in the first stage of the dark adaptation that is preceded by complete light adaptation. Then for a couple of minutes still the fovea is the most sensitive place of the retina and therefore easily holds the fixation steady. One circumstance, indeed, that makes the experiment more difficult is that at this stage of complete light adaptation, as has been already stated, an object, whose visual angle is not greater than that of the fovea and whose intensity is close to the foveal threshold, cannot be easily found except by accident, so to speak. In this case every observer is in a position similar to that of a patient afflicted with so-called *retinitis pigmentosa* whose field of vision is restricted to the region of the fovea. The vision is like that produced by looking through a narrow tube. Accordingly, in the experiments made by SCHAEFER and the writer[2] for measuring the foveal adaptation, the plan was adopted of making the brightness of the test-object distinctly beyond the threshold at first, so that the observer, coming into the dark room, could easily locate it. The field was then quickly darkened by an assistant until it was just on the border of visibility. During the first minute the sensitivity was found to increase about five-fold. However, there was some uncertainty about these determinations. But after the first minute in the dark, the increase of sensitivity can be measured quite accurately. It amounts to about four-fold and lasts from 5 to 8 minutes. In all, therefore, from the

[1] ¶See S. HECHT, *loc. cit.* (H. L.)
[2] *Zeitschr. f. Psychol.* XXXIV. 1904. S. 271.

very beginning of darkness, foveal sensitivity increases about 20 times, which is certainly not an extraordinarily higher value. The writer has not detected any increase of foveal sensitivity beyond the tenth minute.

It is important to realize that foveal adaptation proceeds in exactly the same way and at the same rate for lights of different colours or wave-lengths. Thus, lights that look equally bright to the fovea of the light-adapted eye, will appear the same way when the fovea has been dark-adapted for any length of time. The so-called PURKINJE phenomenon, which will have to be considered presently, does not, therefore, exist in pure foveal vision.

Another thing to be emphasized is that, *generally, in order to demonstrate that there is an increase of sensitivity in the fovea, it is necessary to begin with very thorough light adaptation (looking at the bright sky).* No satisfactory measurements of adaptation like those described can be obtained by merely changing to the dark room from a room illuminated by ordinary daylight. The sensitivity may probably rise a little during the first seconds, and that will be all.

TSCHERMAK[1] has stated that dark adaptation, and particularly the PURKINJE phenomenon, occurs in the fovea too, provided light is excluded for a sufficient length of time. And so he assumes a much slower adaptation in the fovea than in the periphery. Some other writers make the same statement, but the discrepancy between this result and that given above is due to using test-objects that are so large that their retinal images extend beyond the rod-free foveal region. In the immediate vicinity of the fovea, where the rods are all isolated (as to the significance of this, see below, page 344), as a matter of fact, the adaptative increase of sensitivity in darkness is so minute that it takes hours of darkness to detect it at all. But, of course, this is something entirely different from the increase of sensitivity which takes place in the first few minutes of darkness, and which occurs in the fovea as well as in the rest of the retina.

5. Relations between Sensitivity to Light and the Stimulated Area of the Retina

In his experiments in the dark room, AUBERT[2] noticed that it took less illumination to see large areas than small luminous objects of the same intensity. Many investigators since then have studied this matter, in hopes of ascertaining the laws and have sought to find the conditions governing the relations between sensitivity to light and the superficial dimensions of the source of the stimulus. Among the earlier writers may be mentioned TREITEL[3], RICCO[4], and CHARPENTIER.[5] In very recent years the problem has been worked out in the

---

[1] A. TSCHERMAK, PFLÜGERS *Arch. f. d. ges. Physiol.* LXX. 1898. S. 297.

[2] H. AUBERT, *Physiologie der Netzhaut.* Breslau 1865.

[3] TREITEL, Über das Verhalten der normalen Adaptation. v. GRAEFES *Arch. f. Ophthalmologie.* 1887.

[4] RICCO, Relazione fra il minimo angolo visuale e l'intensita luminosa. *Annali d'Ottalmol.* VI.

[5] CHARPENTIER, *C. R.* XCI. 995. 1880; and *Arch. d'opht.* II. 487. 1882.

writer's laboratory from various angles by PIPER[1], LOESER[2], HENIUS[3] and FUJITA.[4]

The relations between sensitivity to light and the area of the surface are different in the two stages of adaptation of the eye; and they are different also in the fovea and in the periphery. The rule formulated by RICCO and confirmed by LOESER, namely, that the product of the area of the retinal image and the intensity of the light is constant for threshold stimuli, or, in other words, that the sensitivity is proportional to the area of the image, is true for purely foveal vision. In the case of a luminous circular field the law may also be stated as follows: The product of the angular diameter of the field and the square-root of the threshold intensity is constant. That this law is approximately true, at any rate, is shown by the following example taken from a set of experiments by LOESER.

Table V
(Distance of object from observer is 8 metres.)

Diameter of object D, in mm	Square-root of light intensity expressed by the diameter of a stop, J	Visual angle $\dfrac{D}{E}$	Product $\dfrac{D.J}{E}$
20	0.87	2.5	2.18
14	1.27	1.75	2.22
8.5	2.4	1.06	2.5
5	3.45	0.63	2.26

For the periphery of the retina, the relations are different. The following table, taken from PIPER's results, refers to the stage of dark adaptation.

Table VI

Area	$\sqrt{\text{Area}}$ or angular size	Threshold value	Relative stimulation value	Product of angular size and threshold value
1	1	10	1	10.0
10	3.15	2.94	3.4	9.3
25	5	1.96	5.1	9.8
100	10	1.02	9.8	10.2

[1] H. PIPER, Über die Abhängigkeit des Reizwertes leuchtender Objekte von ihrer Flächen- bzw. Winkelgrösse. *Zeitschr. f. Psychol. u. Physiol. d. Sinnesorg.* XXXII. 98.

[2] L. LOESER, Über die Beziehungen zwischen Flächengrösse und Reizwert leuchtender Objekte bei fovealer Beobachtung. *Beiträge z. Augenheilk.* Festschrift für J. HIRSCHBERG 1905.

[3] K. HENIUS, Die Abhängigkeit der Lichtempfindlichkeit von der Flächengrösse usw. *Zeitschr. f. Sinnesphysiol.* XLIII. 99. 1909.

[4] T. FUJITA, Versuche über die Lichtempfindlichkeit der Netzhautperipherie unter verschiedenen Umständen. Ibid. XLIII. 243. 1909.

It is evident at once that there is no question here of any proportionality between area and stimulus value, and so, of course, the product of area and threshold value cannot be constant. But there does exist an almost complete proportionality between the stimulus and the square-root of the area (or the visual angle of the retinal image, on the supposition that the objects concerned are geometrically similar). The threshold values are given in this table in terms of a unit that enables us to see easily the connection between the value of the stimulus and the visual angle.

PIPER has shown that, over a wide range, the stimulus value of a luminous surface, at the measured threshold value, is independent of the form of the surface. As a result of his observations, he formulated the following statement: For the dark-adapted peripheral retina, the value of the stimulus of a luminous surface is proportional to the square-root of the area of the retinal image; or in other words, the product of the threshold value by the square-root of the area of the retinal image is a constant.

As shown by the latest investigations of HENIUS and FUJITA, this law is not absolutely true unless PIPER's experimental conditions are observed, that is, unless the light is mixed white light and the angular size of the object is not more than 10°. The departures from the rule are more marked when still larger surfaces are used, as in shown in Table VII (taken from HENIUS's results). The values of the stimulus are computed (like those in Table VI) in terms of a unit defined to be the stimulus due to an object which subtends an angle of 1°. The place of the retina used for observation was 10° above the fovea.

Table VII

1	2	3	4	5
Area	$\sqrt{\text{Area}}$ or diameter of the round object in degrees	Threshold value	Product of 2 and 3	Stimulus value (Sensitivity)
1	1	454	454	1.0
4	2	260	520	1.7
9	3	127	381	3.5
16	4	94	376	4.8
25	5	79	395	5.7
49	7	60	420	7.5
100	10	46	460	9.8
225	15	35	525	13.0
400	20	26	520	17.5
625	25	25	625	18.1
900	30	21	630	21.6

From 10° on, therefore, the sensitivity, as expressed in terms of the value of the stimulus, rises distinctly more slowly as the size of the angle increases. This increase is much less still when the stimulating light is red; even for small angles. Furthermore, in fields smaller than 1° the variations from PIPER's rule are considerable, as FUJITA has shown.

But in the case of vision with light-adapted eye, the relations are essentially different. For luminous areas which subtend an angle that exceeds the foveal visual angle of from 1.5° to 2°, no clear connection has been found between the threshold stimulus and the size of the angle. This is shown distinctly in Table VIII taken from FUJITA's results.

Table VIII

White Light Stimulation, 30° from fovea, Light Adaptation

Visual Angle	Sensitivity (as reciprocal of threshold value)
1°	25
2°	40
3°	50
5°	50
10°	50
15°	50
20°	53
30°	53

However, the last two values indicate a small increase as compared with the preceding ones; but it is extremely likely that a slight admixture of unavoidable dark adaptation is responsible for this. But the falling off of the sensitivity for angles below 3° cannot be accounted for by sources of error. There is a connection here between sensitivity and size of field, which comes out still more clearly in FUJITA's experiments in which values of the stimulus were compared for angles less than 1° (at 10° from the centre, using white light and light adaptation).

The nature of the dependence between the value of the stimulus and the size of the field in the case of these small areas (Table IX) conforms

Table IX

Visual Angle of object	Relative Area of object	Threshold value	Relative sensitivity
1.0°	1.00	2300	1.00
0.5°	0.25	4500	0.51
0.25°	0.06	10000	0.23

very closely to PIPER's rule for large surfaces in dark adaptation. On account of the difficulty of making these measurements, they are to be considered only as being relatively accurate. It is certain, however, that for small objects subtending angles of 2° or less the value of the threshold stimulus of the luminous surface decreases with the visual angle, but not so fast as to obey RICCO's law for the fovea.

In consequence of the fact that the connection between threshold sensitivity and size of object is distinctly different in light and dark adaptation, particularly for surfaces of medium size subtending visual angles between 5° and 15°, the amplitude of adaptation must be different for luminous areas of different size. In fact, it must increase with the size of the field. TREITEL was aware of this fact. By systematic investigation of the process of adaptation with objects of different sizes, PIPER was able to get considerable differences in the rise of the curves of adaptation.[1]

6. Binocular Stimulus Summation[2]

In determining the threshold of the light sensation, it is not immaterial whether the observation is made with one eye or with both eyes. The truth is, in the state of dark adaptation the threshold in binocular vision is distinctly below what it is in monocular vision; being about half as high, according to PIPER's measurements.[3] This result has been confirmed in the writer's laboratory by numerous other observers. It was corroborated also by W. LOHMANN.[4] Testing a number of persons and comparing the results, he found unequivocally that the increase of sensitivity due to the participation of the other eye did not occur to the same extent with everybody. The differences were most marked in the case of subjects who had a squint. This may be the reason why some observers (WÖLFFLIN[5], for example) have found practically the same values of the thresholds of monocular and binocular vision. The writer had no trouble in verifying the fact of binocular summation of stimulus in his own case and in that of numerous other observers.

[1] ¶See H. PIÉRON, De la variation de l'énergie liminaire en fonction de la surface retinienne excitée pour la vision periphérique. (Cones et batonnets.) *Compt. rend. soc. de biol.*, LXXXIII. 1921, 753. Also, Des principes physiologiques qui doivent présider à toute étude de la lumière. *Rev. gén. des sci.*, XXXI. 620 and 656. (H. L.)

[2] ¶W. DE W. ABNEY and W. WATSON, The threshold of vision for different coloured lights. *Phil. Trans. Roy. Soc.*, 216 A. 1916. 91–142 (see page 109). — P. REEVES, Effect of size of stimulus and exposure time on retinal threshold. *Astrophys. Jour.*, XLVII. 1918. 141–146. (H. L.)

[3] H. PIPER, Über das Helligkeitsverhältnis monokular und binokular ausgelöster Lichtempfindungen. *Zeitschr. f. Psychol. u. Physiol. d. Sinnesorg.* XXXII. 161.

[4] W. LOHMANN, Untersuchungen über Adaptation und ihre Bedeutung für Erkrankungen des Augenhintergrundes. v. GRAEFES *Arch. f. Ophthal.* LXV. 1907.

[5] E. WÖLFFLIN, Der Einfluss des Lebensalters auf den Lichtsinn bei dunkeladaptiertem Auge. Ibid. 61. 1905.

FECHNER[1] stated that a bright surface viewed with both eyes does not look brighter than it does in monocular vision. HELMHOLTZ corroborated this, and it is a well known fact so far as vision in a bright place is concerned. The only effect of closing one eye may be to make a faint shadow come over the surface.

In performing this experiment, supposing that the initial adaptation is of that moderate kind customary indoors, it should be borne in mind that a certain degree of dark adaptation takes place very quickly in the eye that is closed or screened with the hand. When the eye is uncovered, it is not as if the free eye were reinforced by a second eye of equal sensitivity, but by an eye which at the instant when it begins to take part has increased sensitivity. As a matter of fact, when light adaptation is very good, and one of the eyes has been closed for a very short time, there is generally no appreciable difference of brightness between monocular and binocular vision.

That there is a real difference between the pair of eyes for photopia and scotopia so far as the summation of binocular stimuli is concerned, has been proved by PIPER. His method consisted in determining the monocular and binocular thresholds alternately throughout the entire test of the dark adaptation. The results of one of these tests, in which the writer acted as observer, are given in Table X; and graphically exhibited in Fig. 66. The experiment was made before the construction of the adaptometer; consequently, the absolute sensitivity values are not directly comparable with those given in other places, but are represented in terms of an arbitrary unit.

Table X

Binocular		Right Eye		Left Eye	
Time in min.	Sensitivity	Time in min.	Sensitivity	Time in min.	Sensitivity
0	86	½	111	1	111
3½	272	4½	498	5	498
8½	2724	9½	2914	10½	3419
14½	11815	15½	13521	16	14516
20½	41649	21½	27778	22½	22957
27½	65746	28½	38447	30	33058
37	81632	39½	40000	40½	36982
52½	97656	56	40000	57	41649
59	97656				

A distinct separation between the curves for monocular and binocular vision is not manifest until after 14 minutes. Investigating various soldiers, who were employed as normal controls in an investigation of hemeralopia, MESSMER (*loc. cit.*) got quite similar results.

[1] FECHNER, Über einige Verhältnisse des binokularen Sehens. *Abhandl. der sächs. Gesellsch. d. Wissensch.* VII. 1860. S. 423. See also Bd. III. S. 424.

When the observations are made with both eyes, one of which is light-
adapted and the other dark-adapted, the light-adapted eye behaves
as if it were shut; that is, in this case the threshold is found to have the
same value in both monocular and binocular vision.   PIPER concludes
correctly that this affords further proof of the independence of the
process of adaptation in the two eyes.   Extending his investigations
further, he was able to show that even with stimuli considerably above
the threshold, a binocular summation of stimulus occurred, provided
both eyes were dark-adapted.   In his method of experiment the
intensity of one of two white surfaces could be regulated at will, and

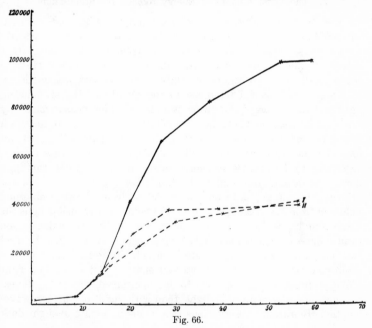

Fig. 66.

this surface was exposed to one eye only, while the other could be seen
by both eyes.   This enabled him to make a comparison between
monocular vision and binocular vision.   In order to obtain the same
apparent brightness with both methods of observation, it was found
that the intensity of illumination of the field seen with one eye must
be from 1.6 to 1.7 times that of the other.   With very low intensities,
near the threshold in fact, the value is approximately double.

Comparing these results on binocular vision with those in which the
determination of the threshold was made for retinal areas of different
sizes, we find a remarkable analogy, as follows: In complete light

adaptation of the eye the stimulating values of the quantities of light that fall on different parts of the retina are not to be added together when the stimulated area exceeds a certain size amounting to a few degrees of visual angle; and, furthermore, when both eyes are light-adapted, the stimulations due to the quantities of light reaching the two eyes are not to be added together. But in the state of dark adaptation the summation occurs distinctly and regularly in both cases. The possible experimental explanations of these facts will be discussed in another place.

7. The Least Amount of Energy Needed for Stimulation[1]

The absolute measure of the least amount of energy that is needed to stimulate the organ of vision has been determined very recently by various observers. Thus, Wien[2] has computed the energy that reaches the eye every second from the most faintly visible stars as being 4×10^{-8} erg. A thorough study of the subject was made by v. Kries[3] with special reference to the quality of the stimulating light and the region of the retina stimulated. The measurements by Dr. Eyster were made on the most sensitive part of the retina, with blue-green light of wave-length $507\mu\mu$, which is the part of the spectrum for which the ratio between visibility and energy has its greatest value, according to Langley's measurements. With the most thorough dark adaptation, and under the most favourable conditions, for utilizing the energy, as to both area and exposure, Eyster obtained values of from 1.3 to 2.6×10^{-10} erg. For continuously visible light the value found was 5.6×10^{-10} erg per second. Dr. Boswell[4] made similar determinations for purely foveal vision. As stimulus he used the longest waves in the spectrum for which König has found a fairly uniform ratio between brightness and energy, that is, sodium light ($589\mu\mu$); because, for reasons to be mentioned presently, foveal fixation is easier with this light than with light of shorter wave-lengths. Boswell's observations were made in a state of slight dark

[1] ¶P. Reeves, The minimum radiation visually perceptible. *Astrophys. Jour.*, XLVI. 1917. 167–174. — P. L. Dunoüy, Energy and vision. *Jour. Gen. Physiol.* III. 743–764. — W. W. Coblentz and W. B. Emerson, Relative sensibility of the average eye to light of different colors and some practical applications to radiation problems. *Bull. Bur. Stand.* 1917 sci. papers, No. 303, 167–236. — H. Piéron, De la variation de l'énergie liminaire en fonction de la durée d'excitation pour la vision peripherique. *Compt. rend. Acad. des Sci.*, CLXX. 1921. 1203–1206. (H.L.)

[2] Wien, Über die Messung von Tonstärken. *Diss.* Berlin 1888.

[3] J. v. Kries, Über die zur Erregung des Sehorgans erforderlichen Energiemengen. Nach Beobachtungen von Herrn Dr. Eyster mitgeteilt. *Zeitschr. f. Sinnesphysiol.* XLI. 373. 1906 (and *Ges. Abhandl. z. Physiol. d. Gesichtsempfindungen*, 3, 4.)

[4] F. P. Boswell, Über die zur Erregung des Sehorgans in der Fovea erforderlichen Energiemengen. *Ibid.* XLII. 299. 1907.

adaptation, perhaps, therefore, under conditions in which the foveal
sensitivity had already reached its highest value; which, according to
the results given above as found by SCHAEFER and the writer, occurs
after 10 minutes of dark adaptation with previous highest light
adaptation.   BOSWELL found the just effective energy for short
exposure, taking the average of numerous measurements, to be $31.6 \times$
10^{-10} erg.   For long exposure from 16 to 20 times as much energy per
second is necessary.

It is extremely remarkable that the amount of energy necessary
to stimulate the peripheral retina is only about 15 times as much as is
required to stimulate the fovea.   Much greater differences might be
expected on account of the considerable differences between the fovea
and the periphery in the perception of very faint light.   However, it
must be remembered that the superiority of the periphery is particularly evident in long continued observations of large objects.   When
the values of the stimuli given by EYSTER and BOSWELL for long exposures are compared, it appears that the periphery under these
conditions is about a hundred times superior to the fovea.   We saw
above, that for simple threshold determination with objects 1° in
diameter, the eye being free to look in a chosen direction for as long a
time as desired, the periphery of the dark-adapted eye is about a thousand times more sensitive than the fovea.   Considering also the fact
that in threshold determinations with the adaptometer, where the eye
is free to move, the observational conditions are more favourable than
in measurements with a spectrum apparatus and an ocular slit, and that
this circumstance is more evident in eccentric vision than in foveal,
we need not wonder any more at the comparatively slight difference
between the stimulation of fovea and periphery as found in v. KRIES's
laboratory.   This is even more readily appreciated in the light of Bos-
WELL's comparative results on energy values when other lights besides
yellow were used.   It was found that the stimulating value of green
light was more than twice that of sodium light.

B. Duplicity Theory and Twilight Vision.

1. The Duplicity Theory

Aside from the quantitative changes that are the result of the
variation of sensitivity, a series of qualitative changes of vision are
also associated with adaptation.   These are manifested especially
with respect to colour vision and in some other connections also
(time relations, etc.).   Some of them have indeed been mentioned
already in the preceding section, particularly those phenomena which
have recently led more and more to a very definite way of regarding

the contrivance and function of the visual organ. Inasmuch as the actual facts of observation can be much more easily described in terms of the assumptions of this theory, the fundamental ideas will be stated here.

In the first edition of the "Physiologischen Optik" HELMHOLTZ had expressed the opinion that it was not likely that the rods were also sensitive to light in addition to the cones (see page 31). In the second edition he accepted the hypothesis of H. MÜLLER and KOELLIKER, which is that the rods also are concerned in sensation of light (see page 30), although he conjectured that their rôle in the localization of the sensations was different from that of the cones. In this connection no allusion was made to the hypothesis which had been advanced by MAX SCHULTZE[1] in 1866. The fundamental ideas of this theory have since been accepted by many writers.[2] According to SCHULTZE, all that the rods do is to mediate simple sensation of light without colour discrimination, the cones being the apparatus of colour perception. SCHULTZE's view received its chief support from the decrease of the colour sense out towards the periphery of the retina; which has its structural correlations in the preponderance of rods over cones in the peripheral parts. It is supported also by comparative anatomy. In animals that either live exclusively in dark places (caves, etc.) or are not active and alert except in dim light, SCHULTZE found the rods developed in much greater numbers than in animals that do not shun bright light. Indeed, in the case of many nocturnal animals he could find no cones at all, and nothing but rods. On the other hand, in the case of animals that live much in bright sunlight, such as lizards and snakes, he found only cones and no rods.

The foundation of SCHULTZE's theory cannot be said today to be perfectly valid. Peripheral colour blindness is explained in a partly different way from SCHULTZE's hypothesis. And, moreover, with respect to the data of comparative anatomy, it is certainly not true that nocturnal animals have rods only. According to more recent anatomical investigations, there are no mammals and birds without cones. Still the general fact is correct that the rod mechanism, as compared with the cone mechanism, is much more highly developed in nocturnal and twilight animals than in those whose habits are distinctly diurnal. The difference, however, is not so much in the number as in the length of the rods and the amount of visual purple they contain.

The theory of the functional difference between the rods and cones

[1] *Arch. f. mikroskop. Ana .* II. 1866. S. 247–261.
[2] For the literature on the subject see TSCHERMAK, *Ergebnisse der Physiologie* I. 2. 1902.

was put on a much firmer basis by the researches of PARINAUD[1] and
v. KRIES.[2] Independently of each other, and proceeding along
different lines, they arrived at a complete confirmation of MAX
SCHULTZE's hypothesis and shaped it into a reasonable theory. By
referring to it as the *duplicity theory* (*Duplizitätstheorie*), which is the
name given to it by v. KRIES, the implication is that there is not simply
a morphological duality of the elements of the retinal neuro-epithelium,
but a corresponding duality of function as well, and that to a certain
extent there are two kinds of vision. One kind is that which is active
when the eyes are light-adapted and stimulated by strong light—*Tages-
sehen* (or *daylight vision, photopia*), as v. KRIES designates it. Opposed
to it is the so-called *Dämmerungssehen* (or *twilight vision, scotopia*),
when the eye is dark-adapted and the light stimulus is weak. On the
duplicity theory the organ for daylight vision is the "daylight mechanism" or brightness-mechanism represented by the totality of the
cones; the "twilight mechanism" or darkness-mechanism being constituted by the rods along with the visual purple absorbed in their
outer segments.

In agreement with each other and with SCHULTZE, PARINAUD and
v. KRIES assumed that only one quality of light sensation can be
mediated by the rods. Thus, to a certain extent the twilight mechanism must be considered as being totally colour-blind, whereas the
daylight mechanism is *farbentüchtig* or capable of discriminating
colours.[3]

The function of the daylight mechanism, pure and simple, is exem-
plified in vision with the foveal region of the retina where there are
no rods. But the function of the twilight mechanism cannot be isolated
so simply. According to the theoretical assumptions, under ordinary
circumstances in not too strong light, rods and cones function together
simultaneously. But the rods are supposed to have a much greater
capacity for dark adaptation. Thus, with low intensity of illumination,
the stimulus may be sufficient to excite the rod or twilight mechanism,
without being adequate to stimulate the cone mechanism. And hence
below a certain limit of intensity, whatever possibility of vision there
may be is to be considered as being due entirely to the mediation of the
rods. As to whether the rods continue to function along with the cones

---

[1] PARINAUD, *Arch. gén. de méd.* April 1881; *C. R. Aug.* 1881, 286; *C. R. Nov.* 1884;
Annal. d'ocul. 1894. CXII. 228; *Arch. d'ophthal.* XVI. 87. 1896.

[2] J. v. KRIES, Ber. naturf. Ges. Freiburg, IX. 1894. Über die Funktion d. Netzhaut-
stabchen. *Zft. f Psychol.* IX. 81. 1895; GRAEFES *Arch. f. Opth.* XLII. 95. 1896.

[3] ¶"Broadly speaking vision with the dark-adapted eye, i. e., scotopic vision, is monochromatic or tone-free. Vision with the light-adapted eye, i. e., photopic vision, is polychromatic or toned. In the former the threshold stimulus intensity is low; in the latter
relatively high." J. H. PARSONS, *loc. cit.* p. 203. (J. P. C. S.)

at high intensities of light, the two kinds of visual epithelium being therefore united for seeing by very bright light, the duplicity theory does not definitely attempt to say. During morning and evening twilight, and in dim light generally, the functions of the two mechanisms are interlinked in a complicated fashion, as will be described in the following sections.

The foundation for the duplicity theory is primarily in the comparison between foveal vision and peripheral rod vision.

In the preceding chapter of this Appendix it was shown (p. 329) that the absolute sensitivity in the centre of the retina at the fovea is not anywhere nearly so high as it is in the parts of the retina to one side of the fovea, say, 10° from it.

On the supposition that the angular diameter of an object which sends out white light is about one degree, and that the eye is thoroughly dark-adapted, the intensity of the light required in order for the object to be just visible when it is fixated directly must be in round numbers one thousand times greater than when the eye views the object with the most sensitive parts of the periphery of the retina; as was stated above. In light adaptation, on the contrary, the sensitivity in the fovea is somewhat greater than in the periphery. The simplest explanation of the superior sensitivity of the dark-adapted periphery of the retina is by assuming that the sensitivity of the rods, which are absent in the fovea but present in the periphery along with the cones, increases in darkness to a much greater degree than that of the cones; and that, therefore, with decreasing illumination, as for example, in the evening twilight, the rods more and more take over the rôle of receptors; until finally, for a certain degree of darkness, the intensity of light is no longer sufficient to stimulate the central part of the retina where there are no rods. Thus the condition is brought about which is characteristic of twilight vision, and in which there is a deficiency of function, a "scotoma", in the centre of the visual field.

2. Quality of the Light Sensation in Twilight Vision

Another striking characteristic of twilight vision is the lack of all colour discrimination. The eye is totally colour-blind, as can be verified without difficulty. The observation may be made at night in any room, with a suitable source of light and a device for regulating its intensity, so that it can be made sometimes dark and sometimes bright. As soon as it is possible to distinguish colour, it is a sure sign that the intensity is already above the threshold of the fovea centralis. Suppose, for example, there is a piece of red paper in the dark room, and that at a certain degree of illumination the red colour can be discerned. Under these circumstances, a little bit of this paper subtending an angle of one or two degrees cannot be made to "disappear" in the foveal region of the retina; as can be done so easily with a white object and sufficiently low degree of illumination, by suddenly looking straight at it (see page 333). The intensity is above the threshold of the foveal sensitivity.

The experiment turns out the same way when the colour of the paper is orange or brown, and to some extent also even when it is green. But in the case of blue objects there are difficulties with experiments of this kind. Many persons will say that a blue paper looks still distinctly blue, although the intensity of illumination of the surface is certainly below the foveal threshold; that is, although a small piece of the blue object of proper size disappears when it is focused in the fovea. It is a fact also that the sky at night when not absolutely devoid of light is frequently a beautiful dark blue[1], and a landscape in moonlight may look as if suffused in a lustre of bluish white.

These observations show that the quality of the light sensation in twilight vision is not always colourless, that is, white or grey, but that, at least under certain circumstances, it may be bluish. This is not a contradiction of the existence of total colour blindness in twilight vision; because that expression does not imply the inability of seeing light of any kind of colour at all, but merely the impossibility of distinguishing colours as qualities that are different one from another. When a person looks through a piece of glass which is transparent only to rays of some one particular colour, a dark red ruby glass, for example, he is practically colour blind. Objects seen through such a glass all appear in various gradations from bright red to black. The colouring in this case is all so intense that there is never any doubt even for a moment as to whether everything is coloured or colourless. It is a different matter when the piece of glass is lightly coloured, and particularly if the glass is blue. Seen through blue goggles everything white looks bright blue at first glance. (Other rays besides the blue rays come through these goggles, and hence red and green objects do not look much changed and often appear almost in their natural colours.) However, after wearing the goggles some hours, the blue disappears more and more from the visual field, and then white objects cease to look blue, and begin to look white. This is particularly the case when the goggles are made like snow-spectacles so as to prevent side light from entering the eye; and consequently comparisons cannot be made with parts of the field that do not radiate blue light.

In a case like this, in large portions of the field in a comparatively short time the specific coloured character of a sensation of blue that is

[1] Dove, Poggendorffs *Ann.* LXXXV. 1851. 397. (See also above, p. 226).

not a very saturated one may disappear and give way to a sensation of colourlessness. And so also in twilight vision something analogous may occur, particularly as the stimulus here is feeble anyhow, and simultaneous contrast between different coloured parts of the field is absent entirely.

On the other hand, it might be supposed that the coloured quality of twilight vision would be particularly manifest when there was a possibility of comparing such a sensation with the sensation aroused in the light-adapted eye under the conditions of daylight vision. The writer has made observations of this sort in the following manner. The observer places his head in front of the open side of a box divided in two parts by a vertical partition, so that each eye looks into one half. The back of the box is made of milk-glass, and behind it there is an annex for holding the contrivances for regulating the illumination of the two halves of the milk-glass plate. There are two iris diaphragms, in which little pieces of milk-glass are inserted. Coloured glasses can be placed over these diaphragms also. In front of each of the apertures a special source of light can be adjusted. By binocular comparison the observer can decide whether the two fields on the inside of the box are equal in luminosity and in colour.

For one of the fields, say, the one on the right, the intensity of the light is so regulated that, although it is below the foveal threshold, it looks as bright as possible to a *thoroughly dark-adapted eye*. (The best way to get this adjustment is by covering the field with black paper with a hole in it subtending an angle of between 3° and 4°. If the piece of milk-glass as seen through this hole when the dark-adapted eye looks straight at it can be made to disappear with certainty, the intensity of the light is far enough below the foveal threshold.)

The observer's right eye is thoroughly dark-adapted by blindfolding it tightly for one hour; the other eye meantime being kept as fully light-adapted as possible. A very bright source of light must be adjusted in front of the left iris diaphragm. Immediately after going into the dark room the luminosity of the two fields is compared, the right field being viewed with the right eye, and the left field with the left eye, the eyes being closed alternately. If the correct intensities of light have been selected, the left field therefore being illuminated about a thousand times more intensely than the right one, the difference of colour in the two fields is manifested in the most striking way. The left field, viewed by the photopic eye, looks generally distinctly yellow-red alongside the greenish blue right half as seen by the scotopic eye. To obtain equality of the fields, a highly coloured blue filter must be interposed in front of the left source of light.

The technical difficulties of this method are so very great that the writer has not yet succeeded in making an accurate determination of the colour of twilight vision in terms of the wave-length of a definite colour of the spectrum. But by a different method v. Kries and the writer together[1] have obtained a basis for a determination of this sort. In experiments which will be described below in another connection matches were made, for the eye of a colour-blind person (namely, the writer)[2], between homogeneous lights and a mixture of spectrum red and blue (using a field considerably larger than the foveal region). For reasons that cannot be fully understood until we get further on in the subject, a colour match of this sort does not generally continue valid when the lights in the two halves of the match are reduced in the same proportion (for example, by narrowing the width of the ocular slit) so as to approach the conditions of twilight vision. The colour match previously made under the conditions of full daylight vision is therefore incorrect from two points of view, first with respect to luminosity, and then also with respect to hue. Thus, the nearer the conditions are to those of twilight vision, the more the specific colour of twilight vision, the cyan-blue mentioned above, blends for the observer into the colour of the field; and indeed, as we shall see, this takes place to an unequal extent for the different colours of the spectrum. Thus depending on the wave-length of the homogeneous light used in making the colour match, this homogeneous light, or the red-blue mixture, will change *more* towards blue, when the intensity of the entire field is reduced. If the mixture were made up of red of $670\mu\mu$ and blue-violet of $435\mu\mu$, what was found was, that a homogeneous light of wave-length $495\mu\mu$ (which is colourless to the colour-blind and corresponds therefore to his so-called "neutral point" in the spectrum[3]) appeared brighter and *bluer* than the mixture when the intensity of the whole colour match was reduced. The same behaviour was observed for all kinds of light up to about $485\mu\mu$. But if the wave-length of the homogeneous light is shorter than 480, the mixture was found to be *bluer* than the homogeneous light when the intensity was lowered. Thus between these limits, 480 and $485\mu\mu$, there is a homogeneous light which for the dichromat does not change its hue in the transition from daylight vision to twilight vision. v. Kries and Nagel called this place the "invariable point" in the spectrum and assumed for reasons which will not be discussed here, that it was situated nearer

---

[1] J. v. Kries and W. Nagel, Einfluss von Lichtstärke und adaptation auf das Sehen des Dichromaten. *Zeitschr. f. Psychol. u. Physiol. d. Sinnesorg.* XII. 29.

[2] ¶Nagel was a deuteranope. (J. P. C. S.)

[3] ¶The *neutral point* of the dichromatic spectrum is the spectrum colour that matches white for this type of colour blindness. (J. P. C. S.)

the upper limit, $485\mu\mu$. Accordingly, it may be conjectured that the quality of the sensation in twilight vision is similar to that which is aroused by this light in daylight vision. This, however, is not pure white, but very distinctly blue. Recent researches[1], which will be taken up later, point to the same conclusion. The statements made here are applicable strictly to colour-blind persons, but they are doubtless true also to a great extent with respect to so-called normal colour vision; because, as numerous observations have shown, the twilight mechanism in the eye of the normal individual and in that of the colour-blind person seem to function in identically the same way.

Incidentally, it is quite conceivable that the light sensations that occur under the conditions of pure twilight vision have a certain range of fluctuation as to their quality, varying from absolute colourlessness to a cyan-blue of no little saturation.

Perhaps this may be connected with a previous colour modulation (*Umstimmung*) of the visual organ. But the writer, judging by his own observations, does not believe this is the case. On the contrary, according to his experience, the blue hue of twilight vision comes out most distinctly right after long dark adaptation, where there cannot be any question of colour adaptation, the indication being rather that the eye must be "neutral" in HERING's use of this term.

The writer would like to guard against what seems to him to be the mistake of using such observations as the above as the origin or basis of any theory as to the rods in the retina being the anatomical substratum of the blue sensation. A conclusive argument against such a view is the fact that, while the peculiar characteristics of twilight vision are lacking entirely in the fovea centralis, still it is undoubtedly capable of mediating the blue sensation. It is only under very special conditions, when the two mechanisms of daylight vision and twilight vision operate together, that it is possible for the blue sensation arising in the twilight mechanism to be blended with colour vision to any noticeable extent.

3. Twilight Values of Pure Homogeneous Kinds of Light

Rays of different wave-lengths originating from one coherent spectrum have unequal stimulating values for the retina operating under the conditions of twilight vision (state of dark adaptation, with intensity of light below the foveal threshold). As the effects of all wave-lengths are qualitatively of the same kind, that is, as no colour

[1] W. NAGEL, Farbenumstimmung beim Dichromaten. *Zeitschr. f. Sinnesphysiol.* 44. 1909.

sensations are aroused whether the waves are long or medium or short, it is possible to make exact matches and quantitative measurements of the effects of individual wave-lengths without much difficulty.

The method employed in investigating spectral light is different from that used in studying more mixed light like that reflected by the colours of pigments. The nature of the reactions to homogeneous kinds of light is naturally of chief interest; and consequently this matter will be considered first.[1] The investigation may be made by means of HELMHOLTZ's spectrophotometer to be described hereafter. Another apparatus is needed in conjunction therewith to enable the experimenter to adjust a comparison light anywhere alongside the various homogeneous kinds of light in the spectrum. It must be possible to regulate the intensity of this comparison light over a wide range, and it should be big enough to subtend in the field of view an angle of from 5° to 10°. Looking through an ocular slit in HELMHOLTZ's instrument, what the observer sees is a circular field of the prescribed size divided by a vertical diameter. One of the semicircles is completely illuminated by light from the comparison lamp, while the other is illuminated in turn by the different kinds of homogeneous light in the spectrum. A homogeneous light, say cyan-blue, is generally used also for the comparison light. It is better not to regulate the luminosity of this half of the field, at least not entirely, by changing the width of the slit, because the range is not sufficient for the necessary changes. An adjustable pair of NICOL prisms is the best contrivance for this purpose. The intensity of the light in the other semicircle is not deliberately changed at all, the width of the slit being the same for each of the various kinds of spectral light that are admitted through it.

In order to make the observations under the conditions of twilight vision, the observer must keep his eyes thoroughly dark-adapted. The intensity of the entire field should be so low that all colour differences vanish; and therefore either very faint sources of light should be used, or merely a small fraction of the radiation of a lamp that is steady enough. This can be accomplished by placing the lamp far away and letting it shine on a sheet of magnesium oxide or white baryta paper held at a suitable angle in front of the collimator slit. Another convenience about this arrangement is that both slits can be illuminated by a single source of light.

[1] See F. HILLEBRAND, Über die spezifische Helligkeit der Farben, mit Vorbemerkung von E. HERING. *Sitz. Ber. K. Akad. Wien. Mathem. naturw. Kl.* XCVIII. III. 1889.— J. v. KRIES u. W. NAGEL, Über den Einfluss von Lichtstärke und Adaptation auf das Sehen des Dichromaten (Grünblinden), *Zeitschr. f. Psychol. u. Physiol. d. Sinnesorgane.* XII. 45; also in: *Abhandlungen zur Physiol. d. Gesichtsempfindungen aus dem physiol. Institut zu Freiburg i. Br.* Herausgeg. von J. v. KRIES. Heft 1.

The stimulus value for the dark-adapted eye of a particular homogeneous kind of radiation may be expressed simply in terms of the value of the intensity of the comparison light when there is a perfect match between the two halves of the field. The relative stimulus values obtained by systematic investigations with different kinds of spectral light may be termed (see v. KRIES and NAGEL, *loc. cit.*) the *twilight values* (or twilight valences), and can be exhibited in the form of a curve.

Table XI (according to v. KRIES and NAGEL)
Twilight Values of Homogeneous Kinds of Light

Wave-length	Twilight value in arbitrary units
670.8μμ	?
656	19.3
642	36
628	110
615	254
603	276
591	599
582	1276
571	2061
561	2477
552	2930
544	3027
536	2820
525	2055
515	1576
505	1015
496	697
488	486
480	318
469	263
460.8	146
448	46
436	17

The typical distribution of the twilight values in the dispersion spectrum of gaslight for the writer's eye is given in Table XI. The relations are exhibited by the curve in Fig. 67. The maximum is in the green at 544 (for other measurements made by the writer it was at 536μμ). The curve falls rapidly on both sides, but most steeply towards the red, while the descent from the blue-green to the violet is very gradual. On the red end near the border between the orange and red, the values are already almost too small to be measured; and in the red from 670μμ on, while traces of twilight vision can still be detected, they cannot be numerically measured; being dependent besides on the almost unavoidable admixture of diffused light in the instrument.

Fig. 1. Prism Spectrum of Sunlight.

Fig. 2. Spectrum in Twilight (or Scotopic) Vision; as it appears to the totally colour-blind.

PLATE II

The statement that this is a typical curve means that it not only represents the case of persons with the same kind of colour vision, but cases of so-called normal colour vision and of various congenital types of colour blindness as well. It applies likewise, as has been shown by the writer, to anomalous trichromats to be described later.

In his experiments on the luminosities of the spectral colours for various absolute intensities, A. KÖNIG (*Ges. Abhandl.* p. 144, and Beiträge zur Psychologie und Physiologie der Sinnesorgane, *Festschrift zu* HELMHOLTZ 70 *Geburtstag.* 1891. p. 309) used for the lowest degree of intensity one that was probably not far from the conditions required for pure twilight vision. On this occasion he got the important result that the great differences in the distribution of spectral brightness, that exist between normal, red-blind, green-blind and totally colour-blind persons when the intensity of the light used is relatively high, disappeared almost entirely when the lowest degree of intensity was employed. More recent investigations have completely corroborated this result and shown that it is valid also for the anomalous trichromats, as above stated.

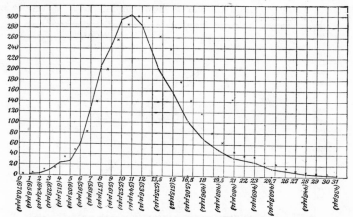

Fig. 67.—Distribution of the twilight values in the dispersion spectrum of gaslight (according to NAGEL). The crosses indicate the results of previous, perhaps rather less accurate determinations.

In repeated parallel experiments with persons of different types of colour vision the same result has been always verified again. *There is no known form of anomalous colour vision for which any noticeable deviation has been found in the distribution of twilight values over the spectrum.* The only cases that have not yet been tested are those of pure tritanopia or violet blindness.

A. TSCHERMAK[1] has stated over and over again that the adaptive ability of the eye for long and short wave-lengths for the two principal types of colour

---

[1] A. TSCHERMAK, *Über physiologische und pathologische Anpassung des Auges.* Leipzig 1900.—Beobachtungen über die relative Farbenblindheit im indirekten Sehen. PFLÜGERS *Arch. f. d. ges. Physiol.* LXXXII. 559. 1900.—Die Helldunkeladaptation des Auges und die Funktion der Stäbchen und Zapfen. *Ergebnisse d. Physiol.* I, 2. 703 and 747. 1902.

blindness (red blindness and green blindness) is regularly different from the two types of colour vision that are presumed to correspond to them. But no proof of the truth of this assertion has ever been given or even so much as attempted.

Evidently, these determinations of the twilight values always apply simply to a particular spectrum, and if the observations are made with an interference spectrum, the curves will have a different form. Moreover, in using a definite apparatus the distribution of the twilight values will be different according to the nature of the source of light. An AUER lamp containing a lot of green light will give a different curve from that of the reddish incandescent electric light.

The most complete determinations of this sort, so far as perfecting the method is concerned, are perhaps those made by SCHATERNIKOFF.[1] The values which he obtains for gaslight are very close to those of the writer. For direct sunlight and reflected skylight the values are given in Table XII and the curve shown in Fig. 68. As was to be

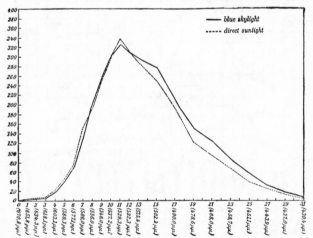

Fig. 68.—Distribution of the twilight values in the dispersion spectrum of sunlight and blue skylight (according to SCHATERNIKOFF).

expected, the peak of the curve (at $529.3\mu\mu$) is a little nearer the blue end than it is in gaslight (537.2). The values for blue skylight are somewhat higher in the blue-green and blue than for direct sunlight.

Even without any spectrum apparatus, an approximate idea of the distribution of twilight values may be obtained, which brings out especially the considerable differences of the luminosities of the colours in the daylight

[1] M. SCHATERNIKOFF, Neue Bestimmungen über die Verteilung der Dämmerungswerte im Dispersionsspektrum des Gas- und Sonnenlichts. *Zeitschr. f. Psychol. und Physiol. der Sinnesorgane* XXIX. 255. Also, *Abhandlungen zur Physiologie der Gesichtsempfindungen,* herausgeg. von J. v. KRIES. Heft 2. 1902.

Table XII (according to SCHATERNIKOFF)

Wave-length	Twilight Values for	
	blue skylight	direct sunlight
670.8	7.7	5.9
651.8	12.5	10.5
634.3	22.2	33.3
618.1	70.7	86.3
603.1	189	214.4
589.3	411	459
577.1	725	752
566.4	1369	1535
556.0	2019	1933
546.0	2578	2546
537.2	3000	3000
529.3	3213	3353
522.3	3060	3067
515.4	2959	2833
502.2	2758	2460
490.0	2067	1935
478.6	1497	1205
468.0	1224	945
458.7	830	658
451.1	580	399
443.8	299	212
437.0	160	112
430.4	69	46

vision and twilight vision. With a good assortment of saturated coloured papers of about post-card size, they can be arranged under very dim illumination in a graded series from the brightest to the darkest. Thorough dark adaptation is necessary and also an illumination correctly adjusted until the colours of the papers are no longer apparent. Afterwards when bright illumination is turned on, it is evident that the order of arrangement is absolutely wrong for daylight vision. Brilliant red papers will be found at the darkest end of the row, and the orange, say, near a dark blue that in daylight vision looks very much less luminous than the orange. On the other hand, the greens are placed near the bright end of the row.

More accurate experiments, in which also numerical values for the differences of luminosity are obtained, can be made by using the colour top. A coloured disc of sufficient size, 18 or 20 cm in diameter, is set to spinning. On it are placed two smaller discs, one black and the other white, which can be shifted over each other, The illumination is lowered until a thoroughly dark-adapted eye can no longer distinguish any colours, and the ratio between the black and white sectors is so adjusted that the grey of the mixture and the dim colourless light of the larger disc appear to have exactly the same luminosity. While this can be quite accurately done, of course no precise twilight values can be obtained in this way, because the colours on the disc are not homogeneous.

The twilight value curves give a picture of the distribution of the luminosity in the spectrum as it must look to a thoroughly dark-adapted observer viewing an entire spectrum under the conditions of twilight vision; that is, at an intensity for which colours are no longer discernible. Observations of a dim, colourless spectrum of this sort were made first by HILLEBRAND[1] in HERING's laboratory; the result being as a matter of fact that under these circumstances the spectrum had a colourless grey appearance. Its brightest place was where pure green or somewhat yellowish green is seen in a bright spectrum. There was nothing visible at all at the places where it would otherwise be red; but towards the violet side the colourless spectrum extended to the end without being noticeably shortened.

The most striking way of showing the changes that take place in the spectrum is to project it on a screen in a dark room and then cut down the intensity by means of a pair of NICOL prisms interposed in the path of the light. If the intensity is not very great to begin with, an episcotister[2] transmitting not more than one three-hundredth of the total amount of light, may be used to produce the necessary dimness. Of course, in order to see the spectrum without any colour in it and yet not too faint, the spectators should previously stay quite a while in the dark or at least in a dim room. In Figs. 1 and 2, Plate II,* the writer has endeavoured to exhibit the appearance of the spectrum in twilight vision as contrasted with the coloured spectrum of higher intensity.

The characteristics of twilight vision, as described here, enable us also to explain (as was done first by LUMMER[3]) an interesting phenomenon which was noted by H. FR. WEBER.[4] He observed that when a body is heated to incandescence in the dark, usually it does not look *red hot* at first, but grey, "dull cloudy grey." This *grey glow* appears at temperatures around 400°C. With rise of temperature there is the appearance of a yellowish-grey radiation, the yellow-green rays being particularly prominent under spectroscopic examination. According to DRAPER[5] it is not until a temperature of 525° is reached that the red glow appears. Although the radiation consists mainly of waves of the lengths of red light, its intensity at 400° is not high enough to stim-

[1] F.HILLEBRAND, Über die spezifische Helligkeit der Farben. *Sitz.-Ber. Wien. Akad.* XCVIII, Abt. 3. 1889. S. 70.

[2] ¶An instrument with rotating sectors for measuring changes in the intensity of the transmitted light, devised by AUBERT. See footnote in Vol. III, towards end of §32. (J. P. C. S.)

[3] O. LUMMER, Grauglut und Rotglut. *Verh. d. D. Physik. Ges.* XVI. 121. 1897; WIEDEM. *Ann.* LXII. 14. 1897.

[4] H. FR. WEBER, Die Entwicklung der Lichtemission glühender fester Körper. *Sitz.-Ber. Akad.* Berlin 1887. 9. June. WIEDEM. *Ann.* XXXII. 256. 1887

[5] *Amer. Journ. of Sc.* (2) IV. 1847; *Phil. Mag.* (3) XXX. 1847; *Scient. Memoirs* p. 33. London 1878.

*Plate II faces page 352.

ulate the colour sensitive mechanism, and yet, owing to the presence of rays of shorter wave-lengths, is sufficient to stimulate the twilight mechanism, which therefore mediates colourless light sensation, as it always does when it operates alone. Thus, as the temperature rises from 400° to 525°, the red portion of the total radiation is not increased in anything like the same proportion. On the contrary, with rising temperature, it is the middle and short-wave radiation that increases. But in consequence of the dark adaptation, the sensitivity of the eye is far better adapted to the medium waves (from yellow to green) than to the long red waves. It hardly needs to be said that a light-adapted observer, entering a dark room, cannot perceive the grey glow, and the first thing of the kind that he can see will be the red glow. He notices it about at the same moment as an observer who has been thoroughly dark-adapted beforehand, and who has been able to see the grey long before.

Two observers, one fully dark-adapted, the other light-adapted, do not obtain the threshold for the red colour at exactly the same temperature of incandescence, the scotopic eye being a little superior to the photopic eye in this respect. The explanation is given by some experiments which the writer got Mr. Boswell[1] to make. The threshold for the appearance of colour on a portion of a surface was determined, first, when the surface was illuminated simply by the coloured light, and second, when it was illuminated at the same time by a certain amount of mixed light. The regular result was that admixture of a slight amount of white light lifts a coloured light over the threshold when it is by itself below the threshold of visibility; the light appearing then in its specific colour. However, admixture of any light of appreciable twilight value, green light, for example, acts in the same way as the addition of white light. Moreover, by this addition a red light, say, that is below the threshold can be lifted above it. The eye being dark-adapted, naturally the green light acts longest on the colour-blind twilight mechanism before it has any effect on the mechanism that is sensitive to colour; and hence the complementary relation between green and red is not manifested at all, but simply the colourless part of the sensation, which to a certain extent paves the way for the perception of the coloured light, that is, the red light in this case. Obviously, this enabling influence can be exerted only by light stimuli whose intensities are themselves not far above the limit of perceptibility of the scotopic eye.

4. The Purkinje Phenomenon

We have seen that in the state of pure twilight vision the retina is not sensitive at all to the long red waves above 670 and is just sensitive to the shorter red waves. Under such circumstances, therefore, objects that are deep red must look perfectly black. In dim twilight the cap of a German infantryman, which is blue with a red band, does not look different from that of a sanitary officer with its dark blue band.

[1] F. P. Boswell, Über den Einfluss des Sättigungsgrades auf die Schwellenwerte der Farben. *Zeitschrift f. Sinnesphysiologie.* XLI, 364. 1906.

This lack of sensitivity to red light in the twilight mechanism is noticeable, however, not only in the case of pure isolated twilight vision, where all colouration disappears, but to a certain extent also in the much more frequent and complicated case when the two mechanisms of twilight vision and daylight vision both operate at the same time. This condition is very pronounced early in the morning at break of day. As a result of the preceding long spell of darkness, the sensitivity of the twilight mechanism that is characteristic of dark adaptation remains enhanced. The dim light is not yet sufficient to overcome dark adaptation and produce light adaptation. On the other hand, however, the light may already be strong enough to stimulate the daylight mechanism and therewith to mediate the sensation of colour also. In most of the retina we must suppose the elements of twilight vision and daylight vision are so interlaced that in observing coloured areas of even moderate dimensions the functions of the two mechanisms are combined. We are accustomed to the function of the daylight mechanism; it is normal colour vision as it occurs in bright light. To that is now added twilight vision, with the peculiarities described above. The most remarkable one is the high stimulating action of the green and cyan-blue rays of medium wave-length, and the ineffectiveness of the red rays. In observing green and blue objects, the colourless or bluish sensation of twilight is associated with the specific colour sensations, and the colours are seen as if white or bluish white were actually mixed with them, and so they look both *brighter* and more *unsaturated* than when the bright colours with the same objective intensity of illumination are viewed by an eye that is not dark-adapted. The contrast between such objects and those which emit or reflect red light only is that, so far as the latter are concerned, there is no difference between the behaviour of the scotopic eye and that of the photopic eye. For the twilight mechanism these rays have no stimulating value, and so nothing is superadded to the effect produced on the daylight mechanism.

The most striking consequence of this special position of the long waves in the combination of daylight vision and twilight vision must be, therefore, that red objects, and even orange ones, appear to be *relatively* darker than blue and green ones. This is familiar to everybody and is known as the PURKINJE phenomenon. The appearance of colours in the morning twilight was described by him as follows[1]: "Blue is what I saw first. The shades of red that are usually brightest in daylight, namely, carmine, vermilion, and orange, are for a long time the darkest, and not to be compared to their ordinary brightness."

[1] PURKINJE, *Neue Beiträge zur Kenntnis des Sehens in subjektiver Hinsicht.* Berlin 1825, S. 109–110.

The reason why PURKINJE speaks here of blue as being the brightest was perhaps due to an accidental choice of the coloured objects, among which the green must have been particularly dark. Thus in case of a spectrum that is dim but not too dark to be void of colour to a dark-adapted eye, the brightest part is not the blue, but the green, which of course looks whitish in the faint light that is there. The blue, violet, and yellow are also whitish and very unsaturated, all the more so, the more completely the eye is dark-adapted. The red alone is very dark and remains a saturated colour, not whitish. For a certain particular (quite weak) intensity of illumination of the spectrum and with a very thorough dark adaptation, almost the whole spectrum can be made to look as if tinged with bright blue, bordered only on one side by deep red.

It is especially instructive to make these observations with only one eye dark-adapted. After staying in a fairly bright room with one eye tightly blindfolded, the observer enters the dark room where the faint spectrum is projected and looks at it first with the photopic eye and then with the scotopic eye. In the latter case it appears as described above, but of course for the photopic eye it lacks the brilliancy and falling off in saturation in the portions corresponding to the medium and short wave-lengths, and the entire spectrum looks very dark but saturated everywhere; the brightest place being in the yellow, although under such conditions it looks more brown.

Perfectly analogous observations may be made also with sets of coloured papers, bundles of wool, etc., but in such cases, owing to the lower saturation of the pigment colours, the characteristic difference in the individual colours is not so distinct.

As is evident from what has been said, two factors are necessary for the production of the PURKINJE phenomenon, namely, dark adaptation and low intensity of the stimulating light. HERING[1] emphasized the importance of the state of adaptation, while HELMHOLTZ and A. KÖNIG[2] paid more attention to the intensity-ratios. The two agencies must act together; and hence it is going too far to say, as HERING does (*loc. cit.*, page 542), that KÖNIG has written about the PURKINJE phenomenon "without being aware of the main characteristic of it." The point that needs rather to be emphasized is that during most of the day there exists already a state of adaptation in which the PURKINJE phenomenon takes place, certainly always indoors. Under these conditions all that is necessary to produce it is

---

[1] E. HERING, Über das sogenannte PURKINJEsche Phänomen. PFLÜGERS *Arch. f. d. ges. Physiol.* **60**, 519.

[2] A. KÖNIG, Über den Helligkeitswert der Spektralfarben bei verschiedener absoluter Intensität. *Gesammelte Abhandlungen zur physiol. Optik.* Leipzig 1903, No. 20, S. 144.

to change the intensity. Special measures are needed, as stated on page 318, to throw out the twilight mechanism for a time, and then it succeeds only for a brief space. By staying quite a long while in a room with ordinary moderate illumination and then suddenly lowering the illumination considerably, all the conditions are present for obtaining the desired effect. If two large pieces of red and blue (or green) paper have been previously selected, so that in full daylight the red looks a little brighter, in the reduced light of the dark room the red piece appears darker at once. Of course, the change of luminosity is much increased by longer dark adaptation, but in the condition of the eye, which may be described as the usual one, the PURKINJE phenomenon can be induced by simply changing the intensity of the light.

A particularly clear demonstration of the phenomenon can be made by projecting sufficiently large patches of red and blue light on a white wall; with some device (like an iris diaphragm, pair of NICOL prisms, or a rotating sector) interposed in the path of the light for reducing the illumination. The two coloured fields can then be shown in strong and weak illumination in rapid alternation; and every time they are darkened, the luminosity of the red falls off relatively much more than that of the blue. In this experiment also the effect is better when the observer has spent some time in the dark or in a dim room, because then the difference in the appearance of the pair of colours in strong and weak light will be more striking. But even with the state of adaptation produced in a moderately bright room, the phenomenon is quite distinct.

In discussing the matters alluded to here, E. HERING[1] makes a distinction between two kinds of adaptations, which he calls *Daueradaptation* (or "time adaptation") produced by long continued exclusion of light, and *Momentanadaptation* (or "instantaneous adaptation"), which occurs the instant darkness begins. These terms are used also by HERING's pupil, TSCHERMAK. But there is no exact definition of what is meant by "instantaneous adaptation," and consequently it is hard to say exactly what those writers have in mind when they speak of a process taking place at the instant darkness occurs. It is a known fact that the sudden darkening of the entire visual field has an appreciable effect on the appearance of a small bright object, because it modifies the light sensation both qualitatively and quantitatively. But there is a sharp distinction between these effects and those of "time adaptation." If, prior to the beginning of "instantaneous adaptation," the eye is *thoroughly light-adapted*, the PURKINJE phenomenon never occurs. The latter effect is associated rather with the existence of some moderate degree at least of "time-adaptation", such as occurs naturally in "indoor adaptation." *Any matches of luminosity or colour as made by the eye in the state of maximum light adaptation are never invalidated by what* HERING *calls*

[1] E. HERING, Über das sog. PURKINJEsche Phänomen. PFLÜGERS *Arch. f. d. ges. Physiol.* LX. 1895.

"instantaneous adaptation," that is, by a sudden proportional dimming of both halves of the match or the total field. In the very nature of what we mean here by dark adaptation, and what HERING calls "time adaptation," the most important factor is the functioning of a new stimulus receptor, working according to different laws from that of the daylight mechanism. We shall find a series of other differences in the way these two mechanisms operate besides those that have already been mentioned. But it must be pointed out here with special emphasis that the process of dark adaptation in the sense intended here is not equivalent to the idea of the simple increase of sensitivity of the retina in darkness; that is, to a purely quantitative change of sensitivity; but that a very fundamental quantitative variation of the retinal function, most plainly indicated by the occurrence of the PURKINJE phenomenon, is an integral permanent part of the concept of "dark adaptation." The term "adaptation of the retina" was used first by AUBERT. Doubtless, he was not then aware of the close connection between the quantitative and the qualitative variations of the sensitivity of the retina in darkness. But the parts of the process of adaptation which he studied are just those that are inseparable from the characteristic conditions of PURKINJE's phenomenon. It is justifiable, therefore, to apply the term "dark adaptation" to the whole complicated process.

What HERING may have meant by "instantaneous adaptation" is not related to those matters at all, or very distantly anyhow; so that the use of this expression results simply in confusion. If the PURKINJE phenomenon is observed immediately by an eye when it is suddenly darkened after having been in a state of medium adaptation (or indoor adaptation, as we called it above), then (to stress this point again) this is the direct consequence of the darkening and the direct consequence of the fact that a *moderate time adaptation* had already occurred previously, but it does not indicate that the instantaneous darkening has induced a process in the eye that is essentially like that caused by long continued darkness.

5. Absence of the Purkinje Phenomenon in the Fovea Centralis

In a central region of the retina corresponding to a visual angle of about 1° 30' the PURKINJE phenomenon cannot be elicited by any means whatever.[1] This area, as will be seen presently, corresponds pretty nearly to the fovea in the most central part of the retina where there are no rods at all. The anatomy of the fovea is extremely hard to determine. It is easy to see why this is the case in the light of what G. FRITSCH[2] tells us concerning the extraordinary diversity in the morphological formation of the centre of the retina. However, what seems to be universal in all normal eyes is a central region where the visual epithelium is composed of nothing but cones, without any rods in between them. In line with this definite anatomical result there is the physiological fact, that there is a central place where the PURKINJE phenomenon cannot occur, and which, if it is capable of adaptation at all, certainly does not show any of the characteristics of it that have

---

[1] ¶See L. T. TROLAND, Apparent brightness; its conditions and properties. *Trans. Illum. Engineer. Soc.* IX. 1916, 947–966. (H. L.)

[2] G. FRITSCH, *Über Bau und Bedeutung der Avea centralis des Menschen.* Berlin 1908.

been described above.[1] Thus what is intended here in speaking of the fovea is always the region that is devoid of rods.[2]

It is extremely easy to verify the absence of the PURKINJE phenomenon in this region. Perhaps the most striking way of doing this is by the method employed first by O. LUMMER.[3] Two large pieces of coloured paper or cloth, from a half to three quarters of a square metre in size, one red and the other blue or green, are attached to the wall of the dark room, touching each other along a straight line. The colours are so selected that by bright gaslight or Argand burner the red looks to the normal eye distinctly brighter than the blue. The observer, supposed to be sufficiently dark-adapted, stands about five or six metres away and looks at the coloured areas. If the illumination is considerably lowered, the PURKINJE phenomenon appears immediately most distinctly, the red becoming deep black red and the blue bright bluish white. With further decrease of illumination still, the colour of the red surface entirely disappears and looks then dark grey or even black. But for the purpose of the present experiment the illumination should be lowered just far enough for the red still to show colour distinctly. The coloured field is then covered by a black curtain leaving just a small circular area exposed, half of it being red and the other half blue. This exposed area should subtend an angle of about one degree from where the observer stands. *As long as the observer continues to look straight at this little spot, even with the dim illumination, the red sems to him to be brighter than the blue; in other words, the* PURKINJE *phenomenon is absent.* But if he looks ever so little away from this spot, the blue comes out with a whitish glow distinctly bright. As soon as the curtain is raised again, immediately the marked difference of brightness in the large field is seen. This alternation can be repeated as often as desired.

The only precaution to be taken is not to lower the illumination until the red disappears. The small red field readily attracts the attention and so insures the formation of the image in the fovea. Otherwise, an inexperienced observer might very easily let his eye wander and thus obtain a "parafoveal" image on parts of the retina where there are rods. Dichromats and anomalous trichromats are more apt to fail with this experiment than those with normal colour vision, because the dim red is not such a striking colour to them and does not hold their attention. Of course, the experiment can also be carried out in another way by using a lantern and glass filters to project

[1] ¶See S. HECHT, *loc. cit.* (H. L.)

[2] ¶W. DE W. ABNEY and W. WATSON, *loc. cit.* (H. L.)

[3] O. LUMMER, Experimentelles über das Sehen im Dunkeln und Hellen. *Verhandl. d. Deutschen physik. Gesellschaft.* VI. No. 2, 1904.

a coloured field on a white wall. A pair of NICOL prisms is employed
for reducing the illumination, and the field is contracted by the insertion of a diaphragm. A similar effect can be obtained very well also
by using the spectrophotometer and pure homogeneous colours;
provided the instrument will give a field of at least 4° in extent (from
10° to 12° is better) which can be conveniently stopped down.

These methods are somewhat unsatisfactory because the two halves
of the field are illuminated by light that cannot be compared *exactly*
as to brightness on account of the difference of colour. The red has
to be such that with brilliant illumination it is undoubtedly brighter
than the blue, and, on the other hand, the dark adaptation must be
sufficient.

The experiment can be performed in a much more conclusive way
on a dichromat, especially if he is what is called green-blind. For with
a subject of this sort it is possible to find two kinds of light that match
perfectly as to colour and yet show a very considerable difference in
their twilight values. Red of wave-length $670\mu\mu$ or longer and green
of wave-length $545\mu\mu$ are two such radiations. In HELMHOLTZ's
spectrophotometer these colours can be thrown on a 7° field, and can
be made to match perfectly by the colour-blind eye thoroughly light-
adapted. Now if dark adaptation is produced (or has been produced
already by bandaging one eye), and the intensity of both halves of the
field at the same time is considerably lowered (say, to one fortieth), the
match is gone completely, the green showing up bright and whitish.
If now the visual field is gradually contracted by means of an iris
diaphragm, the difference between its two halves is very slight even
at a diameter of 3° and disappears entirely at about 1° 30′. The eye
may have been dark-adapted for any length of time, and any total
intensity of the field may be chosen; but the colour match remains good
under all circumstances, provided the eye looks steadily at the centre
of the field. If the line of fixation deviates as much as one or two
degrees, it is enough to make the whitish glow appear again in the
green.

Very similar tests can be made by making a match between blue-
green, about $500\mu\mu$ and a purple mixture (say, $650+460\mu\mu$). The
homogeneous (blue-green) side of this match has the greater twilight
value, and therefore on a large field looks brighter and whiter to the
scotopic eye. The twilight value of the homogeneous light is about
25 times that of the mixed light. In the previous red-green match the
ratio between the twilight values (on the supposition that there are no
red waves shorter than $670\mu\mu$) is at least 1000:1.

It is not possible for observers with normal colour vision to make
true colour matches when the difference of twilight values of the two

halves of the field is even nearly so much as the above. The very highest ratio is 6:1. This is the case with matches between different spectral white mixtures, one half of which is white obtained by mixing red and blue-green, the other being a mixture of yellow and indigo. It was by using such white mixtures that it was first ascertained that the matches did not last when the intensity of illumination was varied. This result was obtained independently and almost at the same time by CHRISTINE LADD-FRANKLIN[1] and H. EBBINGHAUS.[2] Their tests were made with colour-blind persons. A. TSCHERMAK[3] extended these experiments by testing persons with normal colour vision; and according to him colour matches of this kind were not valid for the foveal region of the retina, supposing dark adaptation had been sufficiently long continued. But under the given condition v. KRIES and the writer[4] were not able to find a single instance where a match that had been made at high intensities was not valid in the fovea of the scotopic eye.

KOSTER[5] and SHERMAN[6] have likewise maintained the existence of the PURKINJE phenomenon in the fovea, but there are considerable possibilities of error in the methods they used. The question as to whether there are any traces of the phenomenon in the fovea and what would be the significance of it, will be considered later. It will be sufficient to say here that in the writer's opinion it has not been proved that the PURKINJE phenomenon occurs in the part of the retina where there are no rods.

The size of the central area of the retina where the PURKINJE *phenomenon does not occur* can be determined with some degree of accuracy by making as perfect a spectral match as can be between two halves of the field whose twilight values are as far apart as possible, first, with a light-adapted eye, and then with the eye dark-adapted. If the field is greater than 2°, the dark-adapted eye detects immediately the inadequacy of the match. By means of an iris diaphragm the size of the field is now quickly diminished (to between 1° and 2°) until the two halves again match. A measurement of this sort cannot be

[1] C. LADD-FRANKLIN, On theories of light sensation. *Mind.* (N. S.) II. No. 8, 473–490, 1893.

[2] H. EBBINGHAUS, Theorie des Farbensehens. *Zeitschr. f. Psychol. u. Physiol. der Sinnesorgane* V. 145–238, 1893.

[3] A. TSCHERMAK, Über die Bedeutung der Lichtstärke und des Zustandes des Sehorgans für farblose optische Gleichungen. PFLÜGERS *Arch. f. d. ges. Physiologie.* LXX, 297–328, 1898.

[4] J. v. KRIES and W. NAGEL, *Zeitschr. für Psychol. und Physiol. der Sinnesorgane.* XXIII. S. 162.

[5] W. KOSTER, Untersuchungen zur Lehre vom Farbensinn. GRÄFES *Arch. f. Ophth.* XIV. 1895 and *Arch. d'opht.* XV. 1895.

[6] F. D. SHERMAN, Über das PURKINJEsche Phänomen im Zentrum der Netzhaut. WUNDTS *philosoph. Studien* XIII. 1898.

made very accurately, because naturally the effect of the slightest movements of the eye, involving displacements of the image on the central region of the retina, will be to make the size of the field seem to be too small.

Very much more accurate results were obtained by v. Kries and the writer[1] by a method for the details of which the original publication must be consulted. In the case of the writer's right eye (after being dark-adapted by bandaging it tightly for many hours) the Purkinje phenomenon was found to be absent in a region of the retina whose horizontal extent was 107'. In the left eye it was 88'. In the right eye the vertical extent was 81'. In the writer's case the point used for fixation is not in the centre of this region, but a little to one side. In the right eye the region in question extends from the point of fixation more to the temporal side, and in the left eye more to the nasal side; that is, it is not symmetrical in the two eyes. The longer the dark adaptation, the sharper was the line of demarcation between the central region where the Purkinje phenomenon did not occur and the surrounding retina where it was manifested.

6. The so-called Colourless Interval

In recent literature on the visual sensations there is a lot of discussion of "the colourless interval."[2] It comprises a certain range of low degrees of intensity within which the stimulating light is visible, but the quality of the sensation is too indefinite for any colouration to be perceived. The actual existence of such an interval is implied in what has been already stated, at least for the state of dark adaptation and more extensive areas of the retina. Indeed the possibility of seeing a dimly illuminated spectrum without colour when the eye is dark-adapted depends on it. Another way of expressing this fact is by saying that coloured lights whose intensity is increased from zero intensity cross first the "absolute" (Butz[3]) or "general" (v. Kries[4]) threshold, but need to be at higher intensity before crossing the "specific" threshold where they are discerned as coloured.

The question as to whether *all* lights that appear coloured at high intensity exhibit a colourless interval, has been variously answered.

---

[1] J. v. Kries and W. Nagel, Weitere Mitteilungen über die funktionelle Sonderstellung des Netzhautzentrums. *Zeitschr. f. Psychol. und Physiol. der Sinnesorgane* XXIII. 167–186.

[2] ¶See W. de W. Abney, *Researches in colour vision* (1913); and Abney and Watson, *loc. cit.* (H. L.)

See also H. D. Parsons, *loc. cit.* p. 60. (J. P. C. S.)

[3] Untersuchungen über die physiologischen Funktionen der Peripherie der Netzhaut. *Dissertation*, Dorpat 1883.

[4] Nagels *Handbuch der Physiologie des Menschen.* Bd. III. S. 19. 1905.

PARINAUD states that red is seen as red as soon as it rises above the threshold; and also KÖNIG and v. KRIES are inclined to think that the general and specific thresholds for homogeneous red are identical. But CHARPENTIER, KOSTER, HERING, and TSCHERMAK maintain the existence of a colourless interval for red light also. This difference of opinion is easily accounted.for by taking into consideration the distribution of the twilight values in the spectrum, as given above (p. 352). Beginning at the border between red and orange, say, from wave-length $650\mu\mu$ on downwards, homogeneous kinds of light have measurable twilight values, which means, in other words, that they must show a colourless interval. But for wave-length 670 the twilight value is already almost too small to be measured, and the almost imperceptible real effect on the twilight mechanism of the eye would perhaps disappear entirely if filters were used to exclude from the field every vestige of light of wave-length shorter than $670\mu\mu$. Even in the most accurate measurements hitherto this has not been done, owing to the technical difficulties. The twilight value of light of greater wave-length still, say between 680 and 700, definitely vanishes, and hence there cannot be a colourless interval for these radiations. Now red light of long wave-length by itself is never obtained with pigments, and it is only by special precautions that it can be obtained with light filters. Owing to this circumstance, an observer can easily be made to believe that there is a colourless interval for red light also. But from what has been said this is true only for the shortest red waves on the border of orange, and even here there is just a faint trace of this effect.

Opinion is also divided as to whether the colourless interval can be observed in the centre of the retina where there are no rods. Here again CHARPENTIER, KOSTER, and TSCHERMAK are among those who believe this to be the case; while PARINAUD, KÖNIG, and v. KRIES state that spectral lights are coloured as soon as they rise above threshold value (with the possible exception of greenish yellow of $580\mu\mu$, according to KÖNIG). The writer himself is a dichromat, and of course in his case there is no chance of observing a colourless interval except with the brilliant hues of red, orange, blue and violet. With fields of appropriate size for being imaged in the region of the fovea centralis (that is, with visual angle of about one degree), lights of this kind above the threshold always look coloured to dichromats. The writer finds the same thing with persons who are not colour-blind, although in their case there is also no colourless interval for green. He has not made any tests with yellow light.

In observations of this nature the same difficulties are encountered as in deciding whether or not the PURKINJE phenomenon occurs in the fovea. The trouble lies in the foveal fixation of the coloured field. Without having a point of fixation to rivet the observer's attention, there is much risk of his first seeing the image of the coloured field as formed on the parts of the retina outside the fovea coming over the threshold, and of course the image then will be colourless (unless the light happens to be red of short wave-length).

From the theoretical standpoint it is of slight interest whether, under any conditions at all, some indication of a colourless interval likewise in the foveal part of the retina could be shown for homogeneous spectral lights. What is more important and more certain is the fact that it can simply be a question of some vestiges of such an effect, not to be compared with the pronounced phenomenon that is observed in the dark-adapted peripheral retina.

For larger areas of the retina that have been completely light-adapted, the colours or at any rate red, orange, green, blue and violet appear immediately at the specific threshold. It is easy to verify this, because in this case there is no necessity of local fixation. Of course, such fields cannot be observed with the entire retina, because it is practically impossible to bring the whole retina to a state of complete light adaptation.

Suppose a person, after having been thoroughly light-adapted, enters a dark room where there is a blue or orange coloured surface of suitable size subtending an angle of from 10° to 20°. If the illumination is steadily increased from sub-liminal to super-liminal values, the deeply saturated colour will come out from the blackness. This observation can be repeated several times during the first minutes of darkness. But then a change occurs quite suddenly. The threshold is lowered and at the same time the colour becomes less saturated; and after a quarter of an hour the sensation produced by sub-liminal stimuli is no longer that of the specific colour but that of the vague almost colourless super-liminal hue. There are also other changes. During the first few minutes if the coloured surface is visible at all, it is sharply outlined; and if, for example, it is a square, it is immediately recognized as being such. In the later stage of the adaptation the borders of the surface that is illuminated just above the threshold are vague and confused, and the longer the dark adaptation continues the more hazy the outline becomes. *During the first minutes after light adaptation vision takes place by means of the daylight mechanism, enabling us to discriminate colour and to have keen perception of form, but requiring comparatively strong light stimuli; but during the later stages, it takes place by means of the colour-blind twilight mechanism in which recognition of form is vague, but which is extremely sensitive to light. It is only when the sensitivity of the twilight mechanism has been so increased during the process of adaptation that it exceeds that of the daylight mechanism for the light used in the test, that the conditions are produced for the appearance of the colourless interval.*

In this connection, it should be recalled that the "grey glow" of incandescent bodies cannot be seen unless the eye is dark-adapted. For the photopic eye the glow is red to begin with. Anyhow the grey glow is never seen in the centre of the retina.

7. Capacity of the Retina for Space and Time Discriminations, in Daylight Vision and Twilight Vision

In ordinary daylight vision the ability to make space discriminations, or what is usually meant by the "visual acuity", is greatest in the fovea by far. Even a few degrees to one side of the point of fixation it is quite a good deal less (see page 34). The approximate form of a curve constructed according to DOR'S measurements[1] is shown in Fig. 69,

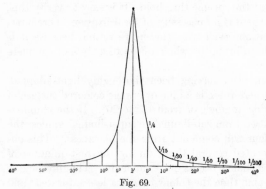

Fig. 69.
Local variation of the visual acuity of the retina (according to DOR).

where the ordinates indicate the visual acuity and the abscissae denote the distances in degrees from the point of fixation designated by *F*. According to BURCHARDT[2], the visual acuity at places from 15′ to 20′ away from the point of fixation was equal to the maximum value, but at a distance of 30′ it was only 80 or 50 percent. of the maximum.

With the enormous superiority of the fovea in the matter of visual acuity, it goes without saying that the visual acuity in pure twilight vision, where the fovea is excluded as a result of "physiological hemeralopia", will under all circumstances remain far below the maximum acuity of daylight vision. Indeed, strictly speaking, visual acuity in bright daylight cannot be compared with that in twilight vision, because it is dependent on the luminosity of the test chart; in other words, the visual acuity diminishes within certain limits as the

[1] *Archiv. f. Ophthalm.* XIX. 3. S. 321. 1873.

[2] BURCHARDT, *Internationale Probe zur Bestimmung der Sehschärfe.* Berlin 1893.

luminosity decreases. And even when the eye is thoroughly dark-adapted, the subjective brightness can never be so great as it is in daylight vision in bright light, without its rising above the threshold of foveal sensitivity and therewith crossing the border between twilight vision and daylight vision. However, a comparison may be made between the visual acuity of a scotopic eye and that of a photopic eye by making observations on the two eyes, either when the objective intensity of illumination is the same for both eyes in different states of adaptation, or when the subjective brightness is the same. In the latter case the objective illumination of the test chart must be much smaller for the scotopic than for the photopic eye. Experiments of this kind were made by BLOOM and GARTEN.[1] When the illumination is very low, their results are that the visual acuity of the dark-adapted periphery is somewhat higher than that of the photopic eye for the same illumination; but that when the illumination is slightly increased, the visual acuity of the photopic eye is the superior of the two. For approximately the same subjective brightness, these authors found the visual acuity of the scotopic eye was invariably less than that of the photopic eye; but v. KRIES[2] found it to be the same in the periphery for both conditions of adaptation. The essential point is that, whatever the differences may be, they are anyhow insignificant as compared with the differences between the absolute maxima of visual acuity of the photopic eye and the scotopic eye.

The quantitative connection between visual acuity and the intensity of illumination is shown by the measurements made by A. KÖNIG.[3] The test-objects used in these experiments were SNELLEN'S hook-shaped characters, painted black on a white background. The state of adaptation always corresponded to the intensity; that is, the more complete the dark adaptation was, the weaker was the illumination. The results are shown in Table XIII. The figures in the first column give the intensity of illumination B, the unit being the intensity of a HEFNER lamp one metre away. The third column gives the values of the visual acuity S expressed in terms of the ordinary SNELLEN unit. It is evident from the table that a curve plotted by taking the intensities B as abscissae and visual acuities S as ordinates would not enable us to get a very good idea of the connection between these magnitudes,

[1] S. BLOOM and S. GARTEN, Vergleichende Untersuchungen der Sehschärfe des hell- und dunkeladaptierten Auges. PFLÜGERS *Arch. f. d. ges. Physiol.* LXXII. 372, 1898.

[2] J. v. KRIES, Über die Abhängigkeit centraler und peripherer Sehschärfe von der Lichtstärke. *Zentralbl. f. Physiol.* VIII. 694, 1895. See also: BUTTMANN, Untersuchungen über Sehschärfe. *Diss.* Freiburg i. B. 1906.

[3] A. KÖNIG, Die Abhängigkeit der Sehschärfe von der Beleuchtungsintensität. *Sitz. Ber. Akad. Wissensch. Berlin.* 13. May 1897. S. 559–575; and *Gesammelte Abhandlungen* S. 378.

Table XIII (results of A. KÖNIG)

B	$\log B$	S	B	$\log B$	S
0.00036	0.56—4	0.031	1.03	0.01	0.692
0.00037	0.57—4	0.046	1.16	0.06	0.564
0.00037	0.57—4	0.038	1.19	0.08	0.596
0.00038	0.57—4	0.038	1.38	0.14	0.615
0.00063	0.58—4	0.046	1.38	0.14	0.577
0.00087	0.80—4	0.055	1.76	0.24	0.692
0.0013	0.94—4	0.055	2.14	0.33	0.744
0.0022	0.11—3	0.077	2.20	0.34	0.795
0.0023	0.35—3	0.062	2.20	0.34	0.795
0.0034	0.36—3	0.092	2.28	0.36	0.923
0.0034	0.53—3	0.062	2.37	0.37	0.744
0.0043	0.53—3	0.062	2.97	0.47	0.667
0.0048	0.63—3	0.077	3.95	0.60	0.769
0.0080	0.68—3	0.088	4.64	0.67	0.654
0.0086	0.90—3	0.088	6.06	0.78	0.846
0.0091	0.93—3	0.096	6.81	0.83	1.115
0.0096	0.96—3	0.092	6.81	0.83	1.038
0.010	0.98—3	0.096	9.97	1.00	1.115
0.012	0.00—2	0.092	12.88	1.11	0.866
0.013	0.08—2	0.088	13.6	1.13	1.000
0.032	0.12—2	0.123	13.6	1.13	0.982
0.035	0.51—2	0.123	13.6	1.13	0.963
0.035	0.54—2	0.123	13.6	1.13	0.872
0.037	0.54—2	0.132	14.1	1.15	1.192
0.051	0.56—2	0.154	15.7	1.19	1.054
0.068	0.71—2	0.154	16.0	1.20	1.192
0.069	0.83—2	0.176	20.6	1.31	1.100
0.11	0.84—2	0.185	26.1	1.42	1.093
0.12	0.04—1	0.242	26.7	1.43	1.154
0.13	0.09—1	0.205	28.3	1.45	1.262
0.15	0.13—1	0.231	47.5	1.68	1.308
0.15	0.16—1	0.205	51.2	1.71	1.430
0.15	0.16—1	0.231	54.5	1.74	1.169
0.16	0.18—1	0.200	80.0	1.90	1.313
0.18	0.19—1	0.246	94.5	1.98	1.458
0.20	0.27—1	0.231	119.—	2.08	1.540
0.22	0.30—1	0.308	123.—	2.09	1.437
0.22	0.33—1	0.262	123.—	2.09	1.283
0.22	0.34—1	0.308	168.—	2.23	1.471
9.22	0.34—1	0.277	264.—	2.42	1.568
0.24	0.38—1	0.269	264.—	2.42	1.556
0.28	0.45—1	0.286	316.—	2.50	1.600
0.29	0.46—1	0.308	494.—	2.69	1.667
0.34	0.53—1	0.346	645.—	2.81	1.683
0.35	0.55—1	0.320	794.—	2.90	1.723
0.36	0.56—1	0.338	824.—	2.92	1.662
0.36	0.56—1	0.359	878.—	2.94	1.700
0.41	0.61—1	0.461	1042.—	3.02	1.744
0.41	0.61—1	0.374	1082.—	3.03	1.631
0.44	0.64—1	0.410	1261.—	3.10	1.643
0.44	0.64—1	0.400	1975.—	3.30	1.667
0.50	0.70—1	0.462	2346.—	3.37	1.703
0.52	0.71—1	0.462	2500.—	3.40	1.708
0.67	0.83—1	0.423	3511.—	3.55	1.700
0.67	0.83—1	0.523	7413.—	3.87	1.651
0.88	0.94—1	0.558	7413.—	3.87	1.708
0.91	0.96—1	0.615	7900.—	3.90	1.683
0.95	0.98—1	0.538	14040.—	4.15	1.708
0.99	0.99—1	0.500	31590.—	4.50	1.733
1.00	0.00	0.596	64480.—	4.81	1.750
1.03	0.01	0.558			

because if the high values of B are to be indicated clearly, the smaller values would all be crowded very close together. And so KÖNIG employed the convenient method of plotting the logarithms of the intensity as abscissae, which shows the connection between the intensity of illumination and the visual acuity in an extremely simple fashion.

The curve (Fig. 70) is composed of two tolerably straight portions which meet each other at an obtuse angle. The break in the curve occurs at an intensity of 0.1 metre-candle. Thus, as the luminosity increases, visual acuity increases at first in proportion to the logarithm of the luminosity, and then for a short interval the relation is more complicated; but soon after the increase becomes again proportional to the luminosity, but the ratio between the two is now much larger, as shown by the steep portion of the curve. In the equation $S = a\log B$ the factor a is about 10 times as large for the steeper gradient of the curve.

A white surface illuminated by one-tenth of a metre-candle is not far from the threshold of daylight vision. Thus the portion of the curve that lies to the left of the abscissa 0.1 corresponds about to the range of twilight vision. On the other hand, it was stated

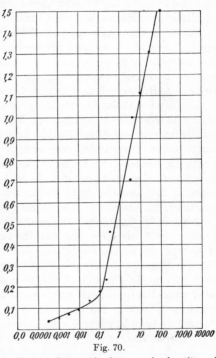

Fig. 70.

Functional connection between visual acuity and the logarithm of the intensity of illumination.

above (page 318) that a white surface illuminated by one metre-candle or more was above the threshold of an eye that has been light-adapted by bright light. This part of the curve therefore lies definitely within the region of daylight vision. As to the intervening segment comprised between intensities of one-tenth and one metre-candle, it may be considered as representing the case of daylight vision that has not been dulled by very high intensities of light. PERTZ[1] found the threshold of

[1] In the article by v. KRIES "über die absolute empfindlichkeit usw." *Zeitschr. f. Psychol. u Physiol. der Sinnesorgane* XV. 1897.

foveal vision to be the luminosity of a magnesium oxide surface illuminated by 0.033 metre-candle. At this intensity the curve, as shown in Fig. 70, begins to bend into the steeper branch, and here for the first time the daylight mechanism is appreciably involved, until when the intensity gets to be about ten times as great, it is the sole factor in the power of the retina to make space-discriminations. Thus it may be said that at the border between twilight vision and daylight vision there is some sudden change in the relations between intensity of illuminations and visual acuity, the daylight mechanism being dependent on the intensity of illumination in a much greater proportion.

Likewise there are marked differences between the photopic mechanism and the scotopic mechanism with respect to *the duration and course of the process of stimulation*. It is true we are not yet in a position to describe exhaustively the course of the stimulation in the two cases. However, it may be stated that the sensational response to a short-lived stimulus is more sluggish with the scotopic mechanism than with the photopic mechanism. This is shown most distinctly by rapidly intermittent stimulation; for example, by interposing a rotating sectored disc between the source of light and the eye, or simpler still, a rotating disc with alternating black and white sectors. As the speed of rotation, slow to begin with, is gradually increased, the sectors, which at first can clearly be distinguished, become more and more indistinct, the alternation from bright to dark being perceived merely as so-called "flicker", until finally at a certain speed the disc appears a uniformly steady grey. Knowing the angular speed and the number of sectors, the number of interruptions can be calculated at which flicker just ceases. It is true it is not altogether easy to determine this limit, because the direction of fixation must be kept constant, and the observation has to be made with a visual angle that it is not too large, say, from 3° to 5°. For the latter purpose, the greater part of the rotating disc can be covered with an opaque surface with an aperture of the correct size.[1]

---

[1] ¶For recent accounts of flicker the following may be consulted:

H. BENDER, Untersuchungen am LUMMER-PRINGSHEIMschen Spectralflickerphotometer. *Ann. d. Physik.* XLV. 1914. 105–132.—W. W. COBLENTZ and W. B. EMERSON, The relative sensibility of the average eye to light of different colors, and some practical applications to radiation problems. *Bull. Bur. Stand.* Sci. paper No. 303. 1917. 167–236.— E. C. CRITTENDEN and F. K. RICHTMYER, An average eye for heterochromatic photometry and a comparison of a flicker and equality of brightness photometer. *Bull. Bur. Stand.* XIV. 1918. 87–114. — U. EBBECKE, Über das Augenblicksehen II. Über das Sehen im Flimmerlicht. PFLÜGERS *Arch.*, 1920. CLXXXV. 181–195.— Idem, Über das Sehen im Flimmerlicht, PFLÜGERS *Arch* CLXXXV. 1921. 196–223. — C. E. FERREE and G. RAND, Flicker photometry. I. The theory of flicker photometry. II. Comparative studies of equality of brightness and flicker photometry with special reference to the lag of visual sensation. *Trans. Illum. Engin. Soc.* 1922. 50 pages. — H. E. IVES, Studies in the

HELMHOLTZ states (page 213) that with a disc of alternate black and white sectors of equal width illuminated by the strongest lamplight, the flicker ceases for him when the stimulus from a single sector lasts for one forty-eighth of a second; and under the illumination of the full moon, when the stimulus lasts one twentieth of a second.

This relation between the brightness of the light and the number of interruptions at which flicker is abolished is easily explained. The black portions of a colour-top of this sort cannot be considered as being absolutely black. Some light is reflected from them, although of course much less than that reflected from the white portions. When the illumination is diminished, the observer gets the impression of a stationary disc with greater diminution in the brightness of the white, which gradually changes to dark grey becoming more and more like the black. This colour acting on the eye alternately with the black fuses with it more easily, that is, for fewer alternations, than a pure white would do. The careful measurements made by SCHATERNIKOFF show that the *fusion frequency*, as v. KRIES calls the number of revolutions necessary to make flicker disappear, depends not only on the absolute objective intensity of the light, but also on the subjective brightness of the white as determined by the state of adaptation. As long as the conditions of twilight vision are completely or at least very approximately maintained, the fusion frequency increases with increasing dark adaptation, since the same effect for the brightness of the white is produced in this way as would be produced by objective increase in the intensity of the light.

SCHATERNIKOFF also compared the fusion frequency of the photopic eye with that of the scotopic eye, his method being similar to that used by BLOOM and GARTEN (*loc. cit.*) in their visual acuity tests; that is, by obtaining a brightness that was subjectively the same for the eye in both states of adaptation, the objective illumination being therefore very different for the two cases. Even under these conditions the photopic eye requires a greater frequency than the scotopic eye, and hence the decrease of the fusion frequency when the illumination is low cannot be attributed simply to the decrease of illumination of the

photometry of lights of different colors. *Phil. Mag.* 6th Ser., XXIV. 1912. 149–188; 744–751; 853–863. —H. E. IVES and E. F. KINGSBURY, The theory of the flicker photometer. *Phil. Mag.* 6th ser. XXVIII. ,1914. 708–728; XXXI. 1916. 290–322.—H. E. IVES, A polarization flicker photometer and some data of theoretical bearing obtained with it. *Phil. Mag.* 6th Ser. 1917. XXXIII. 360–380. — Idem, Hue difference and flicker photometer speed. *Phil. Mag.*, 6th Ser. XXXIV. 1917. 99–112. — Idem, Critical frequency relations in scotopic vision. *Jour. Optical Soc. Amer.*, VI. 1922, 254–268.—Idem, A theory of intermittent vision. *Jour. Optical Soc. Amer.* VI. 1922. 343–361. — E. THUERMEL, Das LUMMER-PRINGSHEIMsche Spectral-Flickerphotometer als optisches Pyrometer. *Ann. d. Physik*, XXXIII. 1910. 1139–1160. (H. L.)

white, but we must assume that the operation of the mechanism of vision depends on other factors besides. SCHATERNIKOFF found that the fusion frequencies of the photopic eye and the scotopic eye were in the ratio of 5 to 3. For as exact a match as possible, as to both brightness and colour, the writer has obtained bigger differences, with his eyes in the two states of adaptation. Discs like those described by HELMHOLTZ in connection with Fig. 42 are convenient for observations of this kind. Experimenting with this apparatus, with one eye thoroughly dark-adapted and the other light-adapted, the writer found that the speed of rotation could be so regulated that for the photopic eye there is no flicker at all in the outside ring, little in the middle, and distinct flicker in the central ring; whereas the entire disc was free from flicker so far as the scotopic eye was concerned. The brightness was the same under the two conditions.

Without paying special attention to the state of adaptation, PORTER[1] compared the fusion frequencies for a series of different intensities of illumination from the highest to the lowest, and obtained the remarkable result that the relation between the frequency and the intensity of illumination can be expressed by a curve composed of two approximately straight portions meeting each other at an angle, similar to the curve in Fig. 70 which represents KÖNIG's measurements of visual acuity. In each of the straight portions the fusion frequency increases in proportion to the logarithm of the intensity, the factor of proportionality, however, being different for the two branches.

The similarity between the two curves, as v. KRIES[2] has pointed out, becomes still more perfect when the intensity is noted at which the bend in the curve occurs. This intensity, at which there is suddenly a new relation between intensity of light and spatial and temporal power of discrimination, turns out to be in fact practically the same in both cases, being the illumination of a HEFNER lamp at a distance of one-tenth of a metre in KÖNIG's experiments and that of a standard candle at a distance of one-eighth of a metre in PORTER's experiments.[3]

Aside from the fusion of periodic luminous stimuli, the time relations in a single brief stimulation are likewise of interest in connection with the duplicity theory. These quite complicated phenomena are to be described hereafter. It will appear then that although it is not yet possible to give a complete explanation of them, still they present a number of characteristics indicating with much probability a difference

[1] *Proceedings of the Royal Society*, London, LXX. 313.

[2] J. v. KRIES, Über die Wahrnehmung des Flimmerns durch normale und durch total farbenblinde Personen. *Zeitschr. f. Psych. u. Physiol. d. Sinnesorg.* XXXII. 113; and *Abhandlungen zur Physiol. d. Gesichtsempfindungen.* Drittes Heft 1908.

[3] ¶See J. H. PARSONS, *loc. cit.*, p. 208. (J. P. C. S.)

of behaviour between the daylight mechanism and the twilight mechanism, and consequently are very easy to comprehend on the basis of the duplicity theory.

8. Total Colour Blindness Considered as being Twilight Vision Alone

At the time the first edition of this work appeared only two kinds of colour blindness were known, namely, red blindness and green blindness, as HELMHOLTZ distinguished them; both afterwards included by HOLMGREN under the name of "partial colour blindness". Each of these types was capable of making certain qualitative colour distinctions. More modern investigations of the vision of such persons will be described below. Here however something should be said about what is now known as *total colour blindness*, a much rarer type discovered about 1880, in which there are no qualitative differences in the appearance of different colours, and which has therefore been called *achromatopia* or achromatic vision. Persons who suffer from this anomaly distinguish merely unequal shades of brightness in objects of different colours, the quality of the light sensation always remaining the same.[1]

In the case of certain totally colour blind individuals, HERING and HILLEBRAND found that the distribution of luminosity in the spectrum was the same as for the thoroughly dark-adapted eye in the state of twilight vision. Further researches conducted by KÖNIG, v. KRIES and others showed that the vision of persons who see with this kind of luminosity distribution has a number of other common propensities also, and that this anomaly, being apparently always congenital, is characteristic of a well-defined class, and may be described therefore as "typical, congenital total colour blindness". At the same time it should be mentioned that there are also achromatopes with a totally different luminosity distribution in the spectrum. In these cases it is nearly always possible to trace the origin of the anomaly to some injury of the optic nerve; and, besides, the other peculiarities of congenital total colour blindness which will be described below are not manifested.

In achromatic vision the spectrum looks like a shaded surface without any differences of colour, a conception of which an achromatope has no notion (see the illustration on Plate II).[*] To him the greatest luminosity (the source being gaslight) is where the green is, between 530 and 540$\mu\mu$. Red light of longer wave-lengths than the line C is not visible to him at all, but towards the violet end the visible spectrum in his case extends about as far as it does for a normal eye.

---

[1] ¶That is, they see only shades of grey. (J. P. C. S.)

[*]Plate II faces page 352.

But whereas in the normal eye this peculiar distribution of luminosity does not occur unless the intensity of the entire spectrum remains below the threshold of colour vision, that is, does not occur except in pure twilight vision, almost the same distribution of luminosity persists for the totally colour-blind whether the illumination of the spectrum is low or high. If the intensity of illumination of a spectrum is gradually increased from the lowest degrees, the instant it begins to appear coloured to an observer with normal colour vision, the only change whatever that will be apparent to an observer who is totally colour-blind will be a mere increase of the total luminosity.

The exact agreement between the luminosities of colours for the achromatopes and a dark-adapted person with normal vision may readily be verified by making twilight matches with the colour-top and especially with the spectrophotometer also. By the same process as described on page 317 for finding the twilight values of the normal eye, these values may be obtained also for the totally colour-blind individual, and not merely when the intensity of illumination of the spectrum is low, but also when it is high. There is an upper limit due to the sensation of glare that is very annoying to colour-blind persons. Curves showing the relative stimulating value in the spectrum of a totally colour-blind person have been obtained by Kö̈nig[1], v. Kries[2]

Table XIV

Wave-length	Twilight Value for W. Nagel	Luminosity Value for for the totally colour-blind H.
628 $\mu\mu$	3.1	—
615	—	10.0
603	10.0	13.2
595	—	26.1
591	25.9	—
580	45.8	30.0
570	57.8	52.7
561	65.0	—
553	76.0	81.8
545	88.1	84.9
535	86.3	88.1
528	81.6	78.3
520	70.2	—
514	61.5	64.5
500	39.0	43.8
488	24.5	33.7
473	13.5	18.8
457	6.2	11.5
446	2.5	—

[1] *Zeitschr. für Psychologie und Physiol. der Sinnesorgane* IV, S. 241. 1892.
[2] Ibid., XIII. S. 293.

and the writer. The results of the investigation of a girl sixteen years old (Miss H.), as made by Dr. May[1] and the writer together, are exhibited in Table XIV and Fig. 71. The luminosity values for Miss H. and the twilight values in the case of the writer (which agree with those that are typically normal) are plotted here side by side. The colour-blind subject made the observations on the HELMHOLTZ spectro-photometer in the bright room with moderate intensities of the spectrum that were not dazzling for her. The writer's observations were

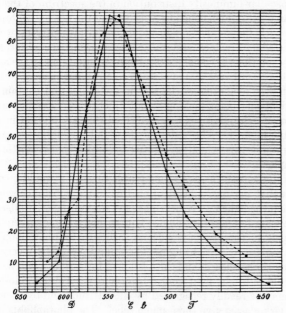

Fig. 71.—Distribution of luminosity for the totally colour-blind ------ and twilight values for a deuteranope———, in the prismatic spectrum of the NERNST light.

made in the dark room after being dark-adapted with eyes bandaged for an hour. The results are for the spectrum of the NERNST lamp. The agreement between the two sets of observations is very obvious, and even better than in a previous comparison made between the writer and another colour-blind girl, which was reported by v. KRIES.[2] Perhaps, the main reason for this is that meanwhile the writer himself had had more practice in making twilight matches, which are not altogether easy to make. In both cases there is a distinct difference in the green and blue between the values of the colour-blind observer

[1] *Zeitschr. für Psychologie und Physiol. der. Sinnesorgane* XLII. S. 69. 1908.
[2] Ibid., XIII. S. 293.

and those of the writer, which can hardly be accounted for as being due to errors in the settings. At these places the twilight values are below the luminosity values for the totally colour-blind subject. The reason for this discrepancy will be discussed later, but here it may be simply mentioned that the difference would not exist, or at any rate would be very much less, if the totally colour-blind observer had also made the observations after previous long-continued dark adaptation, which in the present case was purposely avoided.

The peculiar luminosity distribution in the spectrum of the totally colour-blind eye, which coincides with that of the normal scotopic eye, together with the connection to be explained presently between the curve of twilight values and the curve showing the absorption of energy by solutions of visual purple, led A. König to make the assumption, that in case of eyes that are totally colour-blind vision is performed entirely by the mediation of the rods in the retina that contain visual purple, the cones being lacking or not functioning. Further study of the vision of achromatopes has confirmed this assumption in a very remarkable manner. The vision of these folks exhibits a number of marked peculiarities which are united to form a characteristic symptom-complex.

From the sensitiveness of visual purple to light, it would be natural to expect that persons dependent on this visual substance would see badly when the light was very bright, and that ultimately indeed they would become temporarily blind. This is really the case. Achromatopes are all, to a greater or less degree, light-shy (or photophobic) and averse to looking at a bright light. Their pupils are usually very small, the eyelids almost closed, and the head bent forward in a characteristic way whenever bright light comes from above. Totally colour-blind persons may be readily recognized by this attitude and by their timid glance. Dark glasses give them much relief. The photophobia of such persons as have come under the writer's observations is the effect of a different cause from that of individuals who are light-shy as a result of injury to the eye. Light is not painful or disagreeable to achromatopes; they are simply aware that they do not see well when they look at anything bright. Miss H., the totally colour-blind girl mentioned above, who was most amiable about acting as a test patient in numerous experiments made by Dr. May and the writer, was easily induced to look at an extremely bright light with one eye, the other being blindfolded. It gave her no pain, but in a few minutes she was practically blind and unable at any rate to see luminous bright fields in the spectrophotometer. Nor did she complain when a large area of her retina was brightly illuminated by the Thorner ophthalmoscope, although she was not able to see with this eye for a quarter of an hour afterwards.

Naturally, it was a matter of special interest to see what was the behaviour of the central part of the retina in the case of achromatopes; because here in the region of the fovea there is no visual purple, and there are no rods; and here also the characteristic phenomena of twilight vision are absent.[1] Various possibilities may be conjectured as to the behaviour of this part of the retina of totally colour-blind persons. Thus, the cones might be lacking entirely and their places occupied by rods; or instead of the cones there might be special structures different from the rods, but not able to function or at least not sensitive to light. Lastly, the vacancies due to the absence of cones might be only partly filled by rods. No matter which of these possibilities proves to be the case, the fovea must be either a completely blind spot, or a place which is stimulated by light exactly in the same way as the scotopic eye in the case of twilight vision. In the latter case, especially, a visual acuity is to be expected that continues below that of the normal fovea, having about the same range of values as are found in pure twilight vision under the most favourable circumstances. Now this is actually what is found to be the case, as v. KRIES has showed.[2] In the most favourable conditions the visual acuity of achromatopes may be as high as one-sixth or one-tenth, values even a little higher (as much as one-fourth) being obtained in sporadic cases. Of special interest in this connection is A. KÖNIG's result which indicates that as the illumination is increased the visual acuity of the totally colour-blind eye increases by a different rule from that of the normal eye. There is no bend in the curve (Fig. 70) at the threshold of daylight vision, but even for intensities of illumination higher than 0.1 HEFNER-candle the totally colour-blind curve is fairly straight and continues as a prolongation of the initial, less steep portion. A maximum is then soon attained, where glare interferes with perception of form. These results are entirely in harmony with our previous assumption that for intensities of illumination higher than a tenth of a metre-candle the visual acuity is controlled by the daylight mechanism represented by the cones, this mechanism being lacking in the totally colour-blind.

In some totally colour-blind people a spot has been found in the centre of the retina that is perfectly insensitive to light, that is, a blind spot or "central scotoma"; but in the case of other totally colour-blind persons it is not certain that there is a central scotoma. A. KÖNIG considered it as a particularly impressive proof of the correctness of his view concerning the function of the rods, that there was a central scotoma in the case of achromatopia which he investigated. On the other hand, not being able to find a defective spot of this sort, HER-

---

[1] See W. DE W. ABNEY and W. WATSON, *loc. cit.* (H. L.)

[2] *Zentralblatt für Physiologie*, 1894. S. 694.

ING and HESS used it as an argument to throw doubt not only on KÖNIG's theory but also on the duplicity theory in the form given it by v. KRIES. But v. KRIES, not having found a scotoma in a careful investigation which he made, has pointed out that this particular matter is of no importance for or against the duplicity theory. At present we still know nothing at all certain as to the original cause of total colour blindness, and therefore cannot assert that, because there is lack of cone *function*, the central part of the retina, which is normally crowded with nothing but cones, must be without any functional elements at all. We might just as readily assume that rods have taken the place of the cones. Consequently, it may be considered that the cases with scotoma (GRUNERT lists 10) and those without (GRUNERT lists 8) represent two different modes of origin of total colour blindness in fetal life. There is, however, still another possibility, namely, that even in those cases of total colour blindness in which no scotoma has been found as yet, there may be one present corresponding to the fovea, only it has escaped observation.

The establishment of a scotoma as large as the rod-free region, that is, having an angular diameter of from 1° to 1° 30′, is not easy even when the place in the retina that has become insensitive to light by some pathological process lies to one side of the fovea; but it is far more difficult still to confirm the existence of real central scotoma. The chief difficulty about finding a small defect like this in the visual field consists in maintaining the direction of fixation, and this condition cannot be fulfilled unless foveal fixation is possible. The writer failed to find a central scotoma in the case of Miss H., although a careful search was made; but in spite of this negative result, it is quite possible that it was there, and was simply hard to locate.

Nearly all achromatopes exhibit what is called nystagmos, that is, a restless, frequently very rapid movement of the eyes first one way and then another. Watching the eyes of a patient of this kind, the observer will notice particularly active nystagmos when he tries to rivet his gaze on an object, that is, fixate it. The subject simply cannot do it. This gives a peculiar expression to the eyes of an achromatope in addition to the other characteristics that are the result of photophobia. The tendency to perfect coördination of the movements of the two eyes and for permanent binocular vision is absent or perhaps weak; and the result is a strange sort of disconnection in the movements of both eyes, as was particularly noticeable in the case of Miss H. A permanent squint is sometimes the consequence. Strabismus divergens is reported in so many cases that its occurrence in connection with total colour blindness cannot be an accident. When the tendency to binocular vision is absent, as it is just before going to sleep, or when the eyes are closed, the axes of the two eyes are usually divergent. Apparently when there is a slight divergence the external muscles of the eye are most relaxed; and therefore it might be expected that, when the tendency to binocular fixation is absent from some defect of foveal vision, there is likewise a disposition to let the eyes diverge.

The writer desires to emphasize the fact that the existence of nystagmos and strabismus, or, to put it another way, the lack of a *definite* place of fixation in the centre of the retina, does not necessarily involve the assumption of a central scotoma in place of the fovea. It is just as satisfactory an explanation to assume that the foveal region was occupied by elements with rod-like functions. The absence of a place quite specially adapted for keen vision is sufficient by itself to explain to a certain extent why the eye is so restless in a case of this kind. The explanation is made still clearer by supposing that the rod mechanism is more quickly fatigued than the cone mechanism in the fovea; an assumption which has much to support it.

A characteristic distinction between daylight vision and twilight vision, as we saw above, is the dissimilar reaction to short-lived stimuli recurring in quick succession. In this respect also the vision of the totally colour-blind is similar to twilight vision. As stated above, flicker of a rotating disc with alternate black and white sectors ceases in twilight vision for a much slower speed of rotation than in daylight vision with equal subjective brightness. At the suggestion of v. KRIES, UHTHOFF made special determinations on some totally colour-blind patients whom he had under examination, and found that for even higher intensities of illumination that are above the threshold of daylight vision for the normal eye the totally colour-blind cease to see flicker at a speed of rotation of the disc that is not high enough to make flicker disappear for a person with normal vision. This result was completely confirmed by the writer in tests made with the colour-blind girl above mentioned.

Accordingly here also there is perfect analogy between the vision of the achromatope and twilight vision and a further support for the assumption, that the totally colour-blind person sees regularly only by means of the elements of the retina that under other circumstances mediate twilight vision.

9. Night Blindness as Functional Abeyance of the Rods[1]

PARINAUD regarded the relation between the light sense and colour sense in so-called night blindness or hemeralopia as one of the most essential supports of the duplicity theory. More recent investigations

---

[1] ¶W. DE W. ABNEY, Two cases of congenital night blindness. *Proc. Roy. Soc.* 90. B·
1916. 69–74. (H. L.)

have completely confirmed this view. Night blindness may be considered as a sort of obverse condition to total colour blindness. In the latter, according to the duplicity theory, the rod mechanism is isolated, the function of the cones being in abeyance. Conversely, in night blindness the function of the cones is found to be more or less intact, the rod-mechanism being seriously impaired. It is true that in those cases in which the rod mechanism can be considered as completely lacking, the cone mechanism has perhaps always been considerably impaired too, so that it is not the case of a retina where the rods alone have become incapable of functioning. Still there is a decided approximation to this state of affairs.

In night blindness the faculty of adaptation is much affected, and dark adaptation is so much retarded that the sensitivity usually reached in a half hour will not be attained until after several hours in darkness; or the amplitude of adaptation will be more or less circumscribed, and only a moderate increase of sensitivity to light will be experienced after a long period of darkness. In higher degrees of night blindness both the rate of adaptation and the amplitude are invariably diminished. As was mentioned on page 319, the sensitivity may be enormously reduced. In this case the foveal threshold in the state of light adaptation may be entirely or almost entirely normal; which is an important fact from the theoretical standpoint. With thorough light adaptation and in bright daylight an individual with a moderate degree of night blindness may see practically as well as one with normal vision. On the other hand, with high degrees there is as a rule a certain amount of amblyopia, which, considering the origin of the disease and the processes going on in the retina and choroid, is not surprising. No serious defect of colour vision is manifested unless there is some congenital, typical anomaly. The only thing that is occasionally remarkable is a lowered sensitivity to blue light, particularly in foveal vision. Small, dark blue objects, like corn-flowers that grow in grain-fields, are not seen as blue but simply as "dark". This is similar to the condition in the normal eye when it has been blinded by very bright light.

The reaction of the night-blind to the longer waves of red light is particularly remarkable and important theoretically. After dark adaptation lasting a quarter of an hour, more or less, his sensitivity to an area illuminated by composite white light which extends past the foveal region will be much less than that of a person with normal vision dark-adapted to the same degree; but the threshold for red light in cases of slight night blindness is not at all higher than it is for persons with normal vision, and very little higher in cases of moderate night blindness.

Connected with this is the fact that the PURKINJE phenomenon (see p. 357) is not nearly so distinct in night blindness as in normal vision. Suppose that red and green surfaces are arranged side by side in the dark room, the colours being so selected that they look about equally bright in daylight vision both to a night-blind individual and to a person with normal vision; and then let both observers enter the dimly lighted dark room together. After a few minutes the green will look decidedly brighter to the person with normal vision than the red, before any sign of this difference is apparent to the night-blind. He will not be aware of the phenomenon until much later. Measurement shows that after staying in the dark for about half an hour the increase of brightness of the light of shorter wave-length is from 10 to 100 times greater for the normal eye than for the night-blind eye. In far advanced cases of retinal pigment atrophy, which always accompanies night blindness, twilight vision may be completely destroyed. Under these conditions the visual field is considerably contracted in size, and the PURKINJE phenomenon cannot generally be evoked in the part of the central field that is left. For such patients the brightness relation of a pair of colours is just the same in weak illumination and after long dark adaptation as in bright daylight.

Concerning the time relations of the light sensation in night blindness little is known as yet. It is especially not known whether the "fusion frequency" for regularly intermittent light stimuli (page 373) varies with the state of adaptation in the case of night-blind persons in the same way as it does in normal vision; or whether the entire retina in their case behaves in the same way as only the central region does under normal circumstances. It is very probably that the latter is the case in the earlier stages of dark adaptation, but that in the later stages the part of the twilight mechanism which still continues to function asserts itself, as shown by the more extended course of the process of stimulation and consequent lower fusion frequency. This seems to be the case for normal vision on the basis of SCHATERNIKOFF's experiments mentioned above (p. 373).

The so-called PURKINJE after-image, to be mentioned presently, which apparently represents a peculiarity of rod stimulation, was not obtained by the night-blind patient examined by v. KRIES. Moreover, certain night-blind individuals, to whom the writer tried to show the after-image, could not see it at all even under the most advantageous conditions. In milder cases of this malady the PURKINJE after-image is not absent; still the writer has the impression that it is not so easy to perceive as it is for observers with normal eyes. These observations, as we see, are in good agreement with the duplicity theory and with PARINAUD's way of regarding night blindness. Further experiments would be of interest especially in those cases in which one eye is distinctly hemeralopic, the other eye not being yet so or only in slight measure. Of course, in this case the plan would be to make the subjective brightness of the light-stimuli equal for both eyes.

Although the facts here presented as to the light-sense and colour-sense of the night-blind point to the correctness of PARINAUD's hypothesis, besides many other facts concerning the pathogenesis of the condition of hemeralopia, which cannot be discussed here, but which point in the same direction; HESS[1] has come out recently as vigorously objecting to the use of the results found in night blindness as arguments in favour of the duplicity theory. He maintains that the night-blind persons examined by him were able to perceive the PURKINJE phenomenon; that after dark adaptation they exhibited less sensitivity to light in the centre of the retina than in the periphery; that red pigments in dim light were visible to them without colour, etc. These results are in keeping with some which the writer could instance concerning various night-blind subjects. On the basis of such observations, HESS concludes that PARINAUD's hypothesis of the origin of hemeralopia as being due to the disappearance of visual purple is thus upset. But the hypothesis does not imply that *everybody* that is night-blind is *entirely* without visual purple and the twilight mechanism in v. KRIES's sense. Nobody seriously thinks this. Night blindness is a symptom of a number of ocular diseases and occurs in the most various degrees. In many cases it is progressive, and consequently it is not surprising that in mild and medium degrees of it the effects mentioned by HESS should have been obtained. These effects are explained by v. KRIES, PARINAUD, the writer and others as being the expression of a participation of the twilight mechanism in vision. The process of dark adaptation by which the twilight mechanism is gradually inserted along with the daylight mechanism and made to function is merely accomplished far more slowly in the night-blind patient than in the case of a person with normal vision; and the PURKINJE phenomenon takes a longer time to occur and eventually is fainter, frequently with almost no traces of it. Moreover, in night blindness the sensitivity to light in darkness does not *cease* increasing, but it merely proceeds more slowly and to a less extent. All that HESS's experiments show is that certain qualitative changes in colour vision that go hand in hand with adaptation may occur in spite of the existence of night blindness. This has never been denied. The views which are here advocated would not be affected even if it can be shown (which incidentally HESS has not done) that the cone mechanism in night blindness is sometimes or always impaired

---

[1] C. HESS, Untersuchungen über Hemeralopie. *Arch. f. Augenheilk.* LXII. 1908.

PLATE III

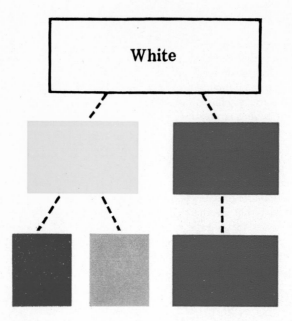

Fig. 83.—Stages 1, 2 and 3 of the actual development of the colour sense.

Fig. 84.—The cleavage products in the three stages of the colour sense. This diagram does not represent the entire light-sensitive molecule, but only the specific cleavage products which, according to the LADD-FRANKLIN theory, constitute the several nerve-excitants for the colour sensations (See WOODWORTH's *Psychology*). For other diagrams, see *Psychological Review*, 23:247, 1916; *Zeitschrift f. Psychologie*, Bd. 6, etc.

also. The outstanding result shown by the symptoms is the *severe damage* of the twilight mechanism compared with which any lesion of the daylight mechanism is quite secondary. Even if it can be inferred from PARINAUD's statements that he meant to assert the occurrence of *damage* to the rod mechanism entirely by itself, it would perhaps be hard to gainsay such a positive statement as this without additional evidence against it.

10. Assumptions of the Duplicity Theory

The experimental observations described in the preceding sections indicate how under the influence of long-continued exclusion from light the retina undergoes fundamental changes in its mode of function. They show also that in the most striking and significant of these changes the centre of the retina, the fovea centralis, does not participate. As a matter of fact, when an eye which has been previously exposed to bright illumination is plunged suddenly in darkness, the sensitivity to light does increase even in the centre of the retina; but, as was stated above, this increase, even under the best circumstances, that is, after previous very thorough light adaptation, amounts only to a small fraction of the increase of sensitivity that takes place in the periphery; and, besides, it disappears in a few minutes, being succeeded by an approximately stationary condition. For the same size of luminous object, the periphery of the retina shows an increase of sensitivity thousands of times greater, lasting from a half hour to an hour, and not complete then. But the most remarkable thing is the difference in the reaction to radiations of different wave-lengths. In the fovea the change of sensitivity is of the same degree for all kinds of light; in the periphery the differences between light of long waves and light of medium and short waves are found to be enormous. The process in the fovea gives the impression of being a simple recovery process, such as takes place in quite similar fashion in other sense organs, the ear, for example. On the other hand, the adaptation of the periphery of the retina to different degrees of intensity is connected with striking qualitative changes in the mode of reaction. The latter, together with the important quantitative changes of excitability, find their most natural explanation on the basis of the theory of the double functions of the rods and cones, as formulated by v. KRIES.[1] His own words are as follows: "Accordingly, we should ascribe to the rods the property of being able to undergo very extensive changes of adaptation, which however arouse merely colourless sensations of brightness; and, lastly, the property of being affected by different kinds of light in just the same proportions as correspond to the distribution of brightness

---

[1] NAGELS *Handbuch der Physiologie des Menschen.* Bd. III. S. 185.

in the spectrum as it occurs in twilight vision. On the other hand, the cones are to be considered as having comparatively little power of adaptation and as being able to discriminate colour in the centre of the retina and its immediate vicinity, although everywhere they are of such nature as to be strongly stimulated even by light of long wave-lengths, and hence by their activity the relations of brightness occur that are peculiar to daylight vision and favourable to light of long wave-lengths."

According to what was stated on page 347, there might perhaps have been included in these propositions the conjecture that the sensation mediated by the rods may vary, according to circumstances, between being colourless or bluish.

On the basis of the determinations of the fusion frequency with rotating discs, we must, moreover, assume, with v. KRIES, that the process of stimulation in the twilight mechanism, presumably therefore in the rods, is longer and more drawn out. In the matter of space discrimination, the parts of the retina where the rods are, never attain anything like the same capacity as the fovea where there are nothing but cones. Finally, the experiments of PIPER and HENIUS (see page 336 above), which shed light on the difference in the relation existing between the sensitivity and the stimulated retinal area in daylight vision and in twilight vision, enable us to realize that a real summation of stimulations is also a very much more important factor in the twilight mechanism than it is in the daylight mechanism.

The question may now be considered whether these differences in the excitability of the rods and cones as postulated by the duplicity theory can be reconciled with the known anatomical, physical and chemical characteristics of the photo-sensitive elements, and to what extent this is possible. Here the anatomical results obtained by RAMON Y CAJAL[1] with respect to the nervous connections of the rods and cones agree very well with the observed physiological facts. So far as the cones are concerned, especially those in the foveal region, at present it is quite generally supposed that each is connected with a single fibre; and that conduction in the retina and optic nerve is isolated to a certain degree at least. On the other hand, the idea is that the rods are collected in groups by cross connections in the retina. According to the views developed by HELMHOLTZ (see page 35), the isolated relation of the cones must be very favourable for nicer space discrimination, whereas the connections of the rods must be comparatively unfavourable. On the other hand, the arrangement of the

[1] See R. GREEFF, Die mikroskopische Anatomie des Sehnerven und der Netzhaut. GRAEFE-SÄMISCHS *Handbuch d. Augenheilk.* 2. Aufl. I. (5) 1901.

rods in groups must be conducive to the integration of separate sources of stimulation. Thus if, say, ten rods are connected together in such fashion that their impulses must all be conducted along a single nerve fibre, the stimulation of two rods in this group will not produce light sensations involving space-discrimination, but rather merely a single sensation so far as the sense of space is concerned, only it will be stronger than if just one rod had been stimulated. Subjectively, the result of this dispersion of a light stimulus over several rods in a group is seen in augmentation of brightness.

Of course, this does not imply that there is no integration whatever of separate stimuli in the cones, for example, in the foveal region. Evidently, the question here is rather one of quantitative differences that are certainly quite considerable in amount.

In trying to explain the inferior power of the twilight mechanism for temporal discrimination, we are on less firm ground. More complicated modes of connection in the retina might be imagined, involving the insertion of several neurones in the transmission system of the twilight mechanism. But even if a marked difference in this respect could not be shown between the routes of conduction from rods and cones, it would not involve any difficulty. For both the rate of reaction and the conductivity in the case of different kinds of tissues, even those particularly distinguished for excitability, exhibit differences that exceed those in question here.

A question of special interest is, what is the reason for the difference of excitability between the daylight mechanism and the twilight mechanism for light of long wave-lengths, and what is it that is mainly responsible for the unequal distribution of the stimulus values in the spectrum for the two mechanisms. There is a possibility here that the stimulus values, like photo-chemical actions, depend on the wave-lengths in some unknown way. To a certain extent this is undoubtedly true. We do not know at all why the so-called infra-red rays do not stimulate the retina of the human eye, although they distinctly stimulate some lower organisms; and we are equally ignorant as to why just those rays of wave-lengths $590 - 600\mu\mu$ produce the brightest sensation of light in the foveal cone-mechanism, although there is no known absorbent material in the cones that absorbs especially these particular waves, and although the maximum energy of spectral radiations is not in this part of the spectrum but in the green.[1] And yet no sooner had the duplicity theory been formulated, and a claim entered

[1] ¶See F. Weigert, Ein photochemische Modell der Retina, Pflügers *Arch.* CXC. 1921. 177–197. Also, Über die Photochemie der Retina. *Zft. f. Elektrochem.* XXI–XXII. 481–487. Also, Zur physikalischen Chemie des Farbensehens. I. Über die Lichtempfindlichkeit der Farbstoffe. *Zft. f. physikalische Chem.* C. 1922. 531–565. (H. L.)

on behalf of the rods as organs of twilight vision, than attention was directed to the very remarkable analogies between rod vision and the chemical action of light on visual purple. KÜHNE's researches had already shown that visual purple was only slightly affected by yellow light and hardly at all by red light. The more precise quantitative relations have been given in a previous section. Here it is sufficient to to say that the results obtained by KÖTTGEN and ABELSDORFF as to the *amounts of energy absorbed* by visual purple and TRENDELENBERG's determinations of the *bleaching values* or chemical effects produced in the visual purple indicate that both of these magnitudes depend on the wave-length. Now these relations are found to accord in most striking manner with the way the *twilight values* depend on wave-length, as can be seen in the graphical representation in Fig. 72.[1]

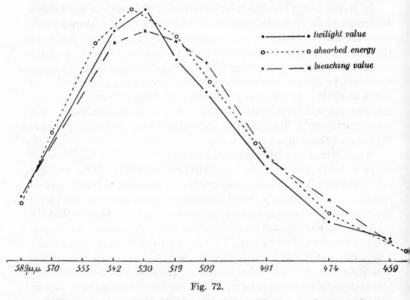

Fig. 72.

This cannot be purely accidental. It would seem rather to indicate beyond doubt that visual purple is of the greatest importance for twilight vision, and especially that its regeneration in darkness is the most fundamental thing in dark adaptation. Just what its special part is, and how it and its decomposition are related to the whole process of the stimulation of the eye by light, are questions that cannot be answered at present.

[1] ¶See S. HECHT and R. E. WILLIAMS, The visibility of monochromatic radiation and the absorption spectrum of visual purple. *Jour. Gen. Physiol.*, V. 1922. 1–34.—See also §18A in this volume, and literature there cited. (H. L.)

The close connection between the optical properties of visual purple and the stimulating effect of spectral lights, which is proved to exist by the researches alluded to above, comes out still more clearly in a series of experiments carried out by STEGMANN under v. KRIES's direction. Visual purple, as is well known, occurs in the outer segments of the rods, colouring them in their entire length, and hence it must be in a layer of some little thickness. Light which traverses the layer with its purple contents will undergo a partial absorption in the layers which it encounters first, and in fact those rays will be most absorbed, and consequently most enfeebled, that have the strongest stimulating actions on the rods, namely, the green rays. The more concentrated the "solution" of visual purple is in the layer of rods, the greater the absorption will be. Thus, the ratio between the stimulating effects of two kinds of light, one of which (say, green) was strongly absorbed, while the other (say, orange) was not much absorbed, would have to depend to a certain extent on the amount (or "concentration") of visual purple in the layer of rods. Now we know it to be a fact that the accumulation of visual purple in the retina is notably increased by long-continued exclusion of light; and therefore matches made under the conditions of twilight vision between two kinds of light like those mentioned above will generally not be independent of the duration of the previous dark adaptation. As a matter of fact, STEGMANN and the writer, working together, found that there was no doubt about it.

If, for example, after being dark-adapted for a period of five or ten minutes, "twilight matches" were made between spectral orange and blue-green (both of which would, of course, look colourless), and if then this match was considered by the same eye after it had been dark-adapted for a much longer time, it ceased to be valid: the light of longer wave-length (orange) looked the brighter of the two, and it was necessary to reduce its intensity to three-fourths of what it had been. Accordingly, this is a change in the opposite sense from that which would correspond to the PURKINJE phenomenon; but it occurs in the direction that was to be expected if the increased accumulation of visual purple has any influence on the stimulating effect. The observation also shows that the place of action of light in the rods cannot be, or at least cannot be entirely, in the inner segment, or at the border between the inner and outer segments, but must be farther outwards. The farther outwards in the rod the place of stimulation is, the more the absorptive action of the visual purple must influence the threshold value. On the other hand, it does not follow from the experiment just described that the place of stimulation is only at the outermost end of the rod. It may just as well take place in the entire outer segment.

On the assumption that typical congenital total colour blindness (achromatopia) is to be considered as vision in which the cones have no share, it is natural to expect in the case of such persons that the difference between matches made with retina poor in visual purple and with retina rich in visual purple will be still more distinctly marked. An achromat can make matches in the spectroscope between orange and blue green in a bright room, whereas observers with normal vision must be already dark-adapted for some time before they can obtain anything like exact matches. In that state of "indoor adaptation", which is sufficient for making observations in the case of achromats, the amount of visual purple to start with is decidedly less.

With the totally colour-blind girl mentioned previously, the writer has made experiments of this sort with the HELMHOLTZ spectro-photometer. One eye was tightly bandaged for a long time, the other being kept always in the state of medium light adaptation. She then made matches with the photopic eye between orange-yellow ($600\mu\mu$) and green-blue ($490\mu\mu$). The width of the slit for the green-blue was 0.44 mm on the average (0.49–0.40). The observations then were made with the eye that had been bandaged for an hour, and for this purpose the intensities of the two fields were considerably lowered, in proportion, of course, by means of an episcotister. The first settings of the slit after removing the bandage amounted to 0.85 and 0.80 mm, but as the experiment continued, these values were lowered to an average of 0.6 mm. After this eye had become light-adapted, the values for it were also between 0.4 and 0.44, whereas for the other eye, that had meanwhile been blindfolded, the values increased to between 0.55 and 0.6.

The fact that the twilight value for blue-green light and, for that matter, for every green and blue, is found to be lower when the eye has been dark-adapted for a long time than when it was darkened simply long enough to make the matches, gives the explanation of the marked separation in the blue between the two curves in Fig. 71. One of these curves represents the twilight values of a normal eye, and the other shows the distribution of spectral brightness for a totally colour-blind person. By long exclusion of light, the observer who was not colour-blind made his retina far richer in visual purple than that of the totally colour-blind girl could possibly have been, because her settings were made in a bright room. Owing to the greater amount of visual purple, the twilight values obtained for green and blue lights, which are strongly absorbed, turn out to be lower than in the case of the totally colour-blind observer.

Comparative physiological investigations on animals whose retinas contain very different amounts of visual purple are also of much interest in the present connection. As was stated above, M. SCHULTZE's argument that animals that are accustomed to live in darkness should have rods only and no cones, has not been altogether verified. But it is a fact that in distinctly nocturnal animals like owls the rods are unusually large and numerous and also particularly rich in visual purple; whereas the retinas of diurnal birds of prey contain little visual purple or none at all.

Functional differences were established first by ABELSDORFF, in the case of the reaction of the pupil under the influence of light of different colours.[1] In diurnal animals he found the greatest pupillary contraction for those spectral rays that also look brightest to the light-adapted eye, that is, at the border of yellow and orange; whereas in nocturnal animals the maximum effect of pupillary contraction appears to be distinctly shifted towards the green, completely corresponding to the subjective impression of brightness of the scotopic eye with its large amount of visual purple.

Quantitative comparisons of photo-electrical reactions for light of different wave-lengths can be made far more accurately than measurements of the "pupillomotor" effect. In a manner similar to that used by earlier investigators (see page 56), HIMSTEDT and the writer together studied the electrical reactions in the frog's eye to light of various colours, the state of adaptation being taken into consideration for the first time. The distribution of electrical reaction in the spectrum was first found for the eye when it was as thoroughly dark-adapted as possible, and then for eyes which had been previously exposed to bright daylight. As might be expected from what is known about the effect of adaptation on the human eye, higher intensities of light were needed to get measurable electrical effects with the photopic eye, whereas very slight intensities were adequate for the scotopic eye. Taking account of the high sensitivity in the state of dark adaptation, the investigators tried not to disturb it any more than was absolutely necessary and therefore used very small amounts of light for producing stimulation. But the connection between the effect and the wave-length varies also with the adaptation. In the dark-adapted eye the maximum effect is shifted considerably towards the violet end of the spectrum.[2]

At the writer's suggestion, H. PIPER measured the stimulating effect of coloured lights on other animals. Some of them were warm-

---

[1] ¶See H. LAURENS, The pupillomotor effects of wave lengths of equal energy content. *Amer. Jour. Physiol.* LXIV. 1923. 97–119. (H. L.)

[2] ¶See E. L. CHAFFEE, W. T. BOVIE and A. HAMPSON, The electrical response of the retina under stimulation by light. *Jour. Opt. Soc. Amer.* VII. 1923. 1–44.—Additional more modern literature on photo-electrical and photo-mechanical effects will be found at end of §18A. (H. L.)

blooded. Invertebrates were represented by the cuttle fish. Here again the comparative observations on diurnal and nocturnal birds proved to be particularly interesting. The results in these latter cases are shown in Fig. 73. Some of the diurnal birds were hawks, chickens and pigeons. Several species of owls were among the nocturnal birds. The difference in the two groups comes out clearly in the figure, especially the entirely different positions of the peaks of the curves. In the individual groups there is quite good agreement; only one curve, that of the mouse-hawk, being different from that of the other diurnal birds by being less steep in its descent towards the violet end of the spectrum.

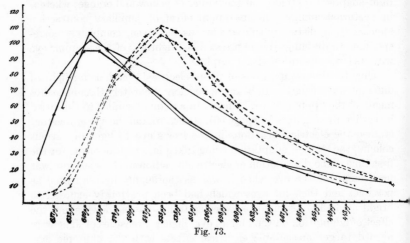

Fig. 73.

These facts certainly are strong indications that in these animals also the cones are the organs of daylight vision and the rods of twilight vision; and the probability is that, especially in their reactions to light of different kinds they behave much in the same way as the corresponding structures in the human eye.[1]

Finally, stimulation of the retina by light is accompanied by certain distinct structural changes, which like the photo-chemical and photo-electrical effects, are unquestionably dependent on adaptation, that is, on whether the retina is illuminated or unilluminated. These

---

[1] However, there is still much here that needs explanation. Thus, it is singular that PIPER failed to find variations in the distribution of stimulations as a result of adaptation in the case of rabbits, cats, and even dogs. In HESS's experiments with chickens the values of the relative brightness were found to be shifted by adaptation more towards the violet end of the spectrum; but this is not so surprising because the retina of a chicken's eye is perhaps not entirely without visual purple.

changes are the migration of the pigment in the pigment epithelium of the retina and the contractions of the cones. It is natural to treat these two processes together, as HERZOG and EXNER and JANUSCHKE have done. According to these authors, we have here a contrivance for throwing in and out the two combined mechanisms in the retina, that is, for throwing in the twilight mechanism and throwing out the daylight mechanism. In dim light or complete darkness the pigment returns into the cells leaving the intervals between the individual rods free. It might be that under these conditions, when a small amount of light comes through the pupil, the portion of it that falls on a single rod is greater (owing to diffusion of light all over the retina) than if the rods were isolated from one another by a thick mantle of pigment. In this case the only light that can get to the rod will be light that traverses the retina in the longitudinal direction of the rod. The supposition is that the cones, which in twilight vision are mostly pushed forward between the rods, remain out of action, because the small amount of light acting on them is not yet above the threshold of stimulation for the cone mechanism.

When, on the other hand, the pigment migrates forward in bright light, that is, under the conditions of daylight vision, an exceedingly large amount of light is prevented from reaching the rod mechanism which has been rendered highly photo-sensitive by accumulation of visual purple in the dark. The result is that the adaptation to the increased intensity of light is more gradual, and meantime the less photo-sensitive cones can emerge from the mantle of pigment to be freely exposed to the stronger stimulus.

While this view of the photo-mechanical processes in the retina is certainly attractive in some ways, still it must be admitted that there are numerous arguments against it that cannot be treated lightly. The writer did not accept it in the summary of the objective changes that take place in the retina as set forth in the *Handbuch der Physiologie des Menschen*, Bd. III, S. 92; nor can he accept it now, especially since GARTEN in his very thorough review of this subject in the third volume of the second edition of GRAEFE-SÄMISCHS *Handbuch der Augenheilkunde* has not been able to adduce any arguments that are favourable to the HERZOG-EXNER hypothesis. The writer still thinks that the fact that the pigment and cone movements could be established very easily in cold-blooded animals and birds, but not in man and the higher mammals, is comparatively the least weighty of all the arguments against it. The mere fact that these processes have not been demonstrated in the human eye is no proof that they do not occur. It may be that they go on more rapidly than in cold-blooded animals. HESS tried in vain to find pigment migrations in monkeys; but GARTEN, employing a more delicate method, did succeed in detecting it to a slight extent. But even if it should be overwhelmingly proved that the photo-tropic reactions of the pigment epithelium do not occur in the human eye, that would be no argument against explaining the processes in the eyes of frogs, fishes, and birds in the above manner, and assuming that the same purpose, namely, adaptation of the eye to different intensities of light, is achieved in the eye of the mammal in a different way. The act of accommodation is performed by different classes of animals in fundamentally different ways.

But there are other considerations against this hypothesis of an in-and-out mechanism. For instance it is not easy to see what is the purpose of the elongation of the cones in darkness. Why do not all of the cones remain immobile on the membrana limitans, as some of them do? What is the object of the pigment in the region of the human eye where there are no rods? How are we to explain the fact that over a considerable portion of the retina in the case of animals with a tapetum, like the dog and cat, there is no pigment at all?

Without being able to answer such questions as these, it is impossible to speak yet of a complete theory of the photo-mechanical processes in the retina. It is very probable that the process of light and dark adaptation is not *rigidly* connected with the existence of photo-tropic movements of retinal elements, but that these changes may accompany adaptation, the most essential basis of it being the formation and bleaching of visual purple.

It is not probable that the pigment as such has anything to do with the formation of visual purple, because the latter occurs in large amounts even in albinos who have no pigment and in the parts of the retina of the cat where there is no pigment. The purpose of the pigment is probably purely optical and consists in the prevention of lateral diffusion of light in the layer of rods. But, as has been said, it is still obscure why with one set of animals this protective mechanism exhibits such plain reactions to light, and yet does not do so with other animals.

Appendix by v. Kries

I. Normal and Anomalous Colour Systems

1. Laws of Mixture of Light

The views developed by HELMHOLTZ as to the nature and origin of the visual sensations and the fundamental mechanism of the organ of vision have recently undergone a certain modification, as was explained in the preceding Appendix; because it has been necessary to assume that twilight vision is a special mode of vision, presumably having to do also with a separate and distinct part of the organ as a whole. Most of HELMHOLTZ's investigations were concerned with the other mode of vision known as *daylight vision*, that is, the vision of the thoroughly light-adapted eye, which is probably confined to a small region belonging to the fovea centralis. Here also later observations have considerably advanced our knowledge. This has been due mainly to improved methods. Thus whereas formerly the laws of light-mixture were merely qualitative, these laws have now been determined quantitatively for normal and anomalous vision.

It would take too much space to enumerate here all the many devices which have been designed in the last ten years for studying the mixture of spectral lights. It must suffice to say that, in so far as they are intended for subjective observation, they are almost all based on a principle which (as well as the writer can ascertain) was introduced first by MAXWELL.[1] Objective spectra are not used in this method, but their real images are focused directly in front of the observer's eye, so that any particular region can be separated and inspected through a slit in the ocular. Accordingly, the observer does not see the spectrum with its hues blending into each other from place to place; but what he sees is the surface of the object-glass illuminated all over by light of the same wave-length and appearing therefore as a uniform field.[2]

---

[1] *Philos. Transactions* CL. p. 57, 1860.

[2] ¶"By far the best method" is HELMHOLTZ's "colour-mixing apparatus," (presumably the same instrument as is described in the text), which "is, in effect, a double spectroscope; there are two collimator-tubes which throw light, after it has passed through a prism, into the two halves of a single telescope. The eye-piece of the telescope has been removed, and a plate carrying a narrow slit put its in place; the effect of this is that an eye looking through the telescope sees, not a narrow image of the collimator-slit, but the whole surface of the prism lighted up by homogeneous light." CHRISTINE LADD-FRANKLIN, Article on Vision in BALDWIN's *Dict. of Philos. and Psychol.* (J. P. C. S.)

Here we shall describe merely a little more in detail the apparatus which was described by HELMHOLTZ himself in the second edition of this work. Except for many special modifications, it is the same instrument as that used so much by KÖNIG and by NAGEL and the writer. It is shown in plan in Fig. 74.

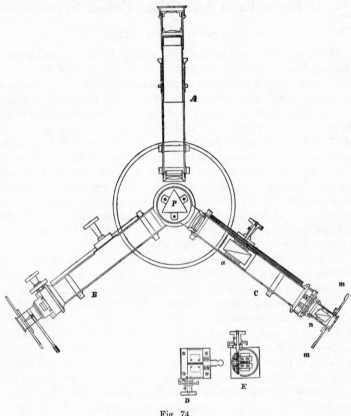

Fig. 74.

"A large equilateral prism is mounted at P and rigidly connected with the massive central base of the instrument. B and C are two collimator tubes that can be turned around a vertical axis which is underneath the prism. The two kinds of light that are to be mixed emerge from these tubes and fall on the prism. The light from B leaves the prism on its right face and that from C on its left face. Thus the observer whose eye is at A sees the light from the right collimator through the left side of the prism, and *vice versa.* For observations of colour mixture the ocular of the telescope is removed, and all that remains in its place is a narrow rectangular slit at the focus of the object-glass. The width of the slit can be adjusted by screws. At the ends of the tubes *B* and *C* there are two other finer slits, whose widths can be read on the heads of micrometer screws for adjusting them. The main thing about adjusting the width of each of these slits is to keep the middle line of the slit fixed, so as to alter the brightness of the image without changing its colour; and hence by turning the same screw the two edges of the slit are shifted equally in opposite directions. The details of the slits are shown in the inserts at *D* and *E*. To unite two colours, one from each of the collimators *B* and *C*, each tube contains a double refracting calc-spar prism (*a* in Fig. 74) so combined with a glass prism that there is no deviation of the mean direction in which the two images are seen. After traversing these prisms, the rays proceed as if they came from two separate images of each slit; these images being farther apart, the farther the prism is from the slit. Each of the calc-spar prisms can be shifted back and forth by means of a rack and pinion. For this purpose a piece is cut out of the side of each of the tubes *B* and *C* to let the prism *a* and its screw be free to move one way or the other. The two bundles of rays, however, that correspond to these two images, are polarised at right angles to each other. If, therefore, a rotatable NICOL prism is inserted in front of each slit, the relations between the two beams of light can be varied at will. One image can be extinguished entirely, while the other attains its greatest intensity. The amount of rotation is measured by means of two graduated circles *mm*, fastened to the pieces of tube that hold the NICOL prisms.

"Each of the two slit images is developed in a spectrum by the prism *P*. But depending on the apparent separation of the images, the two spectra are more or less shifted towards each

Fig. 75.

other so that different pairs of colours can be made to overlap. Finally, a real image of these two pairs of spectra is produced in the plane of the slit at the focus of the object-glass of the telescope. Thus on each side of the prism *P* light of both colours meets here in the slit. Looking towards the prism through the slit, the observer sees therefore a field of the form shown in Fig. 75. The narrow dividing line corresponds to the front edge of the prism *P*, the round edges on the sides to the circumferences of the object-glasses of *B* and *C*. The colour and brightness of the two fields can thus be compared; and the observer can try to make them match, if they do not do so.

"The two colours in each colour mixture can be both made to vary towards red or towards violet by turning the corresponding tube *B* or *C*. On the other hand, by shifting forward the calc-spar prism *a*, one of the colours will change more towards red and the other towards violet. One intensity of the components may be varied in a way that can be accurately measured by turning the Nicol prism *n*. The relative brightness of the two mixtures is adjusted by altering the width of the slit in *B* or *C*.

"For determining the wave-lengths, the ocular lens is inserted in *A*. Then when sunlight is used, the Fraunhofer lines of the four spectra will be visible in the ocular slit. Individual lines can be isolated, and since the wave-lengths of even the finer lines are accurately known, it is possible to determine the wave-lengths of the four average colours of the slit."

The apparatus designed by v. Frey and v. Kries (*Arch. f. Anat. u. Physiologie*. Physiol. Abt. 1881; page 336) is adapted also for scientific observations and measurements; as is also an instrument described by Asher (*Verhandlungen der Deutschen Physikal. Gesellschaft*. V. 1903) and one mentioned by Hering (Pflügers *Arch*. LIV. 1893. 312), which, so far as the writer knows, has never been described any more fully.[1]

Various instruments have been designed for demonstrations of colour-mixing effects: Zoth (Pflügers *Arch*. LXX. 1898. 1), Schenck (*Sitzungber. d. Marburger Gesellschaft z. Bef. d. ges. Naturw.* 1907), Basler (Pflügers' *Arch*. 116. 1907. 628), Samojloff (*Zeitschr. f. Physiol. d. Sinnesorgane*. XLIII. 1909. 237), and Krogh (*Scandinav. Arch. f. Physiol*. XVIII. 1906. 320). The writer has described a simple apparatus designed for laboratory instruction: (*Zeitschr. f. Psychologie u. Physiol. d. Sinnesorgane*, XLIII, 1919. 59). Some instruments intended for purposes of practical investigation will be described later.

In describing the results of these investigations, it is best to consider trichromats and dichromats together. Two facts stand out prominently as being of more general significance and having wide bearing. The first of these is that typical dichromats (for whom according to Helmholtz's way of looking at it the colour triangle would collapse into a straight line) fall into two distinctly separated types. The vision of these two types presents differences which certainly cannot be due to purely physical causes, for example, to more or less yellow colouration in the ocular media; and yet in each type separately there are individual distinctions which are not very great and are doubtless physical in their origin.

The other important fact is that colour matches made by persons with normal colour vision are valid for both types of dichromats.

[1] ¶S. Garten, Herings Farbenmischapparat für spektrale Lichter. *Zft. f. Biol.* LXXII. 1920. 89–100. (H. L.)

Objectively unlike mixtures of light which appear to be alike to persons with normal colour vision appear alike also to dichromats. This is true except for the presumably physical differences just mentioned, such differences as are to be found also among persons with normal colour vision.

The first of these facts amounts to nothing more than what was already known before, for example, that in the case of some dichromats the red end of the spectrum is abbreviated. But the fact comes out far more distinctly in the difference of brightness between two kinds of light belonging to the half of the spectrum that corresponds to the long waves. These may be so chosen that all typical dichromats make correct matches with them for certain definite ratios of intensity; although these ratios have to be entirely different for the two classes of dichromats. In these tests the writer used red light of wave-length $671\mu\mu$ (lithium line) and yellow light of wave-length $589\mu\mu$. The following table[1] exhibits the results obtained with twenty dichromats.

Amount of red that it takes to match a given yellow

1. W.N.	36.5	F.	214
	36.3	V.	213
	36.3	M. Sc.	211
	33.5	E. J.	205
	38.4	H.	196
2. L. V.	37.3	E. I.	198
3. A. V.	37.0	E. II	210
4. Sc. En.	37.0	K.	200
5. O. N.	37.8	W.	210
6. K.Th.	37.0	B.	203
7. H.Th.	36.9	Th.	225
8. O.Th.	38.0		
9. F.	40.0		

It is obvious here that, while the two types are sharply distinguished from each other, there is very close agreement between the individuals of each class.

A detailed and complete determination of the mode of vision of the individual dichromat can be obtained by making a set of systematic observations on colour mixture, that is, by what the writer speaks of as "calibrating a spectrum" (*Eichung eines Spektrums*). The way this is done is to illuminate one of the fields of the apparatus by a mixture of light of short wave-length and light of long wave-length, the other field getting from its collimator a pure spectral light. This latter field is illuminated in turn by a series of pure spectral lights, and the mixture of red and blue light that looks like it in each instance is

[1] v. KRIES *Zeitschrift für Psychologie etc.*, XIII. S. 925

obtained in the adjoining field. Thus for every part of the spectrum the amounts of red and blue are found which are in the mixture that matches this place. The red values of two dichromats, one of each type, are exhibited in Fig. 76, and the blue values in Fig. 77.[1] It will be observed that while the red values are quite different for the two types, the blue values are not characteristically unlike.

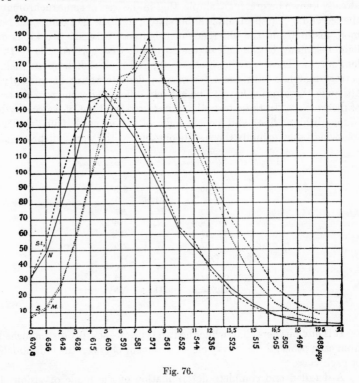

Fig. 76.

The second fact mentioned above might be proved by calculation, in a perfectly exact and general way, provided the spectrum could be "calibrated" in a similar way for an eye with normal colour vision. So far this has been done only for the less refrangible half of the spectrum. In this region a trichromat can match a given colour by a mixture of two others, one on either side of it. This part of the spectrum, therefore, can be "calibrated" by using two standard lights; and then we are in a position to calculate immediately the distribution

[1] See numerical data, *loc. cit.* p. 252 and in NAGEL's *Handbuch d. Physiol.* III. page 153.

of the stimulus values for dichromats, knowing that for one class of dichromats the stimulus value of yellow-green light is about 20 times that of red light and for the other class about twice that of red light.

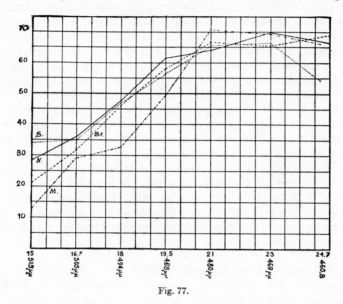

Fig. 77.

The calculated distribution agrees very satisfactorily with that found for dichromats, as the following table shows.

Wave-length of the Homogeneous Light	Amounts of Lights 670.8 and 552μμ in the mixture		Stimulus Value for the eye of the green-blind		Stimulus Value for the eye of the red-blind	
	670.8	552	Calculated	Observed	Calculated	Observed
0 (670.8)	88.5	—	33	33	4.9	4.9
3 (628 μμ)	251	10.0	106	107	28.8	38.5
4 (615 μμ)	276	27	126	147	54.2	63
5 (603 μμ)	270	49	145	151	86	84
6 (591 μμ)	202	67	135	137	108	105
7 (581 μμ)	123	76	114	124	117	113
8 (571 μμ)	73	91	110	103	137	126
9 (561 μμ)	21	80	76	82	111	106
10 (552 μμ)	—	71	64	64	101	101

Thus it may be generally stated as a result of calculation, invariably verified in individual cases by experimental test, that colour matches made by persons with normal colour vision are in fact valid for both kinds of dichromats.[1]

As was stated, the entire spectrum would have to be "calibrated" for persons with normal colour vision in order to make a similar comparison throughout the whole range. Three calibrating lights would be needed for this purpose and therefore much more complicated apparatus. Observations of this kind have not yet been carried out. We are certainly therefore not in a position to prove the above law systematically. And yet it is easy to prove it by means of numerous and varied individual experiments, and there are no exceptions to it, so far as the writer's experience goes. The changes that have to be made in any colour match made by a person with normal colour vision to make it right for a dichromat are usually very slight and such as occur with that particular type, being probably due to physical causes.

The connection thus established and experimentally verified between the two types of dichromats and between both of them and normal trichromats is identical with what HELMHOLTZ had already supposed to be probably the case. In order to have a name for it that expresses simply the experimental results without involving any theoretical consequences, the writer speaks of the two colour systems of dichromats as being *reduction forms* of normal vision. At any rate the simplest and most natural explanation of these abnormalities is to regard them as being *deficiency effects,* in the sense that each of these types lacks one of the component factors of the visual organ as assumed in the HELMHOLTZ theory. This was just the idea that was conveyed by the terms red-blind and green-blind that were formerly in use. And yet these expressions have been the source of much misunderstanding, for which the words themselves are perhaps partly responsible. As a matter of fact, green-blind persons are not really blind to green light, nor red-blind persons to red light; nor can it be assumed that the former lack the sensation of green and the latter the sensation of red[2]. In order to have brief descriptive terms for the relation that has been found to exist here, without expressing any theoretical bias, the writer suggests the names *protanopes* and *deuteranopes* to describe the two kinds of dichromats, that is, persons who lack the first component or the second component, respectively, of the normal visual organ.

[1] A very simple proof of this statement is that matches of pure yellow with a red-green mixture are not the same for both kinds of dichromats unless the relative amounts of red and green are such that the mixture has the same colour as pure yellow for persons of normal vision (see *Zft. f. Psychologie,* etc., XIII. 277.)

[2] Moreover, simply because the dichromat is supposed not to have some one of the three components of the organ of vision, we have no right at all to infer that ordinary heterogeneous daylight which has no colour for a normal eye looks blue-green to one kind of dichromat and purple to the other kind.

It may, therefore, be considered as established that colour matches which are valid for both kinds of dichromatic vision are valid also for trichromatic vision. Starting from this assumption, we can exhibit the laws of colour mixture for trichromats in the form of a colour chart which will not only express the qualitative relations, as was done formerly (see page 139), but will agree also with the quantitative results of observation. On the basis of the measurements of dichromats mentioned above, the writer has constructed a colour chart of this sort.[1]

Moreover, we obtain here something definite as to the way in which the separate components of the organ of vision are affected by light of different kinds. The term *valence* proposed by HERING is usually employed to denote the intensity of the action of a given light on a part of the visual organ.[2] Here, on the other hand, the term *calibration value (Eichwerte)* will be used for the amount of each of the three calibration lights in the mixture that looks the same as the given homogeneous light. *Calibration curves* and *valence curves* are curves for which the ordinate at any point represents one or the other of these two magnitudes as a function of the wave-length in the case of a definite spectrum.

Now a simple consideration shows[3] that the blue valences, that is, the stimulus values for the blue component substance of the eye, depend on the wave-length of the light in the same way as the observed blue calibration values do; whereas the valences of the first and second component substances may be any linear functions of the observed amounts of light of long wave-length.

Owing to the frequency of the occurrence of the two kinds of dichromatism above mentioned and the typical uniformity of the phenomena, this kind of vision is easy to investigate and can be satisfactorily explained. But there is another kind of anomaly which may be called blue blindness or yellow-blue blindness concerning which our knowledge is still quite scanty. With reference to these disorders, it is worth mentioning that they seem to be seldom congenital, but are more apt to be acquired as the result of sundry diseases of the eye, particularly loosening of the retina. The disturbance in such cases is naturally mostly on one side and frequently confined to certain parts of the visual field.

[1] NAGELS *Handbuch der Physiologie.* III. p. 162. Certain peculiarities in the form of this chart will be mentioned later.

[2] ¶HERING's theory presupposes three visual substances or components that furnish the six fundamental sensations. Different kinds of homogeneous light affect these substances differently. "All coloured lights, except the four primary colours, have three values or valencies, corresponding to their action on the three substances. The physiological value or 'moment' of a light depends upon its physical value and also upon the condition of excitability of the visual mechanism." PARSONS, *Colour Vision*, 253. (J. P. C. S.)

[3] NAGEL's *Handbuch der Physiologie.* III. S. 163.

In five cases investigated and described by König[1] the disorder was acquired. These individuals detected no difference between a yellow 566–570$\mu\mu$ or a blue about complementary to it and a colourless mixture. Moreover, special investigations with a series of colour combinations and matches showed that what was involved here was a form of reduction of normal vision. The phenomena are therefore in accord with what might be expected according to the Helmholtz theory, when the blue component is lacking. Consequently, in line with the nomenclature suggested above, this anomaly may be called *tritanopia.*

Some other cases of acquired unilateral anomalies invariably of a similar nature have been described by Collin and Nagel.[2]

In a case described by Vintschgau[3] and Hering[4] the anomaly was on both sides and congenital. Here again yellow and blue lights had the same appearance as composite white light. But not much difference could be noticed for red or green either, so that the condition was to some extent like that of total colour blindness.

Other cases that may be mentioned are the one described by Piper[5] and another one by Levy.[6]

With reference to colour matches, it was stated above that certain individual differences are apparent in persons with normal colour vision and also in dichromats of the same type. This fact seems to have been first noted by Maxwell[7] who also expressed the opinion that possibly the explanation was a physical one and due to the yellow colouration of the fovea, which is different in different individuals. Quite a large mass of experimental work on this subject is available now, which tends to substantiate Maxwell's assumption for a portion of the phenomena anyhow.

At the instigation of Hering, a direct physical investigation of the macular pigment in the isolated human retina was undertaken by Sachs.[8] He found that the long wave-lengths were not appreciably absorbed. The absorption begins in the yellow-green and continues to increase with decreasing wave-length. As to individual differences in colour matches, v. Frey and the writer[9] showed that for them these differences in a large number of trials with all sorts of combinations

[1] *Sitzungsberichte der Berliner Akademie.* 1897.

[2] *Zeitschrift für Physiologie der Sinnesorgane.* XLI. S. 74. 1906.

[3] Pflügers *Archiv.* LVII. 191. 1894.

[4] Ibid. LVII. S. 308. 1894.

[5] *Zeitschrift für Psychologie.* XXXVIII. S. 155. 1905.

[6] *Archiv f. Ophth.* LXII. 3. S. 464. 1906.

[7] *Philos. Transactions* 1860.

[8] Pflügers *Archiv.* 50. S. 574. 1891.

[9] *Archiv für (Anatomie und) Physiologie,* 1881. S. 336.

were of such nature and so related to one another as to be accounted for by assuming a retinal pigmentation.[1]

The corresponding phenomena occuring with dichromats of the same type are very much simpler. In the case of two protanopes who were carefully investigated by the writer, differences of this sort appeared very distinctly and regularly in "calibrating" a spectrum as described above. The amount of absorption for different kinds of light (or, to be more accurate, the ratio between the absorption for one light and for the other) can be ascertained by comparing the amounts of red in the red-blue mixtures that match. Thus the following table was obtained.

Wave-length	670.8	656	692	568	615	603	591	581	571	561 $\mu\mu$
Calculated ratio	1.1	1.1	1.05	1.00	1.00	1.07	1.07	0.98	0.96	1.02

Wave-length	552	544	536	525	515	505	496	488	480	469 $\mu\mu$
Calculated ratio	0.91	0.91	0.97	0.91	0.63	0.63	0.57	0.42	0.41	0.3

The absorption begins to be evident here at about 525$\mu\mu$, in agreement with the results found by SACHS.

The differences observed in the same person between the place of clearest vision itself and the adjacent paracentral places likewise indicate the influence of colouration of the macula on colour matches. Most people can readily notice that, when they try to get a colourless light by mixing red and complementary blue-green, they have to use quite different amounts of the two colours according as the result is obtained by direct fixation or by paracentral observation. If the mixture is correctly adjusted for the fovea, it looks distinctly green when the eye is turned away a little. The differences between colour matches made for the central and paracentral retina have been carefully studied by BREUER[2], and his results likewise support the assumption of an absorbing pigment.

There are difficulties about measuring the absorptions exactly, because the pigmentation, in many cases at least, is quite dilute, and hence colour matches for places that are distinctly outside the macula cannot be made very accurately. The amount of individual variation may be estimated to a certain extent on the basis of observations made on numerous subjects. This method indicates that the strength of the

[1] ¶ABNEY and FESTING, *Phil. Trans. Roy. Soc.* 183A. 1892, p. 532. — W. ABNEY, *Researches in colour vision and the trichromatic theory.* 1913. — L. T. TROLAND, Apparent brightness; its conditions and properties. *Trans. Illum. Engin. Soc.* IX. 1916, 947–966.—HECHT, SELIG and R. E. WILLIAMS, The visibility of monochromatic radiation and the absorption spectrum of visual purple. *Jour. Gen. Physiol.* V. 1922. 1–33. (H .L.)

[2] *Zeitschrift für Psychologie*, etc. XIII. S. 464.

blue light that gets through to the visual substance, after being diminished by absorption, is for persons with least macula pigmentation, and for those with most, about in the ratio of 1 : 0.3.

A general colouration of the ocular media, and particularly perhaps of the vitreous humor and lens, may also be taken into consideration in the same sort of way as in the case of the pigment of the yellow spot. It is well known that the lenses of elderly people are slightly yellowish. We can try to get some idea of the importance and effect of this colouration by testing different people for the *twilight values* of yellow and blue lights, the fovea being out of action under these circumstances. That slight differences do occur here, which are however too great to be attributed to errors of observation, had been already found by NAGEL and STARK.[1] The interpretation of these differences as being due to absorption by the pigment of the lens or vitreous humor is, however, rendered questionable, because the pigment of the macula extends quite far out beyond the central region where there is no twilight vision. The twilight equations too, as above stated, are not entirely constant but depend a little on the degree of adaptation.

HESS[2] has recently made twilight equations between yellow and blue (the wave-lengths not being stated) on a large number of persons, obtaining considerable difference in not a few instances, which he attributes to the colourations of the vitreous humor and lens.

This view of macula pigmentation, and its bearing, which has been pretty generally accepted for a long time, has recently been called in question by GULLSTRAND,[3] as stated on p. 304. Thus far the writer has not been convinced that the objections urged against the hitherto accepted opinion were conclusive and that it would be necessary to adopt GULLSTRAND's proposed explanation in place of it.[4]

Another question is whether there may not be other individual differences besides the physical factors alluded to here, as Miss v. MALTZEW[5] is disposed to think. However, as this has to do with observational methods which will be discussed later, it seems best to defer their consideration.

Since the appearance of the first edition of this treatise, an extensive and important addition to our knowledge has resulted from the more exact investigation of those forms of colour vision which KÖNIG speaks of as *anomalous trichromatic systems*. A fact discovered by RAYLEIGH[6] was the starting point of these researches. If a large number of people are required to make colour mixtures with homogeneous red and

---

[1] STARK, Beitrag zur Lehre von der Farbenblindheit. *Diss.* Freiburg 1897.

[2] *Archiv f. Augenheilkunde* LXIII. S. 164. 1909.

[3] *Arch. f. Ophth.* LXII. S. 1. 1905.

[4] The writer hopes to return to this subject briefly in another place.

[5] *Ztschr. für Physiologie der Sinnesorgane* XLIII. S. 76. 1909.

[6] *Nature* XXV. S. 64. 1881.

yellow-green (671 and 536$\mu\mu$, corresponding to the lines of lithium and thallium) that will match a homogeneous (sodium) yellow (589$\mu\mu$), it is found that the red and green are not always mixed in the same proportion. It is true that in the large majority of cases the differences are only comparatively slight. Moreover, the settings of these persons are always close to one another, so that they are naturally classified in a group of individuals who agree among themselves, not absolutely, of course, but approximately. Anticipating things a little, let us say at once that these are persons whose colour vision may be considered as perfectly normal. We shall have to consider later the differences that occur also in this class with regard to making the RAYLEIGH colour match. At the same time there is found to be a smaller number of persons whose settings are very considerably different from the others. Some of them will use far more green, and others far more red, in the mixture than the large majority do. Thus red-green mixtures which look to these people like sodium yellow are either distinctly green or distinctly red to most people. It is natural to suppose that the way most eyes are found to behave is a better and more perfect way, and to regard deviations in the nature of anomalies; and hence we are warranted here in speaking of *anomalous trichromatic systems*. It should be mentioned at once that the test described above is not the only way, although it is the best and most reliable one, for detecting this peculiar kind of vision, and for that reason it has gained a special importance. Hence, a short name has been invented for colour matches between sodium yellow and lithium-thallium-mixtures, namely, the RAYLEIGH-*equation* (or RAYLEIGH test).

Moreover, for reasons that will be evident as soon as certain facts are stated, as will be done immediately, NAGEL suggested calling that class of these people *protanomalous*, who use more than the normal amount of red in the RAYLEIGH-test; and the other class *deuteranomalous*, who use too much green.

A more exact examination of the anomalous trichromats shows that the deviation from the normal cannot be due to absorption of light by a pigment in the ocular media or in the retina. Were such the case, so that, for example, the amounts of green light reaching the visual substance for a normal and for an anomalous eye were in the ratio of 1:a, then (other properties of the visual organ being alike in the two cases) the anomalous individual would always have to use more green than the normal person, in the ratio of 1:a, in trying to match a red-green mixture with any homogeneous light. But this is by no means the case. The fact is rather that the two red-green ratios (for the normal eye and for the anomalous eye) are found to be very different according to the kind of homogeneous light that is matched, and that the quotient of the two ratios varies in a regular way with the wave-length of the homogeneous light. An illustration is given in the following tables.[1]

Homogeneous light	Quotient of the ratio (red : green) for the two observers
628 $\mu\mu$	4.51
615 "	3.74
603 "	3.15
591 "	3.14
581 "	2.68
571 "	2.48
561 "	2.15
552 "	2.12

Homogeneous light	Quotient of the ratio (red : green) for the two observers
625 $\mu\mu$	0.019
613 "	0.123
601 "	0.230
589 "	0.278
579 "	0.262
569 "	0.249
559 "	0.176
550 "	0.080

As stated above, it may be inferred from this fact that these differences are not due to physical causes, but rather to modifications of some kind in the parts of the visual organ that can be affected by light. In order to express this idea and at the same time to bring out the distinction between these forms of colour vision and the reduction systems, which is an important one so far as theory is concerned, the former may be referred to as *alteration systems*.[2] While all colour equations valid for normal vision are also valid for the reduction systems, a characteristic of the alteration system is that this is not the case. This fact is brought out particularly clearly in the case of the RAYLEIGH-equation. Lights that look alike to the normal eye have to be changed considerably to be made to match for vision of this kind.

[1] See v. KRIES *Zeitschrift für Psychologie* etc. XIX. S. 65.

[2] This distinction between "reduced" and "altered" systems is essentially the same as that made by HERING (PFLÜGERS *Arch*.LVII. 308), although the terms he employs (qualitative and quantitative modifications of colour vision) are not very apt and may easily lead to misunderstanding. The subject is discussed by the writer in his paper: "Über Farbensystem, *Zft. f. Psychol. u. Physiol. der Sinnesorgane*, XIII. pp. 246 and foll.

So far a complete "calibration" of a spectrum has not been made for anomalous trichromats any more than for persons with normal vision. Only the less refrangible half has been "calibrated" just as in the case of normal vision. These "calibrations" have been made by two observers, one of whom had one form of the anomaly, and the other the other form.

If these results are used for making calculations similar to those that were mentioned above as having been made for the normal eye, it is found that the colour matches of one group agree very closely with the results for deuteranopes, and those of the other group with the results for protanopes. Thus, in terms of the HELMHOLTZ theory, the presumption is that in each case only one of the three hypothetical component substances of the visual organ is modified as compared with the normal condition. For instance, if colour matches made by an anomalous trichromat are found to be valid for a deuteranope, it may be inferred that the two are alike so far as the red component substance is concerned, and that vision is normal to this extent. If the anomaly has to do with the green component, the colour matches will not indeed be valid for a normal subject, but will be valid, on the other hand, for a deuteranope who has not got this component substance at all. Now, as a matter of fact, as stated above, this is what seems to be the case. Consequently, we can assume that in the protanomalous an alteration occurs in the red component; and in the deuteranomalous an alteration in the green component.

There is some difficulty about giving a theoretical explanation of these anomalies, because neither of them represents a unique type. Both forms include individuals with minor differences amongst themselves, although these differences may perhaps be regarded as different degrees of the same kind of anomaly. They do not come out so clearly in the RAYLEIGH test as might be expected; perhaps because even with normal persons not altogether slight variations are found in making the RAYLEIGH test which are due to physical causes. On the other hand, in connection with a series of other phenomena, the different degrees of the anomaly are manifested very distinctly.

Aside from differences in making colour matches and "calibrations," a number of important peculiarities are to be found among anomalous trichromats. We are indebted especially to NAGEL's investigations[1] for light on this subject. DONDERS had long ago expressed the view that such persons had a "dim sense of colour." This indeed has now been thoroughly established; that is, the anomaly of the colour system (in the sense of having to make a different setting for the RAYLEIGH-

[1] *Klinische Monatsblätter f. Augenheilk.* XLII. S. 356. 1904.—*Zeitschr. für Psychologie* etc. XLI. S. 239, 319, 455. 1906. — Also GUTTMANN, ibid. XLII. S. 24 and 250. 1907.

equation) can be considered as an important and sure sign of "colour infirmity."

No doubt, to some extent, loss of ability for discrimination is a factor here, but the main thing is an impairment of the faculty of recognizing colours.

So far as the first point is concerned, most anomalous trichromats make the RAYLEIGH-equations, and many of them make matches also between other homogeneous lights and red-green mixtures, almost as accurately as persons with normal vision.

However, even in these cases power of discrimination for variations of wave-length is apparently on the wane. For instance, GUTTMANN made errors at $589\mu\mu$ averaging from 12 to $13\mu\mu$; whereas in the case of normal persons working under the same conditions the error amounted to only one or two units.

But along with this there is another factor that is more complicated. For example, in order to make a colour match with sodium light or with one of longer wave-length, the mixture of red and green has to be pretty nearly in a fixed ratio. On the other hand, if the experiment is made with a homogeneous light whose wave-length is decidedly less than $589\mu\mu$, the settings become entirely uncertain and variable. Moderate amounts of red not only do not upset the match, but the red can even be reduced to nothing. In other words, homogeneous light of $536\mu\mu$ can be displayed alongside the yellow without the two fields ceasing to look at least approximately the same. Evidently, therefore, power of discriminating variations of wave-length in the region from 570 to $535\mu\mu$ is very much diminished here. These are extreme cases of so-called deuteranomaly. Extreme cases of protanomaly also occur, in which homogeneous yellow, and particularly lights of somewhat longer wave-lengths, appear to be almost the same as spectral red. Here too the setting for colour matches between red-green mixtures and certain homogeneous lights may be entirely wrong.

A still simpler indication of infirmity of colour sense is more or less inability with respect to absolute recognition of colour. The coloured object has to be much larger for anomalous persons than for people with normal vision. Mere reduction of the visual angle is sufficient to make the colour of the object unrecognizable, even when it can easily be perceived by a normal eye.

Another regular difficulty that anomalous persons have is that they take a longer time to decide what the colour is. If the coloured object is exposed to view for very brief, measurable intervals of time, the minimum time required by an anomalous person to recognize the colour will be found to be much longer than that required by a normal person.

Perhaps connected with the difficulty of recognizing the right colour, is another peculiarity that NAGEL found to be very noticeable in all anomalous persons. This was what appeared to be an accentuation of certain contrast phenomena. For example, a yellow field viewed by itself is described correctly as yellow; but if it is displayed alongside a red field, it is then called green. This is the explanation of what is practically a very important fact, namely, that in observing two adjacent objects of different colours, anomalous persons are liable to make big mistakes that would be entirely out of the question in normal vision. Thus a gaslight or electric light of the usual pale yellow colour is taken for green if it is put by the side of a red light.

Note by v. Kries

(Prepared specially for insertion here, January 1924)

In recent years extensive studies have been made on the connections between the various forms of anomalous colour vision. HESS[1], in particular, has carried out very thorough investigations on this subject. The writer will limit himself here to a brief discussion of the matter so far as it has to do with typical dichromats (protanopes and deuteranopes).

The old view, as represented by SEEBECK and HELMHOLTZ, namely, that the cases of congenital partial colour blindness were arranged in two typically different groups not connected by any transitions, had been, as stated above, fully established by systematic testing of colour-mixture equations. HESS has again challenged this fact. The particular support on which he relies is that even within each group there are considerable differences in the mode of vision. However, HESS's observations were not made under conditions that insure pure daylight vision, and for this reason alone decisive importance cannot be attached to them. For the point that is of theoretical interest is, whether or not there is a distinct difference between the *mechanisms of daylight vision* in the protanopic and deuteranopic visual organs. This question can only be decided by observations where precautions have been taken to insure practically pure cone vision, by having the eye light-adapted and the observation confined to a small field. If, for

---

[1] v. HESS, Die Rot-Grün-Blindheiten. PFLÜGERS *Archiv*, CLXXXV. 1920.—Idem, Die angeborenen Farbensinnstörungen und das Farbengesichtsfeld. *Archiv. f. Augenheilkunde*, LXXXVI. 1920. — v. HESS gave a very thorough account of the subject in his article on "Farbenlehre" in the *Ergebnissen der Physiologie*, Bd. XX. p. 1. 1922. See v. KRIES's review of this article, Zur physiologischen Farbenlehre, *Klinische Monatsblätter f. Augenheilkunde*, LXX. p. 577. 1923.

instance, it was found that different protanopes disagree more or less about what is the brightest place in the spectrum, this might easily be due to the fact that under the conditions in which the observations were made the relation between rod-activity and cone-activity was very unequally adjusted for different individuals. Now it is a well-known fact, without any particular further significance, that the capacity for twilight vision, and hence also the ratio in which the two component parts of *vision* are concerned in the resultant sensations, differs very much in different individuals. There is another point that is more important. HESS finds not only that protanopes as well as deuteranopes are without the red-green sense, but that in the former the yellow-blue sense also is lowered as compared with that of persons with normal vision or with that of deuteranopes. For this reason he is disposed to regard protanopia as being a transition-stage of that dichromatic condition, which is due to lack of the red-green sense on its way to total colour blindness. If this fact should be established, it would constitute a behaviour of great theoretical interest. On the assumption that the normal visual organ (the only question here is as to the daylight mechanism that has colour vision) is converted into a protanopic eye by the lack of *one* component and into a deuteranopic eye by the lack of the *other* component, it may be the case that both of these organs are indeed adapted for producing the sensation of yellow and the sensation of blue, and yet that the yellow-blue sensation, like the entire daylight vision, has an altogether different basis in the two different visual organs. A whole series of *facts* testifies to the fact that in normal daylight vision it is precisely the red component, the very part that the protanope lacks, that has a specially important, indeed a principal, significance.[1] This being the case, the lack of this component, that is, protanopia, must mean a far more serious injury than the lack of the other component, that is, deuteranopia. According to this, we can understand how it is that both protanopes and deuteranopes have indeed the faculty of seeing yellow and blue, but not equally well, and why the deuteranope is as a rule, or at any rate on the average, superior to the protanope in this respect. Nor would it be

[1] KÖNIG long ago called attention incidentally to the curious fact that the luminosity values of the colours, no matter whether they are determined by the direct impression they produce or are measured as peripheral values or flicker values, turn out to be very nearly the same function of the wave-length for deuteranopes and persons with normal vision. Since in the case of deuteranopes light of long wave-lengths has no effect except on the red component, we must suppose also that this action depends on the wave-length in the same way. But then the further result is that the distribution of luminosity is not affected, or at least almost inappreciably affected, by the addition of the green component by which the deuteranopic visual organ is converted into a normal organ; in other words, that in the case of normal vision also the luminosity goes practically hand in hand with the action of the red component.

strange if under some circumstances, dependent on a vision in which rod-function and cone-function were intermingled, this vision should on the average gain the upper hand more strongly with protanopes than with normal persons and deuteranopes. Then indeed we could speak of an approximation to total colour blindness, of course only in the sense in which that term is understood in the duplicity theory. Unfortunately, the method which Hess used in his observations does not enable us to come to any sure decision about these points. Thus, he ascertained the limits of the visual field for seeing yellow and blue with suitable objects, that is, the extent of the so-called colour-fields of vision. But his own observations show that even with persons whose visual organs are the same in other ways, and particularly in the case of persons with normal colour vision, there are very considerable differences in the extent of these fields among different individuals. And hence in the first place it seems hardly permissible to draw any definite conclusions from the differences in this respect that were found between protanopes and deuteranopes.

2. The Phenomena of Daylight Vision Under Conditions that make it Difficult or Impossible to Recognize Colours

The above description of normal and abnormal vision has been confined principally to perfectly definite conditions, those in fact that are most conducive to distinguishing and recognizing colours. Even in the normal organ of vision there are conditions for which the sensations are modified as to their colour specifications, or they may be entirely lacking. Most important of all is the case when the light does not fall on the fovea but on more or less eccentric parts of the retina; and another case of importance is when the time of exposure or the apparent size of the object is reduced.

The facts concerning the first case have already been partly considered in the main text (p. 154). As was there stated, the coloured character of the sensation produced by a certain kind of light acting on the eccentric part of the retina depends to a very great extent on the absolute intensity of the light and on the luminous area. Along with the fact that the pigments used were not exactly defined, this serves to explain the many conflicting statements of the earlier workers in this field. In numerous details the conditions have been clarified by Hess's investigations.[1] The appearance of most colours is found to alter more and more towards the periphery of the retina. There are just four hues that tend to fade out without losing their quality. These "invariable colours"[2] are a green of $495\mu\mu$, a nearly complementary red (spectral

---

[1] *Archiv f. Ophth.* XXXV. (4). S. 1.
[2] ¶See Parsons, *Colour vision*, p. 70. (J. P. C. S.)

red with a little addition of blue), a yellow of 574.5$\mu\mu$, and a blue of 471$\mu\mu$. The first two lose their colour at a comparatively short distance out from the centre; the last two very much farther out. When the red and green objects are of the same size, saturation and luminosity[1], the limits are found to be the same for both of these colours. The same thing is true with respect to yellow and blue. The limits for yellow and blue being farther out than for red and green, in the case of objects of given size, luminosity and saturation, we can speak of a dichromatic zone; in which the invariable red and green look colourless, and the invariable yellow and blue are seen in their ordinary hues. A simple rule for the qualitative changes of all colours that are comprised between these invariables is that the red (or green) sensation disappears more quickly than the blue (or yellow), and so it approaches the latter. Thus violet and blue-green blend into blue; orange and green-yellow, into yellow.

Vision in the dichromatic zone is, at all events, different from that of the protanopic eye. It might be something like that of the deuteranopic eye; although it is not certain as to whether this agreement is perfectly exact. This matter will be discussed later.

An outermost zone of the retina in which even yellow and blue objects have no colour[2] may be said to be *totally colour-blind* or "monochromatic,"[3] although it must be remembered that the extent of this zone depends very much on the luminosity and size of the object. The

---

[1] What is meant by the "same saturation" is, for instance, when the two equal sectors on the colour top produce a colourless mixture.

As to "same luminosity," there is some uncertainty about this point in HESS's work. His condition is that the two colours must have the same "white valence." This amounts to defining white valences in two ways, (1) as being the same as what we now call twilight value, and (2) as being the same as what we now call peripheral value (see page 415). At that time it was not understood that these two things are entirely different. Presumably, the condition involved here (so far as the light-adapted eye is concerned) means that the peripheral values of the two colours must be the same.

[2] ¶C. E. FERREE and G. RAND, The absolute limits of colour sensitivity and the effect of intensity of light on the apparent limits. *Psychol. Rev.* XXVII. 1921, 1–23.—The extent and shape of the zones of color sensitivity in relation to the intensity of the stimulus light. *Amer. Jour. Physiol. Optics.* I. 1921, 185–213. — The limits of color sensitivity; effects of brightness of preexposure and surrounding field. *Psychol. Rev.* XXVII. 1921, 377–398.—Some contributions to the science and practice of ophthalmology. *Trans. Internat. Cong. Ophthalmol.* Washington, 1922, pp. 1–36—Perimetry; variable factors influencing breadth of color fields. *Amer. Jour. Ophthalm.* V. 1922, p. 886.—A new laboratory and clinical perimeter. *Jour. Exp. Psychol.*, V. 1922, 46–67. (H. L.)

[3] ¶This use of the word "monochromatic," to describe the type of vision of those "people who apparently see all parts of the spectrum of one hue" (PARSONS) is, of course, entirely different from the way it is used in Physics. The physicist is accustomed to speak of "monochromatic" light, meaning light of a definite wave-length, and of "monochromatic aberrations" (as used by HELMHOLTZ and GULLSTRAND in Volume I). The word "achromatic" is in the same predicament. This is a good instance of the "confusion of tongues" among different groups of scientists that often makes it exceedingly difficult for one to understand the terminology of the other even when both have the same thing in mind. Total colour blindness or monochromatic vision is the same thing as "achromatopia." (J. P. C. S.)

disappearance of colour can be noticed best on the nasal edge of the visual field. When bits of coloured paper on a grey background are carefully inserted in the visual field from this side, they always show up at first as brighter or darker spots without any colour. Under these circumstances any pair of lights can be made to look exactly alike by simply adjusting their luminosities in the right proportion. And hence the mode of vision can be determined exactly as in the case of a totally colour-blind eye, by finding out the requisite luminosities of the various parts of the spectrum or the distribution of the spectral stimulus values that have to be taken into consideration here. The writer has found the distribution of these stimulus values, or *peripheral values* (as he terms them), in the dispersion spectrum of gaslight. In order to show at once the theoretically important fact that the peripheral values depend on the wave-length in an entirely different way from the twilight values, both the peripheral values and the twilight values are given in the following table (the values for sodium light being put equal to 100).[1]

Wave-length	680	651	629	608	589	573	558	530	513 $\mu\mu$
Peripheral value	9.6	37.5	77.5	101	100	79.1	52.2	28.5	14.6
Twilight value	?	3.4	14.0	35.5	100	256	351	321	198

The results are exhibited in Fig. 78 in the usual way.[2]

As was mentioned above, the sensation can also be deprived of its coloured character by reducing the time of exposure or the apparent size of the stimulating light. The factors in the first case have not yet been accurately determined. On the other hand, SIEBECK[3] has made a systematic study of the other case. He finds that, with spectral lights of average luminosity, colours cannot be made

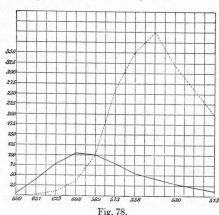

Fig. 78.

Distribution of the peripheral values——— and of the twilight values...... in the prismatic spectrum of gaslight.

[1] ¶See PARSONS, *Colour vision*, p. 71. (J. P. C. S.)

[2] ¶Compare PARSONS, *Colour vision*, Fig. 25, where these curves are called "photopic luminosity curve for the totally colour blind peripheral zone of the retina," and "scotopic luminosity curve." (J. P. C. S.)

[3] *Zeitschrift für Physiologie der Sinnesorgane* XLI. S. 71.

to disappear entirely at the fovea by reducing the size of the field; although it is easy to do so at very small distances from the centre (1.5°). Accordingly, it is possible to determine for what luminosities different lights are visible under these conditions; an investigation that is perfectly analogous to that which has just been described; where the colours are made to disappear by being observed far out from the centre. The stimulus values found in this way may be termed *minimum-field luminosities*. The results obtained by SIEBECK are given in the following table, which shows that the minimum-field luminosities are likewise entirely different from the twilight values, but are in approximate agreement with the peripheral values (the maximum being at 601.3$\mu\mu$).

Wave-length	658.0	650.1	642.4	635.0	627.8	620.8	604.2
Minimum-field luminosity	44.9	56.7	66.6	72.1	84.2	91.5	104.3

Wave-length	607.8	601.3	595.2	598.3	584.2	579.1	574.1
Minimum-field luminosity	112.8	128	110.9	100	90	81.6	79.5

Wave-length	569.3	564.8	560.1	556.4	551.4	547.2	542.9
Minimum-field luminosity	72.9	68.6	62.6	58.5	52	47.3	42.8

In finding the minimum-field luminosities and the peripheral values, it is necessary to compare the luminosities of lights of different colours. It is possible to do this just because under the given conditions the sensations do not reveal differences of colour. This question of comparison of the luminosity of lights of different colours is not only one of general interest but has been the subject of much controversy. In these observations, therefore, we may speak of methods of *heterochromatic photometry*.[1]

A series of other observations will, therefore, be included here, because from this point of view they are connected with those that have just been described. The following fact, discovered first by ROOD, constitutes the starting point of these observations. If, by means of a colour disc, the eye is exposed alternately and regularly to two lights, one coloured and the other not, and if the luminosity of the colourless light is systematically varied, there is a certain definite value for which a minimum number of alternations suffices to make the sensation

---

[1] In the use of this term undoubtedly one has to be on his guard against making a mistake or at least against being misled by very questionable assumptions. It does not mean to imply at all that the luminosity-relations of different lights must necessarily be the same when the colour is made to disappear in some other way; nor does it mean that equality of brightness of two sensations of different colour is any precisely defined relation. See the writer's work on this subject in NAGELs *Handbuch der Physiol.* III. pages 28 and 259.

¶Consult also GLAZEBROOK's *Dictionary of Applied Physics*, IV (1923), pages 453, foll. (J. P. C. S.)

uniform and the flicker disappear. When this luminosity of the colourless light has been found and the disc made to rotate just fast enough for the flicker to disappear, the flicker appears again as soon as the luminosity of the colourless light is increased or decreased. Without implying anything as to the theory of the phenomenon, let us speak of two lights whose intensities are adjusted for the minimum "fusion frequency" as being "equivalent as to flicker"; and call the luminosity of the colourless light which is "equivalent as to flicker" with a given coloured light its *flicker value*. A determination of the flicker values for the prismatic spectrum of gaslight has been made by POLIMANTI.[1] The results are given in the following table.[2]

Wave-length	687	664	642	624	606	588	565	543	526	500 $\mu\mu$
Flicker value	28.3	31.2	56.6	75.2	87.9	100	83.1	48.1	25.0	21.9

Evidently, the distribution of the flicker values agrees, approximately at least, with those of the peripheral values and minimum-field values; but it is entirely different from that of the twilight values.

Quite a number of other methods have been used for comparing the luminosities of lights of different colours; and some have been proposed without ever having been employed.

VIERORDT[3] considered two coloured lights as being equally bright when their luminosities were such that a certain white light added to them could just be perceived. According to another principle, likewise based on flicker phenomena but not to be confused with that of ROOD's mentioned above, lights of different colours may be regarded as being equally bright which, acting intermittently, have to have the same frequency to produce a steady sensation without any flicker in it (HAYCRAFT[4], RIVERS[5]).

Moreover, there is an observation reported by BRÜCKE that indicates something analogous in space-discrimination to ROOD's observation for time-discrimination alluded to above. When a coloured object is displayed against a colourless background, there is a certain perfectly definite luminosity of the background for which it is hardest to recognize the object, no matter what angle it subtends; and the luminosity of the coloured object may then be said to be equal to that of the background.

[1] *Zeitschrift für Psychologie etc.* XIX. S. 263.

[2] ¶See PARSONS, *Colour vision*, Fig. 26. (J. P. C. S.)

[3] POGGENDORFFS *Annalen*. CXXXVII. — *Die Anwendung des Spektralapparates.* Tübingen 1871.

[4] *Journal of Physiology* XXI. S. 126.

[5] Ibid., XXII. S. 137.

One of the methods used by Brücke[1] consisted in mixing small amounts of different greys with the colour to be tested. If a small piece of grey paper is placed on a coloured disc so as to make a ring of the right width when the disc is set in rotation, it can be decided with a comparative degree of certainty whether the ring is brighter or darker than the rest of the disc; that is, whether the grey is brighter or darker than the coloured paper. Fundamentally, this procedure is also a direct comparison of the luminosity of unlike colours (which differ also in saturation). There is the advantage, however, of being able to compare two colours of the same hue that do not differ much in saturation.

Lastly it will be recalled that Fraunhofer tried to compare the luminosity of light of different colours directly by their subjective impression, the colours being visible. This method was subsequently undertaken again by König[2] on a rather bigger scale. His results on five normal subjects are given in the following table.

Wave-length	Luminosity for Observer				
$\mu\mu$	I	II	III	IV	V
670	0.855	1.120	—	—	—
650	2.381	2.137	1.15	—	0.64
625	3.460	3.413	2.06	1.10	1.24
605	3.650	3.247	2.56	1.66	1.56
590	3.030	2.645	2.38	2.05	1.58
575	2.358	1.923	2.00	2.08	1.56
555	1.695	1.389	1.50	1.65	1.36
535	1	1	1	1	1
520	0.554	0.553	—	—	—
505	0.224	0.250	—	—	—
490	0.0994	0.092	—	—	—

Accordingly, in approximate agreement with the peripheral values and flicker values and also with the minimum-field luminosities, the maximum luminosity, on the average anyhow, is on the red side of the sodium line. The results for the different subjects, it is true, vary a good deal, especially too in the position of this maximum. Incidentally, these tests have been shown to be quite uncertain. The setting of two unlike colours at equal luminosity is very variable and often also seems to be somewhat arbitrary. And hence it is difficult too to decide whether the individual differences exceed the degrees of uncertainties and fluctuations of this nature.

Some of the investigations referred to above have been extended to a larger number of persons, normal and anomalous. These results must now be briefly considered, as they are of some theoretical interest.

[1] Pflügers *Archiv* XCVIII S. 90.
[2] Helmholtz *Festschrift*. 1891. S. 350.

In the first place it seems that even normal persons are subject to not altogether inconsiderable variations in this matter. This is apparent in some degree in the above measurements of KÖNIG. But even in those methods where the uncertainty due to difference of colour is eliminated, variations are manifested. Thus POLIMANTI's results for the distribution of the peripheral values in his own case are distinctly, although not considerably, different from those of the writer.

Miss v. MALTZEW's extensive experiments[1] were concerned mainly with flicker values, and showed that even among normal trichromats there are very considerable differences in this respect. Apparently, these variations are regularly connected in some way with the differences alluded to above in making the setting for the RAYLEIGH-equation. Persons who use comparatively much green in the mixture likewise require a high luminosity of green to give it a flicker value equal to that of a certain red.

As to the phenomena in anomalous vision, the results indicate, as might have been expected that the most favourable conditions for such colour sensations as dichromats have are in the fovea. At a certain distance from the centre, assuming that the conditions are suitable in every way, colour determinations are found to be entirely impossible. Accordingly, peripheral values can be determined in their case in the same way as for normal persons. The result then is found to be that the distribution of the peripheral values for *protanopes* is entirely different from that for persons with normal colour vision, as shown in the following table.[2]

Wave-length	680	651	629	608	587	573	558	530	513
Peripheral value for protanopes	4.1?	10.7	34.0		100		110		36.4
Peripheral value for normal persons	9.6	37.5	77.5	101	100	79.6	52.2	28.5	14.6

A similar difference is found also in the case of the flicker values[3], not for the protanopic eye only, but for the protanomalous eye as well. Thus, generally, in order to get the requisite effect here, the luminosities of the red light have to be very much greater for both of these anomalous kinds of vision than for normal vision.

The differences, between normal colour vision, on the one hand, and protanopic and protanomalous vision, on the other hand, are in fact so large as to be apparent without any question, even when lights of different colours are compared simply by the subjective impression

---

[1] *Zeitschrift für Physiologie der Sinnesorgane.* XLIII. S. 76. 1909.

[2] v. KRIES, *Zeitschrift für Psychologie.* XV. S. 266. Similar results were subsequently obtained by v. d. WIJDE, *Onderzoekingen,* Utrecht. 4. III. 2.

[3] POLIMANTI, *loc. cit.* S. 274. — LEVY, *Zft. Psychologie, etc.* XXXVI. S. 83. 1904.

of their brightnesses. This fact has been established by a number of observers.[1]

In the writer's first observations a trifling difference, hardly beyond the limit of error, was found between the peripheral values of a deuteranopic eye and those of a normal eye. But ANGIER[2] believed that he could prove that there certainly was a difference in this respect. However, some doubt has been raised as to the correctness of this conclusion by Miss v. MALTZEW's results as to the individual differences of flicker values that are found to occur among normal trichromats. The differences which she got were very large, as has been stated. The deuteranopic and deuteranomalous persons investigated by her arranged themselves in between the normal trichromats. It is at least conceivable that the individual differences in the ratios of the peripheral values are approximately similar to those of the flicker values; and if this is the case, it would be expected that also the differences in this respect between normal vision and deuteranopic or deuteranomalous vision would anyhow not be so large that they could not be accounted for by individual differences within the same type.[3]

On the assumption that trichromats and deuteranopes agree as to peripheral values, and, further, that lights of equal peripheral values, even when they are seen centrally and therefore in different colours, give the impression of being equally bright, it follows that green and bluish-red lights which look alike to the deuteranope will look about equally bright to a person with normal colour vision. As a matter of fact this is the case, as far as we can tell with the great uncertainty that exists in heterochromatic comparisons of brightness. Certain peculiarities of the colour chart mentioned by SCHENCK are connected with this fact. It has been already shown (§20) that the colours that look alike to dichromats lie on straight lines that must all intersect at one point (in case the dichromatic system is a reduction form of normal vision). This point, which generally is outside of the real part of the colour chart, represents the stimuli which act only on the component that is not present in the dichromatic eye.

The construction of the colour chart, and hence also the position of this point, is arbitrary to the extent that unit quantities of the three calibration lights can be selected in any way we like. It is always possible to choose them in such a way that the point is infinitely distant, that is, so that colours that a dichromat cannot tell apart will fall on parallel lines. In order for this to be the case for a deuteranope, according to the assumptions made here, the unit quantities of the three calibration lights would have to be chosen so as to be about equally bright for the normal eye.

We have had to limit this treatment to a discussion of those anomalies of colour vision that are of particular interest from physiological standpoints. Of course, the subject is of much interest in other direc-

---

[1] LEVY, *loc. cit.* — SCHENCK. PFLÜGERS *Archiv* CXVIII. S. **174. 1907.**

[2] ANGIER, Ibid. XXXVII. S. 401. 1905.

[3] ¶PARSONS, *Colour vision.* p. 179. (J. P. C. S.)

tions. As to the general biological relations (inheritance), statistical data and practical significance, HOLMGREN's work is still the standard book of reference on this subject.[1]

From the practical standpoint, the thing of most importance, as has been shown by NAGEL's recent researches, is that not only dichromats but persons with anomalous vision also are below par in a number of respects, and they are particularly unsuitable for railway or marine service. This, therefore, to a certain extent is the chief reason for improving the methods of investigation. The examination of these people is the right way of going at the problem of finding out all persons with abnormal colour vision and eliminating them.

As to the method of investigation, it is of very little value, as has been stated, to conduct tests which consist in finding out the names that are used in describing objects of different colours. In the writer's judgment this is true likewise concerning deductions by colour-contrasts, although a high estimate is placed on these tests in many quarters. The only methods that have proved to be of real value are those that depend on finding out what colours look alike to the patient. However, it is not easy to obtain absolutely definite colours that look exactly alike to all deuteranopes, say; partly because there are individual variations and partly because the technical production of colours is more or less uncertain and the illumination is different, etc. And therefore the best way of making the test amounts to finding out whether certain colours seem to the patient to be *very nearly* alike. This was the principle of HOLMGREN's method in which the patient was required to pick out of a large assortment of coloured wools those hues that matched certain samples. NAGEL's charts, based also on the same principle, have during the last few years been proved to be the most useful and reliable test, having been officially adopted for the merchant marine and the Prussian railway system after very thorough comparison with other methods. No system can entirely supersede the spectroscopic test of the RAYLEIGH-equation, and sometimes it has to be resorted to still. For making this test easily with comparatively inexpensive appliances, SCHMIDT and HAENSCH have constructed an instrument called an "anomaloscope" designed according to NAGEL's specifications. It is used to test the RAYLEIGH-equation by comparing, therefore, a field illuminated by homogeneous yellow with a red-green mixture.[2]

---

[1] *Die Farbenblindheit in ihren Beziehungen zum Eisenbahn- und Marinedienst.* German edition. Leipzig 1878.

[2] As to the various methods of investigation, see especially NAGEL, *Die Diagnose der praktisch wichtigen angeborenen Störungen des Farbensinnes*, 1899, and also a large number of other works by the same author, some of the most important of which are as follows:

Note by v. Kries

(specially prepared for insertion here, January 1924)

During the past decade some new facts have been ascertained which can be utilized for comparing the luminosity of light of different colours. Consider a small spot on a uniformly white ground. If for a very brief period the white light at this place is replaced by coloured light, the colour cannot be recognized any longer. But what happens is that at the moment when the coloured light acts, that particular place appears brighter or darker than the surroundings, depending on the intensity at that point. For a certain definite ratio between the intensity of the two kinds of light the spot looks neither brighter nor darker than the surroundings, and then the difference between them will not be noticed at all. Thus, just as we speak of "minimum-field luminosity" we can speak here of a *minimum-time luminosity*. Thus, when a coloured light substituted for a very brief time on a colourless ground appears neither bright nor dark it is said to be "equivalent" to that colourless light in "minimum time" (*minimal zeitgleich*). ZAHN's observations have shown that the distribution of minimum-time luminosity in the spectrum is almost, although not absolutely exactly, in agreement with the distribution of minimum-field luminosity and with the distribution of the peripheral values and flicker values.[1]

Moreover, very lately PULFRICH[2] has described a method of comparing the luminosity of light of different colours depending on binocular perception of depth, which therefore is called a *stereophotometric* process. It is based on the following fact. If a dark vertical rod is moved back and forth from right to left and from left to right in a plane in front of a bright background, under ordinary circumstances we get the correct impression of a rod being moved in a frontal plane. But now if a smoked glass is interposed in front of one eye, so as to cut down the light that comes to that eye, we get the impression that each

---

Die Diagnose der anomalen trichromatischen Systeme, *Klin. Monatsblätter für Augenheilkunde* XLII. S. 369, 1904. Zwei Apparate für die augenärztliche Funktionsprüfung (Adaptometer und Anomaloskop), *Zeitschrift für Augenheilkunde* XVII. Fortgesetzte Untersuchungen zur Symptomatologie und Diagnostik der angeborenen Störungen des Farbensinnes, *Zeitschrift für Psychologie und Physiologie der Sinnesorgane*, XLI. S. 237 and 319. 1906. Versuche mit Eisenbahn-Signallichtern an Personen mit normalen und abnormem Farbensinn, Ibid. XLI. S. 455.

[1] ZAHN, Über die Helligkeitswerte reinen Lichter bei kurzen Wirkungszeiten. *Zft. f. Psychologie für Sinnesphysiologie* XLVI. p. 287. 1912.

[2] PULFRICH, Die Stereoskopie im Dienste der isochromen und heterochromen Photometrie. *Die Naturwissenschaften*, 1922. pp. 553, 569, 714, 735 and 751. In book form with the title, *Die Stereoskopie im Dienste der Photometrie und Pyrometrie*. Berlin, 1923.

point of the rod traverses a horizontal ellipse. In the middle of its path it looks therefore farther off when it traverses it one way than when it traverses it the other way. PULFRICH speaks of this phenomenon as that of the "revolving mark." The explanation he gives is as follows. Between the arrival of a stimulus and the production of the sensation in every case there is a certain amount of time lost, which varies however with the intensity of the stimulus, decreasing as the intensity of the stimulus is increased. Thus, for instance, if the right eye is stimulated more highly than the left eye, the image of a moving object in the right eye will be a little ahead of that in the left eye. Hence, in that phase where the rod is moving to the right, the image in the right eye must be a little more to the right and that in the left eye more to the left. On the other hand when the motion is reversed, the case is just opposite; the image in the right eye will be more to the left, and that in the left eye more to the right. Accordingly, we have here the general condition that is necessary for binocular perception of depth, namely, a disparity between what is seen by one eye and what is seen by the other eye, in this case a right-and-left displacement (transversal inequality, binocular parallax). According to the general laws of binocular perception of depth, what is to be expected is that in the case first mentioned the rod would be perceived as being farther away, and in the other case as being closer. And this is exactly how it looks. The rod invariably appears to move in such a way that in the remoter part of the path it proceeds from the eye that is shaded towards the eye that sees brighter. Viewed from above the apparent motion is clockwise when the right eye gets brighter light than the left eye, and counter-clockwise when it is just the other way. Now if a *coloured* glass is inserted in front of one eye instead of the smoked glass, the same effect is produced. This is not surprising, because the coloured glass also absorbs some portions of the light concerned and so tends on the whole to darken it. If, finally, with a coloured glass in front of one eye, colourless glasses of regular gradations of darkness are inserted in front of the other eye, a certain one of them can be found for which the rod will appear to move in a plane; whereas when a brighter or darker glass than this is used, the "revolving" movement will be seen, clockwise in one case and counter-clockwise in the other. Now here we have *one* basis for comparing the luminosity of light of different colours. In PULFRICH's own words, "We get the following definition of equal luminosities: two colours are said to have the same luminosity when the time between stimulation and sensation is the same for both of them, and we can tell when their luminosities are equal by the fact that at the instant the difference vanishes between the times of the two sensations as shown by the revolving mark the circular motion becomes rectilinear" (*loc. cit.*, p. 37).[1]

We must notice that here we are dealing with a definition of equality of luminosity which, however valuable and convenient it may prove to be, still has a conventional significance always, exactly in the same way as if, for example, we should stipulate that a coloured light should be said to be of the same brightness as a light without colour, when under certain special conditions (very eccentric vision, acting on an extremely small part of the field or for a very brief time) it looks precisely the same as the colourless light. In order to express this, the writer has suggested using the term "stereo-equal" when two lights are found to be equal by PULFRICH's method. Thus two lights would be "stereo-equal" when in observing a moving object with both eyes, one eye getting one kind of light and the other eye getting the other kind, no stereoscopic effect of any sort is obtained, that is, the object which actually does move in a frontal plane also appears to move in this plane.

Physiological investigation of the phenomenon[2] has shown that lights, which are equal as to minimum-field and which therefore also have approximately the same peripheral value and minimum-time luminosity, are approximately "stereo-equal" also. However, this is only true with certain limitations, that is, with high light intensities and for the photopic eye. On the contrary, when we change over to reduced intensity of light and more or less dark-adapted eye, there is a very decided shifting of the "stereo-equal" relation. However, it is a remarkable fact that the ratio between the stereo-values for a light of long wave-length and one of short wave-length is not shifted in the sense of the PURKINJE phenomenon, but in the opposite sense. The explanation of this behaviour can readily be found in the fact that both components of the visual organ, that is, the cones and the rods, are concerned to a different extent in the production of the visual impression, and that the reaction of the rods is decidedly more inert, as is shown also by numerous other phenomena (see pages 445, ff). In the transition from daylight-vision to twilight-vision the short waves of light gain in luminosity as compared with the long waves, because they act far more powerfully on the rods. It is exactly the same thing that comes out in the PURKINJE phenomenon. But the rapidity of the reaction, and therefore the stereo-value, is not increased, but diminished, by the greater action of the rods that is in evidence

---

[1] ¶This striking and beautiful phenomenon can be readily observed. PULFRICH's method is both ingenious and interesting, and certainly of much theoretical value. However, it would hardly seem to be capable of sufficient accuracy for purposes of practical heterochromatic photometry. (J.P.C.S.)

[2] v. KRIES, Über das stereophotometrische Verfahren zur Helligkeitsvergleichung ungleichfarbiger Lichter. *Die Naturwissenschaften.* 1923, p. 461.

here. And so it may happen that by lowering the light and by dark adaptation the ratio between the stereo-values of light of long waves and light of short waves is shifted in the opposite sense of the PURKINJE phenomenon, that is, in favour of the light of long waves. The consequence is that in any case the stereo-photometric process cannot give unequivocal and useful results unless these complications are avoided, that is, unless the operation of the twilight mechanism is practically eliminated by using light of high intensity and making the observations with the light-adapted eye.

The *threshold values* supply another set of facts that can be made to bear on heterochromatic photometry. The luminosity of a light may be defined as being inversely proportional to its threshold value, and accordingly another definition will be obtained as to what is intended when we speak of the luminosity of a light or of two lights of different colours as having the same luminosity. In the first place there are known facts here which show that, provided the observation is made with the scotopic eye, and no special precaution is taken to confine it to the central region where there are no rods, the luminosities of lights of different colours are measured by their twilight values. This case can be excluded here, because under these conditions there is no sensation of colour anyhow, and hence also there is no difficulty about making a comparison between the luminosities of lights of different colours. But the results obtained in the case of purely foveal vision are of more interest. Suppose we use the term *threshold luminosity* to denote the luminosity as measured by the reciprocal of the threshold value; then the question arises again whether it is proportional to the minimum-field luminosity, peripheral value, etc. According to BOSWELL's results, apparently it is not. His observations rather indicated that in the middle part of the spectrum, indeed (where the lights that are on the verge of visibility are seen without colour even in *foveal* vision), the threshold luminosities proceed almost side by side with the minimum-field luminosities. But at the two ends of the spectrum, that is, for light of both long waves and short waves, a light that is just over the threshold will immediately begin to appear coloured. Here the threshold luminosities are different from the minimum-field luminosities; the threshold, in fact, being lower, that is, the sensitivity being greater than it would be if there were a proportionality with the minimum-field luminosities. BOSWELL's conclusion from this was that when a light was just on the verge of visibility something more was involved than the colourless luminosity alone, and that the colour-value promotes the visibility, that is, lowers the threshold. This has been confirmed by KOHLRAUSCH's more recent observations, which, however, have shown also that these phenomena are likewise dependent on the state of adaptation of the fovea. The matter requires further investigation.

II. Theories of Vision

1. The Young-Helmholtz Theory

HELMHOLTZ endeavoured to elucidate the whole nature of the visual sensations, and especially the way in which they depend on the effective stimuli, in terms of the theory which is known by his name and which is based on a conjecture of THOMAS YOUNG. In giving a description of this theory and of the numerous subsequent hypotheses that have been conceived along the same line, the writer would like to indicate beforehand the principal point of view which is the motive for doing this.

Even at the present time the theory of HELMHOLTZ is thoroughly justified as to its fundamental conceptions, it is in close agreement with the facts, and as an hypothesis it is qualified to explain a very large mass of actual phenomena. The writer has briefly expounded this elsewhere.[1] The main thing that has to be done now, therefore, is, first, to mention a series of new facts recently discovered which substantiate and support the theory, and then to speak of the limitations, modifications and additions which it certainly must undergo on account of a number of other established results. Incidentally, the opportunity will be afforded at the same time of correcting some misunderstandings under which the theory has laboured in many ways.

It will be necessary also, in the second place, to discuss here the other theories of visions, which, as above stated, are very numerous. However, this will be confined to a general survey and brief outline of the fundamental conceptions, without going into a detailed criticism and weighing all probabilities and dubieties. The writer's views have been stated elsewhere as to the futility of making hypotheses and dissecting and weighing all sorts of possibilities beyond what seems expedient in the light of our positive knowledge.

A perfectly general conclusion should certainly be stated here prominently first of all: Fundamentally, the HELMHOLTZ theory was simply the expression of a direct fact of observation, namely, that *the resultant of all the various light stimuli so far as sensations are concerned can be completely represented as a function of three variables.*[2] It is idle to try to explain this fact except on the assumption that the *result of the stimulation* also can be represented completely as a function of three variables. It is this assumption that is the fundamental conception of the HELMHOLTZ theory. The justification for it has

---

[1] NAGELS *Handbuch der Physiologie* III. S. 266 f.

[2] ¶Some would maintain perhaps that all we are justified in saying here is that an immediate photo-chemical initial process is a function of three variables. (J. P. C. S.)

been shown most of all by the huge difficulties that are encountered by every theory that has been developed on the assumption of a greater number of independent valences.

The next thing to be noticed here is that so far as *dichromatic vision* is concerned and its relation to normal colour vision, the researches described above (page 398) have completely verified HELM-HOLTZ's conjecture, that there are two distinct types of this kind, both being reduction forms of normal vision. In fact, therefore, (just as HELMHOLTZ guessed from less accurate data) the conditions occurring here can be explained most satisfactorily as being *deficiency-effects*, that is, on the assumption that one component of the normal organ of vision is lacking in one case and another component in the other case.

Observations have shown too that any other explanation of the difference between the two types of dichromats (especially as being due to physical conditions of the ocular media) cannot be thought of at all. Undoubtedly, therefore, the simple way in which the theory is able to account correctly for these facts is a strong confirmation of it.

Matters are not quite so simple when we come to consider *anomalous trichromatic vision*.

In order to give a theoretical explanation of the facts which have been assembled above, we must keep steadily in mind, first of all, that the question here, as was pointed out then, is one of *alterations*, that is, variations, the effect of which is that matches that are valid for the normal eye are not valid for the anomalous eye. This immediately excludes the idea that one of the normal components, let us say, instead of being lacking entirely as in case of the dichromats, has simply been reduced to a very small amount without being changed in its character. We might indeed suppose that in this way the ability of discrimination in certain respects was lowered more and more; but matches that were valid for the normal eye would still have to be valid for the anomalous eye. A better plan is to adopt an idea which was developed first by FICK[1], in a different connection, it is true. The different appearance of colours is due to their acting unequally on the various component substances of the eye. Imagine the visual organ modified in such a way that the valence curves of two component substances instead of being considerably different, as they usually are, are almost identical; then no matter how these two substances may combine, there will not be much difference in the effects produced. Thus the result of certain differences in the nature of the stimulating light will be smaller differences in the corresponding physiological

---

[1] *Verhandlungen der physik-mediz. Gesellschaft zu Würzburg.* V 1873. S. 129. —PFLÜGERS *Archiv* XLVII S. 274.

processes, and hence with respect to certain discriminations the
response of the organ of vision will be at fault. If the valence curves
of two components are identical, the result would be a typically
dichromatic organ. Accordingly, we are bound to suppose that the
red component substance in the case of one class of anomalous persons,
and the green component substance in the case of the other class, has
undergone some kind of change by which its valence curve has been so
modified that there is less difference between it and the valence curve
of the other (normal) component substance than there is in the case
of an eye with good colour vision. In this way we can easily conceive
of a series of stages of transition into typical dichromatic vision of
one kind or the other.

At present we still have no way of calculating these changed valence
curves. But if light of all wave-lengths between 589 and $536\mu\mu$ looks almost
exactly alike to the extreme deuteranomalous eye, this means that the
valence curves of both components are very nearly in the same proportion
in this part of the spectrum. And in the most pronounced cases of protanomalous vision also the behaviour seems to be the same in the region of the
long waves about up to the sodium line.

However, as to the connection between dichromatism and normal
vision, a somewhat different view appears to be probable. Taking
everything into consideration, it is quite likely that anomalous trichromatic colour systems are intermediate forms between normal
trichromatism and typical dichromatism; so that, either by separate
steps or continuously, the protanomalous eye represents a transition
between the normal eye and the protanopic eye, and the deuteranomalous eye a transition between the normal eye and the deuteranopic
eye. As a matter of fact, the observations described above show that
as soon as the ability of the anomalous eye for discriminating colour
is lowered by reducing the size of the object, it behaves nearly in the
same way as the dichromatic eye. Whether this agreement is perfect,
has not yet been decided in the milder forms of anomalous vision.
On the contrary, indeed, it is found, for instance, that a person with
pronounced protanomalous vision will make a match between red
($671\mu\mu$) and yellow (589) that agrees with that of the protanopic eye;
explaining, however, at the same time that, while the fields match
mighty nearly, they are not exactly the same. For deuteranopic
vision and deuteranomalous vision the relation is still more sharply
established. When the investigation is made with the small fields of
the spectrum apparatus, persons may behave like typical deuteranopes,
and yet, when tested with large objects, never make the RAYLEIGH-
match perfectly correctly, showing themselves to be, therefore, like

very anomalous trichromats.[1] Another thing to be noted here is that with reference also to luminosities (peripheral values, flicker values, etc.) protanomalous vision and protanopic vision behave in the same way or at least very much alike, and therefore very differently from normal vision; but the differences in deuteranomalous persons (just as in deuteranopes) are no greater than the individual variations from the normal.

Thus if dichromatic vision is regarded as being the highest manifestation of a modification, which in its lower degree is characteristic of so-called anomalous vision, the conclusion is reached that in such cases there is something more than just simply a lack of one of the component substances of the visual organ. Take the case of protanopic vision, for example. The idea is that, in its capability of being acted on by different kinds of light, the first component substance here, instead of having its own normal quality, has that which belongs normally to the second component substance. So also in the case of deuteranopic vision the valence curves of these two component substances would both be the curve that normally belongs to the first, or red, component. It is obvious that an organ of vision of this nature, in which two of the component substances are bound to act in the way described, must behave as a dichromatic eye.

Undoubtedly, alterations are not so easy to comprehend as pure deficiency effects; and the entire subject no longer seems to be quite so clear and lucid as it looked when there was an absolutely typical and fixed organization that could not be modified except by being lacking in some constituent part. But there cannot be any doubt whatever as to the occurrence of such alterations. (No physical explanation can account for the big discrepancy in some colour matches.) A certain variability of the organ of vision is therefore a directly established fact, and every theory must take it into account.

Moreover, from this point of view typical dichromatic vision would be a remarkable case, because the two valence curves are perfectly identical. And in a rather broad sense this case might perhaps be considered as being a deficiency effect. Thus, suppose, for instance, that A and B are two component substances that normally are provided with photo-sensitive materials a and b, respectively. Now if, instead of this, both A and B have the same material b, it would mean simply that the quality of the light-receptor belonging to A was abnormal; or, of course, it can be considered as being an absence of a. Thus, the importance of the fact that perfectly dichromatic systems are reduction forms of normal vision does not seem to be diminished,

[1] NAGEL, *Zeitschrift für Psychologie* etc., XXXIX. p. 96, 1905.

even if in their case it is not a question of deficiency effect in the very simplest meaning of the expression.

Incidentally also, according to this view, the answer is obtained to the question, as to what is the nature of the sensations of dichromats; whether, for example, the protanope sees mixed white light as colourless or perhaps blue-green. Although it is impossible to get any certain information as to the sensation of other persons, this latter assumption always did seem very unlikely, particularly in reference to twilight vision, as well as to the phenomena of acquired and unilateral colour blindness. On the theory of dichromatic vision adopted here, it seems clear that colourless light looks exactly the same way to dichromats as it does to normal persons; and it may be conjectured that long waves of light look yellow and short waves blue to both protanopes and deuteranopes.

An extensive array of facts, mainly phenomena connected with adaptation, has been accumulated since HELMHOLTZ's theory of colour vision was formulated. The phenomena of adaptation are at the basis of the duplicity theory (twilight vision, total colour blindness, the PURKINJE phenomenon, etc.). We shall have to see how HELMHOLTZ's theory can be connected with these facts and with the assumptions of the duplicity theory so far as the explanation of these facts is concerned.

At first glance it might indeed seem that the duplicity theory was diametrically opposed to HELMHOLTZ's theory of the sensations of vision. For according to the latter, the sensation of colourless brightness ought to be produced by a combination of processes which of themselves arouse a red-green and a violet sensation; which cannot be considered at all in the case of the activity of the twilight mechanism. However, by imposing some limitations on the HELMHOLTZ theory, as has to be done also for other reasons, this difficulty will be removed. In thus modifying the original theory it is still a question whether this implies something essentially different from what its author had in mind or whether it amounts merely to introducing definite assumptions as to some matters which HELMHOLTZ himself left open to discussion.

In the first place it must be kept in mind here that when HELMHOLTZ made the assumption that the organ of vision was a structure composed of three parts, he did not mean that the *sensation* itself was a combination of three elements (like the three notes of a musical triad). What he meant rather was that, in spite of the composite nature of the physiological process as made up of three independent constituents, the sensation may very well be something perfectly unitary and not capable of psychological sub-division. He regarded the outstanding position of certain sensations (for absence of colour and the so-called pure colours) as the result of psychological relations, connected with the naming of colours, etc. It is this view that stands in such sharp contrast to the one so often entertained nowadays, that the simple investigation of sensations without any auxiliary appliances is sufficient to enable us to find out their "simple elements." In the writer's opinion, from analogy with what is known about other senses, this way of looking at the matter is certainly much less accurate; and HELMHOLTZ's conception is undoubtedly justified to the extent that sensations of complex physiological origin can sometimes convey the impression of being absolutely unitary and typically steadfast.

Thus, while from this point of view there does not seem to be any positive necessity of modifying the HELMHOLTZ theory as proposed above, there are other facts that point in that direction with greater force. We know by experience that the sensation of absence of colour must certainly be exceptionally significant, because in a great many cases colour perceptions cease, and there is nothing left but a colourless sensation. And this is true, indeed, not only under the conditions of twilight vision (where there is a simple explanation for it on the assumptions of the duplicity theory), but also for daylight vision. The variations of vision in passing from the central to the more and more eccentric parts of the retina belong here. Still more important is the fact that by decreasing the size of an object the colour can be made to disappear; as a person with normal vision can very easily verify by using the eccentric parts of his retina, and as can be shown anywhere in the visual field of an anomalous trichromat. Another point in this same connection is that by limiting the time of exposure it can be made impossible for an anomalous trichromat to recognize colour. And, finally, let us allude also to acquired abnormalities of colour vision due to pathological causes, in which likewise colour discrimination is lost. Perhaps, in some of these cases absence of colour can be attributed, as above, to variations of the valence curves; but this explanation is ruled out for the cases of areal and temporal limitations. We are almost bound to make the assumption here that, even when the degrees of activity of the three hypothetical components of the organ of vision are adjusted to correspond to a colour, still in order for the sensation to be really that of a colour, or at least in order for the colour to be recognized as such, some other conditions besides have to be fulfilled; conditions, which by their very nature are in a certain way analogous to the ascent above a threshold value.

On this basis it may be considered as extremely probable that the organization in three components assumed in the HELMHOLTZ theory does not apply to the organ of vision as a whole, but only to those parts that are directly exposed to the action of light and á more or less extended series of parts connected with them; and that, on the other hand, the final results, the immediate substrata of the sensations, are themselves of a different nature; and hence that somewhere along the route the three independent results of stimulus are transformed into processes of a different kind and composition. As to these processes, nothing can be said with certainty, in the writer's opinion, except that in them the colourless sensation has some outstanding physiological significance.

In order to have some short way of referring to this assumption, let us speak of it as a *zonal theory*. From this point of view there seems to be no particular difficulty about supposing that the sensations of vision may be aroused by two different mechanisms more or less independent of each other, only one of which has the tripartite structure in question, whereas the other, being unitary, reacts to its stimulus in a simple monotone.[1]

Colour blindness of the eccentric parts of the retina is a subject about which it is hard to form a more positive opinion at present. Undoubtedly there are many points of resemblance between the defective colour vision of the eccentric parts of the retina and the colour infirmity of anomalous trichromats, and it would seem natural to try to explain them on the same basis, that is, as variations of the valence curves. This idea was developed and explained by Fick. Formerly, the writer was not able to accept this view, but now that it has been positively ascertained that there are alterations of this sort in anomalous trichromats, it seems to him to be more worthy of consideration. However, according to this explanation we should expect to find deviations in the Rayleigh-equation in the eccentric zones of the retina; and so far they have not been found. Should they occur, hardly any doubt would remain as to the correctness of that conception. On the other hand, if these deviations are not found, and if (leaving out of account the influence of the macula pigment) matches that are valid for the central retina are good for the periphery also,[2] we could perhaps do as the writer formerly suggested and fall back on assumptions as to modifications of those relations which exist when the peripheral processes are transformed into the substrata of sensation. The experimental data on the subject are not yet so complete as they should be; so that it would be somewhat premature to discuss the possibilities in detail.

---

[1] ¶See L. T. Troland, Brilliance and chroma in relation to zone theories of vision. *Jour. Opt. Soc. Amer.* VI. 1922, 3–26. (H. L.)

[2] That this is the case has heretofore generally been tacitly assumed as self-evident, but it can hardly be regarded as having been really proved. Incidentally, it is hard to decide the matter on account of the intermingling of rod functions.

Another point which has not been cleared up, and which incidentally is closely related to that just discussed, is the mode of distribution of luminosity. KÖNIG called attention to the fact that the distribution of luminosity in the spectrum is approximately, though not very exactly (the great individual differences would prevent this from being the case), in agreement with the stimulus values as calculated for the red component. The same thing is true, as later investigations have shown, for peripheral values and flicker values and also minimum-field luminosities. Clearly associated with this is the fact that these relations for deuteranopic vision and deuteranomalous vision are not greatly different from those for normal vision, although their green components are different in their capacity for being stimulated; whereas in protanopic vision and protanomalous vision, in both of which it is the red component that is deficient in this capacity, the peripheral values, etc., are found to be entirely different from those in normal vision.

If we adopt the above suggestion and assume that the operations taking place in the three components are transformed towards the centre into processes of another kind, then in order to explain these phenomena, some hypothesis will have to be made as to the nature of these new processes and how they are related to the former. However, in the writer's opinion, it is idle to try to do this at present because we do not yet know enough about the facts along these lines. In the first place it would have to be definitely decided whether it is really a fact, as it seems to be, that even in the case of persons with normal colour vision there are individual differences in these respects, and how they are connected with each other or with other differences of the organ of vision, etc.[1] As the writer sees it, it is important to bring out clearly that the idea of each of the components having to contribute something to the total luminosity, which at first glance is the most natural supposition, is by no means the only possible conjecture, and it is more likely that the collective effect is the result of other very different modalities.

Briefly, by way of conclusion, it may be said that as regards the group of facts, that is, the so-called laws of colour mixture, which constituted the original primary basis of the HELMHOLTZ theory, the theory has been confirmed in a remarkable manner, even in the light of the present very extensive state of our knowledge. It accounts for the behaviour of the normal organ of vision and its relations to typically dichromatic vision in a simple and accurately satisfactory fashion.

---

[1] Indications in this direction that are worth considering are to be found in Miss v. MALTZEW's work mentioned above, but they need to be elaborated and confirmed.

The somewhat more complicated conditions of anomalous trichromatic vision can be made to fit in it in an intelligible manner, although not quite so simply. And it affords us at least the simplest way of expressing the observed facts in a comprehensive system. If, on the other hand, it has to be stated that it certainly is not a definitive theory of the whole of vision, as HELMHOLTZ supposed, there can hardly be any doubt as to the correctness of its fundamental conceptions. A rather more general discussion of theoretical questions will be deferred until other theories and other groups of facts have been described.

2. Other Theories of the Sensations of Light and Colour

While HELMHOLTZ deemed it illegitimate or at least untrustworthy to draw conclusions as to physiological processes from the direct psychological character of the sensations, most subsequent theories of vision use this very group of facts as their starting point. The results of this mode of treatment are in harmony as to their main features at least, and so all these theories have a common stamp impressed on them. In the first place, they assign a very special importance to the series of *colourless sensations* ranging in all degrees from black to white.[1] A similar importance is also assigned to certain colours, which are accordingly referred to as pure, simple or primary colours, namely, red, green, yellow and blue.[2] Another thing to be mentioned about it is that in sensation each quality of one pair seems capable of being combined with both qualities of the other pair (that is, red with blue as well as with yellow and yellow with red as well as with green); but the two determinations of each pair are mutually destructive, that is, red and green cannot be combined, nor yellow and blue.[3] This conception is a very old one fundamentally. Of late years it has been developed and advocated chiefly by AUBERT, and may be called the *four-colour theory*.

Unfortunately, this theory has been very inadequately tested as to the very points that are capable of being easily investigated. Obviously, it would be important to find out what objective lights can, under proper conditions, give the impression of "pure" colours, and whether in this respect various observers would agree or disagree. Investigations of this kind are very scarce; and among the advocates

---

[1] ¶Sometimes called "toneless" or "untoned" or "grey" sensations as distinguished from the "toned" or coloured sensations, namely, red, yellow, green and blue; as mentioned in the text. (J. P. C. S.)

[2] ¶The so-called "psychological primaries." This is another instance of the confusion of colour terminology in physics and psychology. (J.P.C.S.)

[3] ¶These latter combinations are what Mrs. LADD-FRANKLIN terms *colour-fusions* or *colour-extinctions*, to which attention was called elsewhere. (J. P. C. S.)

of the four-colour theory opinions are very much divided concerning a point of fundamental importance. Thus, AUBERT was of the opinion, and HERING has also espoused this view (as will be seen in the discussion of his theory below), that pure red and pure green mixed in proper proportions lose their coloured qualities and produce white; that is, that pure red and pure green are complementary colours. In opposition to this view, Mrs. LADD-FRANKLIN[1] (in agreement, by the way, with an idea expressed long ago by FICK[2]) affirms that pure red and pure green acting together are not colourless, but look yellow. Of course, there are also great differences of opinion in the further development of the four-colour theory, which will be mentioned below.

In the past decade much attention has been bestowed on this theory mainly in the special form which has been given to it by E. HERING.[3] According to him the visual organ is composed of three constituent parts, one of which (the "black-white substance") furnishes the colourless luminosity sensations, the other two visual substances (the red-green and yellow-blue) being responsible for the sensations of colour. In harmony with HERING's general biological ideas, the theory assumes moreover that in each of these substances processes of an opposite kind take place simultaneously; which HERING calls assimilative and dissimilative (usually spoken of as A and D processes). The *ratio* between these opposite processes is what determines the sensation. When they are in equilibrium in one of the coloured visual substances, this means that the sensation does not have the quality of either colour of that particular pair (that is, is neither yellow nor blue, or neither red nor green). When there is a state of equilibrium in *both* coloured visual substances, the sensation is devoid of colour. Equilibrium in the black-white visual substance corresponds to a particular "mean grey." White, red, and yellow, in increasing luminosity or saturation, is the result of the increasing preponderance of the three D processes; similarly, black, green, and blue result from the preponderance of the A processes. This entire conception was called by HERING a *theory of "Gegenfarben"* or *the theory of opponent colours.*

The hypothetical mode of action of different kinds of light on the separate visual substances is evident at once. All kinds of light would have to act on the black-white substance in the dissimilative (white) sense, but in different degree depending on the wave-length. On the other hand, the long waves as far as pure green (extending neither into the yellow nor into the blue) have a dissimilative (yellow) action on

---

[1] *Zeitschrift für Psychologie* etc. IV. p. 211. 1893.—Article on Vision in BALDWIN's *Dictionary of Philosophy and Psychology.*

[2] PFLÜGERS *Archiv* XLVII. S. 285. 1890.

[3] *Sitzungsberichte der Wiener Akademie,* Mathem.-naturw. Kl. LXIX. S. 131. 1874.

the yellow-blue substance; whereas the short waves from green on have an assimilative (blue) action on it. In the case of the red-green substance there is D action for the less refrangible end of the spectrum as far as pure yellow, and A action from there on up to pure blue, but beyond this point there is D action again in the violet. Pure yellow and blue would have no effect at all on the red-green substance, and pure red or green would have no effect on the yellow-blue substance.

Of particular interest also is the manner in which the effect of the stimulus on the visual organ is considered to take place here, and its dependence on the processes that determine the sensation. If the dissimilative action preponderates, the material substance is diminished and hence the "key" (*Stimmung*) varied in such a way that the effect of the D stimuli is reduced while that of the A stimuli is augmented. The reverse happens when the A processes are preponderant. The conditions are thus regulated automatically, as it were. The only possible permanent condition is that of an equilibrium between D processes and A processes, that is, a colourless grey of definite luminosity.

Now as to the anomalies that we have in colour vision, the four-colour theory assumes that in dichromatic vision there is an absence of the red-green sense, and both forms therefore are included under the name *red-green blindness*. HERING also accepted this way of regarding it, on the assumption that the red-green visual substance is lacking in all cases. The differences in the two types that are now called protanopes and deuteranopes, which even at that time were well understood to a certain extent, HERING tried to account for by attributing them to physical causes (absorption of light in the coloured media of the eye, especially in the pigment of the macula). This assumption, hardly compatible with what was known about the matter then, has been shown by subsequent investigations to be thoroughly untenable. The difference between the protanopic and the deuter-anopic organ of vision in the case of the long waves is so great and so typically fixed thereby, being also just as pronounced in the periphery as in the centre of the retina, that such an explanation cannot be seriously considered.[1]

We have no more right to place side by side the differences in the forms of dichromatic vision and those that are found in normal vision, as TSCHERMAK[2] has recently tried to do. He supposed that there are two types of persons with normal colour vision, just as there are two types of red-green-blind; one of which would be characterized by a relatively high, and the other by a relatively

[1] Concerning the particulars of the investigation by which HERING was led into this error, see v. KRIES, *Zft. f. Psychol.*, etc., XIII. S. 301. 1897.

[2] *Ergebnisse der Physiologie*. I. 2.

low, power of responding to long waves of light. But a normal eye never responds poorly to the long waves in the way the protanopic eye does. Persons with trichromatic vision who have trouble in connection with the long waves are protanomalous. Similarly, there is a kind of trichromatic vision which differs from normal vision in another way, but only in a limited sense, and which is not characterized by particular sensitivity to long waves, or by low sensitivity to the short. This difference however, is associated with deterioration in colour vision and leads by continuous transition to the deuteranopic system.

There are therefore not two kinds of normal colour vision between which there is the same kind of difference as between the two kinds of dichromats. But there is only one normal colour vision which is capable of two modifications. One of these is characterized by "poor use of long waves," to borrow this expression once; whereas this is not the case with the other. But both involve derangements of colour vision and may lead to dichromatic vision.

At present, therefore, there can be no doubt as to the failure of the four-colour theory at this point, and that, in particular, the explanation which HERING tried to give for the two kinds of colour blindness is not compatible with the facts. Of course, this does not imply that the assumptions of the theory, especially the original fundamental propositions of the theory, may not be right in a sense. But it is certain that the anomalies of colour vision point unavoidably to some set of relations that are not considered in the theory, and that thereby necessitate a limitation or extension of it.

The theory of opponent colours has been just as unsuccessful in explaining total colour blindness. Originally, HERING believed that in these cases the organ of vision was without both coloured visual substances, and was therefore limited to the black-white substance only. Thus he believed that by ascertaining the stimulus values for such an eye the *white valences* would be determined; and that a confirmation of this assumption can be found in the fact that the normal organ of vision in the state of dark adaptation in dim illumination (below the colour threshold) has very nearly just this same kind of vision. Apart from the fact that numerous peculiarities of the totally colour-blind eye would be completely incomprehensible from this point of view, this conception is shattered by the fact that these white valences may be totally different for two kinds of light which look alike to dichromats under the conditions of daylight vision; and also by the fact that, although in strong light the extreme periphery of the light-adapted retina has no colour vision anywhere, it can discern differences of luminosity; and chiefly by the whole series of facts which force us to regard twilight vision as a function of some special constituent of the organ of vision.[1]

[1] The assumption that the effects on the black-white visual substance corresponds to the twilight values under all circumstances was found to conflict in some ways also with the luminosity distribution in the coloured spectrum. HERING tried to get around it in his

The theory has come here into still more direct conflict with the actual facts, but it can indeed escape from this difficulty by a simple and unimportant modification. It would simply have to be completed by the assumptions of the duplicity theory; and the peripheral values, not the twilight values, would then have to be regarded as being the measure of the action on the black-white substance, that is, the peripheral values would be the "white valences."

An amplification of the theory in these directions has been attempted by G. E. MÜLLER.[1] Starting with the fundamental concepts of the four-colour theory, he has developed a theory of the organ of vision intended to take account not only of these facts but also of adaptation. He began with the perfectly sound view that, while it is possible to consider the last substrata of sensation in a manner corresponding to that proposed in the four-colour theory, it is also possible that the arrangements in the peripheral sense organ may be of another character. With respect to these latter, MÜLLER then developed a series of ideas which might seem adapted for explaining the facts known at that time (1897), although since then they have become much more complicated. A detailed account of MÜLLER's theory (which would certainly exceed the space allotted to this article) is not so necessary at present, because the theory would perhaps require to be modified still further to be made to agree with the facts which have been discovered in the last ten years.

TSCHERMAK also has tried to develop further the theory of opponent colours, mainly without much success. As was mentioned above, he abandons HERING's physical explanation of the difference between protanopes and deuteranopes, and speaks of a relatively better or poorer "utilization of the long waves." He has not made any attempt to explain the ground for this unequal utilization or the special connections between the different kinds of colour vision on this basis.[2] Incidentally, in this latter respect, as had been stated, TSCHERMAK starts out with certain notions that are contrary to the facts.

---

theory of the *specific brightness of colours*. There is no need to go into this matter because, from what has been said above, it can no longer be considered seriously. The fact that the distribution of luminosity in the coloured spectrum is approximately the same as it is in case of colourless vision with the eccentric parts of the retina in state of light adaptation, shows that the colours have but slight influence on the luminosity.

[1] *Zeitschrift für Psychologie* etc. X. pp. 1 and 321; XIV. pp. 1 and 161.

[2] TSCHERMAK simply alludes to the possibility that the matter may have something to do with peculiarities of structures which are in front of the visual substances proper. Here he adopts a view occasionally advanced by HERING himself, but never really seriously; which DONDERS on the other hand, had actually tried to apply, and which has been the writer's view ever since his earliest publications (*Die Gesichtsempfindungen und ihre Analyse*, 1882, pages 163, foll.)

On the other hand, SCHENCK[1] tried to develop the assumptions of the HELMHOLTZ theory along certain lines, and particularly to explain the hypothetical separation of the organ of vision into three components by means of conceptions as to its evolution. He supposed that not only the rods but the cones also originally contained a single substance not very different from that in the rods, the decomposition of which by light gave a colourless sensation of brightness in the same way as in the rods. This substance, like that in the rods, was originally not very sensitive to long waves, but at first it underwent a change called "pan-chromatization," by virtue of which (just as in photographic plates) it was made relatively very sensitive to long waves also. Next it differentiated or divided into blue and yellow components, and finally the yellow component was subdivided again into red and green components. For the anomalies of colour vision there are various possibilities. Entire absence of the cone mechanism involves the ordinary form of total colour blindness. Other forms are due partly to failure of pan-chromatization, and especially in some cases to failure of splitting up of the yellow process. This latter is responsible for dichromatic vision, which is deuteranopic or protanopic, according as pan-chromatization has, or has not, taken place, respectively.

The theory certainly is calculated to give an attractive explanation of the occurrence of many forms of colour vision like those which are actually found (although it has always been a curious fact that some of the theoretically possible forms have never been observed). But it seems to the writer that the manner in which the special relations between the different kinds of colour vision are explained is not so smooth and simple as to compel conviction, lacking, as it does, objective observations in support of it. Accordingly, it does not seem necessary to give a detailed description of it here.

LADD-FRANKLIN's theory[2], developed long before, is very similar to that of SCHENCK. The writer has mentioned the latter rather more particularly, because it discusses in special detail just the anomalies of colour vision that concern us here. Some other theories of the visual sensations, whose interest is more from another side, will be briefly alluded to presently.

3. Modulations of the Organ of Vision[3]

Although the manifold anomalies of colour vision are certainly best suited for giving us an insight in the normal structure of the organ of vision, and have been studied and discussed chiefly from this point

[1] PFLÜGERS *Archiv* CXVIII. S. 129. 1907.

[2] *Zeitschrift für Psychologie* etc. IV. S. 211. 1893.

[3] ¶It is difficult to find a precise English equivalent to the German *Umstimmungen* as employed here to include both "fatigue" (see PARSONS, *Colour Vision*, 112) and "re-

of view, there are some other groups of phenomena that are valuable for the same reason. These will be only briefly touched on here in order to record facts which have been made known recently. The phenomena of *the modulation* (*Umstimmung*[1]) of the organ of vision will be mentioned here first. While the fundamental facts of these phenomena have been known for a long time, and, incidentally, can be satisfactorily explained too by all theories, certain questions of special theoretical interest have resulted from researches in these fields. First, there is the question as to the *"persistence of optical equations,"* that is, as to whether two mixtures of light, which are not equal objectively, but which appear to be the same for a certain condition of the organ of vision, will continue to look alike for every other condition, or whether they can be made to look unlike by changes in the state of the eye. Facts above stated show that in all parts of the retina where there are both rods and cones the latter is the case, that is, the match does not persist. It will be recalled that mixtures of light which look alike under the conditions of daylight vision may have totally unequal twilight values. Thus, matches of this kind can be destroyed by adaptation, and changed often to an enormous extent. On the other hand, so far as we know, the probability is that in the place where vision is most distinct, and where there are no rods, changes of this nature do not occur at all, or to such a slight extent that there is no sure proof of them at present.[2]

Moreover, as to the parts of the organ of vision that are used in twilight vision, STEGMANN's experiments (page 389) and observations on total colour blindness show that the luminosity relations of different kinds of light are but little affected by changing adaptation. We can therefore assume that for the organ of vision as a whole there is no persistence of optical equations whatever, but that for each of its two mechanisms matches do persist, approximately anyhow.

As to the way in which the response to the stimulus is influenced by the state of the organ of vision at the time and of its component parts, HELMHOLTZ, adopting a suggestion of FECHNER, had conjectured that "the fatigue of the nervous substance of vision has about the same effect on the sensation of fresh incident light as if the objective

---

covery" (or adaptation). The word "modulation" is certainly not an exact rendering of the original, and, doubtless, exception will be taken to it. Still it seems to convey the meaning better than such terms as "mutation," "conversion," etc. (J.P.C.S.)

[1] This term *"Umstimmung"* is employed here instead of HELMHOLTZ's expressions "fatigue" and "recovery," because it is more general and is not prejudiced by any theoretical view.

[2] Concerning researches and controversies on this subject, see NAGELS *Handbuch der Physiologie.* III. pp. 210, foll., and the literature given there.

intensity of this light were diminished by a definite fraction of its amount" (see p. 235).

Accordingly, therefore, if one of the mechanisms of the organ of vision were "tuned" differently, the result would be the same as if all stimuli acting on it were multiplied by a certain coefficient. Incidentally, HERING also made this a fundamental part of his earlier ideas at least, and assumed that the product of the intensity of the light and a coefficient depending on the condition of the organ of vision was a measure of the effect of the stimulus.

The writer calls this the *coefficient law*. So far as its proof and validity are concerned, it must be borne in mind in the first place that the assumption in regard to the functional importance of the eye's being "attuned," which is at the basis of the law, applies merely to the behaviour of a unitary system, that is, of a single component mechanism of the organ of vision. Accordingly, it is to be expected that the law will *not* apply where twilight and daylight vision are in operation together; because, under these conditions, we have to do with changes of condition of both mechanisms, and these changes are generally different. As a matter of fact, BÜHLER[1] found that the effects of dim lights were increased much more by dark adaptation than those of bright lights. Thus, in order to illuminate two adjacent parts of the retina that are "attuned" differently, so as to get the same impression of brightness from them both, the ratio between the two objective brightnesses will have to be reduced (that is, will have to be made nearer unity) as the absolute intensities are increased. And if a match is made between two dim lights, and then both are increased in the same proportion, the stronger light (acting on the fatigued place) will appear too bright. The same result has been obtained recently by DITTLER and ORBELLI.[2]

In apparent conflict with the results of the authors just mentioned, WIRTH[3] found that the coefficient law was valid within fairly wide limits; but the explanation perhaps is that he worked with light-adapted eye and possibly also with stronger lights. Thus an unequivocal answer cannot be given at present to questions that are of peculiar theoretical interest, namely, as to how the ratios turn out for the separate mechanisms of the eye; whether the coefficient law is obeyed here approximately, and if not, in what direction the deviations from it are. To obtain the answers, the test would have to be made with very small fields, directly fixated, and with very bright lights.

[1] Beiträge zur Lehre von der Umstimmung des Sehorgans. *Diss.* Freiburg 1903.

[2] PFLÜGERS *Archiv*, CXXXII. p. 338. 1910. — From the description given by these authors it is not clear whether the conditions were such that the coöperation of the twilight mechanism can be assumed; but they certainly do not indicate that this was not the case.

[3] WUNDT, *Philosoph. Studien* XVI. (4), XVII. (3) and XVIII. (4).

As to more special phenomena, there is a fact connected with the action of white light that should be mentioned here. If in the case of the photopic eye a part of the retina that has been fatigued with white light is tested with coloured light, we find that in order to get the same impression (that is, equal colour saturation) from the adjacent unfatigued places as from this spot, we have to use lights of different intensity but of approximately the same spectral composition. Thus, for instance, if in order to make the match, three times as much white light is required at the fatigued place as on the adjacent parts, this place must be stimulated with approximately three times the amount of coloured light also. Fatiguing the eye by white light appears therefore to modify the effects that stimuli have on the colour discriminations of the sensation.[1]

There are also a number of new results concerning the phenomena of fatigue with coloured lights. If places on the retina that are fatigued for one colour are tested with lights of other colours, the general effect is an appearance which is approximately complementary to that of the colour causing fatigue. We are indebted to HESS[2] for a series of quantitative determinations along this line indicating that these changes are very considerable. A green light ($517\mu\mu$) acting on a portion of the retina fatigued with blue looked the same to him as a slightly greenish yellow ($565\mu\mu$) which he used to make the comparison. The writer[3] found that after red fatigue a yellow looked like green yellow ($556\mu\mu$), and that after green fatigue it looked like orange ($605\mu\mu$). HELMHOLTZ stated that all pure spectral colours seem to be very much more saturated when the eye has been previously fatigued by the complementary colours; and this has since been repeatedly verified.[4] It is especially true with respect to the colours of the less refrangible half of the spectrum and for high intensities.

By making the tests with the same light used for fatiguing the eye, information is obtained concerning the apparent variations that take place in looking at a single colour (or monochromatic light) for a long time. It is a familiar fact that there is loss of saturation under these circumstances; and most colours undergo a change of hue at the same time. According to VOESTE's observations,[5] after steady fixation for a long time, light of long wave-lengths (up to $560\mu\mu$) was found to

---

[1] v. KRIES, *Berichte der Freiburger Naturf. Gesellschaft.* 1894. — WIRTH, *(Archiv. f. Psychologie.* I. page 49) obtained the same result. On the other hand, opposite results have been found very lately by DITTLER and RICHTER in similar experiments, the explanation of which is not clear at the present time. *Zft. f. Sinnesphysiologie* XLV. page 1, 1910.

[2] HESS, *Archiv f. Ophth.* XXXIX (2), S. 45.

[3] v. KRIES, NAGELS *Handbuch der Physiologie* III S. 215.

[4] HESS, *loc. cit.*—v. KRIES, NAGELS *Handbuch der Physiol.* III. S. 214. 220.

[5] VOESTE, *Zeitschrift f. Psychologie* etc., XVIII. S. 257.

look like a test light of shorter wave-length; and light of wave-length between 560 and 500$\mu\mu$ like a light of longer wave-length. Thus in each case they approach yellow in appearance. Light comprised between 500 and 460$\mu\mu$ again begins to look like light of shorter wave-length, that is, tends to look more like blue.

As previously stated, there is a great variety of satisfactory theoretical explanations of the essential qualitative aspects of these phenomena; but no one has yet succeeded in giving a satisfactory explanation of the details and quantitative relations. And hence, with respect to this whole group of phenomena, we should be cautious about drawing conclusions as to fundamental questions concerning the organization of the eye or how it is composed of separate parts.

HELMHOLTZ's assumption of a *fatigue*, which would take possession of the separate components independently, affecting each of them in proportion to its activity, encounters difficulties with respect to the great increase of saturation which can be produced even with spectral lights by fatigue with complementary colours. At any rate this is so if we adhere to the theory of the components as derived from the anomalies of colour vision. And it is doubtful, to say the least, whether these difficulties can be surmounted by making other assumptions as to the components.

As has been mentioned, HERING originally regarded the modulations, conformably to the coefficient law, as being of such nature that the result of the stimulus was measured by the product of stimulus-intensity and a factor depending on the modulation. Later, as HESS had done before, he substituted for this the notion that every light by its colour modulation (*Farbenumstimmung*) must receive a certain value in complementary valence (*Betrag an gegensinniger Valenz*); a conception which cannot be said to be entirely satisfactory. In all cases additions of some sort have to be made to the theory in order to explain the independence between optical matches and the modulation of the organ of vision.[1] And the theory encounters positive difficulties in connection with the facts given above, which show that by fatigue with white light the excitability of even the underlying mechanism of colour determinations is lowered.

4. Temporal Effects of Stimulations

The *temporal relations* of the processes of stimulation are much more complicated than was formerly supposed. These have theoretical bearings in many ways, and hence a review of the more recent studies may be included here also.

---

[1] v. KRIES, *Arch. f.* (*Anatomie und*) *Physiol.* The validity of this view has been questioned by HERING, without justification. See HERING, PFLÜGERS *Arch.*, XLII. 497. — v. KRIES *Arch. f. Physiol.* 1887, page 113; 1888, page 381.

As to the effect of a single short-lived stimulus, peculiar conditions were found to arise from the so-called PURKINJE *after-image* (positive complementary image), which is a phenomenon that has been known for a long time. Thereupon, systematic investigation of the action of short-lived stimuli revealed that this constitutes only a part of a long series of processes.

As to methods, these researches have been conducted along two lines. One way is to let a short-lived stimulus act on a part of the retina and to observe the successive stages of sensation that follow. The other way consists in letting a spot of light glide over the retina of the immobile eye. Moreover, in the latter case each point of the retina is illuminated for a short time (determined by the size and speed of the image), but one after the other. Thus the various phases of the process are watched at the same time, but separate from each other in space, which makes it much easier to analyze and appreciate them.

The phenomena that are perceived under the most favourable conditions for distinguishing their various stages will now be enumerated.[1]

Suppose a bright object is made to move about in the field of view which is otherwise perfectly dark; then under proper conditions the following stages of the entire process connected with brief stimulation may be distinguished.[2]

1. The primary image, the preliminary appearance of light, which is the first and greatest effect of the stimulus. It comes up generally in the same colour that the light has when it acts continuously. As contrasted with the stationary light, it is elongated more or less, depending on the speed of movement.

2. The primary image is followed by a dark stretch.

3. Thereupon follows closely a so-called secondary image indicating a repeated flashing out. When the light itself is coloured, this image is faint and usually indeed complementary to the primary image. It represents what was observed first by PURKINJE, and what has since been called the positive complementary or PURKINJE after-image. Very sharply delineated and as a rule not drawn out much, this image constitutes the most peculiar and most conspicuous phenomenon of the whole region. For when the movement is moderately rapid, it makes the impression of a second luminous object at a fixed distance behind the first, often of considerable brightness, and, as intimated, having a colour about complementary to the primary image. This is

---

[1] This is a brief résumé of the writer's description in NAGEL's *Handb. d. Physiol.* III. 221.

[2] ¶See PARSONS, *Colour vision*, pages 87, foll. (J. P. C. S.)

the reason why the phenomenon was called "recurrent vision" (YOUNG, DAVIS), "the pursuant image" (v. KRIES), "ghost" (BIDWELL), and "satellite" (HAMAKER). For a revolving blue object it is shown in Fig. 2 of Plate III.[*]

4. The secondary image is not sharply terminated behind, and is followed by a second dark gap. Close on this is—

5. Another glow still, which we may call the tertiary image, adopting the term used by SNELLEN and BOSCHA. It has no colour or is faintly coloured like the primary image. It is not sharply outlined, but represents a gradual increase and decrease of brightness extending over several seconds. When the object completes its circuit in from 1.5 to 3 seconds (which is the best speed for seeing the secondary image), this part of the phenomenon, if it is well produced, is like a cloud of light filling the entire circle. Therefore, in order to observe the entire course of the phenomenon, it is better to let the object make only one revolution or part of a revolution.

6. The last phase consists of a darkening following close on the preceding, again without being sharply separated from it. It reveals the path traversed by the bright object as a deep black band. The primary image is by far the brightest, and although the secondary image is much fainter, it is, however, considerably brighter than the tertiary image. Accordingly, supposing that there are certain intensities of the objective light that are best adapted for showing the phenomena in the way they have been described above, we should expect that with lower intensities the primary and secondary images alone would be visible, and with lower intensities still the latter too would disappear. Moreover, the extent of the separate images is variable and depends on circumstances; and hence the primary image may reach as far as the secondary, and the latter again may extend out to the tertiary; and so there will be no dark gaps. In this case the appearance is essentially different in character; and this is manifested especially by the fact that the comparative individuality of the various stimulations supposed to occur here is not clearly brought out any more.

Of the many details only those can be mentioned here that have been most positively observed and are of particular theoretical interest. In the first place, the primary image shows variations which indicate that the different parts of the organ of vision that are affected by the continuous action of light do not all come into activity simultaneously when the light is first turned on. Phenomena of this kind, by the way, can be observed under many conditions, and some of them have been known for a long time. Thus, for example, it has already been stated (p. 255) that for certain rates of rotation of a disc with black and white

[*]Plate III faces page 384.

sectors, the forward edges of the latter appear reddish and the backward edges bluish. Thus it seems as if the red component reacted more quickly than the others. Incidentally, also, KUNKEL's observations[1] are in good accord with this. HESS[2] states that the forward edge of a red object in motion appears to be a more saturated red, which perhaps can be explained in the same way.

These differentiations are especially noticeable in dark adaptation. In this case, vivid colour appears only on the forward edge (the effect is particularly distinct with blue light). Close behind it there is a paler portion which runs out into a white tail. The primary image then has the appearance shown in Fig. 3, Plate III.[*] This shows that *the primary stimulation of twilight vision follows that of daylight vision with a little retardation.* The old phenomenon of the so-called "fluttering heart" belongs here also (see p. 258). Bits of coloured paper are fastened on a background of another colour; and when the whole affair is moved slightly to and fro, the pieces of paper seem to dance about on the background, as if they lagged behind it or ran ahead of it. It is an effect that can be induced by suggestion under very many conditions. By far the best way to get it is with bits of red paper on a dark blue ground (or *vice versa*), and with feeble illumination, so that in case of the blue its rod-action preponderates.

Along a radius of a black disc attach a narrow red strip and a blue strip so that one forms the continuation of the other; and observe it in dim illumination with dark adaptation. When the disc is turned slowly, it is easy to see how the red strip runs ahead and the blue strip lags behind. (Of course, the eye must not try to follow the movement of the disc, but must look fixedly in the same direction.) McDOUGALL[3] estimated the amount of this retardation at about 1/18 second.[4]

The *secondary image* appears from a quarter to a sixth of a second after the primary. The most remarkable thing about this image is that it is absent in the fovea. Thus if it is observed in the way described above as an image coming behind, and if then, without changing the fixation of the eye, the primary image is made to glide over the

[1] PFLÜGERS *Archiv.* VI. S. 197. 1872.

[2] PFLÜGERS *Archiv.* CI. S. 226. 1904.

[3] McDOUGALL, *Brit. Journal of Psychology.* I. 1904.

[4] ¶H. E. IVES, Visual diffusivity. *Phil. Mag.* XXXIII 1917, 18–33.—Idem, Resolution of mixed colors by differential visual diffusivity. *Phil. Mag.* XXXV. 1918. 413–421.—F. W. FRÖHLICH, *Grundzüge einer Lehre vom Licht- und Farbensinn. Ein Beitrag zur allgemeinen Physiologie der Sinne.* 1920. — Idem, Über oscillierende Erregungsvorgänge im Sehfeld. Untersuchungen über periodischer Nachbilder. Zur Analyse des Licht u. Farbencontrastes. *Zft. f. Sinnesphysiol.* LII. 52–59; 60–88; 89–103. — Idem, Über den Einfluss der Hell- u. Dunkeladaptation auf den Verlauf der periodischen Nachbilder. *Zft. f. Sinnesphysiol.* LIII. 79–107.—Idem, Über die Abhängigkeit der periodischen Nachbilder von der Dauer der Belichtung. *Zft. f. Sinnesphysiol.* LIII. 108–121. (H. L.)

[*]Plate III faces page 384.

fovea, the trailing image follows behind it up to a short distance from the fovea, and then disappears there in very singular fashion, just as if it went into a tunnel, to reappear a little the other side of the fixation point.[1] The inference is that the secondary stimulation is a function of the twilight mechanism, which is confirmed by the fact that the luminosity of the trailing image corresponds to the twilight values of the stimulating lights. When light of very long wave-length is used, the secondary image is not observed, at any rate not until the intensity of the light is very considerable. Thus, so far as the luminosity of the secondary image is concerned, we must consider it as being a special temporal characteristic of rod function; and, on the other hand, the reason for its complementary colour is connected with the modulation of the organ of vision that exists during this phase.[2] The way in which the secondary image depends on the adaptation is remarkable and has not yet been explained. Starting with the eye light-adapted and observing the changes that take place in the secondary image, during otherwise constant conditions, as dark adaptation sets in and continues, we notice that for some minutes it is invariably clearer and more beautiful, increasing in brightness and extent. But then it becomes harder to make out, and after very long dark adaptation (two hours or more) the writer cannot see it any longer at all.[3] The tertiary image, being of the same colour as the first, proves to be a second stimulation of the trichromatic mechanism similar to the first, but there seems to be superadded still another, that is, a third luminosity-sensation mediated by the rods.

Thus, the details of the phenomena enable us to keep separate the part in them that is probably taken by each of the two mechanisms of the organ of vision. But at present we are not in the position to give an explanation of the complex temporal configuration of the processes of stimulation in each of these parts.

With respect to the stimulus effects in case of long-continued illuminations, HESS[4] reports that at both the beginning and the end of the stimulus similar oscillatory proceedings can be observed. Long

---

[1] v. KRIES, *Zeitschrift für Psychologie* XII. S. 83. 1896.

[2] Certain deviations from the rule of complementary colouration are due to the fact that the sensation corresponding to twilight vision is often more or less bluish. This is why the blue colouration is particularly clear and easy to see when yellow lights are used. On the other hand, with blue lights, frequently the secondary image seems to be of the same colour provided the stimulating light is of low saturation; not being yellow, as it should be, unless the saturation is high.

[3] NAGEL and various other observers working with him and the writer had the same experience. HESS states that for him the phenomenon is not essentially different whether the dark adaptation is very long or brief.

[4] PFLÜGERS *Archiv*. CI. S. 226. 1904.

ago EXNER[1] carried out experiments and measurements as to the manner in which the process of stimulation increases at the beginning of the stimulus, and especially with respect to the time taken to reach the maximum.

For this purpose, he stimulated two contiguous portions of the retina at an interval apart of from one-fiftieth to one-sixtieth of a second, and then simultaneously extinguished both lights. The exact moment of extinction can be varied, and so the two illuminations can be made to last longer or shorter, however with the same interval always between their instants of beginning. Now if the periods of illumination are so brief that the maximum is not yet reached, then at the moment the lights are extinguished the stimulation due to the first will be nearer the maximum, that is, higher in value. But if the maximum has already been reached, then the stimulation due to the first will already be beyond that, that is, lower in value. EXNER found that the times thus ascertained for the rise of the sensation became shorter with increased intensity. With the intensities which he used, these times were between 0.150 and 0.287 second. Also when the time of action of one stimulus was diminished, it could be determined how its intensity had to be increased in order for it to remain equal to the other, which was kept constant in period and strength. Hence, the mode of rise of the stimulation could be derived.

Similar experiments were made by KUNKEL[2] with coloured (spectral) lights.

As the comparison between the adjacent fields is made mainly during the after-image phase when the illuminations are of such short duration, the principle is correct only on the assumption that, if the stimulations are equal at the moment the stimuli cease to act, they will also die down together. Owing to the complicated temporal relations of stimulation by short-lived stimuli, this supposition is open to some doubt; and so there is some uncertainty about experiments based on it.[3] Still greater difficulties are encountered in comparing the luminosity of a very brief stimulus with that of one that is continuously visible; as was done by MARTIUS[4] in trying also to find how the

[1] *Sitzungsberichte der Wiener Akademie* Math. naturw. Kl. (2) LVIII. S. 601.

[2] PFLÜGERS *Archiv*. IX. S. 197.

[3] On the other hand, the writer cannot see how these results would conflict with the above mentioned observation of HESS concerning the oscillatory way the stimulations begin or how they would be invalidated thereby. EXNER worked with stationary objects and HESS with moving objects, which is a difference that may be worth considering in this matter. But aside from this, there is nothing whatever against the idea that EXNER's determinations relate to the first rise and first maximum of the process of stimulation, as was rightly pointed out by EXNER himself in reply to HESS's criticisms. (PFLÜGERS *Archiv*. CIII. p. 167, 1904).

[4] *Beiträge zur Philosophie und Psychologie*. I. S. 3.

sensation rises. The conditions here for comparing the luminosity are very complex, and the results are variable; as is shown directly by WATT's observations.[1]

The phenomena are far more diversified still when time and space are both factors in the combined stimulus; as, for example, when images more or less complicated in character are made to pass over the retina. These phenomena are as yet only partially understood, and cannot be classified or positively explained. It may suffice to cite here one example which is especially remarkable because very brilliant colour effects are produced by objects without any colour as a result simply of

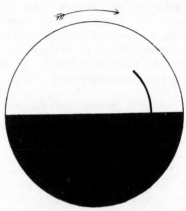

Fig. 79.

special space and time relations. When a disc like that represented in Fig. 79 is made to execute single rotations of about 180° in the direction of the arrow (the best way to do it is by hand, because then the right speed can be easily found), what we see is that a metallic luminous

yellow red tail attached to the black portion comes on behind it. The tail is deep red when the disc is viewed through a yellow glass. If the disc is made to revolve continuously, at about 4 or 5 revolutions per second, the colour spreads over the whole periphery, that is, we see a yellow-red or red ring, in which incidentally a periodic alternation of bright and dark places is noticeable.

The yellow-red colouration occurs on portions of the retina, where the (colourless) illumination begins a little later than on the adjacent parts.

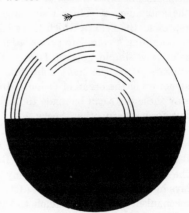

Fig. 80.

In an experiment described by BIDWELL[2] the same thing was ob-

[1] WATT, PFLÜGERS *Archiv.* CVII. S. 531. 1905.
[2] *Proceedings of the Royal Society London.* LXI. S. 268.

served in a little different form. A disc, half white and half black, has a 45° sector cut out of the white half. It is set to spinning rapidly, 180° of black being followed by 135° of white. Black print on a white background seen intermittently through the gap in the rotating disc looks red. This phenomenon, combined with others, can be observed with the so-called BENHAM top[1] (Fig. 80). Rotated slowly, the inner rings here, which are arranged as described above, look yellow-red, and the outer ones bluish. No distinct colour can be discerned in the two intermediate sets of rings.

5. Review of the Status of the Theoretical Questions

Reviewing the facts here mentioned, we can see that perhaps of all theoretical conceptions as to the structure of the organ of vision the assumptions that constitute the *duplicity theory* may be regarded as comparatively the most secure. It is not necessary to take up again in detail the relations that have been described. It may be added, however, that they are connected with perfectly definite anatomical and physical facts, and therefore have the advantage of dealing with something concrete and known rather than with the abstractions of HELMHOLTZ's components or HERING's visual substances.

Connected with this is the fact that we are on less sure ground the moment we try to form more exact pictures of the trichromatic mechanism. As to these matters, it may be said in the first place that the anomalies of colour vision and their relations to normal vision represent the field in which there has been on the whole most success in obtaining a complete survey of a large number of facts in terms of relatively simple general laws. This field affords therefore what appears to be the most solid foundation for conjectures as to the structure of the organ of vision. Moreover, in a comparatively simple way these facts can be made to dovetail with the HELMHOLTZ theory, but not with any other theory.

It must be remembered also that this theory does not pretend to explain the conditions of vision in the thorough and simple manner it seemed to do fifty years ago. But from an unprejudiced view of the facts there can hardly be any doubt that in its assumptions it lays hold of a fundamental characteristic in the structure of the visual mechanism and is very much to the point. There is nothing inconsistent with this in imagining that the hypothetical articulation (*Gliederung*) of the mechanism of vision is true only for one portion of it; the question still being left open, however, as to what those component parts really are. And we may go on using the ideas of com-

[1] Ibid.

ponents, valence curves, deficiency effect, etc., without being deceived as to their merely provisional meanings and without leaving out of account the fact that subsequent investigations will determine their ultimate significance, probably substituting something else for them equivalent in effect.[1]

As to the conceptions of the four-colour theory, the writer thinks that all that can be said with comparative certainty is that in some way the colourless sensations occupy an important position. But whether a similar statement can be made with respect to what are called pure colour sensations is very much more doubtful. But even on the first assumption by itself, we may still regard the three components of the HELMHOLTZ theory as being a satisfactory representation simply of an outer structure of the organ of vision, the processes occurring within them being transformed into others in the interior, in which the colourless luminosity sensation comes to occupy a position of special importance, and which probably may conform in other ways also to the assumptions of the four-colour theory. It is rather curious to note that most theoretical speculations have led, from different points of view, to be sure, to these notions of a different division of the organ of vision in different zones. This is a view which the author advanced in his earliest work. Starting from the theory of opponent colours, G. E. MÜLLER likewise has had to assume other mechanisms for the places where the light acts directly. TSCHERMAK also, by his distinction between stimulus-receptors and sensation-stimulators, takes practically the same position. And SCHENCK has assumed a distinction of this kind and regards it as indispensable.

So far the conception may be said to be on a pretty solid basis of facts. But when we try to designate physiologically the immediate substrata of sensation, we are landed in the midst of all kinds of uncertainty. Certainly, in this respect HERING's theory is the most interesting by reason of its general biological considerations.. But it is precisely from this point of view that there are also weighty objections to it.[2] Moreover, it never seemed plausible to suppose that the state of the sensation both in brightness and darkness has to be adjusted on the average to the same value (neutral grey). And at present it can be regarded as extremely probable that at any rate the greatest changes that go on in the organ of vision are those produced by adapta-

---

[1] ¶C. LADD-FRANKLIN, On color theories and chromatic sensations. *Psychol. Rev.* XXIII. 1916, 237–249. — Eadem, Practical logic and color theories. *Physiol. Rev.* XXIX. 1922, 180–200. Eadem, Tetrachromatic vision and the development theory of color. *Science*, LV. 1922, 1–6. (H.L.)

[2] See, for example, what FICK says in *Sitzungsberichte der Physik. Med. Gesellschaft Würzburg*. 1900.

tion and are connected with the formation of visual purple; in other words, they have an external basis in the sense that they are not directly dependent on the sensation process.—Among hypotheses connected with HERING's fundamental ideas, the proposals made by PAULI[1] and by BRUNNER[2] may be referred to. They are likewise concerned with the nature of the processes underlying sensations, especially with the mode of antagonism that has to be hypothecated between processes combined in one pair. With respect to the anomalies of colour vision, these theories certainly need to be amplified exactly in the same way as the original theory of opponent colours; and, according to what has been stated already, this amplification would have to do with the external part of the organ of vision. As to the basis of sensation itself, the writer thinks that the proposals made by PAULI and BRUNNER amount to far more considerable changes in HERING's theory than they themselves realize; changes which enable the theory to get rid of many difficulties, but also involve it again in many others. The interest of the entire conceptions, and especially the way in which they differ from the original theory, is connected chiefly with general biological questions; and therefore a thorough discussion has to be omitted here and reserved for another occasion.

An idea that is apparently at the basis of many of these attempted explanations was first expressed by DONDERS. He supposed that the sensations are associated throughout by cleavage-processes. The colourless sensations are due to total cleavages (symmetrical or unsymmetrical) of highly complex molecules, whereas the coloured sensations are due to partial cleavages. SCHENCK's theory mentioned above and LADD-FRANKLIN's theory, which is very similar to it, are closely related to this idea.

On the other hand, BERNSTEIN[3] has developed a theory of visual sensations on an entirely different basis. This theory makes use of special conceptions concerning the processes in the central nervous system, including inhibitory effects.

The very diversity of the results of all these speculations, in spite of the fact that they all start from very similar premises, merely serves to show what wide room there is here for hypotheses. The writer has expressed the opinion over and over again that it is idle at present to tackle these questions; and recent experiments (especially one of SCHENCK's) tend to confirm this opinion. Of course, it is a matter of individual scientific disposition and personal taste as to how far one can go in this direction.

[1] PAULI. *Der kolloidale Zustand und die Vorgänge in der lebendigen Substanz.* 1902.

[2] PFLÜGERS *Archiv* CXXI. S. 370. 1908.

[3] *Naturwissenschaftliche Rundschau.* XXI. S. 497. 1906.

As to the main result of the more recent investigations, the writer would not venture to state that they are in harmony with any definite theory of the organ of vision or tend to give it support. The chief outcome has been rather to establish the fact that the different mechanisms of vision, which are different also in their efficiency, are distinguished from each other in very characteristic fashion by the way in which they react to different kinds of light, that is, by the peculiarity of the lights that appear to be the same. The thing to do, therefore, is to find out *what lights look alike to each mechanism*, because, as far as we know at present, this is the only perfectly unobjectionable method of obtaining information in comparatively simple fashion as to the efficiency of an eye in recognizing and discriminating colours.

The reason why König's researches and the vast amount of work that has been carried on in methodical connection with it have had such valuable results is just because, without any theoretical presumption whatever, a certain group of facts was investigated that could be observed directly. And in this way results were obtained which may be regarded, also without any theoretical bias, as general facts as to the mode of behaviour of the different mechanisms of vision, as found by direct observation. It is worth emphasizing this chiefly on account of the great practical value of these tests of colour vision for railway employees, etc. Just such conditions constitute the basis of methods of research, as has been stated before. But these facts must be further emphasized because, although it was formerly supposed that colour matches were particularly adapted for determining the character of vision, for a long time the method was viewed with some doubt, the tendency being to relegate it to a position of subordinate importance. As a matter of fact, Hering's theory of the relative blueness or yellowness of vision as a peculiarity that may belong to the normal eye and the "red-green-blind" eye entirely in the same way, necessarily led to the conception, which is certainly very prevalent, that we are concerned here with peculiarities of comparatively secondary importance, that are of no great scientific interest and certainly without any practical value.[1] On the contrary, we must emphasize that this whole theory has proved to be actually incorrect. The differences in the normal eye are not of a similar kind to those between

[1] Hering's vacillating attitude is responsible for this opinion in great measure. In his work on the subject published in 1885 he left it undecided whether "the division of the red-green-blind into red-blind and green-blind, which is considered more accurate by many persons, can be said to be correct, inasmuch as the higher degrees of blueness or yellowness of vision are more frequent than the medium degrees." Thus he did not think it worth the trouble to come to a definite conclusion on this question. Subsequently, so far as the writer is aware, neither Hering himself nor any of his pupils made any observations of this kind on dichromatic eyes or eyes with poor colour vision.

protanopes and deuteranopes. Normal eyes, colour-blind eyes, and eyes with poor colour vision can be checked in a perfectly regular way by the kind of colour matches they make.

Colour matches are a correct criterion for determining the character of the organ of vision. The differentiation between the different forms of the organ of vision, based on these matches, so as to include normal vision, the two kinds of dichromatic vision (colour blindness), and the two kinds of poor (anomalous) colour vision; the possibility of deciding on the mode of vision of each of these persons and distinguishing them exactly—these are the things in the writer's opinion that constitute the most important outcome of recent investigations. These facts by themselves are not sufficient to constitute a basis of a theory of vision. And as long as there is a lack of objective observations as to the action of light, and as to the morphological or chemical subdivision of the organ of vision, etc., every theory of this kind will float in the air, so to speak. Undoubtedly, however, the chief problem of a future theory supported by determinations of this kind will be to explain these functional facts; and its ability to do this will be the touchstone by which it must be tested.[1]

---

[1] ¶L. KOEPPE, Lässt sich das retinale Sehen neu physikalisch erklären? *Münchner Medizinische Wochenschrift*. No. 16, 1921; and Idem, Die Rolle stehender Lichtwellen im optischen Lamellaraufbaue der lebenden Augenmedien. *Deutsche optische Wochenschrift*. No. 12, 1921. (J. P. C. S.)

The Nature of the Colour Sensations

being a further discussion of this subject

by

CHRISTINE LADD-FRANKLIN[1]

Professor CATTELL, in reviewing for *Science*, in 1898, the second edition of HELMHOLTZ's *Physiologische Optik*, said that this work is "one of the few great classics in the history of science." This very just judgment holds still at the present time, although it is now nearly sixty years since the first edition, which had been some ten years in coming out, was finally issued. Whoever looks over this splendid example of acute scientific thinking and brilliant experimenting will be grateful to the Optical Society of America and to the editor in charge of the translation, Professor SOUTHALL, for having decided to bring out even now (what ought to have been done long ago) an English translation of this great work. Some of the facts here recorded will, it is true, have been superseded by later work, but on the other hand much will be found in it which has been, by accident, simply overlooked in later times. The scientist in the subject of physiological optics will therefore be amply repaid if he reads this translation, and not simply secures it for his bookshelves.

I. The Helmholtz Theory

HELMHOLTZ was a great psychologist as well as a great mathematician, a great physicist, and a great physiologist.[2] If his work were to be brought out now for the first time it would undoubtedly be called Psychological Optics instead of Physiological Optics—there is far more of psychology in it than there is of physiology, and the psychology

---

[1] ¶As stated in the Preface, this chapter is an addition to the original work, for which the editor assumes the sole responsibility. The writer, as everybody knows, is particularly well qualified to discuss this subject. One of the sessions of the International Congress of Psychology in London in 1892 was devoted to new theories of colour sensation. That evening the papers which had been read in the morning were being discussed privately by a group of scientists of whom HELMHOLTZ happened to be one. He had spoken rather disparagingly of one of the contributions, when somebody asked him what he thought of Mrs. FRANKLIN's colour theory. "Ah," said HELMHOLTZ, "Frau FRANKLIN,—*die* versteht die Sache!" (J.P.C.S.)

[2] It happens that his predecessor in the construction of a theory of the colour-sensations, THOMAS YOUNG, was also a man of the first distinction in half a dozen different branches of learning.

is (for the most part) of an extremely acute, as well as of a highly original kind. Organised (non-philosophical) psychology was not definitely in existence when HELMHOLTZ began issuing this book (1856), and he is, very properly, regarded as one of the first investigators in this field. It is, therefore, one of the most inexplicable of psychological occurrences that so great a scientist paid no attention whatever to the fact that, while the necessary *stimuli* for all the colours in the spectrum (and in the world) can be secured by appropriate mixtures of only *three* wave-lengths, the distinct, different, *sensations* that result are not three in number but five—yellow and white are just as good, just as unitary, light-sensations as are red and green and blue.[1] The things to be accounted for, then, in a theory of the visual sensations are, in the order of their phylogenetic development, a primitive achromatic sensation, the dull whites, and *four* chromatic sensations, first yellow and blue (the bees) and then red and green in addition (normal tetrachromatic vision); it may, therefore, be said that the YOUNG-HELMHOLTZ theory is at most three-fifths of a colour theory—it recognizes the existence of three out of five of the actual sensations. But also it takes no account of why the chromata[2] are developed in this peculiar way in pairs: first *yellow* and blue (although yellow does not exist in this theory)—later red and green. (It is also in this order inverted that the colours are lost in the case of diseases of the eye— tobacco amblyopia, progressive atrophy of the optic nerve—and also restored if the disease is recovered from.) Still less has it occurred to the adherents of this theory to pay attention to the extraordinary fact (absolutely unique in the whole range of the sensations) that these very colours constitute "disappearing" colour-pairs[3]—that no human being has ever seen a red-green or a yellow-blue—though he would be very much surprised if he failed to see, on the other two sides of the colour-triangle, the blue-greens and the red-blues, or, in the taste sensations, *all six* of the possible blends, two and two—the bitter-

---

[1] Black, as HELMHOLTZ recognized perfectly, is a definite sensation, but it is a constant permanent, background sensation which becomes evident and forms a dual blend with any of the colours—not with white only—when they are faint. It is a non-light sensation and it belongs in a totally different category from the light-sensations. Its function I have given a theory for (see *Dictionary of Philosophy and Psychology*, II, Art. *Vision*, p. 767, and *Psychological Review*, November, 1924).

[2] I have urged the introduction of this name, *chroma*, in the sense of *colour proper*, *getönte Farbe*, since 1913, in order to obviate the hopeless ambiguity that results from using "colour" in a double sense—now including and now excluding the achromatic sensations.

[3] The term "disappearing" colour pair is very necessary in order not to prejudice the mind of the reader, at first, as between the HERING conception (antagonistic chemical processes) and mine (that of *constituent* chemical processes). Still less is "cancellation" (TROLAND) a permissible term for this, unless one has definitely adopted the HERING theory.

sweets, the sweet-acids, etc. The theory is therefore in absolute contradiction to the first of the admirable "axioms" enunciated by Professor G. E. MÜLLER—that in correlation with every distinct sensation some distinct physiological (cortical in the last instance) process must be assumed to exist. To suppose (as v. KRIES does) that for no assignable reason a three-fold process in the retina turns into a four-fold process in the cortex (or conversely, as DONDERS does) is to make admission of a fact, but does not provide a theory to account for it. Not everybody is interested in hypotheses (theories); some are content with a plain diet of fact. But it is well-known that successful theories of complicated occurrences in nature are not only intellectually satisfying but also most important as guides to further investigation.

Our ancestors thought that redness resides in the rose. They had, very naturally, no conception of the fact—now a commonplace of science (save for the physicists)—that there is no redness until specific light-frequencies have passed through the alchemy of the retina (and not always then—some persons, though they can see, are totally chroma-blind). That HELMHOLTZ himself should have used the word "colour" in its primitive, objective, sense is singular in the extreme; two successive sections of his book are called *Die einfachen Farben* and *Die zusammengesetzten Farben*, when what he is discussing is respectively homogeneous (or pure) and non-homogeneous (or mixed) light-rays. A blue-green sensation-blend may come from a homogeneous beam of light, and on the other hand a unitary yellow sensation may come from a mixture of "red" and "green" lights. While this use of the word "Farben" is a mere momentary inadvertence on the part of HELM- HOLTZ—he puts the matter in the third volume of this work (§26) in perfectly strict scientific terms—that is far from being the case with most of the physicists who write on colour at the present time, *e. g.*, with Sir OLIVER LODGE, BARTON, JOLY, PEDDIE, etc. This is all the more strange when it is remembered that NEWTON (no one, indeed, before him had made this discovery) says plainly: "The rays, to speak properly, are not coloured. In them is nothing else than a certain power or disposition to stir up a sensation of this or that colour . . . . So colours in the object are nothing but a disposition to reflect this or that sort of rays more copiously than the rest."

Moreover, it is to be noted that in the original theory of THOMAS YOUNG it was the *physiological* difficulty of imagining a sufficient number of tuned retinal fibres for all the rays of light, in accordance with the view of NEWTON—"vibrations running along the aqueous pores or crystalline pith of the capillamenta which pave or face the retina"—that led him to substitute a three-part mechanism, with an *overlapping* in various proportions for the intermediate blue-greens, etc.[1] Unquestionably, THOMAS YOUNG would never have called this hypothesis of his (a limited-number-of-constituents-hypothesis) a *trichromatic* theory, nor (what is no improvement) a "triple nerve-excitation theory."

It is for all these purely psychological reasons that the psychologists have never been able to regard the *colour-theory* of HELMHOLTZ as deserving of serious consideration. (The fact that HELMHOLTZ gave no physiological explanation of what v. KRIES[2] has lately furnished a much-needed name for, namely, the "accessory" visual phenomena, is of far less consequence; the recent finding of FRÖHLICH, *e. g.*, that contrast is simply an after-image of scattered light, would fit into any hypothesis regarding the fundamental process of the colour-sensations.) In fact, Professor CATTELL has said of this theory (in the review already quoted from) that "if it were to be proposed at this time [1898] it would not have a single adherent." WILLIAM JAMES said that HELMHOLTZ is, in the science of colour, more eminent for his experimental work than for his theoretical contributions; but it has been pointed out, on the other hand, that the *Physiologische Optik* was the work of his younger days. In any case the physicists ought surely to take notice of the fact that the psychologists, who are experts in questions of *sensation*, find that the HELMHOLTZ theory is wholly inadequate.

II. The Helmholtz-König Facts of Colour Sensation

But however inadequate the HELMHOLTZ theory may be for explaining the characters of the chromatic sensations—however certain it may be that (1) vision is tetrachromatic, (2) that it has undergone a remarkable and a perfectly well made out course of development,

---

[1] It would seem to be impossible for the physicists to realize that when once light has struck the retina, wave-lengths cease to exist — that their place is taken by *three* initial chemical products and *mixtures* of them. Thus no interest attaches to a pair of complementary *wave-lengths*. When red and blue-green, or green and blue-red, or blue and yellow (that is, red-green) mixed in the required proportions, make white, what we have is the fundamental YOUNG-HELMHOLTZ fact that white can be made out of the three physical constituents, red and blue and green. (Yellow does not need to be put in separately—yellow is a secondary chemical product that forms itself. See my theory, to be given presently.) A simple consideration of similar triangles (in the map of colour sensations in terms of trilinear coördinates) will show that lines drawn through the whiteness-point will meet the spectral line in points such that their severally combined red and green and blue constituents will be in the correct proportion for making white. I have, therefore, to aid this process of thought, proposed the use of the term "transformer mechanism" (plainly adumbrated, as above, by THOMAS YOUNG) to accentuate the immediate change that takes place as soon as light performs its initial (photo-chemical) work upon the photo-aesthetic retina. There is everything in having a name when things are in danger of being overlooked.

[2] *Allgemeine Sinnesphysiologie.*

namely—(a) white, (b) yellow and blue in addition, which however
revert to white, and (c) the addition again of red and green, which revert, when mixed, to yellow,—nevertheless the result of the great
work carried out in the HELMHOLTZ laboratory by KÖNIG and his
assistants is plain matter of fact. It is indeed the most fundamental
of all the facts regarding the colour-processes. However, it is not a
fact regarding the *sensations* of colour, but only regarding the initial,
photo-chemical process which starts up conditions resulting finally in
sensation. Colour vision is not *trichromatic*, but it starts up (in the
cones) with an initial "tri-receptor" photo-chemical process.

The distribution-curves of the (four) chromatic sensations which
represent the theory of HERING are all purely the work cf the imagination, and so are the first tentative curves of HELMHOLTZ (still too
frequently reproduced in the books). But the situation is very different
when it comes to the later curves, which represent what I may call the
HELMHOLTZ facts. These curves are drawn in accordance with the
results of a vast number of observations in the game of "matching by
mixtures"—the demonstration, by the eye, that all the colours of the

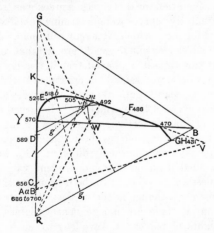

Fig. 81.—The Colour Triangle (KÖNIG).

spectrum can be matched by physical mixtures of red, green and blue
lights. When one-half of the field of view of the great HELMHOLTZ
instrument for mixing specific light frequencies, the *Farbenmischapparat*, is filled with a combination of two different lights and the
other half with a homogeneous light, or a different light mixture, or
white light, and if the proportions and the character of the several
constituents are varied until the two half-fields are indistinguishable,

we are said to have before us a colour equation.[1] The results of these measurements are mapped in a *colour-triangle* (what the metallurgists call a triaxial diagram)—a very natural plan for representing (proportionally) by trilinear coördinates functions of three independent variables. The three distribution-curves picture the same facts by means of a different system of representation. But it was only after the incorporation into this work by König of the results of the equations made by the partially chroma-blind that it acquired its present immense significance.

This triangle should always be drawn with the yellow-white-blue line a fundamental (that is, a horizontal) line, as representing the fact that the yellow and blue system of sensations (that of the common form of partial colour blindness, of the normal human mid-periphery, and of the bees) was the first to be developed.

When it came to deciding what wave-lengths to take for the independent variables in this work of matching by mixture, the choice was a difficult one for green (the two ends of the spectrum were naturally chosen, as a first trial, for red and for blue). In the lack of any determining consideration for this choice, a green was taken somewhat at hazard, and tentative curves were determined. (König's names for these curves and for those which later replaced them, *"Elementarempfindungen"* and *"Grundempfindungen,"* are without present significance). Just at this time it happened that it was possible to secure four individuals who were trained observers, and whose vision was dichromatic (two of each type). Would their curves show any coincidence with the curves of the normal eye? It turned out that while the *blue* curves of these defectives coincided with the blue curve of normal vision, the other two curves (both *yellow* in quality, it cannot be too often repeated) were markedly different. But would they perhaps have coincided if some *other* independent variables had been chosen? The question is easily put to the test: it is a simple matter of mathematics (merely a change in the vertices of the triangle of reference) to find out if there are independent variables, that is, unit quantities of lights of particular wave-lengths, such that the entire spectrum as seen by the three classes of individuals (the normal and the two types of defectives) can be built up out of like amounts of two or three of the several constituents—that is, are such that their curves do actually coincide. As a matter of fact König and Dieterici (König, *Gesammelte Abhandlungen*, p. 317) found that it was only necessary

---

[1] The instrument provides also for the throwing of measured quantities of white light upon either field at pleasure. An improved model has been put on the market quite lately by its makers, Schmidt and Haensch of Berlin. Other equivalent means of securing the same results are now in use in this country.

to make the following substitutions for the colours first chosen to disclose complete coincidence:

$$R = \frac{R - 0.15\,G + 0.1\,V}{0.95}$$

$$G = \frac{0.25\,R + G}{1.25}$$

$$B = V$$

The colours thus fixed upon are (1) a red less yellowish than that of the spectrum, (2) a green of about $505\mu\mu$, (3) a blue of about $470\mu\mu$. To repeat constantly that "these stimuli correspond quite closely with three of the fundamental physiological primaries of HERING" (*Colorimetry Report* 1920-21) is to commit a sad error. The *Urfarben* of HERING are complementary colours and therefore cannot be the same as the colours of the KÖNIG curves. KÖNIG and HERING both are perfectly explicit on this point (PFLÜGERS *Arch.*, XLI, 44, 1887 and XLVII, 425, 1890). The first set of KÖNIG curves prove simply that three stimuli *are enough* to reproduce all the colours of the spectrum—they do not show that the actual constituents of normal vision may not be *more* in number. But the extraordinary circumstance that when vision is dichromatic the sets of two constituents (of two very different types) coincide respectively with one or the other pair of the three normal constituents, the blue and the red *or* the blue and the green, is a fact that can only be accounted for by admitting that we have here discovered the actual limited number of constituents of the wilderness of the colour-sensations. (It is this non-occurrence of either the "red" or the "green" *distribution* curve that has made it almost impossible for the physicist to admit the fact that in the case of undeveloped, second-stage, vision it is the more primitive yellow that the defective sees instead of *either* red or green.) In other words, the colour-systems of the two types of chroma-blindness are "reduction systems" (this admirable term is due to v. KRIES). Another way of stating the fact here involved is this: in the colour-triangle all points on lines drawn through the vertices R and G will represent colours which look alike to the defective concerned, and their quality will be that of the whitish yellow (or blue) point in which the line cuts the fundamental Y-W-B line of the triangle. The continued use of the term "confusion colours" shows great ignorance of all these well-established facts of colour-vision. To say that (*Colorimetry Report*, 1920-21, p. 553) "the results cannot be regarded as sufficiently final to justify their adoption in place of a maximally straightforward [!] representation of the facts of colour mixture," and to reproduce KÖNIG's crude, tentative, curves (*loc. cit.*, page 288), is to have missed this point altogether. The curves may be changed by future more exact methods, but the important thing is that they will both (normal and defective) be changed together, so that the *coincidence* will not be lost.

When it was decided to make the first edition of the *Physiologische Optik* instead of the second the basis of the third edition (1909-1910), the editors automatically left out all of this very important work of König's in the determination of the distribution-curves. Many of the *theoretical* views of König were of such a nature as not to be confirmed by future results—as his belief that the cones have merely a dioptric function and that the photo-chemical process starts (for the chromata) in the epithelium cells. (It is plain that these large cells would have none of the minute space-specificity which is provided for in the cones.) But that is no reason for not recognizing the fact that his *experimental* work is fundamental in the highest degree. His great paper giving the complete account of this work did not appear until after the death of HELMHOLTZ (1896; reproduced in *Abhandlungen*, pp. 214-321), but his final results had been very fully published, and they were expressly incorporated by HELMHOLTZ himself in the *second* edition.[1] To have published an edition of HELMHOLTZ with all this left out was very much like issuing the play of SHAKESPEARE without the part of Hamlet. I therefore give on the opposite page the original diagram of König (*loc. cit.*, p. 310), never before reproduced as it happens, except schematically (HELMHOLTZ); which exhibits the definitive coincidence between the normal distribution curves (König and DIETERICI) and those of two each of the two common types of dichromatic vision (*yellow* and blue, in both cases, as sensations).

III. The Development Theory of the Colour Sensations[2]

It can never be known beforehand what ones of a highly complicated (and apparently contradictory) collection of facts will be the ones to throw light upon the whole bewildering subject—to suggest a theory which will reconcile the facts in question and fuse them into one all-embracing conception. In 1891-92, when I had the good fortune to have successive semesters in the laboratories of G. E. MÜLLER and König, and as a consequence to have the HELMHOLTZ and the HERING points of view both very "warm" in my consciousness, I found the antagonistic states of mind produced by these two absolutely

---

[1] Up to page 640 this edition is the work of HELMHOLTZ solely (as König expressly states in his preface); the account of the work of König is given in pages 357–370.

[2] This has been variously called, by its adherents, the genetic theory, the evolution theory, and the development theory.

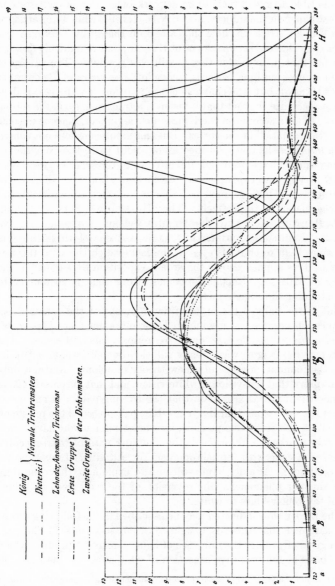

Köníg ⎱ *Normale Trichromaten*
Dieterici ⎰

Zehnder, Anomaler Trichromat

Erste Gruppe ⎱ *der Dichromaten.*
Zweite Gruppe ⎰

Fig. 82.—The HELMHOLTZ-KÖNIG Distribution Curves (final, corrected, form)

incompatible arrays of facts to be very irksome. It was (as I state in my first paper on the subject, *Mind*, N. S. II, 1893) while I was engaged in writing an article to show that a certain theory by DONDERS was better than that of HELMHOLTZ or of HERING, that it suddenly dawned upon me that a far better theory still was possible. The theory of DONDERS does nothing towards reconciling the views of HELMHOLTZ and of HERING; but (the converse of the position of v. KRIES) it does at least recognize the fact that if vision is tetrachromatic in the retina, it must, to take account of the HELMHOLTZ argument, become in some way "trichromatic" in the cortex. But this admission does not constitute a *theory* of the fact. All theories of colour (with the exception of the one which I have proposed) fall into one or the other of two classes —they accept (and explain) *either* the facts of HERING *or* the facts of HELMHOLTZ. Thus we have, as theories of "trichromatism"[1] and tetrachromatism, respectively: The HELMHOLTZ School—LODGE, JOLY, BARTON, etc.; and the HERING School—DONDERS, G. E., MÜLLER, FRÖHLICH, SCHJELDERUP, etc. Not one of these theorists does more than to shut his eyes to the facts which the rival theories explain. This applies also to the ardent exposition by FRÖBES of the theory of MÜLLER, although he comes nearer than is customary to understanding the adverse facts.

But in the light of the order of development of the colour-sense, the question became less insoluble. The remarkable fact of *the double structure and the double function* of the retina (rods and cones—MAX SCHÜLTZE, PARINAUD) was already sufficiently well established to be made the foundation stone of a new theory of colour. And not only was it known that rod-vision is white vision, and that chromatic vision is cone-vision; it was also plain that the chroma-pairs did not occur both at the same time, that the yellow-blue pair preceded the red-green pair. With this it became possible, by what HEGEL might have called a "higher synthesis," to reconcile the YOUNG-HELMHOLTZ tri-receptor process in a cone with tetrachromatism for sensation (LEONARDO DA VINCI, BRÜCKE, AUBERT, HERING), and to explain at the same time those singular phenomena, the reversion of the red-greens to yellow and of the yellow-blues to white.

The theory thus indicated may be described in the following terms. It is assumed that there is a light-sensitive substance in the rods which gives off, under the influence of light, a reaction-product which is the basis of the primitive sensation of whiteness. In the cones, in

[1] This word is a misnomer, if we take *chroma* in its actual significance. The vision of the totally chroma-blind is not monochromatic but achromatic. The initial three-fold photo-chemical process which actually takes place in a cone should be called a *tri-receptor* process.

the next higher stage of development of the colour-sense (the yellow
and blue vision of the bees, and of our own mid-periphery), this same
light-sensitive substance has become, by a simple molecular rearrangement, *more specific* in its response to light, and in such a way
that the two ends of the spectrum act separately to produce nerve-
excitant substances which, however, when they are produced both
at once, unite chemically to form the "white" nerve-excitant out of
which they were developed. In the third and final stage the "yellow"
nerve-excitant has again undergone a development in the direction of
greater specificity, and red and green vision are acquired. These
reaction-products are, however, the constituents of the more primitive
"yellow" nerve-excitant, and hence when they both occur at once—
when red and green light fall together on the retina—they revert to
the "yellow" nerve-excitant. If blue light is now added, the white
sensation is again produced. Thus "yellow" and "white" are, in
tetrachromatic vision, secondary products; at the same time *they are the
identical nerve-excitants* which produced the more primitive forms of
vision. In other words, (1) a light-sensitive "mother substance" in
the rods which, on dissociation by light, gives off a cleavage-product,
W, resulting (in the cortex) in the dull white sensations, becomes (2)
capable of giving off two subsidiary cleavage-products, Y and B; Y is
split off by light of low frequency and B by light of high frequency;
Y is the nerve-excitant for the sensation of yellow, B for the sensation
of blue. But suppose that, chemically $Y + B \equiv W$; then if Y and B
are both split off at the same time in the same cone they (being by
hypothesis the chemical constituents of W) immediately unite to form
W, and the *sensation* produced will be the primitive white. So in the
third stage we shall have, in brief:

$$R + G \equiv Y, \qquad Y + B \; (\equiv R + G + B) \equiv W.$$

The accessory phenomena of colour are also given a perfectly
simple and satisfactory explanation in this theory.

It is not necessary to discuss here the theory of Professor HERING;
in addition to all its other difficulties it is absolutely incompatible with
the HELMHOLTZ fact of the tri-receptor process and consequently
it has, naturally, never appealed to the physicists. There is no occasion
for considering (as does PARSONS) at great length all the minor merits
and demerits of the HELMHOLTZ and HERING theories. The situation
is simply that HERING confutes HELMHOLTZ and HELMHOLTZ confutes
HERING.

Before the time of LAVOISIER, when chemistry was not yet in
existence, the alchemists might by chance have discovered that on

putting hydrogen and chlorine together in a test-tube, under certain conditions both of these substances disappear and hydrochloric acid takes their place. Being not yet chemists, they might have explained this experiment in this way: they might have said, "Hydrogen and chlorine are a naturally antagonistic pair of elements—when they are put together in a test-tube they both vanish, and a hydrochloric acid which was there all the time takes their place." This would be analogous to the HERING explanation of the fundamental event in colour. But since chemistry *does* now exist, it would be a pity not to take advantage of its effectiveness for explaining disappearances and appearances.

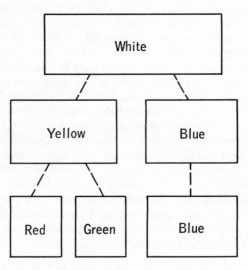

Fig. 83.—Stages 1, 2 and 3 of the actual development of the colour sense

The assumptions which I make (representing the psychological actualities) have been confirmed in a remarkable manner. (1) That the cones are *anatomically* more highly developed rods has now been put beyond question by RAMON Y CAJAL. It is natural therefore to think that the light-sensitive substance which they contain has also undergone development, and that too in the direction of greater specificity. (2) But following upon the discovery of WEIGERT (the photochlorides) that a specific light-sensitive substance need not show colour to the human eye, HECHT has proved that that in the cones actually *is the same substance* as that in the rods, save that it has undergone a "molecular rearrangement"—the very phrase that I am in the habit of using to characterize the change in the colour-molecule made necessary by the *psychological* considerations (the same final whiteness-sensation in the cones as in the rods, though due to a three-part mechanism). (3) Moreover nothing could be simpler, chemically, than this situation. In fact (as Dr. ACREE has pointed out to me) there is a perfect analogy for it in a certain dye-stuff, a rosaniline carboxylate (no longer in practical use because it has been superseded by other less labile dyes). This is a substance such that (under proper conditions of light, heat and moisture), (*a*) hydrogen, chlorine and ethyl alcohol can either one of them be given off separately; but (*b*) when hydrogen and chlorine are given off together, they unite to

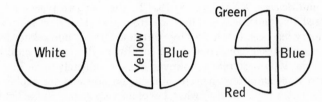

Fig. 84.—The cleavage products in the three stages of the colour sense. This diagram does not represent the entire light-sensitive molecule, but only the specific cleavage products which, according to the LADD-FRANKLIN theory, constitute the several nerve-excitants for the colour sensations (See WOODWORTH'S *Psychology*). For other diagrams, see *Psychological Review*, 23:247, 1916; *Zeitschrift f. Psychologie*, Bd. 6, etc.

form hydrochloric acid (analogue of the yellows); (*c*) when ethyl alcohol and *either* hydrogen or chlorine are given off, they do not unite—they persist as mixtures (analogue of the blue-greens and the blue-reds); (*d*) when all three of these substances are given off at once they unite to form ethyl chloride (analogue of the three-part leucogenic nerve-excitant in the cones). In other words, the ethyl alcohol set free does not unite with either the hydrogen or the chlorine until after they have first united with each other, exactly as a "blue" constituent in the retina does not chemically unite with either a "red" or a "green" constituent *unless* they have first united with each other to make yellow. Nothing could be more perfectly analogous to what is required for the phenomena of colour-vision.

In conclusion it must be kept in mind that no theory of colour-sensation is deserving of consideration which is not built upon, at once, (1) the fact discovered by THOMAS YOUNG (and magnificently confirmed in the laboratory of HELMHOLTZ)—that three light-stimuli are sufficient, as a physical cause, to start up the retinal photo-chemical processes: (2) the apparently contradictory fact that nevertheless the

*Figure 83 and 84 are reproduced in color facing page 385.

sensations are *five* in number—yellow and white have been somehow added; (3) the very illuminating fact that the *order of development* of the colour sense can be made to account fully for this anomaly and also for (4) the disappearance of the red-greens (and of the yellow-blues) and the appearance in their stead of yellow (and of white). Any proposed theory should be subjected to the test: does it meet all of these "minimal requirements"? (See *Journ. Opt. Soc. Amer.*, etc., 7, pp. 66–68.)

A fuller account of the Development Theory of Colour Sensation will be found in: *Zft. f. Psychologie*, 4, 1892; *Dictionary of Philosophy and Psychology*; *American Cyclopedia of Ophthalmology*, 1913; the *Psychological Review*, XXIII, 1916 and XXIX, 1922; *Mind*, 1892, 1893; and *Science*, XXII, pp. 18, 19. In the last two places I have discussed its fundamental difference from the theory of DONDERS. My theory has been taken over by SCHENCK without due acknowledgment, as has been pointed out for me by v. BRÜCKE (*Zentralbl. f. Physiologie*, 1905). SCHENCK, however, failed completely to see all that my theory accounts for: he felt, himself, no necessity for explaining (he was not a psychologist) what I explain very simply in the light of development: namely, the reversion of what we should see as the red-greens and the yellow-blues to the primitive sensations, yellow and white.

Partial Bibliography 1911-1924 for Volume II

The following list of some articles and books that have appeared since the publication of the third German edition of the *Handbuch der physiologischen Optik* has been compiled by the editor with the idea that, very imperfect and far from complete as it necessarily is, it would still be of much use to the student who is interested in the manifold subjects treated in Volume II. The list does not even include some of the more recent works that are cited in the new footnotes. It should be borne in mind that this manuscript was in the hands of the printer in June 1924 and of course contains nothing later than that date.

1911. W. DE W. ABNEY, Colour-blindness and trichromatic theory of colour vision. II. Incomplete colour-blindness. *Proc. Roy. Soc.*, Ser. A. **86**. pp. 43–56.

F. ALLEN, A new method of measuring the luminosity of the spectrum. *Phil. Mag.*, 604–607.

E. ESTANAVE, Synthesis of complementary colours by ruled gratings. *C. R.*, **153**, pp. 1464–1466.

R. STIGLER, A new binocular photometer. *Akad. Wiss. Wien*, Ber. 120, 2a. pp. 1069–1073.

C. ZAKRZEWSKI, The half-shadow interferometer as photometer. *Acad.Sci. Cracovie*, Bull. 8a. pp. 545–547.

1912. W. DE W. ABNEY, Trichromatic theory of colour vision—the measurement of retinal fatigue. *Proc. Roy. Soc.*, Ser. A. **87**, pp. 415–427.

L. ARONS, A chromoscope. *Ann. d. Phys.* **39**, 3. pp. 545–568.

W. E. BARROWS, *Light, photometry and illumination.*

L. BELL, Factors in heterochromatic photometry. *Electr. World*, **59**, pp. 201–203.

A. BRÜCKNER and R. KIRSCH, Untersuchungen über die Farbenzeitschwelle. *Zft. f. Sinnesphysiol.* **46**, 229–287.

W. B. CROFT, Contrast colours in the use of zone-plates. *Nature*, **89**, p. 581.

E. P. HYDE, Spectro-photometry. *Astrophys. Journ.*, **35**, 237–267.

H. E. IVES, Studies in the photometry of light of different colours. *Phil. Mag.*, **24**, pp. 149–188, 352–370, 845–853.

Idem, Primary standard of light. *Astrophys. Journ.*, **36**, pp. 321–329.

A. C. JOLLEY and A. J. BULL, Measurement of colour. *Phys. Soc., Proc.* **24**, pp. 417–421.

H. KRUESS, Spectrophotometer with colour-mixing apparatus. *Zft. Instrumentenk.*, **32**, pp. 6–13.

P. G. NUTTING, New precision colorimeter. *Washington Acad. Sci., Journ.*, **2**, pp. 183–185.

T. C. PORTER, Study of flicker. *Proc. Roy. Soc.*, Ser. A, **86**, pp. 495–513.

H. S. RYLAND, Optical experiments. *Nature*, **89**, pp. 554, 555.

J. THOVERT, Heterochromatic photometry. *Jour. de Phys.*, **2**, Ser. 5, pp. 34–40.

M. WERTHEIMER, Experimentellen Studien über das Sehen von Bewegungen. *Zft. f. Psychol.*, **61**, pp. 162–266.

1913. W. DE W. ABNEY, *Researches in colour vision and the trichromatic theory.*

W. W. COBLENTZ, Radiometer attachment for monochromatic illuminator. *Journ. Franklin Inst.*, **175**, pp. 151, 152.

C. FABRY and H. BUISSON, Absorption of ultra-violet light by ozone and limit of solar spectrum. *C. R.*, **156**, pp. 782–785.

R. A. HOUSTOUN, Luminous efficiency throughout the visible spectrum. *Phil. Mag.*, **25**, pp. 715–722.

O. LUMMER, Rod vision. *Phys. Zft.*, **14**, pp. 97–102.

J. R. MILNE, New types of spectrophotometer on the "flicker" principle. *Proc. Roy. Soc. Edinburgh*, **33**, pp. 257–263.

T. A. NEELIN, The sensitiveness of the eye to light and color. *Trans. Roy. Soc. Canada*, **2**, pp. 195–208.

W. E. and R. PAULI, Objective photometry, *Ann. der Phys.*, **41**, 4, pp. 812–828.

J. P. C. SOUTHALL, *The Principles and Methods of Geometrical Optics.* Rev. ed. New York.

H. C. STEVENS, Flicker photometer and the iris. *Phil. Mag.*, **26**, pp. 180–183.

W. WATSON, Luminosity curves of persons having normal and abnormal colour visions. *Proc. Roy. Soc.*, Ser. A, **88**, pp. 404–428.

Idem, On the luminosity curve of a colour-blind observer. *Proc. Roy. Soc.*, Ser. A, **89**, pp. 36–38.

1914. L. BELL, Types of abnormal colour vision. *Proc. Amer. Acad.*, **50**, pp. 3–13.

H. E. IVES and E. J. BRADY, Apparatus for the spectroscopic synthesis of colour. *Journ. Franklin Inst.*, **178**, pp. 89-96.

Iidem, New form of flicker photometer *Phys. Rev.*, **4**, pp. 222-227.

H. E. IVES and E. F. KINGSBURY, The theory of the flicker photometer. *Phil. Mag.*, **28**, pp. 708–728.

L. A. JONES, Colour analyses of two component mixtures. *Phys. Rev.*, **4**, pp. 454–466.

M. LUCKIESH, Growth and decay of colour sensations. *Phys. Rev.*, **4**, pp. 1–11.

A. MALLOCK, Intermittent vision. *Proc. Roy. Soc.*, Ser. A, pp. 407–410.

P. G. NUTTING, Visibility of faintly illuminated objects. *Nature*, **93**, p. 480.

Idem, Visibility of radiation. *Am. Illum. Engin. Soc., Trans.*, **9**, 7, pp. 633–642.

A. H. PFUND, Contrast photometer. *Phys. Rev.*, **4**, pp. 477–481.

S. P. THOMPSON, Intermittent vision. *Proc. Roy. Soc.*, Ser. A, **90**, pp. 448, 449.

L. T. TROLAND, Adaptation and the chemical theory of sensory response. *Am. Journ. of Psychol.*, **25**, pp. 500–527.

F. H. VERHOEFF and L. BELL, Effect of ultra-violet radiation on the eye. *Science*, **40**, pp. 452–455.

W. WATSON, On anomalous trichromatic colour vision. *Proc. Roy. Soc.*, Ser. A, **90**, pp. 443–448.

1915. W. DE W. ABNEY and W. WATSON, Threshold of vision for different coloured lights. *Roy. Soc., Phil. Trans.*, **216**, pp. 91–128.

W. E. BURGE, Effect of ultra-violet light on the eye. *Electr. World*, **65**, pp. 912–914.

E. P. HYDE and W. E. FORSYTHE, Visibility of radiation in the red end of the visible spectrum. *Phys. Rev.*, **6**, pp. 68-70.

H. E. IVES, Establishment of photometry on a physical basis. *Journ. Franklin Inst.*, **180**, pp. 409–436.

Idem, The transformation of colour-mixture equations from one system to another. *Ibid.*, **180**, pp. 673–701.

Idem, Precision artificial eye. *Phys. Rev.*, **6**, pp. 334–344.

Idem, Physical photometry. *Am. Illum. Engin. Soc., Trans.*, **10**, pp. 101–125.

Idem, On the choice of a group of observers for heterochromatic measurements. *Am. Illum. Eng. Soc., Trans.*, **10**, pp. 203–209.

H. E. IVES and E. F. KINGSBURY, Heterochromatic photometry by CROVA's method. *Am. Illum. Eng. Soc., Trans.*, **10**, pp. 716–723.

Iidem, Flicker photometer measurements with a monochromatic green solution. *Phys. Rev.*, **5**, pp. 220–235.

1915. E. F. KINGSBURY, Flicker photometer attachment for the LUMMER-BRODHUN photometer. *Journ. Franklin Inst.*, **180**, pp. 215–223.

P. G. NUTTING, The visibility of radiation. *Phil. Mag.*, **29**, pp. 301–309.

W. OSTWALD, Theory of pigments. I. Fundamental properties of pigments and size of grain. *Kolloid. Zft.*, **16**, 1, pp. 1–4.

J. H. PARSONS, *An introduction to the study of colour vision.*

I. G. PRIEST, New method of heterochromatic photometry. *Phys. Rev.*, **6**, pp. 64–66.

C. V. RAMAN, Intermittent vision. *Phil. Mag.*, **30**, pp. 701, 702.

M. O. SALTMARSH, Brightness of intermittent illumination. *Phil. Mag.*, **29**, 646–650.

1916. P. W. COBB, Photometric considerations pertaining to visual stimuli. *Psychol. Rev.*, **23**, pp. 71–88.

Idem, The effect on foveal vision of bright surroundings. *Journ. Exper. Psychol.*, **1**, pp. 419–425.

E. C. CRITTENDEN and F. K. RICHTMYER, An "average eye" for heterochromatic photometry, and a comparison of a flicker and an equality-of-brightness photometer. *Am. Illum. Eng. Soc., Trans.*, **11**, pp. 331–367.

F. DITTMERS, Über die Abhängigkeit der Unterschiedschwelle für Helligkeiten von der antagonistischen Induktion. *Zft. f. Sinnesphysiol.*, **51**, pp. 214–232.

CHRISTINE LADD-FRANKLIN, On colour theories and chromatic sensations. *Psychol. Rev.*, **23**, pp. 237–249.

R. A. HOUSTOUN, Theory of colour vision. *Proc. Roy. Soc.*, **92**, pp. 424–432.

H. E. IVES, Minimum radiation visually perceptible. *Astrophys. Journ.*, **44**, pp. 124–127.

H. E. IVES and E. F. KINGSBURY, Mechanical equivalent of light. *Phys. Rev.*, **8**, pp. 177–190, 254–258.

Iidem, The theory of the flicker photometer. *Phil. Mag.*, **31**, pp. 290–321.

W. OSTWALD, Theory of colour. *Phys. Zft.*, **17**, pp. 322–332.

Idem, Absolute system of colours. *Zft. phys. Chem.*, **91**, 2, pp. 129–142.

P. G. NUTTING, The retinal sensibilities related to illuminating engineering. *Am. Illum. Eng. Soc., Trans.*, **11**, pp. 1–21; 131–136.

L. T. TROLAND, Flicker frequency as affected by colour. *Journ. Franklin Inst.*, **181**, pp. 853–855.

Idem, Absence of PURKINJE-effect in the fovea of the eye. Ibid., **182**, pp. 111, 112.

Idem, The heterochromatic brightness discrimination threshold. Ibid., **182**, pp. 112–114.

Idem, Notes on flicker photometry: flicker photometer frequency as a function of light intensity. Ibid., **182**, pp. 261–262.

F. H. VERHOEFF, L. BELL and C. B. WALKER, The pathological effects of radiant energy on the eye. *Proc. Amer. Acad.*, **51**, pp. 630–793.

1917. W. DE W. ABNEY, The fourth colourless sensation in the three-sensation spectrum, measured on the centre of the retina. *Proc. Roy. Soc.*, **94**, pp. 1–13.

F. BEST, Untersuchungen über die Dunkelanpassung des Auges mit Leuchtfarben. *Zft. f. Biol.*, **68**, pp. 111–146.

H. BUISSON, Minimum radiation visually perceptible. *Astrophys. Journ.*, **45**, pp. 296, 297.

Idem, The minimum energy necessary to produce the sensation of light. *Journ. de phys.*, **7**, pp. 68–74.

W. W. COBLENTZ and W. B. EMERSON, Sensibility of the average eye to light of different colours. *Bureau of Stand., Bull.* **14**, pp. 167–236.

Iidem, Mechanical equivalent of light. Ibid., pp. 255–265.

J. GUILD, Mechanism of colour vision. *Proc. Roy. Soc.*, **29**, pp. 354–361.

G. F. GÖTHLIN, Studien über die Energieschwelle für die Empfindung Rot in ihrer Abhängigkeit von der Wellenlänge der Lichtstrahlung. *Kungl. Vetenskapsakadem. Handlingar*, **58**, No. 1, 89 pages.

1917. C. HESS, Der Farbensinn der Vögel und die Lehre von den Schmuckfarben. PFLÜGERS *Arch.*, **166**, pp. 381–426.

A. V. HÜBL, Colour apparatus. *Phys. Zft.*, **18**, pp. 270–275.

H. E. IVES, Visual diffusivity. *Phil. Mag.*, **33**, pp. 18–33.

Idem, Polarization flicker photometer. Ibid., pp. 360–380.

Idem, Hue difference and flicker-photometer speed. Ibid., **34**, pp. 99–112.

Idem, Explanation of persistence of vision as a physical conduction phenomenon. *Journ. Franklin Inst.*, **183**, pp. 779, 780.

Idem, Units of radiation and illumination. *Astrophys. Journ.*, **45**, pp. 39-49.

L. A. JONES, The fundamental scale of· pure hue and retinal sensibility to hue differences. *Journ. Opt. Soc. Amer.*, **1**, pp. 63–77.

R. I. LLOYD, Hemianopsia. *Ophthalmic Record*, Oct. 1917.

M. LUCKIESH, Equality point in spectral energy and luminosity distribution curves. *Journ. Franklin Inst.*, **183**, pp. 633, 634.

Idem, The physical basis of color technology. *Journ. Franklin Inst.*, **183**, pp. 73–93 and **184**, pp. 227–250.

H. E. MERVIN, Optical properties and theory of colour of pigments and paints. *Proc. Amer. Soc. for Testing Materials*, **17**, pp. 1–34.

P. REEVES, Effect of light on pupillary area and retina of the eye. *Eastman Kodak Co.'s Research Lab.*, Comm. No. 52.—*Journ. Franklin Inst.*, **184**, pp. 717–719.

Idem, The minimum radiation visually perceptible. *Astrophys. Journ.*, **46**, pp. 167–174.

H. N. RUSSELL, Minimum radiation visually perceptible. Ibid., **45**, pp. 60–64.

L. T. TROLAND, On the measurement of visual stimulation intensities. *Journ. Exp. Psychol.*, **2**, pp. 1–33.

1918. J. BLANCHARD, The brightness sensibility of the retina. *Phys. Rev.*, **11**, pp. 81–99.

F. EXNER. Some experiments and remarks on colour theory. *Akad. Wiss. Wien*, Ber. **127**. 2a. pp. 1829–1864.

L. W. HARTMAN, Visibility of radiation in the blue end of the visible spectrum. *Astrophys. Journ.* **47**, pp. 83–95.

G. HOLST and J. S. DE VISSER, Brightness of the black body and the mechanical equivalent of light. *K. Akad. Amsterdam Proc.*, **20**, 7, pp. 1036–1042.

R. A. HOUSTOUN, A statistical survey of colour vision. *Proc. Roy. Soc.*, **94A**, pp. 576–586.

E. P. HYDE, W. E. FORSYTHE and F. E. CADY, Visibility of radiation. *Journ Franklin Inst.*, **185**, pp. 829–831.

H. E. IVES, Resolution of mixed colours by differential visual diffusivity. *Phil. Mag.*, **35**, pp. 413–421.

L. LUMIERE, Persistence of luminous impressions on the retina. *C. R.*, **166**, pp. 654–656.

P. METZNER, Adaptation of the eye for low illuminations. *Deutsch. phys. Gesell.*, Verh. **20**, pp. 183–186.

I. G. PRIEST, The law of symmetry of the visibility function. *Phys. Rev.*, **11**, pp. 498–502.

Idem, A precision method for producing artificial daylight. Ibid., 502–504.

P REEVES, The rate of pupillary dilation and contraction. *Physiol. Rev.*, **25**, pp. 330–340.

Idem, Visibility of radiation. *Phil. Mag.*, **35**, pp. 174–181.

J. P. C. SOUTHALL, *Mirrors, Prisms and Lenses*, New York.

1919. F. ALLEN, On the discovery of four transition points in the spectrum and the primary colour sensations. *Phil. Mag.*, **38**, pp. 55–81.

Idem, The persistence of vision for colours of varying intensity. Ibid., pp. 81–89.

E. H. BARTON and H. M. BROWNING, Syntonic hypothesis of colour vision with mechanical illustrations. *Phil. Mag.*, **38**, pp. 338–348.

1919. A. BLONDEL, A physical method of heterochromatic photometry. *C. R.*, **169**, pp. 830–835.

P. W. COBB, Dark-adaptation, with especial reference to the problems of night-flying. *Psychol. Rev.*, **26** pp. 428–453.

M. DRESBACH, J. E. SUTTON, JR., and S. R. BURBAGE, Dark adaptation of the peripheral retina. *Proc. Amer. Physiol. Soc.;Amer. J. Physiol.*, **51**, p. 188.

C. E. FERREE and G. RAND, Effect of colour of light on acuteness of vision. *Am. Illum. Eng. Soc., Trans.*, **14**, pp. 107–116 (discussion, pp. 117–132).

Iidem, Chromatic thresholds of sensation from center to periphery of the retina and their bearing on color theory, *Psychol. Rev.*, **26**, pp. 16–41 and 150–163.

J. W. FRENCH, The unaided eye. *Trans. Opt. Soc.*, **20**, pp. 209–232 and **21**, pp. 1–33 and 127–156.

R. A. HOUSTOUN, Theory of colour vision. *Phil. Mag.*, **38**, pp. 402–417.

E. P. HYDE, W. E. FORSYTHE and F. E. CADY, Brightness of a black body and mechanical equivalent of light. *Phys. Rev.*, **13**, pp. 45–58.

H. E. IVES, Photometric scale. *Journ. Franklin Inst.*, **188**, pp. 217–235.

M. LUCKIESH, Infra-red radiant energy and the eye. *Amer. J. Physiol.*, **50**, pp. 383–398.

O. MEISSNER, Colorimetric measurements according to OSTWALD's scale. *Phys. Zft.*, **20**, pp. 83–85.

Idem, OSTWALD's colorimetry. Ib'd., pp. 344–346.

S. G. RICH, The PURKINJE phenomenon in subtropical moonlight. *Psychol. Bull.*, **16**, pp. 388, 389.

P. WOOG, Variation in persistence of vision in different regions of the retina. *C. R.*, **168**, pp. 1222–1224.

1920. M. BECKE, The nature of colour perception. *Färber-Ztg.*, **31**, pp. 50–52 and 61–64.

U. EBBECKE, Über das Augenblicksehen. Über das Sehen in Flimmerlicht. PFLÜGERS *Arch.*, pp. 181–195, 196–223.

F. W. EDRIDGE-GREEN, *The physiology of vision, with special reference to colour blindness.*

Idem, Colour vision and colour blindness; new spectrometer. *Journ. Soc. Arts*, **69**, pp. 40–47.

F. EXNER, v. HELMHOLTZ's three-colour scheme. *Akad. Wiss. Wien*, Ber. **129**, 2a, pp. 27–46.

C. E. FERREE and G. RAND, The extent and shape of the zones of color sensitivity in relation to the intensity of the stimulus light. *Am. J. Physiolog. Optics*, **1**, pp. 185-213.

C. E. FERREE and G. RAND, An illuminated perimeter with campimeter features. *Trans. Amer. Ophthalm. Soc.* **18**, pp. 164-173.

J. FISON, Position of macula lutea and optic disc. *J. Anat.*, **54**, pp. 184–187.

H. HARTRIDGE, Colourimeter design. *Cambr. Phil. Soc. Proc.*, **19**, pp. 271–282.

Idem, Colour blindness and YOUNG's Hypothesis. *Brit. J. Ophth.*, **4**, pp. 318–322

S. HECHT, The photochemistry of the visual purple. *Journ. of Gen. Physiol.*, **3**, pp. 1–13.

S. HECHT, The dark adaptation of the human eye. *J. Gen. Physiol.*, **2**, pp. 499–517.

H. HENNING, Optische Versuche an Vögeln und Schildkroten übe die Bedeutung der roten Ölkugeln im Auge. PLFÜGERS *Arch.*, **178**, pp. 91–123.

E. HERING, *Grundzüge der Lehre vom Lichtsinn.*

C. v. HESS, Die angeborenen Farbensinnstörungen und das Farbengesichtfeld. *Arch. f. Augenheilk.*, **86**, pp. 317–335.

Idem, Die Rotgrünblindheiten. *Arch. f. d. ges. Physiol.*, **185**, pp. 147–164.

Idem, Untersuchungen zur Lehre von der Wechselwirkung der Sehfeldstellen. Ibid., **179**, pp. 50–72.

Idem, Die Grenzen der Sichtbarkeit des Spektrums in der Tierreihe. *Natur-wissenschaften*, **8**, pp. 197–200.

1920. E. P. HYDE and W. E. FORSYTHE, Colour match and spectral distribution. *Journ. Franklin Inst.*, **189**, pp. 663, 664.

E. R. JAENSCH, Parallelgesetz über der Verhalten der Reizschwellen bei Kontrast und Transformation. *Zft. f. Psychol.*, **85**, pp. 342–352.

L. A. JONES, Subtractive colorimeter. *Journ. Opt. Soc. Amer.*, **4**, pp. 420–431.

Idem, An instrument for the measurement of the visibility of objects. *Phil. Mag.*, **39**, pp. 96–134.

A. JUHÁSZ, Über die komplementär gefärbten Nachbilder. *Zft. f. Psychol. u. Physiol. d. Sinnesorgane II. Zft. f. Sinnesphysiol.*, **51**, pp. 233–263.

K. W. F. KOHLRAUSCH, Contributions to the theory of colour. *Phys. Zft.*, **21**, pp. 396–403.

Idem, Brightness of pigment colours. Ibid., pp. 423–426.

Idem, Remarks on OSTWALD's theory of pigment colours. Ibid., pp. 473–477.

J. KUNZ, Threshold phenomena in radiation. *Phys. Rev.*, **15**, pp. 129, 130.

R. I. LLOYD, The stereoscopic campimeter slate. *N. Y. Med. Journ.*, Dec. 1920.

P. G. NUTTING, Sensitiveness of the eye to light and colour. *Journ. Opt. Soc. Amer.*, **4**, pp. 55–79.

W. OSTWALD, The foundations of colorimetry. *Zft. tech. Phys.*, **1**, 9, pp. 173–175 and **1**, 12, pp. 261–271.

A. H. PFUND, Colorimetry of nearly-white surfaces. *Journ. Franklin Inst.*, **189**, pp. 371–379.

I. G. PRIEST, Note on the relation between the frequencies of complementary hues. *Journ. Opt. Soc. Amer.*, **4**, pp. 402–404.

Idem, Preliminary note on the relations between the quality of color and the spectral distribution of light in the stimulus. Ibid., **4**, pp. 388–401.

P. REEVES, The response of the average pupil to various intensities of light. *Journ. Opt. Soc. Amer.*, **4**, pp. 35–43.

F. K. RICHTMYER and E. C. CRITTENDEN, The precision of photometric measurements. *Journ. Opt. Soc. Amer.*, **4**, pp. 371–387.

F. E. ROSS, Photographic photometry and the PURKINJE effect. *Astrophys. Journ.*, **52**, pp. 86–97.

E. SCHRÖDINGER, Colorimetrics. *Zft. f. Physik*, **1**, 5, pp. 459–466.

M. SO, The visibility of radiation throughout the spectrum. *Phys. Math. Soc. Japan, Proc.*, **2**, pp. 177–184.

J. P. C. SOUTHALL, Refraction and visual acuity of the human eye. *Am. J. Physiol. Optics.* **1**, pp. 277-316.

L. T. TROLAND, The enigma of color vision. *Amer. Journ. Physiol. Optics*, **1**, pp. 317–337.

Idem, The nature of the visual receptor process. *Journ. Opt. Soc. Amer.*, **4**, pp. 3–15

Idem, The "all or none" law in visual response. Ibid, **4**, pp. 160–185.

R. L. WATERFIELD, Sensitiveness of different parts of the retina. *Journ. Brit. Astron. Assoc.* also *Journ. Roy. Astronom. Soc. Canada*, **15**, p. 84.

1921. A. AMES, JR., Systems of color standards. *Journ. Opt. Soc. Amer.*, **5**, pp. 160–170.

F. W. EDRIDGE-GREEN, The effect of red fatigue on the white equation. *Proc. Roy. Soc.*, **92B**, pp. 232–234.

W. EINTHOVEN, Über die Beobachtung und Abbildung dünner Faden. PFLÜGERS *Archiv*, **191**, pp. 60–98.

F. EXNER, Determination of brightness in the red-blind colour system. *Akad. Wiss. Wien, Ber.*, **130**, 2a, No. 7–8, pp. 355–361.

H. S. GRADLE, The blind spot. III. The relation of the blind spot to medullated nerve fibres in the retina. *J. Amer. Med. Assoc.*, **77**, pp. 1483–1486.

H. HARTRIDGE, Apparatus for projecting spectra. *Cambr. Phil. Soc. Proc.*, **20**, p. 480.

S. HECHT, Foveal dark adaptation. *J. Gen. Physiol.*, **4**, pp. 113-139.

H. HONIGMANN, Über Lichtempfindlichkeit und adaptierung des Vogelauges. PFLÜGERS *Arch.*, **189**, pp. 1–72.

1921. S. Hecht, Photo-chemistry of visual purple. II. *J. Gen. Physiol.*, **3**, pp. 285–290.

Idem, Time and intensity in photosensory stimulation. *J. Gen. Physiol.*, **3**, 367–390.

F. L. Hopwood, An auto-stroboscope and an incandescent colour top. *Trans. Opt. Soc.*, **23**, 2, pp. 93–98.

K. Horovitz, Theory of visual space. *Akad. Wiss. Wien., Ber.* **130**, 2a, No. 7–8, pp. 405–420.

R. A. Houstoun, A new method of investigating colour blindness with a description of 23 cases. *Proc. Roy. Soc. Edinburgh*, **42**, pp. 75–88.

R. A. Houstoun and M. A. Dunlop, A statistical survey of colour vision. *Phil. Mag.*, **41**, pp. 186–200.

H. E. Ives, A proposed standard method of colorimetry. *Journ. Opt. Soc. Amer.*, **5**, pp. 469–478.

J. Joly, A quantum theory of vision. *Phil. Mag.*, **41**, pp. 289–304.

H. Koellner, Über theorien des Farbensinnes. *Münch. med. Woch.*, **68**, pp. 1045–1047.

L. Koeppe, *Die ultra- und polarisationsmikroskopische Erforschung des lebenden Auges.* Published by E. Bircher, Bern, Switzerland.

R. I. Lloyd, The stereocampimeter and its uses. *Scientific and Technical Publications of Bausch & Lomb Optical Co.*, Rochester, N. Y., No. 12.

Idem, The stereo-campimeter and its use; presentation of a new instrument for the study of central field defects. *The Journal of Ophthalm., Otology and Laryngology*, Oct., 1921.

T. R. Merton, Spectrophotometry in the visible and ultra-violet spectrum. *Proc. Roy. Soc.*, **99**, pp. 78–84.

G. Michailesco, Sur les variations de la sensibilité autour de la tache de Mariotte. *C. R.*, **173**, pp. 604–606.

P. L. du Noüy, Energy and vision. *J. Gen. Physiol.*, **3**, pp. 743–764.

J. H. J. Poole, The photoelectric theory of vision. *Phil. Mag.*, **41**, pp. 347–357.

Idem, Minimum time necessary to excite the human retina. Ibid., **43**, pp. 345–348.

I. G. Priest, The spectral distribution of energy required to evoke the gray sensation. *Bureau of Stand. Sci. Papers*, No. 417; *Journ. Opt. Soc. Amer.*, **5**, pp. 205–209.

P. Reeves, Reaction of the eye to light; energy required to produce visual sensation. *Trans. Opt. Soc.*, **22**, pp. 1–14.

F. Schanz, Das Sehen. *Munch. med. Woch.*, **68**, pp. 1390–1392.

L. T. Troland, The colors produced by equilibrium photopic adaptation. *Journ. Exp. Psychol.*, **4**, pp. 344–390.

F. Weigert, Ein photochemisches Modell der Retina. *Pflügers Arch.*, **190**, pp. 177–197.

R. S. Woodworth, *Psychology, A study of mental life.*

1922. F. Aigner, Resonance theory of colour vision. *Akad. Wiss. Wien., Ber.* **131**, 2a. No. 4–5, pp. 299–320.

E. H. Barton, Colour vision and syntony. *Nature*, **110**, pp. 357–359.

A. Contino, Measurement of visual acuity. *Riv. Ottica e Mecan.*, **2**, pp. 40–59.

A. Duschek-Frankfurt, Perception of brightness in relation to colour. *Akad. Wiss. Wien.*, Ber. **131**. 2a. No. 3. pp. 171–197.

F. W. Edridge-Green, Colour-vision theories and colour-blindness. *Phil. Mag.*, **44**, pp. 916–920.

F. W. Ellis, The study of visual processes by means of momentary retinal shadows. *Journ. Opt. Soc. Amer.*, etc., **6**, pp. 922–931.

F. Exner, Colour vision. *Akad. Wiss. Wien., Ber.* **131**, 2a, No. 10, pp. 615–641.

C. Fabry and H. Buisson, A universal photometer without diffusing screen. *Rev. d'optique*, **1**, pp. 1–12.

C. E. Ferree and G. Rand, A new laboratory and clinic perimeter. *J. Experim. Psychol.*, **5**, pp. 46–67.

1922. C. E. FERREE and G. RAND, An illuminated perimeter with campimeter features. *Amer. Jour. Ophthal.*, **5**, pp. 455-465.

C. E. FERREE and G. RAND, Perimetry: Variable factors influencing the breadth of color fields. *Am. J. Ophthalm.*, **5**, pp. 886-895.

C. E. FERREE and G. RAND, Some contributions to the science and practice of ophthalmology. *Trans. Internat. Congress Ophthalmol.*, Washington, D. C.

W. E. FORSYTHE, Accuracy in color matching. *Journ. Opt. Soc. Amer.*, etc., **6**, pp. 476-482.

W. P. GRAHAM, The absorption of the eye for ultra-violet radiation. *Journ. Opt. Soc. Amer.*, etc. **6**, pp 605-614.

C. v. HESS, Farbenlehre. *Ergebn. d. Physiol.*, **20**, pp. 1-107.

R. A. HOUSTOUN, An investigation of the colour vision of 527 students by the RAYLEIGH test. *Proc. Roy. Soc.*, **102**, pp. 353-360.

K. HOROVITZ, Heteromorphia due to variation of effective aperture and visual acuity. *Journ. Opt. Soc. Amer.*, etc., **6**, pp. 597-604.

E. P. HYDE and F. E. CADY, New principle in contrast photometry. *Journ. Opt. Soc. Amer.*, etc., **6**, pp. 615-619.

H. E. IVES, A theory of intermittent vision. *Journ. Opt. Soc. Amer.*, etc. **6**, pp. 343-361.

L. KOEPPE, *Die Bedeutung der Gitterstruktur in den lebenden Augenmedien für die Theorie der subjektiven Farbenerscheinungen.* (E. BIRCHER, Bern, Switzerland.)

Idem, Über das Problem der Krümmungen der elastischen Membranen und Lamellen in den lebenden Augenmedien. *Deutsche optische Wochenschrift*, Nos. 36, 37.

Idem, *Die Mikroskopie des lebenden Auges in natürlichen Lichte.* Vol. I (1920) and Vol. II (1922); published by JULIUS SPRINGER, Berlin.

CHRISTINE LADD-FRANKLIN, Tetrachromatic vision and the development theory of color. *Science*, **55**, No. 1430.

Eadem, Practical logic and color theories. *Psychol. Rev.*, **29**, pp. 180-200.

M. LUCKIESH, *Visual illusions, their causes, characteristics and applications.*

W. OSTWALD, What advances has the new colour theory made? *Zft. Elektrochem.* **28**, pp. 398-404.

W. PEDDIE, *Colour vision.*

F. SCHANZ, Theory of vision. *Zft. f. Physik*, **12**, 1 and 2, pp. 28-37.

H. SCHULZ, *Das Sehen.*

M. C. SHIELDS, The visibility function and visibility thresholds for color-defectives. *Journ. Opt. Soc. Amer.*, etc., **6**, pp. 362-368.

L. T. TROLAND, Psychophysics as the key to the mysteries of physics and metaphysics. *Journ. Washington Acad. Sci.*, **12**, pp. 141-162.

Idem, The facts and theories of color vision. *Trans. Internat. Congress of Ophthalm.*

Idem, The present status of visual science. Bulletin No. 27, *National Research Council.*

Idem, Brilliance and chroma in relation to zone theories of vision. *Journ. Opt. Soc. Amer.*, etc., **6**, pp. 3-26.

Idem, Report of the nomenclature and stadards sub-committee on colorimetry for 1920-1921. *Journ. Opt. Soc. Amer.*, etc., **6**, pp. 527-604.

F. WEIGERT, The physical chemistry of colour vision. *Zft. Phys. Chem.*, **100**, pp. 537-565.

1923. F. ALLEN, On reflex visual sensations. *Journ. Opt. Soc. Amer.* etc., **7**, pp. 583-626.

Idem, On reflex visual sensations and color contrast. Ibid., **7**, pp. 913-942.

T. Y. BAKER, Limits of visual acuity. *Phil. Mag.*, **46**, pp. 640-642.

R. T. BEATTY, Monochromator for the ultra-violet, visible, and near infra-red. *Journ. Sci. Instr.*, **1**, pp. 33-42.

L. BLOCH, Colour measurement. *Zft. tech. Phys.*, **4**, 4, pp. 175-182.

E. L. CHAFFEE, W. T. BOVIE and ALICE HAMPSON, The electrical response of the retina under stimulation by light. *Journ. Opt. Soc. Amer.*, etc., **7**, pp. 1-43.

1923. P. W. COBB, The relation between field brightness and speed of retinal impression. *Journ. Franklin Inst.*, **195**, pp. 855–857.

C. C. COLBY, JR. and C. M. DOOLITTLE, A distribution photometer of new design. *Trans. Amer. Illum. Eng. Soc.*, **18**, pp. 273–289.

E. C. CRITTENDEN, The measurement of light. *Journ. Washington Acad. Sci.*, **13**, pp. 69–90.

H. DEMBER, An entoptic phenomenon. *Zft. te h. Physik*, **4**, 1, p. 7.

R. DIETZIUS, The ultra-violet end of the solar spectrum. *Meteorlog. Zft.*, **40**, pp. 297–301.

G. M. B. DOBSON, A flicker type of photoelectric photometer giving high precision. *Proc. Roy. Soc.*, **104**, pp. 302–315.

F. W. EDRIDGE-GREEN, Some curious phenomena of vision. *Journ. Roy. Soc. Arts*, **71**, pp. 469–478.

O. EMERSLEBEN, Theory of vision. *Zft. f. Physik*, **15**, 2 and 3, pp. 180–183.

C. E. FERREE and G. RAND, Theory of flicker photometry. *Amer. Illum. Eng. Soc., Trans.*, **18**, pp. 151–199.

W. E. FORSYTHE, Color match and spectral distribution. *Journ. Opt. Soc. Amer.*, etc., **7**, pp. 1115–1122.

K. S. GIBSON and E. P. T. TYNDALL, Visibility of radiant energy. *Bureau Stand., Sci. Papers*, No. 475, pp. 131–191.

E. GOLDBERG, The grey wedge and its use in sensitometry. FARADAY *Soc., Trans.* **19**. pp. 349–354.

H. HARTRIDGE, Physiological limits to accuracy of visual observation and measurement. *Phil. Mag.*, **46**, pp. 49–79.

F. L. HOPWOOD, Time lag in vision. *Proc. Phys. Soc.*, **35**, p. 214.

R. A. HOUSTOUN, *Light and colour.*

R. A. HOUSTOUN and E. DOW, The evolution of the colours of the spectrum in terms of the three primary colours. *Phil. Mag.*, **45**, 2, pp. 169–176.

R. A. HOUSTOUN and W. M. HEDDLE, Visibility of red light. *Phil. Mag.*, **46**, pp. 699–706.

R. A. HOUSTOUN and W. H. MANSON, A new method of investigating colour-blindness. *Roy. Soc. Edinb.*, Proc. **43**. 2. pp. 216–218. (1922–1923).

H. E. IVES, A colour-match photometer. *Journ. Opt. Soc. Amer.*, etc., **7**, pp. 243–261.

Idem, Simultaneous matches by trichromatic and monochromatic analysis. *Journ. Opt. Soc. Amer.*, etc., **7**, pp. 287–298.

Idem, A chart of the flicker photometer. Ibid., **7**, pp. 363–373.

Idem, Transformation of colour-mixture equations from one system to another. *Journ. Franklin Inst.*, **195**, pp. 23–44.

Idem, A variable aperture rotating sector-disc. *Journ. Opt. Soc. Amer.*, etc. **7**, pp. 683–687.

E. KARRER, A photometric sectored disc. *Journ. Opt. Soc. Amer.*, etc. **7**, pp. 893–899.

M. LUCKIESH, Demonstrating color-mixture. *Journ. Opt. Soc. Amer.*, etc., **7**, pp. 657–660.

MARTIN and GAMBLE, *Color and methods of color reproduction.* New York, 1923.

L. C. MARTIN, The photometric matching field. *Proc. Roy. Soc.*, **104**, pp. 302–315.

T. OTASHIRO, The visibility curve. *Proc. Phys. Math. Soc. Japan*, **5**, pp. 57–59.

W. PEDDIE, Colour vision. *Phil. Mag.*, **45**, pp. 1058–1062.

I. G. PRIEST, The colorimetry and photometry of daylight and incandescent illuminants by the method of rotary dispersion. *Journ. Opt. Soc. Amer.*, etc., **7**, pp. 1175–1209.

Idem, Rotatory dispersion method of colorimetry and heterochromatic photometry. *Am. Illum. Eng. Soc., Trans.*, **18**, pp. 861–864.

H. M. RANDALL, Infra-red spectra. *Am. Phil. Soc., Proc.*, **62**. 6 pp. 326–340.

R. H. SINDEN, Studies based on the spectral complementaries. *Journ. Opt. Soc. Amer.*, etc., **7**, pp. 1123–1153.

1923. J. P. C. SOUTHALL, *Mirrors, Prisms and Lenses.* Rev. ed. New York.

W. WENIGER, Summary of investigations in the infra-red spectrum of long wavelengths. *Journ. Opt. Soc. Amer.*, etc. **7**, pp. 517–527.

1924. F. ALLEN, On the reflex origin of the self light of the retina. *Journ. Opt. Soc. Amer.*, etc., **8**, pp. 275–286.

Idem, A new tri-colour mixing spectrometer. *Journ. Opt. Soc. Amer.*, etc., **8**, pp. 339–341.

Idem, On reflex visual sensations—I. Experimental. *Amer. Journ. Physiol. Optics*, **5**, pp. 341–375.

Idem, On reflex visual sensations. II. Discussion of results. *Am. J. Physiolog. Optics*, **5**, pp. 420-437.

Idem, The reflex origin of color contrast. *J. Opt. Soc. Am.*, etc., **9**, pp. 375-388.

W. A. ANDERSON, Reflex visual sensations and anomalous trichromatism. *Journ. Opt. Soc. Amer.*, etc., **8**, pp. 731–765.

A. BLONDEL and J. REY, New verification of the law of perception of brief illuminations at the limit of their range. *C. R.*, **178**, pp. 276–280.

A. BLONDEL and J. REY. The law of the limiting perception of luminous flashing signals. *Comptes Rendus*, 178. pp. 1245-1247.

E. L. CHAFFEE and ALICE HAMPSON, Effects of varying the wave-length of the stimulating light upon the electrical response of the retina. *Jour. Opt. Soc. Amer.*, etc., **9**, pp. 1–25.

J. H. CLARK, The Ishihara test for color blindness. *Amer. Journ. Physiolog. Optics*, **5**, pp. 269–276.

P. W. COBB, The speed of vision. *Am. Illum. Eng. Soc., Trans.* **19**, pp. 150–163; discussion, pp. 163–175.

H. G. DORSEY, A visual method of measuring short time intervals. *Journ. Opt. Soc. Amer.*, etc., **9**, pp. 351, 352.

H. ERFLE and H. BOEGEHOLD, *Grundzüge der Theorie der optischen Instrumente nach ABBE, von* S. CZAPSKI *und* O. EPPENSTEIN. Dritte Auflage bearbeitet von den wissenschaftlichen Mitarbeitern der ZEISSischen Werkstätte. Leipzig.

C. E. FERREE and G. RAND, Further studies on the extent and shape of the color fields in relation to the intensity of the stimulus light. *Am. J. Physiolog. Optics*, **5**, pp. 409-419.

C. E. FERREE and G. RAND. Effect of composition of light on important ocular functions. *Am. Illum. Eng. Soc., Trans.* **19**, pp. 424-447.

E. F. FINCHAM, A new form of Corneal Microscope with ·Combined Slit Lamp Illuminating Device. *Opt. Soc., Trans.*, **25**. 3. pp. 113–118; Disc., 118–122. (1923-1924.)

H. GEORGE and E. BAYLE, Spectrophotometric Definition of Colours of Fluorescence. *Comptes Rendus*, **178**, pp. 1895–1897.

K. S. GIBSON, Special characteristics of test solutions used in heterochromatic photometry. *Journ. Opt. Soc. Amer.*, etc., **9**, pp. 113–121.

J. GUILD, New flicker photometer for heterochromatic photometry. *Journ. Sci. Instruments*, **1**, pp. 182–189.

A. GULLSTRAND, Optische Systemgesetze zweiter und dritter Ordnung. (175 pages, 4to.) *Kungl. Svenska Vetenskapsakademiens Handligar.* Bd. 63. No. 13 (Supplement).

S. HECHT, Visibility of the spectrum. *Journ. Opt. Soc. Amer.*, etc., **9**, pp. 211–222.

OTTO HENKER, *Introduction to the theory of spectacles.* English translation by R. KANTHACK. Jena School of Optics.

A. HOLLENBERG, Visual sensory reflexes and color blindness. *J. Opt. Soc. Am.*, etc., **9**, pp. 389-401.

H. S. HOLLENBERG, On the verification of the principle of reflex visual sensations. *Journ. Opt. Soc. Amer.*, etc., **8**, pp. 713–730.

H. E. IVES, A primary standard of light. *Journ. Franklin Inst.*, **197**, pp. 147–182 and 359–400.

1924. G. JAECKEL, The faintest visible. *Phys. Zft.*, **25**, pp. 13–17.

D. B. JUDD, The spectral energy distributions produced by rotary mixing of complementary papers. *Journ. Opt. Soc. Amer.* etc., **9**, pp. 95–111.

E. KARRER, An interesting phenomenon in photopsia. *Journ. Opt. Soc. Amer.*, etc., **8**, pp. 319, 320.

Idem, New type of photometric disc. *Journ. Opt. Soc. Amer.*, etc., **8**, pp. 541–543.

E. KARRER and A. PORITSKY, Low brightness photometer. *Opt. Soc. Amer.*, etc., **8**, pp. 355–359.

J. v. KRIES, Über einige Aubgaben der Farbenlehre. *Zft. f. techn. Physik*, 6 Nr. 8, pp. 327-349.

P. LASAREFF, Application of the WEBER-FECHNER law to photometry. *Rev. d'optique*, **3**, pp. 65–70.

C. LEISS, Monochromator for 200μμ to 800μμ. *Zft. f. Physik*, **21**, 1. pp. 60–62.

O. MEISSNER, The OSTWALD double-colour cone. *Zft. f. Physik*, **21**, 1, pp. 68–72.

J. H. PARSONS, *An introduction to the study of colour vision*. Second edition. Cambridge.

W. PEDDIE, The development and present position of colour vision theory. *Science Progress*, No. 72, pp. 635–639.

H. PIÉRON, The minimum of energy in the luminous excitation of the retina by brief illumination. *Comptes rendus*, **178**, pp. 966–968.

I. G. PRIEST, Apparatus for the determination of color in terms of dominant wavelength, purity and brightness. *Jour. Opt. Soc. Amer.*, etc. **8**, pp. 173–200.

I. G. PRIEST, H. J. McNICHOLAS and M. K. FREHAFER, Some tests of the precision and reliability of measurements of spectral transmission by the KOENIG-MARTENS spectrophotometer. Ibid., **8**, pp. 201–212.

I. G. PRIEST (in collaboration with L. B. TUCKERMAN, H. E. IVES, and F. K. HARRIS), The Computation of Colorimetric Purity. *J. Opt. Soc. Amer.*, etc., **9**, pp. 503–520.

C. PULFRICH, The Colours Produced by Rotation of the Plane of Polarisation in a Quartz Plate Gound Perpendicular to the Axis. *Zft. Instrumentenk.*, **44**. p. 261–270.

O. SCHNEIDER. Effect of colour of light on visual fatigue. *Zft. techn. Physik*, **5**, 8. pp. 355-357.

C. SHEARD, On the effects of quantity and quality of illumination upon the human eye and vision. *Am. J. Physiolog. Optics.*, **5**, pp. 468-485.

W. J. SMITH, The law of recurrences and decay of after images. *Proc. Roy. Soc. Edinburgh* (1923-24), **44**, Part III., pp. 211-217.

L. T. TROLAND, The optics of the nervous system. *Journ. Opt. Soc. Amer.*, etc., **8**, 389–409.

Idem, The interrelations of modern physics and modern psychology. *Journ. Franklin Inst.*, **197**, pp. 479–504.

E. P. T. TYNDALL and K. S. GIBSON, Visibility of radiant energy equation. *J. Opt. Soc. Am.*, etc., **9**, pp. 403, 404.

J. W. T. WALSH, *The elementary principles of lighting and photometry.*